MW00784549

Handbook of Cognitive-Behavioral Approaches in Primary Care

About the Editors

Robert A. DiTomasso, PhD, ABPP, is Professor of Psychology and Chairman of the Department of Psychology at the Philadelphia College of Osteopathic Medicine. He is a Diplomate in Clinical Psychology of the American Board of Professional Psychology, a Fellow of the Academy of Clinical Psychology, a Founding Fellow of the Academy of Cognitive Therapy, and a licensed psychologist in Pennsylvania and New Jersey. He obtained his doctoral degree from the University of Pennsylvania, and completed an internship at Temple University School of Medicine, Department of Psychiatry, Behavior Therapy Unit, and Eastern Pennsylvania Psychiatric Institute. He completed extensive postdoctoral training and supervision in cognitive therapy and primary care psychology. He previously served as Adjunct Associate Professor at the University of Pennsylvania, and as Associate Director of Behavioral Medicine at West Jersey Health System Family Practice Residency for many years. He is the coeditor of *Comparative Treatments for Anxiety Disorders* (Springer Publishing, 2002).

Barbara A. Golden, PsyD, ABPP, is an Associate Professor of Psychology and the Director of Clinical Services and Director of the Center for Brief Therapy at the Philadelphia College of Osteopathic Medicine. She received her PsyD in clinical psychology from Loyola College in Baltimore, Maryland, and completed an APA-approved internship at University of Medicine and Dentistry of New Jersey and a postdoctoral fellowship at Robert Wood Johnson Medical School. She is board certified in Clinical Psychology by the American Board of Professional Psychology. As a licensed psychologist, her clinical and scholarly work includes nonpharmacological pain management, somatization disorder, and psychology in primary care. She is a member of several professional organizations, and has published and presented on various clinical health psychology topics.

Harry J. Morris, DO, MPH, is Professor and Chair of the Department of Family Medicine at Philadelphia College of Osteopathic Medicine (PCOM). He received his DO degree from PCOM and his MPH from the Medical College of Wisconsin. He completed his internship and residency in family medicine at PCOM, and a postdoctoral fellowship in Primary Care Curriculum Development from Michigan State University. He previously directed the Family Medicine Residency at PCOM. He currently teaches communication, documentation, and physical examination skills to medical students. Dr. Morris administers the ambulatory health care system at PCOM, which includes four urban health care centers in underserved areas. He was in private practice in Pennsylvania for 11 years before becoming a Family Medicine Residency Director in Orlando, Florida. Dr. Morris is board certified in Family Medicine and Preventive Medicine/Occupational Medicine.

Handbook of Cognitive-Behavioral Approaches in Primary Care

Editors
Robert A. DiTomasso, PhD, ABPP
Barbara A. Golden, PsyD, ABPP
Harry J. Morris, DO, MPH

New York

Springer Publishing Company, LLC
11 West 42nd Street
New York, NY 10036
www.springerpub.com

Acquisitions Editor: Sheri W. Sussman
Production Editor: Pamela Lankas
Cover design: Mimi Flow
Composition: International Graphic Services

Ebook ISBN: 978-0-8261-0384-0

09 10 11 12/ 5 4 3 2 1

Library of Congress Cataloging-in-Publication Data

Handbook of cognitive-behavioral approaches in primary care / edited by Robert A. DiTomasso, Barbara A. Golden, Harry J. Morris.
p. cm.
Includes bibliographical references and index.
ISBN 978-0-8261-0383-3 (alk. paper)
1. Cognitive therapy. 2. Mind and body. 3. Psychophysiology. 4. Primary care (Medicine). I. DiTomasso, Robert A. II. Golden, Barbara A. III. Morris, Harry (Harry J.)
RC489.C63H358 2010
616.89'1425—dc22
2009037638

Printed in the United States of America by Hamilton Printing

This book is dedicated to many people in my life, all of whom are now gone, all of whom have left this earth much too soon, all of with whom I had the pleasure to spend important parts of my life, and all of whom in one or more countless ways have positively touched my life. I enjoyed the pleasure of their company and I think of them fondly and often. Through their losses, I have also come to personally realize how the toll of lifestyle, among other factors, in many instances contributed to the diseases that ultimately took their lives. These special people are: Lucy and William DiTomasso, Mary (Cammarota) and Umberto (Big Albert) Macera, Robert (Bobby DiAntonio) DiGiovannantonio, George M. Vinci, Anne (Cammarota) and John (Johnny Cheeri) Bucciero, Helen (Cammarota) and Dan Carangi, Anthony (Tony Carlo) Carangi, Joan (Barossa) Bucciero, Lena (Granny) Bongiovanni, Anthony Bongiovanni, Luigi and Antoinette DiTomasso, Esther (DiTomasso) Vecere, Rita (DiTomasso) and Mike (The Spike) Maggio, Charles (Charlie Young) DiTomasso, Buddy DiTomasso, Kate (DiTomasso) Buccella, Anthony (Rushy) DiTomasso, Frank DiTomasso, Carmela (DiGiovannantonio) Terlingo, Donato Ezzio, S.Thomas Carter, Jr., MD, and James P. Mahan, PsyD.

—RAD

For my parents, John and Kathleen Golden; my sisters, Kathleen and Carol. Being your daughter and your sister are my greatest blessings.

—BG

To my wife, Joanne, and my family.

—HM

Contents

Contributors

Frank Andrasik, PhD
Distinguished University Professor
Department of Psychology
Senior Research Scientist
Florida Institute for Human and Machine Cognition
University of West Florida
Pensacola, FL

Stephen D. Anton, PhD
Assistant Professor
Department of Aging and Geriatric Research
Department of Clinical and Health Psychology
University of Florida
Gainesville, FL

Immaculate A. Antony, BSc
Ontario Institute for Studies in Education (OISE)
University of Toronto
Ontario, Canada

Michael J. Baime, MD
Director, Penn Program for Stress Management
Abramson Cancer Center
University of Pennsylvania School of Medicine
Philadelphia, PA

Jeff Baker, PhD, ABPP
Professor and Director
Psychology Training Program
Division of Rehabilitation Sciences
University of Texas Medical Branch
Galveston, TX

Michael A. Becker, DO, MS, FACOFP
Vice Chair, Associate Professor
Department of Family Medicine
Philadelphia College of Osteopathic Medicine
Philadelphia, PA

Dorothy A. Borresen, PhD, APN
Assistant Professor, University of Medicine and Dentistry
Robert Wood Johnson Medical School
Family Medicine Residency at Capital Health Systems
Lawrenceville, NJ

Patrick D. Boyle, MA
Doctoral Student, PsyD Program in Clinical Psychology
Philadelphia College of Osteopathic Medicine
Philadelphia, PA

Craig J. Bryan, PsyD
Chief, Primary Care Psychology Service
Wilford Hall Medical Center
San Antonio, TX

Oliver Bullock, DO
Professor, Department of Family Medicine
Chairman of the Division of Community Medicine
Philadelphia College of Osteopathic Medicine Healthcare Center
Cambria Division
Philadelphia, PA

Dawn C. Buse, PhD
Assistant Professor, Department of Neurology
Albert Einstein College of Medicine of Yeshiva University
Assistant Professor, Clinical Health Psychology Doctoral Program
Ferkauf Graduate School of Psychology of Yeshiva University
and Director of Psychology, Montefiore Headache Center
Bronx, NY

Stacey C. Cahn, PhD
Assistant Professor
Department of Psychology
Philadelphia College of Osteopathic Medicine
Philadelphia, PA

Raymond Carvajal, MA
Doctoral Student, PsyD Program in Clinical Psychology
Philadelphia College of Osteopathic Medicine
Philadelphia, PA

Deborah Chiumento, PsyD
Postdoctoral Fellow
Clinical Coordinator, "A Healthier You"
Department of Psychology
Philadelphia College of Osteopathic Medicine
Philadelphia, PA

Andrea L. Cincotta, MS
Research Coordinator
Penn Program For Stress Management
University of Pennsylvania Health System
Philadelphia, PA

Carla Cirilli, MA
Doctoral Student
PsyD, Program in Clinical Psychology
Philadelphia College of Osteopathic Medicine
Philadelphia, PA

Travis A. Cos, PhD
Department of Psychiatry
University of Rochester Medical Center
Rochester, NY

Michael J. Dolan, PsyD, CAC
Licensed Psychologist, Adjunct Faculty
Department of Psychology
Philadelphia College of Osteopathic Medicine
Philadelphia, PA

Rebecca Egner, BS
University of Pennsylvania
Philadelphia PA

Stephanie H. Felgoise, PhD, ABPP
Professor, Vice Chair
Department of Psychology
Director, PsyD Program in Clinical Psychology
Philadelphia College of Osteopathic Medicine
Philadelphia, PA

Amelia G. Findiesen, MS, NCC
Doctoral Student, PsyD Program in Clinical Psychology
Philadelphia College of Osteopathic Medicine
Philadelphia, PA

Larry H. Finkelstein, DO
Associate Professor of Family Medicine
Director of Extended Care Services and Education
Philadelphia College of Osteopathic Medicine
Philadelphia, PA

Arthur Freeman, EdD, ScD, ABPP
Visiting Professor, Department of Psychology
Governors State University
Chicago, IL

Robert J. Gatchel, PhD, ABPP
Professor and Chairman
Department of Psychology
College of Science, The University of Texas at Arlington
Arlington, TX

Scott Glassman, MSEd
Doctoral Student, PsyD Program in Clinical Psychology
Philadelphia College of Osteopathic Medicine
Philadelphia, PA

Elizabeth A. Gosch, PhD, ABPP
Associate Professor
Department of Psychology
Philadelphia College of Osteopathic Medicine
Philadelphia, PA

Kimberly A. Hand, MSc
Graduate Student, Department of Applied Physiology and Kinesiology
University of Florida
Gainesville, FL

Erica A. Henninger, PsyD, MBA
Psychotherapist and Director of Bariatric Behavioral Health
Family Health Psychology Center
Darby, PA

Jenna L. Jebitsch, MS
Doctoral Student, PsyD Program in Clinical Psychology
Philadelphia College of Osteopathic Medicine
Philadelphia, PA

Jeanne R. Kestel, MS
Doctoral Student, PsyD Program in Clinical Psychology
Argosy University
Chicago, IL

Samuel Knapp, EdD
Director of Professional Affairs
Pennsylvania Psychological Association
Harrisburg, PA

Anu Kotay, PhD
Director of Behavioral Science, Family Medicine Residency
Robert Wood Johnson Medical School
New Brunswick, NJ

Stuart L. Kurlansik, PhD
Faculty, West Jersey–Memorial Family Practice Residency at Virtua
The Tatem-Brown Family Practice Center
Voorhees, NJ

Paul Lehrer, PhD
Professor of Psychiatry
University of Medicine and Dentistry of New Jersey
Robert Wood Johnson Medical School
Piscataway, NJ

Richard Levine, MD
Faculty, West Jersey–Memorial Family Practice Residency at Virtua
The Tatem-Brown Family Practice Center
Voorhees, NJ

Eileen Lightner, MA, MS, LPC
Doctoral Candidate, PsyD Program in Clinical Psychology
Philadelphia College of Osteopathic Medicine
Philadelphia, PA

Meghan L. Marsac, PhD
Psychology Fellow, Center for Injury Research and Prevention
The Children's Hospital of Philadelphia
Philadelphia, PA

Roger K. McFillin, PsyD
Department of Psychology
Philadelphia College of Osteopathic Medicine
Philadelphia, PA

Eugene Mochan, PhD, DO
Associate Dean, Primary Care
Philadelphia College of Osteopathic Medicine
Philadelphia, PA

Margaret Nam, BA
Graduate Student, Department of Psychology
Philadelphia College of Osteopathic Medicine
Philadelphia, PA

Arthur M. Nezu, PhD, ABPP
Professor of Psychology, Medicine, and Public Health
Drexel University
Philadelphia, PA

Christine Maguth Nezu, PhD, ABPP
Professor of Psychology and Medicine
Drexel University
Philadelphia, PA

Philip J. Pellegrino, PsyD
Department of Psychology
Philadelphia College of Osteopathic Medicine
Philadelphia, PA

Michael G. Perri, PhD
Interim Dean, College of Public Health and Health Professions
Department of Clinical and Health Psychology
University of Florida
Gainesville, FL

Maurice F. Prout, PhD, ABPP
Professor and Director, Respecialization Program
Widener University, Institute for Graduate Clinical Psychology
Chester, PA

J. Russell Ramsay, PhD
Assistant Professor of Psychology in Psychiatry
University of Pennsylvania School of Medicine
Adult ADHD Treatment & Research Program
and Center for Cognitive Therapy
Philadelphia, PA

Paul M. Robins, PhD
Director of Clinical Services
Codirector, Internship Training Program
Department of Psychology
The Children's Hospital of Philadelphia and
Associate Professor of Psychology
University of Pennsylvania
School of Medicine
Philadelphia, PA

Bradley Rosenfield, PsyD
Assistant Professor
Department of Psychology
Philadelphia College of Osteopathic Medicine
Philadelphia, PA

M. David Rudd, PhD, ABPP
Professor and Chair
Department of Psychology
Texas Tech University
Lubbock, TX

Nancy Breen Ruddy, PhD
Director of Behavioral Science
Mountainside Family Practice Residency
Mountainside Hospital
Mountain Lakes, NJ

Laura Russo-Innamorato, MS
Doctoral Candidate
PsyD Program in Clinical Psychology
Philadelphia College of Osteopathic Medicine
Philadelphia, PA

Jesús A. Salas, PsyD, ACT
Clinical Psychologist, Clinical Assistant Professor
Philadelphia College of Osteopathic Medicine
Department of Psychology
Philadelphia, PA

Marsha S. Singer, PhD
Clinical Assistant Professor
Department of Psychology
Philadelphia College of Osteopathic Medicine
Philadelphia, PA

Clint C. Stankiewicz, PsyD
Department of Psychology
Philadelphia College of Osteopathic Medicine
Phillipsburg, NJ

Rebecca K. Stern, PhD
Research Assistant
Widener University
Chester, PA

Takako Suzuki, PhD
Assistant Professor
Department of Psychology
Philadelphia College of Osteopathic Medicine
Philadelphia, PA

Brenda B. Toner, PhD
Center for Addiction and Mental Health
Toronto, Ontario, Canada

Adam G. Tsai, MD, MS
Assistant Professor of Medicine
University of Colorado
Denver, CO

Kenneth J. Veit, DO, MBA
Senior Vice President for Academic Affairs and Dean
Philadelphia College of Osteopathic Medicine
Philadelphia, PA

Ivette Velez, MS
Department of Psychology
Philadelphia College of Osteopathic Medicine
Philadelphia, PA

Thomas A. Wadden, PhD
Professor of Psychology in Psychiatry
and Director, Center for Weight and Eating Disorders
University of Pennsylvania School of Medicine
Philadelphia, PA

Mark A. Watling, MD, FRCPC
Assistant Professor
Department of Psychiatry and Behavioural Neurosciences
McMaster University
St. Joseph's Healthcare
Hamilton, Ontario, Canada

Beverly White, PsyD
Assistant Professor
Department of Psychology
Philadelphia College of Osteopathic Medicine
Philadelphia, PA

Laura Young, MD, PhD
Clinical Associate Faculty
Department of Medicine
Division of Endocrinology, Diabetes and Metabolism
University of Pennsylvania School of Medicine
Philadelphia, PA

Bruce S. Zahn, EdD, ABPP
Professor
Director of Clinical Training
PsyD Program in Clinical Psychology
Department of Psychology
Philadelphia College of Osteopathic Medicine
Philadelphia, PA

David L. Zehrung, PhD
Director, Counseling and Psychological Services
Greencastle Family Practice, P.C.
Greencastle, PA

Foreword

The premise that mental health and physical health factors affect each other has become widely accepted in our society. By and large, psychotherapists and medical practitioners alike have come to appreciate the ways in which stress, maladaptive attitudes, negative behavioral and lifestyle habits, and physiological pathology interact, typically in vicious cycles, often leading patients to present with problems that are neither quickly nor easily assessed or treated. Similarly, there has been a rising awareness that by coordinating care between psychotherapists and primary care physicians, patients can receive more powerful interventions, and their adherence to treatment and ongoing self-care can be enhanced. The results of such professional collaboration promise better outcomes and maintenance for patients, reduced costs in the long run (for individual patients and for society as a whole), and improved understanding of the etiology, development, and maintenance of health and mental health problems, thus leading to potentially fruitful treatment research directions.

The *Handbook of Cognitive-Behavioral Approaches in Primary Care* is an impressive volume that clearly and comprehensively describes theory, research, and practice on issues pertinent to the mind-body connection, from the level of individual patients to the macro-levels of professional systems and societal access to empirically supported treatments. The editors and authors have a wealth of professional experience as prime movers in the growing trend toward integrative medical and mental health care, and they expertly bring this knowledge to bear in spelling out the issues and problems that need to be addressed so as to maximize the availability and utility of this model.

As interested readers, we learn that there has been a convergence between the rise of the biopsychosocial model in health care, the growing body of data supporting cognitive-behavioral therapies as being at the forefront of "best practices" in the treatment of a wide range of disorders and populations, and the emergence of the overlapping fields of health psychology and behavioral medicine. We also learn some things that may be surprising even to seasoned clinicians, such as the fact that mental health difficulties are among the most common presenting problems in primary health care and about 70% of psychotropic medication prescriptions come from primary care physicians. Nevertheless, there is often a significant disjunction between primary care practitioners and mental health therapists, even when they are fundamentally in agreement that it would be advantageous for patients to avail themselves of both types of care. Appropriate referrals to therapists may be difficult for primary care practitioners to make, and patient follow-through is notoriously poor. Primary care practitioners and cognitive-behavioral therapists have different exigencies (e.g., in terms of time allotments, billing regulations, ethical guidelines on boundaries) and a contrasting nomenclature, thus leading to suboptimal collaboration. However, as the *Handbook of Cognitive-Behavioral Approaches in Primary Care* so clearly details, creating a workable environment and system for better coordination of care can produce markedly improved results for patients and enhanced professional satisfaction for clinicians.

The breadth and depth of this text is astounding. It would be more than sufficient if the book focused only on the major problems encountered in primary care to which cognitive-behavioral methods could be applied in a facilitative manner. Indeed, we learn about the ways in which integrative care can better address such health concerns as hypertension, diabetes, asthma, obesity, headaches, insomnia, chronic pain, and irritable bowel syndrome, as well as behavioral problems such as substance abuse, eating disorders, and suicidality, among others. However, the volume goes well beyond this, tackling such highly relevant issues as patient problems in adherence to medical advice (owing to misunderstandings, memory problems, fears of medical procedures, negative beliefs, and the like), preparing patients to be in an optimal state of mind for medical interventions (a sort of "mental prehab"), and cultural considerations pertinent to the practitioners' sensitivity to the patients' ethnic and familial norms that may affect the patients' receptivity to treatment.

The editors and authors offer extremely helpful guidelines on how to improve collaboration, coordination, and integration of care so as to approach the goal of providing treatments to the "whole person" in the most effective, efficient, and empirically supported ways. They repeatedly make the point that the primary practitioner's office and the cognitive-behavioral therapist's office do not have to be separate worlds—they can be brought together via improved appreciation for what the other venue has to offer its patients, and via improved communication between their disciplines regardless of whether or not they are located in the same physical space. In the same way that health and mental health professionals can become more culturally aware and sensitive when treating patients from a variety of ethnic backgrounds, they also can become better partners if they understand each other's professional "culture," such that timely teamwork is enhanced in a way that adds value to the other's practice. Significantly, the *Handbook of Cognitive-Behavioral Approaches in Primary Care* includes a chapter on the training of primary care residents in cognitive-behavioral methods. Although it is true that they will likely have far too many patients and too little time to apply such methods as guided discovery and motivational interviewing techniques, these future frontline physicians will be better positioned to recognize problems such as patient denial, low adherence, eating disorders, and substance-use disorders, and also will be better oriented to work in tandem with their colleagues doing cognitive-behavioral therapy so as to bring comprehensive care to their patients.

Absorbing the evidence-based principles and experiential wisdom these pages have to offer will be a gratifying experience, whether the reader zeroes in on one or more particular chapters of interest or is determined to read the entire book (and I enthusiastically recommend the latter choice). Many of the chapters include illustrative case examples that exemplify the use of cognitive-behavioral assessment methods, case formulations, and interventions to ameliorate the wide range of clinical problems already noted. As previously stated, these chapters also address cultural considerations, such that practitioners and therapists can adjust their approaches when necessary and appropriate to enhance their partnership with patients from different ethnic backgrounds. Especially useful are the sections on "clinical pearls of wisdom" that summarize so many of the chapters. This will surely be a text to which to refer again and again.

The *Handbook of Cognitive-Behavioral Approaches in Primary Care* makes a compelling case for integrative models of health care and mental health care being the wave of the future, promising significant advantages for all parties. Nonetheless, as with any major "merger," there are formidable challenges in trying to move forward in an organized manner, with well-defined roles and new lines of communication. The new "team" has to learn to work collaboratively and synergistically with the least amount of delay and a minimum of growing pains. The editors and authors of this seminal text do a masterful job in explicating the conceptual and technical details involved, thus guiding this vitally important, soon-to-be burgeoning field in the right direction.

Cory F. Newman, PhD, ABPP
Director
Center for Cognitive Therapy
University of Pennsylvania
School of Medicine

Preface

Our goal in this handbook is to present a comprehensive, up-to-date summary of the integration and applications of cognitive-behaviorally oriented approaches to common issues and problems confronted by practitioners in primary care medical settings. As academics and practitioners ourselves, we have experienced the multitude of issues and problems described in this volume. Each of us has been fortunate enough to have spent her/his career in multidisciplinary medical settings integrating our services on the frontline in a variety of service delivery units, as well as training advanced doctoral students, medical students, family medicine interns, family medicine residents, nurse practitioners, and physician assistants.

Before joining the Department of Psychology at Philadelphia College of Osteopathic Medicine full time in 1998, Robert A. DiTomasso had served for roughly 20 years as Associate Director of Behavioral Medicine at West Jersey Health System Family Practice Residency and its outpatient medical service, the Tatem-Brown Family Practice Center. This program, originally affiliated with the University of Pennsylvania School of Medicine, and later, the University of Medicine and Dentistry of New Jersey, provided rich and priceless opportunities for working side by side on a daily basis with 5 attending family physicians and about 24 residents. Before joining this residency, DiTomasso had completed an internship at the Behavior Therapy Unit at Temple University's Department of Psychiatry/Eastern Pennsylvania Psychiatric Institute, under the direction and supervision of Joseph Wolpe, MD, the father of behavior therapy, and L. Michael Ascher, PhD. The melding of these two experiences—behavior therapy and primary care—was critical in shaping ideas and concepts about the important role of mental health practitioners in primary care. Barbara A. Golden completed her postdoctoral training in Clinical Health Psychology at the University of Medicine and Dentistry of New Jersey/Robert Wood Johnson Medical School. She worked closely with primary care physicians and specialists in the areas of pain management, somatization disorders, and HIV/AIDS. At the Philadelphia College of Osteopathic Medicine (PCOM), this work was continued and expanded by creating, implementing, and overseeing the training of the clinical psychology students from our APA-accredited PsyD program in the area of integrated health care in PCOM's neighborhood health care centers. In these multidisciplinary settings, students have marvelous educational opportunities to complete practica and internship (APPIC) experiences working with chronically ill underserved medical patients. Harry J. Morris worked in family medicine as a solo practitioner for many years. Prior to coming to PCOM, he was the Residency Director for Florida Hospital East Orlando. Since coming to PCOM 14 years ago, he has been the Chair of the Department of Family Medicine and oversees the health care centers. His background in family medicine, public health, and spirituality provides a unique blend for the delivery of health care in these urban settings, as well as training family medicine residents and clinical psychology interns.

There is little doubt that the marriage between psychology and family medicine at PCOM has served as the impetus for this book. We hope to provide practitioners and scholars with the unique and important benefits made possible by integrating cognitive-behavioral models into the delivery of primary medical care. In Part I, General Considerations, chapter 1, with our colleague Deborah Chiumento, postdoctoral fellow in clinical health psychology and Clinical Coordinator of the "A Healthier You" project at PCOM, we describe the importance of three major events influencing primary care: the birth of the biopsychosocial model, the emergence of behavioral medicine and health psychology, and the cognitive-behavioral revolution in psychotherapy. In chapter 2, with Sam Knapp and Ken Veit, we elucidate the roles and functions of the cognitive-behavioral clinician in primary care, with an emphasis on ethical issues. Borresen and Ruddy, in chapter 3, present a comprehensive overview and analysis of the importance of collaboration between mental health providers and primary care physicians. In chapter 4, Cos, DiTomasso, Cirilli, and Finkelstein examine critical issues in the process of conducting patient-centered and consultee-centered consultation in primary care. In chapter 5, DiTomasso, Cahn, Cirilli, and Mochan argue for the absolute importance of incorporating empirically based models and their applications into primary care practice. In chapter 6, Kurlansik and Levine, seasoned educators of family medicine residents, examine their methods and strategies for educating and training family practice residents in cognitive-behavioral approaches and biopsychosocial medicine, with a keen eye focused on cognitive-behavioral clinicians seeking to function effectively as teachers of family medicine. In chapter 7, Felgoise, Becker, and Jebitsch, based on their work with chronically ill medical patients, offer a unique perspective on the role of spirituality in primary care, a frequently neglected topic.

In Part II, Cognitive-Behavioral Techniques, a variety of important cognitive-behavioral strategies are reviewed. In chapter 8, Suzuki, White, and Velez present their ideas on the importance of cultural competence and psychoeducation in working with primary care patients. In chapter 9, Young, Cincotta, and Baime summarize their work on mindfulness from their experience at the University of Pennsylvania's Stress Management Program. In chapter 10, Art Nezu and Christine Maguth Nezu, based on years of work in mind-body medicine and problem-solving therapy at Hahnemann University's (now Drexel's) Department of Clinical and Health Psychology, contribute their comprehensive and useful model of conceptualizing patient problems in primary care. In chapter 11, Zahn, Zehrung, and Russo-Innamorato offer a detailed review of common cognitive assessment and treatment strategies of relevance to the primary care setting. Next, in chapter 12, Gosch, DiTomasso, and Findiesen describe the behavioral model of assessment and treatment and its relevance in working with primary care patients. Finally, in chapter 13, Jeff Baker, based on his work at the University of Texas Medical Branch at Galveston, undertakes the important topic of how to best prepare primary care patients for stressful medical procedures.

Part III, Common Behavioral Problems in Primary Care, opens with chapter 14, in which DiTomasso, Chiumento, Singer, and Bullock describe the challenges of assessing and treating nonadherent patients in primary care. Anton, Hand, and Perri, in chapter 15, address critical issues related to behavioral lifestyle habits, including smoking and physical activity. In chapter 16, Freeman, Lightner, and Golden address the common cold of mental health—depression in primary care. Salas, Henninger, Stern, and Prout, in chapter 17, provide a thorough and eye-opening account of the role of anxiety in clinical presentations and its treatment in the outpatient medical setting. Rudd and Bryan, in chapter 18, present a useful model of understanding suicidality in primary care, coupled with a variety of clinically helpful strategies for

dealing with this challenging issue. In chapter 19, Dolan and Nam offer a practical perspective on identifying and handling substance abuse issues in primary care. Golden, Stankiewicz, and Kestel, in chapter 20, describe the common, complex, and challenging issues presented by somatoform patients. In chapter 21, Watling offers a complete analysis and clinically helpful recommendations for handling the problem of medical phobias that interfere with medical treatment. Robins and Marsac, in chapter 22, tackle the common behavioral pediatric problems presented in the primary care setting. In the final chapter in this section, Cahn and McFillin provide a thoughtful treatment of the complexities of assessing and handling eating-disordered patients.

In Part IV, Common Medical Problems in Primary Care, DiTomasso, Chiumento, and Morris begin with the assessment and treatment of the hypertensive patient in chapter 24. In chapter 25, Kotay and Lehrer of UMDNJ discuss the issue of asthma. In chapter 26, DiTomasso, Boyle, Finkelstein, and Morris address the complicated and challenging problems presented by diabetic patients in primary care. In chapter 27, Tsai, Carvajal, Egner, and Wadden present an academically stimulating review of their well-known work from the University of Pennsylvania on obesity, with implications for primary care clinicians. Golden, Gatchel, and Glassman offer valuable insights in assessing and treating chronic pain in primary care in chapter 28. In chapter 29, Buse and Andrasik provide a thoughtful piece on the headache patient, and in chapter 30, where irritable bowel syndrome is discussed, Toner and Antony offer clinical considerations about the assessment and treatment of this challenging problem.

In chapter 31, Rosenfield, Ramsay, Cahn, and Pellegrino provide a thorough approach to the assessment and treatment of the insomnia patient. Finally, in chapter 32, we offer our insights and conclusions about the future of cognitive-behavioral approaches in primary care.

Acknowledgments

There are many individuals who deserve our appreciation. First, I thank my wife, Deborah, my daughters Natalie and Alexis, and Dahlia Jade for their understanding during those many moments when I was consumed by this project. I also thank my entire "family" in the Department of Psychology at PCOM, especially the Self-Study Committee (Stephanie H. Felgoise, Bruce Zahn, Virginia Salzer, and Angelika Mohnke Weakland), Barbara Golden, Debbie Chiumento, Bob Cuzzolino, Matt Schure, Ken Veit, and Harry Morris. The Pew Charitable Trusts provided grant funds to support the implementation of cognitive-behavioral approaches with chronically ill patients in PCOM's health care centers. Jeanne Kestel, Margaret Nam, Hussain Alhashem, Amelia Findiesen, and Stuart Kurlansik are also recognized. Sheri Sussman and Deborah Gissinger at Springer provided ongoing direction. Finally, I thank my former colleagues and the staff and residents at the Tatem-Brown Family Practice Center. Last, and most assuredly not least, a most special note of acknowledgment is given to the late S. Thomas Carter, Jr., MD, Founding Director of the West Jersey Health System Family Practice Residency. Tom, the quintessential primary care physician, had a most profound and lasting influence on me personally, and on my thinking about primary care medicine. As a "student" of family medicine, I spent my first year at Tatem-Brown joining Tom for office visits with his patients and accompanying him during house calls and nursing home visits. Tom was truly a gifted, brilliant, and dedicated physician with outstanding interpersonal skills and an encyclopedic knowledge base—a true master. Most important, he was a gifted leader and charismatic human being. As my mentor in primary care, he taught me countless things that I use in my clinical practice, administration, and teaching on a daily basis, and for this, I thank him (RAD).

My deepest appreciation goes to my coeditors. Bob has had the desire to write this book for many years. With his experience and mentorship, I have learned much of what I know about cognitive-behavioral therapy and primary care medicine. Harry welcomed the practice of providing psychological services into our health care centers at a time when this multidisciplinary approach was considered "a new way" of doing business. We share a common vision of providing comprehensive health services to urban, underserved persons, and have taught and supervised countless numbers of students. I am most grateful to the Sisters of St. Joseph, Chestnut Hill, PA, and to the Society of Jesus, the Jesuits, who gave me the foundation to become an empathetic psychologist and a knowledgeable teacher, and, in addition, a mission to serve the most vulnerable persons in our society. I am grateful for my dear friend, Thomasina Farley, SSJ, and my aunt, Mary J. Golden, SSJ, without whose constant encouragement

I would never have completed my doctorate. My deepest thanks also go to my colleagues and my students at PCOM, especially Amelia Findiesen, Jeanne Kestel, and Margaret Nam, who remind me of the reasons why I chose to be a teacher. Finally, for all the patients struggling with physical and mental illnesses, I am in awe of their perseverance and strength to overcome many hardships (BG).

I recognize and thank many individuals. My patients have taught me that medical care and caring for the patient are separate and equally important concepts. My family medicine colleagues have shown me how to deliver quality health care and train the next generation of physicians. The Psychology Department has shown me how to implement comprehensive care of the mind and the body. A special thanks also goes to Linda Monger for her dedicated assistance to me over these many years (HM).

Handbook of Cognitive-Behavioral Approaches in Primary Care

Part I

General Considerations

8.27

Primary Care: The Biopsychosocial Model and Cognitive-Behavioral Approaches

1

Robert A. DiTomasso
Barbara A. Golden
Harry J. Morris
Deborah Chiumento

Introduction

Over the past 25 years, we have witnessed a rather dramatic rise in the number of mental health practitioners in medical settings. The primary care setting is no exception, as shown by the call to integrate the biopsychosocial model into patient care. The American Psychological Association calls for strategies to promote collaboration and multidisciplinary practice in health care settings (Bray, 2009). There is little doubt that cognitive-behavioral approaches play a central role in the assessment and treatment of primary care patients. The cognitive-behavioral approach has quickly established itself as the treatment of choice for many of the common problems of patients presenting for care (Sperry, 2008). This phenomenon has likely occurred from the confluence of a number of factors. First, over the past century, the traditional medical model has been sorely lacking in its ability to fully explain, predict, and treat medical patients. This biomedical approach has been found to be inadequate due to its almost exclusive focus on the biological, to the exclusion of other relevant factors. Engel (1977) argued for the adoption of a more comprehensive model that attended to the multifaceted nature of medical problems. This biopsychosocial model has received increasing attention over the past 30 years, serving as a basis for spawning clinical research that addresses the interplay between physical, psychological, and social factors in medical patients and their problems. Second, the average life span of patients has improved, due in large part to dramatic advances in medical technology. On the whole, people are living longer, and are thereby confronting rather unique medical challenges (Seime, Clark, & Whiteside, 2003). Quality of life is, therefore, often compromised and undermines the potential for living a fully functional life. Third, there has been a growing appreciation of the fact that lifestyle habits play a major role in the onset, development, maintenance, and exacerbation of medical problems. For instance, rigorous vaccination protocols have all but eliminated the demise of patients from infectious diseases that were commonly observed in the last century. Broadly speaking, today the culprit is found among the "behavioral pathogens" (Matarazzo, 1984) that set the stage and fuel the rates of morbidity and mortality commonly seen in medical practice. Simply put, factors such as poor diet, minimal physical activity, significant stressors, the abuse of substances, unsafe sex practices, limited coping ability, inadequate emotional support, and nonadherence to medical advice may combine to place patients at great risk for health problems. Fourth, the rise in popularity of primary care medicine, especially family medicine, places the physician in the central role of partnering with patients in the coordination of their health care needs. The basic tenets of primary care medicine (Taylor, 2003), such as continuity of care, comprehensiveness of care, attention to psychosocial issues, and the role of patient education have placed emphasis on the assessment and treatment of the "whole patient," as opposed to disease states. The training of family physicians is a case in point. Allopathic and osteopathic medical education accreditors, including the American Board of Family Practice and the American Board of Osteopathic Medicine, mandate that all interns and residents have exposure and training in the psychological aspects of medical care. Fifth, the emphasis on evidence-based medicine and the rise in popularity of empirically based treatments, as reported in the Cochrane Evidence Based database, has sensitized physicians to the scientifically supported efficacies of cognitive-behavioral therapies. Today, primary care physicians (PCPs) are more aware of the clinical outcomes associated with the cognitive-behavioral approach for problems for which efficacy has been demonstrated. The cognitive-behavioral therapy (CBT) revolution in the field of psychotherapy, the rise of behavioral medicine/health psychology, the application of the CBT approach to medical patients and the crises they experience (DiTomasso, Martin, & Kovnat, 2002), and the popularity of empirically supported approaches has done much to reinforce the view that cognitive-behavioral assessment and treatment protocols have much to offer in the primary care setting. CBT practitioners must rise to the challenge and meet the demands for the care of patients. Given the common medical and psychosocial problems seen in primary care, as well as the literature demonstrating efficacy for treating these problems, the CBT model is a perfect fit. The functional analysis of behavior, cognitive-behavioral case conceptualization, the development and selection of empirically based treatment plans, and the willingness to work side by side with physician colleagues will help to address the needs and enhance the health care of primary care patients.

Theoretical Issues

A number of theoretical models and issues are important to examine when considering the role of CBT clinicians in primary care. Three main areas are relevant here: Taylor's Tenets of Family Medicine, Engel's Biopsychosocial Model, and the Cognitive-Behavioral Model of Behavior and Psychopathology.

There are a number of important tenets of family medicine that must be considered in understanding the unique characteristics of primary care. By embracing these concepts, practitioners will appreciate the context within which primary medical care is embedded, but more importantly, will foster a more effective partnership among PCPs, cognitive-behavioral practitioners, and patients. Taylor (2003) elucidated several important tenets of primary care. Perhaps most important is the construct of *continuity of care*, the idea that patients have their medical care provided by one physician over the course of the life cycle. Continuity of care has profound implications for a number of reasons. Having a consistent medical practitioner who is thoroughly familiar with the patient's history, as well as the unique and idiosyncratic aspects of the patient's medical and psychosocial history, can make a dramatic difference in the quality of patient care. The importance of continuity has far-reaching implications in enhancing the accuracy of problem identification and in fostering the formation of a more effective physician-patient relationship. Continuity is especially relevant in the psychological realm. Having care provided by a physician in a continuous manner over an extended period of time provides a physician with a thorough level of familiarity with the unique and idiosyncratic manner in which the patient adjusts to change. The physician sees how the patient handles the daily stressors associated with living in today's world, and specifically within the community and family environment. Likewise, knowledge about the patient's history, when the patient is likely to become symptomatic, family medical and psychiatric history, the role of stressors in the family, the availability of family support, the implicit trust in the physician, and the like are critical factors that can affect the course of care. These factors are likely to be important in effectively assessing, diagnosing, and treating patients. When continuity does not exist, such as instances in which patients seek primary care from an emergency room, the treating physician is missing the entire picture. Incomplete information results in incomplete assessments and has a significant impact on the validity of diagnoses. Often the patient receives incomplete treatments and treatments aimed at the wrong targets. The consequence may be unnecessary diagnostic tests, patient discomfort and inconvenience, increased patient expense, unnecessary physician time and effort, and waste of precious health care dollars.

Comprehensiveness of care refers to the importance of considering the totality of the patient's experience. In this sense, there is a commitment to understanding and treating the "whole" patient, not just focusing exclusively on one aspect, such as biological functioning. This construct places emphasis on the many advantages of having a thorough understanding of all of the factors that are likely to impinge upon the patient's care. Failure to attend to the total view leaves significant areas ignored in patient assessment and treatment that serve to undermine effective care. Unfortunately, in some instances, physicians may miss an obvious factor that is associated with the onset, exacerbation, and maintenance of a problem. Failure to consider all relevant factors may thus occur, resulting in ineffective treatments or placing patients at undue risks. A balanced view of patient problems that respects the multifaceted causal nature of problems is indicated. For instance, in the diagnostic realm, ignoring important psychosocial patient information in the patient's life is just as serious as overlooking the possibility of a physical, albeit rarer, cause of a problem. Partnering with patients by incorporating their self-observation and monitoring into the assessment process (DiTomasso & Colameco, 1982), as well as maintaining a scientifically skeptical and empirically based attitude coupled with the respect for physical or organic causes of patient problems (Colameco & DiTomasso, 1982), is critical.

The emphasis that PCPs place on the psychosocial aspects of patient care is also of obvious importance. The implicit assumption communicated to patients is simply that patients are welcome to discuss the psychological and social aspects of their lives and their impact on physical and mental functioning. By addressing physical and mental (mind-body) problems in a broad, concurrent, and simultaneous fashion, medical practitioners emphasize the interplay of these factors in explaining patient problems and in ultimately solving them.

PCPs also place a premium on educating patients about their health. The impact of patient education is such that it provides a basis for the patients' understanding their conditions, factors creating them and influencing them, and why specific treatments are offered. Although patient education may not be a powerful treatment in and of itself, it does appear to provide a mechanism for patients to integrate and accept the treatment package. It may be necessary, although not sufficient, for fostering patient change. For example, in the psychological area, patient psychoeducation may serve a variety of useful functions—explanatory, motivational, and practical—in fostering the patient's adoption of the treatment package to orient the patient to the components of the treatment protocol and facilitate treatment assimilation (DiTomasso, Freeman, Carvajal, & Zahn, 2010).

Finally, the emphasis on evidence-based approaches in medicine provides another vehicle for considering the value of CBT approaches and making these strategies relevant to the primary care setting. Primary care has embraced the integration of the different facets of patients, including cognitive, physical, affective, behavioral, and motivational components, and how these unite to provide a thorough understanding and formulation of patient problems and the search for effective interventions.

Biopsychosocial Model

The term *biopsychosocial* stems from George Engel, who, in 1977, introduced the biopsychosocial model of disease in a now-classic article entitled "The Need for a New Medical Model: A Challenge for Biomedicine." This model is based on the interplay of the biological, the psychological, and the social aspects of a person's disease (Engel, 1977). In describing this model, Campbell and Rohrbaugh (2006, pp. 10–11) stated:

> *In the biopsychosocial model, the biological system emphasizes the anatomical, structural, and molecular substrates of disease and their effects on the patient's biological*

functioning; the psychological system addresses the contributions of developmental factors, motivation, and personality on the patient's experiences of and reactions to illness; and the social system examines the cultural, environmental, and familial influences on the expression of, as well as the patient's experiences of, illness.

This revolutionary view of patients strayed from the traditional unidimensional approach of viewing health and illness, and focused on incorporating and viewing biological, psychological, and social aspects of the person and how these factors influenced, precipitated, interacted with, and maintained illness. Not unexpectedly, this novel viewpoint of health and illness (and even wellness) represented a major paradigm shift and, as a result, was met with resistance from the medical community. The social and psychological aspects of a patient's life, unlike the physical biological markers, emerged from the "soft" sciences and were not accorded the same respect or potency in explaining, let alone affecting, patients. Consequently, they were not previously considered or, if so, were minimized, at best. Over the past two decades, volumes of research have attested to the importance of these factors in fully understanding and treating patient problems in the medical setting.

The biopsychosocial approach assesses functioning within the behavioral, emotional, affective, biological, psychological, and social realms. Physiological, behavioral, and cognitive mechanisms may link to an individual's health (Richman et al., 2005), and positive emotions may correspond with a healthy lifestyle *to the extent that* assessing patients on all domains of this model may more accurately measure functioning and risk and protective factors. For example, with hypertensive patients, assessment on the social domain (such as social support) may yield clues about their support network, a well-known buffer to stress and possible key to facilitating adherence to medical regimens. Evidence suggests that individuals who have strong social supports typically manage their hypertension better than those without social support (Marzari et al., 2005).

An explanation of each of the domains and their impact will underscore the importance of this model for the cognitive-behavioral clinician in primary care. The *biological* component encompasses all physical and demographic factors related to the patient. Assessment on this domain specifically addresses the age, sex, race, physical appearance, symptoms, health status, physical examination, vital signs, laboratory data, medications, drugs, psychophysiological data, constitutional factors, genetics, and history of injury, disease, and surgery. The biological domain captures the unique physical portrait of the patient undergoing assessment and warrants exploration of factors such as genetics, medications, substances, and physical conditions. This area, although critically important, represents only one piece of the puzzle.

The *psychological* component encompasses all those things that are related to the psychological functioning of the patient. Assessment on this domain includes any history of psychological problems (including type, nature, duration, and severity), psychological vulnerabilities, disruptions in psychological development from childhood, and psychosocial stressors and coping mechanisms. Cognitive aspects of the patient are assessed here as well, including thoughts, attitudes, beliefs, and assumptions, as well as behaviors and emotions that may be related to illness. These data form the basis for a functional analysis of behavior as a basis for determining, for instance, whether any behaviors are serving a specific purpose, such as escape, avoidance, or secondary gain.

The *social* component of the biopsychosocial model focuses the clinician's attention toward the role of family, friends, significant others, social issues, education, work, housing, income, access to health care services, and legal problems. Especially relevant in this domain is the strength or lack of close interpersonal relationships, the patient's social support network.

Engel's (1977) view of the inadequacy of the traditional medical model opened the way for a new understanding of patients. He emphasized the consequences of failing to factor in other important domains of the patient's life and functioning, and argued for a fuller, richer, comprehensive, and more useful understanding of patients from assessment and treatment perspectives. In the field of psychology, the rise in popularity of learning-based approaches added significantly to the development of empirically based assessment and treatment alternatives.

Learning-Based Models

The development and extension of learning-based approaches to psychotherapy and behavior change have dramatically impacted the course of medical care. The implicit assumptions of these approaches, including operant-based, classically conditioned-based cognitive models and, more recently, the influx of mindfulness-based models, have been quite influential. The most central tenet of these approaches is the critical role of learning in developing, maintaining, extinction of, generalizing, and modifying behavior. The implicit ideas are that behavior is learned to a great extent and, therefore, can be unlearned; maladaptive behavior can be replaced with adaptive behavior; behavior can be replaced by learning and engaging in positive incompatible behaviors; new behaviors can be shaped gradually through reinforcement; and, finally, that laws of learning are powerful models for understanding, predicting, and controlling behaviors. The central role of cognitive factors, including automatic thoughts, implicit assumptions, and underlying conditional and unconditional beliefs and their inherent relationships to behaviors and feelings is also of paramount importance. These models have placed great emphasis on behavior broadly defined as the problem, and moved away from models presuming the importance of some underlying cause. The focus on history of the patient as a learning blueprint provides clues to formulating models that explain the development of problems, their maintenance, and ultimately their treatment. Finally, these models have spawned unique and widely applicable and useful methods of assessment, case formulation models, and specific empirically based treatment strategies. Perhaps no other models in the history of psychology and mental health have provided as much empirical evidence to support the application of psychological principles to the assessment and treatment of patient problems commonly encountered in primary care. More recently, there has been great emphasis on transporting efficacious treatments into the community at large and testing their effectiveness in clinical settings.

In sum, the melding of primary care, the biopsychosocial model, and learning-based approaches have much to offer in enhancing the care of patients in medical settings. However, there are many practical and logistical issues that affect the application of these theories and principles in the practical everyday world of the

PCP. In the next section, we describe these issues and strategies for overcoming them.

Practical and Logistical Issues

There are a number of unique issues that the cognitive-behavioral clinician will confront in working with primary care patients. Practical and logistical issues are those that relate to the day-to-day operations of the medical environment and that impact the delivery and collaborative implementation of service. Whether working onsite with physicians or outside of the medical center independently, a number of considerations must be addressed. Otherwise, care will be compromised and the providers are likely to experience significant frustrations with each other. These include issues related to time constraints, schedules, turn-around of information, and resistance. To ensure success in this regard, the therapist must, for all intents and purposes, become a student of primary care and fully embrace the model, understanding and accepting its basic tenets and its underpinnings. An appreciation of the role of the PCP and filtering what the therapist does through the lens of the physician will help make whatever is offered to the physician most practical and applicable. The medical environment is a time-oriented setting, in which typically there are large numbers of patients being seen in limited time slots. Although mental health clinicians are accustomed to having the luxury of a 50-minute hour in which to provide service, most physicians spend about 15 minutes or even less with patients. Likewise, the sheer volume of patients in a typical primary care practice for which a physician is responsible dwarfs the usual patient panel of the mental health clinician. These factors usually place physicians under a great deal of pressure to balance multiple priorities simultaneously, with limited time to spend talking with other providers. Considering the typical schedules of most therapists, arranging time to collaborate may present a significant challenge. Likewise, what time is available is typically limited, placing further constraints on the situation. In consulting with physicians, this means avoiding overelaborate, highly theoretical, and overly detailed explanations of the patient's problem (e.g., a theoretical aspect of an aspect of an aspect of a patient's problem) that may be completely unnecessary and not well received by the physicians. A consideration of what the physician needs to know versus does not necessarily need to know will streamline an already time-pressured encounter and will be appreciated by the physician. Seizing available opportunities to discuss a patient on the fly and openly accepting one's role as a consultant are helpful. A related time issue is office staff, who may see it as their role to buffer the physician from undue distractions and to keep the schedule flowing. Coordinating office space and differences in the manner in which services are billed may also be problems. Many physicians are frustrated by the lack of flow of information back to them about their patients, as well as the timing of the response when they do receive information. These issues necessitate educating physicians about unique confidentiality issues in psychotherapy and obtaining permission from patients as a prerequisite for treatment at the outset to share relevant information. Patients may not initially appreciate the mind-body connection and the value and importance of integrating care. Failure to include the physician may seriously compromise care and create mixed messages when the physician and therapist are not on the same page, so to speak. Dealing with resistant physicians who may not appreciate the role of the therapist is another matter. It is often valuable to use medical metaphors as a means of explaining problems and situations to physicians. For example, the use of standardized psychological tests, such as the Beck Depression Inventory (Beck, Ward, Mendelson, Mock, & Erbaugh, 1961) and the Beck Anxiety Scale (Beck, Epstein, Brown, & Steer, 1988), may be likened to screening blood work. To deal with a physician who views a serious suicidal threat as an attention-getting device, the seriousness of hopelessness and suicidal intent as cardinal indicators may be likened to crushing substernal chest pain and shortness of breath on exertion as impending signs of a heart attack. Forging positive relationships with physicians, educating them about your role, collaborating with them, respecting their role as coordinator of patient care, and demonstrating the value of your services are critical for success. There are also a number of clinical and professional issues to consider.

Clinical and Professional Issues

Clinical issues relate to specific assessment, diagnostic, and treatment issues that arise in collaboration with physicians. The therapist would be wise to consider a number of unique considerations in patients presenting in primary care settings. First, most patients presenting in primary care are seeking care from their physician as a result of physical symptoms that they are experiencing. Their illness representations are frequently physical, as opposed to psychological. Coupled with this fact is that many problems are presented to physicians in an undifferentiated state, requiring the therapist to anticipate what a symptom could represent and to be prepared for early detection. A proportion of patients will, as a result, resist the idea of a psychological interpretation as a cause of a problem. It takes a great deal of skill and coordination between the physician and therapist to present an explanation that the patient will accept. This may involve framing the patient's problem in terms that the patent will accept, such as initially referring to the patient's problem as stress, as opposed to depression. A patient may be more willing to accept stress management as a treatment, as opposed to psychotherapy. Of course, the timing of a referral is also important (Belar & Deardorff, 1995). Physicians who espouse a true biopsychosocial model help patients entertain the interrelationship of these factors early on and may be more likely to accept the involvement of a therapist, unlike the patient who would naturally assume that a referral means the problem is only in their head. The primary care therapist must also be cognizant of the fact that the types of problems often seen in primary care patients are directly related to the setting in which they are seeking care. For example, one may be more likely to encounter medical phobias in the primary care setting than in a typical mental health population.

Other important clinically related problems confronted by the therapist may include issues related to differential diagnosis, inappropriate treatment for problem, specific assessment and diagnostic and treatment issues that arise, recommendation and use of nonempirically based treatments, poor quality of information originally obtained by the physician, lack of a thorough biopsychosocial conceptualization of the patient's problem, failure to appropriately address nonadherence issues, and improper handling of problematic, difficult cases. The therapist must also appreciate that some clinical problems are more common than others in primary care settings, and these base rates must be considered in diagnostic decisions. A thorough understanding of common presenting problems and their clinical and typical manifestations, including depression, anxiety, and substance abuse, should be considered. Physical symptoms may be signs of a depressive equivalent or mask an underlying psychological diagnosis. Likewise, physicians often think of patients as sick versus not sick or emergent versus nonemergent, which allows them to quickly ascertain the necessity for responding quickly to a patient problem. These issues warrant great skill on the part of the therapist in negotiating a win-win solution while allowing the physician to save face, and ultimately providing optimal care to the patient.

Professional challenges confronted by therapists may stem from role-related issues (therapist versus physician), differing models of patient care, role status, or confusion (e.g., a physician expecting a recommendation for a psychotropic medicine from the therapist), expecting the therapist to do something outside of his/her prescribed role and unique norms in medical settings. Regarding the latter, violation of norms may alienate the physician from the therapist. For example, the therapist should avoid telling patients that their physician needs to order a particular test, such as an MRI. These types of matters are more appropriately handled by the physician.

Ethical Issues

There are a number of special ethical considerations in medical settings, and the astute clinician will make him/herself aware of such before embarking on practice. These issues reflect problematic ethical concerns and dilemmas that are raised in collaboration (e.g., confidentiality, informed consent, charting, appropriateness of information for the chart, competence issues, and boundary violations). These issues are discussed in more depth elsewhere in this book, and should be carefully considered to avoid unethical practice.

Recommendations for Effective Practice

To function effectively in collaborating with PCPs, there are a number of important recommendations for effective practice. Therapists should consider the following:

1. Understand and learn as much as possible about the primary care model of medical care. A thorough appreciation of the tenets of primary care, as well as the role of the PCP, will enhance the likelihood of successful handling of the patient.
2. Respect the mores, norms, and customs of practicing within a medical environment, and find the common ground between medicine and mental health practice with a commitment to collaboration and consultation.
3. Embrace the biopsychosocial and learning-based cognitive-behavioral model of assessment and intervention, with an emphasis on empirically based and tested approaches.

4. Educate physicians about the biopsychosocial model of patient care and the cognitive-behavioral approach and its relevance for assessing, conceptualizing, and treating common problems in primary care.
5. Educate physicians about the role of the cognitive-behavioral therapist, the assessment and treatment model, and the effectiveness of this approach in helping patients.
6. Emphasize an empirically based approach to practice that is commonly accepted in medical circles today, emphasizing the outcomes associated with this approach. Educate physicians about the CBT approach as a psychosocial model of empiricism.
7. Respond to physicians and keep them informed in a timely manner, sharing the case conceptualization and treatment plan with the physician and patient.
8. Provide assistance that is practical, understandable, applicable, useful, and easily adopted in the primary care setting.
9. Use medical metaphors to communicate the rationale of assessment and treatment procedures.
10. Avoid turf wars and emphasize the common ground between physician and therapist, which is the welfare of the patient. Coordinate the care of the patient with the physician and reinforce the role of the physician as the coordinator of patient care.

References

Beck, A. T., Epstein, M., Brown, G., & Steer, R. A. (1988). An inventory for measuring clinical anxiety: Psychometic properties. *Journal of Consulting and Clinical Psychology, 56*(6), 893–897.

Beck, A. T., Ward, C. H., Mendelson, M., Mock, J., & Erbaugh, J. (1961). An inventory for measuring depression. *Archives of General Psychiatry, 4*(6), 561–571.

Belar, C. D., & Deardorff, W. W. (1995). *Clinical health psychology in medical settings: A practitioner's guidebook.* Washington, DC: American Psychological Association.

Bray, J. H. (2009). Future of psychology practice. *Pennsylvania Psychologist, 16*(1), 3–4.

Campbell, W. H., & Rohrbaugh, R. M. (2006). *The biopsychosocial formulation manual: A guide for mental health professionals.* New York: Routledge.

Colameco, S. M., & DiTomasso, R. A. (1982). Arachnoid cyst associated with psychological disturbance. *Journal of the Medical Society of New Jersey, 79*, 209–210.

DiTomasso, R. A., & Colameco, S. M. (1982.) Patient self-monitoring of behavior. *Journal of Family Practice, 15*(1), 79–83.

DiTomasso, R. A., Freeman, A., Carvajal, R., & Zahn, B. (2010). The cognitive model of anxiety. In D. Stein, E. Hollander, & B. O. Rothblum (Eds.), *Textbook of anxiety disorders* (2nd ed., pp. 103–116). Washington, DC: American Psychiatric Press.

DiTomasso, R. A., Martin, D. M., & Kovnat, K. (2002). Crisis in medical patients. In F. Datillio & A. Freeman (Eds.), *Cognitive behavioral strategies to crisis intervention* (pp. 409-428). New York: Guilford.

Engel, G. L. (1977). The need for a new medical model: A challenge for biomedicine. *Science, 196*(4286), 129–136.

Marzari, C., Maggi, S., Manzato, E., Destro, C., Noale, M., Bianchi, D., et al. (2005). Depressive symptoms and development of coronary heart disease events: The Italian longitudinal study on aging. *Journals of Gerontology: Series A: Biological Sciences and Medical Sciences, 60A*(1), 85–93.

Matarazzo, J. D. (Ed.). (1984). *Behavioral health: A handbook of health enhancement and disease prevention.* New York: Wiley.

Richman, L. S., Kubzansky, L., Maselko, J., Kawachi, I., Choo, P., & Bauer, M. (2005). Positive emotion and health: Going beyond the negative. *Health Psychology, 24*(4), 422–429.

Seime, R. J., Clark, M. M., & Whiteside, S. P. (2003). Health psychology practice in medical settings. In L. M. Cohen, D. E. McChargue, & F. L. Collins, Jr. (Eds.), *The health psychology handbook* (pp. 3–16). Thousand Oaks, CA: Sage.

Sperry, L. (2008) *Treatment of chronic medical conditions: Cognitive-behavioral therapy strategies and integrative treatment protocols*. Washington, DC: American Psychological Association.

Taylor, R. B. (2003). Family medicine: Now and future practice. In R. B. Taylor (Ed.), A. K. David, S. A. Fields, D. M. Phillips, & J. E. Scherger (Assoc. Eds.), *Family medicine: Principles and practice*. New York: Springer Publishing Company.

The Cognitive-Behavioral Clinician: Roles and Functions and Ethical Challenges in Primary Care

2

Robert A. DiTomasso
Samuel Knapp
Barbara A. Golden
Harry J. Morris
Kenneth J. Veit

Introduction

More psychologists are practicing as clinical health psychologists, as opposed to just providing mental health services. Clinical health psychology can be broadly defined as the psychological assessment of and intervention with physical health problems. The clinical health psychologist may treat patients individually (e.g., a psychologist is working with a patient who wants to stop smoking), treat patients as part of a larger multidisciplinary team (e.g., a psychologist who is providing relaxation treatment to a patient who is also receiving treatment for a medical condition), or provide a brief service to the patient of another health care provider (e.g., a psychologist who evaluates medical patients to determine their capacity to consent to medical procedures).

Several factors suggest that the importance of health psychology will increase in the near future. First, the population is getting older and will have more illnesses that are likely to manifest themselves in older years, such as arthritis and neuromuscular diseases (Yali & Revenson, 2004). Also, there is a greater emphasis on promoting long-term behavior and lifestyle changes (healthy eating, exercise, abstention from smoking, etc.), as opposed to simply treating diseases once they emerge. Furthermore, the knowledge base on how psychological interventions can promote physical health has increased. Finally, medicine is putting greater emphasis on the body and mind interaction, the development of a biopsychosocial model, and health care for the whole person (Belar, 2008; Kaslow et al., 2007).

In the primary care setting, the CBT clinician may function in one or more of a variety of different roles, each of which may directly or indirectly impact the quality of patient care delivered. These roles include that of teacher, clinician, consultant, researcher, and administrator. There are a number of reasons for the placement of CBT in primary care. There is little doubt that the traditional biomedical model fails to serve the needs of patients by ignoring critical factors that are relevant to effective assessment and outcome. Limited access to comprehensive, quality evidence-based care is a major issue facing the U.S. health care system. Over the past several years, there has been an increasing emphasis on evidence-based approaches in primary care. Many of the serious and prevalent problems that undermine the health of individuals by increasing morbidity and mortality rates through a vicious cycle, perpetuating poor health outcomes and premature deaths, are behaviorally based. Failure to comprehensively attend to the needs of these patients is a critical contributory factor. There is an ever-increasing body of empirical evidence (Smith, Keith, & Kendall, 2002), however, supporting the effectiveness of psychological interventions in improving a wide range of physical problems, including both acute and chronic illness (Coumos & Goldfinger, 2006; Jason, Corrodi, & Torres-Harding, 2005). For the past several years, the American Psychological Association (APA) has strongly supported initiatives promoting the integration of psychological services in the primary care setting (www.apa.org/ppo/issues/psycare.html; apa.org/practice/pu/jun98/primary).

The rationale and evidence base that supports these proposed activities has been clearly elucidated in published, refereed series of studies throughout the health-psychology and behavioral-medicine outcome literature. Based on a set of stringent methodological criteria, these treatments have also been listed as efficacious by the Division 12, APA Task Force on the Dissemination of Evidence-Based Treatments. There is currently a plethora of clinical-outcome research studies demonstrating the efficacy of the treatments, as shown in evidence-based treatment manuals and treatments and strategies that have been tested on clinical populations. These evidence-based cognitive-behavioral treatments (APA, 1995, 2005) will maximize the likelihood of positive outcomes. Examples include the work of Brownell, Wadden, and Foster (2002) on obesity; DiTomasso (1987; DiTomasso & Mills, 1990) on hypertension; Lynch and Zamble (1989), Payne and Blanchard (1995), and Blanchard (2005) on IBS; Gatchel (2005) and Okifuji and Ackerlind (2007) on chronic pain; Surwitt (2002) on diabetes; Meichenbaum and Turk (1987) on facilitating treatment adherence; and Hill et al. (1993), Stevens and Hollis (1989, Cinciripini et al. (1994), and Cinciripini (1995) on smoking cessation.

Cognitive-behavioral clinicians can contribute by thoroughly addressing the interface between critical factors that are likely to undermine the health status of these primary care patients by attending to the key components for comprehensive care, assessing and targeting specific problem areas, and delivering evidence-based treatments aimed at each target. Based on a thorough assessment process, a specific comprehensive treatment plan can be tailored for each patient and must include specific interventions to address the relevant target problems for each patient coupled with close, on-going systematic monitoring of progress. This chapter will review theoretical issues, practical and logistical issues, ethical issues, and recommendations for effective practice. A significant amount of literature will be presented for ethical practice for clinicians working in primary care.

Theoretical Issues

Cognitive-behavior theory has considerable relevance to the assessment and treatment of patients in primary care. Cognitive therapy has several basic principles that are the guidelines for practice and empirically supported treatments (A. T. Beck, 1964; J. Beck, 1995). The first principle is *cognitive therapy is based on the formulation of the patient and presenting problems in cognitive terms*. Throughout this volume, brief case histories and cognitive conceptualizations will identify patients' distorted thoughts and problematic behaviors regarding various medical and mental health concerns. Suggestions will be made regarding how developmental events have contributed to enduring patterns of interpreting events, leading to increased feelings of depression, anxiety, and the exacerbation of physical symptoms. The second principle is *cognitive therapy requires a sound therapeutic alliance*. It is common knowledge that if a relationship is marked by trust, the outcomes are generally favorable. For primary care patients, physicians, and mental health clinicians, this relationship should be empathetic, caring, and genuine. This will generate more mutual collaboration and willingness to proceed where significant obstacles may otherwise predict potential failure. Principle three *emphasizes collaboration and active participation* on the part of all persons. If a patient sees and experiences more control over physical, psychological, and social factors, they are more likely to exercise active participation in changing thoughts about health behaviors that will lead to behavioral change. The fourth principle suggests that *cognitive therapy is goal-oriented and problem-focused*. For primary care patients and very busy physicians working with a specific plan, focused goals and clear objectives toward empirically supported outcomes is quite motivating and can be challenging. Thus, working in a multidisciplinary model will generate the most success. Principle five says that *cognitive therapy is designed to be educative*, leading the person to become independent from the therapist and ultimately self-guide treatment. This will help to prevent relapse. In the primary care setting, as patients learn more about illness and the biopsychosocial model of illness, it is more likely that they will be able to generate greater solutions to problems, instead of a narrow focus only on the physical symptoms. Principle six states that *cognitive therapy is time-limited*. This factor is appealing to all individuals: the patient, family, physician, employer, and health care insurers. The seventh principle states that *cognitive therapy is structured*. Because every session follows an agenda and a treatment plan that has been developed collaboratively, more attention is paid to the priorities of the patient and use of time is maximized for all individuals. The eighth principle says that *cognitive therapy teaches the patient to identify, evaluate, and respond to dysfunctional beliefs*. For most patients, this is an entirely new way of life. As the patient learns to identify the distortions that exacerbate distress, they begin to experience a greater sense of hope for a future of change. The ninth principle states that *cognitive therapy uses a variety of strategies to change thoughts, mood, and behaviors*. The patient is constantly learning new strategies to implement for different problems and obstacles that may be present in the course of health care treatment.

Cognitive therapy is designed to be active, collaborative, and empirically sound. The various roles of the clinician allow for therapy to be implemented for a variety of presenting problems in primary care.

Teacher

In the role of teacher, the CBT practitioner engages in one or more informal or formal educational activities designed to increase the knowledge, skill, or attitudes of the medical practitioner in a given area. In this role, the CBT practitioner serves a variety of functions. First, the information imparted may provide new, insightful, and useful information that improves the quality of health care delivered by the medical practitioner. Here, the physician may have a knowledge deficit, lack of skill, or a blind spot that warrants correction. The implicit assumption is that the information imparted would alter the manner in which the physician conceptualizes the patient's problem and intervenes. Second, the clinician may correct misconceptions held by the practitioner that may undermine effective treatment delivery. For example, the physician who interprets a suicidal threat or gesture as means of obtaining attention may unwittingly place a patient at undue risk. Third, the information may reinforce the existing knowledge base of the physician and result in continued good practice. Fourth, the information may provide the physician with a number of testable hypotheses that may account for the patient's problem and serve as a basis for sound care. Fifth, an indirect by-product of teaching is that it may serve to reinforce the role of the CBT clinician as a resource for specific cases. This could lead to the physician seeking consultation from the clinician or referring patients to the clinician. Finally, the learned information may help to focus attention on critical issues and previously ignored aspects of patient functioning. In our own clinical practices, we note a consistent rise in the number of referrals based on topics presented at case conferences.

There are innumerable opportunities for teaching, both formally and informally, in the primary care setting. These didactic opportunities depend on the role one has with the physician, and varies on a continuum where clinicians practice separately in different settings to one where the CBT practitioner is practicing side by side in the primary care clinic with the physician. In either case, the practitioner would do well to view each encounter with a physician as a teachable opportunity. This role may involve imparting information about theory, knowledge on practical tips on handling patients, or sensitizing the physician to important issues related to diversity. These moments occur in the context of real patient encounters, and provide unique and valuable opportunities to apply theory and knowledge for the benefit of the patient. The important consideration here is that the physician and CBT clinician are on the same page with congruent information, reducing the likelihood of the patient receiving mixed messages. These educational opportunities provide an invaluable interchange where the physician and therapist learn from each other as well. In this manner, one may find the physician developing a more healthy respect for the biopsychosocial view, and the therapist developing more respect for the biological aspects of the patient's problems. This can form the basis for a mutually beneficial relationship where it is the patient who actually receives most benefit.

Formalized teaching opportunities offer another unique advantage. In every medical setting, physicians are required to earn continuing medical education credits. There are excellent opportunities for the CBT clinician to present empirically based approaches to assessment and treatment. Teaching opportunities manifest themselves in a number of formats, including curbside consults or side bar consults, precepting of interns and residents, formal presentations, and teaching curricular components in residency settings.

Clinician

Cognitive-behavior therapists in the primary care environment are in a unique position to make a contribution to patient care. There are a number of important issues to address. First and foremost, one must consider the tenets of primary care as important in understanding patients. PCPs usually aim to provide comprehensive care and continuity of care over the course of the life cycle. Sir William Osler is credited with saying, "It is more important to know what sort of person has a disease than what sort of disease a person has" (Chehab & Fealy, 2008). These words of wisdom underscore the importance of the biopsychosocial model in medical care. As early as 1747, Gaub aptly noted, "The reason why a sound body becomes ill, or an ailing body recovers, very often lies in the mind" (Gaub, cited in Lipowski, 1977, p. 234). The fact is that a significant majority of patients presenting for care in the primary care setting are suffering from psychological distress. We must consider that base rates are critically important from the standpoint of understanding that what is common is common.

In the role of clinician, the CBT therapist may perform one or more of a variety of functions. These functions include: individual psychotherapy, group therapy, couples therapy, family therapy, and psychological assessment. The CBT clinician must comprehensively address the concerns of patients presenting in primary care, who will often seek out their family physician in time of need. Early recognition is crucial to ward off the potential for more serious complications and possible debilitation. Fortunately, CBT clinicians are trained to be familiar with critical questions to ask, and the use of appropriate clinical instruments to determine problems early on in undifferentiated states.

Patients often become symptomatic at times of life events or life-cycle changes, requiring adjustment on the part of the patients.

From a clinical perspective, the CBT therapist must do the following:

1. Determine the primary problem, which problem came first, which problem resulted from the initial problem, and which problem is causing the most impairment for the patient?
2. Use the continuity of care to the patient's benefit.
3. Know the patient's history and when, how, and to what extent the patient will react symptomatically.
4. Use the "family" in family practice to serve as important informants about the patient's presenting problem.
5. Prescribe empirically supported treatments for the patient.
6. Educate all health care staff to the biopsychosocial model.

Physicians have usually attended to the biological presentation of the patient. This may be an inadequate explanation of the patient's problem, and results in partial treatment. The key to the solution often lies in the psychosocial arena.

Consultant

In the primary care environment, there are numerous opportunities for consultation. Despite commitment to training in the biopsychosocial model, physicians are often lacking the skill mix that is necessary to accurately *diagnose, assess, conceptualize, and intervene* with their patients from other than a basic biomedical framework. Even those who have the training and desire to comprehensively address their patients and their problems frequently do not have the time that it takes to do so. The result is a situation in which significant pieces of information are lacking, including information that may be essential to fully and successfully help the patient. As a case in point, take the middle-aged diabetic male who has poor eating and exercise habits and is not contemplating the need for behavior change. From a psychological perspective, this patient is currently at the precontemplative stage of change (Prochaska & DiClemente, 1992). Diabetic education, although necessary, in and of itself is clearly not sufficient to set the stage for meaningful and consistent behavioral change. Efforts aimed at motivational interviewing designed to assist the patient in progressing to the contemplative and planning stages of change coupled with diabetic education and nutritional counseling are more likely to yield a positive outcome. Telling the patient to lose weight and handing him a 1500-calorie diabetic diet to follow will most likely not result in weight loss.

Clinicians may be called upon to provide any one of a number of consultative services to physicians. These services often include the need to provide the physician with a diagnostic opinion. Pure *Diagnostic and Statistical Manual of Mental Disorders* (*DSM-IV-TR*; American Psychiatric Association, 2000) diagnoses, however, may be inadequate in fully explaining the patient's problem and providing a basis for intervention. The ability to comprehensively and accurately assess patients is undoubtedly critical. Knowing the most critical questions to ask in establishing reasonable explanatory hypotheses is perhaps even more important. The cognitive-behavioral clinician who asks important and relevant questions may be able to provide data that convincingly demonstrate meaningful and important considerations to the physician. One of the authors was consulted about a 35-year-old female patient with unexplainable, persistent epigastric pain that had been extensively evaluated from a medical standpoint and was unresponsive to treatment. The consultant arranged to interview the patient with the physician present. One key question turned out to be related to the temporal onset of the problem. The patient reported that the pain began about one year earlier and named the month. Gentle probing around significant events at that time uncovered that the patient's sister, after a night of heavy drinking with her, had committed suicide at that time. Further probing revealed that the patient's sister had left several unanswered desperate phone calls pleading for help on the patient's cell phone. Not coincidentally, the victim had shot herself in the abdomen with a shotgun and was found by the patient. The patient's treatment was then shifted appropriately from antacid medication to grief and trauma work surrounding the patient's guilt and unresolved grief. As a consultant, the CBT clinician may also be helping in identifying and selecting empirically based treatment options and clinicians in the community who offer such services.

Researcher

The psychologist in the primary care setting functioning as a researcher is able to conduct various outcome studies reviewing various situations related to the office staff, settings, diagnostic strategies, and intervention strategies. As a researcher, the importance of accessing outcomes in these settings is critical.

Administrator

In functioning as an administrator, the CBT therapist may be called upon to help in the staff-selection process, resolve conflicts, solve problems, and develop and implement strategies. In addition, the ability to teach and encourage communication skills among all staff members is paramount to effective office functioning. Cognitive-behavioral constructs are frequently useful in explaining organizational phenomena.

Practical and Logistical Issues

In whatever role the clinician finds him/herself, there are a number of practical and logistical issues to address. Practical and logistical issues are those that relate to the day-to-day operations affecting implementation of our roles and functions. A consideration of relevant factors related to the medical environment is critical to the success of any role. These factors deserve careful attention, as they may undermine anything a CBT clinician does in the medical setting, be it teaching, consulting, therapy, research, or administration.

First and foremost, the clinician must develop a thorough understanding of the audience with whom he/she is working. Physicians are usually trained to place a premium on time, meaning that they often work under significant time pressures and are frequently overburdened. This time sensitivity, based on the reality of their role, may affect the manner in which they perceive our interactions with them. They are usually balancing multiple priorities and anything that takes their time must be perceived as valuable, lest it be regarded as a waste of valuable time. This means that whatever the CBT clinician does with or for the physician must be presented in a manner that is the most helpful and without unnecessary frills. Second, the clinician must capitalize on available time to provide the most salient and most important information. Generally speaking, information that would likely be of great interest to other therapists may not be important for physicians. Information must be practical, and formed in a manner that is useful to the physician. Third, when communicating information, physicians usually need the critical highlights as they are accustomed to thinking in terms of markers or indicators in their problem solving. Fourth, as a prioritizing strategy, physicians typically think of patients in terms of criterion, such as sick versus nonsick. Finally, they usually approach problems in smaller graduated fashion over a period of time and number of visits, delineating between emergent and nonemergent situations.

Timing issues include scheduling time to collaborate, time constraints, and availability of office space and office staff. Billing issues that may be problematic necessitate a prompt response in order to keep the office running. Other issues include: appreciating the role of the physician; filtering our experience through the lens of the physician; finding common ground between the physician and CBT clinician; being practical; and providing useful information. Effective work with physicians presupposes that one fully understands and appreciates the role of the medical practitioner. Otherwise, whether we are teaching, consulting, or providing direct care to a physician's patient, what we are doing may not seem relevant to the physician. In fact, it may appear outrageous. This requires understanding the role of the physician, considering what is reasonable, being aware of time, and providing practical information that can easily be used. This means avoiding focusing on esoteric, highly theoretical aspects of a problem that truly have little relevance for the physician. It is most helpful to use the BLUF Method: **Bottom Line Up Front!** (Munsey, 2007). What may seem exciting and most interesting to the CBT clinician may be written off as somewhat irrelevant by the physician. Carefully consider what the physician needs to know in order to function effectively with the patient.

Clinical and Professional Issues

We see clinical issues having to do with specific assessment, diagnostic, and treatment issues that arise in the primary care setting. These issues relate to questions of differential diagnoses, inappropriate treatment for the problem, and treatment issues that arise. This calls for mutual respect and collaboration by all staff members. If the PCP does not conceptualize the process according to the biopsychosocial model, the results may be nonadherence and significant problems for patient care. Be aware that psychological problems may mimic medical problems. Collaboration with the physician helps to exhaust all possible realistic causes. When appropriate permissions have been granted, read the chart and look for patterns and themes. It is helpful to interview the patient with and without the physician, so all perspectives may be honestly assessed. Be sure to spend time with the physician and gain her/his perspective in light of the history that may be present with the case.

Professional issues relate to role-functioning issues of psychologists versus physicians, differing models of patient care, role status or confusion (e.g., a doctor expecting a recommendation for a psychotropic medicine from a psychologist), and expecting the psychologist to do something outside of her/his role. PCPs may resist a psychological interpretation of a presenting problem. Perhaps the physician may insist on continuing to reinforce behavior or expose a patient to unnecessary tests or diagnostic workups. These obstacles may be negotiated in a mutually respectful fashion, and generally become easier as the professional relationship grows. Neither party should attempt to "pull rank." This only serves to facilitate an impasse that ultimately affects patient care.

Ethical Issues

The ethical issues related to primary health care and health psychology are, in part, the application of general ethical principles to psychologists working in the area of clinical health psychology. That is, psychologists need to ensure that they are competent, protect patient privacy, get the informed consent of patients, refrain from entering into clinically contraindicated or exploitative multiple relationships, and follow the other standards of the profession, as found in the APA Ethics Codes, state laws, and other governing authorities. However, some of the applications of ethical issues in primary care or health care psychology are distinct because of the uniqueness of the work settings, the populations served, and the problems encountered.

For example, everyone would agree that psychologists working in clinical health psychology need to be competent. However, many psychologists working in health care psychology were originally trained in other areas of practice and respecialized, often informally, later in their careers. Consequently, discussions of competence in the field of health psychology should give more attention to the issue of retraining.

Another example is that everyone would agree that psychologists need to protect the privacy of patient information. However, much health psychology is conducted as part of a formal interdisciplinary team, or an informal system of different health care professionals. Consequently, psychologists working in health psychology may have to make more decisions about sharing information with other professionals than they traditionally had to do when working with short-term outpatients in an independent practice.

This section will look at the overall ethical principles and comment on their unique applications to health care psychologists, such as competence, informed consent, and confidentiality. This section is informed by the perspective of "positive ethics." As with any other professional psychologist, health psychologists who fail to follow the standards of the profession are placed at risk for a malpractice suit, ethics charge, or other forms of civil liability or disciplinary actions. Although the legal risks in health psychology are real, clinical health psychologists are motivated by more than just the desire to avoid being disciplined. Clinical health psychologists will want to strive for delivering the highest standard of care possible, consistent with deeply held ethical values. Consequently, the section will review moral foundations of behavior. Suggestions for practitioners include a discussion of risk-management strategies that are consistent with ethical principles, and a desire to promote a culture of safety in which probable risks are identified and steps taken to minimize the risk of harm.

Positive Ethics

Some psychologists think of ethics only as a fixed set of prohibitions derived from the statutes, regulations, or court cases governing the profession, or perhaps the legal procedures that govern the deliberations of adjudicative bodies. Consequently, the study of ethics is thought of primarily in terms of ways to avoid punishment. A different view is that ethics should also be concerned with ways that psychologists can adhere to foundational ethical principles, and strive to reach their highest ideals. This view, called positive ethics, does not mean that the laws and standards of the profession need to be ignored. Indeed, they are important for practical purposes and, for the most part, rest upon some ethical foundation. However, the laws and standards are not the sum total of the body of knowledge called ethics. A more complete view of ethics requires consideration of the individual's goals and values, and the ways that their lives can be uplifted.

According to the perspective of positive ethics, it is necessary to have a moral philosophy to guide behavior. Positive ethics does not specify what that philosophical system could be; it could be utilitarian, Kantian (deontological), feminist, virtue-based ethics, principle-based ethics, or some other ethical system of thought. This book will use the language and formulations of principle-based ethics, although other ethical systems could be used as well.

Sir William David Ross (1877–1940) developed principle-based (prima facie) ethics as a result of his dissatisfaction with the two dominant philosophical systems of his day: utilitarianism and deontological ethics. According to utilitarianism, a moral agent evaluates the morality of an action according to the amount of happiness it creates for all of the persons who are affected by that action, regardless of their relationship to the actor (the "greatest good for the greatest number"). However, Ross believed that moral agents sometimes have special obligations to parents, children, friends, employers, or others that take priority over their obligations to the public in general.

According to deontological ethics, a moral agent evaluates the morality of an action according to whether the actor is fulfilling a duty, with no exceptions allowed. However, Ross believed that the duties of moral agents sometimes appear to conflict, and that sometimes moral agents must break one rule in order to protect another.

As a result, Ross developed principle-based ethics that postulates several duties, ethical intuitions, or prima facie principles that should be followed, unless overridden by another moral obligation. Ross identified several of these duties, such as gratitude, justice, beneficence (coming to the assistance of others), self-improvement, and nonmaleficence (avoiding harming others), although Ross acknowledged that there may be other prima facie duties as well, or that others may classify the duties differently.

In recent years, philosophers at Georgetown University, Thomas Beauchamp and James Childress (2001), have applied Ross's principle-based theories to health care and have identified four moral principles especially important in the field of health care ethics (respect for client/patient autonomy, nonmaleficence, beneficence, justice). Others have added fidelity as a fifth principle (Bersoff & Koeppl, 1993; Kitchener, 1984), which refers to an obligation to keep one's promises, such as the promise of confidentiality, and general or public beneficience as a sixth principle (Knapp & VandeCreek, 2004), which refers to an obligation to protect the public or persons who are not clients or patients of the health care provider. The next section reviews several of these principles and how they apply to medical settings.

Competence

Competence is anchored on the moral principles of beneficence and nonmaleficence. That is, psychologists can fulfill their moral obligations of beneficence and nonmaleficence by ensuring that they are competent to deliver services. Competence entails emotional competence (ability to withstand the stressors of being a psychologist), cultural competence (knowledge of the ways that culture impacts behavior), and technical competence and knowledge.

A variety of mechanisms are in place to ensure that health care professionals have competence. These include the requirement of a graduate degree (the assumption is that the program will only graduate qualified persons), a license (the assumption is that the licensing standards of training, supervision, and performance on examinations will ensure that only competent persons will get licensed), or other mechanisms, such as mandated continuing education as a condition of continued licensing (the assumption is that this requirement will ensure that licensees stay current in their skills).

However, the license to practice psychology is generic and there is a risk that a psychologist may go into a new area of practice without adequate training. Belar et al. (2008) have identified a self-assessment template for psychologists to ensure that they are competent in clinical health psychology. This includes questions concerning the relevant knowledge base of psychology (such as the biological, cognitive, social-affective, and developmental bases of behavior), skill and knowledge in implementing empirically supported interventions and assessments, and an understanding of the context of service delivery and the ethical, legal, and professional issues involved. Knapp and VandeCreek (2006) have opined that any respecialization should involve some external review. Although much can be learned from self-study, feedback from an impartial expert is also required. This feedback could occur through a formal respecialization program or through a proctorship, wherein a licensed psychologist hires an expert to review his or her work product. Failure to have the technical skill or to understand the medical culture of the appropriate role of a clinical health psychologist could compromise the quality of patient care.

Case Example One

A patient shows a psychologist the psychotropic medication he received from his physician and asks him whether he should still take it. "It doesn't seem to do any good," the patient said. "Besides, it makes me constipated." The medication did not appear appropriate for the patient's condition.

In responding, an appropriately trained psychologist would consider the legal restrictions on her ability to advise patients on medications, the need for the patient to have a trusting relationship with the prescribing physician, and enough awareness to realize that physicians may sometimes prescribe off label for legitimate medical reasons that may not be obvious. Only having technical information about the properties of the psychotropic medication and the patient's diagnosis is not sufficient to guide the response of the psychologist.

Confidentiality

Confidentiality is anchored to the ethical principle of fidelity, or the commitment of the psychologist to keep his/her promises to the patient. The patient's control over the release of information is also consistent with the principle of respect for patient decision-making autonomy. Also, because confidentiality is often essential to ensure patient progress, it may also be linked to beneficience or nonmaleficence.

Confidentiality in health care is highly regulated by state and federal law, although patient information tends to be more highly regulated for psychologists and other mental health professionals. All health care psychologists need to be aware of the confidentiality statutes, regulations, and case law governing their professional behavior, including privileged communications laws, laws mandating the reporting of child or elder abuse, how to respond to subpoenas and court orders, laws concerning patient access to records, rules regarding the protection of copyrighted test materials, and other laws concerning patient information.

For example, a combination of state and federal laws (HIPAA; Health Insurance Portability and Accountability Act) determine patient access to records, including HIPAA's preemption clause that holds that state laws that are more protective of patient privacy, from the standpoint of the patient, trump HIPAA. HIPAA permits patients to see their medical records, except for psychotherapy notes that, according to HIPAA, are defined as those "recorded (in any medium) by a health care provider who is a mental health professional documenting or analyzing the contents of conversation during a private counseling session or a group, joint, or family counseling session and that are separated from the rest of the individual's medical records." In addition, a psychotherapy note "includes medication prescription and monitoring, counseling session start and stop times, the modalities and frequency of treatment furnished, results of clinical tests, and any summary of the following items: diagnosis, functional status, the treatment plan, symptoms, prognosis, and progress to date" (45 CFR 164.501).

Several features of these regulations are relevant. First, the treatment does not have to be mental health treatment for the note to constitute a psychotherapy note. Instead, the requirement is that the notes have to be dictated by a mental health professional, which would include a clinical health care psychologist. Second, according to HIPAA, a note written in the medical chart in a hospital by a psychologist would not be considered a psychotherapy note because the note was not separated from the medical records. Consequently, patients could have legal access to that note, if they wanted. For that reason, some psychologists working in health care settings keep a separate set of more detailed notes for some patients if the information is especially sensitive. Finally, HIPAA's definition of psychotherapy notes excludes the results of clinical tests, which means the results of psychological tests and evaluations. Consequently, HIPAA requires that all patients may receive their assessment results, thus necessitating that psychologists use discretion and diplomacy in their reporting of sensitive patient information.

Another issue related to confidentiality in health care settings is that clinical health psychologists need to keep other members of the health care team informed of relevant events in treatment. This may require discretion in what information to include or exclude in a patient's medical record. If a patient in a rehabilitation unit appears to have a histrionic personality disorder, it will probably provide little information to the treating staff to include that diagnosis in the patient's chart. However, it may be useful to note that the patient expresses emotions very openly and provide suggestions on how to respond to the patient (Benefield, Ashkanazai, & Rozensky, 2006).

Finally, following hospital protocols in documentation is important. Hospitals may have protocols for writing notes, such as the color of the pen, procedure for correcting a note, and format of the signature (Robinson & Baker, 2006). Prudent psychologists are careful about the scope of practice issues, as they may raise ill feeling. For example, Tovian (2006) recommends that the documentation of a medical diagnosis include the physician who made that diagnosis.

Also, working in a multidisciplinary setting requires sensitivity to accidental breaches of confidentiality.

Case Example Two

A psychologist was approached by a nurse in the hallway who started to tell her important information about one of the patients on the ward. Although no other patients or visitors were nearby, the psychologist sensed that the conversation could get into very personal material, and she motioned to the nurse to continue the conversation in a nearby vacant room.

Although HIPAA recognizes that health care personnel need to exchange information on the ward, and permits conversations like this to occur in semipublic places, the psychologist appropriately believed that it would be better to have the conversation in a more private location.

Case Example Three

A psychologist complained that the physicians seemed to ignore the recommendations in his reports, even though he spent much time writing them. A cooperative physician took him aside and explained that his reports were too long and contained too much jargon. He explained that the notes were more likely to be read if they were concise and direct.

This case example illustrates the importance of tailoring the notes for the audience intended. Although the detailed reports might be appropriate for some professionals under some circumstances, in this context, patient interests are better served by a brief and to-the-point note.

Informed Consent

Informed consent is the general theory that patients should be informed of the benefits and risks of treatments and allowed to make their own decisions, assuming they are competent to do so. Informed consent standards are based on the ethical principle of respect for patient autonomy. Informed consent has a long legal history within American history, including the right of patients to have basic information before they make decisions about their health care treatment, such as the risks and benefits of agreeing to the procedure. Although the specific formulations of informed consent vary according to state law, the general goal is to give patients the information that a reasonable person would want under the circumstances. The medical profession has seen a shift toward information consent and away from a paternalistic attitude where "the doctor knew best." In part, this shift occurred because of an increased emphasis on patient rights, and in part, it occurred because the public was more educated and sophisticated and better able to weigh the options presented. Nonetheless, in actual practice, the informed consent process in medicine tends to be highly legalistic for some medical procedures and consists of detailed forms that list every possible side effect that could occur, no matter how remote.

According to the APA Ethics Code, informed consent in therapy should include, at the minimum, "the nature and anticipated course of therapy, fees, involvement of third parties, and limits of confidentiality and provide sufficient opportunity for the client/patient to ask questions and receive answers" (APA, 2002, 10.01 [a]). However, conscientious clinical health care psychologists want to go beyond just ensuring that the minimal legal standards are met. Consistent with good clinical care and the spirit of respecting patient autonomy, good clinical health care psychologists will actively work to solicit patient perspectives and input into treatment decisions. This is so important that some authors redefine informed consent as shared participation, informed participation (Knapp & VandeCreek, 2006), or informed collaboration (Zuckerman, 2008).

Working within clinical health psychology may present certain unique issues with informed consent. First, psychologists may be evaluating the consent of individuals whose capacity to give consent is unclear. The APA Ethics Code states that psychologists do not need to get informed consent when "one purpose of the testing is to evaluate decisional capacity" (APA, 2002, 9.03 [a]). This may occur if the patient is suspected of having a dementia or perhaps has serious or profound mental retardation. Often, these individuals have not been adjudicated incapacitated and are therefore legally deemed competent to make health care decisions.

Nonetheless, the patient may show an inability to understand the nature of the assessment, let alone agree to it, or may not show the ability to make other health care decisions. At times, the patient may initially appear alert, but only after some interaction does it become clear that the patient fails to appreciate the nature of the health care assessment. Psychologists need to proceed with caution here. At times, it may be appropriate to speak to relatives about a hearing for declaring the patient incapacitated.

Another issue in informed consent in hospitals deals with the professional identity of the psychologist. In hospital settings, the psychologists need to identify themselves and the general nature of their intervention. The psychologist may be one of several health care professionals that the patient has seen that day. Some patients, in the midst of all of the emotional demands of a hospitalization, may become confused as to the role of the psychologists who visit them and why they are there. Nonetheless, as much as possible, psychologists should clarify their role. The patient may see the letters "Dr." before the name of the psychologist and assume that the individual is a physician. Some physicians are especially sensitive about the use of the term "Dr." by those who are not physicians, unless that term is qualified by informing the patient of the professional identity of the provider.

Recently, the House of Delegates of the American Medical Association passed a resolution requesting that states make it a felony for any health care providers to misrepresent themselves as a physician (AMA, 2008).

Other Ethical Issues

Clinical health psychologists may encounter other ethical issues simply by the fact that they are working in a health care system. Cultures of individual hospitals vary considerably. Some hospitals make a very deliberate effort to treat all employees and patients with respect. Nonetheless, hospitals are hierarchical institutions that, by their very nature, include periods of intense pressure, as the staff deal with sick and injured patients, life and death situations, and demands from insurers, families of patients, and others. At times, the hospital practice experience can be very unpleasant and dehumanizing for both patients and staff.

Although medical reformers are pushing for more empathy-based and patient-centered medicine, many physicians may appear gruff when under stress; some may be rude, and a few are despotic. Most physicians welcome other health care professionals as collaborators, others tolerate them, and a few openly disdain other professions, which they see as competitors. Psychologists will survive, or even thrive, in these environments when they appreciate the formal and informal rules governing institutional behavior. On the formal level, they need to understand the role of accrediting agencies like the Joint Commission for the Accreditation of Health Care Organizations (JCAHO), the rules concerning the mission of the medical staff or adjunctive medical staff, and the roles of credential and peer review committees (Rozensky, 2006). On an informal level, they need to show respect for the skills and roles of other professionals, make a concerted effort to focus on patient welfare, know how to build positive relationships with other staff members, and know when to let an issue slide and when to take a stand.

No one response is appropriate for all the conflicts that may arise when working in a health care setting. It is best that psychologists start by consulting with someone to determine whether their perceptions of the ethical issues are accurate and, if it is determined that their instincts about the ethical issues are accurate, it is recommended that the psychologist start to document attempts to rectify the situation. Usually, it is best to start with a low-key educational approach and move into more formal organizational complaints later.

Basics of Risk Management

Generally, the relationship between competence and the likelihood of being the subject of a disciplinary complaint or malpractice suit is positive, but low to moderate. That is, psychologists who act poorly are more likely to be subject to complaints. However, an element of arbitrariness occurs in the disciplinary process, and often, competent and ethical mental health professionals have complaints filed against them.

Bennett and colleagues (2006) have identified certain types of patients and types of situations where complaints are more likely to occur. Patients who have difficulty forming productive relationships are more likely to file complaints. This

2.1 Strategies and Their Moral Foundations

	Transparency	Moral Foundation
Informed Consent	Be clear as possible about what you want to do together, how you propose doing it, and why.	Respect for patient autonomy and decision making
Consultation	When seeking consultation, be honest with yourself about your strengths and limitations. The best way to receive accurate information about yourself is from others.	Beneficence
Documentation	Be accurate, honest, and diplomatic in documentation.	Beneficence
Redundant protections	Be clear as to the purpose of the redundant strategy.	Beneficence, nonmaleficence

includes those who have a background of being abused, who have a serious personality disorder (especially borderline narcissistic), or who are seriously suicidal or homicidal. Wealthier persons are also more likely to file complaints. Complaints are more likely to occur when there is an assessment with external implications (employment testing, child custody evaluation, etc.), or when the patient is involved in some kind of litigation. It is certainly desirable to avoid complaints or to avoid the types of situations that are likely to lead to patient dissatisfaction.

Unnecessarily defensive or insensitive risk-management strategies increase the vulnerability of mental health professionals to an allegation of misconduct, to the extent that they distance professionals from authentic and meaningful relationships with their patients. Of course mental health professionals need to be cognizant of and to consider disciplinary consequences, and to have a certain healthy amount of fear for personal liability. However, proper risk management should be driven primarily by a concern to be consistent with moral principles and designed to promote patient or public welfare. It should not be driven by excessive fear or distrust of patients.

When faced with difficult patients or high-risk situations, professionals are wise to give special attention to the four risk-management strategies (documentation, informed consent, and consultation identified by Bennett et al. [2006], and redundant protection identified by Knapp and VandeCreek [2006]). They both enhance patient welfare and, at the same time, protect the professional in the event that a patient alleges misconduct. All of these risk-management strategies can be linked to ethical principles. Generally speaking, these strategies should be implemented openly and with transparency. That is, the psychologists should be up front with themselves, their patients, and other staff as to why these procedures are being followed. Those risk-management strategies and their implementation principles are shown in Table 2.1, as well as their relationship to transparency and their basis in ethical principles.

These strategies, when used together in a responsible manner by conscientious employees, create a *culture of safety* (Bennett et al., 2006; Knapp & VandeCreek, 2006), in which the professional plans for a *safety net* when working with high-risk situations. A *culture of safety* is a practice environment that recognizes that sometimes "a perfect storm" can arise. Sometimes the confluence of patient characteristics and external events is such that a tragedy will be likely to occur. Just as every airplane has a second set of electrical fuses in the event that one fails, every practitioner working in an emergency needs to have a second set of eyes looking at a case. The culture of safety occurs when risk-management strategies are a common and expected element of practice. Each of the four risk-management strategies will be reviewed in more detail.

Consultation differs from supervision. Consultation occurs between those who are legally peers, and the person receiving the consultation can reject or accept the recommendations given. Consultation has at least two benefits. First, it may provide the consultee with new information about the patient's condition or treatment strategies. Second, it may provide the consultee with the opportunity to talk about a difficult situation. The mere fact of talking about the situation may help reduce emotional arousal and help individuals think through the situation on their own. The quality of services is likely to improve if the psychologist has the benefit of wisdom from other knowledgeable professionals. In a health care environment, the consultation may come from another psychologist, but it may also come from other health care professionals, as well.

Documentation enhances the quality of patient care. Documentation ensures that other members of the health care team are aware of relevant facts concerning the case. It may also provide the clinical health psychologist with the opportunity to reflect on a difficult case. Generally speaking, the details in documentation should be increased when patients are not responding well to treatment. As noted before, psychologists need to be circumspect on what they write in the medical chart of the patients that all staff can see and that the patient may have access to. However, in high-risk situations, it may be prudent for the psychologist to keep a separate set of records as psychotherapy notes. The decision making of the psychologist should be transparent in the documentation. The notes should never ignore nor minimize salient features of the patient's condition.

In addition to improving the quality of health care, documentation can also be essential in a defense in the case that the judgment of the psychologist was called into question. The general rule in risk management is "if it isn't written down, it didn't happen." In the event of a tragedy and a law suit, courts will give very high deference to medical records. The general assumption is that the medical records are accurate, and it is a very high threshold for a plaintiff to successfully challenge what is written in the medical record.

Informed participation, or informed consent, becomes especially important when treating patients who are at a high risk to have emergencies. As noted above, certain elements of informed consent are mandated by law and professional standards. However, as a risk-management technique, informed participation or informed consent means to actively engage the patient in treatment decisions as much as is clinically indicated. From a clinical perspective, patients will be more motivated to comply with treatment when they understand its rationale and purpose.

Redundant protections refer to a second source of information about a patient. The information may come from a screening instrument, information from a family member or close friend of the patient, or another treating health care professional. Redundant protections are the core strategy for reducing medical errors in hospitals. Medical errors are greatly reduced in an environment that expects cooperation, good communications, and redundant protections. For example, in a good medical environment, a pharmacist would be expected to double check on a prescription if the handwriting was unclear, or a nurse would be expected to double check before administering a medication that appeared to be medically contraindicated. Patient involvement and understanding also creates another layer of protection. There is a story, perhaps apocryphal, of a Spanish-speaking patient who was given a prescription that read "once a day," but "once" is also the Spanish word for eleven. She took the pills 11 times a day instead of the 1 time a day that was prescribed.

In a well-run health system, the philosophy is that patient care is everyone's business, and that any employee, including clinical health psychologists, should ask questions if they perceive a risk to patient safety. For example, psychologists who become aware of apparently clinically contraindicated medical interactions should ask questions, especially because polypharmacy is common among older adults (Arnold, 2008). As it applies to their own work, psychologists should nondefensively accept feedback from other staff members who comment on or ask about their work. When the health of a patient is precarious, the psychologist can actively seek out feedback from other health professionals on the progress of their treatment and the health of the patient.

Although this section has focused on positive risk-management principles, it will also warn against "false risk-management principles," which are those that violate foundational moral principles. Bennett et al. (2006) warn that "any purported risk management strategy that tells you to do something that appears to harm a patient or violates a moral principle needs to be reconsidered" (p. 32). They identified several of these, such as "always get a suicidal patient to sign a safety contract," or "never keep detailed records when patients present a threat to harm themselves or others" (Bennett et al., 2006, p. 33). These are false risk-management principles because sometimes it may be clinically contraindicated to get a patient to sign a safety agreement, or because detailed records should help improve the quality of treatment and are in the patient's interest. Although the examples provided by Bennett et al. (2006) deal primarily with mental health treatment, the same basic principles apply to clinical behavioral health, as well. As much as possible, treatment decisions should be transparent, anchored on foundational moral principles, and done with the benefit of the patients in mind.

Ethics Summary

Adherence and sensitivity to foundational ethical principles can help improve patient satisfaction and the quality of patient care. The practice of clinical health psychology can be very rewarding. Indeed, it can be argued that the development of behavioral factors in medicine is at the forefront of health care advances in the 21st century. Ethical considerations and patient-focused risk-management strategies should not be viewed as a burden or a nuisance ("let's get this informed consent stuff out of the way so we can get down to business"). Instead, it should be viewed as an opportunity to improve the quality of services.

Recommendation for Effective Practice

Practitioners who are partnering between primary care medicine and clinical health psychology are working in an area with history and promise for the future. We are called to recognize the value of the biopsychosocial model, and to implement this model in a multidisciplinary approach to provide superior health care. By practicing in this manner, the cost of health care will be reduced, health disparities among different populations will diminish, and valuable patient care will be recognized as the ultimate goal. When practitioners are knowledgeable and respectful of diverse roles and functions, the organization and day-to-day operations of health care facilities will flow smoothly. Effective practice includes the resolution of problems and the flexibility to work through change as needed to develop superior patient care. Ethical practice calls us to consider the patient's goals and values, and always work to instill hope that lives may be uplifted and the most holistic quality of life may be possessed by all persons.

References

American Medical Association. (AMA). (2008). *Report of the Committee B.* Retrieved October 28, 2008, from www.AMA-assn.org/AMA/pub/upload/mm/471/annotatedb.doc

American Psychiatric Association. (APA). (2000). *Diagnostic and statistical manual of mental disorders* (4th ed., text revision). Washington, DC: American Psychiatric Press.

American Psychological Association. (1998). *Practice pointer: Psychology practice in primary care settings.* Retrieved September 10, 2009, from http://www.apa.org/practice/pu/jun98/primary.html

American Psychological Association. (202). Ethical principles of psychologists and code of conduct. *American Psychologist, 57,* 1060–1073.

American Psychological Association. (2006). *Psychology in primary care. APA Government Relations: Education Policy.* Retrieved September 10, 2009, from http://www.apa.org/ppo/issues/psycare.html.

APA Task Force on Evidence-Based Practice. (2006). Report of the 2005 Presidential Task Force on Evidence-BAsed. *American Psychologist, 61,* 271–285.

Arnold, M. (2008). Polypharmacy and older adults: A role for psychology and psychologists. *Professional Psychology: Research and Practice, 39*(3), 283–289.

Beck, A. T. (1964). Thinking and depression. II. Theory and therapy. *Archives of General Psychiatry, 10,* 561–571.

Beck, J. (1995). *Cognitive therapy: Basics and beyond.* New York: Guilford.

Beauchamp, T., & Childress, J. (2001). *Principles of biomedical ethics* (5th ed.). New York: Oxford.

Belar, C. (2008). Clinical health psychology: A health care specialty in professional psychology. *Professional Psychology: Research and Practice, 39*(2), 229–233.

Belar, C., Brown, R. A., Hersch, L., Rozensky, R., Sheridan, E., Brown, R. T., et al. (2003). Self-assessment in clinical health psychology: A model for ethical expansion of practice. *Prevention and Treatment, 6*(1), ArtID 25A.

Benefield, H., Ashkanazai, G., & Rozensky, R. (2006). Communication and records: HIPAA issues when working in health care settings. *Professional Psychology: Research and Practice, 37*(3), 273–277.

Bennett, B., Bricklin, P., Harris, E., Knapp, S., & VandeCreek, L. (2006). *Risk management: A patient focused approach.* Washington, DC: APAIT.

Bersoff, D., & Koeppl, T. (1993). The relation between ethical codes and moral principles. *Ethics and Behavior, 3*(3/4), 345–357.

Blanchard, E. B. (2005). A critical review of cognitive, behavioral, and cognitive-behavioral therapies for irritable bowel syndrome. *Journal of Cognitive Psychotherapy, 19,* 101–123.

Chehab, E. L., & Fealy, S. (2008). Aseptic loosening in total shoulder arthroplasty. In S. Fealy, J. W. Sperling, R. F. Warren, & E. V. Craig (Eds.), *Shoulder arthoplasty.* New York: Thieme.

Cinciripini, P. M. (1995). Current trends in smoking cessation research: Psychological therapy, nicotine replacement and changes in smoking behavior. *Cancer Bulletin, 47,* 259–263.

Cinciripini, P. M., Lapitsky, L. G., Wallfisch, A., Mace, R., Nezami, E., & Van Vunakis, H. (1994). An evaluation of a multicomponent treatment program involving scheduled smoking and relapse prevention procedures: Initial findings. *Addictive Behaviors, 19,* 13–22.

Cournos, F., & Goldfinger, S. M. (Eds.). (2006). Frontline reports. *Psychiatric Services, 56*(3), 353–355.

DiTomasso, R. A. (1987). Essential hypertension: A methodological review. In L. Miehelson & L. M. Ascher (Eds.), *Anxiety and stress disorders: Cognitive-behavioral assessment and treatment* (pp. 520–582). New York: Guilford.

DiTomasso, R. A., & Mills, O. (1990). The behavioral treatment of essential hypertension: Implications for medical psychotherapy. *Medical Psychotherapy, 3,* 125–134.

Gatchel, R. J. (2005). *Clinical essentials of pain management.* Washington, DC: American Psychological Association.

Hill, R. D., Rigdon, M., & Johnson, S. (1993). Behavioral smoking cessation treatment for older chronic smokers. *Behavior Therapy, 24*(2), 321–329.

Jason, L. A., Corradi, K., & Torres-Harding, S. (2005). Preventive psychology in primary care settings. *Journal of Primary Prevention, 26*(1), 37–51.

Jones, C. (2002). *Held to a higher standard. APA Practice Organization.* Retrieved September 10, 2009, from http://www.apa.org/practice/pf/winter02/higher_standard.html.

Kaslow, N., Bollini, A., Druss, B., Glueckauf, R., Goldfrank, L., Kelleher, K., et al. (2007). Health care for the whole person: Research update. *Professional Psychology: Research and Practice, 38*(3), 278–289.

Kitchener, K. (1984). Intuition, critical evaluation, and ethical principles. The foundation of ethical decisions in counseling psychology. *Counseling Psychologist, 12*(3), 43–55.

Knapp, S., & VandeCreek, L. (2004). A principle-based interpretation of the APA Ethics Code. *Psychotherapy: Theory/research/practice/training, 41,* 247–254.

Knapp, S. J., & VandeCreek, L. D. (2006). *Practical ethics for psychologists: A positive approach.* Washington, DC: American Psychological Association.

Lipowski, Z. J. (1977). Psychosomatic medicine in the seventies: An overview. *American Journal of Psychiatry, 134*(3), 233–243.

Lynch, P. M., & Zamble, E. (1989). A controlled behavioral treatment study of Irritable Bowel Syndrome. *Behavior Therapy, 20*(4), 509N523.

Meichenbaum, D. C., & Turk, D. (1987). *Facilitating treatment adherence: A practitioner's guidebook.* New York: Plenum Press.

Munsey, C. (2007). Supplying therapy where it's needed most. *Monitor on Psychology, 38*(1), 42–44.

Okifuji, A., & Ackerlind, S. (2007). Behaviroal medicine approaches to pain. *Medical Clinics of North America, 91*(1), 45–55.

Osler, W. (1899). Address to the students of the Albany Medical College. *Albany Medical Annals, 20,* 307–309.

Payne, A., & Blanchard, E. B. (1995). A controlled comparison of cognitive therapy and self-help support groups in the treatment of irritable bowel syndrome. *Journal of Consulting and Clinical Psychology, 63*(5), 779–786.

Prochaska, J. O., & DiClemente, C. C. (1992). Stages of change in the modification of problem behaviors. *Progress in Behavior Modification, 28,* 183–218.

Robinson, J., & Baker, J. (2006). Psychological consultation and services in a general medical hospital. *Professional Psychology: Research and Practice, 37*(3), 264–267.

Ross, W. D., & Statton-Lake, P. (2002). *The right and the good.* New York: Oxford University Press.

Rozensky, R. (2006). An introduction to psychologists treating medically ill patients: Competent practice and seeking credentials in organized health care settings for routine or incidental practice. *Professional Psychology: Research and Practice, 37*(3), 260–263.

Smith, T. W., Kendall, P. C., & Keefe, F. (2002). Behavioral medicine and clinical health psychology: Introduction to the special issue, a view from the decade of behavior. *Journal of Consulting and Clinical Psychology, 70,* 459–462.

Stevens, V. J., & Hollis, J. F. (1989). *Journal of Consulting and Clinical Psychology, 57*(3), 420–424.

Surwit, R. (2002). Type 2 diabetes and stress. *Diabetes Voice, 47,* 38–40.

Tovian, S. (2006). Interdisciplinary collaboration in outpatient practice. *Professional Psychology: Research and Practice, 37*(3), 268–272.

Wadden, T. A., Brownell, K. D., & Foster, G. D. (2002). Obesity: Responding to the global epidemic. *Journal of Consulting and Clinical Psychology, 70*(3), 510–5525.

Yali, A. M., & Revenson, T. (2004). How changes in population demographics will impact health psychology: Incorporating a broader notion of cultural competence into the field. *Health Psychology, 23*(2), 147–155.

Zuckerman, E. L. (2008). *The paper office: Forms, guidelines and resources to make your practice work ethically, legally, and profitably* (4th ed.). New York: Guilford.

Collaboration With Medical Professionals in the Primary Care Setting

3

Dorothy A. Borresen
Nancy B. Ruddy

Introduction

Almost 20 years ago, McDaniel and colleagues (1990) warned against "psychosocial fixation," which they described as "overfocusing on the psychological experience and avoiding the somatic." Today, most clinicians are very aware of the close link between physical and mental health. The biopsychosocial model, first described by George Engel in 1977, challenged the traditional, reductionistic biomedical perspective, which separated the mind from the body. Engel's theory that body, mind, relationships, and social context interact with and influence each other and shape overall health revolutionized both medicine and psychology. In 2001, the American Psychological Association (APA) amended its mission statement to include the word "health." This change reflected an understanding that the traditional separation of mental health and physical health was no longer an adequate paradigm.

Efforts to integrate psychology into the health care field have resulted in more mental health professionals, including psychologists, practicing alongside their medical colleagues in health care settings (Department of Health and Human Services, 2007). Today, most psychologists would acknowledge the importance of collaboration when psychological and medical problems co-occur or when medical professionals prescribe psychotropic medications. However, the typical psychologist continues to collaborate infrequently, if at all, with primary care medical professionals ("Psychologists and Physicians," 2008). More than a decade ago, the Committee for the Advancement of Professional Practice Task Force on Primary Care within APA discussed practical tips for psychologists willing to expand their practice into primary care (Haley et al., 1998). This chapter will expand on these practical tips for those clinicians interested in working within this larger context. We will define the collaborative psychotherapist and discuss barriers, advantages, and benefits to collaboration for psychologists, patients, and medical colleagues. We will discuss various models of collaboration, as well as practical and logistical issues. The professional and ethical issues that are unique to collaboration will also be delineated. Finally, we will outline recommendations for effective practice in the current health care environment and discuss the future of fully integrated health care systems. We will also discuss trends that support the role of the cognitive-behavioral therapist. Our goal is to help mental health clinicians appreciate the benefits of collaboration and adopt practices that are consistent with their patients' needs, preferences, and legal and ethical issues, as well as their personal styles and approaches to treatment.

Theoretical Issues

The Collaborative Psychotherapist

Altering practice from a traditional model to a model of collaboration requires a paradigm shift. Collaboration may require the psychotherapist's role and focus to expand or alter during the course of treatment with a medically ill patient. Collaboration is much more than making the occasional phone calls to a patient's physician, nurse practitioner, or physician's assistant. It conveys teamwork, partnership, cooperation, and working together toward common goals. It requires a broader, systemic approach to patient care that may include the patient, significant others, the psychotherapist, and various medical professionals. A willingness to partner and negotiate with both the patient and medical professional is necessary for this approach to be successful.

Most psychotherapists are more accustomed to the practice of referring and collaborating with their psychiatric medical colleagues. Expanding collaboration to include the patient's medical professionals requires a greater degree of commitment and involvement. Although psychologists have embraced the "mind-body" paradigm, the level of collaboration between psychologists, particularly those in office-based practice, and their medical colleagues has not changed significantly and occurs infrequently.

Most therapists are taught to assess patient's physical health, especially during the initial interview. However, this is frequently a cursory review. In contrast, the collaborative therapist has an expanded view of what constitutes the patient's health. He/she should obtain the past medical history of the patient and family, relevant health events, and current physical health, lifestyle habits, and risk factors. During the initial evaluation, patients should be asked details about their physical health, including their last visit to a primary care professional, recent laboratory studies, chronic and acute illnesses, and current medications. Obtaining a release(s) to communicate with pertinent medical professionals is routine for the collaborative psychotherapist. If the health information indicates a medical exam is overdue or indicated, a collaborative clinician will recommend seeking medical consultation.

This simple intervention of referring the patient to his/her primary care professional is often the first step in the collaborative process. The referral ensures the medical professional is aware that the patient currently is receiving psychological treatment. The medical professional reviews specific symptoms in order to evaluate possible physical causes of symptoms that brought the patient to the therapist. Communication, whether direct between the therapist and medical professionals or indirect via the patient, provides a bridge between the medical and mental health providers. This is particularly useful when patients' medical issues affect mental health or vice versa. Typically, patients see communication between their health care professionals as the norm, rather than the exception, and as an important part of providing comprehensive, patient-centered care.

Benefits of Collaboration

Relationships among medical professionals offer many benefits to the patient, the medical professional, and the psychotherapist. Primary care has been described as "the de facto mental health care delivery system" for three decades (Regier, Goldberg, & Taube, 1978). Because mental health issues are endemic in primary care settings, collaboration has the potential to provide more integrative treatment and generate referrals to the therapist, who actively collaborates with primary care professionals. More than 40% of patients with mental health problems initially seek care in primary care settings (Chapa, 2004). Twenty-five percent of patients who present in an emergency department with chest pain have depression or panic disorder (Fleet et al., 1996). These patients are usually referred from the emergency department back to their primary care professional. Primary care continues to provide the initial and often only opportunity to access mental health. Primary care medical professionals rather than psychiatrists prescribe 60–70% of the psychotropic medications in the United States (Lewis, Marcus, Olfson, Druss, & Pincus 2004). Many of these patients never see a mental health professional.

The presence of nurse practitioners in the primary care setting has increased over the years (Bonsall & Cheater, 2008; Miller, 2006). Patients with chronic illnesses benefit from an evidence-based step-wise care approach with the use of nurses in organized health care systems (Katon, Von Korff, Lin, & Simon, 2001). Nurse practitioners and physician assistants have helped to hold down health care costs and provide care to underserved patient populations, and are key personnel for collaboration in primary care (Atwater, Bednar, Hassman, & Khouri, 2008).

When a patient's problem exceeds a medical professional's expertise or time constraints, making treatment unrealistic, physicians make efforts to refer the patient to a mental health provider. For the medical professional, this referral process is frequently challenging because of many factors including stigma, access to care, and financial constraints. Medical professionals who collaborate routinely with mental health providers can suggest a consultation with a specific professional they know and respect. This personal relationship often will enhance the likelihood of a successful referral. Further, when there is an established relationship between the therapist and medical professional, the therapist can provide prereferral consultation to facilitate the reluctant patient's referral. Therapists frequently see those patients who were not helped in the primary care setting and require more than the medical professional can provide.

The collaborative psychotherapist sees every patient as an opportunity to develop new relationships with medical professionals or to revisit old ones. They develop ongoing relationships with medical professionals that enable them to provide optimal treatment. This is especially true when the patient is confronted with complex medical problems like obesity, hypertension, diabetes, and asthma, and psychological issues like depression or anxiety. Working collaboratively provides a support structure for not only the patient, but for everyone who works with the patient.

Collaboration is particularly helpful when working with challenging patients that are sometimes confusing, discouraging, frustrating, and even infuriating (Ruddy, Borresen, & Gunn, 2008). A patient-centered and collaborative environment can be reassuring to the patient who has had difficulty making effective use of the health care system. The psychological and medical professionals can benefit from the variety of perspectives, explanations, and treatment suggestions that collaboration can generate. Different areas of expertise, different values regarding what issues are important, different views of the patients and their problems, although potentially causing complications, have the potential to provide integrated, creative treatment. Ultimately, collaboration has the potential to facilitate a better understanding and treatment of our patients, as well as insight into clinical blind spots.

Models of Collaboration

There is a continuum of collaboration that ranges from therapists who seldom contact their patient's medical professionals to those who collaborate closely in a partly or completely integrated system. Most collaborative therapists in office-based practice vary the level of collaboration from case to case, depending upon the patient needs, the level of preexisting relationships with medical professionals, and specific logistical issues. Several collaboration models have been described, based on various combinations of characteristics. These include model characteristics such as how patients are best served (Doherty, McDaniel, & Baird, 1996), the type of communication between those collaborating (Holloway & David, 2005), extended, continuous collaboration (Butler & Turkal, 2005), and routine and intensive collaboration (Ruddy et al., 2008). These collaboration models reflect the varying ways that psychologists and medical professionals work together.

Various levels of collaboration were described by psychologists as early as 1996 (Doherty et al., 1996). The following nomenclature is based upon their work and still has relevance. They described many psychologists who rarely communicate with medical professionals, believing that confidentiality issues outweigh collaboration's benefits. Today, *minimal collaboration* in which there is a separation of mental health and medical care is still the norm in most communities. *Basic collaboration at a distance* is another model in which the psychologist practices independently, but does communicate with the medical professional as patient need dictates. Often, psychologists and medical professionals who practice in this model eventually develop a referral relationship. There is neither a formal referral process nor a structure for communication between the psychologist and medical professional (Doherty et al., 1996). Any communication that occurs is usually informal and brief. The patient best served by this model has routine medical and psychological issues where there are few management difficulties or clinical questions, and little interaction between the physical and psychosocial issues. This model may be appropriate for many patients. However, routine notification of the medical professional by the treating psychologist that their shared patient is receiving psychological treatment could prove beneficial, especially if the situation becomes more complex. Even minimal contact has the potential to open the door to greater collaboration. The medical professional may begin referring to the psychologist who communicates routinely or may seek consultation concerning challenging patients.

Basic collaboration on site refers to psychologists who practice in the medical setting, but focus on the provision of traditional psychotherapy. There is some communication about shared patients, but this communication may be haphazard. In this model, billing structures, record keeping, and other elements of practice remain separate. *Close collaboration in a partly integrated system* describes colocated practices in which some operational elements overlap (e.g., billing or charting) and collaboration occurs in a routine, structured manner. However, in this case, psychologists typically become involved in patient care only when the medical provider initiates a referral. Finally, the most seamless model of collaboration is *close collaboration in a fully integrated system*. Psychologists work side by side with medical professionals, meeting with patients during their regular medical visits. Reimbursement structures are the same, and all charting occurs together. Medical professionals and patients view the psychologist as part of the health care team. Psychological intervention can occur directly and without a referral by a medical professional. Often, psychologists provide very little "traditional" psychotherapy, shifting toward brief consultations and interventions. Psychological care is integrated into medical care such that behavioral aspects of medical illness and the impact of medical illness on mental health are recognized as interdependent.

Holloway and David (2005) describe the "complexion of collaboration" as focusing on the health and well-being of the patient. This model is flexible and suggests using a variety of models, including informal and formal consultation, the co-provision of care, and co-therapy between physician and psychologist, depending on the specific situation and conditions of the collaboration. This model stresses the importance of agreed-upon goals, ongoing communication, and problem solving to address barriers between collaborative partners. The model of *routine and intensive collaboration* (Ruddy et al., 2008) recommends building collaborative relationships into the routine of daily practice and varying the intensity depending on medical complexity, needs of the patient, and treatment team.

Practical and Logistical Issues

Barriers, Myths, and Stereotypes

There are very real barriers to collaboration, as well as myths and stereotypes that may discourage therapists. The issues of confidentiality and time pressure are probably the major barriers to most therapists. For example, psychology has traditionally emphasized the dyadic relationship between the psychologist and patient, and absolute confidentiality. Many psychology providers erroneously believe that their patients will be hesitant or even unwilling to disclose sensitive, personal information. They may believe that their patients will be offended by a request to talk to their medical professionals, or that sharing information will adversely affect the psychotherapeutic process. Some psychologists have concerns about how medical professionals will manage confidential information. These beliefs can pose a significant barrier to the psychologist who is considering practicing more collaboratively. Psychologists may need to see clear benefits to collaboration before they will be willing to come out of their "confidentiality comfort zone" (Ruddy et al., 2008).

The therapist's lack of experience with collaboration may reduce their motivation to even suggest collaboration to their patients. They may be uncertain about how to justify collaboration to a reluctant patient, fearing that they will not have a good answer if a patient asks them, "Why do you need to talk to my doctor?" In our experience, the psychologist or therapist who asks her/his patients for a release to speak to the other health care professionals rarely encounters resistance. In fact, patients are often pleased and reassured that there will be communication between the members of their health care team. Many patients assume that professionals involved in their care do talk and are surprised when this is not the case. Patients need an explanation of how sharing information can positively affect their health care. In addition, therapists can reduce patient concerns about information disclosure by clarifying and negotiating the information that will be shared with the medical professional. Patients need to be reassured that particularly sensitive information that is not relevant to their medical care will not be shared. Throughout the collaboration process, the patient needs to understand that they can rescind their permission at any time. Once the therapist establishes a working relationship with specific medical professionals, they can openly discuss how to maintain the safety of patient information to their satisfaction. Therapists may not realize that HIPAA (Health Insurance Portability and Accountability Act) regulations have increased pressure on medical professionals to maintain privacy, and their practice is more in line with mental health standards than in the past.

The belief that collaboration requires too much time and is rarely appreciated by medical professionals may be the greatest obstacle to collaboration. Collaboration does mean that the role and function of the therapist is expanded to include ongoing communication with medical professionals. This process need not be onerous or anxiety producing. Communication can and should be brief. This may require the therapist to develop new working styles. Medical professionals want pertinent information like diagnosis, symptom profile, and treatment plans. They appreciate regular updates about the patient's progress, especially if they are prescribing psychotropic medications or if the patient's medical problems and emotional status are intertwined. They appreciate suggestions that will help them provide better care, especially when the issues are lifestyle change and adherence to treatment. Technology has the potential to promote regular, brief, and effective communication. Medical professionals desire written communications that are brief and to the point, but do not always respond directly to this information. Unfortunately, some therapists interpret this lack of response as a brush off. Actually, primary care medical providers only respond to incoming information from medical specialists (e.g., cardiologists) and mental health specialists (e.g., psychologists) if they have questions or concerns.

Therapists who reach out to primary care medical professionals may sense enormous time pressure. This reflects the reality of the time pressure in primary care. In contrast to psychotherapists who practice the 50-minute hour, they are always being interrupted by beepers, pagers, faxes, e-mail, and phone calls. They have only 15 minutes with each patient to conduct a differential diagnosis, negotiate and implement a treatment plan and, ideally, discuss preventative care.

Negative stereotypes held by mental health providers and medical professionals can also be barriers to collaboration. The stereotype of the arrogant, hierarchical, uninterested medical professional is as limiting as the stereotype that the therapist is inaccessible, always "in session," and secretive about his/her work. One negative experience for either party can be generalized and deter further efforts to collaborate. They fuel isolation and deter therapists and medical professionals from initiating collaboration. Like many stereotypes, this one has a grain of truth to it. Medical professionals seem busy and rushed because they are busy. Also, receptivity and a willingness to collaborate vary. Some medical professionals may not value communication from therapists. The fear of disinterest, rejection, or criticism of the assessment of the patient can be a powerful deterrent to collaboration to the psychologist. The fact that mental health and medical professionals are usually not trained together only heightens these feelings and beliefs. Separate cultures and the physical distance between practice locations perpetuate the status quo. Often, the only link between medical professionals and therapists is the patient whose needs straddle both the medical and the mental health treatment worlds, particularly in the cases of those with concomitant mental health and chronic physical problems. Yet, psychotherapists usually do not consider themselves part of their patient's overall health care team, and consequently, rarely consult other involved professionals.

Therapists may not appreciate the depth, importance, and permanence of the relationship that develops among a patient, family, and medical professionals. They may believe that because medical professionals see patients for 15 minutes or less that there is little opportunity for a relationship development. They may believe that medical professionals see so many patients in a day that they could not possibly feel a personal connection to their patients. This relationship, although very different from the therapist and their patient, may be no less significant and emotionally powerful. Some patients and their families have seen the same primary care medical professional for many years. The relationships can be extremely important when the patient has a serious, chronic, or life-threatening condition. Patients have contact with their medical professional in times of health and illness; they share births, deaths, diagnoses of new illness, and declining health. This continuity of care creates a shared history that can result in a relationship that is extremely important to both the patient and the medical professional, and should not be underestimated by the therapist.

Working collaboratively requires overcoming barriers and stereotypes, and expanding our notions of what is possible. In collaboration, our role and tasks may change depending on each clinical situation. Although collaboration is considered to be ideal practice by forward-thinking leaders in psychology and medicine, it is not yet the standard of care. In the current environment, this "best" practice may seem unrealistic to many psychologists who lack an experiential understanding of the process of becoming a collaborative provider. Yet, collaboration has the potential to improve patient care, enhance referral networks, and increase professional satisfaction (Doherty, 2007).

Much as cognitive-behavioral therapists help patients change maladaptive cognitions and behaviors, they must examine their own thoughts and behaviors regarding collaboration with medical professionals and begin to change their day-to-day practice. This can be accomplished by taking a series of steps. First, it is necessary to make a genuine commitment to routine collaboration, and set specific goals to increase collaboration from your current level. Therapists must be willing to examine their own beliefs about collaboration with medical professionals, and identify any biases or fears that are likely to interfere with successful collaboration. Most therapists encounter some challenges as they make a shift toward routinely interfacing with the medical system. Understanding one's own motivation and goals may facilitate perseverance in stepping outside the comfort zone.

The second step is to expand assessment, conceptualization, and treatment planning processes to determine the appropriate level of collaboration for each patient presentation. One factor to consider is the quality of the relationship between the medical professional and the patient. Therapists with a collaborative mindset and practice are in a unique position to facilitate optimal patient/medical professional relationships. Patients with multiple or chronic medical conditions often experience frustration and disempowerment during their interface with the medical system. It is not uncommon for patients to complain about their medical care in psychotherapy. Therapists who do not collaborate and hear only the patient's perspective may inadvertently exacerbate relationship issues between the patient and their medical professionals. Collaborative clinicians hear both sides of the story, and can help each participant better understand the perspectives of the other. They can evaluate behavioral patterns and suggest empowering strategies for patients who experience frustration. They can recognize when a collaborative approach is necessary to prevent fragmentation of the treatment team. They can help patients and medical professionals decide when the relationship is beyond salvaging and when it is best for the patient to move to a new medical provider. Without collaboration, the therapist cannot help the patient optimize their medical care in any of these ways.

Another area that a therapist with a collaborative mindset must assess is the interplay of physical illness, medications, and mental health. Fatigue and concentration difficulties could signal depression or hypothyroidism. Patients with anxiety issues often have unspoken somatic concerns and fears. Many medical conditions can present as symptoms frequently associated with mental health conditions. Collaborative psychotherapists must know which medical conditions have symptoms similar to depression or anxiety, and understand how some medical conditions and treatments can exacerbate mental health issues. In general, any patient who has not had a general physical for 2 or more years, or who presents with somatic concerns, substance abuse, an eating disorder, or significant vegetative symptoms, should be referred for medical examination. When the medical professional initiates the referral for psychotherapy, prescribes psychotropic medication, or has a long-standing relationship with the patient, collaboration is particularly important. Yet, many therapists do not consider or assess these variables in their treatment-planning process, leading to disjointed, suboptimal treatment.

But how is a therapist to make time for all of this extra communication? As with any behavioral change, attempting a collaboration "practice overhaul" is probably not realistic. Rather, it is more advisable to start with the techniques that are the least time-consuming or difficult, and allow their collaboration practices and style to evolve with time and experience. For example, many psychologists find it helpful to create a "tool box" of communication aids. The following suggested "form letters" can allow psychotherapists to add patient-specific information to a prewritten letter, reducing the time and energy necessary for successful collaboration.

1. **Postreferral/intake letter:** Develop a standard "thank you for the referral" letter and send it after the first appointment. The letter may simply inform the medical professional that the patient has entered into the care of a psychotherapist. Often, medical professionals are unaware that their patients are in psychotherapy. Patients frequently neglect to inform their medical professionals that they are engaged in psychotherapy. Rather than relying on informal communication between the patient and the medical professional, it is more helpful to fax or mail a form letter with a space for diagnosis and a few words about the intended treatment plan. The minimal extra time and effort to include this information helps the medical professional provide optimal medical care.
2. **Clarification of communication expectations and means:** Include contact information (e.g., cell phone and e-mail) and request the same from the medical professional in the postreferral letter. Ideally, include your preferred methods of communication, which should facilitate information exchange. All forms of potential communication methods should be included, as psychotherapists and medical professionals are notoriously difficult to contact directly. Because communication norms are so different between the medical and mental health cultures, it is helpful to clarify the best way to contact the medical professional under emergent and nonemergent situations. For example, in the medical culture, it is normative to interrupt medical professionals during patient care, or to use a paging system to facilitate communication. In contrast, these methods are typically used only under emergent conditions in the mental health culture. Because many psychotherapists are reluctant to use these methods without the expressed permission of the medical professional, simply ask the medical professional's preference directly. Therapists can include a form with a checklist of communication methods and frequency in the postreferral letter, and ask that the medical professional return mail or fax it back to them.

3. **Termination letter:** It is important to tell the medical professional when treatment is completed. The letter can simply state that treatment has stopped, or it can go into more detail about the treatment and future options. Medical professionals find it very helpful to be made aware of the symptoms or warning signs that would indicate a relapse, so that they can suggest the patient return to treatment with the therapist. When termination is mutually agreed upon by the patient and the therapist, they can draft a termination letter together during one of the final sessions. This saves time, and it is a therapeutic exercise in and of itself.

As noted earlier, mental health providers will find variability in medical professionals' interest and ability regarding collaboration. Over time, it will become obvious which medical professionals desire a "shared care" process and which are not willing to put the time and energy into collaboration. By its very nature, this process entails some rejection by medical professionals who are not psychosocially oriented. Yet, research indicates that disinterested medical professionals are relatively rare in primary care. Brazeau, Rovi, Yick, and Johnson (2005) found that 13.5% of family physicians have psychologists providing services in their offices, and an additional 60.2% would consider having an in-house psychologist.

Finding collaboration partners often occurs via the referral networking process. Investigating which medical professionals practice nearby is useful. Geographic proximity facilitates collaboration, particularly when practices are in the same office building or office park, where there is opportunity for face-to-face interaction among the professionals. Additionally, a convenient and familiar office location is often a consideration to patients when they seek mental health services. Identify which medical professionals are known to be psychosocially focused and/or particularly skillful in working with distressed patients. Contact medical and nursing professional associations and offer to give medically relevant talks on topics such as depression in primary care, managing chronically ill patients, or increasing patient compliance with medical regimens. Presenting provides an opportunity to directly interact with medical professionals interested in detecting and treating these issues in their practices.

Nonetheless, the medical professionals of current patients are the best source of potential collaborators. During the intake process, ask patients the name, phone number, and address of their primary care medical professional and obtain a release of information. Patients rarely balk at this request, especially when the request includes a rationale for collaboration. After obtaining the necessary information and permissions, contact the medical professionals of current and recent patients. It is generally best to first send a postreferral letter and then make a follow-up phone call, fax, or e-mail.

To build collaborative contacts beyond the medical professionals of current patients, call those who have made referrals in the past to express interest in developing a collaborative relationship and offer assistance in prereferral consultations. Suggest visiting their office for a brief meeting. Those medical professionals who have made referrals previously are likely to be interested in collaboration. In general, referrals beget referrals, and collaboration begets collaboration, in both directions. During the initial phone call or meeting, conduct a needs assessment. How often do they refer their patients to psychotherapists? Do they have a cadre of psychotherapists with whom they usually work? Are they satisfied with the level of communication and the outcomes they obtain with these psychotherapists? Do they have patients with mental health needs who are reluctant to see a psychotherapist? Describe credentials, areas of expertise, and strategies that will optimize patient care via prereferral consultation and ongoing communication about shared patients. Medical professionals tend to prefer therapists who use a solution-oriented approach. Patients often complain that the therapist "just listens" and does not offer any suggestions or pragmatic help. Most primary care medical professionals seek a therapist who will offer this kind of partnership in optimizing the care they offer their patients.

It can be time-consuming to have personal conversations with medical professionals, but the time is well spent in reaching the goal of establishing working relationships. Medical professionals often need to convince and cajole patients into seeing a therapist. A psychotherapy referral has been likened to a blind date; ambivalent, anxious patients need motivation and encouragement to take a leap of faith by initiating psychotherapy. Medical professionals who can reassure the patient that they personally know the therapist to be competent and personable can erode the patient's ambivalence and anxiety and facilitate the referral.

Leave business cards with medical professionals, office managers, and front-desk staff. If the practice employs a managed-care referral specialist who processes referrals and helps patients navigate the managed-care system, ensure that you make contact with this person. He or she can guide appropriate patients to your practice based on factors such as your practice's location, hours, and accepted insurances. These initial conversations lay the groundwork for collaboration, and help identify medical professionals interested in collaboration. However, it is the collaboration itself that will engender and maintain a mutually beneficial working relationship.

Follow the initial conversation regarding a shared patient with a note reviewing details of the patient's clinical presentation, target symptoms, and treatment plan, and review the collaboration agreement in general and patient-specific terms. This will demonstrate to medical professionals that their concerns and requests were heard and internalized and will remind them that you can help them with this and other patients. In addition, doing so can help you keep track of agreements made with different medical professionals and offices.

Create a collaboration tracking system to ensure that agreements with different medical professionals regarding different patients do not become confused. Some therapists track collaboration separately from progress notes, listing the contact information for medical professionals, copies of letters sent, and notes regarding any verbal communication in a segregated section. Others create space on their normal progress notes to track communication with medical professionals, such as a separate prompt or check box. Integrated tracking can also serve as a reminder to collaborate.

The level of collaboration will vary from patient to patient. Minimally, inform the medical professional when treatment begins and ends. Sometimes it is necessary to send routine letters to update information and review salient treatment issues. This gives the medical professional information regarding ongoing stressors and helps them support the psychotherapy. Suggestions should always be pragmatic and helpful to the medical professional.

In some circumstances, reciprocal conversation is necessary. This tends to be the case when patients have complex medical conditions affecting their mental health, when the patient or family has questions about the patient's medical condition, or when the patient has expressed dissatisfaction with their care. The energy spent on an occasional phone conversation or reciprocal e-mails can ultimately save time and frustration. Challenging situations may resolve when the therapist has health status information and understands the medical professional's impressions of the patient's coping and treatment progress. Medical professionals can provide information about the patient's history or context, ongoing assessment, and provide an alternate perspective potentially broadening the therapist's understanding of the patient. The following questions can frame the conversation with the medical professional:

1. What is the medical professional's primary concern for this patient?
2. What would constitute therapy "success" for this patient?
3. How well does the medical professional know this patient and his/her social situation?
4. Does the medical professional have any advice about developing a working relationship with this patient?
5. Are there any medical problems now or in the past that might be relevant to the patient's psychological distress?
6. How well does the patient follow medical advice? If this is an issue, how can the psychotherapist help the medical professional with these issues?
7. Does the patient require psychotropic medication?
8. How would the medical professional like to proceed with communication and collaboration regarding this patient?

These questions reflect the need to be organized, focused, and specific when exchanging information with medical professionals.

Finally, advise medical professionals when psychotherapy ends prematurely. It may be their only notification that their patient is no longer receiving psychological treatment. After premature termination, they may need to provide ongoing care and address the patient's decision in subsequent medical appointments. These dialogues with a trusted medical professional may result in referral to another psychotherapist or a return to treatment.

Clinical and Professional Issues

It is important for therapists and primary care medical professionals to be aware of the other's competencies, skills, and scope of practice. A study of collaboration between nurse practitioners and family physicians demonstrated that these factors were necessary in order to foster trust and respect (Kaspereski, 2000). Initially, the therapist may need to educate the medical professional about the broad range of problems they treat in their practice. A description of evidence-based psychological treatment interventions used by the therapist may facilitate appropriate referrals from the medical professional. Many primary care medical professionals, especially those trained in family medicine in the United States, are aware that psychologists are trained in evidence-based interventions for adjustment problems and psychiatric disorders. They may be less knowledgeable about the effectiveness of psychological interventions with acute and chronic health conditions, like cardiovascular disease, cancer, asthma, chronic fatigue, pain, and insomnia (Nezu, Nezu, & Lombardo, 2001). They may not be aware that the psychologist has expertise in helping patients make lifestyle changes that have the potential to improve overall health and well-being.

Before beginning to share professional opinions and recommendations regarding a specific patient, a discussion of expectations of the collaboration process is ideal and may help avert boundary issues. As we noted, establishing the methods for ongoing communication early in the collaboration relationship is crucial to success. A Canadian survey (Grenier, Chomienne, Gaboury, Ritchie, & Hogg, 2008) exploring family physicians' knowledge of psychologists' training, roles, and skills found that the most common reasons for referring their patients to psychologists was their belief that psychologists' services were appropriate for the patient's problems. They placed the highest importance on receiving feedback from psychologists on their clinical findings and recommendations. However, they did not think that psychologists provided adequate feedback when patients had been referred to them. In general, medical professionals are more often interested in the psychologist's diagnosis, symptoms, prognosis, and treatment plan.

For collaboration to be most effective, there should be agreed-upon goals of treatment and collaboration. These should be established initially and may be renegotiated throughout the collaboration. When the latter occurs, it may take place between the patient, medical professional, and therapist, but it always needs to be communicated to everyone involved.

Both the therapist and medical professional may have questions about the differential diagnoses of a patient and the best possible treatment outcome. Throughout this process, the professionals should be mindful of each person's relevant expertise. The different perspectives and skill sets each practitioner brings to the clinical question can be both an advantage and a disadvantage to the collaborative process. Not all medical professionals have biopsychosocial conceptualizations of their patients. They may be unaware of the patient's emotional struggles because they are not comfortable discussing these issues. The therapist's role may be expanded to include educating the medical professional about the interaction between the patient's physical and mental health. The therapist, too, benefits from being educated about the medical issues affecting their patients. They may need additional training about medical problems and pharmacology. The medical professional may have a specific diagnostic question or hope for regular updates on improvement or worsening of target symptoms when patients have anxiety, depression, or more serious psychiatric problems. Understanding that medical professionals may approach patient care issues differently than psychotherapists is another key to successful collaboration.

Cognitive-behavioral therapists working in primary care need to adapt their language and presentation styles to brief descriptions of assessment, symptoms, techniques, and progress toward treatment goals. Although medical professionals are time-pressured, they find time to routinely give and receive consultation from other medical specialists about their patients. They expect routine feedback from consultants that may be informal, but is usually a concise, written report. When therapists fail to update the referring medical professional, it may be interpreted as rude, secretive, and confusing within the medical culture. This failure to communicate is a lost opportunity to provide optimal patient care and initiate collaboration. Even simple, brief communication about the patient's emotional and psychological issues has the potential to alter the medical outcome. The therapist, too, benefits from being educated about the patient's medical issues.

Clinical and treatment issues that were not obvious at the outset of treatment may arise and necessitate more intensive collaboration. This is more likely when the patient's problems are complex, life-threatening, involve substance use or abuse, or involve chronic pain or adherence issues. These situations can be frustrating, confusing, and disheartening to everyone involved and, unless addressed, will have an adverse effect on treatment. Feelings of frustration and hopelessness can affect the medical professional, therapist, or both. The patient, too, may be angry, frustrated, and disillusioned with their treatment and the team. Although collaboration is not a panacea, it often reduces each person's sense of isolation and hopelessness, and the synergy of sharing information and ideas often leads to a new approach or, at a minimum, an adjustment of expectations.

When more intensive or longitudinal collaboration is necessary, the therapist should discuss the rationale with the patient. Longitudinal collaboration may require renegotiating the collaboration process with the patient and the medical professional, as well as revising treatment goals as new challenges arise (Butler & Turkal, 2005). When the patient understands the rationale and accepts the plan, the medical professional can be included at a different level (Ruddy et al., 2008). This situation can also happen in reverse. The medical professional may desire more intensive collaboration with the therapist and should follow the same process. If medical professionals practice patient-centered medicine, they will include their patient by giving them the opportunity to negotiate and discuss their concerns. In contrast, some medical professionals will contact the therapist before talking to the patient. This strategy has inherent dangers. The patient may feel left out of their treatment and be less willing to participate in an increased level of collaboration, and the therapist risks becoming triangulated between their patient and the medical professional. This can occur in the context of a patient or family member feeling dissatisfied with the medical or psychological treatment. Although it is important that the therapist listen and understand the patient's confusion, frustration, or concern, treatment will be undermined if this information is not shared and addressed. The therapist or medical professional should have the opportunity to respond to the patient's concerns and to provide elucidating feedback. In these situations, patients should be encouraged to directly discuss their concerns. Joint sessions and conference calls are potential strategies for handling the pitfalls of triangulation.

In summary, clinical issues that arise during collaboration will be unique to each patient, to their particular medical and psychological problems, and to the "health" of the collaborating team. When disagreements arise between the therapist and medical professional concerning the patient and their treatment, communication becomes not only desirable, but essential. Sensitivity to criticism or discomfort with conflict on the part of therapist or medical professional can quickly disrupt and derail the treatment. If the therapist has the ability to resolve conflict and work systemically, these potential pitfalls can be avoided. In more intensive, longitudinal collaboration, the therapist must be flexible, versatile, and adhere to a high professional standard of clinical competence (Butler & Turkal, 2005). They must acknowledge the importance of the relationship between the patient and their medical professionals, and actively consult or refer when the clinical situation is outside of their competency. Expectations and goals for treatment may need to be redefined and fluid, based on factors such as the patient's particular medical condition, his/her readiness to change, agreement on treatment strategies, and flexibility of all of the professionals involved. This expanded role has the potential to be enriching, rewarding, and challenging for the therapist.

Ethical Issues

In this section, we discuss ethical challenges facing cognitive-behavioral clinicians in primary care. Clinicians who collaborate must be attentive to several legal and ethical guidelines in their communication with other medical professionals. Because cognitive-behavioral clinicians come from a variety of professional backgrounds (psychology, psychiatry, nursing, social work, counseling), the reader is urged to consult the ethical guidelines published and adhered to by his or her own professional group. Most issues fall under the umbrella of confidentiality and scope of practice, and we use psychologists to demonstrate these issues. For example, psychologists are bound by HIPAA and by the privacy and confidentiality practice standards and ethical guidelines that have governed the professional behavior of psychologists for decades whenever they deal with protected health information (APA Practice Directorate, 2002). The guidelines are somewhat different when a psychologist sees a patient who has been admitted to a general medical hospital.

Confidentiality

In both office-based and hospital settings, the psychologist must ensure that patients understand the rationale and agree to the disclosure of protected health information. Patients should be informed that they can restrict at any time the sharing of psychological information, simply by requesting information be kept confidential. Despite a strong commitment to collaboration, it is incumbent on the psychologist to avoid pressuring a reluctant patient. There is a fine line between explaining the benefits of collaboration in order to help the patient understand the rationale, and putting undue pressure on the patient to release information. This is particularly important when a patient discloses information of a sensitive nature that may be relevant to their medical care. For example, although the psychologist believes that a medical professional might find it helpful to know about their shared patient's history of sexual abuse, particularly for provision of gynecologic care, the patient always has the right to restrict disclosure of this information.

Throughout the collaboration process, the prudent psychologist will discuss and review with the patient information that will be shared with medical professionals to ensure that the patient is in agreement. It may take some time before they are willing to consent to sharing private information that is relevant to their medical treatment. However, informed consent must always be the psychologist's guiding principle. One of the original mandates of the policies that would become

HIPAA was to improve fluidity of care. As a result, those health care professionals practicing on a team in a hospital setting may freely communicate with others on the patient's team once a referral has been received (Benefield, Ashkanazai, Rozensky, 2006). Psychologists in office-based practice who consult with health care professionals in medical settings are subject to state laws pertaining to practice and ethical guidelines and the principles of the APA.

A psychologist practicing in a hospital setting generally completes a formal credentialing and privileging process. They must adhere to the specific hospital protocols that pertain to consultations and progress notes. Patients are not required to sign specific releases of information in order for team members to exchange information. However, the psychologist should still involve the patient in the process of deciding what psychological information or history is put in their medical chart. The psychologist must use caution and observe standards of confidentiality when writing in the chart, and should avoid sensitive information that is not relevant to the patient's medical treatment plan. Concise information that includes objective findings, assessment, diagnosis, treatment plan, and progress toward goals is appropriate for the medical chart and useful to the primary treatment team.

These clinical notes are in contrast to the traditional psychotherapy note that may contain historical information that may be sensitive and does not have immediate relevance to the patient's treatment, and thus, should not be included. The HIPAA privacy rule defines psychotherapy notes as "notes recorded by a health care provider who is a psychologist documenting or analyzing the contents of the conversation…and are separated from the rest of the individual's medical record" (Jones, 2002). Progress notes in the medical chart, like clinical notes that are not considered psychotherapy notes, do not have the same degree of confidentiality as the psychotherapy notes in the psychologist's private office. Many people have access to the patient's medical record. Therefore, it is important to consider the purpose of the note and only include information that is relevant to their medical conditions. It has been recommended, but is not required by HIPAA, that psychotherapy or clinical notes that include sensitive information be kept separately, as they are more protected than standard treatment notes under HIPAA (Benefield et al., 2006). When the psychologist uses psychotherapy notes, they should become part of a separate patient file in the psychologist's office.

The informal "curbside consult" that frequently occurs in hospital settings can also occur in an office-based group or shared settings. Although they have a casual feel that may lend itself to a sharing of information, this situation has the potential to breach a patient's confidentiality unless the consultant is officially part of the treatment team. In the office-based setting, explicit release of information is required before any consultation can occur.

Scope of Practice

As collaborative relationships develop, medical professionals may increasingly look to the psychologist for guidance on various aspects of medical care, particularly the prescription and monitoring of psychotropic medications. Psychologists must remain guided by the APA Ethical Standard on Competence, section 2.01, which states that a psychologist provide services "only within the boundaries of their competence, based on their education, training, supervised experience, consultation, study or professional experience" (APA Practice Directorate, 2002). These are very broad guidelines, and they suggest that the more knowledgeable and experienced psychologist may participate more actively in the medical treatment decisions than those who are less experienced or less trained. The psychologist can actively work with adherence to treatment issues, but they must take care to not make specific recommendations about the medical treatment plan unless they have specific expertise. Although this may seem obvious, the more psychologists work with patients who have medical problems, the more likely it is that they will have experiences relevant to the clinical presentation.

The APA Ethical Standards do not directly address the standard informed-consent process. The standards do indicate that use of treatments that are different from the community standard requires the psychologist to discuss all available, established treatment options, which may include medications. It is important not to recommend specific medical treatment options to the patient without first discussing them with the medical professional. Further, psychologists must take care that their ideas regarding medical care be offered to the medical professional as an experience that might be helpful rather than a recommendation. Often, posing the idea as a question to the medical professional can avoid scope-of-practice issues, particularly if the psychologist is inexperienced or lacking in knowledge. The psychologist who is knowledgeable about medical problems and pharmacology needs to be diplomatic in offering suggestions depending on the relationship with the medical professional. For example, a psychologist who has worked with many patients with diabetes and routinely collaborates with a particular endocrinology group may wonder if a specific patient would benefit from an insulin pump. Such a discussion would be appropriate in the context of the psychologist's experience and expertise, and the established collaborative relationship. In contrast, the psychologist with little medical knowledge or training in health psychology might approach the situation by asking for further information regarding what types of patients benefit from pumps, and why this particular patient is or is not a good candidate for that course of treatment. Both of these psychologists are practicing within their scope of practice. Subsequently, if the medical professional were to desire exploring this option with the patient, they might initiate a conversation at the next medical appointment, which could then be continued during psychotherapy.

It is essential for both the psychologist and the medical professional to respect one another's areas of competence and expertise. These clinical situations are opportunities for both to exchange information and educate one another. The psychologist can expand his/her medical knowledge and understanding of the patient's specific medical options. Another technique in this situation would be to hold a joint appointment with the patient.

Preston and Elbert's (1999) discussion of the psychologists' role in the successful use of psychotropic medication is still quite relevant today. They outline the information about the patient and her/his psychotropic medication that the primary care professional may not know. Patients frequently tell their psychologists about side effects that are barriers to adherence, such as sensitive side effects like sexual side effects including inorgasmia or lack of sexual desire. Patients may disclose to the psychologist that they are not taking medications or following medical recommendations. This discontinuation could be critical and even life-threatening to the patient. Discontinuing specific antidepressants can result in serious discontinuation symptoms. The psychologist may also become aware of an inadequate medication response that may warrant dosage adjustments. Similarly, she/he might know of a history of substance abuse or a current substance problem that might impact the choice of medications. He/she is in a better position to notice the emergence of subtle side effects like emotional blunting, lack of motivation, or involuntary movement. Each of these examples illustrates how opportunities for treatment enhancement are lost when psychologists and medical professionals do not collaborate.

Vandebos and Williams (2000) indicate that over 80% of psychologists in their survey have consulted with physicians about changing a patient's medication, whereas over 85% participated in the initial decision to prescribe psychotropic medications. Medical professionals commonly request assistance in choosing and managing psychotropic medications. Psychologists who have not received post-graduate training in psychopharmacology must limit their input to discussions of the patient's symptom profile and the medications themselves. Currently, only a few psychologists are prescribing psychotropic medications, although many are obtaining advanced training and certification. These psychologists are within their scope of practice when they discuss medications, dosages, and side effects with the medical professionals with whom they collaborate.

Another scope-of-practice issue can arise when the psychologist is uncomfortable with the quality of a patient's medical care. Patients have a right to a second opinion, and psychologists are within their scope of practice to encourage or suggest this, especially when the patient expresses concerns about his/her care. However, this can be somewhat more awkward when the psychologist and medical professional have a close collaborative relationship. Ideally, the psychologist would discuss his/her concerns directly with the medical professional.

Another challenging issue can arise when the psychologist has concerns about the relationship between the medical professional and the patient. This can be a very difficult area to discuss with the patient and medical professional. The latter may become burned out by patients with complex mental health needs and chronic illnesses. Even dedicated, compassionate, energetic physicians can become tired, cynical, and angry at patients and the health care system, a situation described as "compassion fatigue" (Pfifferling & Gilley, 2000). If patients feel rushed or ignored, they too may become angry and frustrated. Frequently, these patients are uncomfortable discussing their concerns directly and will bring it up with the psychologist. There may come a point when the psychologist feels the patient's best interest is met by a transfer of care. Again, it is recommended that the psychologist discuss these concerns with both the patient and the medical professional. Sometimes a joint session is an opportunity for the patient to discuss his/her concerns, and such a meeting may successfully clear the air. If the patient reports that the medical professional is engaging in ethically inappropriate behavior (e.g., sexual advances toward the patient), the psychologist must encourage the patient to transfer care and report the specifics to the appropriate state board.

In summary, psychologists and other mental health professionals who collaborate with medical professionals will frequently encounter issues involving confidentiality, scope of practice, and competency. The APA Ethical Guidelines and Procedures (2002) provide specific guidance in these areas. The psychologist must always be guided by the patient's best interest and the standard of care. The psychologist should make every effort to protect the patient's psychological and medical information whenever possible. The HIPAA privacy rule includes provisions to protect the confidentiality of patient records and facilitate communication between medical professionals. Psychologists working in different settings should be knowledgeable about setting-specific guidelines. Psychologists are held to a higher standard when protecting patient records under HIPAA if they write psychotherapy notes that are process-oriented. Clinical notes are considered a more appropriate choice when writing in the patient's hospital chart in order to protect sensitive patient information. The psychologist's scope of practice depends on their level of competency as defined in the APA Ethical Guidelines (2002). Frequent collaboration with medical professionals will inevitably challenge the psychologist to be thoughtful, careful, and attentive when medical illness and pharmacology are central to the patient's treatment.

Recommendations for Effective Practice

There are increasing opportunities for cognitive-behavioral therapists in the current health care market to collaborate with primary care and other medical professionals. When they begin to collaborate with medical professionals, they will invariably encounter patients with a variety of medical problems. A basic understanding of these medical problems and the physical and psychological implications for patients will enable the psychologist to provide competent, integrative care that has the potential to improve outcomes, as well as patient and professional satisfaction.

Therapists interested in expanding their clinical skill set can seek postgraduate programs that include courses and certifications such as health psychology, behavioral medicine, and behavioral health. Continuing education programs offer many topics related to collaboration, health promotion, and illness management (e.g., motivational interviewing skills when working with patients who need to make lifestyle changes).

Although effective collaboration is possible in most settings, practicing onsite with medical professionals has many advantages. Therapists who locate their offices near hospitals and in close proximity to other medical professionals have opportunities for both formal and informal consultation. Co-location with medical professionals ensures ongoing collaboration, and can be all or part of a therapist's clinical practice.

Effective collaboration can grow out of collaboration that begins when a patient is hospitalized for medical problems. In order to collaborate during medical hospitalization, psychologists should be credentialed in their community hospitals and larger medical centers. This will enable them to see patients outside their offices. This flexibility is necessary when the psychologist is in an office-based practice and treats patients with medical problems. Psychologists can bill for consultation in the hospital or in another medical professional's office by using the health and behavioral reimbursement codes under the current procedural terminology (CPT) coding system. These codes may also be used in the psychologist's office-based practice. The development of these codes involved the efforts of the APA Practice Directorate and the Interdivisional Healthcare Committee

(IHC) that represented several APA divisions. They are considered a "milestone in the recognition of psychologists as health care providers...and apply to behavioral, social, and psychophysiological procedures for the prevention, treatment, or management of physical health problems" (APA Practice Directorate, 2002, para. 1).

The health and behavior codes apply to a wide range of physical health issues, including adjustment to physical illness, health-promoting behaviors, patient adherence, and symptom management. They give the therapist many new opportunities to work with patients whose primary diagnoses are physical in nature. The physical health diagnosis will have already been made by the medical professional and will be represented by *International Statistical Classification of Diseases and Related Health Problems (ICD-9)* codes. However, there is an important caveat when using these codes. When the patient has a physical and mental illness, the therapist must be particularly careful about the billing codes that are chosen. The health and behavior codes cannot be used for psychotherapy that addresses the patient's mental health diagnosis. The therapist must report the predominant service performed on any given day. They cannot use a health and behavior and a psychiatric code on the same day. Intentional or unintentional coding violations are serious infractions, and are considered health care fraud. They may result in serious consequences that include a revocation of one's license to practice by a state board of examiners. The interested reader is referred to *Behavioral Consultation in Primary Care* (Robinson & Reiter, 2007) for detailed instructions on the use of these codes, including how to choose the appropriate CPT and diagnostic codes, and what documentation is required. It should be noted that some private insurers may not reimburse these codes, but Medicare currently reimburses for five of the six health and behavior codes (Robinson & Reiter, 2007).

The future direction of health care policy is unclear; however, the trend seems to point toward more integrative health care approaches. Some federally qualified community health care centers (FQHC) already provide whole-person care that includes psychiatrists and psychologists alongside physicians, nurse practitioners, physician's assistants, social workers, and others. The "medical home," which could include psychologists trained in behavioral health, is a family medicine initiative that requires integrative, collaborative treatment. Reimbursement of mental health services in these settings continues to present challenges because of mental health carve-outs that have fragmented and marginalized mental health treatment (Mauch, Kautz, & Smith, 2008). Some community mental health care centers include primary care medical professionals in an effort to provide more integrated health care. Health and behavior codes may potentially provide a billing payment structure that supports including psychologists in all kinds of primary health care settings. The military and medical residencies currently offer opportunities for psychologists interested in working in fully integrated systems.

Collaboration with medical professionals provides an exciting opportunity. It is our hope that cognitive-behavioral therapists will be eager and willing to expand their scope of practice and expertise to include collaboration with all patients, not just those who have medical conditions. This may require additional and ongoing education, training, and consultation; however, the potential for improved patient care is more than worth the effort. Successful collaboration depends on the willingness of the therapist to work with others in a team. It may require therapists to redefine their roles and preconceptions about what treatment of the patient should look like. Collaboration is a dynamic, reciprocal process that benefits from flexibility and creativity. Michael Hoyt, PhD, a leader in promoting the roles of psychologists in behavioral health care, stated that the collaborative psychologist "must be able to build alliances, communicate respectfully, be helpful, and have a sense of humor" (Ruddy et al., 2008). Cognitive-behavioral therapists who possess the confidence and curiosity to venture out of their offices and into medical settings have the opportunity to become an integral part of the larger health care system as they provide whole-person care to their patients.

References

American Psychological Association. (2002). *Ethical principles of psychologists and code of conduct.* Retrieved December 21, 2008, from http://www.apa.org/ethics/code2002.html

American Psychological Association Practice Directorate. (2002). *APA practice directorate's explanation of new health and behavioral CPT codes.* Retrieved December 20, 2008, from http://www.apa.org/practice/cpt_2002.html

Atwater, A., Bednar, S., Hassman, D., & Khouri, J. (2008). Nurse practitioners and physician assistants in primary care. *Disease-a-Month, 54*(110, 728–744.

Benefield, H., Ashkanazi, G., & Rozensky, R. (2006). Communication and records: HIPAA issues when working in health care settings. *Professional Psychology: Research and Practice, 37*(3), 273–277.

Bonsall, K., & Cheater, F. (2008). What is the impact of advanced primary care nursing roles on patients, nurses and their colleagues? *International Journal of Nursing Studies, 45*(7), 1090–1102.

Brazeau, C., Rovi, S., Yick, C., & Johnson, M. (2005). Collaboration between mental health professionals and family physiciains: A survey of New Jersey family physicians. *Primary Care Companion Journal of Clinical Psychiatry, 7*(1), 12–14.

Chapa, T. (2004, September). *Mental health care services in primary care settings for racial and ethnic minorities populations.* Rockville, MD: Office of Minority Health.

Daw, J. (2002). Psychology as "comprehensive health profession." *Monitor on Psychology, 33*(6). Retrieved September 10, 2009, from http://www.apa.org/monitor/jun02/psychology.html.

Department of Health and Human Services. (2007). *Healthy people 2010: Midcourse review.* Retrieved November 23, 2008, from http://www.healthypeople.gov/publications/html

Doherty, W. J. (2007). Fixing healthcare. *Psychotherapy Networker, 31*(3), 24–31.

Doherty, W. J., McDaniel, S. H., & Baird, M. A. (1996). Five levels of primary care/behavioral healthcare collaboration. *Behavioral Healthcare Tomorrow, 5*(5), 25–27.

Engel, G. L. (1977). The need for a new medical model: A challenge for biomedicine. *Science, 196*(4286).

Fleet, R. D., Dupuis, G., Marchand, A., Burelle, D., Arsenault, A., & Beitman, B. D. (1996). Panic disorder in emergency department chest pain patients: Prevalence, comorbidity, suicidal ideation, and physician recognition. *American Journal of Medicine, 101*, 371–380.

Grenier, J., Chomienne, M. H., Gaboury, I., Ritchie, P., & Hogg, W. (2008). Collaboration between family physician and psychologist's: What do physicians psychologists'know about psychologists' work? *Canadian Family Physician, 54*(2), 232–233.

Haley, W. E., McDaniel, S. H., Bray, J. H., Frank, R. G., Heldring, M., Johnson, S. B., et al. (1998). Psychological practice in primary care settings: Practical tips for clinicians. *Professional Psychology: Research and Practice, 29*(3), 237–244. Retrieved November 23, 2008, from http://www.apa.org/practice/primarycare99.html

Holloway, R. L., & David, A. K. (2005). The complexion of collaboration. *Clinical Case Studies, 4*(2), 115–125.

Jones, C. (2002). Practice organization: Held to a higher standard. *APA Online.* Retrieved December 21, 2008, from http://www.apa.org/practice/pf/winter02/higher_standard.html

Kasperski, M. J. (2000). *Implementation strategies: Collaboration in primary care-family doctors and nurse practitioners delivering shared care.* Retrieved November 23, 2008, from www.ocfp.on.ca

Katon, W. (2001). Rethinking practitioner roles in chronic illness: The specialist, primary care physician, and the practice nurse. *General Hospital Psychiatry, 23*(3), 138–144.

Lewis, E., Marcus, S. C., Olfson, M., Druss, B. G., & Pincus, H. A. (2004). Datapoints: Patients' early discontinuation of antidepressant prescriptions. *Psychiatric Services, 55*, 494.

Mauch, D., Kautz, C., & Smith, S. (2008, February). *Reimbursement of mental health services in primary care settings.* Rockville, MD: U.S. Department of Health and Human Services, Substance Abuse and Mental Health Service Administration, Center for Mental Health Services. www.samhsa.gov

McDaniel, S. H., Campbell, T. L., & Seaburn, D. B. (1990). *Family-oriented primary care: A manual for medical providers.* New York: Springer-Verlag.

Miller, D. (2006). Reflections. *American Journal of Nursing, 106*(12), 88.

Nezu, A. M., Nezu, C. M., & Lombardo, E. R. (2001). Cognitive-behavioral therapy for medically unexplained symptoms: A critical review of the treatment literature. *Behavior Therapy, 32*(3), 537–583.

Pfifferling, J. H., & Gilley, K. G. (2000). Overcoming compassion fatigue. *Family Practice Management, 4*(1), 37–46.

Preston, J., & Elbert, B. (1999, October). Psychologists' role in the discussion of psychotropic medication with clients: Legal and ethical considerations. *California Psychologist, 32*(10), 32–34.

Psychologists and physicians: Tips for collaboration. (2008). *Monitor of Psychology.* Retrieved December 6, 2008, from http://www.apa.org/monitor/2008/05/collaboration.html

Regier, D. A., Goldberg, I. D., & Taube, C. A. (1978). The de facto U.S. mental health services system: A public health perspective. *Archives of General Psychiatry, 35*, 685–693.

Robinson, P., & Reiter, J. (2007). *Behavioral consultation and primary care: A guide to integrating services* Boston: Springer.

Ruddy, N., Borresen, D. A., & Gunn, W. B. (2008). *The collaborative psychotherapist: Creating reciprocal relationships with medical professionals.* Washington, DC: American Psychological Association.

VandenBox, G. R., & Williams, S. (2009). Is psychologists' involvement in the prescribing of psychotropic medication really a new activity? *Professional Psychology Research and Practice, 31*(6), 615–618.

The Consultation Process in Primary Care

4

Travis A. Cos
Robert A. DiTomasso
Carla Cirilli
Larry H. Finkelstein

Introduction

The words "primary care physician" (PCP) or "family doctor" can often conjure up heartwarming images of Norman Rockwell paintings. Depictions of physicians tenderly caring for the people in their community, listening intently to their concerns, and helping them recover from illness and minor injuries fill the cultural landscape and color our perceptions of our doctors. Primary care providers develop long-term relationships with their patients, caring for them in sickness and in health over the course of the life cycle, building a degree of closeness in the process (Bray, 2004). Primary care medicine is patient-centered and relies on several skill sets, most notably emphasizing interpersonal communication, empathetic understanding and care, collaborative decision making, empowering patient self-management strategies, and the successful use of preventive and behavioral change interventions to improve overall health (Belar, 2003; Schulte, Isley, Link, Shealy, & Winfrey, 2004). To effectively accomplish this venture, an integrative approach is necessary, considering the biological, cognitive, affective, and sociocultural needs and circumstances for the patient (McDaniel, Belar, Schroeder, Hargrove, & Freeman, 2002).

In reality, general practitioners face a difficult juggling act. They must balance the expectations that arise from having a large, diverse caseload of individuals presenting with a wide range of medical illnesses and ailments, and working within the confines of managed-care insurance reimbursement and best evidence practice (Robinson & Reiter, 2007). Over the past two decades, managed-care insurance companies have emphasized cost-effectiveness strategies, such as capitation (e.g., physician bonuses for reducing unnecessary or marginally beneficial referrals to specialists) and specialty referral preauthorizations (Hillman, Pauly, & Kerstein, 1989; Kassirer, 1995; Kerr et al., 1995; St. Peter, Reed, Kemper, & Blumenthal, 1999). This has placed PCPs in a more prominent "gatekeeper role," determining and limiting how patients access different health care resources, such as specialty medical care (Pace, Chaney, Mullins, & Olson, 1995; Stephens, 1989). These processes have increased the medical severity and range of problems physicians address in their patient panels, and provided fertile ground for disagreements and conflicts between physicians and patients over referral decisions. One out of four PCPs surveyed feels the scope of their practice is too great (St. Peter et al., 1999). This is further compromised by the fact that the average primary care visit appointment is limited to 15 minutes, and patients tend to report 3 distinct complaints per office visit (Kaplan, Gandek, Greenfield, Rogers, & Ware, 1995).

The Nature of Mental Health Difficulties in Primary Care Practice

Mental health difficulties are among the most common presenting problems in primary care. This is reflected across the U.S., where the number of primary care facilities that provide some form of mental health treatment has steadily increased from 62% in 2000 to 79% in 2006 (U.S. Department of Health & Human Services Centers for Disease Control, 2007). Full-time primary care providers spend an average of 12.1 hours per week providing care for psychiatric disorders (Pruitt, Klapow, Epping-Jordan, & Dresselhaus, 1998), and in one study, 81% of general practitioners reported addressing emotional difficulties on a daily basis among their patients (Vasquez, Nath, & Murray, 1988). It has been estimated that 25% of primary care patients have a diagnosable psychiatric disorder (Olfson et al., 1997), and 50% of those with mental health problems are seen exclusively only in primary care settings, although 70% of all psychotropic medication prescriptions come from primary care providers (Beardsley, Gardocki, Larson, & Hidalgo, 1998; Pincus, 1998). A study by Olfson and colleagues (2000) found that 19% of consecutively scheduled primary care patients met criteria for major depressive disorder, 15% for generalized anxiety disorder, 8% for panic disorders, and another 8% for substance use. When considering that patients experiencing distress often seek out their primary care provider first, these findings are not surprising. However, the mental health problem is further exacerbated by the fact that nearly half of the patients with active psychiatric disorders are missed and not diagnosed by primary care providers (USDHHS, 1999).

The Mind-Body Interaction: The Role of Psychosocial Factors in Medicine

In addition to traditional psychiatric disorders, PCPs treat many medical conditions that can be significantly impacted by stress, such as irritable bowel syndrome, tension headaches, insomnia, and chronic nonspecific pain (Robinson & Reiter, 2007). Psychosocial factors significantly contribute to most of the ten leading causes of death and chronic illness in the United States (USDHHS, 2000). Of particular concern are behavioral risk factors like insufficient exercise, poor diet, smoking, and unsafe practices (e.g., unprotected sex, not using seatbelts [CDC Behavioral Risk Factor Surveillance System, 2007]).

A landmark study conducted by Kroenke and Mangelsdorff (1989) studied the most common complaints primary care providers experience, including chest pain, fatigue, dizziness, headache, swelling, back pain, shortness of breath, insomnia, abdominal pain, and numbness. When these patients' presenting complaints were followed for a year by researchers, only 15% of these problems were linked directly to a sound biological cause. The consensus opinion on this research is that psychosocial difficulties have a more crucial role in the pathogenesis of medical problems than previously appreciated (Gunn & Blount, 2009). It is critical for primary care providers to consider the interaction between mental health and lifestyle challenges on medical illness and injury. For example, research has shown that psychological distress (e.g., anxiety and depressive disorders) is a major predictor for ongoing disability for osteoarthritis from knee injuries (Salaffi, Cavalieri, Nolli, & Ferraccioli, 1991; Sobel, 1995).

Managing Psychiatric Disorders From the PCP Perspective

Given the prevalence of psychiatric disorders in primary care practice, the influence of psychosocial factors in medical illness, and the obstacles that exist in getting patients successfully referred to mental health providers, PCPs are taking a more active role in the treatment and management of psychiatric disorders. PCPs have become the largest treatment source for mental health difficulties, primarily via psychotropic medications (Beardsley, Gardocki, Larson, & Hidalgo, 1988; Reiger, Narrow, Rae, Manderscheid, Locke, & Goodwin, 1993). Since the introduction of newer antidepressants (selective serotonin reuptake inhibitors [SSRIs]), PCPs have also been able to greatly increase their reach in the mental health care of their patients. One noticeable trend that has been observed since Prozac was introduced in 1986 is an inverse linear relationship between increased rates of pharmacological treatment of depression by primary care doctors and decreased rates of individuals receiving psychotherapy for depression (Olfson, Marcus, & Druss, 2002).

PCPs are keenly aware that mental health and psychosocial difficulties cannot be simply "cured" by writing prescriptions for psychotropic medications. Interventions to promote healthy lifestyle choices and proper adherence to prescribed medication are needed to make significant differences in reducing chronic diseases, especially because 60% of patients with chronic health problems display poor medication adherence (Dunbar-Jacob & Mortimer-Stephens, 2001; Robinson & Reiter, 2007). Medical school and residency training plays a significant role in a primary care provider's orientation and capabilities in managing psychosocial problems in their clinical practice, especially their skills in recognizing and treating behavioral health problems (Pace et al., 1995). Medical training is extremely limited in providing physicians with specific psychotherapeutic interventions to help ameliorate psychological distress, despite increased efforts to build psychosocial knowledge for primary care and family medicine physicians. There are several obstacles that physicians experience in using psychosocial interventions for behavioral health problems (Pincus, 2003). First, psychotherapeutic treatments are highly specified for the given psychiatric disorder (e.g., problem-solving therapy for depression, exposure and ritual prevention for OCD) that makes it difficult for physicians to have the necessary knowledge, training, and practice to deliver evidence-based treatments for mental health difficulties. Second, psychiatric disorders are less easily defined and diagnosed than physical health problems, with the *Diagnostic and Statistical Manual of Mental Disorders* (*DSM-IV-TR*; American Psychiatric Association, 2000) being rather cumbersome for use in primary care. Third, many physicians are often not clear where their roles begin and end in servicing psychosocial problems, with multiple systems and individuals involved in these issues (e.g., behavioral health providers, families, workplaces, social welfare agencies), reducing their motivation to get involved at all with psychotherapeutic techniques. Finally, large patient registries that limit the frequency of appointments, minimal reimbursement for psychosocial interventions, and brief office visit encounters are additional prohibitive factors for physicians in delivering mental health treatments to their primary care patients.

The Obstacles in Referring to Traditional Behavioral Health Services

There are a number of barriers to engaging primary care patients in traditional outpatient psychotherapy. There are a limited number of behavioral health providers, not nearly enough to meet the greater mental health needs of a given community (Jenkins & Strathdee, 2000). Primary care providers tend not to have established relationships with mental health providers, and frequently they lack a good sense of referral options in the communities they serve (Gunn & Blount, 2009). This is further exacerbated by the managed care system, when there may be mismatches between the few behavioral health providers the physician may know, the insurance panels these providers belong to, and the patient's insurance, if any. For the growing population of the uninsured, available community services may be limited, with community mental health centers often being overwhelmed, and private care is frequently cost-prohibitive (DeLeon, Giesting, & Kenkel, 2003). When primary care providers are able to refer patients to mental health providers, they often face a lack of direct contact (e.g., voicemail exchanges), long waiting lists, and lack of knowledge on how to provide the most useful and specific referral information (James, 2006). Furthermore, most insurance companies provide psychotherapy reimbursement for only diagnosable *DSM-IV-TR* (APA, 2000) psychiatric disorders, which prevents behavioral health providers from being able to bill for services to those with subthreshold presentations, as well as those with primary health problems that may benefit from psychotherapy (e.g., smoking, obesity, diabetes adherence). This further limits the ability for people to access treatment that could be helpful for improving their daily functioning and health functioning, as well as for gaining assistance in making healthy lifestyle changes (Robinson & Reiter, 2007).

Frequently, patients exhibit low follow-up rates on outside referrals to mental health specialty care (Callahan et al., 2002; Kessler, Stafford, & Messier, 2009; Williams, Palmes, Klinepeter, Pulley, & Meschan, 2005). In the limited time physicians have with patients, they are often not able to assess patient motivation and prominent obstacles that may impede follow-up on the mental health referral, as well as having limited training on addressing this issue (Robinson & Reiter, 2007). Stigma and fear can often prevent patients from addressing mental health concerns with their physicians, as they are reluctant to admit emotional difficulties and they sometimes worry about the ramifications of such disclosures (e.g., Will I be locked up? Deemed crazy?). Defensiveness and discomfort about the issue of a mental health diagnosis and/or referral can be a significant barrier to broaching the subject for patients, as well as for the provider. Copayments for psychotherapy, transportation limitations (e.g., is the therapist on an accessible bus route?), child care concerns, and availability conflicts with the patient's work schedule can be additional barriers that limit mental health referral follow-up.

Theoretical Issues

Background on the Genesis of Behavioral Health Consultation in Primary Care

The growing recognition of the need to address all aspects of health, particularly psychosocial difficulties, in the provision of medical care has slowly initiated a movement toward having behavioral health providers working within primary care, as well as in specialty practices, such as gynecology and cardiology (Johnstone et al., 1995; Schulte et al., 2004). The first example of psychological integration in medical settings may have occurred during World War II (Cummings, O'Donohue, & Cummings, 2009). General William Menninger began using well-trained young psychologists providing brief, immediate behavioral interventions, embedded in military units and encamped right outside the battlefront. This advancement received attention in the popular media of books and film, and helped to further public interest in the psychotherapeutic process.

Evolving trends in the fields of primary care medicine, psychiatry, and psychology played a significant role in limiting integration and collaboration in the subsequent decades after World War II (for further description of this history, please refer to the article by Cummings et al., 2009). Successful demonstration projects were initiated in many states and clinics, most notably the Hawaii Project I (Cummings & Follette, 1968; Follette & Cummings, 1967), which showed that primary care patients and practices benefited from having psychologists operating directly in the medical setting. Grants funded the integration of behavioral health providers in medical settings in the 1960s; however, the services were not self-sustaining and ended when the funding stopped (Robinson & Strosahl, 2009). Unfortunately, the potential benefits afforded to future patients were undermined by the failure to support ongoing efforts of professional collaboration in this regard.

A seminal moment in the integrated behavioral health movement occurred in 1971, when family medicine residencies began to require that a behavioral scientist be a member of the teaching faculty (Robinson & Strosahl, 2009). Pioneering work was started, developing strategies to integrate psychotherapy and consultation in the context of family practice and medical training programs. With the increasing involvement of academic researchers, greater sophistication of treatment delivery in the primary care setting occurred, such as adapting existing consultation and liaison models being used in hospital settings (Lipowski, 1967; Pomerantz, Corson, & Detzer, 2009). This movement spawned an increase in effectiveness studies examining the impact of embedded services (Cummings et al., 2009; Kilbourne et al., 2006; Oxman, Dietrich, & Schulberg, 2003; Skultety & Zeiss, 2006; Smith, Monson, & Ray, 1986). The Hawaii Integrated Healthcare Project II (Laygo et al., 2003) and the U.S. Air Force (Runyan, Fonseca, & Hunter, 2003) were among the first major effectiveness studies to demonstrate the utility of adapting behavioral-health services to better fit the primary care model. Effective models of integrated behavioral health services within a primary care context have been also demonstrated by the Veterans Administration, the Cherokee Health System TriCare, U.S. Navy, and more recently, Kaiser Permanente.

In response to the growing empirical support, in 1984, the World Health Organization began to advocate for the greater integration of physical and medical health services (Jenkins & Strathdee, 2000). In an issued policy statement, the World Health Organization (1984) recommended increased: (a) colocation of mental health services within health clinics; (b) training primary care health workers, nurses, physicians, and medical assistants to better manage basic mental health difficulties; and (c) bringing mental health professionals into training and providing support to health workers. In 1997, the U.S. Senate Appropriations Committee recognized mental health and substance abuse services as essential elements of primary care provision (American Psychological Association, 1998; Johnson, Stewart, Brabeck, Huber, & Rubin, 2004). The U.S. government has also continued to financially support training opportunities for psychologists as part of interdisciplinary teams, particularly in high-need areas, such as rural and underserved communities.

Strosahl (1998) suggests that the three crucial factors to successful primary care-oriented mental health services are colocation, collaboration, and integration. Colocation focuses on having the mental health provider located directly within the primary care clinic, which can help to optimize communication between providers and lower the stigma of mental health treatment. Collaboration emphasizes a biopsychosocial orientation, with an open exchange of information between primary care and behavioral health providers, as well as mutual contributions to the patient's overall treatment plan. Integration emphasizes the growth of the behavioral health provider as a true, functioning member of the primary care team by the health providers and staff. The development of sound professional working relationships characterized by mutual respect, cooperation, and a professional give-and-take perspective is likely to yield a coherent and integrated plan for addressing patient problems.

The practice of behavioral health consultation in primary care can generally be grouped into two categories (Caplan, 1970; Mendoza, 1993). A *client-centered consultation* model is focused on providing clinical behavioral health services directly to the primary care patient, usually depending on joint collaboration and follow-up by the primary care provider and behavioral health clinician. In a *consultee-oriented* model, the behavioral health clinician provides consultation and troubleshooting of service delivery problems, on both individual and system levels, to better improve patient care. The following sections will discuss each model.

Client-Centered Behavioral Health Consultation

Gatchel and Oordt (2003) examined the various models of behavioral health services being implemented within the primary care setting and found five distinct approaches of patient-focused consultation, with increasing aspects of collaboration and integration. The simplest arrangement is to have a *colocated* mental health clinic model, in which a specialty, traditional mental health clinic is located on the premises of a primary care office, in a distinctly separate space. There likely will be minimal direct collaboration, except for referrals and basic correspondence, and the mental health model will likely mirror standard outpatient services (e.g., 45- or 50-minute sessions, comprehensive assessments). The colocation of services in this model helps to lower the stigma and difficulty in accessing mental health services, but may not do much to increase integration and professional collaboration, as the behavioral health and medical practices often will be distinctly separate services.

In the *primary care provider* model, the mental health provider works within the primary care practice and is considered part of the health care team, yet often continues to function rather independently, providing psychotherapy services in a similar manner as the colocated clinic model (Gatchel & Oordt, 2003). The amount of integration and collaboration can vary across clinics, depending on the context and individual preferences of the providers.

One exemplar of the primary care provider model is medical family therapy (McDaniel, 1995). Medical family therapy is a collaborative approach focused on the idea that all human problems have a biopsychosocial systemic component, and the emphasis is on enhancing a sense of choice in medical decisions, personal agency, and interpersonal connection and communication for families dealing with health problems. The provider should view his/her role as helping to enlarge the system in which the patient lives to include the patient's family and medical providers. This process helps increase patient motivation to engage in therapy and make personal changes to improve health. Behavioral health practitioners from this perspective will often join doctors' visits to further the collaboration, as well as occasionally requesting physicians to join the provider on a visit to the patient's home (McDaniel, Campbell, Hepworth, & Lorenz, 2005).

A third level of collaboration involves the *staff advisor* approach, in which a behavioral health provider functions within the primary care team as a consultant to the health care providers (Gatchel & Oordt, 2003). In the staff advisor model, the clinical responsibilities of the behavioral health provider are generally limited to working alongside the primary care providers during their patient visits, or via telephone consultation, with limited independent patient contact. The *health psychology* model (Pomerantz et al., 2009) often resembles many facets of the staff advisor approach. Clinical health psychologists who use this model frequently interpret their role as focused on preventive and wellness interventions to enhance physical and mental health (Stanton, Revenson, & Tennen, 2007). Health psychologists often meet with individuals during their medical visits, using brief-intervention strategies spending only a short time with the individual, and the contact generally is not ongoing in the same nature as traditional psychotherapy. Clinical health psychologists will often frequently refer individuals with primary psychiatric problems to behavioral health providers in the community. A consultation and liaison service within primary care is another model of the staff advisor approach (Pomerantz et al., 2009). Assessment services are provided by the behavioral health clinician to help clarify diagnostic questions by the health providers, and are often followed by treatment intervention recommendations. The consultant may administer brief primary care interventions directly to the patient; train health providers on how to conduct simple, primary care-friendly, disorder-specific interventions (e.g., relaxation techniques for anxiety, behavioral activation and problem-solving strategies for depression); or be instrumental in referring the patient to pertinent community behavioral health services.

The fourth level of collaborative care, according to Gatchel and Oordt (2003), is the *stepped-care approach*, based upon on the medical model for specialty care. A stepped-care approach emphasizes matching the intensity of intervention services to the complexity of the patient's illness(es) (Glascow, 1995; Katon, Von Korff, Lin, & Simon, 2001). At the lowest intensity, known as Level 1 care, PCPs assess and diagnose problems, and provide educational and preventive measures, focusing on patient self-management. At Level 2, the system expands to incorporate nurses or other allied health professionals in providing active treatment to enhance patient education and help to support illness management. Level 3 care would involve the consultation of a specialist for illness persisting after a period of Level 2 care, or for complex initial presentations. Level 4 care would be a referral to specialists for more intense care, after the previous stepped levels could not, or were not able to, ameliorate the presenting problems. In this model, a behavioral health provider offers a variety of different services, depending on patient need, including consultation and training with the primary care providers on specific preventive and intervention strategies and one-time brief interventions with the patient, up to frequent, 30–50-minute psychotherapy visits (Gatchel & Oordt, 2003).

The fifth level of collaboration that Gatchel and Oordt (2003) examined is Robinson and Reiter's (2007) *primary care behavioral health* (PCBH) model. In this approach, colocation, collaboration, and integration are maximized, because the behavioral health consultant works side by side with the primary care providers, using the same office space the patients are seen in by their health providers. They function similarly to primary care providers, seeing 10–15 patients per day for relatively brief periods of time, and average between one to four consultation visits with each patient. Eschewing the longer traditional psychosocial intake, a brief, general assessment of functioning (e.g., history of presenting problem, suicidality) is conducted, with emphasis on problem-focused assessment, and a physician-friendly treatment plan is developed. Brief interventions, tailored to coping with the specific behavioral health problems (e.g., depression, smoking cessation), are enacted. Primary care providers receive training on how to follow up with psychosocial problems, and they then follow the specific behavioral health treatment plan in their primary care visits with the patients, using the behavioral health consultant for a given patient on an as-needed basis. Generally, outpatient, offsite referrals are made only for more extensive mental health difficulties (e.g., substance dependence, chronic mental health difficulties). In general, in this model behavioral health consultants will meet with patients for 15–30 minutes with the aim of maximizing their services to a population greater than the primary care clinic services. An essential component of this model is "warm handoffs," which refers to immediate, same-day visits by the behavioral health specialist upon referral from the primary care provider.

A similar approach is used by the Veterans Administration (VA), known as the "White River Model," after the White River Junction VA in Vermont, where the approach was first piloted (Pomerantz et al., 2009). Like the previously discussed PCBH model, this approach embeds behavioral health providers in primary care and uses a brief intervention model to provide immediate, open-access services to the primary care patient. By reducing the need for scheduled appointments, the VA has significantly been able to cut down on missed appointments and referral no-shows, and it has been demonstrated in one clinic that over 75% of patients were able to have their mental health needs addressed in the primary care clinic without the need for an outside referral (Grembowski et al., 2002; Pomerantz et al., 2009; Van Voorhees, Wang, & Ford, 2003).

The integration of behavioral health services in primary care is slowly becoming a more widespread phenomenon. However, Robinson and Strosahl (2009) suggest that on dissemination of the efficacy of this approach is in its infancy. The demonstration projects discussing colocated, integrated primary care have previously established the potential efficacy of these efforts. Newer research is seeking to explore how these services are best delivered and in what ways they are truly effective. Cumulative research has demonstrated that integrated care is most effective with colocation of mental health services at primary care sites (Aitken & Curtis, 2004). Integrating behavioral health providers in primary care settings leads to increased screening of mental health disorders, reducing the number of undiagnosed psychiatric disorders (Katon et al., 1995, 1996). Likewise, collaborative care has been shown to increase proper adherence to psychotropic medication and reduce the use of medication for subclinical presentations of psychiatric disorders (Katon et al., 1996). Symptomatic benefits have also been demonstrated by the use of integrated behavioral health models (Hine, Howell, & Yonkers, 2008). In a sample of teenagers presenting with symptoms of depression in primary care, a randomized-control study was conducted, and patients either received usual primary care treatment for depression or collaborative, integrated manualized cognitive-behavioral therapy (CBT; Asarnow et al., 2005). The teenagers who received integrated CBT experienced significantly improved health outcomes, quality of life, and depressive symptoms. Another collaborative model focused on low-income Latina patients with breast or cervical cancer, and comorbid depression (Dwight-Johnson, Ell, & Lee, 2005). Using a 7-week problem-solving therapy approach, coupled with antidepressant medication, those women receiving the integrated care were significantly more likely to experience a 50% reduction in symptoms of depression than those only receiving usual medical care.

Cost-effectiveness research has also shown the important value of integrated behavioral health services. Looking at the published research on integrated collaboration, the following trends have been observed (Cummings et al., 2009). Follow-through on referrals increased from 10% for traditional outpatient therapists to 85–90% for immediate, in-house handoffs to behavioral care providers. Medical costs were found to be reduced by 20–30% over and beyond the cost of behavioral care (Cummings, O'Donohue, & Fergusson, 2003). PCPs experience increased freed-up time, allowing them to engage in more medically based care. In the landmark Hawaii Project I, among the people who were randomly assigned to either an integrated primary care clinic or a traditional primary care clinic, a major cost savings was found for the heaviest users of medical services (top 15%) when they received their health care in the integrated clinic, where they were exposed to brief, targeted behavioral interventions (Cummings et al., 2009). Katon and Unutzer (2006) found that collaborative care costs were more expensive in the first 12 months, but downstream benefits led to significant cost savings in the subsequent 12–28 months after services were initially provided. For example, a mean medical costs savings of $240 was found for individuals with panic disorder when they received an integrative care model relative to a usual medical treatment (Katon et al., 2006).

Consultee-Centered Behavioral Health Consultation

Perhaps the earliest formal theoretical model describing the process of mental health consultation was posited by Caplan (1970). Caplan (1970) defined consultation as follows: "a process of interaction between two professionals—the consultant who is a specialist, and the consultee, who invokes the consultant's help in regard to a current work problem with which he(she) is having some difficulty and which he(she) has decided is within the other's area of specialized competence" (p. 19). In consultation, one may distinguish between case, or patient, consultation, in which the consultant is expected to offer an expert opinion about assessment, diagnosis, conceptualization, or treatment of the consultee's patient, and consultee-focused consultation, emphasizing the consultee's reaction to the patient.

A useful and more recent behaviorally based model of patient-centered consultation has been offered by Kratochwill (1990). Combining concepts from Caplan (1970), Kratochwill (1990), and Beck (1991), one of the authors has proposed a cognitive model of psychological consultee-centered consultation in primary care. Before describing this model, a consideration of the rules of consultation and necessity for consultation is warranted.

Almost 40 years ago, Caplan (1970) elucidated the unique characterisitics of consultation and differentiated it from other forms of service. Caplan (1970) proposed that in the strictest sense consultants do not deliver direct services, do not assume professional responsibility for the patient, and offer information and data about the patient. The consultee may choose whether or not to accept the suggestions offered by the consultant. There is an inherent assumption that this process will improve the consultee's ability to effectively handle similar cases in the future. Consultation clearly differs from supervision and psychotherapy in a number of ways.

Cognitive-behavioral clinicians in primary care can benefit from having a useful model for formulating and conceptualizing the work of consultation in a given case. Those readers familiar with the cognitive-behavioral model will notice the application of concepts to this topic. To elucidate this cognitive model of primary care consultation (DiTomasso, 2009), we will use the example of consultee-centered consultation.

The point of contact and reason for consultation in this case is often rooted in the physician's frustration with a particular patient, or group of patients. The central problem may be rooted in the consultee's subjective perspective on the patient, highlighted by the thoughts, beliefs, attitudes, and underlying assumptions the physician holds about the patient, or about him/herself in relation to the patient. This notion is similar to what Caplan (1970) termed *theme interference*. This model posits that the physician's response to the patient may be explained by the activation of a schema, or set of schemas, that guide and determine the physician's thoughts, feelings, and behaviors in relation to the patient. The goals of consultation in this instance are: to assist the physician in identifying the specific problem being experienced in this context; to identify the relationship between the consultee's thoughts, feelings, and behaviors as they relate to this patient; to recognize underlying assumptions related to the physician's thoughts, feelings, and behaviors; and to assist the physician in challenging these unrealistic cognitive products.

The basic assumptions of this model are as follows: (a) Physicians actively process their professional encounters with patients before, during and after an office visit; (b) the thoughts, beliefs, attitudes, and assumptions a consultee has about a patient influence his/her feelings about and behaviors toward the patient; (c) a consultee may distort his/her experience through errors in cognitive processing; (d) when a consultee disorts his/her experience with a patient, what results are behaviors and feelings that may interfere with treatment and undermine the consultee's ability to effectively handle the patient; (e) helping the consultee become aware of his/her thoughts, assumptions, feelings, and behaviors is an important step in resolving the consultee's difficulties in dealing with the patient; (f) teaching a consultee how to formulate his/her experience with the patient and how to challenge dysfunctional thoughts and schema will resolve the consultee's difficulty; and (g) modifying dysfunctional schema will allow the consultee to handle similar cases more effectively in the future. This approach involves building rapport, setting goals and an agenda, gathering relevant information about the patient, orienting the physician to the model, forming and sharing a conceptualization, obtaining feedback about the formulation, challenging thoughts and assumptions, developing strategies for handling the case, evaluating the process, and gathering follow-up data about outcomes.

Case Example

To illustrate the model, consider the case of Dr. M., a 37-year-old female physician board certified in family medicine. Dr. M. has been in practice for 7 years at a university-affiliated family medicine program. She has a reputation as an excellent physician and is popular with patients, the medical staff, and the office staff. A patient Dr. M. sought consultation for is a 42-year-old White woman married to an alcoholic husband, who frequently and repeatedly calls the office on a daily basis to speak to the physician. This patient has seen Dr. M. for several months (e.g., 12 visits in the last 3 months), and has seen several other physicians before transferring to Dr. M.'s practice. Dr. M. has experienced marked difficulty in managing the visits, which too often last for over an hour. The patient was being treated at a counseling center and was diagnosed as suffering from "adjustment disorder with mixed features and a borderline organization." Dr. M. reported to the consultant that she feels anxious, emotionally overwhelmed by the patient, ineffectual with this patient, frustrated, and worried that the patient will take her own life (in the absence of hard evidence). The goals for seeking consultation were to feel less overwhelmed, anxious, and ineffectual, and to develop some specific strategies for handling this difficult patient.

A sample of Dr. M.'s thoughts and beliefs about this patient proved important. Dr. M. reported the following thoughts: " I am a failure, I can't help her, I'm stupid, I can't fix this situation—there is nothing I can do to help her, and she makes too many demands on me." She frequently visualizes the patient "holding a sign in front of my face saying 'You're not a good doctor.' " Dr. M.'s behaviors were also informative. She avoided the patient as much as possible, made her a low priority for a call back, and also communicated this attitude to the office staff. One relevant underlying core schema was, "If I do not know how to intervene with this patient, then I am not a good doctor," which she believed strongly. A number of strategies were used to assist Dr. M., including identifying cognitive distortions about the patient and her own abilities; examining her definition of a good doctor; explaining how she employed a double standard with this patient whose previous physicians Dr. M. saw as competent but were also unable to help; gathering evidence against, and in favor of her beliefs, and comparing the weight of evidence; and engaging in cognitive reframing. Additionally several behavioral strategies were recommended, which included: (a) developing a specific agenda and time limit for each patient encounter (i.e., office, phone); (b) obtaining a release of information to talk with the patient's therapist to improve collaboration; (c) seeing the patient on a regular schedule, rather than emphasizing the ongoing "crisis" visit model; (d) directly assessing for suicidal risk in the patient and discussing this with the treating therapist, to reduce worries; (e) developing a collaborative suicide prevention plan with the patient and her therapist; and (f) engaging in validation of the patient's support and care from Dr. M. and the therapist.

Consultee-focused consultation is critical in primary care because of the heavier load of mental health treatment that primary care providers typically offer. Patients suffering from mental health problems frequently seek help from their PCP and occupy a great deal of physician time. Not surprisingly, these patients have the capacity to elicit negative reactions from their physicians that can interfere with medical care.

Practical and Logistical Issues

The successful delivery of behavioral health services in a colocated primary care setting depends on addressing a number of logistical and interpersonal hurdles.

C. J. Peek, an expert in integrating behavioral health and primary care services, summarized the enormity of this task by saying the "stars need to align" for this enterprise to work (Peek & Heinrich, 1995). Effective collaboration depends on the ability of the behavioral health provider to cooperatively address administrative, clinical, financial, and communication barriers within the primary care practice; relative failure in one of these domains can easily sabotage the collaborative process. The following paragraphs will discuss the most common challenges that behavioral health providers experience when developing and maintaining a colocated, integrated practice in primary care.

Administrative Barriers

The physical space and organizational policies of a medical clinic can pose unique challenges for collaborative behavioral health services. A behavioral health provider will have to contract with the medical director on how and where patients will be seen (Gunn & Blount, 2009). If an embedded, traditional behavioral health service is being created, will there be separate rooms reserved for therapy, and will they be available at convenient times for patients? In an integrative model, a behavioral health provider needs to determine whether clinic flow will allow them enough time to see patients in their medical room or if they will need to be escorted to another space.

The model of collaboration that the behavioral health provider uses will often be heavily influenced by the expectations of the clinic's administration (Peek & Heinrich, 1995). This will depend on how behavioral health services will be funded and the target population for services (e.g., consultation for the health care providers, addressing the most significant mental health needs, providing preventive and intervention services for the greater community of patients). Colocation is advantageous, but it can present barriers when services are not further integrated, including staffing difficulties, long waits for referred mental health services, and a difficulty syncing traditional mental health services with the speed of primary care (Robinson & Strosahl, 2009). A lack of administrative support in scheduling appointments and answering phones can be an obstacle for primary care psychologists being available for consultations and can slow the referral process (Kessler et al., 2009).

Financial Barriers

Managed care insurance-reimbursement policies play a significant factor in how mental health services can be delivered, particularly in the primary care setting (Bray, 2004). Health insurances generally reimburse only for psychotherapeutic services delivered for individuals who meet specific criteria for *DSM-IV* psychiatric disorders, and very few plans support behavioral health consultation claims (Cummings et al., 2009). This poses a significant challenge for integrated behavioral health services, because referrals frequently include individuals with diagnosable psychiatric disorders, subthreshold psychosocial problems (e.g., minor depression, grief, elevated stress), or disease management needs (e.g., smoking cessation, diabetes adherence).

A brief overview of the managed care system of funding behavioral health services is warranted. In the 1980s, facing steeply increasing costs for providing behavioral health services, many third-party insurance parties turned to "carve-out" services, where the provision of mental health services is separated from the standard medical care and managed differently (Feldman, 1998; Grazier & Eselius, 1999; Paharia, 2008). A managed behavioral health organization often administers the mental health services for employers/health insurance companies, and helps to keep costs down through a network of behavioral providers and use reviews (i.e., approving or denying requested services, via formulaic consideration of appropriate treatment selection and/or treatment durations, based upon the specific psychiatric disorder). The carve-out model was essentially designed to cater to the traditional model of outpatient psychotherapy delivered by private-practice therapists and mental health clinics.

Carve-out services have changed the way behavioral health is provided. It has been argued that, through these cost savings, insurance-funded behavioral health services continue to remain financially viable (Paharia, 2008). However, concerns have been raised that the carve-out movement may be lowering the quality-of-care standard, via lifetime benefit caps for how much mental health service one can receive, increased co-pays and deductibles, and greater reliance on psychotropic medications over psychotherapy to treat psychiatric conditions (Gray, Brody, & Johnson, 2005; USDHHS, 1999).

The widespread use of carve-out psychological services limits the application of colocated, integrated collaborative models of PCBH. Given the limitations in obtaining reimbursement for most of the duties a behavioral health provider delivers in a collaborative model (e.g., consultation to physicians, preventive services, interventions for medical problems), a primary care practice faces difficult challenges in implementing behavioral health services. The practice could rely on managed care reimbursement for the behavioral health provider(s), but the collaborative involvement would likely be limited to a colocated mental health clinic or psychologist as primary care provider model. These models would generally provide traditional outpatient psychotherapy services, restricting open access for new referrals, and would service a limited percentage of the mental health needs of the primary care practice. On the other hand, a more integrative, consultative model (e.g., staff advisor model, primary care behavioral health consultant) would allow a behavioral health specialist to provide diverse services for the psychosocial and health needs of a greater proportion of the clinic, but reliance on managed care reimbursement is not self-sustaining. Many primary care practices are often not willing, or able, to fund the cost of imbedded behavioral health providers (Azocar, Ciemins, & Kelleher, 2006; Kessler et al., 2009). However, cost-effective indicators often do not fully estimate the time that is devoted by health-care providers, nurses, medical assistants, and front desk staff in their direct involvement with individuals with psychosocial problems (Kessler et al.). Despite the amount of man-hour support used and extent of contact, these patients often do not receive specific problem resolution and frequently decline to take prescribed medications, or discontinue before a therapeutic effect could be reached.

As these questions arise about the effectiveness and cost vs. quality balance of carve-out behavioral health provision, more managed care companies are looking at "carve-in" services, where behavioral health providers work side by side with primary care providers (Gray et al., 2005). This model provides for greater possibility of integration, collaboration, and broadened consumer access for behavioral health services, based upon a model of medical cost offset. The medical cost offset model suggests that integrated behavioral health services in medical settings may lead to sizeable medical savings (estimated between 20–40%) for managed care insurance companies, through behavioral health prevention and treatment of problems that can contribute, directly and indirectly, to both acute and chronic physical health problems (e.g., depression, anxiety, obesity, asthma management, chronic pain) (Strosahl, 2001; Strosahl & Sobel, 1996). Primary care practices also can see the long-term cost savings in greater physician availability via "warm-handoffs" of patients with psychosocial or behavioral medicine needs (Robinson & Reiter, 2007).

An additional promising factor for collaborative primary care services is the expansion of federal funding allowances for behavioral health. In 2002, additional Medicare billing codes were created for psychologists, known as Health and Behavioral Codes, that allowed for the expansion of reimbursements to psychological assessments and interventions that are geared toward physical health problems, as opposed to specific psychiatric disorders (Department of Health and Human Services, Centers for Medicare and Medicaid Services, 2001). This is a welcomed development for behavioral health providers in primary care, and hopefully will be adopted by the private managed care industry as the cost-effectiveness is demonstrated in Medicare (Schulte et al., 2004).

Clinical and Professional Issues

"Speaking Different Languages"—Problems in Communication

Research clearly demonstrates that communication regarding shared patients is rather poor between PCPs and traditional mental health providers (Kessler et al., 2009). Physicians often complain that behavioral health providers are not timely and are inconsistent in returning and maintaining communication on shared patients (Knowles, 2009). Additionally, for those family practitioners and psychologists who are able to develop an initial exchange of patient communication with a behavioral health provider in the referral and evaluation process, frustration occurs when information is frequently not shared as treatment progresses (Kessler et al.). Colocation of behavioral health within primary care does seem to improve communication across providers, especially through hallway exchanges and drop-in communications (Robinson & Strosahl, 2009). However, colocation puts a higher onus on establishing and maintaining communication with health providers. Obtaining referrals and maintaining continuity of care will depend on open channels of communication with multiple providers, which can be difficult in the fast-moving, busy primary care environment.

One of the most difficult challenges of an integrated primary care model is reconciling differences in language, philosophy, and professional practice across the different disciplines of medicine and psychology. As discussed earlier, the fields of primary care and family medicine are based on brief encounters, with problem-focused interventions, addressing a wide range of problems. This philosophy permeates the way health care providers assess, conceptualize, and treat medical conditions. There can be a tendency for behavioral health providers to overemphasize process-related therapeutic factors in discussions with physicians and nurses, which can obscure the problem-focused diagnostic questions and treatment recommendations that the medical providers will often be requesting (Seaburn, Lorenz, Gunn, Gawinski, & Mauksch, 1996). Similarly, the overuse of discipline-specific terminology, otherwise known as jargon, can impair effective communication between providers (Gunn & Blount, 2009). Behavioral health providers in practice in primary care need to become "multilinguistic," developing the ability to effectively communicate with patients, health care providers, mental health referral sites, and, in some cases, managed care companies. An integrative practice requires that the behavioral health clinician become a quick study in effectively understanding, and confidently communicating in, medical terminology.

Another significant hurdle is the issue of documentation and record keeping. There are many key differences in how psychologists and physicians document their patient contacts (Knowles, 2009). Thematically, a physician's note will be problem-focused, emphasizing signs and symptoms, whereas psychologists often have a developmental focus in their notes, addressing the evolution of the problem across the individual's lifespan. In regard to language, there are sharp differences in the jargon and professional language used in notes. The professions have subtle differences in managing informed consent, release of information authorizations, and patient confidentiality. Ethical, regulatory, and legal aspects of access to medical charts by psychologists, and sharing of their behavioral health records, are important issues to address when developing a collaborative practice (Kessler et al., 2009). Barriers can develop when there is format rigidity, unrealistic expectations, and/or poorness-of-fit for behavioral records in existing medical charting systems. Psychologists in medical settings, given the special protections that are offered to psychotherapy session records, have to maintain a fine balance between exercising restraint in protecting patient privacy and confidentiality, and releasing information to help coordinate care (Knowles). This greatly influences what information is documented in the medical chart, and how notes and assessments are written.

Several barriers may result when engaging in consultee-focused behavioral health consultation. It can be quite challenging to open dialogue if the health care provider does not accept the biopsychosocial model. Likewise, a nonpsychologically oriented provider may have little interest in reflecting on how patient care is directly influenced by their approach to conceptualizing and treating a patient, not to mention the influence of their personal well-being and biases on their clinical delivery. On occasion, providers may exhibit personal blind spots, where they may externalize the problems they are experiencing to their patients, and are not willing or able to accept constructive feedback on this theme. Many health care providers may fear the stigma of consulting with a behavioral health provider, worrying that others may think that the provider cannot handle their caseload or needs a "shrink." Motivational factors, such as secondary gain, may be difficult to address through consultation, such as when a provider is set on discharging a "difficult" patient to no longer have the stress of encounters with this individual.

Limited time for consultation can also be a significant barrier for health care providers.

Treatment Delivery Challenges

A collaborative, integrated primary care service poses some professional challenges for clinical delivery. The biggest transition is shifting from the traditional 45–50-minute duration of psychotherapy, with 60- to 90-minute initial intake sessions, to the primary care medicine model of 15- to 30-minute sessions, combining assessment, diagnosis, and treatment in one meeting (Pomerantz et al., 2009). Likewise, the emphasis in integrated primary care interventions requires a switch from a graduated, process-oriented therapy model to problem-focused interventions, emphasizing immediate patient self-management, through skills training and motivational enhancement. Pomerantz and colleagues (2009) discuss that many providers would be unwilling to make the switch from traditional private practice to primary care due to the rapid pace, brief therapeutic duration, and reliance on problem-oriented interventions. A position in primary care often requires a behavioral health specialist to function in a proactive manner, with flexibility, independence, and considerable multitasking abilities.

Working in a primary care practice means that a behavioral health specialist will have to address a diverse assortment of individuals, presenting with a wide range of biopsychosocial problems in a time-limited fashion, on a daily basis (Robinson & Strosahl, 2009). This equation makes it difficult to rely upon disorder-specific evidence-based treatments. Therefore, primary care interventions must emphasis common underlying processes in helping to provide tools to manage psychological distress, improve personal functioning, and instill behavioral change. The need to balance disorder-specific interventions (e.g., exposure, behavioral activation), while emphasizing common processes, such as the use of values to maximize willingness to make behavioral changes, or teaching relaxation techniques, can be a difficult challenge.

A vital component of successful primary care collaboration is to quickly process physician referrals. It is crucial, in a brief model of treatment, to identify and treat psychosocial problems in the early stages of development, because increased acuity and chronicity of mental health problems will require more intensive behavioral health interventions (Kessler et al., 2009). Failing to see patients in a timely manner will reduce the likelihood of physicians to refer patients, and will greatly lower the effectiveness of the behavioral health specialist for the primary care practice. There are also roadblocks to developing an embedded specialty practice that emphasizes "warm handoffs" from physicians, particularly limited session time with patients, difficulty finding time to write notes, ongoing availability to the health providers throughout the clinical day, and reduced opportunities to make phone calls and engage in collaborative discussions with other providers.

Ethical Issues

There are a number of ethical challenges facing behavioral health clinicians in primary care who serve as consultants. Many of these challenges have been elucidated by DiTomasso, Knapp, Golden, Morris, and Veit in chapter 2 of this volume, and the reader is invited to refer to this information for a more detailed discussion. Potential issues surrounding informed consent, confidentiality, charting, billing, clinical competency, and boundaries/dual relationships are relevant considerations and must be weighed carefully. The astute clinician must be cognizant of the unique aspects of medical environments, differences in ethical standards and expectations, professional courtesy norms, and other pressures, including time and finances, that may impact the manner in which practice is affected. Two examples will help demonstrate the ethical challenges faced by behavioral health clinicians in primary care. It is not uncommon for PCPs to provide medical care to close friends and family members, even to the point of prescribing psychotropic medication. The clinician may be confronted with requests that directly or indirectly conflict with ethical standards and pose potential conflicts of interest, such as providing a professional opinion or even a request for therapy for a medical colleague's family member. Physicians routinely cross-refer family members to other medical specialists who are friends and colleagues. Of course, there is a great difference between a physician referring his wife for an upper GI to the local gastroenterologist on staff at the hospital, and referring her to the psychotherapist who works side by side with him on a daily basis. One of the authors worked for about 20 years in a family medicine outpatient center with 24 physicians, and had numerous such requests that had to be refused in a delicate, professional, and educative manner.

Similarly, some physicians, by nature of engaging in what mental health practitioners would call boundary crossings, may fail to see how their relationships obscure and impact their professional decision making and responsibility. Again, one of the authors worked on-site with a medical practitioner who routinely treated individuals with whom he socialized and conducted business. One of these patients had been referred through this physician to the mental health program that held a contract for the practice. The psychologist, working on-staff at the family medicine center, in this instance was also a consultant to this HMO (health maintenance organization) mental health provider and conducted evaluations. During the course of this evaluation, the psychologist discovered that the patient was sexually abusing his 4-year-old son. When the psychologist reported this case to the local division of youth and family services, the patient complained to his physician and friend who became infuriated with the psychologist who was appropriately discharging his legal and ethical responsibilities. The patient, of course, vehemently denied what he had earlier admitted, and the physician attempted to pressure the psychologist to change the story. After the case went to the district attorney for prosecution, the physician never referred another patient to the psychologist.

Recommendations for Effective Practice

The Role of Colocation

Effective coordination of care between behavioral health and primary care providers depends on communication and accessibility (McDaniel, 1995). Colocating behavioral health providers in primary care provides a great advantage by making communication more convenient. Colocation increases the frequency of referrals, particularly through "warm handoffs," hallway consultations, and greater familiarity with the behavioral providers (Robinson & Reiter, 2007). Likewise, referred individuals are often more likely to follow through on the referral, ranging from "striking while the iron is hot" in a warm handoff by a health care provider, to capitalizing on the patient's familiarity with the clinic and the primary care provider's ability to provide a more glowing recommendation of the behavioral health specialist, due to an established relationship with that specialist.

Colocation benefits are greater than just direct clinical delivery. Frequently, behavioral health specialists become involved in leading lunch-time seminars, training (e.g., quick consultations for a specific provider on how to manage a specific problem, formal workshops for multiple providers on a given topic), journal clubs, and developing practice-wide screening and assessment initiatives (Robinson & Reiter, 2007). The presence of a behavioral scientist in the primary care clinic may also provide greater opportunities for researching the efficacy of new clinic initiatives (e.g., screening for depression in diabetes mellitus patients) and patient outcomes (Robinson & Strosahl, 2009). A simple initiative to increase primary care observation of programmatic outcomes is called *Plan-Do-Study-Act* (PDSA) (Institute for Healthcare Initiatives, 2009). This method is gaining popularity, and involves simply identifying a problem that has arisen in the primary care setting, developing a plan to address it, monitoring the outcome, and instituting clinic changes based upon the outcomes. Behavioral specialists who are colocated in primary care settings can be very helpful in instituting PDSAs, training health care providers and administrative support on how to develop quick and easy PDSAs, and disseminating successful program outcomes via conference presentations and journal publications.

Colocation also can lead to unique consultative roles for the behavioral specialist. In the primary care setting of one of this chapter's authors, a large community clinic is divided into six separate medical suites. In addition to providing behavioral health services across all six suites, each provider is assigned to one specific suite, serving as a member of the medical team with the particular emphasis of being actively involved in weekly team meetings. As a team contributor and process consultant, the behavioral health specialist helps in addressing staff conflicts, suggesting and monitoring PDSAs for clinic problems, emphasizing positive communication (e.g., praising staff accomplishments, encouraging fun dialogue), providing suggestions to enhance meeting effectiveness, and providing minilectures on health psychology topics (e.g., quick interventions for anxiety). This form of involvement builds staff morale and enhances service delivery, and also enhances the behavioral health specialist's sense of community, collaboration, and belonging.

Enhancing Communication Across Providers

Behavioral health specialists who can effectively learn to communicate like primary care providers will have considerably fewer barriers in their collaborative practice. Literature across primary care consultation venues seems to suggest that effective collaborating behavioral health providers engage in frequent, outcome-oriented communication with primary care providers, supplying clear diagnostic information, treatment goals, and recommended interventions (Bray, 2004; Cummings et al., 2009; Robinson & Strosahl, 2009). In the Linkages Program (Bray & Rogers, 1995, 1997), a formalized training to enhance collaboration between health care providers and psychologists, Bray (2004) demonstrates that effective communication was maintained best via colocation of service delivery, and additive impacts were observed when the psychologist maximized the use of in-person meetings (e.g., during lunch or dinner) and electronic communication (e.g., faxes and e-mails).

Effective collaborative communication is based upon shared understanding of the duties and responsibilities of the different service providers. In addition to learning about the language, process, and responsibilities of primary care providers, it is equally important for a behavioral health specialist to teach the primary care providers about their services (Robinson & Strosahl, 2009). This will include education on the referral services the behavioral health specialist can offer, a brief, cogent description of the philosophy and method of clinical delivery, and how collaboration may work best between the providers on behavioral health problems.

Collaboration seems to work best when the behavioral health specialist takes the time to teach the primary care providers the specific strategies that are provided during consultation (e.g., deep-breathing techniques, self-assessment tools, behavioral activation, etc.). This approach of educating primary care providers works best when it is brief, direct, and jargon-free, and can effectively be conducted by brief didactics, patient educational materials, newsletters, chart notes, and hallway meetings.

In colocated settings, the behavioral health specialist should negotiate how documentation will be shared with the primary care providers, so collaboration can be most effective, and balancing the behavioral health specialist's adherence to professional ethics. Shared information between providers can be helpful in coordinating care and in jointly motivating patients, particularly when the information contains clearly expressed clinical hypotheses, treatment goals/recommendations, discussion of treatment progress, and delineation of the roles of collaborators (Knowles, 2009). When behavioral health specialists receive referrals from physicians, the subsequent communication is most effective when it emphasizes diagnostic features and specific treatment recommendations. Knowles (2009) recommends that psychologists share their mental status exam, multidimensional diagnostic information, a brief clinical formulation, and specified treatment recommendations and goals. Communication should be brief, to the point, jargon-free, and emphasize a biopsychosocial philosophy. Psychologists should be proactive in discussing the limits of their disclosure of information to physicians, and that they will work to provide the necessary, pertinent information to enhancing coordination of care, in an ongoing, regular fashion.

Tailoring Interventions to the Primary Care Environment

A number of the aforementioned barriers to collaborative behavioral health services involved referral bottlenecks and mismatches between the delivery of services in primary care and behavioral health. For effective collaboration to occur in the primary care setting, behavioral health providers will need to tailor their services to fit the environment and specific clinic needs. In reality, this is no different than how we uniquely conceptualize and shape treatments to match individual needs and presentations.

The most logical remedy may be to parallel the primary care delivery model in how behavioral health services are carried out. An emphasis on brief, problem-focused orientations will likely provide the greatest match and service the widest demand for behavioral health interventions across the primary care setting. Success has been found most when the emphasis is placed not on symptomatic improvement, but rather assessments of functioning and quality of life (Robinson & Strosahl, 2009). In the simplest form, service delivery may best match primary care delivery by several models. One method is to emphasize single-session consultations, as previously discussed in the Staff Advisor, Stepped Care, and PCBH models, with specific communication and instructions to the primary care provider on how they can continue to follow up with the patient, as well as when they should refer back to the behavioral health specialist. Primary care interventions can be supercharged for those patients who are not responding well to standard behavioral health consultation services (Katon et al., 1996). Behavioral health providers can increase the frequency and length of clinical services delivered to these struggling patients, enhance the monitoring of symptom change, and increase patient empowerment in managing their illness. Referrals to community therapists may also be another option for more intensive outpatient psychotherapy. Another potential remedy, to match clinical delivery to the primary care model, is to reduce session-duration time, with 30-minute extended visits for initial visits and crisis appointments, and 15-minute regular follow-up visits, which would better dovetail with the medical visit model (Kessler et al., 2009).

Service delivery seems to work optimally when the behavioral health specialist is available to take warm handoffs from the primary care providers at the time of the patient's medical visit (Robinson & Strosahl, 2009). Developing a practice model that can provide immediate services and be financially self-sustaining, through a combination of managed care insurance reimbursement, salaried employment by the clinic, and grant funding for providing clinical services to the underserved, would be a particularly sound remedy to many of the challenges to establishing effective collaboration. Warm handoffs are best achieved when there are sufficient behavioral health providers available to meet the clinic's demand; an ideal ratio of one behavioral health provider per six primary care providers has been reported, with at least two available behavioral health providers to keep the hallway handoff process active without frequent bottlenecks (Cummings et al., 2009).

Tips to Enhance Consultee-Focused Consultation

First and foremost, the consultant must forge a relationship with the health care provider, cultivating the trust and willingness to accept feedback from the consultee. Joining activities, such as "small talk" and understanding what the providers enjoy about their jobs, can be effective ways to establish rapport. Second, consultants must remember that they are catering their services to the needs of the provider, and ultimately their feedback is only a suggestion. Embracing this approach requires expertise in pitching ideas and not forcing a specific agenda with a provider. Consequently, openness and patience are important qualities to foster as a consultant. Third, for the providers that are less receptive to a behavioral health consultant's feedback, cultivate experience and positive results with more receptive providers first. Their positive feedback and any available data that demonstrate the value of consultants may help sway the willingness of the providers who are wary of consultants. Finally, the consultant should embrace flexibility and convenient access as ways to address time and other logistical barriers in being available for health providers.

References

Aitken, J., & Curtis, R. (2004). Integrated health care: Improving client care while providing opportunities for mental health counselors. *Journal of Mental Health Counseling, 26,* 321–331.

American Psychiatric Association. (2000). *Diagnostic and statistical manual of mental disorders* (4th ed., text rev.). Washington, DC: American Psychiatric Press.

American Psychological Association. (1998, June). *Interprofessional health care services in primary care settings: Implications for the education and training of psychologists* (for Work Order Requisition No. 97M220s464). U.S. Department of Health and Human Services, Project on Managed Behavioral Health Care and Primary Care.

Asarnow, J. R., Jaycox, L., Duan, N., LaBorde, A., Rea, M., Murry, P., et al. (2003). Effectiveness of a quality improvement intervention for adolescent depression in primary care clinics. *Journal of the American Medical Association, 293,* 311–319.

Azocar, F., Ciemins, F., & Kelleher, D. (2006). Behavioral health outreach: Integrating medical and behavioral health care. *Psychiatric Services, 57*(12), 1807–1808.

Beardsley, R., Gardocki, G., Larson, D., & Hidalgo, J. (1988). Prescribing of psychotropic medications by primary care physicians and psychiatrists. *Archives of General Psychiatry, 45,* 1117–1119.

Beck, A. T. (1991). Cognitive therapy: A 30 year retrospective. *American Psychologist, 46,* 368–375.

Belar, C. D. (2003, March). Competencies for quality health care. *Monitor on Psychology, 34*(3), 38.

Bray, J. H. (2004). Training primary care psychologists. *Journal of Clinical Psychology in Medical Settings, 11,* 101–107.

Bray, J. H., & Rogers, J. C. (1995). Linking psychologists and family physicians for collaborative practice. *Professional Psychology, Research and Practice, 26,* 132–138.

Bray, J. H., & Rogers, J. C. (1997). The linkages project: Training behavioral health professionals for collaborative practice with primary care physicians. *Families, Systems, and Health, 15,* 55–63.

Callahan, E. J., Bertakis, K. D., Azari, R., Robbins, J. A., Helms, L. J., & Leigh, J. P. (2002). Association of higher costs with symptoms and diagnosis of depression. *Journal of Family Practice, 51,* 540–544.

Caplan, G. (1970). *The theory and practice of mental health consultation.* New York: Basic Books.

Centers for Disease Control (CDC). *Behavioral Risk Factor Surveillance System.* Atlanta, GA: U.S. Department of Health and Human Services. Retrieved November 15, 2007, from http://www.cdc.gov/brfss

Centers for Disease Control (CDC). (2007). *Healthy people 2010 focus area 17: Mental health and mental disorders, progress review.* Retrieved November 15, 2007, from http://www.cdc.gov/nchs/hphome.htm

Cummings, N. A., & Follette, W. T. (1968). Psychiatric services and medical utilization in a prepaid health plan setting: Part 2. *Medical Care, 6,* 31–41.

Cummings, N. A., O'Donohue, W. T., & Cummings, J. L. (2009). The financial dimension of integrated behavioral/ primary care. *Journal of Clinical Psychology in Medical Settings, 16,* 31–39.

Cummings, N. A., O'Donohue, W. T., & Ferguson, K. E. (Eds.). (2003). *Behavioral health in primary care: Beyond efficacy to effectiveness. Cummings Foundation for Behavioral Health: Health utilization and cost series* (Vol. 6). Reno, NV: Context Press.

DeLeon, P. H., Giesting, B., & Kenkel, M. B. (2003). Community health centers: Exciting opportunities for the 21st century. *Professional Psychology, Research and Practice, 34,* 579–585.

Department of Health and Human Services, Centers for Medicare and Medicaid Services. (2001). 42 CFR part 405 et al. Medicare Program; Revisions to payment policies and five-year review and adjustments to the relative value units under the physician fee schedule for calendar year 2002, final rule. *Federal Register, 66*(12), 55245-55503.

DiTomasso, R. A. (2009). *Cognitive model of primary care consultation*. Unpublished manuscript, Department of Psychology, Philadelphia College of Osteopathic Medicine, Philadelphia.

DiTomasso, R. A., Knapp, S., Golden, B. A., Morris, H. J., & Veit, K. J. (2010). The cognitive-behavioral clinician: Rules and functions and ethical challenges in primary care. In R. A. DiTomasso, B. A. Golden, & H. Morris (Eds.), *Handbook of cognitive-behavioral approaches in primary care* (pp. 15–34). New York: Springer Publishing Company.

Dunbar-Jacob, J., & Mortimer-Stephens, M. K. (2001). Treatment adherence in chronic disease. *Journal of Clinical Epidemiology, 54*, 857–860.

Dwight-Johnson, M., Ell, M., & Lee, P. (2005). Can collaborative care address the needs of low-income Latinas with comorbid depression and cancer? Results from a randomized pilot study. *Psychosomatics, 46*, 224–232.

Feldman, S. (1998). Behavioral health services: Carved out and managed. *American Journal of Managed Care, 4*, SP59–SP67.

Follette, W. T., & Cummings, N. A. (1967). Psychiatric services and medical utilization in a prepaid health plan setting. *Medical Care, 5*, 25–35.

Gatchel, R. J., & Oordt, M. S. (2003). *Clinical health psychology and primary care: Practical advice and clinical guidance for successful collaboration*. Washington, DC: American Psychological Association.

Glascow, R. (1995). A practical model of diabetes management and education. *Diabetes Care, 18*, 117–126.

Gray, G. V., Brody, D. S., & Johnson, D. (2005). The evolution of behavioral primary care. *Professional Psychology: Research and Practice, 36*, 123–129.

Grazier, K. L., & Eselius, L. L. (1999). Mental health carve-outs: Effects and implications. *Medical Care Research and Review, 56*, 37–59.

Grembowski, D. E., Martin, D., Patrick, D. L., Diehr, P., Katon, W., Williams, B., et al. (2002). Managed care, access to mental health specialists, and outcomes among primary care patients with depressive symptoms. *Journal of General Internal Medicine, 12*, 258–269.

Gunn, W. B., Jr., & Blount, A. (2009). Primary care mental health: A new frontier for psychology. *Journal of Clinical Psychology, 65*, 235–252.

Hillman, A. L., Pauly, M. V., & Kerstein, J. J. (1989) How do financial incentives affect physicians' clinical decisions and the financial performance of health maintenance organizations? *New England Journal of Medicine, 321*, 86–92.

Hine, C. E., Howell, H. B., & Yonkers, K. A. (2008). Integration of medical and psychological treatment within the primary health care setting. *Social Work in Health Care, 42*, 122–134.

Institute for Healthcare Initiatives. (2009). *Plan-Do-Study-Act (PDSA) worksheet (IHI tool)*. Retrieved May 4, 2009, from http://www.ihi.org/IHI/Topics/Improvement/ImprovementMethods/Tools/Plan-Do-Study-Act+(PDSA)+Worksheet.htm

James, L. C. (2006). Special section on proceedings of the Clinical Health Psychology Institute: Integrating psychology into primary care settings. *Journal of Clinical Psychology, 62*, 1207–1212.

Jenkins, R., & Strathdee, G. (2000). The integration of mental health care with primary care. *International Journal of Law & Psychiatry, 23*, 277–291.

Johnson, C. E., Stewart, A. L., Brabeck, M. M., Huber, V. S., & Rubin, H. (2004). Interprofessional collaboration: Implications for combined-integrated doctoral training in professional psychology. *Journal of Clinical Psychology, 60*, 995–1010.

Johnstone, B., Frank, R. G., Belar, C. D., Berk, S., Bieliauskas, L. A., et al. (1995). Psychology in health care: Future directions. *Professional Psychology: Research and Practice, 26*, 341–365.

Kaplan, S. H., Gandek, B., Greenfield, S., Rogers, W., & Ware, J. E. (1995). Patient and visit characteristics related to physicians' participatory decision-making style: Results from the medical outcome study. *Medical Care, 33*, 1176–1187.

Kassirer, J. P. (1995). Managed care and the morality of the marketplace. *New England Journal of Medicine, 333*, 50–52.

Katon, W., Robinson, P., Von Korff, M., Lin, E., Bush, T., Ludman, E., et al. (1996). A multifaceted intervention to improve treatment of depression in primary care. *Archives of General Psychiatry, 53*, 924–932.

Katon, W., Russo, J., Sherbourne, C., Stein, M., Craske, M., Fan, M., et al. (2006). Incremental cost-effectiveness of a collaborative care intervention for panic disorder. *Psychological Medicine, 36*, 353–363.

Katon, W., & Unutzer, J. (2006). Collaborative care models for depression. *Archives of Internal Medicine, 166*, 2304–2306.

Katon, W., Von Korff, M., Lin, E., & Simon, G. (2001). Rethinking practitioner roles in chronic illness: The specialist, primary care physician, and the practice nurse. *General Hospital Psychiatry, 23*, 138–144.

Katon, W., Von Korff, M., Lin, E., Walker, E., Simon, G. E., Bush, T., et al. (1995). Collaborative management to achieve treatment guidelines: Impact on depression in primary care. *Journal of the American Medical Association, 273*, 1026–1031.

Kerr, E. A., Mittman, B. S., Hays, R. D., Siu, A. L., Leake, B., & Brook, R. H. (1995). Managed care and capitation in California: How do physicians at financial risk control their own utilization? *Annals of Internal Medicine, 123*, 500–504.

Kessler, R., Stafford, D., & Messier, R. (2009). The problem of integrating behavioral health in the medical home and the questions it leads to. *Journal of Clinical Psychology in Medical Settings, 16*, 4–12.

Kilbourne, A. M., Pincus, H. A., Schutte, K., Kirchner, J. E., Haas, G. L., & Yano, E. M. (2006). Management of mental disorders in VA primary care practices. *Administration and Policy in Mental Health and Mental Health Research, 33*, 208–214.

Knowles, P. (2009). Collaborative communication between psychologists and primary care providers. *Journal of Clinical Psychology in Medical Settings, 16*, 72–76.

Kratochwill, T. R. (1990). *Behavioral consultation in applied settings*. New York: Springer-Verlag.

Kroenke, K., & Mangelsdorff, A. D. (1989). Common symptoms in ambulatory care: Incidence, evaluation, therapy, and outcome. *American Journal of Medicine, 86*, 262–266.

Laygo, R., O'Donohue, W., Hall, S., Kaplan, A., Wood, R., Cummings, J., et al. (2003). Preliminary results from the Hawaii Integrated Healthcare Project II. In N. A. Cummings, W. T. O'Donohue, & K. E. Ferguson (Eds.), *Behavioral health as primary care: Beyond efficacy to effectiveness. Cummings Foundation for Behavioral Health: Healthcare utilization and cost series* (Vol. 6, pp. 111–143). Reno, NV: Context Press.

Lipowski, Z. J. (1967). Review of consultation psychiatry and psychosomatic medicine: II. Clinical aspects. *Psychosomatic Medicine, 29*, 201–224.

McDaniel, S. H. (1995). Collaboration between psychologists and family physicians: Implementing the biopsychosocial model. *Professional Psychology: Research and Practice, 26*, 117–122.

McDaniel, S. H., Belar, C. D., Schroeder, C., Hargrove, D. S., & Freeman, E. L. (2002). A training curriculum for professional psychologists in primary care. *Professional Psychology: Research and Practice, 33*, 65–72.

McDaniel, S. H., Campbell, T. L., Hepworth, J., & Lorenz, A. (2005). *Family-oriented primary care* (2nd ed.). New York: Springer Publishing Company.

Mendoza, D. W. (1993). A review of Gerald Caplan's "Theory and Practice of Mental Health Consultation." *Journal of Counseling and Development, 71*, 629–635.

Olfson, M., Fireman, B., Weissman, M. M., Leon, A. C., Sheehan, D. V., Kathol, R. G., et al. (1997). Mental disorders and disability among patients in primary care group practice. *American Journal of Psychiatry, 154*, 1734–1740.

Olfson, M., Marcus, S. C., & Druss, B. (2002). National trends in the outpatient treatment of depression. *Journal of the American Medical Association, 287*, 203–209.

Olfson, M., Shea, S., Feder, A., Fuentes, M., Nomura, Y., Gameroff, M., et al. (2000). Prevalence of anxiety, depression, and substance use disorders in an urban general medicine practice. *Archives of Family Medicine, 9*, 876–883.

Oxman, T. E., Dietrich, A. J., & Schulberg, H. C. (2003). The depression care manager and mental health specialist as collaborators within primary care. *American Journal of Geriatric Psychiatry, 11*, 507–516.

Pace, T. M., Chaney, J. M., Mullins, L. L., & Olson, R. A. (1995). Psychological consultation with primary care physicians: Obstacles and opportunities in the medical setting. *Professional Psychology: Research and Practice, 26*, 123–131.

Paharia, M. I. (2008). Insurance, managed care, and integrated primary care. In B. A. Boyer & M. I. Paharia. *Comprehensive handbook of clinical health psychology* (pp. 31–51). Hoboken, NJ: Wiley.

Peek, C., & Heinrich, R. (1995). Building a collaborative healthcare organization: From idea to invention to innovation. *Family Systems Medicine, 13*, 327–342.

Pincus, H. A. (2003). The future of behavioral health and primary care: Drowning in the mainstream or left on the bank? *Psychosomatics, 44*, 1–11.

Pincus, H. A., Taniellen, T. L., Marcus, S. C., Olfson, M., Zarin, D. A., Thompson, J., & Zito, J. M. (1998). Prescribing trends in psychotropic medications. *Journal of the American Medical Association, 79*, 526–531.

Pomerantz, A. S., Corson, J. A., & Detzer, M. J. (2009). The challenge of integrated care for mental health: Leaving the 50 minute hour and other sacred things. *Journal of Clinical Psychology in Medical Settings, 16*, 40–46.

Pruitt, S., Klapow, J., Epping-Jordan, J., & Dresselhaus, T. (1998). Moving behavioral medicine to the front line: A model for the integration of behavioral and medical sciences in primary care. *Professional Psychology: Research and Practice, 29*, 230–236.

Rieger, D. A., Narrow, W. E., Rae, D. S., Manderscheid, R. W., Locke, B. Z., & Goodwin, F. K. (1993). The de facto U.S. mental and addictive disorders service system. *Archives of Psychiatry, 50*, 85–94.

Robinson, P. J., & Reiter, J. T. (2007). *Behavioral consultant and primary care: A guide to integrating services.* New York: Springer Publishing Company.

Robinson, P. J., & Strosahl, K. D. (2009). Behavioral health consultation and primary care: Lessons learned. *Journal of Clinical Psychology in Medical Settings, 16*, 58–71.

Rosenbaum Asarnow, J., Jaycox, L., Duan, N., LaBorde, A., Rea, M., Murray, P., et al. (2005). Effectiveness of a quality improvement intervention for adolescent depression in primary care clinics. *Journal of the American Medical Association, 293*, 311–319.

Runyan, C. N., Fonseca, V. P., & Hunter, C. (2003). Integrating consultative behavioral healthcare into the Air Force medical system. In N. A. Cummings, W. T. O'Donohue, & K. E. Ferguson (Eds.), *Behavioral health in primary care: Beyond efficacy to effectiveness. Cummings Foundation for Behavioral Health: Healthcare utilization and cost series* (Vol. 6, pp. 145–163). Reno, NV: Context Press.

Salaffi, F., Cavalieri, F., Nolli, M., & Ferraccioli, G. (1991). Analysis of disability in knee osteoarthritis: Relationship with age and psychological variables but not with radiographic score. *Journal of Rheumatology, 18*, 1581–1586.

Schulte, T. J., Isley, E., Link, N., Shealy, C. N., & Winfrey, L. L. (2004). General practice, primary care, and health service psychology: Concepts, competencies, and the combined integrated model. *Journal of Clinical Psychology, 60*, 1011–1025.

Seaburn, D., Lorenz, A., Gunn, W., Gawinski, B., & Mauksch, L. (1996). *Models of collaboration: A guide for mental health professionals working with medical professionals.* New York: Basic Books.

Skultety, K. M., & Zeiss, A. (2006). The treatment of depression in older adults in the primary care setting: An evidence based review. *Health Psychology, 25*, 665–674.

Smith, G. R., Monson, R. A., & Ray, D. C. (1986). Psychiatric consultation in somatization disorder: A randomized controlled study. *New England Journal of Medicine, 314*, 1407–1413.

Sobel, D. S. (1995) Rethinking medicine: Improving health outcomes with cost-effective psychosocial interventions. *Psychosomatic Medicine, 57*, 234–244.

St. Peter, R. F., Reed, M. C., Kemper, P., & Blumenthal, D. (1999). Changes in the scope of care provided by primary care physicians. *New England Journal of Medicine, 341*, 1980–1985.

Stanton, A. L., Revenson, T. A., & Tennen, H. (2007). Health psychology: Psychological adjustment to chronic illness. *Annual Review of Psychology, 58*, 565–592.

Stephens, G. (1989). Family medicine as counter culture. *Family Medicine, 21*, 103–109.

Strosahl, K. (1998). Integrating behavioral health and primary care services: The primary mental health model. In A. Blount (Ed.), *Integrated primary care: The future of medical and mental health collaboration* (pp. 139–166). New York: W.W. Norton.

Strosahl, K. (2001). The integration of primary care and behavioral health: Type II change in the era of managed care. In N. A. Cummings, W. O'Donohue, S. C. Hayes, & V. F. Follette (Eds.), *Integrated behavioral healthcare: Positioning mental health practice with medical/surgical practice* (pp. 45–69). San Diego, CA: Academic Press.

Strosahl, K. D., & Sobel, D. (1996). Behavioral health and the medical cost offset effect: Current status, key concepts, and future applications. *HMO Practice, 10*, 156–162.

United States Department of Health & Human Services (USDHHS). (1999). *Mental health: A report of the Surgeon General.* Rockville, MD: USDHHS, SAMHSA, NIH, NIMH.

United States Department of Health & Human Services (USDHHS). (2000). *Healthy people 2010: Understanding and improving health* (2nd ed.) Washington, DC: U.S. Government Printing Office.

U.S. Department of Health and Human Services (USDHHS). (2007). *Progress review. Mental health and mental disorders.* Retrieved September 10, 2009, from http://www.healthypeople.gov/Data/2010prog/focus18/default.htm

Van Voorhees, B. W., Wang, N. Y., & Ford, D. E. (2003). Managed care organizational complexity and access to high quality mental health services: Perspective of US primary care physicians. *General Hospital Psychiatry, 25*, 149–157.

Vasquez, A., Nath, C., & Murray, S. (1988). Counseling by family physicians: Report of a survey and curriculum modification in West Virginia. *Family Systems Medicine, 6*, 463–466.

Williams, J., Palmes, G., Klinepeter, K., Pulley, A., & Meschan, J. F. (2005). Referral by pediatricians of children with behavioral health disorders. *Clinical Pediatrics, 44*, 343–349.

World Health Organization. (1984). *Mental health care in developing countries. Report of a WHO study group* (Technical Report Series 698). Geneva, Switzerland: Author.

Evidence-Based Models and Interventions in Primary Care

5

Robert A. DiTomasso
Stacey C. Cahn
Carla Cirilli
Eugene Mochan

Introduction

This chapter focuses on the rationale, development, and applications of evidence-based models and interventions in the primary care setting. We begin this chapter with a provocative quote from Rachman and Wilson (2008, p. 294): "A conversation between a psychologist and a senior engineer: The psychologist was explaining the steady adoption of demands for evidence-based psychological treatments, and the engineer listened with interest but was puzzled, and asked this question: 'What was it based on before?' " This quote underscores the relative lag in the suitable evaluation of techniques within the field of psychology. Over the past several years, the evaluation of psychological approaches and techniques has emerged as one of the most important phenomena in the history of psychology. The application of psychological approaches, especially cognitive-behavioral models, to both mental health and medical problems has underscored the value of careful evaluation of outcomes attributable to assessments and interventions.

In this age of accountability, the demonstrated efficacy and effectiveness of assessment tools and interventions now properly rests on a foundation of demonstrated and replicable findings, providing a critical foundation for the selection and implementation of techniques in the clinical setting. The plain truth is that traditionally, not all approaches that have been labeled *therapeutic* deserve the distinction of this branding. By definition, anything that is called *therapeutic* should, in fact, provide some level of clinically significant benefits to the patients who entrust clinicians with their care. Statistically significant findings, of course, do not necessarily imply a level of change that results in clinically meaningful change. In the medical setting, this issue assumes as much, if not even more, importance. Physicians are accustomed to practicing from an evidence-based model where clinical trials set the standard of care. Behavioral and cognitive-behavioral approaches have a long, rich history of commitment to the benefits of empiricism. Of course, the extent to which science affects practice is not always so direct, and the lag time between demonstration of an effect and application in the office is frequently protracted. To date, the volume of research on psychotherapeutic interventions conducted specifically in the primary care setting lags behind those conducted in more traditional settings. This state of affairs often requires the transporting of findings from one setting to another, assuming generalizability until it is demonstrated. In the meantime, it is incumbent upon those clinicians practicing within the primary care setting to commit to evaluating the outcomes of their interventions, and to contribute to the further development of an empirical database by disseminating their findings.

Testing models of therapeutic assessment and intervention provides a sound basis for assisting clinicians in selecting among the myriad of therapies included under the category of "psychological therapies," and poses a challenge for clinicians seeking the most beneficial option. Clinical research provides a vehicle for evaluating and selecting therapies that hold the greatest potential for helping patients. In this manner, only refereed published scholarly work that has survived the scrutiny of professionals in the field enjoys the privilege of publication, helping to create a data-driven base and solid foundation for the current and future practice of psychological therapies in the medical setting. In 2006, the APA Presidential Task Force on Evidence-Based Practice proclaimed psychology's commitment to evidence-based psychological practice through an emphasis on the application of empirically based principles of psychological assessment, case formulation, therapeutic relationships, and intervention. The implications of this proclamation are extensive, especially when one considers the poignant words of the Task Force (2006), proclaiming that "psychology—as a science and as a profession—is distinctive in combining scientific commitment with an emphasis on human relationships and individual differences" (p. 6).

In the primary care setting, patients frequently present with psychosocial and medical problems that undermine long-term mental health and physical status. There is little doubt that these problems are inextricably intertwined. The mental health of patients clearly affects physical health and vice versa. Both types of symptoms may co-occur as part of a single syndrome, or one may temporally precede the other, as in the case of insomnia, which can be seen as a risk factor for depression or a "prodrome," or early marker of a subsequent full depressive episode (Lustberg & Reynolds, 2000). It is difficult to identify a medical problem in which psychosocial factors do not play a role in the precipitation, maintenance, or exacerbation of the patient's condition. As a "soft" science, in which there is a clear absence of identified biological markers, behavioral science may be viewed by many physicians as insufficiently scientific and lacking in an empirical basis.

This viewpoint has considerable implications for the manner in which behavioral clinicians and the information and services they offer are perceived by the medical establishment. Despite this intricate association of physical and psychosocial symptoms, different models of understanding, conceptualizing, and treating problems between the medical and psychological professions may undermine the integration of services. Particularly within the medical establishment, this skeptical perspective has considerable implications for the perception of behavioral science, which includes the field's information, services, and even the professionals themselves. Working closely with physicians and illustrating the empirical basis of practice is critical in setting the stage for shared and integrated, effective care. Cultivating broader acceptance of the cognitive-behavioral model, the biopsychosocial model, and the multifaceted nature of problems seen in primary care may be demonstrated by elucidating and sharing the common ground on which all effective therapies are based, empirical evidence.

The establishment of a common ground across professional roles may be created by a commitment to four basic principles. First, the development and maintenance of an empirical database necessitates a commitment to promoting a reciprocal relationship between scientific and practical knowledge, whereby science affects practice and practice affects science. Second, effective practice requires a thorough understanding of the clinical disorders commonly presenting in primary care. The efficacy of cognitive-behavior therapy (CBT) approaches is likely based, in part, on the fact that clinical researchers continue to investigate the characteristics of certain disorders and patients that serve as a basis for promoting useful case formulations. CBT is unique, in that it targets treatment toward the cognitive, behavioral, and affective components of behavioral disorders. Third, use of valid and reliable outcome measures provides a useful yardstick with which to measure the impact of treatment. Finally, the use of clinical research to test and advance theory for the ultimate benefit of patients is essential. Assessment of outcomes in the clinical setting is imperative in this sense.

In understanding the role of empiricism in the development of a science-based practice of psychology in primary care, it is important to define what an empirically supported treatment (EST) is and what it is not. An empirically supported approach is simply one that is subject to empirical validation. This type of approach to assessment and treatment implies that there is a scientific basis of support for what cognitive-behavioral clinicians offer in the clinical setting. An EST is a psychological treatment for a specific clinical disorder that has previously demonstrated efficacy in carefully conducted clinical research with real patients (e.g., randomized-controlled trials [RCTs]). By definition, an EST has been shown to be efficacious and yield desirable clinical outcomes by producing results that are clinically significant, by helping clinically disordered patients become nonclinically disordered, or less so to some significant degree (Kendall, Kipnis, & Otto-Salaj, 1992; Persons & Silberschatz, 1998).

Further, an EST has been evaluated in internally valid research designs, through which one can confidently associate the observed outcome to the treatment and not to some alternative competing hypothesis (Kendall et al., 1992; Persons & Silberschatz, 1998). An EST must also have been replicated by other clinical researchers in different treatment settings with a different set of patients. The APA Task Force has established the following criteria (Chambless et al., 1998) for well-established treatments and probably efficacious treatments, respectively:

Well-Established Treatments:

1. At least two good between-group design experiments demonstrating efficacy in one or more of the following ways:
(a) Superior (statistically significantly so) to pill or psychological placebo or to another treatment;
(b) Equivalent to an already established treatment in experiments with adequate sample sizes;

or

2. A large series of single-case design experiments ($n > 9$) demonstrating efficacy. These experiments must have:
(a) Used good experimental designs;
(b) Compared the intervention to another treatment as in 1(a).

Further Criteria for Both 1 and 2:

3. Experiments must be conducted with treatment manuals;
4. Characteristics of the client samples must be clearly specified;
5. Effects must have been demonstrated by at least two different investigators or investigating teams.

Probably Efficacious Treatments:

1. Two experiments showing the treatment is superior (statistically significantly so) to a waiting-list control group;

or

2. One or more experiments meeting the well-established treatment criteria 1(a) or 1(b), 3, and 4, but not 5;

or

3. A small series of single-case design experiments ($n > 3$) otherwise meeting well-established treatment criteria (p. 2).

These treatments are typically based on a theory of personality and therapy for which empirical support exists. Support is also shown for principles underlying the therapeutic approach that delineates the techniques based upon the principles underlying the theory (Beck, 1993). Theory then guides the development of assessment and therapeutic strategies. Further, demonstrated support for the techniques (Beck) and replication by other clinical researchers in different settings, with different patients, and with different therapists is critical. In this sense, clinical practice in the medical setting is never a haphazard or arbitrary decision-making process. Rather, it demands deliberate thought, planning, and decision making, followed by the systematic application of a treatment protocol that must be simultaneously tailored to the individual patient. This is what some may refer to as the art of practice.

Thus far, the APA has identified ESTs for a number of psychiatric conditions, as well as chronic pain, fibromyalgia, rheumatologic pain, chronic headache, chronic low back pain, and insomnia (APA Presidential Task Force on Evidence-Based Practice, 2006). Many of the common psychological disorders seen in primary care, such as depression and anxiety, also have ESTs. There is a vast literature supporting the application of cognitive-behavioral approaches to a variety of other problems seen in primary care, including nonadherence, hypertension, obesity, and diabetes.

Notably, in the United Kingdom where there is national health care, the government has established the National Institute for Clinical Excellence (NICE), which reviews the body of research supporting both pharmacological and psychological treatments for major disorders. NICE then grades the level of empirical support for each treatment from "A" (strong empirical support from well-conducted randomized trials) to "C" (expert opinion without strong empirical data). The evaluation criteria place great emphasis on methodological rigor of supporting research, with less weight given to clinical judgment and experience. In the case of bulimia nervosa (BN), for example, CBT was given the grade of "A," whereas antidepressant medication was given a "B," reflecting the greater empirical support for the efficacious treatment of bulimia with CBT than medication. This marked the first time a psychological treatment was advanced as the first-line treatment over a medication (Wilson & Shafran, 2005). In this way, the government of the United Kingdom through the National Health Service has established that CBT should be the first-line treatment for BN and widely available to the public. Accordingly, the British government has already budgeted $600 million, in part to train clinicians in the delivery of this first-line treatment, "with the goal of introducing '3600 more newly trained psychological therapists giving evidence-based treatment' in the first 3 years, steadily rising to a total of 8000. An immediate challenge is to develop more efficient and effective ways of training therapists to administer evidence-based treatments in a manner consistent with research findings" (Rachman & Wilson, 2008, p. 293). This massive current undertaking by the United Kingdom is an excellent and timely example of the current zeitgeist of the increasing emphasis on ESTs and accountability.

Manual-Based Treatments

Manual-based treatments (MBTs) offer the advantages of established efficacy and transportability, as well as a practical way to train and supervise clinicians in specific techniques (Wilson, 1998). Although standardized treatments have been common in randomized controlled trials (RCTs) to ensure treatment fidelity, they have been adapted for clinical training and use in clinical practice.

RCTs Versus Real-Life Patients in Clinical Practice

In clinical trials, patients are carefully screened and outcomes are reported for the average patient. Most important, these patients often differ from those in physicians' offices who have multiple problems, coexisting disorders, and personality disorders. Also, the manner in which results are reported often undermines the applicability of these data. Results are often reported in terms of how the average or typical subject has fared, with an emphasis on statistical significance versus clinical significance. More recently, alternative approaches have been employed, such as the percentage of patients who improve according to some stringent clinical criterion.

The degree to which such differences undermine the applicability of these treatments to real-life clinical situations, if at all, is controversial. Some have argued that the most common reason that individuals are excluded from clinical trials is that, in fact, their problems are *not severe enough* to meet inclusion criteria (Crits-Cristoph, Wilson, & Hollon, 2005; Wilson, 2007). Moreover, another argument that has been made is that it is generally assumed that individuals in RCTs have less comorbidity (of both axis 1 and axis 2 conditions) than real-life patients. First, this may or may not be the case. Second, whether a comorbid psychiatric condition affects treatment outcome is dependent upon the diagnosis in question, rather than a universal truth (Wilson, 2007). For example, research on the treatment of some disorders such as panic disorder and BN fail to find significant differences in outcome with comorbid axis 1 or axis 2 conditions (Wilson, 1998). Alternatively, one would imagine that the prognosis may be poor for treatment of an individual with comorbid schizoid personality disorder, regardless of whether the treatment is manualized/empirically supported, assuming such patients would likely seek psychological treatment at all.

Also, some would argue that empirically supported therapy protocols may fail to address common problems seen in everyday practice that undermine treatment (e.g., nonadherence, transference issues; Persons & Silberschatz, 1998). There are simply critical differences between therapy as practiced and therapy as delivered in clinical research (Seligman, 1995), including the fact that therapy is not always time-limited or fixed, and is arguably self-adjusting, though the evidence does not always support this view (e.g., Kendall et al., 1992). Real-life therapy also involves patients seeking therapy who often present with complex problems and frequent comorbidity. We note that the field may be moving toward less specificity in diagnosis, however. For example, Moses and Barlow (2006) have developed and promoted a "unified protocol" directed at the treatment of emotional disorders in general. Christopher Fairburn has also advanced a "transdiagnostic" protocol for the treatment of eating disorders covering anorexia nervosa, BN, and binge eating disorder (Fairburn, 2008).

Clinicians using CBT in primary care may struggle with the decision of whether to use an MBT for a complicated patient. The rule of parsimony would appear to dictate an EST, if one exists, as a first-line course of treatment, unless there is clear reason to proceed otherwise (e.g., lack of treatment acceptance by patient). Many patients, however, will not be treatment successes, may relapse quickly, or may otherwise need, or demand, alternative approaches for subsequent courses of treatment. Additionally, MBTs are often more flexible, allowing for more individualization, than many realize. For example, part of Fairburn's (2008) manualized CBT protocol for eating disorders specifically calls for the creation of a model depicting the specific maintaining processes of each patient's disorder, as well as an individualized treatment plan.

There are also a number of potential legal issues in the use of empirically based treatments. Knapp and Vandecreek (2003) have called attention to the duty to treat patients in a reasonable manner, recognizing that harm may be caused by what is or is not done. In the context of empirical models, a critical issue is whether a patient received a treatment that is unrecognized or unaccepted by the profession. Perhaps the relevant question here is, "What is the definition of unrecognized or unaccepted?" By publishing a list of efficacious treatments, some believe there is the risk that other treatments may be construed as unrecognized. The alternative risk, however, is that more patients will otherwise receive treatment that may be ineffective or even harmful. Take the tragic example of Candace Newmaker, the 10-year-old girl who died while receiving "rebirthing" treatment for a presumed attachment disorder (Lowe, 2001). At the time, there was no empirical support for rebirthing therapy, nor is there currently.

To more fully appreciate the importance of empirically based treatments, it may be helpful to place oneself in the role of the patient with a serious problem for a moment and answer several questions posed by Persons and Silberschatz (1998). These questions are:

1. Would you choose a treatment that has never been formally tested through scientific research?
2. Would you choose a treatment that has been tested and found to be equal to receiving no treatment at all?
3. Would you choose a treatment found to be significantly better than receiving no treatment?
4. Would you choose a treatment found to be better than a placebo?
5. Would you choose a proven treatment and with less adverse side effects?
6. Would you choose a treatment found to be superior to all other available treatments?
7. If your condition did not exactly meet the screening diagnostic criteria used in the clinical research, would you want your clinician to extrapolate the findings to your case?

One may also reasonably ask a related series of questions about the type of therapist characteristics one may seek when searching for a therapist. Empirical evidence dictates that certain therapist characteristics and skills appear to promote better outcomes (see Norcross, 2002).

Although these questions and answers may help to orient us to the significance of this issue, there are some important considerations and disclaimers to address.

Just because an approach is not identified as empirically supported does not mean that this approach is not or could not be effective. All that it means is that the approach is as of yet insufficiently tested for the presenting problem. Even an approach that is empirically supported does not guarantee that its delivery will always result in a positive outcome. There are a host of factors that may enhance or undermine the delivery of an effective treatment. These factors have to do with the accuracy of the formulation of the problem, competence in delivering the treatment, tailoring the treatment protocol to the patient, removing barriers to treatment implementation, and the like. There are likely to be many things that competent clinicians do with patients that may work but have yet to be tested. In fact, although not the focus of this chapter and book, there are some non-CBT treatment protocols that are efficacious. Fourth, clinicians must recognize that patients with a given diagnosis are not necessarily equivalent to other patients with the same diagnosis (Kiesler, 1973). Similarly, therapists with a given theoretical orientation are not necessarily equivalent to other therapists with the same theoretical orientation (Kiesler). Simply put, there are a host of factors that are likely to impinge on the delivery of any treatment.

Fortunately, a body of translational evidence is emerging, substantiating the *effectiveness* of psychological treatments that have previously demonstrated *efficacy* in RCTs. These benchmarking studies have demonstrated comparable effectiveness for a treatment in common clinical settings with fewer exclusion criteria and a more heterogeneous sample of arguably greater clinical complexity and comorbidity. Comparable *effectiveness* has been established in clinical outpatient settings for the treatment of panic disorder (Wade, Treat, & Stewart, 1998), social phobia (Gaston, Abbott, Rapee, & Neary, 2006), and depression (Merrill, Tolbert, & Wade, 2003). Less evidence exists for benchmarking studies in primary care, perhaps due to health insurance reimbursement issues inherent in the United States' current health care system.

The dissemination of ESTs into practice has many obstacles for the field of psychology. Simply put, there is not the same "business model" as exists for pharmaceutical companies, where massive budgets are devoted to training and marketing their treatments. Consider that from January to September of 2007 alone, Sepracor spent $246.4 million in direct-to-consumer marketing of the sleep drug Lunesta, *a decline from the previous year* ("Spending Review," 2008). Indeed, careful analyses of unpublished pharmaceutical company-funded clinical trials have cast doubt on the empirical evidence behind some antidepressants that would justify such robust sales. Once such study, in fact, found marginal benefit over placebo when the data from unpublished clinical trials were included (Turner, Matthews, Linardatos, Tell, & Rosenthal, 2008). In fact, 94% of the favorable studies were published in the medical literature, when only about half of the studies supported the efficacy of antidepressants (Turner et al., 2008). The marketing-fueled popularity of such antidepressants may, in some ways, be a mirror image to empirically supported psychological treatments such as CBT: rigorous methodological support, and negligible, if any, marketing budget.

The literature, clinical experience, and clinical wisdom all behoove clinicians to consider the entire picture by reviewing the APA Task Force list of ESTs, realizing that in some instances, an EST may not have yet been identified. Such is the case in anorexia nervosa, where there is no "gold standard" treatment with significant efficacy. Naturally, we wish to find the most efficacious treatments possible for the patients whom we serve. The costs and risks to patients (and for providers!) are too high to do otherwise. In the medical setting, it is important for clinicians to use all available information and data at their disposal to apply the art of helping in an effective manner. Although most of the focus in this chapter thus far has been on ESTs, there is just as much reason to consider the inclusion of empirically supported assessment tools in our discussion. Tools such as the Beck Depression Inventory (Beck, Steer, & Brown, 1996), the Beck Anxiety Inventory (Beck & Steer, 1993), the Beck Hopelessness Scale (Beck & Steer, 1988), the PRIME MD (Spitzer et al., 1994), and the Millon Behavioral Medicine Diagnostic (MBMD; Millon, 1982) should be considered (Maruish, 2000). These tools may make the difference in identifying an accurate diagnosis, and are likely to alter initially determined diagnoses. One particularly important tool is the MBMD, which the editors of this volume are employing in a grant-funded project supported by the PEW Charitable Trusts, designed to deliver empirically based interventions into a primary care setting with chronically ill, underserved, vulnerable adults. The data provided by this tool are quite helpful in consulting with primary care physicians about their patients.

The MBMD (Millon, 1982) provides a comprehensive analysis of medical patients, including diagnostic data, coping styles, and medically related constructs (e.g., pain sensitivity, problematic compliance) that are critical for providing a thorough patient formulation. Particularly relevant, this scale provides suggestions for managing medical patients, as well as explicit recommendations for the primary care physician. Consider that although physicians frequently rely on comprehensive blood work panels and sophisticated diagnostic tests, such as MRIs, to rule out hypotheses and determine diagnoses, they are more likely to rely upon subjective impressions when dealing with psychological issues in their patients. In this sense, clinicians must be willing and prepared to use all information available to help their patients.

There are several good reasons to consider doing so. In the marketplace, some reliable and documented information about what mental health providers can offer in working with medical patients is better than no information at all. Patients do have the right to receive, and therapists have the responsibility to offer, treatments that have the best likelihood of yielding a positive outcome (Persons & Silberschatz, 1998). Otherwise, there is really no added benefit of integrating psychological services with physicians in the primary care setting. If mental health providers do not question what they do, someone else surely will. Knowledge, basic and applied, is powerful in helping to grow the field of psychotherapy as an applied science. Offering services that have demonstrated potential for being effective is critical for both patients and providers, as the delivery of ineffective treatments may undermine public confidence, as well as confidence of our medical colleagues that psychological therapies have anything at all to offer. The added value must be clearly elucidated through clinical work with patients to demonstrate how psychosocial interventions contribute to making a difference. Managed-care companies, let alone physicians, may fail to appreciate the contributions made by cognitive-behavior clinicians to the treatment team. The direct marketing of pharmacotherapy to patients as a "quick proven fix" may undermine the public belief that psychological therapies have anything to offer. The result may be that medical patients may then be less likely to seek nonpharmacological therapies.

Theoretical Issues

The theoretical issues underlying the establishment of empirically based approaches lie well within the arena of clinical outcomes assessment. Research design and methodology have a direct impact on the development of valid, reliable, and replicable data. An important consideration is to examine how information for empirically based practice is generated. There are a variety of available research designs for evaluating outcomes, each of which offers specific advantages under different circumstances (Greenberg & Newman, 1996). At the most basic level is clinical observation, often forming the foundation for developing testable hypotheses. The case study, a cornerstone of clinical psychology, provides an intensive study of a given individual that may have implications for working with other patients. Case studies, of course, are extremely limited for drawing firm conclusions about relationships (Kazdin, 2007). A series of systematically obtained case studies, all pointing to the same conclusion, provides further "evidence," albeit quite limited, of the possible relations that may exist between important variables (Kazdin). There is, in all likelihood, a seemingly endless amount of potentially useful information, albeit untapped, embedded within the patient files in a physician's office.

In fact, Stricker and Trierweiler (1995) have advocated that psychologists adopt a local clinical scientist model, encouraging clinicians to develop and test clinical hypotheses and case formulations with each client, adopting a scientific approach even with an "*n* of 1" as a proposed way of bridging the much discussed gap between science and practice. This concept is similar to that advocated by Jaqueline Persons in her case formulation approach, where the scientific method is used to develop, test, and refine clinical case formulations and working problem lists for each client (Persons, 1989).

Single-case experimental designs (Kazdin, 1982), in which the dependent variable is systematically observed during baseline and the independent variable is delivered under more controlled alternating conditions or phases, provide more definitive evidence. RCTs are, of course, considered the gold standard in evaluating outcomes, but these, too, have their limitations. Some have argued that random assignment to treatment conditions and delivering treatments in the absence of case formulations for an a priori agreed-upon limited period of time (e.g., 15 sessions) in no way mimics real psychotherapy (e.g., Persons & Silberschatz, 1998; Seligman, 1995). Seligman (1995) has argued that such approaches to evaluation of effects preclude the self-correcting nature of therapy.

Meta-analytic findings are valuable studies of bodies of clinical research, and a quantitative alternative to narrative literature reviews that provide evidence of the magnitudes of effect observed in a given defined area of research. The data from these reviews allow clinicians to determine how much better off the typical or average treated patient is relative to the untreated patient. However, effect sizes are averaged across studies and potentially risk losing the direct application to the individual client. Qualitative methods provide evidence of common themes or patterns observed in regard to particular phenomena of importance. These approaches provide a useful alternative to understanding clinical phenomena. Finally, mixed-method approaches incorporate both quantitative and qualitative information, perhaps representing the best of both worlds.

All of the previous methods, although valuable in their own right, are obviously not without limitations. Medical practitioners today frequently rely on published reviews of efficacious treatments stored in databases such as the Cochrane evidence-based database. They rely on this resource as a means of selecting treatments for which the most evidence currently exists. Clinicians practicing in areas in which they interface with primary care physicians would be wise to adopt an empirical model. There are a number of reasons to support this assertion. Medical practitioners today frequently use published systematic review of efficacious treatments. These reviews provide an overview of primary qualitative or quantitative studies that contain specific objectives, materials, and methods that are analyzed in an explicit quantitative and transparent manner. The most extensively used systematic reviews are meta-analyses. Meta-analysis involves performing a statistical synthesis of quantitative results from several relevant studies that address the same question. The fundamental goals of meta-analyses are to combine results across studies to yield an overall estimate effect, and to compare effects between studies in order to understand moderating factors. The most widely cited organization performing these analyses is the International Cochrane Collaboration. These types of reviews have made very important contributions in the management of health care knowledge. Good systematic reviews are usually regarded as the "strongest form of medical evidence." However, in many areas of medicine, updating is necessary.

Evidence-based medicine (EBM) resulted from a desire by many physicians to apply epidemiology to clinical problems. Pioneers in this movement include John Paul, MD, David Sackett, MD, and Alvan Feinstein, MD. They argued that clinical epidemiology should serve as "the basic science of clinical medicine." Sackett and colleagues (Sackett, Rosenberg, Gray, Haynes, & Richardson, 1996) defined EBM as "the conscientious, judicious and explicit use of current best evidence when making decisions about the care of individual patient" (p. 71). He and others took the classic approach of epidemiology (i.e., defining a population, assessing exposures, and measuring outcomes) and used it to answer clinical questions relating to causation, therapy, diagnosis, and prognosis. This new emphasis on EBM represents a renaissance of empiricist thinking cast into modern language that deals with bias, chance, and modern analytical tools. This approach has the potential to contribute to resolving the controversy associated with whether disease mechanisms or appropriately analyzed outcomes play a central role.

One of the important aims of EBM is to identify aspects of medical practice that are subject to scientific methods that enhance prediction of analytical outcomes in medical treatment. In essence, EBM represents a new paradigm for medical practice that de-emphasizes intuition, pathophysiologic rationale, and unsystematic clinical experience, and stresses the examination of clinical research evidence. EBM also requires new skills, including efficient literature searching and critical assessment of pertinent medical literature in daily practice. This new paradigm gives a structural process to help both professionals and patients with making decisions based on the best available health care interventions to produce the desired outcome. As demonstrated in the following example, this approach can be used as a means of improving diagnostic accuracy.

Case Example

A 48-year-old woman presented to her primary care physician with a 3-week history of painful swollen hands and moderate morning stiffness. Based on the history, physical exam, and laboratory tests, the patient was told by the physician that she had undifferentiated arthritis that could be early rheumatoid arthritis (RA). She was given pain medication and told to return in 1 month. The patient was very concerned about her risk of RA and left in a state of apprehension regarding her health status.

What should she do? In the past, physicians had limited information on risks for developing RA for this type of patient. Today, the situation has changed. With the use of EBM clinical prediction rules, the physician in this case could determine the risk of this patient having RA. In order to do this, it would be necessary for the physician's coordinator to conduct a literature search to determine whether any new information was available to help this patient. A question was formulated as follows: Which adults with "undifferentiated arthritis" have a high risk of developing RA? They conducted a computerized literature search using the appropriate terms and found eight citations. After surveying the titles, abstract, and method sections of these research papers, the coordinator found only three that appeared relevant. Analysis of these articles provided evidence that this patient's risk for developing RA in 1 year is 57%.

The physician informed the patient that people with her symptoms have a 6 out of 10 chance of having RA in 1 year. With this type of information, the physician now discussed with her the results of recent studies of the risks and benefits of therapy for treating RA, and referred her to a rheumatologist at an early arthritis clinic for further evaluation.

It is not difficult to imagine many other examples in which a similar process may reveal important information that affects the course of care. Data about the factors related to the therapy alliance, for example, may also be important in identifying strategies for enhancing the outcomes of treatment. Although the bedrock of ESTs are accurate diagnosis and the identification and application of a well-established or probably efficacious EST for a given diagnosis, significant research has highlighted the importance of several additional factors; namely, the therapeutic alliance and the impact of individual therapist factors. There is considerable correlational evidence to support the association between certain characteristics of providers, the therapy process, and clinical outcomes. Decades of correlational-type research (Norcross, 2002) support that certain characteristics of the therapy relationship are consistently associated with positive treatment outcome. As Norcross (2002) has noted in summarizing these data, estimated proportions of total outcome variance accounted for by various factors reveals the following: 15% attributable to expectancy (placebo, client knowledge of treatment, client beliefs in treatment techniques and rationale); 30% result from common factors (empathy, warmth, acceptance, client and therapist characteristics, therapeutic alliance); 40% accounted for by extratherapeutic factors (spontaneous remission, fortuitous events, social support), and 15% attributable to therapeutic techniques. In addition, there are unique characteristics in primary care settings that may significantly impact patient outcomes. As DiTomasso, Chiumento, Singer, and Bullock (2010) have argued in this volume, the literature clearly supports the efficaciousness of the physician-patient relationship. Mental health clinicians working with primary care patients must capitalize on all possible factors that may, in combination, enhance the potency of available interventions.

With the above points in mind, practitioners in primary care settings must commit themselves to evaluating the outcomes of their assessments and interventions (Borrego & Follette, 2003). This approach entails arranging the clinical environment to support the systematic collection of information that may shed light on questions of clinical relevance in the office. Clinicians must be prepared to test the impact of their individual and group interventions by contrasting them with appropriate and available control conditions existing naturally with the setting. In group-delivered treatments, for example, these comparison groups may be wait-list control groups, contact control groups, or patients receiving standard medical care only. With single cases (Kazdin, 1982), practitioners must be prepared, when ethically appropriate and possible, to alternate baselines and treatment conditions or to collect baseline data across several patients simultaneously, and stagger the delivery of interventions to different individuals over time to test the impact of services being delivered. The use of sensitive, appropriate, valid, and reliable measures is essential, just as the use of available standardized and manualized protocols would be beneficial. For example, for two common problems in primary care such as panic disorder and obesity, Barlow's Panic Control Therapy and Brownell's LEARN Program can be easily applied (see Hofmann & Spiegel, 1999; Wadden et al., 2005). Developing and incorporating systems for assessing the effects of one's clinical work should become an integral aspect of the armamentarium of all clinicians (Borrego & Follette, 2003). As Palm, Mutnick, Antonuccio, and Gifford (2003) have suggested, if the true aim of health care is to identify, develop, and implement effective care, then the use of empirical strategies for evaluating services is critical for facilitating dissemination of empirical treatments.

Practical and Logistical Issues

The clinician will discover that the introduction of empiricism into the clinical setting is fraught with challenges. There are a number of practical and logistical issues that impede this process of transporting ESTs into clinical settings. We highlight some of the major issues unique to primary care in the following text.

Clinicians and physicians often speak different languages, which creates communication problems. Clinicians need to exert great care in explaining the rationale of psychological treatments that may seem foreign and, in some instances, even outrageous to medical practitioners. For example, physicians may not understand the inherent value, let alone the theoretical underpinnings, of hyperventilating a panic patient in the office as an exposure treatment.

Moreover, mental health practitioners and physicians may value different things. This may result in differing goals in handling a patient problem. Physicians are trained to provide patients with treatments and prescriptions, and value doing something for the patient each visit. They may need to understand the rationale of using themselves as tools for listening to and understanding patients.

Physicians and cognitive-behavior practitioners read different journals, often emphasizing different approaches to conceptualizing and treating problems. Physicians obtain a great deal of their clinical learning experiences in clerkships that are dominated by attending physicians who are likely to be completely unfamiliar with psychological interventions. For example, one of the authors encountered a situation in which a family practice resident who had just completed a urology rotation had learned that medication was the treatment for bedwetting in pediatric patients. It was necessary to educate the resident and attending physician about the effectiveness of the bell-and-pad method as a treatment without the risk of medication side effects.

Clinical and Professional Issues

There are also a variety of clinical and professional issues that may affect the use of empirically supported models in practice. Problems of transportability abound, and must be addressed to facilitate application to the clinical setting.

First, physicians and clinicians may have competing or conflicting case formulations about the patient's problem. This may require carefully negotiating a treatment plan that attends to each practitioner's concerns. Second, as described in a previous section, the clinician must carefully judge the extent to which a patient in the primary care setting is similar to patients studied in published clinical trials. This information serves as the basis for determining whether to apply the treatment protocol in question to the patient in the office, and whether the treatment may be expected to be successful. Third, in the clinical setting, the cognitive-behavioral clinician must address a number of factors that may undermine the delivery of treatment. Problems related to nonadherence, factors affecting the therapeutic alliance, issues of transference and countertransference, and the existence of Axis 2 psychopathology may impact the delivery of treatment. In other words, the direct application of a manualized treatment protocol to the primary care office is more complex than it appears. The seasoned clinician must negotiate these challenges and demonstrate flexibility in the application of the protocol, tailoring it to the needs of the patient, collaborating with the primary care physician, and maximizing the likelihood of a successful outcome.

Ethical Issues

There are a number of ethical issues related to empirically based models. Clinicians must be sure to obtain appropriate training, consultation, and supervision to maximize the efficacy of their services. Simply reading a manual is not enough to ensure competence in delivery. In the primary care environment, the clinician must be aware of his/her limitations and scope of competence. When obtaining informed consent, Persons and Silberschatz (1998) have called for clinicians to provide patients with information about findings from clinical trials that relate to the patient's problem. Further, they have argued for clinicians to exert responsibility for recommending ESTs over non-ESTs or those that have never been tested (Persons & Silberschatz, 1998).

The central message from an ethical perspective is clear. First, cognitive-behavior therapists in primary care must have a sound scientific foundation for their psychotherapeutic work. Second, they must always be careful by never overstating the case or sensationalizing clinical research findings to patients or physicians. Finally, therapists must be competent to deliver the treatments that they offer and seek training, consultation and supervision, whenever indicated.

Recommendations for Effective Practice

CBT clinicians in primary care settings have an obligation to employ approaches that represent "best practices." The clinical research literature is a useful resource for choosing assessment tools and treatment protocols that have a maximum likelihood of yielding positive outcomes.

Practitioners must be aware of the multitude of factors that are likely to affect outcomes. Recognizing and capitalizing on the power of the physician-patient relationship, as well as the psychotherapeutic alliance, is likely to promote more positive outcomes. Working toward the creation of therapeutic relationships for which empirical evidence exists (Norcross, 2002) is likely to enhance the impact of ESTs offered in the primary care setting.

The use of valid, reliable, and appropriate assessment tools, especially those normed on medical patients, may be expected to yield more accurate and definitive diagnoses, case formulations, and recommendations that may yield more positive outcomes.

Given the multitude of mind-body problems seen in primary care patients, the clinician would be wise to become educated and skilled in treating the common problems encountered in this setting.

There is likely to be an enormous amount of useful clinical information and relationships tucked away in the charts of patients in primary care. As empirically based practitioners, CBT therapists should consider exploring and investigating this archival data as a unique source of hypotheses to be tested in clinical practice.

References

American Psychological Association Presidential Task Force on Evidence-Based Practice. (2006). Evidence-based practice in psychology. *American Psychologist, 61*(4), 271–285.

Beck, A. T. (1993). Cognitive therapy: Nature and relation to behavior therapy. *Journal of Psychotherapy Practice and Research, 2*(4), 345–356.

Beck, A. T., & Steer, R. (1988). *Beck hopelessness scale manual*. San Antonio, TX: Psychological Corporation.

Beck, A. T., & Steer, R. A. (1993). *Beck Anxiety Inventory manual*. San Antonio, TX: Psychological Corporation.

Beck, A. T., Steer, R. A., & Brown, G. K. (1996). *Manual for the Beck Depression Inventory-II*. San Antonio, TX: Psychological Corporation.

Borrego, J., Jr., & Follette, W. C. (2003). Evaluating outcomes in health care settings. In L. Cohen, D. McChargue, & F. Collins (Eds.), *The health psychology handbook: Practical issues for the behavioral medicine specialist* (pp. 525–536). Thousand Oaks, CA: Sage.

Chambless, D. L., Baker, M. J., Baucom, D. H., Beutler, L. E., Calhoun, K. S., Crits-Christoph, P., et al. (1998). Update on empirically validated therapies, II. *Clinical Psychologist, 51*(1), 3–16.

Crits-Christoph, P., Wilson, G. T., & Hollon, S. D. (2005). Empirically supported psychotherapies: Comment on Westen, Novotny, and Thompson-Brenner (2004). *Psychological Bulletin, 131*, 412–417.

DiTomasso, R. A., Chiumento, D., Singer, M. S., & Bullock, O. (2010). Nonadherence in primary care. In R. A. DiTomasso, B. A. Golden, & H. Morris (Eds.), *Handbook of cognitive-behavioral therapy in primary care* (pp. 291–315). New York: Springer Publishing Company.

Fairburn, C. G. (2008). *Cognitive-behavior therapy and eating disorders*. New York: Guilford.

Gaston, J. E., Abbott, M. J., Rapee, R. M., & Neary, S. A. (2006). Do empirically supported treatments generalize to private practice? A benchmark study of a cognitive-behavioural group treatment programme for social phobia. *British Journal of Clinical Psychology, 45*(1), 33–48.

Greenberg, L. S., & Newman, F. L. (1996). An approach to psychotherapy change process research: Introduction to the special section. *Journal of Consulting and Clinical Psychology, 64*(3), 435–438.

Hofmann, S. G., & Spiegel, D. A. (1999). Panic control treatment and its applications. *Journal of Psychotherapy Practice and Research, 8*, 3–11.

Howard, K. I., Moras, K., Brill, P. L., Martinovich, Z., & Lutz, W. (1996). Evaluation of psychotherapy: Efficacy, effectiveness, and patient progress. *American Psychologist, 51*(10), 1059–1064.

Kazdin, A. E. (1982). *Single-case research designs: Methods for clinical and applied settings*. New York: Oxford University Press.

Kazdin, A. E. (2007). Systematic evaluation to improve the quality of patient care: From hope to hopeful. *Pragmatic Case Studies in Psychology, 3*(4), 37–49. Retrieved August 10, 2009, from http://hdl.rutgers.edu/1782.1/pcsp_journal

Kendall, P. C., Kipnis, D., & Otto-Salaj, L. (1992). When clients don't progress: Influence on and explanations for lack of therapeutic progress. *Cognitive Therapy and Research, 16*, 269–282.

Kiesler, D. (1973). *The process of psychotherapy*. Chicago: Aldine.

Knapp, S., & Vandecreek, L. (2003). An overview of the major changes in the 2002 APA ethics code. *Professional Psychology: Research and Practice, 34*(3), 301–308.

Koocher, G. P., & Keith-Spiegel, P. (1998). *Ethics in psychology: Professional standards and cases*. New York: Oxford University Press.

Lowe, P. (2001, April 21). Rebirthing team convicted: Two therapists face mandatory terms of 16 to 48 years in jail. *Rocky Mountain News*. Retrieved August 10, 2009, from http://www.rockymountainnews.com/drmn/local/article/0,1299,DRMN_1 5_340350,00.html

Lustberg, L., & Reynolds, C. F. (2000). Depression and insomnia: Questions of cause and effect. *Sleep Medicine Reviews, 4*(3), 253–262.

Maruish, M. E. (2000). *Handbook of psychological assessment in primary care settings*. New York: Routledge.

Merrill, K. A., Tolbert, V. E., & Wade, W. A. (2003). Effectiveness of cognitive therapy for depression in a community mental health center: A benchmarking study. *Journal of Consulting and Clinical Psychology, 71*(2), 404–409.

Millon, T. (1982). *Millon Behavioral Health Inventory Manual*. Minneapolis, MN: National Computer Systems.

Moses, E. B., & Barlow, D. H. (2006). A new unified treatment approach for emotional disorders based on emotion science. *Current Directions in Psychological Science, 15*(3), 146–150.

Norcross, J. C. (2002). Empirically supported therapy relationships. In J. C. Norcross (Ed.), *Psychotherapy relationships that work* (pp. 3–16). New York: Oxford University Press.

Palm, K. M., Mutnick, J. L. M., Antonuccio, D. O., & Gifford, E. V. (2003). Practical research in a medical setting is good medicine. In L. Cohen, D. McChargue, & F. Collins (Eds.), *The health psychology handbook: Practical issues for the behavioral medicine specialist* (pp. 525–536). Thousand Oaks, CA: Sage.

Persons, J. B. (1989). *Cognitive therapy in practice: A case formulation approach*. New York: W. W. Norton.

Persons, J. B., & Silberschatz, G. (1998). Are results of randomized controlled trials useful to psychotherapists? *Journal of Consulting and Clinical Psychology, 66*(1), 126–135.

Rachman, S., & Wilson, G. T. (2008). Expansion in the provision of psychological treatment in the United Kingdom. *Behaviour Research and Therapy, 46*(3), 293–295.

Sackett, D. L., Rosenberg, W. M. C., Gray, J. A. M., Haynes, R. B., & Richardson, W. S. (1996). Evidence based medicine: What it is and what it isn't. *British Medical Journal, 312*(7023), 71–72.

Seligman, M. E. P. (1995). The effectiveness of psychotherapy: The *Consumer Reports* study. *American Psychologist, 50*(12), 965–974.

Spending review: 11 of top 15 brands increase advertising spending in 2007's Q1-Q3. (2008). *DTC Perspectives, 7*(1), 10.

Spitzer, R. L., Williams, J. B. W., Kroenke, K., Linzer, M., deGruy, F. V., Hahn, S. R., et al. (1994). Utility of a new procedure for diagnosing mental disorders in primary care: The PRIME-MD 1000 study. *Journal of the American Medical Association, 272*(22), 1749–1756.

Stricker, G., & Trierweiler, S. J. (1995). The local clinical scientist: A bridge between science and practice. *American Psychologist, 50*(12), 995–1002.

Turner, E., Matthews, A. M., Linardatos, E., Tell, R. A., & Rosenthal, R. (2008). Selective publication of antidepressant trials and its influence on apparent efficacy. *New England Journal of Medicine, 358*(3), 252–260.

Wadden, T., Berkowitz, R. I., Womble, L. G., Sarwer, D. B., Phelan, S., Cato, R., et al. (2005). Randomized trial of lifestyle modification and pharmacotherapy for obesity. *New England Journal of Medicine, 358*(3), 252–260.

Wade, W. A., Treat, T. A., & Stuart, G. L. (1998). Transporting an empirically-supported treatment for panic disorder to a service clinical setting: A benchmarking strategy. *Journal of Consulting and Clinical Psychology, 66*(2), 231–239.

Wilson, G. T. (1998). Manual-based treatment and clinical practice. *Clinical Psychology: Science & Practice, 5*(3), 363–375.

Wilson, G. T. (2007). Manual-based treatment: Evolution and evaluation. In R. M. McFall, T. A. Treat, R. R. Bootzin, & T. B. Baker (Eds.), *Psychological clinical science* (pp. 105–132). New York: Routledge.

Wilson, G. T., & Shafran, R. (2005). Eating disorders guidelines from NICE. *Lancet, 365*(9453), 79–81.

9.3

6 Training Primary Care Residents

Stuart L. Kurlansik
Richard Levine

Introduction

Cognitive-behavioral clinicians work closely with primary care physicians (PCPs) as faculty members in Family Practice residency programs. Family practice residents include physicians who have completed their medical school education and who are obtaining training in the specialty area known as family medicine. As the individual responsible for resident training in behavioral medicine, the cognitive-behavioral therapist can become an integral part of the education and training of physicians who will ultimately steer the course of medical care in surrounding communities. Over a 20-year span, for example, the therapist who has trained eight graduates per year will have influenced 160 practicing physicians. If the average physician in a solo practice has a panel of 3,000 patients in his practice, then the therapist will have indirectly affected the care of over 480,000 patients. The potential impact on medical care necessitates a careful consideration of not only what residents are taught, but how to do so effectively. The purpose of this chapter, then, is to describe a model for training family medicine residents in psychosocial interventions using a cognitive-behavioral format.

Why should we be concerned with training primary care providers in mental health interventions in general, and in cognitive-behavior therapy (CBT) methodology specifically? The answers to this question are compelling. Mental illness is the leading cause of disability in the United States for individuals between the ages of 15 and 44, and by 2020, major depression is expected to be the leading cause of disability in the world for women and children (Chapa, 2004). It is estimated that 26.2% of Americans ages 18 and older suffer from a diagnosable mental health disorder in a given year. This comprises 57.7 million Americans. One in five adolescents, over 14 million, have a diagnosable mental health disorder (National Institute of Mental Health, 2008, in "The Numbers Count: Mental Disorders in America").

Given the aforementioned information, one can easily appreciate why mental health issues are so common in the primary care setting. In addition, approximately 60% of patients with a diagnosable mental health disorder seek treatment from their PCP, not a mental health professional (Girgis & Sanson-Fisher, 1998), and it is estimated that half of patients with a psychiatric disorder go undiagnosed by their PCP (Rosenbaum, Ferguson, & Lobas, 2004).

There are estimates that about 40% of patients in treatment with a PCP at any particular time have a mental health or psychosocial component that must be addressed. Without question, family physicians need to be able to recognize, diagnose, and treat emotional disorders *effectively*. They also need to recognize, as well as treat or triage, a host of other psychosocial issues seen in the office. All family medicine residencies are required to incorporate education in human behavior and mental health, as well as to address the psychosocial issues of all patients; these authors believe that the cognitive-behavioral model is the format of choice for this task. Its effectiveness has been established, it has a strong research basis, and it has a well-deserved reputation as being effective in treating a host of emotional disorders. As a result, once taught, the resident has powerful tools at their disposal, tools that can be used throughout their career to relieve patient suffering. Although there is abundant literature (although most of it relatively recent) with regard to training psychiatric resident physicians in CBT methodology, there is little published information about training primary care (family medicine, internal medicine) residents in this modality, and even less research.

Mental health treatment in the primary care setting can be daunting. Kates and Craven (1998) state that "while myths and misconceptions abound as to the kind of mental health conditions that primary care providers actually handle, in reality they treat a broad spectrum of problems, many of which are severe and enduring." They continue: "The challenge that the non-psychiatrist faces is to detect the mental health problem, which more often than not presents with a physical symptom, assess it, and come up with a management plan—perhaps in as little as 10 minutes" (pp. vi, vii).

Presenting problems that are well known to the primary care practitioner include depressive disorders, anxiety disorders, psychoses (including bipolar disorder), and attention deficit hyperactivity disorder, among others. It is incumbent upon the physician, at a minimum, to recognize that a problem that is primarily biological in nature may have a psychosocial component that requires targeted treatment. In fact, medical issues that may require forms of CBT are numerous in the primary care setting. Belar and Deardorff (1996) list the following areas that may benefit from psychological intervention (including CBT): adherence to treatment regimens (i.e., patient compliance); arthritis and rheumatology; asthma; cancer; cardiovascular disorders; chronic illness; death, dying, and bereavement; diabetes; gastrointestinal disorders; habit management; human immunodeficiency virus disease; insomnia; occupational health; organ donation and transplantation; pain; pediatric issues; surgery/stressful medical procedures; prevention; rehabilitation; and women's health issues. Other target areas not specifically noted by Belar and Deardorff may include men's health issues, erectile dysfunction, conception difficulties, and genetic counseling.

It is a requirement of all family medicine residency programs that residents be taught the concepts for counseling their patients. The ACGME Program Requirements for Graduate Medical Education in Family Medicine (2007), which sets the standards and guidelines for the training of residents in family medicine, states the following with regard to education in the areas of human behavior and mental health:

> 1. *Training should be accomplished primarily in an outpatient setting through a combination of longitudinal experiences and didactic sessions. Intensive short-term experiences in facilities devoted to the care of chronically ill patients should be limited.*
> 2. *There must be faculty who are specifically designated for this curricular component who have the training and experience necessary to apply modern behavioral and psychiatric principles to the care of the undifferentiated patient. Family physicians, psychiatrists, and behavioral scientists should be involved in teaching this curricular component.*
> 3. *There must be instruction and development of skills in the diagnosis and management of psychiatric disorders in children and adults, emotional aspects of non-psychiatric disorders, psychopharmacology, alcoholism and other substance abuse, the physician/patient relationship, patient interviewing skills, and counseling skills. This should include videotaping of resident/patient encounters or direct faculty observation for assessment of each resident's competency in interpersonal skills. This will require sufficient faculty who participate on an on-going basis in the program, and in the Family Medicine center, in particular. (p. 29)*

As noted previously, family physicians do not have the time to spend 50 to 60 minutes counseling a patient. The average appointment time in a typical outpatient family medicine office is 10 to 15 minutes. That is not a considerable amount of time to diagnose, counsel, and treat the multiple complaints patients bring to the table.

From the moment the family physician picks up the patient's chart (or, more recently, looks in the electronic medical record), the search for an accurate differential diagnosis begins, and the physician must consider the role of psychosocial factors in the diagnosis and for the treatment plan. Could the patient's back pain be caused by stress? Does depression contribute to the diabetic patient's unwillingness to follow a low-sugar diet, exercise, or take their medication regularly? Whereas specialists tend to focus on the chief complaint, the family physician needs to have a more comprehensive understanding of the patient's problem. It is a simple matter to send the patient for an X-ray. Rather, determining just how the pain is affecting the patient, addressing their concerns regarding future functioning, and helping the patient cope with chronic pain are just some of the concerns the family physician must address.

Since it first became an area of specialization, family medicine has tried to distinguish itself from internal medicine. Using the biopsychosocial model of health and disease, behavioral science has been one of the mainstays of family medicine (Searight, 1999). Most family medicine residency programs have at least one psychologist or behavioral science specialist on the faculty to help train their residents. However, it is beyond the scope of a family medicine residency program to train residents to deliver 50 minutes of formal psychotherapy. From a practical standpoint, the standard 15-minute appointment time makes this unfeasible. Rather, the behaviorist may help the residents and residency faculty understand the impact that a disease has on the patient's mental health, as well as how to help the patient more effectively cope with problems that may confront them. What tends to distinguish family medicine from internal medicine is its focus on taking care of the "whole" person, from birth to death, addressing not only the physical or "biological," but also considering emotional and interpersonal functioning in the context of the family and greater environment. In this chapter, we examine how to effectively train family medicine residents in cognitive-behavioral methods appropriate to the primary care setting.

Theoretical Issues

Cognitive-behavioral therapy is one of a number of cognitive-behavioral models, whose modern developers include Beck, Rush, Shaw, and Emery (1979), Ellis (1973), Lazarus (1971), Meichenbaum (1977), and Burns (1980), among others. Although the authors of this chapter employ many of the methods derived from the theoretical base underpinning CBT, there is no unified theory known to us that guides the training of primary care residents in the many areas of psychosocial intervention used in the primary care setting. Family practice residents are expected to acquire the requisite knowledge, skills, attitudes, and competencies that will ensure their effectiveness as a practitioner. Although behaviorists in their respective residencies may network and confer with each other about methods for implementing the curriculum, each picks and chooses the methods based mostly on residency needs, personal experience, and perhaps intuition. Given the aforementioned, the remainder of this chapter will address those methods used in the authors' residency program with apparent success, based on observation and resident feedback. The cognitive-behavioral therapist with an interest in working in this setting may benefit from adapting this model.

Practical and Logistical Issues

For family medicine residents, education in behavioral medicine, including cognitive-behavioral techniques, occurs in both structured and less-structured fashions. The setting in which the authors work is a combined family medicine residency program and primary care practice. As a result, faculty members not only provide didactic and experiential training, but also carefully monitor and provide feedback about the resident's practice of medicine over the course of the three-year residency program. Although family medicine residencies almost always have a "behaviorist" on faculty, the theoretical orientation and even the discipline of that faculty member can vary considerably. Thus, although behaviorists are often psychologists, there is no RRC requirement that they must hold to the cognitive-behavioral theoretical orientation. Additionally, within the overall theoretical orientation known as cognitive-behavioral therapy, practitioners are of varying stripes, and certainly do not function in lockstep with regard to treatment methodology. They may use different approaches, emphasize different concepts, and may pick and choose different tools from the techniques available to them. Some family medicine residencies do not, in all instances, have a psychologist on faculty. Rather, they may have a social worker, or perhaps a psychiatrist. In some residencies, the behaviorist is full-time, whereas in others they may be part-time, or perhaps function as a consultant. As a result, the exposure to cognitive-behavioral approaches that the resident receives can range from extensive to none at all.

Our focus here is on the residency with a behaviorist who holds to the general cognitive-behavioral theoretical orientation, and although we will discuss curriculum elements, the emphasis will be on the specific tools used within those elements that advance the resident's knowledge of cognitive-behavioral and related methods. In addition, we will describe these methods in roughly the order in which they are introduced, from the resident's intern (first) year, to the third (and currently last) year of residency.

The curriculum includes cognitive-behavioral elements, and this approach is interwoven throughout the day-to-day resident/patient interactions. One important aspect of CBT is for the therapist to arm the patient with the tools he or she needs to solve their problems. As a result, part of our approach to our patients is didactic education in the methods of CBT—the "nuts and bolts" of the approach, taught in the service of helping patients add adaptive tools to their repertoires. In addition, we assign homework to our patients, an essential piece of the therapy process. We tell our patients, for example, that there are 168 hours in a week, but the (weekly) patient meets with the therapist for only about 1 hour. The rest of the time, when the patient is at home, work, or school, is where the "lessons" learned during the treatment hour are truly put into practice. Without practice via homework, the patient cannot implement the more adaptive methods discussed during the therapy hour.

The residency experience is analogous. We introduce concepts and methods during the 3 years of residency. The "homework" involves implementing the new material in a new context, during the doctor–patient interaction. Although we may not directly make the comparison with therapy, the similarity in approach is certainly not lost on the skilled cognitive-behavioral therapist.

The path to educating medical residents is not always smooth. Logistical issues may often interfere, and we discuss several in the text that follows.

Scheduling

One of the issues that often arises is simply getting the residents together in the same place at the same time in order to teach them. Residents are on a variety of schedules, and these schedules typically change monthly. This is a function of the various rotations in which they must participate, as well as work-hour rules. In our family medicine residency, in which each year we may have eight residents, each resident is often on a different schedule. One resident may be on a surgery rotation, one may be in the family medicine office seeing patients, and yet another may be on a night-float rotation in the hospital, and so on. Additionally, because of work-hour rules that dictate the number of hours a resident may work in a given period of time, it is often mandated that they stay home (to catch up on sleep), because, for example, they were on a rotation that required them to remain in the hospital the night before.

This makes getting all of the residents together for a lecture almost impossible. As a result, programs must assume that those residents who miss a lecture will eventually obtain the knowledge later in their residency career. Unfortunately, it is possible that because of conflicting schedules, certain residents never hear a specific lecture or presentation. In addition, residents may be required to attend only a certain percentage of the lectures or presentations given, in order to fulfill graduation requirements.

Predominance of Biological Model

To further complicate matters, faculty colleagues of the behaviorist can present a unique set of problems. Although family medicine espouses a biopyschosocial approach, it becomes immediately apparent to the behaviorist that for some physician faculty, the "bio" predominates in the mind of the physician. It is also possible that not all physicians, both physician faculty as well as residents, uniformly see addressing psychosocial issues as a high priority. As a result, they may attend primarily to the biological issues, with psychosocial aspects treated secondarily. This problem may create some inconsistencies for residents.

Although it cannot be argued that it is essential for biological issues to be ruled out even in cases in which psychosocial issues appear to be the root cause of the patient's problem, there are times when blind adherence to this approach can marginalize the behaviorist's role. In doing so, the physician faculty member establishes a powerful role modeling for the resident, who quickly learns to listen to the words of the physician faculty member above all others. In some instances, then, the behaviorist must work diligently to assist the faculty to develop an appreciation of the model.

Role Issues as Teacher

A physician faculty member may even come to believe, again erroneously, that he or she is responsible for supervising the behaviorist. Consequently, there is the risk of the behaviorist becoming a "second class citizen" in the medical domain. This situation can seriously undermine the role, let alone the potential contributions, of the behaviorist. Carefully negotiating one's role and finding the common ground, resident learning and patient care, and simultaneously respecting the role of the physician faculty, is indicated here.

Because physician faculty members have been taught to apply the biopsychosocial approach, they often engage in counseling of their own patients, and when they consider it appropriate, teach residents to counsel their own patients. The behaviorist in this situation can use his or her consultation skills to assist faculty, which in and of itself can have an indirect positive influence on resident training.

Politically, the behaviorist must be careful in this context to team up with the medical faculty to provide accurate information to the resident in a situation requiring a psychosocial intervention. Imagine that you are the behaviorist. You are in the precept room with your medical faculty colleague and a resident who has returned from the exam room to discuss the history, diagnosis, and treatment of the patient they have just interviewed and examined. You've not only listened to the resident's presentation of the case, but you've also observed the interaction between resident and patient on video monitor. After the resident has presented the patient's history, the patient's subjective account of the problem, and the results of the physical exam, the resident begins to discuss the assessment of the patient's problem and treatment plan. However, the resident sizes up the situation inaccurately, and presents a diagnosis and treatment plan that, in your professional estimation, is incorrect. Before you can correct the resident's incorrect synthesis of the information gathered, the physician preceptor affirms the resident's thought process and quickly puts their stamp of approval on the diagnosis and treatment plan.

What is a behaviorist to do? If he or she corrects the physician preceptor in the presence of the resident, he/she may be seen as undermining a medical colleague, and if he/she says nothing, he /she is implicitly endorsing a treatment that at best may be ineffective, and at worst may cause harm. If the behaviorist waits until the resident leaves the room, the opportunity may be lost. If the behaviorist asks the resident to leave the room while the preceptors discuss the matter, it may be too late. In addition, the physician preceptor may ultimately not defer to the behaviorist. The correct course should be clear. First, the behavioral clinician teacher is in a consultative role and must recognize that the physician teacher may or may not choose to seek or use his or her input in a given instance. Second, forging relationships with physician colleagues over time and demonstrating how the information provided adds value to the situation is important. Finally, it is incumbent upon the behaviorist to proactively address these issues with his medical colleague beforehand, so as to enhance the quality of the precepting experience on a more consistent basis.

When working with physician faculty in general, the behaviorist would be wise to present the evidence basis for any suggested interventions and use medically relevant metaphors to explain the concepts to facilitate understanding and acceptance by the physician. This approach necessitates that the behaviorist has a firm grasp of the appropriate literature. With residents, the task is a bit easier. They may be more willing to integrate psychosocial interventions in order to comply with residency requirements, particularly when they know they are being observed. Interestingly, one of the authors has seen that once a resident begins to "think psychosocial," the resident becomes more facile with psychosocial approaches, ultimately finding value in them.

Given these obstacles, it might seem almost miraculous that a resident is able to incorporate principles of human behavior, mental health, and psychosocial education in such a complex and busy schedule. However, with 3 years and using methods that are designed to fit into the resident's schedule, as well as through continued shaping by the behaviorist and physician faculty, residents typically can and do acquire the necessary tools. In the next section, we will describe the curriculum and its elements that allow the resident to emerge with a strong background in CBT-related methods, strong interview skills, and enhanced empathy for their patients.

Clinical and Professional Issues

When residents enter our program, they initially attend a formal, structured orientation designed to set the stage for enhancing their clinical and professional skills. During the orientation period, residents attend training sessions with the psychologist, typically accompanied by a physician faculty member. During the first meetings, residents are presented with faculty expectations regarding their approach to patients, in the form of Patient Encounter Guidelines (see Exhibit 6.1), at which time the behaviorist describes the essential elements of the initial patient encounter. The guidelines begin the coaching of the resident in the patient interview process.

Patient Interviewing

The basic elements of patient interviewing (open-ended questions, empathy, unconditional positive regard for the patient, reflection, etc.) cross theoretical lines and form the common or nonspecific bases of the art of helping. The cognitive-behavioral approach considers strong interview skills to be essential to the therapy process, because these skills lay the groundwork for the rapport and collaborative relationship necessary for success in treatment. This process incorporates elements of interview skills that help to foster a positive doctor-patient interaction. These elements are reiterated, practiced, and honed throughout the resident's tenure in the residency program. It is expected that they adhere, when appropriate, to the guidelines and implement these skills. When they stray from the expected approach, they receive appropriate feedback designed to shape and refine their skill set. The bond between doctor and patient may make the difference between compliance and noncompliance with treatment. Therefore, a central tenet of CBT, supported by considerable research, is that rapport and collaboration between patient and treating professional are essential ingredients of successful outcomes.

The same is true with medical treatment. For example, using open-ended questions followed by more focused, close-ended questions is an essential skill for the resident. Interestingly, respect for this approach is often difficult to instill in a resident; residents habitually tend to employ lists of specific questions in order to get the patient to adhere to a preconceived agenda. Open-ended questions allow the patient to go where they want to go, and because residents function within time constraints, they are often reluctant to open up areas of discussion that will draw the appointment time out. As a result, they need to learn to redirect patients, another essential interview skill.

Obtaining a Problem List

At the very beginning of each appointment, the resident must obtain an exhaustive problem list, similar to what cognitive behaviorists do when treating psychotherapy patients. He or she then needs to prioritize the list to determine what is emergent and what can be treated in a future appointment.

Exhibit 6.1

Patient Encounter Guidelines

1. Review the chart *before* entering the room.
2. Knock – open the door – greet the patient – smile – shake hands.
    a. Introduce yourself to everyone in the room.
    b. Be friendly (yet professional) – put the patient/family at ease.
    c. Use people's names – this includes babies and young children.
    d. Suggest that the patient sit in a chair if they are sitting on the exam table.
3. Be empathic (verbalize genuine empathy/sympathy) when appropriate.
4. Get an exhaustive problem list initially ("anything else; anything else?" etc.).
    a. Prioritize the list, using patient input.
    b. Determine, with patient input, what problems can be dealt with today and what problems require a separate appointment.
5. Always consider the possibility of psychosocial factors and explore them when present.
6. Be aware of cultural/religious factors which might have bearing on the treatment plan.
7. Conduct an orderly interview; don't repeat questions unnecessarily.
8. Use open-ended questions.
9. Speak clearly and distinctly, using a moderate pace with correct pronunciation and correct use of idiomatic expressions.
10. Ask unnecessary individuals (e.g., parents, spouse) to leave the room for privacy of questioning.
11. Don't hesitate to use the translation line if language is a problem.
12. Don't let the patient/others control the content or the pace of the interview.
13. Be efficient – remember, you have other patients waiting for you.
14. Always wash your hands before examining the patient.
15. After the exam, suggest that the patient return to a chair.
16. If you need to leave the room to precept, say, "I'm going to review your chart and I'll be back in a minute." Don't undermine your professional credibility by saying that you need to check with your attending/supervisor/preceptor.
17. Present the diagnosis and treatment plan, and get patient "buy-in" by asking if the patient is OK with the treatment plan. Negotiate a fall-back treatment plan if necessary. This will enhance likelihood of patient compliance.
18. Consider if you need to write out non-prescription medications with dosage, as well as complicated treatment plans, to insure patient understanding/compliance.
19. The last question should be, "Do you have any questions about ***what we talked about today?"***
20. Walk the patient to the front desk.

Empathic Skills

Residents also need to learn to be empathic. Because residents come to the program with a wide range of interpersonal skills, not every resident has a natural ability to display warmth, empathy, and support. In fact, less than adequate interpersonal skill is as much a reason for problems within the residency program as is lack of medical knowledge and skill.

Use of Detailed Handouts

Although the Patient Encounter Guidelines present more general and global behaviors expected from the resident, more specific interview approaches, drawing on cognitive-behavioral methodology, are also introduced somewhat later in the orientation period. These are distributed to the residents in the form of double-sided, laminated handouts. The first of the handouts, called "Interviewing—Patient Management—Diagnostics: Basic Skills for Primary Care Physicians," covers some of the material noted in the Patient Encounter Guidelines, but incorporates much greater detail. On the first side (see Exhibit 6.2), the information is primarily interview-skills-related, but also includes slightly more advanced patient-management skills. It includes examples of how to ask nonleading questions, empathic comments that apply to many different situations, and a number of "do's and don't's" for the beginning resident. Patient-management hints include not making a patient wait, establishing an exhaustive problem list that can be prioritized in order to determine what might be covered in the current appointment and what should wait, as well as how a resident should approach a patient with multiple agenda items.

Important Concepts for Practitioners

The concept of "availability, affability, ability" is prominently highlighted. This phrase is presented to the resident early on and reinforced. It is intended to convey the belief that these are among the most important behaviors a physician can manifest, *and in that specific order*. Thus, it is immediately apparent to a patient whether he or she can quickly and easily obtain an appointment with the doctor, as well as whether the doctor is friendly and caring. It is less apparent to the patient, at least initially, that the physician is "able" (i.e., competent). Thus, the physician needs to manifest the first two of the three qualities to help ensure that the patient will *return* in the future, thereby becoming part of the physician's panel of patients. The most skilled PCP will probably not succeed in practice if his or her patients cannot make an appointment with their physician in a timely manner; if the physician lacks friendliness and empathy; is too paternalistic; or is cold, aloof, or dismissive. Other detailed information related to common problems in primary care is also provided.

Use of Screening Questions, Mnemonics, and Scripts

On the second side of the handout (see Exhibit 6.3), the resident is introduced to the assessment of depression, suicidality, and anxiety. These issues are widely

Exhibit 6.2

Interviewing—Patient Management—Diagnostics: Basic Skills for Primary Care Physicians

BASIC INTERVIEW SKILLS - DO:

Use good grooming and hygiene.
Dress professionally.

Read the chart *before* entering the room.

Smile and say, "Hi, I'm *Doctor*________."
Greet everyone in the room.
Sit in a chair initially; have patient sit in a chair, not on the exam table.
Assume a relaxed posture.
Be professional, friendly.
Use the patient's name.
(For babies, too!)

Look at the patient, not in the chart.

Use open-ended questions to begin (i.e., questions that *can't* be answered with "yes" or "no") :
"What brings you in today?"
"When did it start?"
"How did you do it?"
"Tell me about…"
"What does it feel like?"
"Could you describe your symptoms?"

Use closed-ended questions later, for focus.

Display empathy.
"Wow, sounds like you've had a rough time."
"I'm sorry to hear that."
"That's great!"
"You've really worked hard at that."

Let patient know what you intend to do before you do it. Be gentle.

Try to "win your patient over." A satisfied patient returns.

BASIC INTERVIEW SKILLS – DON'T

Don't make your patients wait.

Don't *lead* the patient; e.g., Don't say:"You're not feeling fatigued, right?"

Don't give the patient "possible" answers; let the patient answer your question;
e.g., Don't say:
"How does the medicine make you feel? – tired, sluggish, energized?"

Don't interrupt; let the patient talk.

Don't end sentences with, "or…?"

Don't pontificate, *educate*.

Never argue with a patient; negotiate.

Don't say, "Let me do a quick exam." "Quick" implies not thorough. Rather, say, "Have a seat up here so I can examine (take a look at) you."

Don't use technical terminology; use layman's terms. If you can't say it in words the patient can readily understand, you probably don't know the subject well enough.

Don't forget to ask the parent(s) to leave the room when you interview adolescents.

Don't treat the "disorder" – Treat the patient.

PATIENT MANAGEMENT:

ELICIT A "PROBLEM LIST" AND PRIORITIZE IT.

With a multiple agenda, schedule another appointment for non-emergent issues you can't cover today.
Say, "I want to be sure we do justice to all of your problems; let's schedule a follow-up appointment to devote the time we really need to deal with them."

Think "efficiency." Extra time with one patient may mean your next patient waits/has less time.

Is there a hidden agenda?

Schedule extra time for follow-up counseling.

Let an unaware patient know the appointment is over by casually standing up, opening the door.

Upon leaving to precept, say, "I'm going to step out for a minute; I'll be right back" or "Let me review your chart and I'll be right back."

When the visit is over, walk your patient to the front desk.

Always return telephone calls promptly.

AVAILABILITY, AFFABILITY, ABILITY

encountered in the primary care setting, and family medicine physicians, adhering to the biopyschosocial model, must be aware of and sensitive to symptomotology in these domains. The handout contains the two USPSTF (US Preventive Services Task Force) recommended screening questions for depression. The USPSTF recommends that these questions are asked of every adult patient upon initial meeting, and when the physician suspects that depression may exist.

Following this, the more detailed depression questions are listed. Rather than present the well-known SIG E CAPS mnemonic (sleep, interests, guilt, energy, concentration, appetite, psychomotor retardation, suicidality), one of the authors has developed a somewhat more detailed (and perhaps more memorable) mnemonic, "SPACE PIGS, MA!," which captures all the elements of SIG E CAPS, and adds three additional letters: an additional P for pessimism, an additional A for anxiety, and an M for mania. It is reasoned that because a pessimistic outlook ("hopelessness") tends to be correlated with a greater likelihood of a later suicide attempt, it would be important to assess this construct. The anxiety question is seen as important because anxiety is often comorbid with depression. Additionally, if this is the case, it is important to determine the primary disorder, as treatment may differ depending on the sequential development of symptoms. Finally, it is essential to determine whether a manic episode has occurred, as presence of a current or prior manic episode indicates that the depression is not unipolar, but rather bipolar, and the treatment plan will almost certainly differ from that of a unipolar depression. A mania assessment is included as well, including *Diagnostic and Statistical Manual of Mental Disorders* (American Psychiatric Association, 2000) criteria for mania.

Suicidal ideation is often confronted in the primary care setting, and the resident must be prepared to assess for its presence. In Exhibit 6.3, the resident is presented with a logically ordered script to follow if they believe that the patient may be experiencing suicidal ideation. Following the script, and only if there is suicidal ideation present, the resident learns that they must assess obstacles to attempting suicide, and how to reinforce those obstacles. The last column of the Exhibit is devoted to assessment of anxiety. It includes typical symptoms of anxiety, as well as how to elicit indicators of the presence of anxiety from patients. Panic and agoraphobia symptoms are also listed. The resident is directed to always ask how the patient deals with stress, in order to assess coping mechanisms.

Specialized Techniques

A second handout comprises a compendium of techniques for interviewing children and adolescents. On the first side (see Exhibit 6.4), the resident is initially introduced to methods for interviewing very young children, including techniques to help the physician with the physical examination of the young child. To help the physician establish rapport with the parent of a young child, it is suggested that the physician use the child's name, and find something to praise about the child, reflecting the concept of "affability." It is suggested that the physician develop specific interview questions geared to the developmental level of the child or adolescent. A structured "well-child" interview results in a more efficient office visit, and combined with knowledge of developmental tasks at different ages, the physician can present herself as an expert by providing anticipatory

Exhibit 6.3

Interviewing—Patient Management—Diagnostics: Basic Skills for Primary Care Physicians

DEPRESSION ASSESSMENT:

USPSTF DEPRESSION SCREEN
Over the past 2 weeks:
1. **Have you been down, depressed, hopeless?**
2. **Do you have little (less) interest, pleasure in doing things you used to enjoy?**

If yes to above, then do:

DEPRESSION EVALUATION:

SIG E CAPS or...
SPACE PIGS, MA!

Sleep (more/less)
Pessimism (hopelessness)
Appetite (more/less)
Concentration
Energy

Psychomotor ret.
Interest (loss)
Guilt Feelings
Suicidality

Mania?
Anxiety?

Verbal Cues:
- No energy
- Always tired
- Can't sleep
- Irritated; angry
- Diminished libido
- Cry a lot
- Overwhelmed
- Can't concentrate
- Exhausted

Behavioral Cues:
- Tearful
- Wrings hands
- Sad expression
- Slouched posture
- Furrowed brow
- Apathetic
- Slow moving
- Limited reactivity
- Decreased school performance
- Withdrawal from friends/activities

SUICIDE ASSESSMENT:

DON'T ASSESS FOR SUICIDE UNLESS YOU HAVE GOOD REASON

Put questions in an appropriate order and in context. Never ask "out of the blue."

"Feeling as though life isn't worth living; or you just didn't want to wake up, or wished you were dead?"
IF YES: "Have you been thinking about committing suicide? ("Killing yourself ?")
IF YES: "Have you thought about how you would do it?"
IF YES: "How?"
THEN: "Do you have the means available to you?"
IF YES: "Are you planning to do it?"
IF YES: "When were you going to do it?"

Assess obstacle(s).
"What's stopped you from doing it?"
Reinforce obstacle(s).
e.g., "You're right about that – your family *would* be devastated."

If necessary, obtain a verbal safety plan/ agreement.

MANIA ASSESSMENT

Elevated, expansive or irritable, angry mood
Inflated self-esteem; grandiosity
Decreased need for sleep
Greatly increased energy
Pressure to talk; talk loudly
Racing thoughts; flight of ideas
Increase in goal directed behavior or agitation
Risky behavior

ANXIETY ASSESSMENT:

Anxiety Symptoms:
- Restless, keyed up
- Easily fatigued
- Poor concentration
- Irritable
- Muscle tension
- Sleep disturbance
- Rumination
- Worrying

You might ask, "Do you consider yourself to be an anxious/nervous person?"
"Are you a worrier?"
"Are you a what if'er'?"
"What do you tend to worry about?"
"Do you take your worries to bed with you?"

TO ASSESS COPING SKILLS, ALWAYS ASK HOW THE PATIENT DEALS WITH STRESS.

Panic Symptoms:
Palpitations, sweating, shaking, s.o.b., choking, chest pain, nausea/abdominal distress, dizzy, lightheaded, faint, derealization, depersonalization, fear of going crazy or control loss, fear of dying, paresthesias, chills, hot flashes.

Agoraphobia Symptoms
- Fear places where escape is difficult/embarrassing
- Fear places where help might not be available
  - Alone outside
  - In a crowd
  - Standing in line
  - On a bridge
  - On a bus, train

guidance information, as well as highlighting current developmental tasks that the child has mastered.

Red Flags

The physician is advised to be aware of certain "red flags" that may alert the doctor to the possibility of emotional, physical, or sexual abuse. These include being cognizant of expressions on the child's or the parent's face, unusual behavior in parent or child, and the more obvious physical signs of abuse, such as bruises or broken bones. If suspicion of abuse is present, the physician is mandated to alert the local child protective agency, which has the responsibility of determining whether abuse has occurred and the disposition.

With young children, we typically infer emotional upset from the child's behavior because they are generally not capable of articulating the source of their emotional distress. Thus, much of the information residents gather regarding the mental health/behavioral problems of a child will come from the parent's report (and because parents are not trained in spotting mental health problems, it is essential that the physician is particularly observant here, and cognizant of the more subtle signs of problems).

As a result, residents need to be keenly attuned to out of the ordinary behaviors in the children they examine. In very young children (below the age of 5), mental health/behavioral interventions are typically made through the parents (e.g., modifying behaviors through rewards/discipline, developing better parenting skills, changing the environment, etc.).

In the section dealing with interviews with middle-school children, the physician is reminded to include the child in the interview, using "kid-sized" words, and open-ended questions if possible. It is important to note that some children may not have developed sufficient language skills to process and respond to a physician's open-ended questions; therefore more focused, close-ended questions may be required.

It is essential that the physician have some knowledge of the child's world, including the current games, fads, toys, and hobbies that are likely of interest at each developmental level. The child's world consists primarily of home, school, and peers/play, and each area should be assessed. After the child has passed the stage where visits to the doctor because of viral infections, usually of the upper respiratory variety, are not as frequent, the physician may have to be fairly comprehensive in questioning during office visits, as the visits may be few and far between. As a result, and due to the brevity of allotted appointment times, the physician needs to combine comprehensiveness with efficiency. If the physician establishes a structured framework from which to work, and can populate the framework with the developmentally appropriate exam requirements and interview questions, the elements of comprehensiveness and efficiency are present.

A fairly frequent issue that arises in child office visits is the issue of unruliness. Some parents maintain a laissez-faire attitude when it comes to establishing appropriate out-of-home behavior limits. As a result, the physician needs to have, as part of her or his arsenal of skills, behavioral methods by which to reduce chaos and gain appropriate control. As an initial approach, and assuming the parent does not take the lead, the physician may politely ask the parent to reign little

Exhibit 6.4

Interviewing Children and Adolescents: Basic Skills for Primary Care Physicians

INTERVIEWS WITH YOUNG CHILDREN

Stand in the doorway initially to allow the child to become comfortable with your presence. Introduce yourself to the child and all others in the room. *Use the child's name*. Relax, smile, and be friendly.

Have a seat – try to remain on the child's physical level.

Develop and memorize a structured well-child interview, so that you appear to be both comfortable and knowledgeable. Anticipatory guidance (e.g., forthcoming developmental milestones) during the interview educates the parent and highlights your expertise.

During the exam, the parent may hold the child if it is calming. You may try to soothe an upset child by gently stroking the child's arm, and speaking softly. *Be gentle.*

Find something to praise about the child.

Never let a baby remain on the exam table without an adult making certain that they will not roll off.

Be alert for abuse "red flags."
- Expression on child's face
- Expression on parent's face
- Unusual behavior/glances in child or parent.
- Suspicious marks or bruises on a child.

You must report any suspicion of physical abuse, sexual abuse, or parental neglect to DYFS. You don't need to know with certainty that such abuse has occurred; you only need to be appropriately suspicious – DYFS will make the ultimate determination.

INTERVIEWS WITH MIDDLE SCHOOL CHILDREN

Include the child in the interview. Use "kid sized" words when speaking with them. *Use open-ended questions.*

Always observe the relationship between child(ren) and parent(s).

Learn the current fads, games and toys that kids like and ask about them.
Ask about hobbies.
Ask about the sports they play.
Ask about their school, how they like it, what they like most, least. Favorite subjects.
Ask about their favorite TV shows, movies, video games, food, etc.
Ask about worries, fears. What makes them happiest, saddest?
You might start with "What do you like to do for fun?" or "What is your favorite __________?"

If necessary, request that the parent set appropriate limits with an unruly child (e.g., by asking the child to remain seated, by physically holding or gently restraining the child, or by asking the child to obey a request). The physician may need to model appropriate limit setting for the parent.

"Projective" questions can be used to gain additional information:
- e.g. "If you could have three wishes for anything at all, what would you wish for?"
- "If you could put on a magic ring that would make you invisible, what would you do?"
- "If you could change anything at all about yourself, what would you change?"

Johnny in, to hold him, or ask him to sit in a chair. If that doesn't work, the physician may need to set limits, modeling appropriate child discipline techniques for the parent. This approach allows the physician to empathize with the parent regarding the difficulty of obtaining adequate results from current discipline methods, and may lead to remedial parent education in this area.

The second side of the handout (see Exhibit 6.5) addresses appropriate interview skills with adolescents, as well as common mental health issues in children and adolescents. With adolescents, it is important for the physician to spend time alone with the patient. Thus, the physician needs to request that the accompanying parent leave the room. In most instances, this doesn't present a problem, and the parent understands and acquiesces.

However, in certain instances, and for a variety of reasons, the parent may believe that he or she should remain in the room. Although the physician should not force the parent to leave, neither should he or she immediately comply with parent wishes without making an effort to persuade the parent that it is in the adolescent's best interest to have a measure of privacy. As a result, we have established a script that addresses parent concerns, which helps to pave the way for alone time with the adolescent. The script is essentially, "Just as you have a confidential relationship with your doctor, Kenny is at an age where he needs to have the same kind of relationship." The physician may empathize with the parent's emotional reaction if the parent continues to hesitate. Finally, the physician may need to add, "I know it's hard, but Kenny is growing up."

Our residents are taught to do a "HEADSS" assessment with adolescents. This mnemonic stands for Home, Education, Activities, Drugs, Sex, and Suicidality (mood assessment), all areas of interest for the physician who follows the biopyschosocial model. The resident is also taught never to assume that the adolescent has a heterosexual orientation. Making an incorrect assumption in this regard can be uncomfortable for the recipient, and runs the risk of rupturing the doctor-patient bond.

The adolescent is advised by the physician that what he or she discusses remains confidential, unless the physician believes that the patient presents an imminent risk to self or others. The limits of confidentiality are made explicit to the adolescent. This level of privacy extends to drugs, alcohol, sexual activity, and even minor illegal behavior. In this manner, the patient is much more likely to trust their doctor, allowing the physician to address issues that might not have been discussed otherwise.

In the section dealing with diagnostic concerns, common childhood mental health diagnoses are listed, as well as areas the physician should explore with the patient. There is a more detailed reiteration of the importance of covering home, school, and peer group, including rationales and specific areas to question.

Elements of the Cognitive-Behavioral Model

The last training aid (see Exhibits 6.6 and 6.7) residents receive at orientation covers basic elements of CBT, and is entitled "Cognitive Behavior Therapy for Primary Care Physicians." In this aid, residents are introduced to basic principles of CBT. For example, they learn how thoughts and images fuel emotions, and that it is the perception of the event, not the event itself, that results in the

Exhibit 6.5

Interviewing Children and Adolescents: Basic Skills for Primary Care Physicians

INTERVIEWS WITH ADOLESCENTS

At an appropriate point in the interview, ask the parent to leave the room.

Script (if needed): "Just as you have a confidential relationship with *your* doctor, your son/daughter is at an age where they need to have the same kind of relationship."

Empathize with the parent if they have an "emotional" reaction to your request that they leave the room.

If needed: "I know it's hard, but your son/daughter is growing up."

If a parent refuses to leave the room, consider the possibility of abuse.

Perform a "HEADS" Assessment

- **Home**
- **Education**
- **Activities**
- **Drugs (educate)**
- **Sex (educate)**
- **Suicidality**

Don't assume a heterosexual orientation. Script: "Are you attracted to males, females, both?"

Let the teen know that what they say will remain confidential, unless they are a clear danger to themselves or others. You can let the parent know this as well. This extends to drugs, alcohol and sexual activity.

Don't attempt to meet the teen on his or her level (i.e., don't try to "be cool" to achieve rapport – it is not likely to work); you're an adult and the teen is fully aware of it.

Be an *empathic* listener; help the teen to make decisions that work for *them*.

DIAGNOSTIC CONSIDERATIONS

Common Childhood Diagnoses:

Anxiety Disorder
Depressive Disorder
Oppositional Defiant Disorder
Conduct Disorder
Attention Deficit Hyperactivity Disorder
Learning Disorder
Borderline Intellectual Functioning
Mental Retardation
Receptive/Expressive Language Disorder
Phonological Disorder
Enuresis/Encopresis
Pica
School Avoidance
Autism/Aspergers/PDD

Primary Diagnostic Areas for Parents and Youths:

Home: Relationships with parents and siblings (and anyone else living in the home). Hobbies, interests. Disciplinary methods and need to employ such measures. Family interactions. Problem areas.

School: It's the youth's *job,* and forms a major part of their life. Social, academic, and behavioral issues should be explored in detail.

Peer Group: How do peers treat the youth? Does he/she feel respected, accepted? Does he/she have good friends?

Try to get beyond the superficial responses youths may initially give, but don't "interrogate" either. Developing rapport is essential in order for the child to feel safe enough to be unguarded. Use Socratic questioning, when appropriate, to help older youths solve their problems.

emotional response. They learn that if we can change our perceptions of an event to a more accurate one, we are able to change the emotional response associated with the perception to a more benign response, and as a result, influence the behavior that might follow from the perception/emotion. The aid briefly diagrams how early life experiences help form core beliefs/schemas, which, in turn, give rise to rules, attitudes, and assumptions. These beliefs are triggered by precipitating situations or events that may generate automatic thoughts and painful symptoms, as well as maladaptive behavior. Residents also learn that by forming a collaborative relationship with a patient, and by using Socratic questioning, they can help the patient challenge inaccurate perceptions (cognitive distortions) and thereby attain a more positive emotional stance, which might then result in more adaptive behavior.

Cognitive Distortions

Drawing from Burns (1980), the most frequent cognitive distortions (e.g., overgeneralization, jumping to conclusions, emotional reasoning, etc.) are presented and described. The importance of the Socratic approach is emphasized. It is important that the resident learns that the best solutions to a patient's psychosocial problems are typically generated by the patient, not the physician. The resident is advised that solutions that may work well for him/her may not be helpful for their patient. Thus, telling the patient what to do is generally not useful.

The resident is advised to truly listen to their patient, in order to determine whether the patient is engaging in cognitive distortions. Then, helping the patient to determine (find the evidence) whether her or his cognitions are accurate is the next step. Plausible alternatives to the original view are generated, and questions that may help the patient challenge the original distortion are presented.

Behavioral Interventions

Finally, the residents are introduced to four behavioral interventions, and are made aware that CBT is a multimodal approach to treatment, encompassing thoughts, behaviors, physiology, and emotions (Greenberger & Padesky, 1995). The interventions include behavioral activation, problem solving, assertiveness, and progressive muscle relaxation. It should be noted that the aids are a work in progress. They are revised from time to time to incorporate refinements as a result of research evidence as well as resident needs, and should be viewed with that in mind.

Additional Educational Objectives and Methodologies

Precept-Assist

Throughout the residency experience, a variety of teaching methods are used to acquaint the resident with CBT and related approaches. A universal approach,

Exhibit 6.6

Cognitive-Behavioral Therapy for Primary Care Physicians

BASIC PRINCIPLES

The primary assumption in cognitive behavior therapy (CBT) is that perceptions fuel emotions/behavior, and not vice versa. That is, what we think, assume or believe influences how we feel, and how we feel influences how we respond. It is not the event or situation that is important, but rather our *perception* of the event. If we can change our perception (meaning) of the event, we can change the unpleasant emotion it may generate, and the (maladaptive) behavior it may elicit.

Two individuals confronting the same situation may respond to it with entirely different emotional states. Thus, one may experience a neutral or even a positive emotional state, while the other person may respond with anxiety, sadness or depression.

Why should this be the case? The answer lies in the fact that the people with negative emotional states probably apply **cognitive distortions**.

Cognitive distortions occur automatically, so we call them "automatic thoughts" or "hot thoughts." People typically distort only in certain situations, likely a function of early life experiences which predispose them to exhibit this behavior in those situations.

Early Life Experiences
↓
Core Beliefs /Schemas
↓
Rules, Attitudes and Assumptions
↓↑
Precipitating Situation/Event
↓
Automatic/Hot Thoughts
↓
Symptoms / Behavior

As a result, CBT involves actively collaborating with the patient, and through the use of Socratic questioning, helping the patient to challenge their distortions and replace them with more accurate thoughts ("cognitions"). In doing this, we help the patient attain a more positive emotional state, which has a greater likelihood of resulting in more adaptive behavior.

COGNITIVE DISTORTIONS*

1. **All-or-nothing thinking**: You see things in black and white categories. If your performance falls short of perfect, you see yourself as a total failure.
2. **Overgeneralization**: You see a single negative event as a never-ending pattern of defeat.
3. **Mental filter:** You pick out a single negative detail and dwell on it exclusively so that your vision of all reality becomes darkened, like the drop of ink that discolors the entire beaker of water.
4. **Disqualifying the positive**: You reject positive experiences by insisting they "don't count" for some reason or other. You maintain a negative belief that is contradicted by your everyday experiences.
5. **Jumping to conclusions**: You make a negative interpretation even though there are no definite facts that convincingly support your conclusion.
6. **Mind reading**: You arbitrarily conclude that someone is reacting negatively to you and don't bother to check it out.
7. **The Fortune Teller Error**: You anticipate that things will turn out badly and feel convinced that your prediction is an already-established fact.
8. **Magnification (catastrophizing) or minimization**: You exaggerate the importance of things (such as your goof-up or someone else's achievement), or you inappropriately shrink things until they appear tiny (your own desirable qualities or the other fellow's imperfections).
9. **Emotional reasoning**: You assume that your negative emotions necessarily reflect the way things really are: "I feel it, therefore it must be true."
10. **Should statements**: You try to motivate yourself with "shoulds" and "shouldn'ts." "Musts" and "oughts" are also offenders. The emotional consequence is guilt. When you direct should statements toward others, you feel anger, frustration, and resentment.
11. **Labeling and mislabeling**: You attach a negative label to yourself: "I'm a loser." When someone else's behavior rubs you the wrong way, you attach a negative label to him: "He's a jerk." Mislabeling involves describing an event with language that is emotionally loaded.
12. **Personalization:** You see yourself as the cause of some negative external event or other person's emotional state for which, in fact, you were not primarily responsible.

*Burns, D. (2000). *Feeling Good.* (pp. 42-43) New York: Quill.

Exhibit 6.7

Cognitive-Behavioral Therapy for Primary Care Physicians

COGNITIVE INTERVENTIONS

Establish rapport! – It's an essential component of successful treatment.

Apply the *Socratic* method, using open-ended questions to elicit responses from the patient; the object is to have the patient describe their problem, their thoughts about the problem, and what solutions might work best for *them*. Keep in mind that solutions that work best for you might not be what works best for *them*. Telling the patient "what to do" is rarely useful.

Listen to the patient to determine whether they are generating cognitive distortions. Although it might be helpful to classify the distortion(s), it isn't necessary. Rather, helping them to determine whether their cognitions are accurate or inaccurate is key. *Use the Socratic approach.*

If the patient is distorting, ask them whether they believe this to be the only way of looking at the problem – that is, ask if there might be *plausible alternatives* to what they currently believe to be true. Help them to explore alternative ways to look at the problem. You can use a Thought Record (available in *Feeling Good*) to help structure this task.

- Helpful questions you might ask the patient are: "What is the evidence that the thought is true? Not true?" "Might there be an alternative explanation?"
- You might also ask: "What is the worst that could happen if it were true?" "Would you be able to live through it?" "What is the best that could happen?" "What is the most likely outcome?" "What is the effect of believing the automatic thought?" "What would be the effect of changing your thinking?" "What would you tell your closest friend if he or she were in the same situation and had the same thought?"

Additionally, help the patient to recognize that they have powerful resources upon which to draw. That is, they have their own skills, intellect, and imagination (i.e., their *internal* resources) which they can use in order to gain control of the situation. The patient can also draw on external resources (friends, family, and professionals). Helping a person to recognize that they can achieve a measure of control is particularly empowering, and can help *inoculate* them against future problems in which they might otherwise feel impotent or helpless.

BEHAVIORAL INTERVENTIONS

In depression, patients often withdraw and limit engagement in activities they had previously found enjoyable. Recent research has found that they can experience a reduction in symptoms of depression by a method known as **Behavioral Activation**. In its simplest form, the patient schedules a number of pleasant activities over a predetermined period of time. Several enjoyable activities over the course of a week may be sufficient, although this can vary by patient. This technique easily lends itself to a primary care setting.

For anxious or worried patients who take their worries to bed with them, an effective method of alleviating their worries and helping them to get to sleep more quickly is to have them write down everything they are worrying about *before they go to bed*. They might be told that we can't do much in the way of solving problems between 11 p.m. and 7 a.m., and that spending time worrying during those hours is not particularly helpful. After they have listed their worries, they can prioritize them and resolve to take care of their concerns, one by one, during "working hours." Once they begin to actually take care of the issues which concern them, they begin to realize that they no longer need to worry about them at bedtime, and their sleep is less disturbed. This is an example of the **Problem Solving** method.

Assertiveness: For patients who let others take advantage of them, assertiveness training may be helpful. Patients lacking in assertiveness skills may suffer from or develop low self-esteem, depression, and anxiety. To acquire this skill, the physician can suggest that they first choose a situation in which they would like to assert themselves, but have not yet done so. The situation should not be so anxiety provoking that the patient might avoid it entirely. The basic template for an assertion is *: "I really feel upset/annoyed/ angry when you _____. I'd appreciate it if you'd do _____ instead."* It's important to know that being assertive does not guarantee that the patient will get the desired result; it only maximizes the possibility of success. Also, the patient should be told that assertiveness is *not* aggressiveness, and the dignity of the person on the receiving end of the assertion should be preserved.

Assertiveness Resource: Alberti, R and Emmons, M. (2005). *Your Perfect Right*. Atascadero, CA: Impact Publishers, Inc.

Relaxation can reduce physical concomitants (e.g., muscular tension) of anxiety. *Diaphragmatic breathing* and *progressive muscle relaxation* are useful techniques which are evidence-based and have broad application. Progressive muscle relaxation has been found to reduce blood pressure when used on a regular basis. The patient can be given an explanatory handout with a homework assignment to practice the techniques.

practiced to varying degrees in all residencies, is called 'precepting.' Precepting is a process whereby an attending (faculty) physician meets with a medical resident before (for new residents) and after each patient encounter. Advanced residents (in family medicine, third-year residents) may be exempt from precepting, and can request precepts when desired. In our program, we precept using a unique computer-based program called Precept Assist©. Precept Assist was developed by Mary Willard, MD; James Gamble, MD; and Robert A. DiTomasso, PhD, ABPP (Willard, Gamble, & DiTomasso, 1999). It is a system that rates individual precepts and compiles multiple precepts both within and among residents. Entries into Precept Assist are made for virtually every resident-patient encounter, and each resident is rated with regard to her or his diagnostic accuracy during the encounter, skill in carrying out medical procedures (if the encounter involved a procedure), and the level of clinical competency the resident demonstrated during that encounter. Within the clinical competency spectrum, Precept Assist rates (when applicable) residents with regard to their clinical acumen, interview skills, business practices, and office skills. Clinical competency "packages" are arranged according to the resident's year, as well as the arena in which the rating occurs (i.e., in the precept room only, combining precept room with video monitor observations of the resident and patient, video monitoring only, and the resident's charting comprehensiveness and accuracy). The resident can view his or her own Precept Assist ratings for any time period he or she chooses. In addition, every resident receives quarterly feedback regarding her/his average Precept Assist scores for that quarter as part of the quarterly resident-advising process. Residents also receive a summary score by which they are compared with a residency-year standard, in an effort to determine whether they are meeting educational expectations. Precept Assist lends objectivity to a process that would otherwise rely on the sometimes faulty memory of faculty raters, and is, therefore, a more accurate (and fair) means of determining resident proficiency and progress.

BATHE

As an effective method of incorporating counseling education within the residency experience, the "BATHE" technique was developed by Stuart and Lieberman (1993). This counseling technique is quite simple, and can be performed in a relatively brief period of time. As a result, it fits nicely within the limited time constraints of the doctor-patient encounter. The BATHE technique requires the physician to ask the patient about the problem, that is, what is "bothering" him/her? (B), How is it affecting him/her (A)? What about it troubles him/her (T)? How is he/she handling the problem (H)? After which the physician makes an empathic statement (E) regarding the problem. When a physician BATHEs a patient, he or she is implementing a form of psychotherapy that conforms to certain elements of a CBT approach.

Video Monitoring and Videotaping

Video monitoring of doctor-patient encounters occurs on a daily basis, although not all encounters are observed. Over the course of a morning or afternoon patient session, however, all residents are usually observed several times. All video monitoring occurs with patient permission, and monitors are turned off if a patient must disrobe. Watching a resident from the moment he or she enters the exam room to the end of the encounter provides a wealth of information that cannot be duplicated by a simple case presentation. Using a competency-based curriculum, there are a variety of criteria to observe and rate. For example, the preceptor observes whether the physician introduced himself and properly greeted the patient using the patient's name. The preceptor observes whether the physician greeted others in the room and determined their relationship to the patient. The preceptor also observes whether the resident obtained an exhaustive problem list and, with the patient's help, prioritized it. Additional observations include whether the physician reviewed the chief complaint and obtained enough history to make a diagnosis and determine the treatment plan; determined whether a hidden agenda needed to be addressed; and whether the physician maintained an empathic, caring, and yet professional stance.

Video monitoring is a valuable tool by which the preceptor can determine the degree of skill with which the resident accomplished these tasks. In addition, because the resident-patient interactions are being observed in real time, the preceptor can personally intervene in instances when this is required.

Cofacilitation of a Visit

Finally, there are instances when the examining physician may request that the behaviorist enter the exam room to help explicate complex mental health issues or to provide information to the patient. At these times, the behaviorist may model appropriate history taking and intervention methods for the resident.

Reviewing Videotaped Patient Encounters of the Resident

Patient encounters are videotaped, with written patient permission, twice yearly in our residency. This allows the behaviorist to carefully review the tape with the resident to examine all aspects of the encounter, in an effort to improve physician performance. As noted earlier, during the precept, the psychologist and physician preceptor provide feedback and guidance to the resident. It is also a time when cognitive-behavioral approaches to psychosocial issues are discussed. If it is still early in the resident's career, the preceptors might, through Socratic questioning, help the resident uncover the psychosocial issues with which the patient is dealing, and provide feedback with regard to additional questions that might be necessary to obtain a more accurate diagnosis of the patient's mental health problem. It is also the time when the behaviorist, typically with input from the physician preceptor, may suggest appropriate cognitive-behavioral interventions, as well as physician-recommended pharmacological interventions.

Following the precept, the resident returns to the patient's exam room and presents the diagnosis and treatment plan. The physician is expected to ask the patient how comfortable she or he is with the treatment plan (i.e., to be certain that there is patient "buy-in"). If the patient indicates directly or the resident gets the sense that the patient may not want to follow the treatment plan, it is incumbent on the physician to discuss the patient's concerns, and perhaps educate the patient sufficiently so she or he understands, when appropriate, that it is in her or his best interests to follow the original plan. If the patient is hesitant or refuses to do so, the physician may need to negotiate a new management plan with the patient that better addresses the patient's concerns. Thus, the resident's stance is that in most instances, adapted management of the patient's issues is better than no management at all, and may be more effective in the long term if the patient has participated in the development or evolution of the plan.

Motivational Interviewing

In the same vein, one of the important functions of the behaviorist is to help residents move their patients from a lack of concern with an extant problem, to a desire and motivation to make a positive change. Psychologists use motivational interviewing (Rollnick, Miller, & Butler, 2008) to help their patients in this regard, and strive to educate physicians in this method of intervention. Motivational interviewing is used in a variety of patient health areas, including smoking cessation, weight management and loss, substance abuse, and interpersonal issues, as well as a number of other treatment foci, both biological and psychosocial.

Electronic Communication

Communication via the Internet has become ubiquitous in the population in general, and is an important method of communication in most residency programs. E-mail is used extensively to disseminate important administrative information within and among residency programs. It is self-evident that behaviorists and physicians would be missing an educational opportunity if they did not use the Internet for educational purposes as well. We are an Internet-dependent society, with the current crop of residents steeped in the Internet culture. It is probably accurate to say that the Internet and cell phone are the preferred methods of communication for current medical residents in the United States.

One method by which our residency uses the Internet for dissemination of CBT methodology is through regular e-mails containing "mental health hints" that residents can put to immediate use in their day-to-day interactions with patients. These "hints" are essentially information "bites" (or perhaps "bytes") designed to promote relatively painless and efficient knowledge enhancement by virtue of their brevity and succinctness.

Physician Frustration

As noted earlier, patients are often noncompliant with medical advice, a source of frustration for the treating physician. If there is one source of physician concern that comes to the attention of behaviorists in medical settings, it is the frustration they feel when confronted by patients who do not follow doctor's orders. The cause of this frustration is at least threefold: (a) physicians often can't understand why a patient would not want to do what is in his or her best interests; (b) if the physician has a paternalistic bent, she or he is upset because his or her authority is implicitly (and occasionally explicitly) challenged, similar to the teenager not following a parent's house rules; and (c) the physician may feel frustrated with his or her powerlessness to influence the patient.

It may fall on the behaviorist to help the physician move from a stance that results in frustration regarding his or her patients. The risk of frustration on the part of the physician is that it may alienate the patient and lead to even greater noncompliance and to a stance in which the physician is not able to empathize with the patient. The cognitive-behavioral clinician may help the physician to more effectively collaborate with the patient in an effort to develop a management plan that although not perfect, may be a reasonable compromise between what the physician considers to be the ideal versus what the patient will accept.

Balint Group

Empathy for the patient is also fostered in residents through participation in a Balint Group, a regularly scheduled group for residents specifically designed with this goal in mind. The behaviorist is often a leader or coleader of the Balint Group, which is designed to assist physicians in handling their own reactions to patients. This group process involves working with the resident physicians in examining their cognitive activity about the patient, their emotional reaction to the patient, their behavior toward the patient, and what they believe about the patient. This process may help to alter their reaction and reestablish a helpful and more collaborative interaction with the patient. It is also a matter of physician self-preservation. If a physician becomes upset and stressed because he/she feels thwarted or not given the "respect" due him/her, avoidable burnout can occur. Physicians will encounter patients of all stripes, and must learn to accommodate them within their practice.

Delivering Bad News

Learning how to deliver bad news is a disliked task, although a necessary skill. Although people tend to equate bad medical news with a terminal illness, it can be anything that the patient may perceive as having a negative impact on their future (Vetto, Elder, Toffler, & Fields, 1999). Unfortunately, there is very little training in medical schools in how to deliver bad news to patients, and most residency training programs have no formal training in the appropriate techniques for doing so (Girgis & Sanson-Fisher, 1998). If not delivered empathically and clearly, patients might not understand their illness, and the doctor-patient relationship suffers (Rosenbaum et al., 2004).

There are a number of articles concerning how to deliver bad news to patients. One useful strategy is the SPIKES model, developed by Buckman (1992). "SPIKES" represents the following:

Setting: Establish patient rapport by creating an appropriate setting that provides for privacy, patient comfort, uninterrupted time, sitting at eye level, and inviting significant other(s) if desired.

Perception: Elicit the patient's perception of his or her problem.

Invitation: Obtain the patient's invitation to disclose the details of the medical condition.

Knowledge: Provide knowledge and information to the patient. Give information in small bits, check for understanding, and avoid medical jargon.

Empathize: Empathize and explore emotions expressed by the patient.

Summary and Strategy: Provide a summary of what you said and negotiate a strategy for treatment or follow-up.

In this section, we have presented a number of strategies that the cognitive-behavioral clinician may use in teaching and training residents. These strategies are an integral part of the residency environment and, in large part, help to define the role of the therapist as physician educator.

Ethical Issues

Psychologists in medical settings may encounter unique situations with regard to patient confidentiality. Requirements may differ somewhat with regard to sharing of patient information, including written records, verbal transmission of patient information, coordination of treatment, video monitoring and videotaping, and duty to warn. Psychologists adhere to the tenets of the Ethical Principles of Psychologists and Code of Conduct (American Psychological Assdociation, 1992). The American Medical Association (2001, para. 2 –10) has adopted and published a set of ethical standards that state:

- A physician shall be dedicated to providing competent medical care, with compassion and respect for human dignity and rights.
- A physician shall uphold the standards of professionalism, be honest in all professional interactions, and strive to report physicians deficient in character or competence, or engaging in fraud or deception, to appropriate entities.
- A physician shall respect the law and also recognize a responsibility to seek changes in those requirements that are contrary to the best interests of the patient.
- A physician shall respect the rights of patients, colleagues, and other health professionals, and shall safeguard patient confidences and privacy within the constraints of the law.
- A physician shall continue to study, apply, and advance scientific knowledge, maintain a commitment to medical education, make relevant information available to patients, colleagues, and the public, obtain consultation, and use the talents of other health professionals when indicated.
- A physician shall, in the provision of appropriate patient care, except in emergencies, be free to choose whom to serve, with whom to associate, and the environment in which to provide medical care.
- A physician shall recognize a responsibility to participate in activities contributing to the improvement of the community and the betterment of public health.
- A physician shall, while caring for a patient, regard responsibility to the patient as paramount.

- A physician shall support access to medical care for all people.

Understanding these principles may further assist the behaviorist in his or her role as educator.

Recommendations for Effective Practice

Cognitive behaviorists functioning in residency settings should consider the following recommendations for effective practice:

1. Be cognizant of evidence-based practices and use them wherever possible. It is important to be a credible partner in medical care, and "flying by the seat of your pants" is rarely a good idea, as medical professionals may marginalize you if they don't believe that your diagnostic skills and interventions are sound. You need to be able to support your consultations with evidence that what you suggest has a good likelihood of being effective.
2. Adhere to the ethical standards of your discipline. Each discipline has its own standards and the behaviorist must never be convinced that it is appropriate to conform to a standard that your own discipline might eschew.
3. Be inventive—develop educational methods that residents will actually use. Using a variety of modalities to get your message across increases the likelihood that the message actually does get across. Think brevity, and be succinct. Residents have many competing demands, are often tired and stressed, and need to get the most out of free time available to them. Give them what they need in a format that they can quickly and easily digest.
3. Develop strong, positive relationships with both resident and faculty. Practice what you preach: heed "availability, affability, ability." If you make yourself available to residents and fellow faculty members, and are a friendly, approachable colleague, your value will increase. Of course, ability is also essential, and if you employ the first two qualities, you will likely have the opportunity to demonstrate your ability over time.
4. Keep in close contact with fellow behaviorists with similar job functions. This is particularly important for individuals who are new to residency training programs. Your colleagues have a wealth of information to help you gain expertise in the field more rapidly. They are also a valuable resource when you are negotiating difficult situations, and can help you avoid burnout.
5. Read, attend conferences, and keep up with the latest evidence-based developments in the field. Your worth to your colleagues and residents depends, in a large part, on your continuing expertise.
6. Understanding the norms and mores of the medical environment and becoming knowledgeable about and skilled in treating common problems in primary care will be critical.

References

ACGME Program Requirements for Graduate Medical Education in Family Medicine. Effective July 1, 2007.

American Medical Association. (2001). *American Medical Association code of medical ethics.* Retrieved September 15, 2009, from http://www.ama-assn.org/ama/pub/physician-resources/medical-ethics/code-medical-ethics/principles-medical-ethics.shtml

American Psychiatric Association. (2000). *Diagnostic and statistical manual of mental disorders* (4th ed., text rev.) Washington, DC: Author.

American Psychological Association. (1992). *Ethical principles of psychologists and code of conduct.* Washington, DC: Author.

Beck, A., Rush, A., Shaw, B., & Emery, G. (1979). *Cognitive therapy of depression.* New York: Guilford.

Belar, C., & Deardorff, W. (1996). *Clinical health psychology in medical settings: A practitioner's guidebook.* Washington, DC: American Psychological Association.

Buckman, R. (1992). *How to break bad news: A guide for healthcare professionals.* Baltimore: Johns Hopkins University Press.

Burns, D. (1980). *Feeling good: The new mood therapy.* New York: Avon Books.

Chapa, T. (2004). *Mental health services in primary care settings for racial and ethnic minority populations* (draft issue brief). Rockville, MD: Office of Minority Health.

Ellis, A. (1973). Rational emotive therapy. In R. Corsini (Ed.), *Current psychotherapies* (pp. 167–206). Itasca, IL: F.E. Peacock.

Girgis, A., & Sanson-Fisher, R.W. (1998). Breaking bad news 1: Current best advice for clinicians. *Behavioral Medicine, 24*(2), 53–59.

Greenberger, D., & Padesky, C. (1995). *Mind over mood: Change the way you feel by changing the way you think.* New York: Guilford.

Kates, N., & Craven, M. (1998). *Managing mental health problems: A practical guide for primary care.* Seattle, WA: Hogrefe & Huber.

Lazarus, A. (1971). *Behavior therapy and beyond.* New York: McGraw-Hill.

Meichenbaum, D. (1977). *Cognitive-behavior modification: An integrative approach.* New York: Plenum Press.

National Institute of Mental Health (NIMH). (2008). *The numbers count: Mental disorders in America.* [Data file]. Available at: http://www.nimh.nih.gov/health/publications/the-numbers-count-mental-disorders-in-american/index.sntml

Rollnick, S., Miller, W., & Butler, C. (2008). *Motivational interviewing in health care: Helping patients change behavior.* New York: Guilford.

Rosenbaum, M., Ferguson, K., & Lobas, J. (2004). Teaching medical students and residents skills for delivering bad news: A review of strategies. *Academic Medicine, 79*(2), 107–117.

Searight, H. R. (1999). The outsider: Reflections on behavioral science in family medicine. *Family Medicine, 31*(4), 232–234.

Stuart, M. R., & Lieberman, J. A. (1993). *The fifteen minute hour: Applied psychotherapy for the primary care physician* (2nd ed.). Westport, CT: Praeger.

Vetto, J., Elder, N., Toffler, W., & Fields, S. (1999). Teaching medical students to give bad news: Does formal instruction help? *Journal of Cancer Education, 14*(1), 13–17.

Willard, M., Gamble, J., & DiTomasso, R. (1999). Precept Assist: A computerized data-based evaluation system. *Family Medicine, 31*(5), 346–352.

7 Spirituality

Stephanie H. Felgoise
Michael A. Becker
Jenna L. Jebitsch

Introduction

G. A. is a 72-year-old African American grandmother (with a known history of type II diabetes, hypertension, coronary artery disease, congestive heart failure, spinal stenosis, and narcotic-dependent chronic back pain), who presents to the office following a recent hospitalization for pneumonia. After her acute care admission, she was transferred to a skilled rehabilitation facility. During her acute inpatient stay, the patient nearly required mechanical ventilation because of profound dyspnea and hypoxemia. She describes her experience as exceedingly frightening, as she thought she would die. She has recovered well and is happy to be home with her family. In discussing her case with her family physician, G. A. reports that she was given "strength" to persevere with her sickness. She adds that in addition to the physicians and clinical staff who tended to her, she is quite thankful to God for bringing her through this illness successfully. She adds that although she is hoping one day to be with her "Savior" in heaven, she is not quite ready for that particular journey at this time. She requests that her physician prays with her for wellness.

Religion in America

America is described in the literature as a highly religious nation (Waldfogel & Wolpe, 1993). A Gallup poll published on July 28, 2008, reported that 78% of Americans believe in God, and an additional 15% of Americans stated that they believe in a higher power (Gallup, 2008). These results are similar to statistics published from a Gallup poll 20 years ago that reported that 95% of Americans believe in God (Spaeth, 2000). The U.S. Religious Landscape Survey was recently published by the Pew Forum on Religion and Public Life (2008). Thirty-five thousand Americans age 18 and older were surveyed. The data received were illuminating, in that it reported on the diversity and fluidity of American religious affiliation. The Christian tradition was the major religious tradition identified in the survey; 78.4% of the respondents described themselves as Christian. The breakdown of Christian faiths was reported as follows: 26.3% Evangelical Christian, 23.9% Catholic, 18.1% mainline Protestant, 6.9% historical African American churches, 1.7% Mormon, 0.7% Jehovah's Witness, and 0.6% Orthodox Christian. Respondents who described themselves as "unaffiliated" consisted of 16.1% of those Americans surveyed. The "unaffiliated" respondents were further categorized as follows: 6.3% "secular unaffiliated," 5.8% "religious unaffiliated," 2.4% agnostic, and 1.6% atheist. Other religions accounted for 4.7% of the Americans studied. Jewish respondents were 1.7% of those surveyed; 0.7% of the sample size identified as Buddhist, and Muslims accounted for 0.6% of those studied. Twenty-eight percent of respondents left the faith that they were raised in as children. The survey also commented on the role of immigration to the US as a cause of constant change in religious affiliations. Nearly 20% of men and 13% of the women said that they have no formal religious affiliation. Among married U.S. citizens, 37% responded that they were married to a spouse of another faith tradition. The geographic areas of the United States displayed regional variation of religious makeup. The Northeast region of the US has the greatest concentration of people endorsing the Catholic faith, and the South has the heaviest percentage of people identifying as Evangelical Protestants. The Midwest regional data most closely matched the religious makeup of the entire country. The Western US had the largest proportion of unaffiliated residents, and the largest percentage of atheists and agnostics (Pew Forum on Religion & Public Life, 2008).

Spirituality and Medicine

In the last two decades, the topic of spirituality and medicine has exploded in the medical literature, as well as in the media, public opinion polls, and funding initiatives. Additionally, in the past 10 years, there have been great developments in the understanding of mind-brain relations and the associations between the brain and peripheral biological systems that are important for health and sickness (Davidson, 2008). The complex mechanisms by which the brain can influence the body's physiology have been examined more closely. Because of the upsurge in these studies, the medical profession as a whole has become increasingly more open to the importance of these issues for providing good medical care (Davidson, 2008). Investigators worldwide, using public and private funding sources, are studying spirituality and medicine, as governments try to develop cost-effective health care systems for their citizens (Bjerklie, 2009). A major issue within the body of literature is whether spirituality and medicine can be discussed in the same context. As many clinicians know from their experiences, the practice of medicine is more than just regurgitating medical knowledge when encountering a clinical problem. The art of medicine is based in a holistic assessment of a human being, who is responding to a deleterious change in his or her own homeostasis; it considers that which gives the patient meaning and purpose, and his or her beliefs, loves, priorities, and fears (Fosarelli, 2008). One might ask, then, how can medicine be discussed *without* speaking of spirituality? This chapter intends to review how religion and spirituality may present as topics to be addressed in the primary care setting.

Overview

Following an introduction, the theoretical issues involving spirituality, religion, spirituality and health, prayer, and cultural competency shall be described. Practical issues dealing with spirituality in primary care shall be examined that include healing, coping strategies, end-of-life care, medical disease, psychological treatment, and medical decision making. The professional issues pertaining to spirituality for both physicians and psychologists shall be presented. Conflicts and ethical dilemmas involving spirituality and medical care delivery shall be explored. Finally, spirituality measurements and assessment of patients shall be presented.

Biopsychosocial to Bio-Psycho-Social to Biopsychosocial-Spiritual Approach to Patient Care: A Historical Synopsis

The history of medicine demonstrates a relationship between spirituality and health across many cultural traditions (Modjarred, 2004). This connection has continued to current medical care. Holy men in ancient societies ministered to both the spiritually ill and the physically sick. This has been documented from the early Chinese dynasties to the native and aboriginal empires of the Americas. A shaman, or medicine man, tended to all of the diseased tribesmen, spiritually and physically. Throughout civilization, as man came to understand the physical world, the metaphysical world became separated, and it was addressed by the religious leader or priest; the doctor cared for the physical body. With the dawn of psychology, the metaphysical component of man was divided further, and this triggered the psychologist to care for the soul and the religious leader to care for the spirit (Spaeth, 2000). The earliest hospitals of western civilization were erected, operated, and administered by religious orders of various religious faiths.

The foundation of contemporary primary care has been impacted by Engel's biopsychosocial model of medicine (1977). Hiatt (1986) added spirituality to the biopsychosocial model in order to address a person's spirituality as an integral part of his or her life. Within this model, the relationship between mind, body, and spirit is recognized, and the clinician is able to see how these aspects of a person interact with and influence each other (Kaut, 2002). Recently, another medical reference (Katerndahl, 2008) also calls for this integration, suggesting that attention to spirituality has not been universally adopted, and there is a need to give this further consideration. Declaration of this integration represents the zeitgeist of practice of primary care physicians as they have been challenged to address spirituality during clinical encounters.

In the last 10 years, the World Health Organization (WHO) included spiritual welfare with physical, mental, and social well-being in its definition of health (Calman, 2008). It has been reported that 20% of all community hospitals who are registered with the Centers for Medicare and Medicaid Services are affiliated with a faith-based organization (Modjarred, 2004). In 2001, the Joint Commission on Accreditation of Healthcare Organizations (JCAHO) revised its accreditation standards to require spiritual assessments of patients. Spiritual assessments are now mandated in all hospitals, home care organizations, long-term care facilities, and some behavioral health facilities that are seeking quality certification from JCAHO (Hodge, 2006).

Professional organizations including the American College of Physicians, Association of American Medical Colleges, and JCAHO have also acknowledged the importance of spirituality and have included spirituality as a part of patient care (Puchalski, 2002). Using survey data of members from the American Academy of Family Physicians, Daaleman and Frey (1998) reported that 80% of physician respondents refer patients to clergy and pastoral care, giving evidence to the importance of the spiritual needs of patients, and the willingness of physicians to collaborate with clergy and pastoral care teams. Yet, in the field of clinical psychology, psychologists in traditional settings do not often address spirituality in their assessment of or intervention for patients in their care. Perhaps this is because only a small percentage of mental health professionals endorse religion or spirituality as part of their belief system (Brawer, Handal, Fabricatore, Roberts, & Wajda-Johnston, 2002; Russell & Yarhouse, 2006), in comparison with the overall statistic of 93% of Americans, as a whole. A larger percentage of physicians endorse religious or spiritual beliefs (Fortin & Barnett, 2004), thus highlighting the complexity of mental health professionals addressing spirituality in primary care settings.

As the demand for holistic and spiritual care has increased, medical education has been compelled to train the future physicians of tomorrow about the importance of spirituality in a patient's health. Only 17 of the 126 accredited American medical schools presented courses on spirituality and medicine in 1994; by 2004, 84 of 126 schools had formalized curriculum on this topic (Fortin & Barnett, 2004). Today, over 75% of US medical schools provide teaching on spirituality (Calman, 2008). These concepts may also be taught in courses on holistic medicine or complementary and alternative medicine (CAM) in other medical schools.

Psychology training is not as progressive as medical training in the area of religion and spirituality. There are numerous faith-based graduate programs in psychology that emphasize faith-based counseling, but these programs tend to focus on predominantly one faith. Most programs attend to spirituality as an "individual difference" or a topic to be addressed in multiculturalism (Hage, 2006; Russell & Yarhouse, 2006), but with much variation in degree of attention or direct training, and few courses focusing primarily on this topic. When looking at how predoctoral clinical psychology internships address spirituality within the training of interns, spirituality and religiosity is usually addressed if the client brings it up to the intern, and then it is addressed in supervision (Russell & Yarhouse, 2006). This is also true in professional practice (Hage, 2006). Few sites offer formal training on spirituality and religiosity. Of all the internship sites surveyed, 35.3% reported having didactic training in spirituality and religiosity (Russell & Yarhouse, 2006). Other ways spirituality and religiosity were addressed included supervision, consultation, in-services, crisis services, and teaching. Within the professional practice of clinical psychology, Brawer and colleagues (2002) reported that about 5% of clinical psychologists report that they had spirituality or religiosity addressed in their clinical training, and that none of the internship programs that were attended offered this type of training. They suggest that training programs incorporate spirituality and religiosity into their course work, have more guest speakers on the topic, and have mentors for students who can help them address these issues. Thus, as psychologists have increased their presence in primary care practices, ethically and practically they need to enhance their knowledge, skills, attitudes, and understanding of the roles and functions of religion and spirituality in health care.

Theoretical Issues

Spirituality and Religion

There are many ways to define spirituality and religiosity, and the relationship between those two terms. In the majority of the literature, spirituality is seen as a quest for meaning. Spirituality can also be seen as an inclusive term that encompasses religiosity. Spirituality has a broader scope, and describes a person's life journey toward finding answers about life's value and meaning (Bekelman et al., 2007; Brady, Peterman, Fitchett, Mo, & Cella, 1999). A spiritual person senses there is more to life than what one can see or understand (Fetzer Institute, 1999). This sense also encompasses belief in a higher power (Dein & Stygall, 1997).

Religiosity is specific; it describes the actions and rituals of a religion (Brady et al., 1999; Sulmasy, 2006) and the framework or system from which these actions and rituals come (Dein & Stygall, 1997). It includes behavioral, social, doctrinal, and denominational characteristics (Fetzer Institute, 1999). The root of the word "religion" means "to bind," and this can be interpreted as a bind to God, or a bind to rules that shape behaviors toward a better life in God or a higher power (Roche, 1989).

Bremer, Simone, Walsh, Simmons, and Felgoise (2004) separated religiosity and spirituality by describing them both as a search for the divine, but those who are religious find the divine through an organized faith group, whereas those who are spiritual find the divine through life experience. Religiosity has also been described as a link between spirituality and religion (Szaflarski et al., 2006). Those who describe themselves as spiritual do not always describe themselves as religious, and those who participate in religious worship may not aspire to find meaning in life, hence giving disparity between these two terms. Spirituality and religiosity can be a part of a person's life to the very end of life, even when oral communication is difficult or not possible. When other forms of coping and communication are not available to those with chronic or terminal illness, spirituality and religiosity can continue to be a comfort.

Striving for meaning in life has been the topic of prominent psychologists, including Jung, Erikson, and Frankl (Patton, 2006; Wink, 1999). For Jung, the way to achieve psychological wholeness involves the search for spiritual meaning in our lives. The process of individuation invokes many questions about a person's reasons for living, and those questions bring the individual on a spiritual journey to find the answers (Wink). Related to spirituality, Erikson's discussions on wisdom include the acceptance of ambiguity in life, and having the feeling of contentment with the unknown and nonmaterial (Patton; Wink). Frankl purposes that humans have the affinity to seek meaning in their lives, and sought to incorporate spiritual meaning into treatment (Wink).

From a cognitive-behavioral perspective, spirituality and religious values may represent core beliefs or belief systems that influence individuals' thoughts, feelings, and behaviors. Religious and spiritual practices may be viewed as behaviors that may have adaptive or maladaptive social, cognitive, and emotional consequences. Prayer may be considered one such behavior, and is addressed in more detail below. Thus, in the holistic care of medical patients, religiosity and spirituality deserve attention with regard to how these beliefs and practices positively or negatively affect individuals' beliefs about health care, prevention, intervention, life and death, and interactions between health care providers, patients, and families. As with other behaviors, cognitions, and beliefs, spirituality and religiosity are dynamic constructs that need repeated assessment and attention for each individual patient.

Prayer and Health

Using data from the 2003 Complementary and Alternative Medicine supplement to the 2001 California Health Interview Survey (CHIS-CAM), Ambs et al. (2007) investigated religious and spiritual practices as they related to cancer and other chronic illness, and whether this relationship is modified by perceived health status. These individuals were compared with the healthy individuals who participated in the study. The CHIS-CAM consisted of 9,187 individuals from California who participated in a computer-assisted telephone interview, and 8,903 were used for this study due to providing information about use of religious or spiritual practices. Using questions constructed by the researchers, participants were asked about religious and spiritual practices, religious and spiritual identification, and chronic disease status and perceived health. Forty-six percent of participants identified as religious or spiritual, and self-directed prayer was the most commonly used practice (45%). Overall, the use of religious and spiritual practices, including prayer, increased when perceived health status was poorer. Those with cancer and other chronic illness used religious and spiritual practices more than healthy individuals, and individuals with cancer used these practices more than those with other chronic illness. This could mean that those with chronic illness may use religious and spiritual practices in order to alleviate suffering, and that those with poorer prognoses reach out to these types of interventions more often than their healthy counterparts.

Prayer is a way to connect to the sacred (Pargament, 1997), and is viewed as important in communicating with God (McGrath, 2003). When a person is suffering or needs guidance, the desire to connect to the divine has the potential to be stronger when compared with other times in life. When a person is experiencing health-related problems, he/she may look to find answers that are beyond the scope of what is tangible, and can use prayer as a source of connection and strength. Prayer can be defined as uniting with a higher power, and having a personal relationship with this power (Pargament, 1997). Intercessory prayer is prayer with a purpose; praying for an outcome, praying for those with poor health so that they will become healthy, or for an ease in their suffering. This type of prayer can make a person feel that they have some sort of control over the outcome of an illness.

The concept of prayer is different for each person. Some view prayer as a private, one-on-one experience with God; others view prayer as joining with others in a group. Other rituals and actions can also be viewed as prayer, such as chanting or repeating mantras. Prayer chains and networks have been established around the world via religious and spiritual communities, the internet, and health-based companies such as pharmaceutical companies in order for people to request intercessory prayer for themselves or a loved one in need (Pargament, 1997). Prayer practices, like spirituality and religiosity, need to be assessed in health care settings to identify and understand individual and cultural needs of patients, and for their expectations of health care provider participation to be made clear.

Clinical and Practical Issues

M. M. is an 85-year-old Roman Catholic woman, who was seen by her family physician in the long-term-care facility where the patient resides. M. M. was receiving skilled nursing care following a fall, which resulted in her suffering a left hip fracture. Due to her frailty, coronary artery disease, and severe osteoporosis, the patient was unable to receive corrective hip surgery. M. M. received a palliative pinning of the joint, but was unable to even bear weight on the hip again. The family physician assessed her patient following her morning bed bath and bed change. The doctor was very impressed by the marked pain that the woman was experiencing. The physician told the patient that she was prescribing a PRN dose of oxycodone to be used prior to baths and bed changes, so as to lesson her discomfort. The woman refused the pain medication, because she stated that Jesus Christ suffered more than her during his crucifixion, and that her pain was not as intense as his.

The case of M. M. represents a patient's perspective of how spirituality and/or religion may influence medical decision making, request for care, or refusal of care. If medical recommendations differ from patients' desires, mental health professionals may be asked to provide support for patients, or for the physicians themselves. When medical recommendations or practices are impacted by patients' personal beliefs, it may be difficult for patients and practitioners to function collaboratively or for respective parties to understand choices made. Certain health care practices are prescribed by religious traditions and spiritual beliefs. Others are influenced by mass media on related topics, which has played its part in creating challenges in the doctor-patient relationship.

Clinical Implications for Religious and/or Spiritual Beliefs and Practices

Health care professionals should be aware that spiritual and religious beliefs may be related to patients' choices for the gender of their health care provider, organ transplantation, organ donation, use of blood products, diet, willingness to take medication and the types of medication they are willing to take, choice in birth control, assisted reproductive technology, concerns about privacy, and preferences for end-of-life care.

For instance, culturally based practices of Buddhism, Orthodox Judaism, Hinduism, and Islam may mean that modesty is of concern and same-sex medical practitioners are expected or required for care. Compliance with prescribed medication may be low if the formulary is produced using any animal-based products: such concerns may be relevant to persons adhering to Buddhist, Muslim, or Hindu traditions. Other aspects of medical care that may warrant consideration of religious practices include end-of-life care and needs, cleansing practices, organ transplantation, organ donation, and use of blood products, as examples; such concerns may vary among Catholic patients, Jehovah's Witness patients, Jewish patients, and persons from other traditions. If practitioners are not well informed, religious requests may present as challenges to care.

Differences across religious traditions and between medical practitioners, mental health practitioners, and patients can raise important questions about how to work collaboratively and effectively. Psychologists may be instrumental in educating physicians in religious beliefs, if this is within their knowledge base. Likewise, mental health practitioners must be willing to learn about these aspects of patient care from medical practitioners. The later discussion on ethical issues presents a problem-solving approach to clinical decision making (Nezu, Nezu, & Lombardo, 2004) as a paradigm to help practitioners attend to the different world views held by parties involved in patient care, and a structure for offering comprehensive assessment and intervention.

Impact of the Media on Health Care Practices

The American public has been introduced to the body of medical literature through the lay press (Kluger, 2009), Internet, and other media. Patients are increasingly more educated regarding all issues concerning health. They typically submit questions to their primary care physicians on material that they have read in print or on the World Wide Web, or that were broadcast on television or radio. Physicians and mental health practitioners alike need to be prepared to address information in the mass media and respond when an opinion or comment is requested. Background literature is presented here to provide practitioners with some insight into what is commonly promulgated on the topic of spirituality, religion, and medicine.

The positive effects that spirituality and religion have on health have been well documented since the late 1980s. In 2001, the *Handbook of Religion and Health* was published (Koenig, McCullough, & Larson, 2001). This comprehensive text reported on studies that were both published and unpublished regarding the extensive research on the relationships between religion and health from the years 1990 through 2000. Koenig et al. (2001) concluded that involvement in a religious community is consistently related to lower mortality and longer survival. Mueller, Plevak, and Rummans (2001) verified this point in their 2001 review article, that stated that at least 18 prospective studies have shown that religiously involved persons live longer. Facts obtained from a recent issue of TIME also stated this point: People who attend religious services have a lower risk of dying in any one year than people who don't attend. Those who never attend religious services have twice the risk of dying over the next eight years as people who attend once a week. Church attendance accounts for two to three additional years of life (Kluger, 2009). The community support that occurs from attending religious services is one component of spirituality that assists in good health. However, church attendance is not the only factor that contributes positively to a patient's health. Mueller et al. (2001) also wrote that religious involvement and spirituality are associated with better health outcomes, coping skills, and health-related quality of life; they reported that in the several studies reviewed, it was found that addressing the spiritual needs of patients may enhance recovery from their illness (Mueller et al.). Some specific examples from the empirical literature follow.

Studies have shown that patients who are found to be more religiously involved have less cardiovascular disease. Both Mueller et al. (2001) and Koenig et al. (2001) referred to studies involving Jewish men and women who were Orthodox, secular, or nonreligious. One controlled study that was reported by both authors pertained to secular Jewish patients; there were significantly higher odds of first myocardial infarction in secular Jews compared with orthodox Jewish patients (Koenig et al.; Mueller et al.). Also, in a 23-year prospective study of 10,059 male Israeli civil servants, there was a 20% decreased risk of fatal coronary heart disease compared with nonreligious Israeli men. These data were adjusted for major risk factors such as age, blood pressure, lipids, smoking, diabetes, body mass index (BMI), and baseline coronary disease (Mueller et al.). Koenig et al. (2001) also reported on a study that showed religiousness was associated with a longer survival for Jewish patients who had surgery for coronary artery disease (CAD).

The literature illustrates the positive effects of spirituality and religion on blood pressure. Koenig et al. (2001) and Mueller et al. (2001) described many studies that concluded that religious involvement was associated with lower blood pressure. Mueller et al. (2001) reviewed 14 out of 16 studies that found that religious involvement was associated with lower blood pressure. Spiritual practices, such as prayer and meditation, can significantly reduce blood pressure; they also reported that 9 out of 13 studies found that religious or spiritual practices (meditation) significantly lower blood pressure (Mueller et al.). Koenig et al. (2001) discussed the phenomenon of lower blood pressure in Seventh-Day Adventists and Mormons that can be attributed to healthy lifestyle practices that are related to these faith traditions; these religions prescribe vegetarianism, and abstinence from smoking and alcohol. Levin and Vanderpool (1989) proposed the positive effect of religion and blood pressure may be from a combination of biological, social, psychological, and behavioral factors, including healthy lifestyle behaviors, genetic predispositions, and adaptive coping and use of social support systems.

The promotion of a healthy lifestyle through religious communities can have positive effects on the development of cancer in patients. Mormons and Seventh-Day Adventists have cancer rates one-half to two-thirds less than the general population (Koenig et al., 2001). This phenomenon may be due to these sects' healthier diets, and avoidance of smoking and alcohol. Koenig et al. (2001) reported that Protestants have the lowest risk of developing cancer among traditional Christians. He also wrote on the fact that Jewish patients are more at risk for certain cancers (some types of breast cancer and ovarian cancer, leukemia, lymphoma, and colorectal cancer); this is likely because of genetic factors. Jewish people are at lower risk for other cancer types, such as cancers of the cervix and penis, and cancers of the respiratory and upper gastrointestinal systems; this is likely due to circumcision and possibly due to less smoking and alcohol use (Koenig et al.). Regardless of religious denominations, many faith communities emphasize family values and strong communities that may promote prevention or early detection of cancer. Early detection clearly improves the prognosis of the cancer disease state. Places of worship frequently have health fairs and screenings; information about mammography and colonoscopy is disseminated in church halls and synagogue meeting rooms. The relationship between spirituality and cancer is well documented in the literature with regard to cancer and end-of-life care. Spirituality is used in this capacity as a coping strategy that assists the patient through his/her journey with this illness.

From a practical standpoint, the review of the literature suggests that mental health and medical practitioners alike need to be aware of information that is in the lay media, and be prepared to help patients understand the legitimacy of claims made and how to interpret research data. That which has the power to instill hope, such as research suggesting prayer and religious affiliation may aid spiritual persons in their healing, may also provoke upset, concern, guilt, or discouragement for individuals who have not embraced these practices in their lives. Thus, inviting dialogue about spirituality and religiosity and patients' beliefs about these ideals for their own well-being is the best way to recognize how the media may be affecting their coping, and allow them to share the questions they ponder as a result.

Practical and Logistical Issues

Spirituality and religious beliefs and practices surface as practical issues for patient care in primary care settings, as patients' world views will affect all aspects of medical compliance, coping, medical decision making, and health care practices. Where possible, clinicians should embrace and find ways to enhance effective spiritual and religious practices that may increase medical and psychosocial well-being in prevention, intervention, and palliative care. Yet, practitioners also must be aware of how one's spiritual or religious beliefs may be personally challenged in the face of medical crises or end-of-life circumstances. Examples of these issues are addressed in the following.

Coping Strategies/Stress Reduction

Coping strategies are the actions people choose when confronted with stress in their lives, with the ultimate goal being to reduce the amount of stress. According to Pargament (1997), each person has an orienting system—the way one views the world, which includes attitudes, habits, beliefs, and values—that affects coping with stress. Spirituality and religion are part of this orienting system, and how important it is as a part of the system depends on the individual. However, if a person has strong spiritual or religious beliefs, he/she is more likely to gravitate toward these beliefs and use them to cope with stressful situations. Overall, a person's spiritual or religious beliefs and practices can ultimately reduce the amount of stress he/she perceives in his/her life. Individuals who have strong spiritual and religious beliefs can potentially lead a lifestyle that is less prone to experiencing stress (Koenig et al., 2001). Those who practice spiritual and religious rituals such as prayer or attending social gatherings can use these rituals to reduce stress.

Meditation is used as a form of stress reduction and, at times, is also seen as a spiritual ritual. Meditation uses deep breathing and focus, sometimes on a specific word, sound, or phrase, in order to help an individual clear his/her mind. At times, meditation is also used as part of mindfulness training, in which a person is to let thoughts and feelings enter the mind "as is," with no judgments (Kabat-Zinn, 1994). Numerous studies have concluded that meditation is a positive tool for stress reduction, and can help alleviate symptoms related to anxiety disorders, cancer, coronary heart disease, hypertension, pain control, and substance abuse (Koenig et al., 2001).

According to Pargament (1997), 90% of Americans reported that they pray. People look to prayer as a source of healing; they pray for those who are suffering, prayer chains are made in order to pray for those in need. Some individuals make religious pilgrimage to places of healing (Puchalski, 2006). What began with shamans, who healed the ailments of others through spiritual means, is now done by medical professionals, especially doctors, who cure illness. However, within some religions, including Christianity and Eastern philosophies, comes the understanding that physical health is not removed from spiritual health; they are a part of each other. There is a unity of the body, mind, and spirit (Puchalski). And with this unity comes the medical means to end suffering and cure illness, and also the use of prayer to ask for healing and comfort (Koenig et al., 2001).

Treatment of Mental Health Conditions

An overall statement can be made that there is a link between increased spirituality and religiousness and lower levels of depression (Koenig et al., 2001). Some research has shown that Jewish people and those who are not affiliated with any religious group show more incidences of depression than the general population. However, these higher rates of depression have been found to be contributed to by genetics, lifestyle differences, exposure to historical events (i.e., the Holocaust or World War II), and differences in religious involvement (Kennedy, 1998). Those who are involved in a religious community or highly value their faith have a lower risk for depression. If these individuals become depressed, they improve faster than those who are not religious. This is due to the role religion has in helping them cope with adversity.

For treating depression, religious versions of cognitive-behavioral techniques have been proposed, including cognitive restructuring (i.e., assimilation and accommodation) and rational-emotive behavior therapy. Cognitive reframing includes finding meaning, and patients appraising their symptoms as less harmful due to spiritual coping (Greenstreet, 2006; Siegel, Anderman, & Schrimshaw, 2001). Persons can gain control by using problem-solving approaches that incorporate their spirituality. Many religious traditions incorporate healing into their system of beliefs, and this can help individuals have hope for recovery or improving their condition (Puchalski, 2002). On a macro level, people turn to religion for its intact support system; congregations help those in their membership at times of need.

In terms of cognitive restructuring, a person who is experiencing depression can assimilate his/her experiences or beliefs into an already existing schema relating to his/her spiritual beliefs to explain his/her circumstances. For those who experience symptoms that cannot be assimilated into an existing spiritual schema, a person may go through a psychospiritual transformation, and change his/her schema to make sense of the experience (Marrone, 1999). This takes the form of cognitive accommodation: changing how one thinks of a situation in order to make sense of it. The use of these types of cognitive-behavioral techniques are said to be equivalent to traditional cognitive-behavioral therapy, but with more focus on religious themes (Propst, 1996).

Although historically spirituality and religious rituals have been linked to anxiety and obsessive-compulsive traits, overall, those who use their spiritual and religious beliefs as coping mechanisms for anxiety have positive results (Koenig et al., 2001). These results are especially true if the person is intrinsically religious, meaning the person lives the religion he/she has chosen; religion is the inspiration for his/life, and guides all decisions. Extrinsically, religious persons are considered not completely involved with the religion, and use it as a means to obtain an end. Spiritual and religious interventions such as devotional meditation, mindfulness, and even religious pilgrimage have been cited as effective in reducing anxiety (Kabat-Zinn, 1994; Koenig et al., 2001).

As part of the biopsychosocialspiritual model, spirituality is an important aspect of a person's life that may be a factor in treatment. A person's spirituality may be integrated into his/hertreatment plan, and this aids in the therapeutic process for the client, allowing his/her to trust the health care professional and feeling that his/her concerns are being heard. This integration is especially important for medical patients. Knowing that his/her beliefs are being respected and that there is a safe place to discuss the spiritual journey, can ease a great deal of anxiety for patients engaged in medical treatment that brings uncertainty, fear, and concerns about the future with it.

Suicide

The discussion of suicide and spirituality and religious practices began in 1897 with Emil Durkheim, a prominent sociologist who wrote a book called *Suicide*. This book presented Durkheim's findings and sparked a discussion about how different groups may be more prone to suicidal behavior. Since Durkheim's time, studies have shown rates of suicide are related to certain religious affiliations. However, when looking at the data as a whole, it appears that the results are inconsistent; overall, no specific religious affiliation is linked to greater or lesser risk of suicide. However, it does appear that conservative Protestants and Muslims have lower rates of suicide when compared with other groups. Overall, those who have strong spiritual beliefs and are involved in religious rituals are less prone to attempt suicide, display suicidal behavior, and have suicidal ideation (Koenig et al., 2001). Similarly, spirituality has been associated with lower levels of despair and suicidal ideation when facing a chronic or terminal illness (Reiner, 2007).

Of note is that an individual's spiritual or religious beliefs may be a protective factor for suicide, and can be used as a tool for discussing the difficult topic of suicide. However, this does not imply that suicide assessment is any less important if a patient reports high levels of spirituality or religiosity, or belongs to a particular religious group. On the contrary, these patients may need more support, if they do present with suicidal ideation and they recognize these feelings and thoughts go against their spiritual beliefs.

Negative Effects of Spirituality and Religion on Patient Health

There are some negative effects of spirituality and religion with regard to a patient's health. Mueller et al. (2001) commented that few systematic population-based studies demonstrated an association between spirituality and religious involvement and negative physical and mental health outcomes. However, some adverse outcomes have been noted. Negative effects of religion and/or spiritual beliefs and practices on physical health may include stopping life-saving medications, failing to seek timely medical care, refusing blood transfusions, refusing childhood immunizations, refusing prenatal care and physician-assisted delivery, fostering child abuse, refusing the rights of children to receive medical care, condoning other forms of religious abuse, and replacing mental health care with religion. Of course, although physical well-being may be negatively affected by spiritual or religious beliefs or practices, clinicians are reminded to be mindful of their own values and judgments of patients' decisions that have these results. Clinicians are to help patients make informed decisions, and decisions that have the best outcomes as perceived by their patients, even if this means physical health decline is imminent.

In contrast to patients making spiritually or religiously congruent medical decisions that result in negative medical outcomes, some medical outcomes may result in negative reflections or beliefs about one's own spirituality or religious practices. Patients who are at the end of their lives, either by natural progression of life or as a result of poor medical conditions, may experience spiritual suffering. End-of-life considerations often cause persons to reflect on their religiosity or spirituality, their morals, values, and behaviors in concert with these beliefs. If regrets and misgivings surface, existential or spiritual crises may ensue. The following discussion brings these issues to light.

Spirituality and End-of-Life Issues

Part of spirituality is finding meaning and purpose in one's life. Individuals can use spirituality as a coping mechanism in order to alleviate their suffering and find comfort and meaning at the end of life. When one is facing suffering, especially at the end of life, a struggle ensues: holding on to that meaning, in the midst of suffering. If one has not examined the meaning of life, then the suffering becomes spiritual suffering: trying to make sense of life in the context of pain (Puchalski, 2006).

A theoretical framework by Fennel (2003) describes four phases a person will experience during chronic illness related to spiritual conflict. The first phase, disease denial, is when the person is in denial of his/her condition. Once the conditions of the disease ensue, the individual has difficulty denying the illness and may begin to experience a spiritual crisis. Some will feel anger toward God, that God has abandoned them in their time of need; or that they are being punished for the negative aspects of their lives. Atheists also experience a similar crisis in that there is existential conflict and questioning the reason to continue living. In phase two, those who have a belief in God turn from thinking that God has abandoned them to thoughts that God has turned his attention from them. Those who have turned away from religion may resume religious practice in order to alleviate their symptoms; for example, if they pray more, God will reward them and they will become healthy. Others will reject past ideas of what God is like and look for other spiritual outlets that are more fulfilling. Spiritual change occurs in phase three, when a person develops a new identity and sense of self. The individual searches for explanations for illness and renewed purpose in life. This may include new spiritual resources that are congruent with his/her new self. There is also a realization that who he/she is is not the illness, and he/she will always be an individual regardless of what happens with his/her health (Hall, 1997). In phase four, the individual searches for meaning in relationships and daily activities. He/she searches for meaning in all aspects of the illness and strives to make all activities meaningful.

Similarly, Doka (1993) identified that there are three spiritual tasks that one must complete in order to feel at peace with death. The first is to find meaning and significance in life. When one has difficulty finding meaning in life, this can cause a person to feel unfulfilled in a spiritual sense. Second, a person must die "an appropriate death." This means that a person must feel comfortable with dying on his/her terms, synonymous with personal values and identity. The last task is transcendence. This entails having spiritual insights that bring comfort to the dying person, that his/her legacy will live on after death.

Medical and mental health practitioners who invest time into spiritual and religious assessment of their patients early in their care relationship will have established rapport that allows for a cooperative and peaceful death to be planned, according to religious and spiritual values. Professionals who know their patients well or who have asked about preferences for family involvement or care for their loved ones will be more prepared to assist the individual and family at the end of life. Mental health professionals specifically should address patients' wishes for expressing concern to the family and paying respects after the patient dies. As clinicians partake in primary health care, more attention must be given to how confidentiality and boundaries will be maintained once patients die. Specifically, sending cards, flowers, or attending funerals may represent breaches in confidentiality if not specifically addressed with patients prior to death. Mental health practitioners are reminded that medical practitioners and mental health practitioners have different practices, ethical guidelines, and standards of behavior in these situations, and these differences are best made clear to patients, families, and health team collaborators when work together begins. Additional clinical and professional issues are highlighted in the following, with attention to physicians' practices for edification of mental health professionals.

Clinical and Professional Issues

A family physician responded to an urgent phone message from his patient, Mrs. W. (Mrs. W. was on vacation with her family at the beach prior to phoning her physician). Mrs. W.'s brother-in-law just phoned Mrs. W. to tell her that her sister was gravely ill. (Mrs. W.'s sister is a 52-year-old female patient who was diagnosed with metastatic pancreatic cancer earlier that morning.) The physician contacted Mrs. W. on her cell phone, as she and her family abruptly ended their vacation and were racing from 3 hours away to get to her sibling's bedside. Mrs. W. is crying and very upset as she speaks with the doctor. She states that she is overwhelmed by the news and that she does not want her sister to see her in this most fearful state. The family doctor can appreciate the severe anxiety and tragedy that his patient is experiencing through this event. He attempts to console the patient on her cell phone, and states that he would call in a prescription for some low-dose lorazepam, which will be waiting for her at a local pharmacy near her sister's home. The physician also states that he would pray for Mrs. W., her sister, and the entire family.

Since the late 1980s, spirituality associated with physicians has been reported in the medical literature. The concept of spirituality has been addressed regarding both the existence of spirituality within physicians themselves, and in the patient-physician relationship. An early study described the spiritual dimension that "can enhance the ethical aspects of medical practice by providing a larger context of meaning and purpose from which action and thoughts can flow naturally" (Hiatt, 1986, p. 736). In a physician's perspective regarding the issue of spirituality among physicians, Dr. Plotnikoff states, "How we address spiritual issues with patients depends upon what we see and our own ability to recognize, articulate and address our own spirituality" (Hatgidakis, Timko, & Plotnikuff, 1997, p. 10). Many physicians report that religion and spirituality are central to their lives; these commitments were thought to be contributory to their choice of a career in medicine (Waldfogel, 1997). In another early study of physicians' spirituality, Koenig, Beron, Hover, and Travis (1991) reported on a sample of 130 physicians. Koenig and his colleagues found that 93% of physicians believed in a higher power. Belief in a higher power was generally high among all specialties, except for a slight drop among obstetricians, pediatricians, and psychiatrists. Church attendance was reported to be highest among family physicians and surgeons, and lowest among psychiatrists and neurologists. Religious coping was also highest among family physicians and surgeons, and lowest among psychiatrists and neurologists. Male physicians scored slightly higher than females on all religious characteristics measured, which was contradictory to trends within the lay population (Koenig et al., 1991). In a national study of family physicians, 79% of those doctors reported a strong spiritual and religious orientation, with 35% participating in private spiritual or religious practices daily (Anandarajah & Mennillo, 2007).

The patient-physician relationship and spirituality is also described in the medical literature in various contexts. In an observational study of 20 academic physicians in a large, urban, East Coast academic medical center, two researchers observed the dynamic that existed in the physicians' weekly meetings. These physicians met weekly to study theological concepts through a Christian perspective; within this group, the physicians openly discussed the meaning and purpose of being a doctor, among other topics related to medicine and spirituality. Through their observations of the dialogue that occurred within these physician meetings, the researchers keenly described the patient-physician encounter within a spirituality framework:

> *In our view the clinical encounter is the place, par excellence, in modern society where medicine and spirituality meet each other—in a deeper and more integrated way than the mere presence of a hospital chapel, mediation room, or chaplain's office would suggest. The clinical encounter is the stage on which the drama of the human condition unfolds over and over again in the individual and collective lives of patients and caregivers, raising existential questions of meaning for both. (Messikomer & De Craemer, 2002, p. 572)*

It has been written that the challenge for primary care physicians, who care for patients and their families, is to recognize the spiritual health of their patients, and make resources available to those patients who desire them (McKee & Chappel, 1992; Waldfogel, 1997).

The literature is in agreement with the many barriers that prevent physicians from addressing a patient's spirituality during an office visit. An early described barrier was that physicians were uncomfortable addressing issues on which they were never trained in school (Koenig, George, Titus, & Meador, 2004; Spaeth, 2000). Certainly, medical education has addressed this specific concern of physicians, and has introduced spirituality concepts into the curriculum. Other barriers cited were physicians' unease with discussing spiritual matters, personal discomfort with and fear of the subject of spirituality, the challenges of physicians to support patients' spiritual matters with which the physician does not agree, the concern of physicians that they may be viewed as proselytizing, the physician's lack of knowledge regarding the patient's personal faith tradition, perceived conflicts between science and spirituality, and fear of losing patients from the practice. One of the biggest barriers reported that physicians have in addressing spirituality with a patient involved the physician's personal comfort level with his/her own spiritual well-being. Therefore, it is important for a physician to examine his/her own spiritual health prior to addressing these issues with a patient (Spaeth).

A common clinical dilemma can occur when a patient asks the physician to pray with him/her. Koenig et al. (2001) review numerous studies that describe a significant amount of patients (from 48% to 67%) who would like to have their physicians pray with them. Anandarajah and Mennillo (2007) addressed this challenge by providing helpful recommendations; they first recommended that the physician consider his/her own attitudes and issues with praying with a patient (see Table 7.1). Mental health practitioners are encouraged to consider the same guidelines and questions, in the context of the American Psychological Association's Ethics Code of Conduct, as discussed in the following.

Following self-reflection on this issue, the authors next recommended that the physician understand both the patient's motivation for the actual prayer request, and the necessity of this prayer request. Is the patient asking for this

7.1 Questions to Help Physicians Gain Self-Knowledge About Praying With Patients

How do I feel about prayer in general? How do I feel about prayer in relation to health, specifically?
How prominently does prayer figure into my own life?
How do I feel about public, vocal prayer versus private, silent prayer?
How would I respond to specific clinical situations in which prayer becomes an issue?
Would I remain present for prayer of any type?
Would I join a patient in silent prayer?
Would I wait silently while a patient prayed aloud?
Would I pray aloud with a patient?
Would I participate in group prayer, rites, or rituals?
Would I pray with a patient from a different branch of my religion or from a different religion?
Would I wish to know the general purpose for the prayer (or specifically what would be prayed for) before participating?

Note: Adapted from Anandarajah and Mennillo (2007, Table 1).

activity to achieve more support and connection with the physician, or is it an attempt to change the physician's practice style? The patient may desire to know the physician's own faith beliefs or want to convert the physician to the patient's personal religious belief system. The last suggestion that the authors provided is for the physician to have some idea of what the patient would do if the doctor declined the offer to pray. The authors wisely related this clinical scenario to other challenges that could interfere in the patient-physician relationship. They advise seven steps: the physician should be aware of his/her own personal beliefs and biases, the physician must explore the motivations and needs of the patient, the physician must have the ability to refocus the attention back onto the patient and away from the physician, the physician should seek common ground for an acceptable compromise, the physician must be aware of boundaries in the patient-physician relationship, the physician must maintain a compassionate and patient-centered approach, and the physician should have a prepared response to say "no" to a patient. Rejecting a request for prayer with a patient, if handled skillfully by the physician, may still allow for a clinically productive and compassionate relationship with a patient.

A second clinical scenario in which spirituality is involved with the patient-physician relationship can occur with caring for patients at the end of life. Patients near the end of life may have their spiritual and religious concerns awakened or deepened. It is the physician's duty to provide comfort at the end of a patient's life. The Working Group on Religious and Spiritual Issues at the End of Life (Lo et al., 2002) published an article in 2002 that was designed to be a practical guide for physicians providing end-of-life care. The authors recommended three guidelines for responding to spiritual and religious concerns with patients at the end of life. First, physicians are advised to respect the patient's views and follow the lead in exploring how these issues may affect decisions regarding the patient's medical care, cause problems, or relieve suffering. Second, physicians are advised to appreciate their own role, limits of expertise, and training; physicians should not convert patients, enlist them in theological conversations, or invite them to participate in specific religious rituals. Finally, physicians are urged to maintain their own integrity and not go against their own spiritual or religious beliefs in word or deed, while trying to respectfully care for their patient. The authors also presented four goals for physicians when discussing spiritual or religious matters with patients and their families. Physicians are recommended to clarify the patient's concerns or beliefs and follow hints that the patients are mentioning relative to spiritual or religious issues. Second, physicians should connect with the patient by careful listening, acknowledging the patient's concerns, exploring emotions, making empathetic statements, and using wish statements. Next, physicians need to identify common care goals and reach agreement on clinical decisions. Last, the physician is urged to rally sources of support for the patient. Physicians are also cautioned in the article against a few pitfalls that can occur in discussions about spiritual and religious issues near the end of life. Physicians should not try to solve the patient's problems or attempt to answer certain existential questions that are unanswerable. Physicians must not reach beyond the accepted role as "doctor," nor should the physicians impose any of their religious beliefs on the patient. Finally, physicians are obligated to not provide premature reassurance (Lo et al., 2002). Although these guidelines are geared toward physicians, they are largely appropriate for mental health professionals working in primary care settings, and should be adapted to fit within ethical practices of the profession, which are next to be discussed.

Ethical Issues

Spirituality may often be an independent strength for physicians, patients, and psychologists in collaborative health care. Each person's spirituality may offer unique ways for individuals to cope with illness, and offers strength, hope, or ways of accepting medically related circumstances. Because spirituality is predominantly a belief system, physicians and psychologists are required to know about each person's beliefs to address spiritual needs. Religions, however, offer unified beliefs that inform specific behavioral practices that are fairly standard across believers of each denomination. Thus, health care practitioners need to be aware of religious practices common to different religious traditions. Ethical guidelines also remind practitioners of their responsibility to be competent practitioners in their areas of practice, and to function only within the boundaries of competence. As a psychologist working in primary care, diversity in religion, spiritual beliefs and practices, and other aspects of individual difference may be more varied than in niche practices in specialties of psychology. The American Psychological Association's Code of Ethics states, "Psychologists provide services, teach, and conduct research with populations and in areas only within the boundaries of their competence, based on their education, training, supervised experience, consultation, study, or professional experience" (APA, 2002a, p. 4). Competence here is relevant globally to the concept of knowing how to address spiritual and religious aspects of one's worldview as it pertains to medical intervention, health, and psychosocial well-being. One's competence to work with medical populations, in general, is addressed elsewhere in this book. The Code of Ethics further states,

> *Where scientific or professional knowledge in the discipline of psychology establishes that an understanding of factors associated with age, gender, gender identity, race, ethnicity, culture, national origin, religion, sexual orientation, disability, language, or socioeconomic status is essential for effective implementation of their services or research, psychologists have or obtain the training, experience, consultation, or supervision necessary to ensure the competence of their services, or they make appropriate referrals.* (APA, 2002a, p. 5)

The application of this standard is clear as it pertains to spirituality and religion. Specifically, psychologists need specialized training in clinical health psychology to function within health care teams effectively, and to be able to consider the interactive effect of the health care system on individuals of different religious, spiritual, and cultural backgrounds, among other factors, and the impact of religion and spirituality on the medical system and those within it. For instance, in the United States, privacy and confidentiality are regulated strictly with regard to medical information and communication of personal information by health care practitioners. However, some cultures and religions sanction group prayer and community involvement in healing. Patients' practices need to be respected, yet handled within the legal requirements of the practitioners, as well. This circumstance requires critical knowledge of ethics, health policy, religious/spiritual and multicultural competence to be handled appropriately.

The American Psychological Association's "Guidelines on Multicultural Education, Training, Research, Practice, and Organizational Change for Psychologists" (2002b) explains in Guideline #2, "Psychologists are encouraged to recognize the importance of multicultural sensitivity/responsiveness, knowledge, and understanding about ethnically and racially different individuals" (p. 25). Because individuals' religious traditions are often steeped in rich cultural histories, the complexity of understanding the patient as he/she presents in the doctor's office is guided by this standard as well. Of course, psychologists and physicians are not expected to be experts in all religions and cultures, but they are expected to be sensitive and responsive to these aspects of one's biopsychosocial well-being.

Religious beliefs and practices may affect ethical decision making when the patient's religious beliefs, practices, and therefore requests for medical care (or resistance to care) are in conflict with the psychologist's or physician's personal religious beliefs. Thus, practitioners are encouraged to be aware of their own personal religious beliefs and how their beliefs may affect their ability to care for patients who are different from themselves in this regard. Consider the following case as an example of how an ethical dilemma may present itself based on religious ideals.

Case Example

Rachel is a 23-year-old Caucasian female who has been a patient in Dr. John's practice for the past 5 years. She is typically quiet and has not shared much personal information regarding social relationships in the past. At her annual check-up with her OB/GYN, she announced to Dr. John that she is in a committed relationship with a 29-year-old female, Maria. They have decided to form a family, and she would like Dr. John's guidance on in vitro fertilization and sperm donation so that she can be the carrier of their future child.

The social problem-solving approach to clinical decision making (Nezu, Nezu, Friedman, & Haynes, 1997; Nezu, Nezu, & Lombardo, 2004) suggests that clinicians' worldview or personal beliefs, biases, or frames of reference will affect their clinical problem solving either positively, negatively, or with a neutral outcome. The patient's worldview will do the same. When the physician and the patient do not share similar views on matters of health care, difficult decisions may be encountered. In the case of Rachel, if Dr. John is religiously opposed to her social construction of a family, or to in vitro fertilization, he will need to decide whether he can still act in the best interest of his patient and make objective critical decisions and recommendations for her in a rational and systematic way. Is he able to moderate the impact of his beliefs on his feelings toward Rachel and Maria by his belief in the Hippocratic Oath and the ethical principle of beneficence? If this is so, perhaps he may be able to offer Rachel unbiased information and treatment options. If his religious beliefs do not allow him to act outside of this system, ethically he will need to ensure his patient is transferred to appropriate care that will give her the best options available to meet her needs sensitively and professionally. The important point to consider is that if physicians or psychologists are unaware of how their beliefs affect their emotions, and in turn, their behaviors, then their behaviors may be less supportive and helpful than the patient would prefer, and may even be unethical.

Within the problem-solving model (Nezu et al., 2004), problem solving requires identification of the problem to be solved, generation of alternative solutions, decision making, implementation of the solution selected, and verifying the outcome of the alternative implemented. One's worldview may bias the way a problem is defined. The "problem" is the patient's presenting problem(s) to be "solved" or treated. The clinician's or patient's worldview, or both, may directly influence the goal sought for attainment. For instance, some religious traditions may lead patients to try all forms of life-saving treatment, although other traditions may specify that certain interventions are not consistent with religious teachings (i.e., use of blood products). Spiritual beliefs about the meaning or purpose of life may lead others to come to individualized conclusions about treatment goals and options. Thus, religious, cultural, or spiritual worldviews may also limit or maximize the alternative solutions considered for medical treatment. Treatment alternatives offered by a physician may be affected by religious or spiritual beliefs, such that for example, some physicians may not choose to recommend or provide abortions or morning-after birth control pills. In reverse, patients may suggest complementary or alternative treatments to traditional western medicine that are in line with their own spiritual beliefs that may not be sanctioned by their medical doctor (i.e., use of herbal remedies or spiritual shaman). Decisions about self-care, wellness, and prevention and treatment of disease will also be affected by one's worldview, based on all the factors previously described. Yet, if the health practitioner is not knowledgeable about or does not assess a patient's belief system with regard to medical care, religiosity, or spirituality, recommendations may be made that will be met with noncompliance or a patient not returning for treatment.

Psychologists hold various interesting roles in medical care, as they are not offering or denying medical intervention that may conflict with their own belief systems, but they may be bridging the gap between physicians and patients in their attempt to help patients cope with the medical information and decisions to be made, or to help physicians increase patients' compliance with recommended treatments. Therefore, psychologists' religious and spiritual worldviews must also be self-reflected to ensure objectivity and clarity in executing their skills. In the case of fertility treatment, for example, psychologists may be required to psychologically assess the female who is the recipient of egg or sperm donation, and possibly her partner for emotional stability and readiness to engage in fertility treatment. The psychologist may conduct a psychological screening of the egg donor, and may offer psychoeducation to medical staff and fertility patients, and therapy for newly created families surrounding issues of parenting, disclosure, and integration with society regarding issues of nontraditional family constellations. The ethical responsibilities and areas of competence surrounding medical technology, religious, cultural, and societal beliefs are numerous (Childress-Beatty, 2009). Psychologists constantly need to evaluate their own boundaries of competence and areas of expertise. Mere exposure to medical phenomena does not qualify most psychologists to give medical advice. For example, discussion of fertility treatments provides a richness for consideration of religious and spiritual considerations particularly, as donors and egg or sperm recipients and the treating physicians must consider and explore their own feelings about selective reduction of embryos in multiple gestation pregnancies, and the disposition of surplus frozen embryos (Childress-Beatty, 2009). Therefore, personal beliefs must be reconciled with the professional expectations articulated in the APA Ethics Code (2002a), the "Guidelines for Psychotherapy with Lesbian, Gay, and Bisexual Clients" (2000), and the "Guidelines on Multicultural Education, Training, Research, Practice, and Organizational Change for Psychologists" (APA, 2002b).

Fertility treatment is but one example of numerous topics in medical care that have germane religious and spiritual considerations. End-of-life care, assisted suicide, contraception, organ donation, organ or bone marrow transplantation, palliative care, and even taking routine medication could be affected by religious and spiritual beliefs and practices. As such, the best approach for the health care team is to ensure a biopsychosocial-spiritual assessment is done for each patient upon entering a practice or approaching a medical or developmental milestone when decisions may need to be considered. Likewise, physicians, psychologists, and other health care practitioners are encouraged to regularly self-reflect on their own biopsychosocial-spiritual worldview as it pertains to self-care, and prevention of, and intervention for, maladies common to the medical practice within which they work and to specific patients.

Recommendations for Effective Practice

Addressing Spirituality: Clinical Application

Koenig et al. (2001, p. 440) have created a valuable list that describes tasks that health care professionals can do to address the spiritual and religious needs of patients. They are as follows:

1. *Take a religious/spiritual history.* This information can be sought as part of a routine evaluation and kept in the patient's file. Knowing whether a patient uses spirituality or religion to help cope with illness can help the health care professional provide appropriate care, and shows the patient that he/she is open to this as part of treatment. If the provider does not feel he/she is able to address this part of the patient's care, then a referral to a chaplain or religious/spiritual leader can be made.
2. *Support or encourage the patient's beliefs.* Health care professionals should support and encourage beliefs and rituals that the patient cites as useful. Instead of feeling obligated to find new outlets for the patient, the provider should incorporate the beliefs and rituals the patient already uses into the treatment or care plan.
3. *Ensure access to religious and spiritual resources.* When a patient is hospitalized, the health care professional can take part in making sure the patient's religious or spiritual leaders have been notified, if the patient desires. The health care professional can also refer to a chaplain, and give the patient access to religious or spiritual readings and recordings, as well as religious and spiritual radio and television programs.
4. *Respect visits by clergy or other religious/spiritual leaders.* As health care providers, these visits should not be interrupted, if possible. In reference to the biopsycho-social-spiritual model, this shows the patient that this part of their treatment is as important as other treatments provided. Health care providers should also make efforts to meet the clergy or religious/spiritual leader in order to collaborate as members of the patient's treatment team and as a discharge resource.
5. *View chaplains as a part of the health care team.* Chaplains should be involved in patient rounds and be viewed as specialists in the spiritual care of patients.
6. *Be ready to address spiritual needs when clergy are unavailable.* When chaplains are unavailable or not desired by the patient, yet the patient is in spiritual need (for example, upset family members, no access to chaplains in outpatient settings), health care providers may be the only people to address these needs.
7. *Use advanced spiritual interventions cautiously.* These include praying with patients, giving specific reading materials, or suggesting new spiritual or religious activities. Each patient should have an individualized treatment plan when it comes to spiritual or religious matters, and the health care provider should focus on the needs of the patient when performing these interventions. For example, if praying with a patient is warranted, the patient should lead the prayer, unless the patient specifically asks the health care provider to lead the prayer. The health care provider should minimize the risk that his or her own beliefs will persuade the patient.

Measurements of Spirituality/Religiosity

There are numerous measures that can be effective in assessing an individual's spirituality and religiosity. Some popular and widely used measurements include, but are not limited to, the FACIT-Sp (Peterman, Fitchett, Brady, Hernandez, & Cella, 2002), The Fetzer Brief Multidimensional Measure of Religiousness/Spirituality (BMMRS; Fetzer Institute, 1999; Idler et al., 2003), the Idler Index of Religiosity (Idler, 1987), the Religious Coping Activity Scale (Miller, McConnell, & Klinger, 2007; Pargament et al., 1990), the RCOPE (Pargament, Koenig, & Perez, 2000), Spiritual Well-Being Scale (Bello-Haas et al., 2000; Buford, Paloutzian, & Ellison, 1991), Spiritual Involvement and Beliefs Scale-Revised (Hatch, Burg, Naberhaus, & Hellmich, 1998; Litwinczuk & Groh, 2007; Rowe & Allen, 2004), Purpose in Life Scale (Crumbaugh, 1968; Litwinczuk & Groh, 2007), and the General Well-Being Schedule (Dupuy, 1984). Using different measures may elicit different responses from patients because of the nature of a specific measure such as layout or wording of items, as well as the differences in what they are measuring. For example, the Purpose in Life Scale assesses meaning and purpose in life, whereas the Religious Coping Activities Scale assesses how much a person turns to religion to cope with stressful events (Litwinczuk & Groh, 2007; Pargament et al., 1990). Using different measures can assess different aspects of spirituality and religiosity, and offer a better picture of how a patient is using these mechanisms to cope with an illness. Most instruments are relatively short and easy to complete.

Assessing Spirituality

Specific assessments have been purposed to identify the spiritual needs of patients. Puchalski and Romer (2000) proposed assessing spirituality in patients using FICA—Faith and beliefs, Importance and influence, Community, and Address/Action in care—to get a better sense of what the spiritual needs of the patient are. These elements guide the clinician on how to start a spiritual history and what themes to listen for as the patient tells his or her story. In the first step, "faith and beliefs," questions such as "do you consider yourself spiritual or religious?" or "do spiritual beliefs help you cope with stress?" can help the health care professional find out what is important to the patient. If the patient does not endorse any spirituality, this can open the door to a discussion of how the patient does find meaning in his or her life or what she or he considers important. In the "Importance" step, the health care professional can gain a sense of the importance of faith in the patient's life, and whether this faith guides him or her in the treatment of his or her illness. This can be a time to ask the patient about advance directives and other plans for future care. In "Community," the health care professional can find out whether there are any spiritual or religious communities to which the patient belongs, and how these communities can be a source of support for the patient. In the "Address/Action in care" step, health care professionals can use the information from the patient to find spiritual interventions that will be helpful for the patient. Some examples of interventions are: referring to spiritual leaders (chaplains, clergy, rabbi, spiritual directors, shaman, etc.); spiritual practices such as yoga, prayer, and meditation; practicing rituals or sacraments; worship and spiritual/religious services; sacred readings; journaling; reading groups; nature walks; time for solitude; music and guided imagery; or art.

In a similar assessment, Anandarajah and Hight (2001) proposed the acronym HOPE. The "H" stands for sources of Hope, and spiritual resources the patient may have. Referring to the resources as "sources of hope" broadens the scope of how the patient may answer, and the health care professional can gain information about nonreligious patients' view of hope. This can include internal or external support systems. The "O" refers to "organized religion," in order to find out whether the patient does follow a certain religion, and how important or helpful he or she finds religion to be in times of need. The "P" refers to "personal spirituality and practices" that may be different from organized religion, including meditation, prayer, and belief in God. Separating these two concepts can give the health care provider more information about how the patient views his or her spiritual life. If a person does not identify any religious or spiritual practices, the health care provider can end the assessment or choose to ask further questions, such as whether religion or spirituality was important to the patient in the past. Last, the "E" stands for "effects of spirituality and beliefs on medical care and end-of-life issues." These questions can include specific plans of action for care, including restrictions on medical care or any spiritual guidance the patient would want from spiritual leaders.

When a person is suffering or at the end of life, seeking comfort and reducing pain is the main concern. Individuals obtain medical treatments for their specific symptoms and hope that these treatments will alleviate their suffering. But seeking comfort goes beyond medical intervention. Comfort is often found in social and family interactions, and in the personal relationship one has with spirituality or religion. Those with health-related problems turn to their religion more often than those individuals with other kinds of issues (Benjamins, Musick, Gold, & George, 2003). Spirituality has become more of a focus in the assessment of patients facing chronic or terminal illness, especially as one prepares for their death (Ayalon, 2003; Breitbart, Gibson, Poppito, & Berg, 2004; Reiner, 2007).

Cultural Competency

Although there are specific ways to define spirituality, different cultures view spirituality in different ways. Health care professionals have the responsibility of educating themselves about the ways their clients from different cultures view their spirituality, and how they can be helped to use their belief system as a tool for healing. The General Principles of the APA Ethical Principles of Psychologists and Code of Conduct (2002a) include "do no harm" (Principle A), and "respecting the dignity and worth of all people, and eliminate biases" (Principle E). These principles signify the foundation of what it means to be culturally competent. When addressing the spiritual needs of patients, health care professionals should take into account their own assumptions about human behavior (Sue & Sue, 2003), which include assumptions about spirituality and religious practices. This may also include asking difficult questions of themselves and their clients. It is necessary to understand patients' spiritual and religious views when tailoring appropriate interventions and discussing their beliefs about illness (Sue & Sue). Seeking out diverse personal experiences and training opportunities, and seeking supervision with clinicians who have had diverse cultural experiences can broaden cultural competence (Sue & Sue). In cases in which the patient is culturally different, as with all patients, the patient is the greatest teacher about his or her own belief system, but a foundation of open-mindedness, sensitivity to cultural differences, and a commitment to respecting others' values is critical for building positive, respectful relationships.

References

Ambs, A. H., Miller, M. F., Smith, A. W., Goldstein, M. S., Hsiao, A.-F., & Ballard-Barbash, R. (2007). Religious and spiritual practices and identification among individuals living with cancer and other chronic disease. *Journal of the Society for Integrative Oncology, 5*(2), 53–60.

American Psychological Association. (2000). *Guidelines for psychotherapy with lesbian, gay, and bisexual clients.* Washington, DC: Author.

American Psychological Association. (2002a). *Ethical prinicples of psychologists and code of conduct.* Washington, DC: Author.

American Psychological Association. (2002b). *Guidelines on multicultural education, training, research, practice, and organizational change for psychologists.* Washington, DC: Author.

Anandarajah, G., & Hight, E. (2001). Spirituality and medical practice: Using the HOPE questions as a practical tool for spiritual assessment. *American Family Physician, 63*(1), 81–89.

Anandarajah, G., & Mennillo, R. (2007). Responding to a patient's request to pray. *American Family Physician, 76*(1), 133–134.

Ayalon, L. (2003). Providing care in the end of life: Ethical and therapeutic considerations. *Clinical Case Studies, 2*(2), 107–126.

Bekelman, D. B., Dy, S. M., Becker, D. M., Wittstein, I. S., Hendricks, D. E., Yamashita, T. E., et al. (2007). Spiritual well-being and depression in patients with heart failure. *Journal of General Internal Medicine, 22*, 470–477.

Bello-Haas, V., Andrews-Hinders, D., Bocian, J., Mascha, E., Wheeler, T., & Mitsumoto, H. (2000). Spiritual well-being of the individual with amyotrophic lateral sclerosis. *Amyotrophic Lateral Sclerosis & Other Motor Neuron Disorders, 1*(5), 337–341.

Benjamins, M. R., Musick, M. A., Gold, D. T., & George, L. K. (2003). Age-related declines in activity level: The relationship between chronic illness and religious activities. *Journals of Gerontology, Series B: Psychological Sciences and Social Sciences, 58*, S377–S385.

Bjerklie, D. (2009, February 12). Keeping (or finding) the faith. *Time, 173*(7), 84.

Brady, M. J., Peterman, A. H., Fitchett, G., Mo, M., & Cella, D. (1999). A case for including spirituality in quality of life measurement in oncology. *Psycho-Oncology, 8*, 417–428.

Brawer, P. A., Handal, P. J., Fabricatore, A. N., Roberts, R., & Wajda-Johnston, V. A. (2002). Training and education in religion/spirituality within APA-accredited clinical psychology programs. *Professional Psychology: Research and Practice, 33*(2), 203–206.

Breitbart, W., Gibson, C., Poppito, S. R., & Berg, A. (2004). Psychotherapeutic interventions as the end of life: A Focus on meaning and spirituality. *Canadian Journal of Psychiatry, 49*(6), 366–372.

Bremer, B. A., Simone, A.-L., Walsh, S., Simmons, Z., & Felgoise, S. H. (2004). Factors supporting quality of life over time for individuals with amyotrophic lateral sclerosis: The role of positive self-perception and religiosity. *Annals of Behavioral Medicine, 28*(2), 119–125.

Buford, R. K., Paloutzian, R. F., & Ellison, C. W. (1991). Norms for the spiritual well-being scale. *Journal of Psychology and Theology, 19*, 56–70.

Calman, K. (2008). Spirituality and medical education. *Medical Education, 42*, 123–124.

Childress-Beatty, L. (2009, February). Ethical practice in a reproductive medicine setting. *Monitor on Psychology, 40*(2), Retrieved August 10, 2009, from http://www.apa.org/monitor/200902/ethics.html

Crumbaugh, J. C. (1968). Cross-validation of purpose in life test based on Frankl's concepts. *Journal of Individual Psychology, 24*, 74–81.

Daaleman, T. P., & Frey, B. (1998). Prevalence and patterns of physician referral to clergy and pastoral care providers. *Archives of Family Medicine, 7*, 548–553.

Davidson, R. (2008). Spirituality and medicine. *Science and Practice Annals of Family Medicine, 6*(5), 388–389.

Dein, S., & Stygall, J. (1997). Does being religious help or hinder coping with chronic illness? A critical literature review. *Palliative Medicine, 11*, 291–298.

Doka, K. J. (1993). *Living with a life-threatening illness.* New York: Lexington.
Dupuy, H. J. (1984). The psychological general well-being index. In N. K. Wenger, M. E. Mattson, C. D. Furberg, & J. Elinson (Eds.), *Assessment of quality of life in clinical trials of cardiovascular therapies* (pp. 170–183). New York: LeJacq.
Engel, G. L. (1977). The need for a new medical model: A challenge for biomedicine. *Science, 196*(4286), 129N136.
Fennel, P. (2003). *Managing chronic illness: Using the four-phase treatment approach.* Hoboken, NJ: John Wiley.
Fetzer Institute. (1999). *Multidimensional measurement of religiousness/spirituality for use in health research: A report of the Fetzer Institute/National Institute on Aging working group.* Kalamazoo, MI: Author.
Fortin, A. H., & Barnett, K. G. (2004). Medical school curricula in spirituality and medicine. *Journal of the American Medical Association, 291*(23), 2883.
Fosarelli, P. (2008). Medicine, spirituality, and patient care. *Journal of the American Medical Association, 300*(7), 836–838.
Gallup, Inc. (2008, July 28). *Belief in God far lower in western U.S.* Retrieved March 27, 2009, from http://www.gallup.com/poll/109108/Belief-God-Far-Lower-Western-US.aspx
Greenstreet, W. (2006). From spirituality to coping strategy: Making sense of chronic illness. *British Journal of Nursing, 15*(17), 938–942.
Hage, S. M. (2006). A closer look at the role of spirituality in psychology training programs. *Professional Psychology: Research and Practice, 37*(3), 303–310.
Hall, B. A. (1997). Spirituality in terminal illness: An alternative view to theory. *Journal of Holistic Nursing, 15*(1), 82–96.
Hatch, H. L., Burg, M. A., Naberhaus, D. S., & Hellmich, L. K. (1998). The spiritual involvement and beliefs scale: Development and testing of a new instrument. *Journal of Family Practice, 46*(6), 476–484.
Hatgidakis, J., Timko, E. R., & Plotnikoff, G. A. (1997). Spirituality and practice: Stories, barriers, and opportunities. *Creative Nursing, 3,* 7–11.
Hiatt, J. (1986). Spirituality, medicine, and healing. *Southern Medical Journal, 79*(6), 736–743.
Hodge, D. R. (2006). A template for spiritual assessment: A review of the JCAHO requirements and guidelines for implementation. *Social Work, 51*(4), 317.
Idler, E. L. (1987). Religious involvement and the health of the elderly: Some hypotheses and an initial test. *Social Forces, 66*(1), 226–238.
Idler, E. L., Musick, M. A., Ellison, C. G., George, L. K., Krause, N., Ory, M. G., et al. (2003). Measuring multiple dimensions of religion and spirituality for health research: Conceptual background and findings from the 1998 General Social Survey. *Research on Aging, 25*(4), 327–365.
Kabat-Zinn, J. (1994). *Wherever you go, there you are: Mindfulness meditation in everyday life.* New York: Hyperion.
Katerndahl, D. (2008). Impact of spiritual symptoms and their interactions on health services and life satisfaction. *Annals of Family Medicine, 6*(5), 412–420.
Kaut, K. P. (2002). Religion, spirituality, and existentialism near the end of life: Implications for assessment and application. *American Behavioral Scientist, 46*(2), 220–234.
Kennedy, G. J. (1998). Religion and depression. In H. G. Koenig (Ed.), *Handbook of religion and mental health* (pp. 129–145). San Diego, CA: Academic Press.
Kluger, J. (2009, February 12). The biology of belief. *Time, 173*(7), 94.
Koenig, H. G., Beron, L. B., Hover, M., & Travis, J. L. (1991). Religious perspectives of doctors, nurses and patients and families. *Journal of Pastoral Care, 45*(3), 6–8.
Koenig, H. G., George, L. K., Titus P., & Meador, K. G. (2004). Religion, spirituality, and acute care hospitalization and long-term care use and older patients. *Archives of Internal Medicine, 164,* 1579–1585.
Koenig, H. G., McCullough, M. E., & Larson, D. B. (2001). *Handbook of religion and health.* New York: Oxford University Press.
Levin, J. S., & Vanderpool, H. Y. (1989). Is religion therapeutically significant for hypertension? *Social Science Medicine, 29*(1), 69–78.
Litwinczuk, K. M., & Groh, C. J. (2007). The relationship between spirituality, purpose in life, and well-being in HIV-positive persons. *Journal of the Association of Nurses in AIDS Care, 18*(3), 13–22.
Lo, B., Ruston, D., Kates, L. W., Arnold, R. M., Cohen, C. B., Faber-Langendoen, K., et al. (2002). Discussing religious and spiritual issues at the end of life: A practical guide for physicians. *Journal of the American Medical Association, 287*(6), 785.

Marrone, R. (1999). Dying, mourning, and spirituality: A psychological perspective. *Death Studies, 23*, 495–519.
McGrath, P. (2003). Religiosity and the challenge of terminal illness. *Death Studies, 27*, 881–899.
McKee, D. D., & Chappel, J. N. (1992). Spirituality and medical practice. *Journal of Family Practice, 35*, 201–208.
Messikomer, C. M., & De Craemer, W. E. (2002). The spirituality of academic physicians: An ethnography of a scripture-based group in an academic medical center. *Academic Medicine, 77*(6), 562–573.
Miller, J. F., McConnell, T. R., & Klinger, T. A. (2007). Religiosity and spirituality: Influence on quality of life and perceived patient self-efficacy among cardiac patients and their spouses. *Journal of Religion and Health, 46*(2), 299–313.
Modjarred, K. (2004). Medicine and spirituality. *Journal of the American Medical Association, 291*(23), 2880.
Mueller, P. S., Plevak, D. J., & Rummans, T. A. (2001). Religious involvement, spirituality, and medicine: Implications for clinical practice. *Mayo Clinic Proceedings, 76*(12), 1225–1235.
Nezu, A. M., Nezu, C. M., Friedman, S. H. & Haynes, S. N. (1997). Case formulation in behavior therapy: Problem-solving and functional analytic strategies. In T. D. Eells (Ed.), *Handbook of psychotherapy case formulation* (pp. 368-401). New York: Guilford.
Nezu, A. M., Nezu, C. M., & Lombardo, E. R. (2004). *Cognitive-behavioral case formulation and treatment design: A problem-solving approach.* New York: Springer Publishing Company.
Pargament, K. I. (1997). *The psychology of religion and coping.* New York: Guilford.
Pargament, K. I., Ensing, D. S., Falgout, K., Olsen, H., Reilly, B., & Haitsma, H. V. (1990). God help me: Religious coping efforts as predictors of the outcomes to significant life events. *American Journal of Community Psychology, 8*, 793–825.
Pargament, K. I., Koenig, H. G., & Perez, L. M. (2000). The many methods of religious coping: Development and initial validation of the RCOPE. *Journal of Clinical Psychology, 56*, 519–543.
Patton, J. F. (2006). Jungian spirituality: A developmental context for late-life growth. *American Journal of Hospice and Palliative Medicine, 23*(4), 304–308.
Peterman, A. H., Fitchett, G., Brady, M. J., Hernandez, L., & Cella, D. (2002). Measuring spiritual well-being in people with cancer: The functional assessment of chronic illness therapy-spiritual well-being scale (FACIT-Sp). *Annals of Behavioral Medicine, 24*(1), 49–58.
Pew Forum on Religion & Public Life. (2008). *U.S. Religious Landscape Survey.* Retrieved March 27, 2009, from http://religions.pewforum.org/reports
Propst, L. R. (1996). Cognitive-behavioral therapy and the religious person. In E. P. Shafranske (Ed.), *Religion in the clinical practice of psychology* (pp. 391–408). Washington, DC: American Psychological Association.
Puchalski, C. M. (2002). Spirituality and end-of-life care: A time for listening and caring. *Journal of Palliative Medicine, 5*(2), 289–294.
Puchalski, C. M. (2006). *A time for listening and caring: Spirituality and the care of the chronically ill and dying.* New York: Oxford University Press.
Puchalski, C. M., & Romer, A. L. (2000). Taking a spiritual history allows clinicians to understand patients more fully. *Journal of Palliative Medicine, 3*, 129–137.
Reiner, S. M. (2007). Religious and spiritual beliefs: An avenue to explore end-of-life issues. *Adultspan: Theory, Research and Practice, 6*(2), 111–118.
Roche, J. (1989). Spirituality and the ALS patient. *Rehabilitation Nursing, 14*(3), 139–141.
Rowe, M. M., & Allen, R. G. (2004). Spirituality as a means of coping with chronic illness. *American Journal of Health Studies, 19*(1), 62–67.
Russell, S. R., & Yarhouse, M. A. (2006). Training in religion/spirituality within APA-accredited psychology predoctoral internships. *Professional Psychology: Research and Practice, 37*(4), 430–436.
Siegel, K., Anderman, S. J., & Schrimshaw, E. W. (2001). Religion and coping with health-related stress. *Psychology and Health, 16*, 631–653.
Spaeth, D. G. (2000). Spirituality in history taking. *Journal of the American Osteopathic Association, 100*(10), 641–644.
Sue, D. W., & Sue, D. (2003). *Counseling the culturally diverse: Theory and practice.* New York: Wiley.
Sulmasy, D. P. (2006). Spiritual issues in the care of dying patients. *Journal of the American Medical Association, 296*(11), 1385–1392.
Szaflarski, M., Ritchey, P. N., Leonard, A. C., Mrus, J. M., Peterman, A. H., Ellison, C. G., et al. (2006). Modeling the effects of spirituality/religion on patients' perceptions of living with HIV/AIDS. *Journal of General Internal Medicine, 21*, S28–S38.
Waldfogel, S. (1997). Spirituality in medicine. *Primary Care Clinics in Office Practice, 24*, 963–976.

Waldfogel, S., & Wolpe, P. (1993). Using awareness of religious factors to enhance interventions in consultation-liaison psychiatry. *Hospital and Community Psychiatry, 44*, 473–475.
Wink, P. (1999). Addressing end-of-life issues: Spirituality and inner life. *Generations, 23*(1), 75–80.

Part II

Cognitive-Behavioral Techniques: Empirical Bases and Findings

Psychoeducation and Cultural Competence in the Primary Care Setting

8

Takako Suzuki
Beverly White
Ivette Velez

Introduction

Psychoeducation intervention originated in a family counseling session by Alfred Adler in the 1920s (Carlson, Watts, & Maniacci, 2006). The aim was to educate and inform a public audience in the skills needed for healthy family living. To this end, it is used to help people with mental illnesses and those interested in learning about mental illnesses access information in a clear and concise manner. It also provides a way of learning strategies to deal with mental illness and its effects.

Psychoeducation has been used by many health care providers as an effective way to increase patient understanding of illnesses, diagnoses, and treatments, and to enhance patient motivation and behavioral compliance to treatment and self-care. This is especially helpful when providing care for individuals from diverse cultural backgrounds. Illnesses and disorders are experienced personally and subjectively. An individual's cognitive core beliefs and schemas largely inform his or her perceptions regarding the causes of illness and ability to treat or manage its consequences. These core beliefs and schemas are, in turn, significantly influenced by cultural norms, traditions, language, and direct experience (Angel & Williams, 2000).

Theoretical Issues

In the primary care setting, psychoeducation is described as the presentation of systematic, structured, didactic information on the illness and its treatment. It integrates the information of the biological, psychological, and social nature of illness, and as such, it reflects a view of the mind-body conceptualization of disorders (Belar, 2003). This framework provides a holistic approach, and enables the physical health and mental health care providers to conceive and collaboratively present diagnoses and treatment to patients using an integrated biopsychosocial method (Gatchel & Oordt, 2003).

Psychoeducation enables patients and key caregivers to accept the illness by increasing their knowledge of the symptoms, risks, clinical course, and treatment options of the specific disorder to cope with the illness (Elliot & Rivera, 2003; Fawzy, Fawzy, & Canada, 2001; Rummel-Kluge, Pitschel-Walz, Bauml, & Kissling, 2006). "Providing psychoeducation as a part of individual evidence-based treatment can help significant others understand what their loved one is going through, and help clients engage in and adhere to treatments that work but aren't a piece of cake" (DeAngelis, 2008, p. 44). Psychoeducation interventions effectively help patients change behaviors related to biopsychosocially based issues such as smoking, diet, physical activity, chronic illness management, pain management, screening, sexual behavior, and additional issues (Emmons & Rollnick, 2001; Taplin et al., 2000; Resnicow, Jackson, Wang, Dudley, & Baranowski, 2001). Health behaviors, such as obtaining screening and diagnostic tests, treatment adherence, such as medication compliance, and lifestyle changes, such as adopting a healthy diet and increasing exercise, become the target behaviors.

Psychoeducation Intervention in General Psychology

The most-reported effectiveness of psychoeducational interventions with psychological disorders is its use with schizophrenia (American Psychiatric Association [APA], 2004; Dixon et al., 2001). The American Psychiatric Association stated that when psychoeducation interventions are used as a part of a standard therapy program in acute and postacute phases of patients with schizophrenia (APA, 2004), it assists in providing a higher level of compliance, lower rate of relapse, and improved psychopathological status of patients (Pekkala & Merinder, 2002). Fundamentally, this is achieved by providing the patients and their significant caregivers with the needed comprehensible information to understand the mental illness, and the ways patients and their caregivers can be active participants in improving their quality of life (Rummel-Kluge et al., 2006).

Generally, psychoeducational programs for people with schizophrenia consist of didactic presentations of the history of schizophrenia, its hypothesized causes, its various symptomatic presentations, the diagnostic criteria, relevant medications, and an interactive discussion of problem-solving techniques (Elliot, Shewchuk, & Richards, 2001; North et al., 1998). The various successful usages of the psychoeducational approach with patients with schizophrenia and their families included the multifamily group psychoeducation program (Bauml, Frobose, Kraemer, Rentrop, & Pitschel-Walz, 2006; Glynn, Cohen, Dixon, & Niv, 2006; Goldstein & Miklowitz, 1995; North et al., 1998;) and Internet Web-based psychoeducation programs (Rotondi et al., 2005).

The effectiveness of group psychoeducational intervention is reported for women with bulimia nervosa (Davis, Marion, & Rockert, 1990), for family-focused treatment of adults with bipolar disorder (Rea et al., 2003; Simoneau & Miklowitz, 2001), and with childhood mood disorders (Ong & Caron, 2008). For childhood mood disorders, providing parents and key adult caregivers with psychoeducation has been noted as the key factor in the children's recovery process, due to the children's dependency on parents physically and psychologically, including access to treatment and treatment compliance. Parent and child beliefs about the child's mood disorder and need for treatment may affect willingness of the patient and family to adhere to treatment recommendations.

Psychoeducation Intervention in the Primary Care Setting

A model for providing psychological care in the primary care setting includes the use of behavior health consultants (BHCs). The BHCs are the mental health professionals who serve as second-tier providers on behalf of primary care physicians. Psychoeducation is a significant component of cognitive-behavioral therapy (CBT). Wright, Basco, and Thase (2006) suggest that the three principal reasons to provide psychoeducation in CBT are to: (a) teach and build competency in areas such as communication, social problem solving, cognitive reconstruction, and coping skills; (b) reinforce knowledge with relevant information that will help to reduce the risk of relapse; and (c) train patients to monitor and manage their disorders after being discharged from therapy.

The BHCs often use CBT techniques to impart patients and caregivers with specialized knowledge, to increase motivation, and to help develop the skills necessary to improve and manage their illnesses (Rowan & Runyan, 2005). The self-help quality of the psychoeducation provides an overall plan for identifying problem areas, changes dysfunctional ways of thinking, provides rationales for particular interventions, and motivates behavioral changes (Wright et al., 2006). For example, a patient went to his primary care provider (PCP) with complaints of elevated blood pressure, indigestion, shortness of breath, and heart palpitation. In addition to a thorough medical evaluation, the PCP referred him to a BHC to learn stress-management techniques. The BHC clinician provided psychoeducation about the mechanisms of anxiety and how thoughts cause stress that affects the body. The BHC provided cognitive-behavioral techniques for stress management, such as identifying triggers to the patient's physical discomfort, taking deep breaths, and staying in the present moment in order to deal with any distorted thinking. The patient was amazed to know that there were things he could do to make himself feel better, and he felt empowered.

Assessment Methods

Interviewing Skills and Cultural Issues for Medical Students

Illness and health-seeking behaviors are extensively informed by how the patient perceives and understands his or her illness, and thus, how he or she perceives the benefit of using the health care system. Health-maintenance behaviors include preventive care, such as following guidance on food intake, exercise, hygiene, etc. (Tseng & Streltzer, 2008). These behaviors are subject to factors such as education, past experiences, and culture. Clearly, health care providers should be aware of and understand the function of culture, how the meaning of illness is interpreted, and how help is sought within various cultural groups. "Without an appreciation of the role of culture in human perception (including scientific observation), we run the risk of misinterpreting and misdiagnosing illness because of our own ethnocentric biases" (Angel & Williams, 2000, p. 30).

Freeman (2003) pointed out that in the 1970s, medical education began to include cultural issues as a part of the patient-centered approach to building interviewing skills. The BELIEF instrument was developed to teach preclinical medical students how to elicit patient health beliefs. The instrument is formatted using the word BELIEF as an acronym, as follows (p. 317):

B: Health beliefs (What caused your illness/problem?)

E: Explanation (Why did it happen at this time?)

L: Learn (Help me understand your belief/opinion.)

I: Impact (How is this illness/problem impacting your life?)

E: Empathy (This must be difficult for you.)

F: Feelings (How are you feeling about it?)

This approach provides a good initial method for medical clinicians to obtain valuable information from patients about their particular health beliefs and to initiate a collaborative relationship. Many patients who are of ethnic minority groups, the poor, and less educated report that they generally mistrust the health care system (Nelson, 2002). The BELIEF instrument can help uncover patient preferences, treatment refusal, help-seeking behaviors and attitudes, and differences in clinical presentation of symptoms and culturally bound health beliefs.

As the nation becomes more diverse, the need for culturally aware health care providers becomes increasingly important (Yali & Revenson, 2004). According to the U.S. Census Bureau News (2008), the 2007 estimated census was as follows: 66% non-Hispanic White, 15.2% Hispanic, 12.3% African American, 4.4% Asian American, 0.1% Native Hawaiian/Pacific Islander. The Medical Expenditure Panel Survey 2004 data (Agency for Healthcare Research and Quality, 2007) indicated that family physicians were the most common clinician type accessed by more disadvantaged groups with lower incomes, public insurance, or rural residence than those with higher incomes, private insurance, or urban location in the United States among primary care (Ferrer, 2007).

Clearly, there is a need for a culturally sensitive approach to providing health care. The core factors necessary to move toward cultural competence include an awareness of one's own cultural values, knowledge of the patient's cultural background, and application of this awareness and knowledge to treat culturally diverse individuals effectively (American Psychological Association, 2003; Rundle, Carvalho, & Robinson, 2002; Sue, Arredondo, & McDavis, 1992; Tseng & Streltzer, 2008). A respected and collaborative relationship between the patient and health care provider is important in order to develop the strategies and compliance needed for the management of the patient's illness. This can be established most effectively when the health care provider gains an understanding of a patient's health belief system as it is influenced by cultural values, religion, and his/her interaction with the immediate society (Freeman, 2003).

Rundle and colleagues (2002) emphasize the importance of establishing safe environments where the patients and caregivers are able to communicate effectively. To this end, the provider should observe body language, personal and interpersonal space, and other nonverbal cues, such as seating arrangement. As a way of displaying courtesy and respect, it is important to ask the patient and family their preferences about how to be addressed. Also, through general conversation, the provider can assess the patient's and family's English proficiency, usage of slang and complex sentences, and comfort levels with medical and psychological terminologies (Rundle et al.). During psychoeducational interventions, it is important to assess reading ability before providing written material (Kleinman, 1980). More about language will be discussed later in the chapter.

Increasing Awareness of Provider's Own Cultural Health Worldview

As previously stated, one of the basic factors for cross-cultural awareness and sensitivity needed for health care providers is mindfulness of their own values, beliefs, and biases. Medical and psychological practices in the United States are generally based on Western values (Wrenn, 1985). Consequently, when providing care to individuals from cultural minority groups, it is important to be aware of the differences in our health beliefs as health care professionals, and the way patients may view their illness, its causes, and treatment strategies.

Group-oriented societies value the welfare of the group, cooperation, and interdependency, rather than competition and independence (American Psychological Association, 2003; Sue & Sue, 2008). The role of the family and of the extended family is important. The concept of "privacy" may not apply the same way as providers from a western cultural base may assume. Commonly in the United States, for example, when a male obstetric-gynecological physician performs an examination, a female nurse is present in the room, presumably for the comfort of the female patient. In many Muslim cultures, for the married female patient, the husband may expect to be present, and for the Micronesian unmarried female patient, her mother or sister may be expected to be present in the exam room (Tseng & Streltzen, 2008). Often, having consensus with family members during the decision-making process of many health-related issues is very important. Interpreting patient requests to have family closely involved as a lack of self-esteem and assertiveness, and thus trying to encourage the patient to be more independent, would violate cultural norms and values and may adversely impact the patient-provider relationship (Galanti, 2008; Kanagawa-Singer & Kassim-Lakaha, 2003).

In an individualistic culture, the concept of independence comes with the right of the individual. The concept of confidentiality, therefore, belongs to an individual. In contrast, in a group-oriented culture, group harmony may override an individual's right to confidentiality, in most cases. For example, according to Age of Consent to Mental Health Treatment Act in Pennsylvania, "A juvenile age 14–18 can consent to outpatient mental health examination and treatment for him/herself without parental consent....The same rules regarding consent and abrogation of consent apply as in the outpatient setting" (Pennsylvania Psychiatric Society, 2005, pp. 1–2). For parents and caregivers of many group-oriented cultures where family members must look after one another, however, these stipulations may be viewed as disrespectful and offensive. The Japanese culture, in which it is important for the family to decide whether or not the patient should know about terminal diagnoses such as cancer (Aboud & Rabiau, 2002), provides another example.

Although preventive medicine is an important aspect of health care in the United States, in many other cultures, it is not practiced (Rundle et al., 2002). As an internal locus of control is implied within an individualistic culture for people who believe they can control the environment, an external locus of control is implied within group-oriented cultures, where a basic value is to be in harmony with others in the group (Sue & Sue, 2008). For example, in a group-oriented culture, if you wanted to marry someone you loved, group considerations must be made. Although it is your marriage, you do not have decision-making power, because marriage is a family, and often community, matter. This may present in the patient and health care provider relationship as the provider's dominant value about the nature of man's mastery over nature (Ho, 1987, 1997), that is, his belief in being able to cure the disease, clashes with what patient and family may want to do or not do regarding treatment options. They may have more fatalistic beliefs and refuse the aggressive treatment approaches the physician suggests. When the cause of illness can be attributed to fate based on religious and spiritual beliefs, though the physician may suggest medically sound treatments for the illness, the patient may not see these treatments as being viable options until his/her way of dealing with the illness (e.g., special prayer) is satisfied (Sue & Sue, 2008; Tseng & Streltzer, 2008). This is illustrated by the story of Justine, a 5-year-old Laotian refugee, who needed surgery for a congenital heart defect. Her mother and grandmother worried that the scar left by the operation would damage Justine in her next reincarnation. The physician, through an interpreter, discussed surgery as the most viable treatment option with the family. The family sought advice from religious leaders in the local Buddhist temple, and Justine's mother eventually decided against the surgery (Grainger-Monsen & Haslett, 2003).

Racial and Ethnicity Issues

Researchers have examined the psychological, social, and physiological effects of perceived racism among African Americans (Clark, Anderson, Clark, & Williams,

1999; Lewis et al., 2009; Sanchez-Hucles, 1999; Williams & Williams-Morris, 2000). They have presented evidence that psychosocial stressors, such as racism, are positively related to hypertension risk (Lewis et al., 2006). In fact, exposure to racial stressors under laboratory conditions reliably predicted cardiovascular reactivity. Such responses have been associated with longer term cardiovascular risk, although few empirical studies of the relationship between perceived racism and blood pressure or cardiovascular reactivity exist (Wyatt et al., 2003). Several studies indicated that people who experience racial and socioeconomic status (SES) discrimination also showed higher levels of psychological distress, anxiety, and depression (Kessler, Lloyd, Lewis, Gray, & Cross, 1999; Ren, Amick, & Williams, 1999).

In a correlational study of over 5,000 public school fifth-graders from Los Angeles, Houston, and Birmingham, researchers found that African American children (20%), Hispanic children (15%), and children identified as "other" (15%) reported perceived racial or ethnic discrimination at school, as compared with Caucasian children (7%) (Coker et al., 2009). Seventy-three percent of the respondents were from households with incomes "under 300% of the federal poverty level" (Coker et al., 2009, p. 879). Those children who reported perceived discrimination were more likely to have symptoms of one or more of the following mental health disorders: depression, attention-deficit/hyperactivity disorder, oppositional defiant disorder, and conduct disorder. All four conditions were observed among the Hispanic children, whereas the African American children were more likely to report depression and conduct disorder.

Religious Issues

Medical and psychological research suggests that spirituality and religious beliefs can have significant effects on one's general health, such as helping lower blood pressure levels, and generally improving quality of life and survival rates from illness and life-threatening injuries (Matthews & Larson, 1998). For some patients, faith factors can be key coping mechanisms for dealing with illnesses. It is important for providers to ask questions regarding patients' spiritual and religious beliefs and concerns or barriers to treatment compliance (King, 2000; Rundle et al., 2002). In a study of traditional Israeli Arab women, participants expressed traditional, as well as modern, beliefs about cancer-screening procedures. Barriers to treatment included concern about defying cultural modesty, responses of spouses, and stigma related to screenings (Kulwicki, 2003). Despite these fears and the associated emotional stress, the women pursued screening procedures (Cohen & Azaiza, 2008). In the past, many Jehovah's Witnesses, who generally have positive beliefs regarding medicine and the health care system, believed that accepting blood and blood products for medical purposes directly violated the teachings of the Bible (Knuti, Amrein, Chabner, Lynch, Jr., & Penson, 2002). In Knuti et al.'s (2002) article, the case of a 50-year-old Jehovah's Witness with acute myelocytic leukemia who declined blood products was presented. "Respecting her religious beliefs during chemotherapy required balancing risk and benefit, watching her suffer while unable to intervene with what the staff saw as simple treatment, and eventually undertaking a complicated grief process" (Knuti et al.,

p. 371). In 2000, the Watch Tower Bible and Tract Society slightly altered its policy, allowing their followers to accept blood (Muramoto, 2001).

Language Issues

Primary care physicians have been found to have less effective communications with ethnic minorities, which, in turn, generally results in noncompliance and decreased quality of care (Harmsen, Meeuwesen, vanWieringen, Bernsen, & Bruijnzeels, 2003; Williams, Weinman, & Dale, 1998). Communication styles among North Americans tend to be linear, direct, and to the point, whereas the communication styles of non-Westerners are more narrative and stylized. The non-Western patterns of communication may also be based on the concept of time. In African American, Asian, and Hispanic cultures, time is present oriented or past oriented, and taking time to build relationships is important (Ho, 1987, 1997).

For new immigrants and for many Asian American and Hispanic populations, language can be one of the main barriers to communication between the patient and the provider. Education level may also determine the patient's degree of comprehension. There may be some illiterate individuals who will not admit that they cannot read. For example, Asians, Hispanics, and patients from low socioeconomic levels of society may have difficulty accessing health care information, including facts about prescription drugs, due to language and education barriers (Belar, 2003).

Awareness of communication barriers is particularly essential when ensuring that the patient clearly comprehends issues associated with informed consent. As the American Psychological Association (APA) Code of Ethics standards state in 4.02a:

> *"Psychologists discuss with persons…with whom they establish a…professional relationship (1) the relevant limit of confidentiality and (2) the foreseeable uses of the information obtained through their psychological activities," and 4.02b, "Unless it is not feasible or is contraindicated, the discussion of confidentiality occurs at the outset of the relationship and thereafter as new circumstances may warrant." (APA, 2002, p. 1066)*

Professionally translated explanations and informed consent agreements may be necessary in order to comply with these standards.

Treatment Approaches

Often, the most challenging aspect in providing health care from the perception of the health care provider is obtaining patient compliance with treatment and self-care. Compliance, according to Haynes (1979), is the extent to which a person's behavior coincides with medical advice. Adherence is explained as the active and collaborative involvement of the patient with the clinician in planning and implementing the treatment regimen. Nonadherence is the lack of participation by the patient in a mutually acceptable course of behavior to produce a desired preventative or therapeutic result (Meichenbaum & Turk, 1987). Health care professionals have sought ways to increase patient compliance and appropriate use of services, especially among minority and poverty groups.

Patients in primary care settings are referred to psychologists by physicians who recognize the benefit of working with mental health professionals to facilitate compliance and maintain patient well-being. Acknowledging the multicultural characteristics of many patients seen in primary care settings, psychoeducation interventions are often customized for patients. The following vignettes illustrate how psychoeducation interventions are modified depending on illnesses and the unique cultural characteristics and issues of the patients.

Case Examples

Reggie

A 62-year-old divorced, unemployed, African American male who presented with non-insulin-dependent diabetes mellitus illustrates the successful behavioral changes that can occur from brief psychoeducational interventions. Reggie sought services for diabetes management from an integrated health care system. The program is based on the combination of psychoeducation and behavioral change to help adults with chronic illnesses. The necessary consent and release of information forms were completed, the role of the behavioral health clinician was delineated, and it was made clear that the services provided through this program should only be seen as supplemental to a doctor's care and recommendations.

Reggie spoke openly about growing up in a culture where suffering in silence is highly valued. He attributed this cultural belief to how black slaves attempted to retain their dignity during slavery. He admitted to being a proud man, and stated that this core belief lead to thoughts that he was weak or less masculine when he talked about his illnesses and pains. Reggie admitted that it was a big step for him to seek help in the first place, and that his diabetes often made him think of himself as weak.

Reggie revealed that it had been six years since he had seen a doctor or taken any prescription medications. He stated that although he attempted to comply with medication recommendations in the past, the aversive side effects ultimately led him to discontinue treatment. The shooting pain in his foot, and the fact that he had many friends with type II diabetes who were now amputees as a result of complications caused by diabetes, motivated him to explore the program. Reggie's apprehensions regarding possible complications were validated and used to reinforce the idea that he should seek appropriate medical care. Reggie was advised to see a doctor as soon as possible and communicate his concerns about medication side effects, so that treatment could be tailored to his needs. It came as a surprise to him that he could ask the doctor to tailor treatment to meet his particular needs. Reggie also indicated that he had not received psychoeducation from a health care provider in the past.

When questioned about the methods he employed to manage his diabetes, Reggie reported that he exercised about four times a week regularly.

A major psychoeducational objective is the development of motivation and commitment to treatment through recognition of one's own coping history and the impact of a lack of health-promoting behaviors. During the first session, Reggie was presented with psychoeducational material about diabetes and relevant self-care behaviors. Specifically, key points from a National Institutes of Health (NIH) informational packet entitled *Prevent Diabetes Problems: Keep Your Diabetes Under Control* were reviewed (National Diabetes Education Program, 2005). This helped Reggie to better understand his illness and how he could best manage it. In addition, a motivational technique known as a decision balance (Miller & Rollnick, 2002) was used to assess Reggie's resistance and motivation by eliciting his reasons to change and his reasons for allowing things to remain the same. The session ended with Reggie setting the goal to replenish his supply of blood glucose test strips and record his blood glucose levels for a week.

In the context of the primary care setting, brief adaptations of motivational interviewing are recommended for physicians and nurses, because there is limited patient contact in terms of duration or frequency of patient visits (Resnicow et al., 2002). The goal may simply be to engage the patient so he/she will consider accepting a referral or to think about making future changes. Psychologists in primary care settings use motivational interviewing to increase motivation and teach problem-solving skills to remove barriers for the change behavior.

Reggie demonstrated initiative, problem-solving skills, and an increased level of motivation and investment in his self-care during his second session. He reported that he had called the manufacturer to replace his outdated blood glucose machine after the pharmacist could not supply the needed test strips. A second obstacle presented itself after he obtained the new meter. Reggie decided that although the meter took digital recording of his blood glucose readings, he wanted to manually record his blood glucose levels because he acknowledged that it would increase his self-awareness.

Other psychoeducational materials were also reviewed with Reggie. An NIH informational packet entitled *What I Need to Know About Eating and Diabetes* (National Diabetes Information Clearinghouse, 2007) and a handout from the American Diabetes Association entitled *All About Carbohydrate Counting* (American Diabetes Association, 2004) provided important information for meal planning. In particular, the diabetes food pyramid, recommended serving sizes, and the purpose of carbohydrate counting were discussed. Reggie's goals for the following week were to eat one healthier meal a day, replenish his supply of test strips, keep a diabetes management record, and contact his physician. In order to promote effective communication with his physician, a discussion and role-plays were conducted during the session to help Reggie discern what and how to ask questions about medication times and meal options, medication side effects, and options should he experience intolerable side effects.

An NIH informational packet entitled *What I Need to Know About Physical Activity and Diabetes* (National Institutes of Health, 2008) was reviewed and discussed in the subsequent session. Reggie reported that eating unhealthy meals often made him feel drowsy and he napped soon after eating. Conversely, eating fruits and salads seemed to increase his energy levels, and he could accomplish more during the day. The exploration of this topic was helpful in making the rewards of eating healthier more salient for Reggie. He acknowledged that his increased levels of energy also motivated him to walk and exercise more during the week. He expressed gratitude for the information that was provided, and said that it made him focus more on managing his diabetes, as opposed to ignoring it. He stated that the knowledge had allowed him to both understand and experience the benefits of managing his diabetes.

The next week, Reggie reported having visited the doctor and getting his prescriptions filled. When questioned about the medication, Reggie indicated that he had begun to take the medication just a day prior and had already seen drastic improvements in his blood sugar and blood pressure readings. Although Reggie was happy to see such quick results, he also expressed some concern as to whether these results were within the norm. He resolved to monitor readings for the rest of the week and call the pharmacist or his doctor if his readings continue to drop or if he did not feel well. Reggie's confidence and ability to take the medication was assessed and possible barriers were discussed. Additionally, Reggie stated that he was satisfied with the level of care that he was provided from his doctor, who had clearly answered all of his questions.

A motivational approach was employed throughout the sessions to reinforce and maintain the progress that Reggie made. As seen previously, he moved along the stages of change fairly quickly, going from *contemplation* to the *action* stage in three weeks. Open-ended questions and reflective listening were used to elicit his values and to relate them to the management of his diabetes. This illustrated for him how they affected one another. Reggie was able to acknowledge that diabetes management was central to being able to enjoy the process of aging and continuing to live the active lifestyle to which he was accustomed. Over all, Reggie was able to recognize all of the changes that he had made, and it was difficult for him to see his efforts as work. Furthermore, goals for improving self-care and his management of diabetes were established each week, and relapse prevention was integrated into each session through the evaluation and problem solving of possible barriers to fulfilling his goals. This remarkable change happened in four sessions. Another significant factor in this relationship was the ethnicity and age of the BHC. The BHC was a 26-year-old Latina, master's-level clinical psychology student in a practicum setting. The differences in age and appearance did not seem to interfere with Reggie's motivation to get better.

The following vignette illustrates the intricate biological, psychological, and sociocultural nature of the cases in primary care and the role of psychoeducation in facilitating the treatment process.

Pilar

Pilar, a 56-year-old divorced Latina, lives in one of Philadelphia's low socioeconomic areas. A physician at a health care center referred her to the BHC. The reasons for referral were lack of adherence for the management of hypertension and depression as a consequence of the death of her son. Pilar was not able to provide much motivation to take care of her health because her focus was on dealing with the problems of her 24-year-old, heroin-addicted daughter and 16-year-old niece, both of whom lived with her. She was angry all the time, and would eat unhealthy "comfort" food, and had no energy to exercise. Additionally, Pilar blamed herself for not being able to protect her son, who was killed in a drug-related incident. Her BHC explained the cognitive-behavioral approach to help Pilar better understand how her biopsychosocial-based issues, that is, how her thoughts (believing she should have been able to protect her son) and social condition (low SES and drug-addicted daughter and niece depending on her) contributed to her behaviors (unhealthy food choices) and her depressed mood. Pilar did not do any homework or goal setting, and kept saying, "I just need to talk to someone."

The BHC provided psychoeducation about the grief process as it related to her son. During this discussion, Pilar acknowledged that her guilt was so enormous that she could not forgive herself, and, therefore, punished herself by not taking care of herself. In turn, she allowed her daughter and her niece to take advantage of her. By examining and challenging Pilar's thoughts and reframing some of her dysfunctional cognitions, Pilar began to think, "I did everything I could do to protect my son from harm, his death is not my fault." Soon after making this realization, Pilar became more assertive toward her daughter and niece by refusing to take unreasonable responsibility for their care.

Pilar was, however, still emotionally weighted by her anger, especially toward her daughter and niece. The BHC helped Pilar to build anger-management skills by first providing psychoeducation related to understanding the various aspects of anger and its role. After understanding mechanisms of emotion and how to control it in order to achieve her goals, Pilar was able to communicate firmly, assertively, and effectively with her daughter and niece. After working on problem-solving skills, Pilar's daughter finally gained employment and moved out within three months.

Psychoeducation on the consequences of unmanaged hypertension was also provided. Discussions were conducted regarding how stress, anger, poor diet, and lack of exercise contribute to hypertension. To help her better manage many of these contributors, Pilar found social support by reconnecting with her church, rejoining the organization advocating for the antidrug movement, taking her hypertension medication regularly, exercising, and including more fresh vegetables and fruits in her diet.

Two months after she was discharged from seeing the BHC, Pilar was diagnosed with stage-two breast cancer. She was frightened, but told her BHC that she was going to talk to a few relatives who had cancer, contact the cancer society to get information, and talk to her doctor for treatment recommendations. This was a good sign that Pilar was able to generalize the knowledge and skills she had acquired regarding her hypertension, and use them to help manage other health challenges and focus effectively on self-care.

This next vignette illustrates another complex interaction of physical illness, psychological issues, and sociocultural conditions with the geriatric population.

Mary

Mary, a 70-year-old widowed Asian American female, lives alone; her one son is in the Army. Mary's physician referred her because she was not taking her pain management medication for arthritis and fibromyalgia, and because she appeared anxious and depressed. She was on a limited income, and, despite her pain, she would park her car a half-mile away and walk the uphill road to the health care center to avoid the $5.00 parking fee. Mary explained that the side effects of her pain medication worsened her inoperable glaucoma. Mary stated that she had related this to her physician, and he seemed to understand what she was saying and gave her another prescription. She found out at the pharmacy that the alternate prescription also adversely affected her glaucoma. Mary did not go back to her doctor.

The BHC noticed Mary had a hard time coming to the session on time and she apologized about it furiously. After careful questioning, the patient shared that it was difficult for her to leave home because she wound up doing little things around the house before she left for her appointment. Mary was, in fact, suffering from severe obsessive-compulsive disorder (OCD). Her behaviors included repeatedly rearranging her clothing drawers, checking the stove gas burners and the locks in her home. These activities consumed so much of her time and attention that she would forget about her appointment times. She was also a hoarder. Her living room, bedroom, guest room, and hallways had paths so that she could move around the house. One day, very upset, she stated that her rent would go up soon and she may not be able to move. The BHC asked the referring physician whether Mary was eligible for disability, and she was eligible. However, Mary was unable to complete the form because of her excessive checking symptoms caused by the OCD. The BHC provided psychoeducation on OCD and discussed the information extensively with Mary. From Mary's cultural health belief system, it was difficult for her to accept that she had a mental disorder.

As the BHC was explaining her role at the health center, she noticed Mary had an accent, and occasionally had difficulty understanding what the BHC was telling her. This was most apparent when the BHC was explaining technical issues, such as brain function. Mary was getting slightly nervous. The BHC assessed her language ability, and Mary admitted she could understand everyday tasks, but she had some difficulty when starting to talk about more formal situations, such as medical/psychological coverage. This lack of comprehension could be the reason why there were misunderstandings with the physician.

It was also difficult for Mary to communicate and collaborate effectively with her physician. The BHC provided options, rationales, and employed role-plays to help Mary with problems with her physician, such as clear communication and assertiveness. Being of Asian descent, Mary was not keen on being assertive with the physician because he was an authority figure to her. She also had issues with receiving a disability benefit from government, because she felt shameful to receive social welfare. The therapist understood her concern was culturally based, and used motivational interviewing methods such as reflecting, reframing, and rolling with resistance (Miller &

Rollnick, 2002). Mary realized she was not dealing with Asian doctors and an Asian cultural setting, so she needed to learn to be more assertive and communicative in this situation.

This vignette also alerts us to the fact that when obtaining informed consent, special consideration should be paid in the primary care setting. Many individuals from minority cultures perceive doctors as authority figures, and do not think to ask questions. This perception may generalize to the overall context of the primary care setting. For many patients, being referred to a mental health clinician may be confusing and misinterpreted. The role of the mental health clinician with respect to the treatment of the patient's illness, therefore, will need to be clarified. With regard to informed consent, an explanation of the collaborative team approach between all the health care providers also needs to be provided. Given patient confidentiality rights, this fosters an understanding of the reasons for and implications of signing authorizations for the release of information to be shared among their physicians, physicians' assistants, nurses, and social workers and so on, especially if the primary care is not in an integrated multidisciplinary setting.

Issues may arise regarding patients' language, educational level, and cultural perspectives as they relate to understanding the written consent forms. It is, therefore, important to have written translated forms available (Rundle et al., 2002; Tseng & Streltzer, 2008). For the issues of educational level, some clients may not be able to read and are embarrassed to let you know about it. Practitioners should be sensitive, not assume everyone reads, and consider reading aloud for these clients.

In conclusion, clearly, psychoeducation can be a significant and valuable tool to promote the cognitive and behavioral changes necessary to elicit patient understanding of illness, diagnosis, and treatment in the primary care setting. It also promotes an understanding of the health care environment and clarifies the role the patient and provider play in the treatment and management of illness. Often, this results in empowering and motivating the patient to be an active and compliant participant in the treatment and management of their illness. This is especially important for individuals of minority groups, where perceived barriers to quality health care may be due to their avoidance to engage with health care professionals because distrust, miscommunications, or lack of knowledge contribute to the creation of unnecessary barriers.

References

Aboud, F. E., & Rabiau, M. A. (2002). Health psychology in multiethnic perspective. In P. Pedersen, J. Draguns, W. Lonner, & J. Trimble (Eds.), *Counseling across cultures* (5th ed., pp. 297–316). Thousand Oaks, CA: Sage.

Agency for Healthcare Research and Quality (AHRQ). (2007, March). *Expenses for office-based physician visits by specialty, 2004*. Retrieved February 25, 2009, from http://www.meps.ahrq.gov/mepsweb/data_files/publications/st166/st at166.pdf

American Diabetes Association. (2004). *All about carbohydrate counting: Toolkit no. 10*. Retrieved February 23, 2009, from http://www.diabetes.org

American Psychiatric Association. (2004). *Guidelines for treatment of schizophrenia*. Washington, DC: Author.

American Psychological Association. (2002). Ethical principles of psychologists and code of conduct. *American Psychologist, 57*, 1060–1073.

American Psychological Association. (2003). Guidelines on multicultural education training, research, practice and organizational change. *American Psychologist, 58*(5), 377–402.

Angel, R. J., & Williams, K. (2000). Cultural models of health and illness. In I. Cuellar & F. A. Paniagua (Eds.), *Handbook of multicultural mental health: Assessment and treatment of diverse populations* (pp. 25–44). San Diego, CA: Academic Press.

Bauml, J., Frobose, T., Kraemer, S., Rentrop, M., & Pitschel-Walz, G. (2006). Psychoeducation: A basic psychotherapeutic intervention for patients with schizophrenia and their families. *Schizophrenia Bulletin, 32*, S1–S9.

Belar, C. (2003). Models and concepts. In S. Llewelyn & P. Kennedy (Eds.), *Handbook of clinical health psychology* (pp. 7–19). San Francisco: Wiley.

Carlson, J., Watts, R. E., & Maniacci, M. (2006). Consultation and psychoeducation. In J. Carlson, R. E. Watts, E. Richard, & M. Maniacci (Eds.), *Adlerian therapy: Theory and practice*. Washington, DC: American Psychological Association.

Clark, R., Anderson, N. B., Clark, V. R., & Williams, D. R. (1999). Racism as a stressor for African Americans. A biopsychosocial model. *American Psychologist, 54*, 805–816.

Cohen, M., & Azaiza, F. (2008). Developing and testing an instrument for identifying culture-specific barriers to breast cancer screening in Israeli Arab women. *Acta Oncologica, 47*(8), 1570–1577.

Coker, T. R., Elliot, M. N., Kanouse, D. E., Grunbaum, J. A., Schwebel, E. D., Gilliland, M. J., et al. (2009). Perceived racial/ethnic discrimination among fifth-grade students and its association with mental health. *American Journal of Public Health, 99*(5), 878–884.

Davis, R., Marion, P., & Rockert, W. (1990). Brief group psychoeducation for bulimia nervosa. Assessing the clinical significance of change. *Journal of Counseling and Clinical Psychology, 58*, 882–885.

DeAngelis, T. (2008). PTSD: Helping families cope with PTSD. *Monitor on Psychology, 139*, 40–41.

Dixon, L., McFarlane, W. R., Lefley, H., Lucksted, A., Cohen, M., & Falloon, I. (2001). Evidence-based practices for services to families of people with psychiatric disabilities. *Psychiatric Services, 5*, 903–910.

Elliot, T. R., & Rivera, P. (2003). The experience of families and their carers in health care. In S. Llewelyn & P. Kennedy (Eds.), *Handbook of clinical health psychology* (pp. 61–77). San Francisco: Wiley.

Elliot, T. R., Shewchuk, R. M., & Richards, J. S. (2001). Family caregiver social problem-solving abilities and adjustment during the initial year of the caregiving role. *Journal of Counseling Psychology, 48*, 223–232.

Emmons, K. M., & Rollnick, S. (2001). Motivational interviewing in health care settings: Opportunities and limitations. *American Journal of Preventive Medicine, 20*, 68–74.

Fawzy, F. I., Fawzy, N. W., & Canada, A. L. (2001). Psychoeducational intervention programs for patients with cancer. In A. Baum & B. L. Andersen (Eds.), *Psychosocial interventions for cancer*. Washington, DC: American Psychological Association.

Ferrer, R. L. (2007) Pursuing equity: Contact with primary care and specialist clinicians by demographics, insurance, and health status. *Annals of Family Medicine, 5*, 492–502.

Freeman, J. (2003). The BELIEF instrument: A preclinical teaching tool to elicit patients' health beliefs. *Family Medicine, 35*, 316–319.

Galanti, G.-A. (2008). *Caring for patients from different cultures*. Philadelphia: University of Pennsylvania Press.

Gatchel, R. J., & Oordt, M. S. (2003). *Clinical health psychology and primary care: Practical advice and clinical guidance for successful collaboration*. Washington, DC: American Psychological Association.

Goldstein, M. J., & Miklowitz, D. J. (1995). The effectiveness of psychoeducational family therapy in the treatment of schizophrenic disorders. *Journal of Marital and Family Therapy, 21*, 361–376.

Glynn, S. N., Cohen, A. N., Dixon, L. B., & Niv, N. (2006). The potential impact of the recovery movement on family interventions for schizophrenia: Opportunities and obstacles. *Schizophrenia Bulletin, 32*, 451–463.

Grainger-Monsen, M., & Haslett, J. (2003). *Worlds apart: Jastine Chitsena's story (11:19). A four-part series on cross-cultural healthcare*. Fanlight Productions. Retrieved January, 12, 2009, from http://www.fanlight.com/catalog/films/912_wa.php

Harmsen, H., Meeuwesen, L., van Wieringen, J., Bernsen, R., & Bruijnzeels, M. (2003). When cultures meet in general practice: Intercultural differences between GPs and parents of child patients. *Patient Education and Counseling, 51*, 99–106.

Haynes, R. B. (1979). *Compliance in health care*. Baltimore, MD: John Hopkins University.

Ho, M. K. (1987). *Family therapy with ethnic minorities*. Newbury Park, CA: Sage.

Ho, M. K. (1997). *Family therapy with ethnic minorities* (2nd ed.). Thousand Oaks, CA: Sage.

Hunter, C. L., Goodie, J. L., & Oordt, M. S. (Eds.). (2009). *Integrated behavioral health in primary care: Step-by-step guidance for assessment and intervention*. Washington, DC: American Psychological Association.

Kanagawa-Singer, M., & Kassim-Lakaha, S. (2003). A strategy to reduce cross-cultural miscommunication and increase the likelihood of improving health outcomes. *Journal of Medical Education, 78*, 577–587.

Kessler, D., Lloyd, K., Lewis, G., Gray, D. P., & Cross, I. (1999). Sectional study of symptom attribution and recognition of depression and anxiety in primary care. *British Medical Journal, 318*, 436–440.

King, D. E. (2000). *Faith, spirituality, and medicine: Toward the making of the healing practitioner*. Binghamton, NY: Haworth Press.

Kleinman, A. (1980). *Patients and healers in the context of culture: An exploration of the borderland between anthropology, medicine, and psychiatry*. Los Angeles: University of California Press.

Knuti, K. A., Amrein, P. C., Chabner, B. A., Lynch, T. J., Jr., & Penson, R. T. (2002). Faith, identity, and leukemia: When blood products are not an option. *Oncologist, 7*(4), 371–380.

Kulwicki, A. D. (2003). People of Arab heritage. In J. D. Purnell & B. J. Paulanka (Eds.), *Transcultural healthcare: A culturally competent approach* (2nd ed., pp. 90–105). Philadelphia: F. A. Davis.

Lewis, T. E., Everson-Rose, S. A., Powell, H., Matthews, K. A., Brown, C., Ravolos, K., et al. (2006). Chronic exposure to everyday discrimination and coronary artery calcification in African-American women: The SWAN heart study. *Psychosomatic Medicine, 68*, 362–368.

Lewis, T. T., Barnes, L. L., Bienias, J. L., Lackland, D. T., Evans, D. A., & Mendes de Leon, C. F. (2009). Perceived discrimination and blood pressure in older African American and white adults. *Journals of Gerontology Series A: Biological Sciences and Medical Sciences*. Retrieved May 9, 2009, from http://biomedgerontology.oxfordjournals.org/cgi/content/full/glp062v1

Matthews, D. A., & Larson, D. B. (1998). *The faith factor; An annotated bibliography of clinical research on spiritual subjects* (Vol. 3). Washington, DC: National Institute of Health Care Research.

Meichenbaum, D. C., & Turk, D. (1987). *Facilitating treatment adherence: A practitioners's guidebook*. New York: Plenum Press.

Miller, W. R., & Rollnick, S. (2002). *Motivational interviewing: Preparing people for change*. New York: Guilford.

Muramoto, O. (2001). Bioethical aspects of the recent changes in the policy of refusal of blood by Jehovah's Witnesses. *British Medical Journal, 322*, 37–39.

National Diabetes Education Program. (2005). *Information about diabetes and related Medicare benefits: The power to control is in your hands* (NIH Publication No. 00–4849). Washington, DC: U.S. Department of Health and Human Services & National Institutes of Health and the Centers for Disease Control and Prevention.

National Diabetes Information Clearinghouse. (2007, October). *What I need to kno about eating and diabetes* (NIH Publication No. 08–5043). Washington, DC: U.S. Department of Health and Human Services, National Institutes of Health.

National Institute of Diabetes and Digestive and Kidney Disease. (2008, February). *Prevent diabetes problems: Keep your diabetes under control* (NIH Publication No. 08–4349). Washington, DC: National Institutes of Health: National Diabetes Information Clearinghouse.

National Institutes of Health, National Diabetes Information Clearinghouse, U.S. Food and Drug Administration. (2008, March). *What I need to know about physical activity and diabetes* (NIH Publication No. 08–5180). Washington, DC: U.S. Department of Health and Human Services, National Institutes of Health.

Nelson, A. (2002). Unequal treatment: Confronting racial and ethnic disparities in health care. *Journal of The National Medical Association, 94*, 6666–6668.

North, C. S., Pollio, D. E., Sachar, B., Hong, B., Isenberg, K., & Bufe, G. (1998). The family as caregiver: A group psychoeducation model for schizophrenia. *American Journal of Orthopsychiatry, 68*, 39–46.

Ong, S. H., & Caron, A. (2008). Family-based psychoeducation for children and adolescents with mood disorders. *Journal of Child Family Study, 17*, 809–822.

Pekkala, E. T., & Merinder, L. B. (2002). Psychoeducation for schizophrenia [Abstract]. *Cochrane Database of Systematic Reviews*. Retrieved November 19, 2008, from http://mrw.interscience.wiley.com/cochrane/clsysrev/articles/CD00 2831/frame.ml

Pennsylvania Psychiatric Society. (2005). *Age of consent to mental health treatment in Pennsylvania: Effects of Act No. 2004-147*. Retrieved January 12, 2009, from http://www.papsych.org/publicarticles/act147analysisqa.pdf

Rea, M. M., Tompson, M. C., Miklowitz, D. J., Goldstein, M. J., Hwang, S., & Mintz, J. (2003). Family-focused treatment versus individual treatment for bipolar disorder: Results of a randomized clinical trial. *Journal of Consulting and Clinical Psychology, 71*(3), 482–492.

Ren, X. S., Amick, B. C., & Williams, D. R. (1999). Racial/ethnic disparities inhealth: The interplay between discrimination and socioeconomic status. *Ethnicity & Disease, 9*(2), 151–165.

Resnicow, D. C., Soet, J. E., Borrelli, B., Ernst, D., Hecht, J., & Thevos, A. K. (2002). Motivational interviewing in medical and public health settings. In W. R. Miller & S. R. Rollnick (Eds.), *Motivational interviewing: Preparing people for change* (2nd ed., pp. 251–269). New York: Guilford.

Resnicow, K., Jackson, A., Wang, T., Dudley, W., & Baranowski, T. (2001). A motivational interviewing intervention to increase fruit and vegetable intake through black churches: Results of the eat for life trial. *American Journal of Public Health, 91*, 1686–1693.

Rotondi, A. J., Haas, G. L., Anderson, C. M., Newhill, C. E., Spring, M. B., Ganguli, R., et al. (2005, November). A clinical trial to test the feasibility of a telehealth psychoeducational intervention for persons with schizophrenia and their families: Intervention and 3-month findings. *Rehabilitation Psychology, 50*(4), 325–336.

Rowan, A. B., & Runyan, C. N. (2005). A primer on the consultation model of primary care behavioral health integration. In L. C. James & R. A. Folen (Eds.), The *primary care consultant: The next frontier for psychologists in hospitals and clinics* (pp. 9–37). Washington, DC: American Psychological Association.

Rummel-Kluge, C., Pitschel-Walz, G., Bauml, J., & Kissling, W. (2006). Psychoeducation in schizophrenia—Results of a survey of all psychiatric institutions in Germany, Austria, and Switzerland. *Schizophrenia Bulletin, 32*, 765–775.

Rundle, A., Carvalho, M., & Robinson, M. (Eds.). (2002). *Cultural competence in health care: A practical guide*. San Francisco: Jossey-Bass.

Sanchez-Hucles, J. V. (1999). Racism: Emotional abusiveness and psychological trauma for ethnic minorities. *Journal of Emotional Abuse, 1*(2), 69–87.

Simoneau, T. L., & Miklowitz, D. J. (2001). Integrating psychiatric illness into healthy family functioning: The family psychoeducational treatment of a patient with bipolar disorder. In S. H. McDaniel, L. Don-David, & C. L. Philpot (Eds.), *Casebook for integrating family therapy: An ecosystemic approach* (pp. 359–372). Washington, DC: American Psychological Association.

Sue, D. W., Arredondo, P., & McDavis, R. J. (1992). Multicultural counseling competencies and standards: A call to the profession. *Journal of Counseling and Development, 70*(4), 477–486.

Sue, D. W., & Sue, D. (2008). *Counseling the culturally diverse: Theory and practice* (5th ed.). San Francisco: Wiley.

Taplin, S., Barlow, W., Ludman, E., MacLehose, R., Meyer, D., Seger, D., et al. (2000). Testing reminder and motivational telephone calls to increase screening mammography: A randomized study. *Journal of the National Cancer Institute, 92*, 233–242.

Tseng, W., & Streltzer, J. (2008). *Cultural competence in health care: A guide for professionals*. New York: Springer Publishing Company.

U.S. Census Bureau News. (2008). *U.S. Hispanic population surpasses 45 million: Now 15% of total*. Retrieved February 25, 2008, from http://www.census.gov/PressRelease/www.releases/archives/populati on/011910.html

Watch Tower Bible and Tract Society of Pennsylvania. (1977). *Jehovah's Witnesses and the question of blood*. New York: Watchtower Bible and Tract Society of New York.

Williams, D. R., & Williams-Morris, R. (2000). Racism and mental health: The African American experience. *Ethnicity & Health, 5*(3 & 4), 243–268.

Williams, S., Weinman, J., & Dale, J. (1998). Doctor-patient communication and patient satisfaction: A review. *Family Practice, 15*, 480–492.

Wrenn, C. G. (1985). Afterward: The culturally-encapsulated counselor revisited. In P. Pedersen (Ed.), *Handboook of cross-cultural counseling and therapy* (pp. 323–329). Westport, CT: Greenwood Press.

Wright, J. H., Basco, M. R., & Thase, M. E. (Eds.). (2006). *Learning cognitive-behavior therapy: An illustrated guide*. Washington, DC: American Psychiatric Press.

Wyatt, S. B., Williams, D. R., Calvin, R., Henderson, F. C., Walker, E. R., & Winters, K. (2003). Racism and cardiovascular disease in African Americans. *American Journal of Medical Science, 325*, 315–331.

Yali, A. M., & Revenson, T. A. (2004). How changes in population demographics will impact health psychology incorporating a broader notion of cultural competence into the field. *Health Psychology, 23*, 147–155.

Mindfulness

9

Laura Young
Andrea L. Cincotta
Michael J. Baime

Introduction

Mindfulness is an important component of a variety of promising new cognitive-behavioral treatments of direct relevance in primary care. It can be grouped with a variety of innovative therapies that are more contextual, process-oriented, and experiential than traditional behavior therapies or cognitive therapies (Hayes, 2004). Although mindfulness can be described very simply, on closer inspection, it is a complex concept with no single definition and a wide variety of applications in both medicine and psychology. It can be used as a primary treatment modality or combined with other cognitive-behavioral approaches. It has been used in numerous clinical situations, including the treatment of anxiety, chronic pain, depression, and addiction; to decrease distress and suffering for patients with many medical illnesses; as a more general psychotherapeutic and stress-reduction approach; and to support growth and enhance quality of life in general populations. In this chapter, we will provide some definitions of mindfulness, discuss its history, mention some theoretical considerations about its use, detail ways in which mindfulness can be measured in both the clinical and research setting, and review the growing body of evidence that documents its value as a treatment modality.

Theoretical Issues

Mindfulness and Meditation

Mindfulness describes a particular type of attention that connects to experience in the present moment. The word mindfulness is derived from the Pali word *sati*, meaning "to remember," with secondary meanings of "attention" and "awareness." The remembering that is signified is not the recollection of a past event, but rather a reconnection to the immediate moment of experience. A popular current definition of mindfulness is offered by Jon Kabat-Zinn, the originator of mindfulness-based stress reduction (MBSR). He states that mindfulness is the awareness that emerges through, "paying attention on purpose, in the present moment, and nonjudgmentally, to the unfolding of experience moment to moment" (Kabat-Zinn, 2003, p. 145). Similar descriptions are put forward by Baer: "Mindfulness is the nonjudgmental observation of the ongoing stream of internal and external stimuli as they arise" (Baer, 2003, p.125), and Brown and Ryan: "A receptive attention to and awareness of present events and experience" (Brown & Ryan, 2003, p. 824). The presence of attention in the present moment is a central theme in all definitions, as is a particular attitude that has been described as acceptance, openness, receptivity, or nonjudgment. This two-component model, made explicit in 2004 by an influential group of mindfulness clinicians and researchers (Bishop et al., 2004), has been subject to some critiques (Hayes & Shenk, 2004), but still remains a useful and widely accepted definition. Many modifications to this formulation have been proposed; for example, Shapiro adds another primary factor, intention (Shapiro, Carlson, Astin, & Freedman, 2006), and others have postulated more specific attributes of the attention, such as flexibility, stability, and clarity (Brown, Ryan, & Creswell, 2007). Because mindfulness and attention are mental events, not objects that can be objectively measured or quantified, it is understandable that there are variations in its definition. In fact, it is surprising how much the core description of mindfulness has remained relatively constant during thousands of years of practice in many very different cultures, as part of a wide array of cultural and religious traditions.

Mindfulness is closely linked to meditation. Mindfulness meditation is a mental technique that strengthens the capacity to establish and sustain mindfulness. It is important to distinguish between the experience of mindfulness and the specific meditation-based practices that are used to cultivate that experience. Meditation practices cultivate attentional focus and stability by directing the mind to remain connected to experience in the present moment. This is more difficult than it sounds, as can be demonstrated by just a few minutes of attempting to keep attention focused without wandering. Without training, attention is prone to drift off, and quickly leaves the present moment, becoming lost in the world of memory and events from the past or wandering into a future world of planning and fantasy. Meditation trains attention by using it, in the same way that exercise strengthens a muscle through repeated use against resistance. Mindfulness meditation trains the practitioner to continually return to the present moment of sensation and experience, and to remain balanced in the present moment as the future unfolds as the present and then fades into the past. With practice over time, remaining in the present becomes easier and is more likely to occur spontaneously.

The majority of mindfulness meditation techniques are based on traditional Buddhist meditation practices, many of which originated more than 2,500 years ago. One of the most widely used mindfulness meditation practices directs the practitioner to focus his or her attention on the sensation of the breath and to follow the flowing cycle of breathing with their full attention. Other meditation practices might focus on a different sensation in the body, or on the experience of the body during movement, or a sound, or on a visual focus like a candle flame, a picture, or a statue or other object. Some mindfulness meditation exercises simply direct the practitioner to remain aware of whatever enters the field of awareness. Although the object of focus may vary, in all instances, the goal of the practice is to train attention to remain fully engaged with experience and in the present.

Like many other capabilities, attentional performance is improved with practice. Meaningful changes in the ability to direct and manage attention have been demonstrated after relatively short periods of mindfulness meditation training. Computer-based measures of attentional performance have demonstrated significant improvements in the ability to focus and direct attention after only eight weeks of regular mindfulness meditation practice, (Jha, Krompinger, & Baime, 2007), and one recent article demonstrated measurable changes after only five days of training (Tang et al., 2007). A robust and growing body of knowledge describes the many cognitive, behavioral, affective, and neural changes that accompany mindfulness meditation training (Siegel, 2007). Recent research has even suggested that long-term mindfulness meditation is associated with increased size of the right prefrontal cortex, which is the location of the neural networks that manage attention (Lazar et al., 2005). It has been suggested that the function of attention is central to a variety of psychological maladies, and that many psychotherapeutic techniques work in part through a modification of attentional processes and mechanisms (Posner & Rothbart, 2007). This is not implausible, because attention is the doorway through which the outer world and inner mental experience enter into consciousness. The ways in which we interact with thoughts, emotions, and the external world are all mediated by attention. Because variations of these techniques have been used for millennia to cultivate peace, equanimity, and compassion, it is not surprising that they would be found to have measurable benefits when examined with modern scientific methods. Meditation techniques have been passed from teacher to student, and from culture to culture, for thousands of years because when they are practiced, they create an experience that is valued.

The intentional cultivation of the experience of mindfulness during everyday life is sometimes referred to as "informal" mindfulness practice, and "formal" practice refers to an actual meditation session. Despite the many demonstrated benefits of interventions that include formal meditation training, it is not known to what extent meditation is a necessary ingredient for the benefits that accompany mindfulness, and we do not know the specific role that meditation plays in the cultivation of mindfulness. The optimum duration of meditation practice is not known, nor is there any useful research comparing different types or traditions of mindfulness training. There is a wide range of baseline mindfulness among individuals, and some individuals sustain a high level of ongoing mindfulness even in the absence of formal training. Research has demonstrated that increased levels of baseline or trait mindfulness is associated with better psychological and interpersonal functioning, although at least among students with no meditation experience, the capacity to practice mindfulness meditation was not associated with everyday mindfulness (Brown & Ryan, 2003; Thompson & Waltz, 2007). Most notably, acceptance and commitment therapy (ACT), which will be described in more detail later in this chapter, uses applied mindfulness and trains patients in mindfulness without using formal meditation practice. The importance of formal meditation practice in the cultivation of ongoing mindfulness, especially in a therapeutic context, is unclear.

Assessment Methods

Measurement of Mindfulness

One of the most daunting obstacles to the use of mindfulness in the clinical setting is the difficulty of measuring it. As mindfulness is integrated into psychological and medical interventions, researchers and clinicians have attempted to better quantify and operationalize it. Until recently, no empirical tools existed to measure mindfulness in a standardized way. To better understand the psychological effects of mindfulness training, several self-report psychometric assessments have been developed to measure mindfulness. Although predominantly used as a research tool, all scales are self-administered and can be easily integrated into clinical practice. The eight different mindfulness assessments and their proposed uses are described in detail below. They are of interest not only because they provide measures that can be used to characterize individuals and groups, and to measure change over time, but also because they demonstrate the many ways in which mindfulness has been conceptualized.

The Mindfulness Attention Awareness Scale

The Mindfulness Attention Awareness Scale (MAAS; Brown & Ryan, 2003) is a 15-item self-report instrument that measures one's tendency to attend to present-moment experiences in everyday activities. The MAAS uses a Likert scale ranging from 0 (almost always) to 6 (almost never) to assess such items as, "I find myself listening to someone with one ear, doing something else at the same time," and "I tend to walk quickly to get where I'm going without paying attention to what I experience along the way." The MAAS has a single factor structure and therefore yields a single score. It has demonstrated reliable internal consistency ($\alpha = 0.82$). MAAS scores are significantly higher for practitioners of mindfulness meditation than those of nonmeditators.

Freiburg Mindfulness Inventory

The Freiburg Mindfulness Inventory (FMI; Buchheld, Grossman, & Walach, 2001) is designed to measure nonjudgmental present-moment awareness and openness to negative experiences. Although many of the questions may seem ambiguous or be falsely construed by individuals without prior training in mindfulness techniques, its intended use is in individuals with previous training and experience in mindfulness meditation. The FMI contains 30 descriptive statements that are rated on a Likert scale of 1 (rarely) to 4 (almost always). Higher scores indicate higher degrees of mindfulness. The developers reported high internal consistency: preretreat score ($\alpha = 0.93$) and postretreat score ($\alpha = 0.94$). Examples of questions asked include, "I accept myself as I am," "I avoid unpleasant feelings," and "I observe how my thoughts come and go." The authors highlight that this scale captures several aspects of mindfulness, including a cognitive component, a process component, one that relates to the acceptance of experience, and one that involves a nonjudgmental stance. Although these aspects are closely interrelated, based on their analyses, the authors recommend considering mindfulness as a one-dimensional measure, and therefore, using a single score when interpreting the results.

A shortened version of the FMI, called the Freiburg Mindfulness Inventory–Short Form (FMI-SF), has been subsequently created; it represents the core components of the mindfulness construct as conceptualized by the metric's authors (Walach, Buchheld, Buttenmüller, Kleinknecht, & Schmidt, 2006). It can be used in populations with no previous mindfulness training. It demonstrates good internal reliability ($\alpha = 0.86$), and is very highly correlated with the full scale ($r = 0.95$) suggesting similar elements of mindfulness are being measured with both scales. Longer meditation experience, more frequent meditation, and the increased frequency in mindfulness experienced through events such as a retreat, can be demonstrated by the scale. Similar to the 30-question FMI, the shortened version measures mindfulness as a general construct that has some interrelated facets.

Cognitive and Affective Mindfulness Scale

The Cognitive and Affective Mindfulness Scale (CAMS; Kumar, 2005) was the first questionnaire designed to assess mindfulness. The CAMS consists of 18 items designed to capture a broad conceptualization of mindfulness. The items on the CAMS were designed to assess four core characteristics of mindfulness, including: (a) the ability to regulate attention ("I have a hard time concentrating on what I am doing"), (b) an orientation to present or immediate experience ("I focus on the present moment"), (c) awareness of experience ("It's easy for me to keep track of my thoughts and feelings"), and (d) an attitude of acceptance or nonjudgment toward experience ("I believe it is OK to be sad or angry"). The wording is not specific to any type of mindfulness training, and can be used in a range of samples. Although this tool was sensitive to change and valid, it lacked internal consistency and many of the items lacked direct assessment of key mindfulness constructs. As a result, a revised scale was created called the cognitive and affective mindfulness scale–revised (CAMS-R). The CAMS-R consists of 12 items. Scores from the CAMS and CAMS-R have been shown to be strongly intercorrelated ($r = .66$) (Feldman, Hayes, Kumar, Greeson, & Laurenceau, 2007). Internal consistency for the CAMS-R is good ($\alpha = .76$). Participants answer the 12 items after being given the prompt, "People have a variety of ways of relating to their thoughts and feelings. For each of the items below, rate how much each of these ways applies to you." Ratings range from 1 (rarely/not at all) to 4 (almost always). Higher values reflect greater mindfulness qualities.

South Hampton Mindfulness Questionnaire

The South Hampton Mindfulness Questionnaire (SMQ; Chadwick et al., 2008) was designed to assess the degree of mindful responding to distressing thoughts and images. The SMQ is one of the most recent psychometric tools designed to assess mindfulness. It was formerly called the mindfulness questionnaire (MQ). The SMQ is internally reliable ($\alpha = 0.89$), significantly correlated with other measurements of mindfulness, and shows significant correlation with mood ratings. Furthermore, scores accurately discriminated between meditators, nonmeditators, and those with psychosis. The SMQ has a single-factor structure and contains 16 items that are rated on a 7-point Likert scale, worded "strongly disagree" (0) to "strongly agree" (6), yielding a total range of 0–96. Eight items are framed positively, eight negatively.

Kentucky Inventory of Mindfulness Skills

The Kentucky Inventory of Mindfulness Skills (KIMS; Baer, Smith, & Allen, 2004) measures mindfulness in daily life, and does not require previous training in mindfulness meditation or practice. The questionnaire contains 39 items that are ranked on a 5-point, Likert-type scale (never or very rarely true to always or almost always true). The KIMS assesses four elements of mindfulness as outlined in Linehan's dialectical behavioral therapy (DBT; Lynch, Chapman, Rosenthal, Kuo, & Linehan, 2006). These elements include observing ("I notice when my moods begin to change"), describing ("I am good at finding words to describe my feelings"), acting with awareness ("I get completely absorbed in what I am doing, so that all my attention is focused on it"), and accepting without judgment ("I tend to make judgments about how worthwhile or worthless my experiences are"). A score is generated for each element. Internal reliability is good ($\alpha = 0.76–0.91$) for the four scales. Although the KIMS was developed largely based upon the key concepts of DBT, the authors made a conscious effort to have the descriptive statements be consistent with descriptions found in other evidence-based mindfulness interventions, including MBSR and MBCT; therefore, this is an appropriate assessment tool for a variety of mindfulness interventions.

Five-Factor Mindfulness Questionnaire

The Five-Factor Mindfulness Questionnaire (FFMQ; Baer, Smith, Hopkins, Krietemeyer, & Toney, 2006) was constructed based on exploratory factor analysis in a large sample of college students who completed the KIMS, CAMS, FMI, MQ, and MAAS (Baer et al., 2006). Evaluating mindfulness in this way allowed for items from different instruments to combine to create factors and, in essence, integrated the attempts to operationalize mindfulness by the authors of the various mindfulness metrics. The results of this analysis suggested that there were five components of mindfulness, including observing, describing, acting with awareness, nonjudging of inner experiences, and nonreactivity to inner experience, that represent mindfulness as it is currently conceptualized. The FFMQ contains 39 questions and its scoring is similar to the KIMS. Later analyses suggest that at least four of the factors, with the exception of observing, are components of an overall mindfulness construct (Baer et al., 2008). The authors point out that the factor structure may vary with meditation experience, and additional testing is necessary. The significant length of time required to complete this scale is one of the potential draw backs of this tool.

The Philadelphia Mindfulness Scale

The Philadelphia Mindfulness Scale (PMS; Cardaciotto, Herbert, Forman, Moitra, & Farrow, 2008) is the most recently developed tool to assess mindfulness. It measures mindfulness using a two-factor design, and assesses present-moment awareness and acceptance. The concept of mindfulness used in this questionnaire is based strictly on the definition created by Kabat-Zinn and held by many of the leaders in the field of MBSR. None of the other aforementioned metrics assess mindfulness in a way that adequately captures these two key constituents of mindfulness as separate and distinct ideas. In strictly limiting the assessment to measuring present-moment awareness and acceptance, the authors not only attempt to avoid redundancy, but have also created a tool that is shorter in length. The PMS contains 20 items that are ranked on a 5-point Likert Scale (0 = never, 1 = rarely, 2 = sometimes, 3 = often, 4 = very often), according to the frequency that the subject experienced the described item within the past week. The Scale assesses present-moment awareness ("Whenever my emotions change, I am conscious of them immediately") and acceptance ("I am aware of what thoughts are passing through my mind"). There is good internal consistency and the validity was excellent, with the two subscores highly correlated with the corresponding subscores on the KIMS. The authors point out that further validation of this Scale in additional clinical populations and in meditating samples has yet to be done.

The Toronto Mindfulness Scale

The Toronto Mindfulness Scale (TMS; Lau et al., 2006) is designed to assess the attainment of a mindful state immediately following a meditation session. The original scale has been refined to a two-factor model that defines mindfulness as a state of de-centered, curious awareness of one's experience. Types of questions include, "I experienced myself as separate from my changing thoughts and feelings," and "I was receptive to observing unpleasant thoughts and feelings without interfering with them." The TMS contains 13 items that subjects rate on a 5-point Likert scale, ranging from 0 (not at all) to 4 (very much). The TMS assesses the state of mindfulness as a single point in time, therefore, it may not reflect the true capacity of an individual to evoke a state of mindfulness, nor is it clear how the TMS score can be generalized to "everyday mindfulness" (Thompson & Waltz, 2007).

The existing measures of mindfulness each present unique advantages and disadvantages, in terms of their conceptual coverage of the components of mindfulness, their item content, their length, and their generalizability. As highlighted by Grossman, it is important to recognize the inherent complicated issues surrounding the accurate assessment of mindfulness using the current psychometric tools (Grossman, 2008). Grossman (2008, p. 405) warns that "facile operationalizations of the originally Buddhist psychological construct of mindfulness may serve to trivialize the concept and substantially alter its original meaning." Without a standardized, mutually agreed-on definition of mindfulness, other than "attention to experience in the present moment," there are inherent limitations that must be acknowledged when attempting to quantify mindfulness (Grossman, 2008, p. 405). As outlined previously, there are dramatic differences in the content and structure of the scales designed to measure mindfulness. Furthermore, scores from the various measures of mindfulness are, in some cases, not correlated or only modestly correlated with each other, suggesting that different constructs are being measured. Many of the scales have been developed by researchers with limited training and understanding of the complex, Buddhist psychological theory that underlies mindfulness, further biasing the measurement of mindfulness. Finally, as with any type of subjective self-measure, there are concerns about discordance between actual mindfulness and self-reported mindfulness. It is important to carefully consider what one desires to measure prior to choosing a mindfulness scale. When using these questionnaires for research purposes, it is recommended that several of the mindfulness assessments most appropriate to the research question be employed.

Treatment Approaches

In the first section that follows, we summarize the primary cognitive-behavioral mindfulness interventions that exist to date. These are the interventions based on the tenets of mindfulness and acceptance that Stephen Hayes, the founder of Acceptance and Commitment Therapy, refers to as "third wave" therapies, following in the footsteps of behavioral therapy and cognitive-behavioral therapy. This is then followed by a review of specific psychological and medical problems that are relevant to the primary care provider that have been demonstrated to respond well to mindfulness interventions.

Mindfulness-Based Stress Reduction

Developed in the 1970s by Jon Kabat-Zinn at the University of Massachusetts as a behavioral intervention for patients with chronic pain and stress-related conditions, MBSR has expanded globally and can now be found in a variety of health care and community settings (Kabat-Zinn, 2005) and in over 400 hospital and medical school settings in the United States. MBSR is a standardized program conducted as an 8-week class with weekly sessions typically lasting 2.5–3 hours. Table 9.1 outlines the mindfulness practices that are taught during a typical MBSR training course. These skills are practiced both in class and as homework. Homework is viewed as an important factor in the development of mindfulness skills, and participants are expected to complete approximately 45 minutes of formal mindfulness practice at least 6 days per week during the 8-week period. Between sessions six and seven, there is a 7-hour "all-day" retreat. Participants are mostly silent during the day-long session, and have the opportunity to practice their newly acquired mindfulness skills during a sustained and uninterrupted period of time. The stated goal of this intensive experience is to spend the day in the present moment while maintaining a nonjudgmental focus. An essential component of the weekly classes includes discussion about the experiences that occur during the practice of mindfulness, both in and out of the classroom. Group leaders generally do not provide advice, but instead help the participants explore in depth their experiences of mindfulness. Discussion of obstacles or problems that arise during the practice of the mindfulness exercises is also a key component of the classes. It has been recently shown that number of hours spent in MBSR class is not related to the degree of improvement in psychological distress, suggesting that adaptations that include less class time may be useful for those who are unable to fully commit to the full 8-week course (Carmody & Baer, 2009). The authors caution, however, that most research has been done in the 8-week course, and further investigation is necessary to examine this issue more fully.

Mindfulness-Based Cognitive Therapy

Mindfulness-based cognitive therapy (MBCT), developed by Segal, Williams, and Teasdale (2002), is largely based on the concepts of mindfulness derived from MBSR; unlike MBSR, however, the focus is on the treatment of depression rather than stress (Segal et al., 2002). The intervention was specifically designed for use in the prevention of depression relapse. Its theoretical foundation rests upon research that has shown that those individuals most vulnerable to depression relapse are those who have mood-related reactivation of negative thinking patterns and inappropriate responses to negative thoughts and emotions. MBCT is delivered in a group format, and combines more traditional cognitive therapy for depression with mindfulness techniques. Classes generally meet for eight consecutive weeks for two-hour sessions, plus one all-day session between weeks five and seven. Classes generally accommodate 8–15 people. Outside of class, participants are expected to use audio recordings with guided meditations that support their developing mindfulness practice. During classes, participants discuss their experiences with the home practice, obstacles that arise, and strategies to deal with challenging situations skillfully. Each class is developed around a theme that is explored in class and through mindfulness practice. The body scan, sitting meditation, mindful movement, walking meditation, and informal mindfulness practice are all important components of MBCT. Table 9.2 highlights the main components of each of the eight sessions. The first four sessions focus on learning how to be present. The general concept is that living in the present moment prevents repetitive automatic functioning that can aid in the maintenance of negative mood states. The second portion of the intervention involves the effective handling of mood shifts. MBCT trains patients who have recovered from a depressive episode to recognize the patterns of negative thinking associated with depression and to disengage from them. The cognitive therapy exercises that are integrated into the group classes in the later sessions cultivate a de-centered approach to internal experience and are unlike traditional CBT exercises that attempt to change thoughts; in MBCT, the focus is on acceptance rather than change.

9.1 Mindfulness Practices Taught During MBSR

Mindfulness Practice	Description of Mindfulness Practices Employed During MBSR Training
Sitting meditation	Focus is initially placed on the breath. Participants are warned that the mind will wander and when it does, attention should be gently returned back to the breath. After comfort is developed with following the breath, participants are then encouraged to notice bodily sensations. When pain or discomfort is noted, nonjudgmental acceptance is encouraged. In later classes, attention is shifted to thoughts and emotions. Instruction is given to observe thoughts and emotions briefly and without becoming captivated by them. Audio CDs are provided to guide daily meditation.
Body scan	In either a supine or sitting position, with the eyes closed, participants are guided to focus their attention in a sequential pattern on various parts of the body, and to notice the sensations in each part of the body. Although relaxation may occur during this exercise, the goal is to practice the deliberate direction of attention, notice when the mind has wandered, and nonjudgmental acceptance of the observed sensations. CDs are provided to guide daily practice.
Mindful movement	Gentle yoga-based movement is introduced during weeks 3–6 to promote mindful awareness of the body during stretching and movement. Because the movements are gentle and slow, they are appropriate for nearly all ages and abilities. Participants are instructed to move at their own pace and ability. During these exercises, participants practice awareness and nonjudgmental acceptance of the body.
Walking meditation	Focus is intentionally placed on the sensations in the body while walking. Walking meditation, although classically practiced at a slow pace with the gaze directed straight ahead, can be performed while walking at a quicker pace, as well. This practice can be particularly useful for individuals who experience a high degree of anxiety during the sitting meditation or body scan. The constant flow of the body during walking facilitates the development of continuous, present-moment awareness of the mind and body.
Mindfulness in daily life	Often referred to as "informal mindfulness practice," applying mindful awareness to daily activities is intended to increase insight and reduces habitual, automatic, maladaptive behaviors.

Dialectical Behavior Therapy

Originally developed for the treatment of borderline personality disorder (BPD) by Marsha Linehan at the University of Washington, this treatment program is a modified cognitive-behavioral therapy program, drawing from principles in behavioral science, dialectical philosophy, and Zen meditation practice (Linehan, Armstrong, Suarez, Allmon, & Heard, 1991). The term "dialectic" means "weighing and integrating contradictory facts or ideas with a view to resolving apparent contradictions." Therapists and clients work to balance change with acceptance. Traditional cognitive-behavioral therapy helps the participant change inappropriate behaviors, thoughts, and emotions, whereas mindfulness training

9.2 Description of MBCT Session Content

Session	Description of Class Content
Session One: *Automatic Pilot*	Controlled breathing and mindful eating are introduced. These exercises are intended to get participants to begin to be fully aware of and experience bodily sensations. For homework, the body scan is practiced. To facilitate the incorporation of mindfulness into daily life, participants are asked to take an ordinary activity like taking a shower, and consciously and fully experience every sensation and perception as the activity is performed.
Session Two: *Dealing With Barriers*	This session is devoted to becoming aware of the constant "chatter of the mind." Highlighted is the fact that this chatter often controls reactions to life. In the case of depression, sad or negative feelings can lead to a downward spiral. Rumination on negative thoughts furthers the problem. A short sitting meditation is introduced. Homework entails further practice of the body scan and a breathing exercise. Participants are instructed to also keep a detailed diary of pleasant events that occur during the week.
Session Three: *Mindfulness of the Breath*	During this session, the breathing-based meditation taught during week two is expanded to 30–40 minutes. Often a difficult session for participants, it addresses common difficulties encountered during the learning process, including mind wandering, physical discomfort, judgment of thoughts and control of thoughts. The "mini-meditation" is introduced. Also called the "3-minute breathing space," this exercise is intended to raise the awareness of participants about the differences between automatically reacting and skillfully responding. This session also includes a yoga-like set of stretching exercises. In addition to practicing 30–40 minutes of daily sitting meditation, mindful movement and the "mini-meditation" homework also includes recording unpleasant events that occur during the week in a detailed fashion.
Session Four: *Staying Present*	The main goal of this session is to learn how to stay present even when things become uncomfortable. In class, meditation time is now 40 minutes. A variant of the "mini-meditation" is taught, intended to be used during times of emotional distress. Homework involves daily meditation using the guided audio CD and to practice the "mini-meditation" regularly during daily life.
Session Five: *Allowing and Letting Be*	The main theme of this session is learning to allow an experience to exist without feeling the need to judge or fix it. Again, participants practice a 40-minute in-class meditation, and watch a video that provides tips/tools on how to deal with chronic issues such pain and anxiety. Participants are asked to bring to mind an active problem and as a means to practice noninterference, they are instructed to allow themselves to be with the negative feeling associated with the problem. The goal is to fully experience the feelings and sensations when the mind moves toward rather than away from painful thoughts and feelings. Homework is continued sitting meditation and practicing the "mini-meditation."

(continued)

Table 9.2 *(continued)*

Session	Description of Class Content
Session Six: *Thoughts are Not Facts*	This session is the most cognitive of the course. Participants discuss the concept of thoughts as "objects of awareness." Participants do a mood and thoughts exercise to show how mood can determine how a situation is interpreted. In-depth analysis of how congruent the thought and situation are also occurs. For homework, new audio CDs are given out with new meditations.
Session Seven: *How Can I Best Take Care of Myself*	Practical by design, this session is devoted to how to optimally participate in self-care. When feelings of depression arise, participants are advised to take a "breathing space" for a few minutes before deciding how to respond to the feelings. Discussion of warning signs of depression relapse and action plans to prevent relapse are discussed. In addition to continued daily meditation practice, as homework, participants are encouraged to identify personally relevant early warning signs of depression relapse and to set up an individualized plan to recognize and prevent relapse.
Session Eight: *Using What's Been Learned to Deal with Future Moods*	This session is focused on how to maintain balance in life. During the session, both large group and small group discussions occur with the goal of summarizing all learning points presented during the previous sessions.

helps to facilitate acceptance and change. Participants are asked to make a one-year commitment to the therapy. A successful DBT program consists of five essential functions that include: (a) enhancing client capabilities, (b) enhancing client motivation, (c) ensuring generalizability, (d) structuring the environment, and (e) enhancing therapists' capabilities. There are four different modes of therapy within DBT. The first is traditional dyadic therapy. Skills training, primarily done in a group setting, is the second mode of therapy and includes four modules. Table 9.3 outlines each module and the mindfulness-based elements within each one. The third mode of therapy is skills generalization, and helps participants unite the skills learned in DBT with real-world situations. Often, this is accomplished through brief telephone calls between the therapist and the client. The final mode of therapy is therapist consultation, in which the therapists undergo DBT sessions with each other. This is considered to be an essential component of any DBT program and helps to keep the therapists actively living the concepts of DBT. In simplified terms, the goal of the treatment approaches outlined previously can be broken down into the process of the reduction of ineffective action tendencies linked with dysregulated emotions (Lynch et al., 2006). This is a very brief overview of a very complex program. For more in-depth information, readers are referred to the DBT training manual (Linehan, 1993).

Acceptance and Commitment Therapy

Acceptance and Commitment Therapy (ACT) is a psychological intervention developed by Steven Hayes that uses acceptance and mindfulness strategies together with commitment and behavior-change strategies, with the ultimate goal

9.3 The Main Goals of the Four Modules in DBT With Emphasis on the Mindfulness Aspects in Each Module

Module	Goal of the Module and Specific Mindfulness Skills Taught
Core mindfulness	Provides rationale for why the practice of mindfulness is useful. Trains participants how to use mindfulness to comprehend what is true and subsequently act wisely based upon this truth. *States of Mind Participants are taught about three states of mind. The *reasonable mind* is logical, sensible, rational, makes plans, and solves problems. The *emotion mind* is passionate, and in this state, emotions control thoughts and behaviors. The *wise mind* is the integration of the reasonable mind and the emotion mind into a "centered" type of knowing that can include intuition. In DBT, the development of a wise mind is a skill that all are able to cultivate with appropriate training. *Mindfulness "What" Skills The "what" skills identify our actions when one is mindful. *Observing* is paying attention to what is happening in the present moment without trying to change it. *Describing* is the conscious application of words to the observed experience. *Participating* refers to actively and consciously partaking in whatever is happening in life, not just seeing or understanding it. *Mindfulness "How" Skills The "how" skills identify the manner in which to carry out actions. *Nonjudgmental* refers to taking a nonevaluative stance toward experience. Being *one-mindfully* teaches participants the importance of focusing undivided attention on one thing at a time. *Effectively* refers to doing what works.
Interpersonal effectiveness	Designed to help clients interact with others in a manner that will allow them to improve relationships while simultaneously maintaining their own personal values and self-respect. *No specific mindfulness training.
Emotion regulation	Trains participants how to observe emotions, describe emotions, reduce emotional vulnerability, and decrease emotional suffering. *Mindfulness skills of observing and describing are developed. *Mindfulness of current emotions is also taught.
Distress tolerance	Emphasizes that pain is an inevitable part of life and participants are presented with techniques to more skillfully deal with emotional distress. *Acceptance of reality even if it is unpleasant or unwanted. *Radical acceptance, which is the concept that painful realities need to be fully acknowledged and futile efforts to change things that cannot be changed should be abandoned. *To accomplish the above, skills in mindful breathing are taught.

of increasing emotional flexibility. Experiential avoidance is a key concept of the therapy, and is defined as the tendency to avoid unpleasant thoughts, feelings, and experiences. Avoidance is positively associated with psychological illness (Hayes, Wilson, Gifford, Follette, & Strosahl, 1996), and experimental research has demonstrated that the attempt to avoid a specific thought actually induces that thought (J. J. Gross, 2002). A variety of experiential exercises are employed to help participants learn to safely and effectively reencounter the thoughts, feelings, memories, and physical sensations that induce anxiety, fear, or other aversive emotions. Six main concepts that are employed to assist in the development of emotional flexibility are described in Table 9.4. Participants are taught to apply these concepts to reevaluate and accept private internal events, to redefine personal values, and ultimately, to commit to behavior change. The length of therapy is variable and depends upon the participant's needs. Whereas ACT was originally developed as an individual therapy, recent modifications have allowed it to be successfully employed in group settings. Further details about the implementation of ACT can be found in the ACT manual (Luoma, Hayes, & Walser, 2007).

Although all four of the previous interventions have mindfulness at their core, it is important to note that there are differences between them. MBCT and MBSR have meditation as a key component. DBT and ACT use shorter, more directed mindfulness exercises. MBSR and MBCT are designed to be delivered within a group context over an 8-week period. ACT was initially intended to be delivered on an individual basis, but it has recently been adapted for group delivery. The duration of ACT can last from weeks to months, depending on the participant. DBT includes both group and individual sessions that last for at least a year. A key difference between the four interventions is that MBSR and MBCT generally are not oriented toward behavior change, whereas ACT and DBT encourage both acceptance and behavior change. Finally, MBSR is the only intervention that directly focuses on the alleviation of stress and has wide heterogeneous audience appeal, and DBT and MBCT traditionally have been developed for specific patient populations.

Specific Clinical Treatment Applications

The number of well-designed clinical studies examining the effects of mindfulness training, although still limited, is growing. Limitations in many previous studies include small sample sizes, insufficient statistical power, unmeasured compliance, and lack of an appropriate control group. Nonetheless, there is growing, high-quality evidence that mindfulness training can have beneficial effects in both clinical and nonclinical populations (Chiesa & Serretti, 2009; Grossman, Niemann, Schmidt, & Walach, 2004). The primary mindfulness intervention that has been studied in nonclinical populations is MBSR. Most that enroll in this type of course do so with the primary intent of achieving improved stress-management skills. In a heterogeneous, community population, it was shown that following MBSR training, participants reported statistically significantly enhanced health-related quality of life, reduced physical symptoms, and decreased psychological distress (Reibel, Greeson, Brainard, & Rosenzweig, 2001). Furthermore, in a different community sample of MBSR class participants, increases in mindfulness were shown to completely mediate the relationships between meditation practice and improvements in psychological symptoms and perceived stress (Carmody & Baer, 2008).

9.4 The Six Main Concepts of ACT

Acceptance	This involves nonjudgmental awareness and openness to thoughts, feelings, emotions, and sensations as they occur. During therapy, participants study their current efforts to avoid unpleasant situations and determine whether this type of strategy effectively works for them. More focus is placed on the participant's appraisal than the therapist's view of the situation. The goal is to fully experience thoughts, feelings, and situations that were previously avoided.
Cognitive diffusion	Through this practice, participants change the way they interact with and relate to thoughts, refocusing attention on the process of thinking rather than the specific thought. Diffusion leads to a realization that thoughts may be inaccurate, and decreases the automatic belief of thoughts rather than their occurrence.
Self-as-context	Through a variety of exercises, participants are able to explore the concept of self. The *conceptualized self* is a person's natural tendency to assign characteristics to the concept of self. The *self as process* relates to experiences that are occurring and the way a person relates to them. The *self as an observer* is a stable, ever-present state from which both wanted and unwanted experiences can be witnessed and evaluated neutrally.
Contact with the present moment	Participants learn to experience life as it occurs, in a more direct fashion. This allows thoughts and actions to become more flexible and in accordance with personal values.
Values	ACT helps participants better define their true values in life. There are nine domains in which the program assists in defining values, and they include: (a) marriage/couples/intimate relationships, (b) family relationships, (c) friendship/social relations, (d) career/employment, (e) education/personal growth and development, (f) recreation/leisure, (g) spirituality, (h) citizenship, and (i) health/physical well-being. Participants begin to understand that rather than a means to an end, a value defines a way of living.
Committed action	This concept helps people undertake actions that are coherent with their values.

In the remainder of this chapter, we highlight the clinical applications in which mindfulness interventions have the highest quality of evidence supporting its use. The reader will note that the problems discussed are common issues frequently encountered in the primary care setting.

Mental Health

Depression

Although most clinical trials studying the effectiveness of mindfulness interventions show improvements in depressive mood in a variety of patient populations, some clinicians believe that mindfulness interventions are not appropriate for people who are actively suffering from acute clinical depression. It has been theorized that the intensity of negative thoughts, poor concentration, and restlessness that often accompany an episode of acute depression might make meaningful participation in mindfulness exercises difficult and uncomfortable. Developing the necessary attentional control skills may be difficult during a major depressive episode. These assumptions have been recently challenged. Results of several uncontrolled trials of MBCT in subjects with acute depression or residual depressive symptoms have shown clinically and statistically significant decreases in depression and anxiety (Finucane & Mercer, 2006), possibly mediated through decreased rumination (Kingston, Dooley, Bates, Lawlor, & Malone, 2007). Acutely depressed patients with symptoms resistant to drug therapy have also shown to benefit from MBCT (Eisendrath et al., 2008; Kenny & Williams, 2007). Furthermore, these studies have qualitatively shown that MBCT treatment was acceptable and beneficial from the patients' point of view (Finucane & Mercer, 2006). To date, there is only one rigorous, randomized controlled trial examining the effects of MBCT in actively depressed patients (Barnhofer et al., 2009). The findings showed those who received treatment as usual had no change in their depression symptoms, although those in the MBCT group had self-reported symptoms of depression that changed from severe at the beginning of the intervention to mild by the conclusion. The number of patients who met criteria for major depression decreased in the MBCT group, but remained unchanged in the treatment-as-usual group.

ACT has also been examined in patients with moderate-to-severe depression and anxiety, and been shown to lead to improvements in depression, anxiety, functioning difficulties, quality of life, life satisfaction, and clinician-rated functioning (Forman, Herbert, Moitra, Yeomans, & Geller, 2007). These changes were equivalent to changes seen in patients receiving traditional cognitive-behavioral therapy; however, the mechanism of action across the two groups was different. Improvements in "observing" and "describing" one's experiences were shown to mediate outcomes for the traditional cognitive-behavioral therapy group, in contrast to the ACT group, where "experiential avoidance," "acting with awareness," and "acceptance" mediated the improved outcomes. Although promising, our understanding of the role of mindfulness interventions in the treatment of acute depression will benefit from the many active investigations currently in progress.

MBCT was specifically developed to prevent depression relapse, and there is a significant body of research documenting its efficacy. Two randomized controlled trials have demonstrated that MBCT plus usual care (vs. usual care alone) decreased the rate of depression recurrence by 50% over a 60-week follow-up among people who had experienced three or more previous episodes of major depression. This effect was not due to differences in antidepressive medication between the two groups (Ma & Teasdale, 2004; Teasdale et al., 2000). Further work has demonstrated that MBCT is as effective as maintenance antidepressant medication therapy in preventing depression relapse (47 vs. 60%); however, MBCT was more effective than pharmacotherapy in reducing residual depressive symptoms and psychiatric co-morbidity, as well as in improving quality of life in the physical and psychological domains (Kuyken et al., 2008). Additionally, rates of antidepressant medication usage in the MBCT group were significantly lower compared with the treatment-as-usual group, and 75% of patients were able to completely discontinue antidepressant medication in the MBCT group.

General Anxiety Disorder

General anxiety disorder (GAD) is characterized by chronic worry that seems to not have any substantive cause, a focus on the future, and avoidance of the present. Mindfulness seems to be an ideal intervention to foster cognitive and behavioral flexibility in people with GAD, and should be expected to ultimately lead to decreased habitual responses (Roemer & Orsillo, 2002). The contemporary use of mindfulness as a treatment for anxiety was first demonstrated by Kabat-Zinn in the mid-1980s in pioneering work at the University of Massachusetts. He showed that in subjects with GAD who completed the 8-week MBSR program, there were both clinically and statistically significant decreases in depression and anxiety (Kabat-Zinn et al., 1992). At 3-year follow-up, these improvements were maintained, and the majority of participants reported ongoing meditation practice (Miller, Fletcher, & Kabat-Zinn, 1995). In a more recent randomized trial of MBSR versus cognitive-behavioral therapy, clinically meaningful changes on measures of social anxiety, mood, disability, and quality of life were reported for both groups with GAD (Koszycki, Benger, Shlik, & Bradwejn, 2007). The traditional cognitive-behavioral therapy group reported greater improvements in the core symptoms of GAD, compared with the MBSR group. In a recent Cochrane database review of meditation interventions and anxiety, the authors concluded that no recommendations could be made on the effectiveness of meditation therapy for anxiety disorders, given the lack of high-quality studies (Krisanaprakornkit, Krisanaprakornkit, Piyavhatkul, & Laopaiboon, 2006). To date, the studies of MBCT in anxiety disorders, although small, have yielded promising results. In a small, uncontrolled trial of MBCT for treatment of anxiety, subjects receiving MBCT had significantly lower anxiety, tension, worry, and depressive symptoms following the 8-week program (Evans et al., 2008). Although not statistically significant, clinically significant improvements in self-reported mindfulness were seen following MBCT training, such that the mindfulness scores at the conclusion of training approached values of a normative population. Compared with anxiety disorder education, subjects with anxiety or phobia disorder receiving MBCT had greater reductions in depression and anxiety following 8 weeks of therapy (Kim et al., 2009).

Pain

Individuals with chronic pain tend to become overly focused on their pain, have negative cognitions about their chronic situation, and develop unsuccessful patterns of coping with their pain that lead to reduced physical and psychological functioning. Attempts to directly control the sensation of pain has been shown to be associated with higher degrees of distress and disability (McCracken, Vowles, & Eccleston, 2005). In contrast, acceptance of chronic pain is associated with improved emotional, social, and physical functioning (McCracken & Eccleston, 2003). Furthermore, in structured laboratory experiments, the acceptance of pain leads to improved pain tolerance when compared with a condition of focused pain control (Gutiérrez, Luciano, Rodríguez, & Fink, 2004). Mindfulness training enables patients with chronic pain to allow the experience of pain without struggle or avoidance, and to be fully present and nonreactive in the face of chronic pain. Mindfulness has been shown to account for significant variance in measures of depression, pain-related anxiety, and physical and psychosocial disability, with higher degrees of mindfulness associated with improved functioning on all of the previously mentioned variables (McCracken, Gauntlett-Gilbert, & Vowles, 2007).

Some of the earliest studies of mindfulness were conducted in populations with chronic pain. In his original work, Kabat-Zinn showed that patients with chronic pain who participated in a 10-week mindfulness-skills training program had statistically significant reductions in measures of present-moment pain, negative body image, inhibition of activity by pain, symptoms, mood disturbance, and psychological symptomatology, including anxiety and depression. Also, pain-related drug use decreased and activity levels and feelings of self-esteem increased (Kabat-Zinn, Lipworth, & Burney, 1985). The durability of these changes was assessed at 15 months following the mindfulness training, and all outcomes remained significantly improved from baseline except for present-moment pain. Limitations of this work include the lack of an appropriate control group. More contemporary studies of pain and MBSR have shown that although pain tolerance significantly improved for mindfulness-trained participants, it was not related to the acquisition of mindfulness skills (Kingston, Chadwick, Meron, & Skinner, 2007). In a longitudinal study of 133 chronic pain patients nested within a larger prospective cohort study of heterogeneous patients participating in MBSR at a university-based integrative medicine center, investigators found significant improvements in pain intensity and functional limitations in patients with arthritis, back/neck pain, or two or more comorbid pain conditions following MBSR training. Patients with arthritis showed the greatest treatment effects for health-related quality of life and psychological distress. Patients with chronic headache/migraine experienced the smallest improvement in pain intensity and health-related quality of life, whereas patients with fibromyalgia had the smallest improvement in psychological distress (Rosenzweig et al., in press).

In an uncontrolled study of ACT therapy in patients with chronic back pain who participated in a 3–4 week residential program, investigators found a 41.2% reduction in depression, 25.0% reduction in physical disability, 39.3% reduction in psychosocial disability, 61.8% reduction in hours of rest during the day related to pain, and 48.2% improvement in a directly measured, repeated sit-to-stand performance (McCracken et al., 2005). They also reported significant reduction of pain medication use and primary care visits. All outcomes were related to increases in acceptance, although mindfulness was not assessed in this study. Mindfulness training appears to be useful for those who are experiencing chronic pain, although further rigorous, randomized, case-controlled studies are required to better investigate the impact of these interventions in patients with severe pain.

Cancer

Because of the potentially life-threatening outcome and treatment-related side effects, most people diagnosed with cancer report elevated levels of stress. Given this highly stressful situation, many patients with cancer develop depression, anxiety, and other mental health disturbances. From diagnosis, to treatment, to survivorship, and even the end of life, training in mindfulness can be valuable for those living with cancer. Several studies have evaluated the psychological effects of mindfulness training in patients with cancer, and shown significant improvement in psychological function following MBSR training (Carlson, Speca, Patel, & Goodey, 2003, 2004; Carlson & Garland, 2005; Chadwick et al., 2008; Hebert et al., 2001; Lengacher et al., 2009; Saxe et al., 2001; Speca, Carlson, Goodey, & Angen, 2000). A recent meta-analysis evaluating the impact of these studies revealed that most of the patients with cancer in the trials of MBSR have been highly educated women with breast cancer who are either early in their disease course or in remission (Ledesma & Kumano, 2009). The meta-analysis showed that overall mental health effect (of both controlled and observational studies) following MBSR training showed a moderate mean effect size ($d = 0.48$). A much smaller effect size for overall physiological change following MBSR training was reported in the meta-analysis ($d = 0.18$), and the authors suggest interpreting this result with caution, given the small number of subjects studied. Overall, whereas the improvements in mood, quality of life, sleep, and other subjective psychological outcomes are promising, research in this field is still in its infancy.

Geriatric Populations

Aging has been associated with increased psychological distress, which can be especially detrimental in older individuals whose health is often already compromised by chronic medical conditions. Interest is growing in the use of mindfulness interventions as a means to promote healthy aging (Yuen & Baime, 2006). In preliminary work from our community MBSR classes, we have shown that participants 60 years of age and older had improvements in overall psychological distress following MBSR training (Baime & Young, 2008). Clinically and statistically significant improvements in confusion, energy, depression, anxiety, anger, and vigor were also noted. Others are beginning to investigate the role of mindfulness in older populations, and it has recently been shown to be a potentially useful intervention in older individuals with chronic back pain (Morone, Greco, & Weiner, 2008). Although the initial findings are promising, additional work is necessary to more fully evaluate the theoretically beneficial impact of mindfulness on aging.

Chronic Medical Disease

Mindfulness would seem to offer significant benefits to individuals with chronic medical conditions. Unfortunately, there are few well-designed RCTs to support this notion. Many of the studies of the use of MBSR in chronic medical disease are limited by small sample sizes and suboptimal control groups. Small studies have suggested benefits of MBSR in patients with diabetes (Rosenzweig et al., 2007), heart disease (Tacón, McComb, Caldera, & Randolph, 2003), fibromyalgia (Goldenberg et al., 1994; Grossman, Tiefenthaler-Gilmer, Raysz, & Kesper, 2007; Kaplan, Goldenberg, & Galvin-Nadeau, 1993), rheumatoid arthritis (Zautra et al., 2008), HIV (Creswell, Myers, Cole, & Irwin, 2009), and organ transplantation (C. R. Gross et al., 2004, 2009; Kreitzer, Gross, Ye, Russas, & Treesak, 2005). Recently, a large RCT studying the effects of MBSR compared with an educational support group in patients with congestive heart failure (CHF) showed reductions in anxiety and depression. This effect was maintained at 1-year follow-up. Furthermore, the MBSR group had significantly better symptoms of CHF at 12 months, compared with control subjects. Given the promising beneficial effects of MBSR in the management of chronic disease, other large-scale trials similar to the well-designed CHF trial are warranted.

Conclusions

Each time that mindfulness and meditation have been introduced into a new culture, they have changed to meet the needs of that specific time and place (Fields, 1992). In our own culture, mindfulness is undergoing a transformation that is more radical than what has ever been seen before. Mindfulness is shifting from a traditionally spiritual discipline into a medical treatment. We do not know the final form that mindfulness will take in our culture, and we cannot predict the specific needs that it will be used to meet. But it is clear that our medical system—and our culture—have begun to recognize what other cultures have known for thousands of years: that mindfulness and meditation provide tools that help individuals to cope and to grow. Although much remains to be learned, it seems certain that mindfulness-based interventions have a future in both Western medicine and Western life.

References

Baer, R. A. (2003). Mindfulness training as a clinical intervention: A conceptual and empirical review. *Clinical Psychology: Science and Practice, 10*(2), 125–125.

Baer, R. A., Smith, G. T., & Allen, K. B. (2004). Assessment of mindfulness by self-report: The Kentucky inventory of mindfulness skills. *Assessment, 11*(3), 191–206.

Baer, R. A., Smith, G. T., Hopkins, J., Krietemeyer, J., & Toney, L. (2006). Using self-report assessment methods to explore facets of mindfulness. *Assessment, 13*(1), 27–45.

Baer, R. A., Smith, G. T., Lykins, E., Button, D., Krietemeyer, J., Sauer, S., et al. (2008). Construct validity of the five facet mindfulness questionnaire in meditating and nonmeditating samples. *Assessment, 15*(3), 329–342.

Baime, M. J., & Young, L. A. (2008). Mindfulness-based stress reduction decreases psychological distress in older adults [Abstract]. *Journal of Behavioral Medicine, 35*(Suppl. 1), s103.

Barnhofer, T., Crane, C., Hargus, E., Amarasinghe, M., Winder, R., & Williams, J. M. (2009). Mindfulness-based cognitive therapy as a treatment for chronic depression: A preliminary study. *Behaviour Research and Therapy, 47*(5), 366-373.

Bishop, S. R., Lau, M., Shapiro, S., Carlson, L., Anderson, N. D., Carmody, J., et al. (2004). Mindfulness: A proposed operational definition. *Clinical Psychology: Science and Practice, 11*(3), 230–241.

Brown, K. W., & Ryan, R. M. (2003). The benefits of being present: Mindfulness and its role in psychological well-being. *Journal of Personality and Social Psychology, 84*(4), 822–848.

Brown, K. W., Ryan, R. M., & Creswell, J. D. (2007). Mindfulness: Theoretical foundations and evidence for its salutary effects. *Psychological Inquiry, 18*, 211–237.

Buchheld, N., Grossman, P., & Walach, H. (2001). Measuring mindfulness in insight meditation (vipassana) and meditation-based psychotherapy: The development of the Freiburg mindfulness inventory (FMI). *Journal for Meditation and Meditation Research, 1*, 11–34.

Cardaciotto, L., Herbert, J. D., Forman, E. M., Moitra, E., & Farrow, V. (2008). The assessment of present-moment awareness and acceptance: The Philadelphia mindfulness scale. *Assessment, 15*(2), 204–223.

Carlson, L. E., & Garland, S. N. (2005). Impact of mindfulness-based stress reduction (MBSR) on sleep, mood, stress and fatigue symptoms in cancer outpatients. *International Journal of Behavioral Medicine, 12*(4), 278–285.

Carlson, L. E., Speca, M., Patel, K. D., & Goodey, E. (2003). Mindfulness-based stress reduction in relation to quality of life, mood, symptoms of stress, and immune parameters in breast and prostate cancer outpatients. *Psychosomatic Medicine, 65*(4), 571–581.

Carlson, L. E., Speca, M., Patel, K. D., & Goodey, E. (2004). Mindfulness-based stress reduction in relation to quality of life, mood, symptoms of stress and levels of cortisol, dehydroepiandrosterone sulfate (DHEAS) and melatonin in breast and prostate cancer outpatients. *Psychoneuroendocrinology, 29*(4), 448–474.

Carmody, J., & Baer, R. A. (2008). Relationships between mindfulness practice and levels of mindfulness, medical and psychological symptoms and well-being in a mindfulness-based stress reduction program. *Journal of Behavioral Medicine, 31*(1), 23–33.

Carmody, J., & Baer, R. A. (2009). How long does a mindfulness-based stress reduction program need to be? A review of class contact hours and effect sizes for psychological distress. *Journal of Clinical Psychology, 65*(6), 627–638.

Chadwick, P., Hember, M., Symes, J., Peters, E., Kuipers, E., & Dagnan, D. (2008). Responding mindfully to unpleasant thoughts and images: Reliability and validity of the Southampton Mindfulness Questionnaire (SMQ). *British Journal of Clinical Psychology, 47*(Pt. 4), 451–455.

Chiesa, A., & Serretti, A. (2009). Mindfulness-based stress reduction for stress management in healthy people: A review and meta-analysis. *Journal of Alternative and Complementary Medicine, 15*(5), 593-600.

Creswell, J. D., Myers, H. F., Cole, S. W., & Irwin, M. R. (2009). Mindfulness meditation training effects on CD4+ T lymphocytes in HIV-1 infected adults: A small randomized controlled trial. *Brain, Behavior, & Immunity, 23*(2), 184–188.

Eisendrath, S. J., Delucchi, K., Bitner, R., Fenimore, P., Smit, M., & McLane, M. (2008). Mindfulness-based cognitive therapy for treatment-resistant depression: A pilot study. *Psychotherapy and Psychosomatics, 77*(5), 319–320.

Evans, S., Ferrando, S., Findler, M., Stowell, C., Smart, C., & Haglin, D. (2008). Mindfulness-based cognitive therapy for generalized anxiety disorder. *Journal of Anxiety Disorders, 22*(4), 716–721.

Feldman, G., Hayes, A., Kumar, S., Greeson, J., & Laurenceau, J. (2007). Mindfulness and emotion regulation: The development and initial validation of the cognitive and affective mindfulness scale-revised (CMS-R). *Journal of Psychopathology and Behavioral Assessment, 29*(3), 177–190.

Fields, R. (1992). *How the swans came to the lake: A narrative history of Buddhism in America* (3rd ed.). Boston: Shambhala Publications.

Finucane, A., & Mercer, S. W. (2006). An exploratory mixed methods study of the acceptability and effectiveness of mindfulness-based cognitive therapy for patients with active depression and anxiety in primary care. *BMC Psychiatry, 6*, 14.

Forman, E. M., Herbert, J. D., Moitra, E., Yeomans, P. D., & Geller, P. A. (2007). A randomized controlled effectiveness trial of acceptance and commitment therapy and cognitive therapy for anxiety and depression. *Behavior Modification, 31*(6), 772–799.

Goldenberg, D. L., Kaplan, K. H., Nadeau, M. G., Brodeur, C., Smith, S., & Schmid, C. H. (1994). A controlled study of a stress-reduction, cognitive-behavioral treatment program in fibromyalgia. *Journal of Musculoskeletal Pain, 2*(2), 53–66.

Gross, C. R., Kreitzer, M. J., Reilly-Spong, M., Winbush, N. Y., Schomaker, E. K., & Thomas, W. (2009). Mindfulness meditation training to reduce symptom distress in transplant patients: Rationale, design, and experience with a recycled waitlist. *Clinical Trials, 6*(1), 76–89.

Gross, C. R., Kreitzer, M. J., Russas, V., Treesak, C., Frazier, P. A., & Hertz, M. I. (2004). Mindfulness meditation to reduce symptoms after organ transplant: A pilot study. *Advances in Mind–Body Medicine, 20*(2), 20–29.

Gross, J. J. (2002). Emotion regulation: Affective, cognitive, and social consequences. *Psychophysiology, 39*(3), 281–291.

Grossman, P. (2008). On measuring mindfulness in psychosomatic and psychological research. *Journal of Psychosomatic Research, 64*(4), 405–408.

Grossman, P., Niemann, L., Schmidt, S., & Walach, H. (2004). Mindfulness-based stress reduction and health benefits: A meta-analysis. *Journal of Psychosomatic Research, 57*(1), 35–43.

Grossman, P., Tiefenthaler-Gilmer, U., Raysz, A., & Kesper, U. (2007). Mindfulness training as an intervention for fibromyalgia: Evidence of postintervention and 3-year follow-up benefits in well-being. *Psychotherapy and Psychosomatics, 76*(4), 226–233.

Gutiérrez, O., Luciano, C., Rodríguez, M., & Fink, B. C. (2004). Comparison between an acceptance-based and a cognitive-control-based protocol for coping with pain. *Behavior Therapy, 35*(4), 767–783.

Hayes, S. C. (2004). Acceptance and commitment therapy and the new behavior therapies: Mindfulness, acceptance, and relationship. In S. C. Hayes, V. M. Follette, & M. M. Linehan (Eds.), *Mindfulness and acceptance: Expanding the cognitive-behavioral tradition.* (pp. 1–29). New York: Guilford.

Hayes, S. C., & Shenk, C. (2004). Operationalizing mindfulness without unnecessary attachments. *Clinical Psychology: Science and Practice, 11*(3), 249–254.

Hayes, S. C., Wilson, K. G., Gifford, E. V., Follette, V. M., & Strosahl, K. (1996). Experiential avoidance and behavioral disorders: A functional dimensional approach to diagnosis and treatment. *Journal of Consulting and Clinical Psychology, 64*(6), 1152–1168.

Hebert, J. R., Ebbeling, C. B., Olendzki, B. C., Hurley, T. G., Ma, Y., Saal, N., et al. (2001). Change in women's diet and body mass following intensive intervention for early-stage breast cancer. *Journal of the American Dietetic Association, 101*(4), 421–431.

Jha, A. P., Krompinger, J., & Baime, M. J. (2007). Mindfulness training modifies subsystems of attention. *Cognitive, Affective & Behavioral Neuroscience, 7*(2), 109–119.

Kabat-Zinn, J. (2003). Mindfulness-based interventions in context: Past, present, and future. *Clinical Psychology: Science and Practice, 10*(2), 144–156.

Kabat-Zinn, J. (2005). *Full catastrophe living: Using the wisdom of your body and mind to face stress, pain, and illness: 15th anniversary edition.* New York: Delta Trade Paperback/Bantam Dell.

Kabat-Zinn, J., Lipworth, L., & Burney, R. (1985). The clinical use of mindfulness meditation for the self-regulation of chronic pain. *Journal of Behavioral Medicine, 8*(2), 163–190.

Kabat-Zinn, J., Massion, A. O., Kristeller, J., Peterson, L. G., Fletcher, K. E., Pbert, L., et al. (1992). Effectiveness of a meditation-based stress reduction program in the treatment of anxiety disorders. *American Journal of Psychiatry, 149*(7), 936–943.

Kaplan, K. H., Goldenberg, D. L., & Galvin-Nadeau, M. (1993). The impact of a meditation-based stress reduction program on fibromyalgia. *General Hospital Psychiatry, 15*(5), 284–289.

Kenny, M. A., & Williams, J. M. G. (2007). Treatment-resistant depressed patients show a good response to mindfulness-based cognitive therapy. *Behaviour Research and Therapy, 45*(3), 617–625.

Kim, Y. W., Lee, S. H., Choi, T. K., Suh, S. Y., Kim, B., Kim, C. M., et al. (2009). Effectiveness of mindfulness-based cognitive therapy as an adjuvant to pharmacotherapy in patients with panic disorder or generalized anxiety disorder. *Depression and Anxiety, 26*(7), 601–606.

Kingston, J., Chadwick, P., Meron, D., & Skinner, T. C. (2007). A pilot randomized control trial investigating the effect of mindfulness practice on pain tolerance, psychological well-being, and physiological activity. *Journal of Psychosomatic Research, 62*(3), 297–300.

Kingston, T., Dooley, B., Bates, A., Lawlor, E., & Malone, K. (2007). Mindfulness-based cognitive therapy for residual depressive symptoms. *Psychology & Psychotherapy: Theory, Research & Practice, 80*(2), 193–203.

Koszycki, D., Benger, M., Shlik, J., & Bradwejn, J. (2007). Randomized trial of a meditation-based stress reduction program and cognitive behavior therapy in generalized social anxiety disorder. *Behaviour Research and Therapy, 45*(10), 2518–2526.

Kreitzer, M. J., Gross, C. R., Ye, X., Russas, V., & Treesak, C. (2005). Longitudinal impact of mindfulness meditation on illness burden in solid-organ transplant recipients. *Progress in Transplantation, 15*(2), 166–172.

Krisanaprakornkit, T., Krisanaprakornkit, W., Piyavhatkul, N., & Laopaiboon, M. (2006). Meditation therapy for anxiety disorders. *Cochrane Database of Systematic Reviews (Online), 1*(1). Retrieved November 27, 2009, from http://www.ncbi.nlm.nih.gov/pubmed/16437509

Kumar, S. M. (2005). *Grieving mindfully: A compassionate and spiritual guide to coping with loss.* Oakland, CA: New Harbinger.

Kuyken, W., Byford, S., Taylor, R. S., Watkins, E., Holden, E., White, K., et al. (2008). Mindfulness-based cognitive therapy to prevent relapse in recurrent depression. *Journal of Consulting and Clinical Psychology, 76*(6), 966–978.

Lau, M. A., Bishop, S. R., Segal, Z. V., Buis, T., Anderson, N. D., Carlson, L., et al. (2006). The Toronto mindfulness scale: Development and validation. *Journal of Clinical Psychology, 62*(12), 1445–1467.

Lazar, S. W., Kerr, C. E., Wasserman, R. H., Gray, J. R., Greve, D. N., Treadway, M. T., et al. (2005). Meditation experience is associated with increased cortical thickness. *Neuroreport, 16*(17), 1893–1897.

Ledesma, D., & Kumano, H. (2009). Mindfulness-based stress reduction and cancer: A meta-analysis. *Psycho-Oncology, 18*(6), 571–579.

Lengacher, C. A., Johnson-Mallard, V., Post-White, J., Moscoso, M. S., Jacobsen, P. B., Klein, T. W., et al. (2009). Randomized controlled trial of mindfulness-based stress reduction (MBSR) for survivors of breast cancer. *Psycho-Oncology.* Epub ahead of print. Retrieved August 18, 2009, from http://www.3.Interscience.Wiley.com/cgi-bin/fulltext/122202000/PDFSTART

Linehan, M. M. (1993). *Skills training manual for treating borderline personality disorder.* New York: Guilford.

Linehan, M. M., Armstrong, H. E., Suarez, A., Allmon, D., & Heard, H. L. (1991). Cognitive-behavioral treatment of chronically parasuicidal borderline patients. *Archives of General Psychiatry, 48*(12), 1060–1064.

Luoma, J. B., Hayes, S. C., & Walser, R. D. (2007). *Learning ACT: An acceptance and commitment therapy skills-training manual for therapists.* Oakland, CA: New Harbinger.

Lynch, T. R., Chapman, A. L., Rosenthal, M. Z., Kuo, J. R., & Linehan, M. M. (2006). Mechanisms of change in dialectical behavior therapy: Theoretical and empirical observations. *Journal of Clinical Psychology, 62*(4), 459–480.

Ma, S. H., & Teasdale, J. D. (2004). Mindfulness-based cognitive therapy for depression: Replication and exploration of differential relapse prevention effects. *Journal of Consulting and Clinical Psychology, 72*(1), 31–40.

McCracken, L. M., & Eccleston, C. (2003). Coping or acceptance: What to do about chronic pain? *Pain, 105*(1-2), 197–204.

McCracken, L. M., Gauntlett-Gilbert, J., & Vowles, K. E. (2007). The role of mindfulness in a contextual cognitive-behavioral analysis of chronic pain-related suffering and disability. *Pain, 131*(1-2), 63–69.

McCracken, L. M., Vowles, K. E., & Eccleston, C. (2005). Acceptance-based treatment for persons with complex, long standing chronic pain: A preliminary analysis of treatment outcome in comparison to a waiting phase. *Behaviour Research and Therapy, 43*(10), 1335–1346.

Miller, J. J., Fletcher, K., & Kabat-Zinn, J. (1995). Three-year follow-up and clinical implications of a mindfulness meditation-based stress reduction intervention in the treatment of anxiety disorders. *General Hospital Psychiatry, 17*(3), 192–200.

Morone, N. E., Greco, C. M., & Weiner, D. K. (2008). Mindfulness meditation for the treatment of chronic low back pain in older adults: A randomized controlled pilot study. *Pain, 134*(3), 310–319.

Posner, M. I., & Rothbart, M. K. (2007). Research on attention networks as a model for the integration of psychological science. *Annual Review of Psychology, 58,* 1–23.

Reibel, D. K., Greeson, J. M., Brainard, G. C., & Rosenzweig, S. (2001). Mindfulness-based stress reduction and health-related quality of life in a heterogeneous patient population. *General Hospital Psychiatry, 23*(4), 183–192.

Roemer, L., & Orsillo, S. M. (2002). Expanding our conceptualization of and treatment for generalized anxiety disorder: Integrating mindfulness/acceptance-based approaches with existing cognitive-behavioral models. *Clinical Psychology: Science and Practice, 9*(1), 54–68.

Rosenzweig, S., Greeson, J. M., Reibel, D. K., Green, J. S., Jasser, S. A., & Beasley, D. (in press). Mindfulness-based stress reduction for chronic pain conditions: Variation in treatment outcomes and role of home meditation practice. *Journal of Psychosomatic Research.*

Rosenzweig, S., Reibel, D. K., Greeson, J. M., Edman, J. S., Jasser, S. A., McMearty, K. D., et al. (2007). Mindfulness-based stress reduction is associated with improved glycemic control in type 2 diabetes mellitus: A pilot study. *Alternative Therapies in Health and Medicine, 13*(5), 36–38.

Saxe, G. A., Hebert, J. R., Carmody, J. F., Kabat-Zinn, J., Rosenzweig, P. H., Jarzobski, D., et al. (2001). Can diet in conjunction with stress reduction affect the rate of increase in prostate specific antigen after biochemical recurrence of prostate cancer? *Journal of Urology, 166*(6), 2202–2207.

Segal, Z. V., Williams, J. M. G., & Teasdale, J. D. (2002). *Mindfulness-based cognitive therapy for depression: A new approach to preventing relapse.* New York: Guilford.

Shapiro, S. L., Carlson, L. E., Astin, J. A., & Freedman, B. (2006). Mechanisms of mindfulness. *Journal of Clinical Psychology, 62*(3), 373–386.

Siegel, D. J. (2007). *The mindful brain: Reflection and attunement in the cultivation of well-being.* New York: W. W. Norton.

Speca, M., Carlson, L. E., Goodey, E., & Angen, M. (2000). A randomized, wait-list controlled clinical trial: The effect of a mindfulness meditation-based stress reduction program on mood and symptoms of stress in cancer outpatients. *Psychosomatic Medicine, 62*(5), 613–622.

Tacón, A. M., McComb, J., Caldera, Y., & Randolph, P. (2003). Mindfulness meditation, anxiety reduction, and heart disease: A pilot study. *Family & Community Health, 26*(1), 25–33.

Tang, Y., Ma, Y., Wang, J., Fan, Y., Feng, S., Lu, Q., et al. (2007). Short-term meditation training improves attention and self-regulation. *Proceedings of the National Academy of Sciences of the United States of America, 104*(43), 17152–17156.

Teasdale, J. D., Segal, Z. V., Williams, J. M., Ridgeway, V. A., Soulsby, J. M., & Lau, M. A. (2000). Prevention of relapse/recurrence in major depression by mindfulness-based cognitive therapy. *Journal of Consulting and Clinical Psychology, 68*(4), 615–623.

Thompson, B. L., & Waltz, J. (2007). Everyday mindfulness and mindfulness meditation: Overlapping constructs or not? *Personality and Individual Differences, 43*(7), 1875–1885.

Walach, H., Buchheld, N., Buttenmüller, V., Kleinknecht, N., & Schmidt, S. (2006). Measuring mindfulness—The Freiburg Mindfulness Inventory (FMI). *Personality and Individual Differences, 40*(8), 1543–1555.

Yuen, E. J., & Baime, M. J. (2006). Meditation and healthy aging. In E. R. Mackenzie & B. Rakel (Eds.), *Complementary and alternative medicine for older adults: A guide to holistic approaches to healthy aging* (pp. 233–270). New York: Springer Publishing Company.

Zautra, A. J., Davis, M. C., Reich, J. W., Nicassario, P., Tennen, H., Finan, P., et al. (2008). Comparison of cognitive behavioral and mindfulness meditation interventions on adaptation to rheumatoid arthritis for patients with and without history of recurrent depression. *Journal of Consulting and Clinical Psychology, 76*(3), 408–421.

Cognitive-Behavioral Case Formulation and Treatment Design

10

Arthur M. Nezu
Christine Maguth Nezu

Introduction

As attested to throughout this book, the evidence-based nature characterizing the wide variety of contemporary cognitive and behavioral therapies (CBT) has increasingly led primary care professionals to adopt this approach when making a psychotherapy referral, either alone or in combination with medication, in order to address various mental health problems initially identified in their practice (Durham, Swan, & Fisher, 2000). However, similar to standard mental health outpatient clinics, routine primary care facilities and their referral sources are unlikely to exclusively provide services to those patients who mirror the research participants meeting all the inclusion/exclusion criteria required by rigorous randomized clinical trials. In other words, due to the complexities of most presenting cases in a primary care setting (e.g., comorbid psychiatric diagnoses, comorbid medical illness, diverse ethnicities), the CBT practitioner often needs to develop a unique case conceptualization for a given patient that helps guide the process of treatment planning (Nezu & Nezu, 1989, 1993). The influence of an accurate and valid case formulation on subsequent treatment planning can be observed in various notable quotations, such as "a problem well-defined is half-solved," and "measure twice—cut once." In other words, the more accurate an initial formulation, the more likely that a treatment plan designed for a given patient will be appropriate and effective, especially with regard to more complicated cases. In this chapter, we address these issues by providing a problem-solving-based model of CBT case formulation and treatment design that is quite useful for therapists treating primary care medical patients.

What Is Case Formulation?

Case formulation across psychotherapies can be viewed as a set of hypotheses, generally framed by a particular personality theory or conceptual orientation, regarding what variables serve as causes, triggers, and/or maintaining factors of an individual's emotional, psychological, interpersonal, and behavior problems (Eells, 1997). It is a description of a patient's complaints and symptoms of distress, as well as an organizing mechanism to help the clinician understand how such complaints came into being, how various symptoms co-exist, what environmental or intrapersonal stimuli trigger such problems, and why such symptoms persist (Nezu, Nezu, & Cos, 2007; Nezu, Nezu, & Lombardo, 2004).

During this process, it can be said that the therapist begins to develop a "patient story." Such a story offers a description of the variety of variables within the person's life that are involved in both the emergence and maintenance of a given set of distressing symptoms (i.e., the reason for seeking, or being referred for, psychotherapy), as well as a proposed ending representing treatment goals. Having such a narrative provides a concrete framework within which the practitioner can begin to think about the means required to reach such goals (i.e., the treatment plan).

What Is Cognitive-Behavioral Therapy?

Before we describe our model of case formulation, it is important to provide a definition of CBT. We begin by noting that "cognitive-behavior therapy" is not a singular therapeutic strategy, but rather the umbrella term for an expanding group of behavioral and cognitive treatment techniques and approaches that share a common history and worldview. For example, O'Donohue, Fisher, and Hayes (2003) include over 65 differing behavioral and cognitive therapy techniques in their encyclopedic compendia (see also Freeman, Felgoise, Nezu, Nezu, & Reinecke, 2005). Such clinical strategies include those emanating from the application of learning theories, such as those based on operant (e.g., contingency management strategies) and classical (e.g., exposure-based approaches) conditioning paradigms, more cognitive-based approaches, such as cognitive restructuring strategies, self-control therapies, and problem-solving-based therapies, as well as those recently characterized as "third wave" treatment strategies, such as acceptance and commitment therapy, dialectical behavioral therapy, and functional analytic psychotherapy.

As such, a more accurate label for this approach would be *behavioral and cognitive therapies* (or cognitive and behavioral therapies). Therefore, the acronym *CBT* used throughout this chapter will refer to the myriad of such treatment strategies and not a specific singular approach. Note that the order C-B-T, rather than B-C-T, is used for convention's sake, rather than suggesting the primacy of one type of strategy over the other.

CBT Case Formulation

Our model of CBT case formulation is based on three general principles. First, we attempt to understand, describe, and predict human functioning, including psychopathology, within the framework of a functional analysis. Second, we rely heavily on the empirical literature as a means of identifying meaningful clinical targets that are specific to a given psychological problem, as well as clinical interventions geared to impact meaningfully on such problems. Last, we deliberately characterize the CBT clinician as a "problem solver."

Functional Analysis

A functional analysis involves a CBT practitioner's assessment-derived integration of the important functional relationships among variables; that is, the effects of a given variable on others. Haynes and O'Brien (2000) define a functional analysis as a synthesis of several judgments about a patient's problems and goals, related causal and mediating variables, and the functional relationships among such factors.

In conceptualizing treatment goals, it is helpful to differentiate between ultimate outcome and instrumental outcome goals (Rosen & Proctor, 1981). *Ultimate outcome* (UO) goals are those general therapy goals that represent the reason why treatment is initially undertaken, for example, to improve a marital relationship, decrease a blood-injury phobia, or become less depressed. In addition, such outcomes reflect the objectives toward which treatment efforts should be directed. *Instrumental outcome* (IO) goals are those outcomes that represent the "instruments" by which other outcomes can be attained. More specifically, IOs, depending on their functional relationships to other variables, can have an impact on UOs (e.g., decreasing one's ruminative thinking patterns might reduce depression), or influence other IOs within a hypothesized causal chain (e.g., improving individuals' coping ability can increase their sense of self-efficacy, which, in turn, may decrease depression).

Clinically, we suggest that IOs represent a clinician's hypotheses regarding those variables that are posited to be causally related to the UOs. Alternatively, using language from the research laboratory, IOs can be thought of as *independent variables* (IV), whereas UOs reflect *dependent variables* (DV). As such, IOs can further be viewed as *mediators*, which are those elements that account for or explain the relationship between two other variables, similar to a causal mechanism (i.e., the mechanism of action by which the IV influences the DV). In addition, they can also serve as *moderators*, or those types of factors (e.g., patient characteristics) that can influence the strength and/or direction of the relationship between two or more other variables (Haynes & O'Brien, 2000). In general, the underlying assumption of a functional analysis is that influencing various IOs will, either directly or indirectly, lead to achieving various UOs. As such, IO variables represent potential targets for clinical interventions and crucial ingredients of the case formulation.

Evidence-Based Approach

A CBT orientation has traditionally defined itself as being an evidence-based approach to understanding and treating human problems. For example, a CBT conceptualization regarding the etiopathogenesis of a particular psychological disorder is based less on a given therapist's experience and theoretical conjecture, and more on well-controlled research studies involving actual patient populations. This is not to suggest that noncontrolled research sources of information are worthless; rather, a CBT worldview extends primacy to the validity of information if derived from scientific endeavors.

However, as noted previously, the extant empirical literature regarding the pathogenesis of any psychological disorder, as well as its treatment, is limited in its ability to provide idiographic prescriptions for *all* patients experiencing that given disorder. One reason is the difference between clinical reality and the necessarily restrictive nature of research studies regarding the need to impose limiting inclusion and exclusion criteria, thus only infrequently addressing various individual difference factors (e.g., comorbidity, ethnic background, age, socioeconomic status [SES]).

In addition, a variety of causal hypotheses often exist regarding various IO–UO relationships for a given clinical disorder. For example, several theories exist regarding the etiopathogenesis of major depression, one of the most common disorders in primary care. These conceptual models differ in the degree to which they emphasize or prioritize certain IO variables, such as maladaptive cognitions (Dozois & Beck, 2008), decreased levels of positive social experiences (Hoberman & Lewinsohn, 1985), ineffective problem-solving ability (Nezu, Nezu, & Clark, 2008), ruminative response style (Wisco & Nolen-Hoeksema, 2008), deficient social skills (e.g., Hersen, Bellack, & Himmelhoch, 1980), and negative cognitive style (Alloy, Abramson, Keyser, Gerstein, & Sylvia, 2008). Although these particular IO–UO relationships are generally supported by research, no singular independent variable has been found to account for 100% of the variance in explaining why a given individual becomes depressed. Thus, prematurely taking an "off the shelf" intervention, even if it has been found to be effective via scientific scrutiny, and applying it to a given primary care patient in the absence of assessing the specific mechanism of action responsible for the presenting problem can not only be ineffective, it can also be considered potentially unethical.

Given the previously mentioned limitations of the extant empirical literature, the CBT clinician needs to adapt existing evidence-based nomothetic knowledge in a tailored fashion to multitudes of differing patients in a meaningful way. We suggest that casting the practitioner in the role of problem solver can facilitate the effectiveness of this adaptation, which reflects the third major precept of our model.

Therapy as Problem Solving

In viewing the therapist as a problem solver, we define a "clinician's problem" as one where he or she is presented with a set of complaints, distressing symptoms, and/or concerns by an individual seeking help to reduce or minimize such difficulties. This situation can be defined as a problem in the sense that patients' "current states" represent a discrepancy from their "desired states," whereby a variety of impediments (e.g., obstacles, conflicts, lack of resources) prevent or make it difficult for such individuals to reach their goals without a professional's aid. Such barriers to goal attainment can include characteristics of patients themselves, as well as aspects of their physical and/or social environment.

Given this perspective, it can be suggested that the clinician's "solution" is defined by a treatment plan that is geared to help patients achieve their goals. Identifying the most efficacious treatment plan for a given client who is experiencing a particular disorder, given his or her unique history and current life circumstances, by a certain therapist, becomes the overall goal of therapy.

The Problem-Solving Process

In conceptualizing the CBT practitioner as a problem solver, we draw heavily from our work regarding a prescriptive model of social problem solving (e.g., D'Zurilla & Nezu, 2007; Nezu, 2004; Nezu, Nezu, & D'Zurilla, 2007). Adapted for the current purpose, our model of CBT case formulation incorporates two major problem-solving processes—problem orientation and rational problem solving.

Problem orientation refers to the set of orienting responses (e.g., general beliefs, assumptions, appraisals, expectations) one engages in when attempting to understand and react to problems in living. Basically, this set can be thought of as an individual's *worldview* regarding problems. In the present context, a *clinician's worldview* would involve a cohesive framework that guides attempts to understand, explain, predict, and change human behavior. Our particular CBT world view emphasizes two major themes—planned critical multiplism and general systems.

Planned critical multiplism is the methodological perspective that advocates the use of "multiple operationalism" (Shadish, 1993). With regard to case formulation, this underscores the idea that a particular symptom or set of symptoms can be engendered by multiple permutations of multiple causal factors amid multiple causal paths. For example, when developing a case formulation for a depressed client, the CBT practitioner should search for both confirming *and* disconfirming data to determine whether certain empirically supported causal variables (e.g., cognitive distortions, medically related difficulties, poor self-control skills, ineffective problem solving, low rate of positive reinforcement) is relevant, operative, and meaningful to *this* particular patient. This suggests a more broad-based initial assessment that includes multiple lines of inquiry, as compared with using only one's favorite assessment tool (Nezu, Nezu, & Foster, 2000). Moreover, the primary care physician is not likely to have previously engaged in a comprehensive assessment, but may offer an initial set of recommendations regarding either the nature of the problems (e.g., major depressive disorder) and/or the suspected mechanisms of action "causing" the problem (e.g., poor coping ability). Whereas such sources of information are important, they should only be used within the context of a more comprehensive assessment.

A *general systems* perspective emphasizes the notion that IO and UO variables can relate to each other in mutually interactive ways, rather than in a simple unidirectional and linear fashion (Nezu, Nezu, Friedman, & Haynes, 1997). As an example, consider how various biological, psychological, and social factors can interact with each other in initiating and maintaining various nonbiologically caused distressing physical symptoms (e.g., noncardiac chest pain, fibromyalgia). Early imitative learning within a family, where a parent responds to stress with undue physical symptoms, can serve as a psychological vulnerability factor that influences the manner in which a child interprets the experience of physical symptoms (i.e., gastrointestinal distress) under stressful circumstances. Such cognitive factors then can influence his or her behavior (e.g., avoiding stress, seeking out his or her parents' reassurance, focusing undue attention on the distress "caused" by the symptoms). This, in turn, can lead to parental reinforcement of the behavior and an exacerbation of the symptoms, which can then lead to an intensification of the child's beliefs concerning appropriate behavior under certain circumstances, and so forth (Nezu, Nezu, & Lombardo, 2001).

As such, the CBT clinician should assess the manner in which such variables interact with each other as a means of obtaining a more complete picture of a patient's *unique network or set of behavioral chains*. This allows one to better identify those IO variables that play key roles within the case formulation in order to prioritize such variables as initial treatment targets. In addition, this approach enables the therapist to delineate numerous potential targets to decrease depression simultaneously (e.g., changing negative thinking, decreasing maladaptive behavior, improving negative mood), thereby increasing the likelihood of success if a group of such variables all become targets of effective interventions.

Rational problem solving entails a set of specific cognitive and behavioral operations that help to solve problems effectively. These include: (a) *problem definition and formulation* (i.e., specifying a set of realistic goals to better direct further problem-solving efforts and delineating specific barriers to goal attainment), (b) *generation of alternatives* (i.e., brainstorming a pool of possible solutions to increase the likelihood that the most effective ideas will be ultimately identified), (c) *decision making* (i.e., conducting a systematic cost-benefit analysis of the consequences of these alternatives if carried out and developing an overall solution plan based on selecting the more effective solution ideas), and (d) *solution evaluation* (i.e., monitoring and evaluating the effectiveness of a solution plan after it is implemented). Using these specific problem-solving operations, within the context of the specified problem orientation, provides for the process by which to conduct an effective case formulation, as well as to design an efficacious treatment plan.

Developing a Case Formulation

The steps in developing a CBT case formulation include: (a) delineating patient-specific UOs goals, (b) identifying patient-specific IO variables, (c) conducting a functional analysis, (d) developing a clinical pathogenesis map, (e) selecting initial treatment targets, and (f) evaluating the validity of the case formulation for a given patient.

Step 1: Identifying UOs

In beginning this step, we advocate conceptualizing the overall assessment process as a "funnel" in order to be consistent with our critical multiplism orientation.

This view suggests that the CBT clinician identify possible difficulties that a patient is experiencing across a wide range of life domains, such as interpersonal relationships (e.g., marital, family, parent-child, friends), career, job, finances, sex, physical health, education, leisure, and religion, rather than exclusively focusing on a singular domain. As accumulating evidence indicates that no problems exist in a given domain, the focus of the assessment process narrows ("going down the funnel"). UOs are likely to be couched in terms of possible treatment goals, such as "improving my marriage," "making an important career decision," "improving my physical health," "decreasing my depression," or "getting over my anxiety." As a function of changes that can occur due to continued assessment or treatment, UOs may be discarded, modified, or new ones added by the patient or therapist.

Step 2: Identifying Patient-Specific IO Variables

This next step involves identifying those IO variables that are hypothetically related to the delineated UO goals. To ensure that one is able to conduct a comprehensive review of the possible relevant IO variables, we strongly recommend that the following dimensions be considered: (a) patient-related variables, and (b) environment-related variables.

Patient-Related Variables

This dimension refers to those factors that involve the patient him- or herself, including behavioral, affective, cognitive, biological, and sociocultural variables. For the purposes of the case formulation process, problem *behaviors* can be globally categorized as either behavioral deficits or excesses. Examples of behavioral *deficits* include poor social skills, deficits in daily living skills, or poor self-control. Behavioral *excesses* might include compulsive behavior, avoidance of anxiety-provoking stimuli, frequent negative self-evaluation, or aggressive actions. Problematic *affect* involves the wide array of negative emotions and mood states, such as anxiety, depression, hopelessness, fear, anger, and hostility.

Cognitive factors include both deficiencies and distortions. *Cognitive deficiencies* can be considered absences or limitations in one's thinking processes, such as the failure to contemplate the consequences of one's actions. *Cognitive distortions* refer to errors in one's processing or interpretation of information, such as misperceptions of certain events due to dichotomous thinking.

Biological variables include the wide array of physiological, medical, and physical factors that can be problems by themselves, or variables that are functionally related to a patient's psychosocial problems. These can include such factors as a medical illness, physical limitation or disability, side effects of medication, or a biological vulnerability to heightened arousal under stress. In addition, this category can include certain demographic characteristics, such as a patient's gender or age, particularly when such variables serve as a moderator of the prevalence or manifestation of a particular disorder or set of symptoms.

Sociocultural variables include the myriad range of individual background variables, including ethnicity, sexual orientation, sex roles, culture, and SES. The importance of considering ethnic background when developing a case formulation is emphasized in the most recent version of the *Diagnostic and Statistical Manual of Mental Disorders* (*DSM-IV-TR*; American Psychiatric Association, 2000). Specifically, the *DSM-IV-TR* recommends that clinicians consider five categories when working with multicultural environments: (a) the cultural identity of the individual (e.g., what is the person's self-identified cultural group, his or her degree of acculturation, as well as his or her current involvement in the host culture?); (b) the cultural explanation of the individual's disorder (e.g., what are the causal attributions and significance of the "condition" that is promulgated by the individual's culture?); (c) cultural factors related to one's psychosocial environment and levels of functioning (e.g., what is the availability of social support? What is the cultural interpretation of social stressors?); (d) cultural elements of the relationship between the person and the clinician (e.g., what are the differences in both culture and social status between the clinician and the patient?); and (e) overall assessment for diagnosis and care (e.g., what are the cultural factors that might impact upon the patient's diagnosis and treatment?).

We would argue that a similar set of considerations be adopted when working with gay, lesbian, and bisexual patients, persons who identify strongly with a particular religious or spiritual philosophy (be it traditional or nontraditional), and individuals of extreme SES backgrounds (either poor or wealthy). In this manner, we are better able to understand what might be considered "normal" within the parameters of a given patient's world, as well as to identify problems that might exist simply due to differences between the person's ethnic status and other groups in society, be they dominant or minority in nature.

Environment-Related Variables

This category includes those IO variables related to a patient's physical and/or social environment. Physical environmental variables can include such factors as poor housing, crowding, severe climate, and negative physical living conditions. Social environmental factors can include a patient's relationships with friends and family, spouse, partner, and other members of his or her social and work communities. This latter category also addresses a variety of socio-cultural aspects, but here we emphasize the need to assess the reactions of others (both within and outside of) the patient's self-identified (sub)culture.

Consistent with the problem-solving focus of our model, we advocate using the generation-of-alternatives (GOA) approach in order to increase the probability that the most important and patient-specific IO variables are ultimately identified within the case formulation. This strategy involves a two-step process: (a) searching the evidence-based literature, and (b) applying the brainstorming method of idea production.

First, we suggest that the CBT practitioner search the evidence-based literature to identify those IO variables that have been found to be causally related to a given UO goal. For example, a search of the literature regarding social anxiety would include the following list of major IO objectives: (a) decrease heightened physiological arousal, (b) decrease anxiety-related dysfunctional beliefs, (c) enhance interpersonal skills, (d) decrease general stress, (e) improve specific social skills deficits, (f) decrease focus on bodily sensations, and (g) influence related comorbid disorders if present (see Nezu et al., 2004).

Next, we recommend that the CBT therapist further identify those additional IO variables that may be relevant to a specific patient using brainstorming guidelines. Brainstorming advocates use of the following three general problem-solving principles: (a) *generate quantity* (i.e., the more ideas that are produced, the more likely that the potentially most effective ones are generated); (b) *defer judgment* (i.e., more high-quality alternatives can be generated if evaluation is deferred until after multiple ideas have been identified); and (c) *think of strategies and tactics* (i.e., identifying solution strategies, or general approaches, in addition to specific tactics, increases idea production).

Related to the process of case formulation, the strategies-tactics principle refers to the concept of identifying response classes. *Functional response classes* are those groups of behaviors that on first glance may appear very different in form, but are similar in their functional relationships to the UO (Haynes, 1992). For example, there are many ways that a person can obtain money—investing in stocks or real estate, working for a paycheck, begging, stealing, selling possessions, prostituting, or borrowing money from a bank (i.e., various tactics). These behaviors are all topographically different, yet the effects of these behaviors may be similar—all lead to obtaining money (i.e., a functional strategy).

Step 3: Conducting a Functional Analysis

The CBT clinician is next directed to conduct a functional analysis in order to identify patient-specific IO-UO relationships, as well as various IO-IO associations. Functional relationships represent the reliable covariation that exists between or among two or more variables. Such an association can represent "causation" (i.e., A "caused" B), as well as a simple noncausal reciprocal relationship (i.e., A changes when B changes, and vice versa). In the latter case, the covariation might describe a functional relationship whereby one variable serves as a maintaining factor of the second variable. For example, B may not be the original "cause" of A, but serves as the reason why A continues to persist (e.g., B might serve as a stimulus that triggers A, or B serves to increase the probability of A persisting because of its reinforcing properties in relation to A).

SORC Nomenclature

One means of summarizing the various functional relationships among variables is using the acronym S-O-R-C. For example, if the presenting problem (e.g., phobic behavior) is identified as the *response* **(R)** to be changed (i.e., the UO), then assessment can determine which variables function as the *stimulus* **(S)** that serve as antecedent triggers (e.g., phobic object), which serve as *consequences* **(C)**, such as increases in anxiety and subsequent avoidance of the phobic object, and which function as *organismic* **(O)** or patient-related mediators (e.g., ruminative worrying) or moderators (e.g., presence of comorbid problems) of the response. Within this framework, a variable can be identified as the *S* (i.e., intrapersonal or environmental antecedents), the *O* (i.e., biological, behavioral, affective, cognitive, or sociocultural variables), the *R* (e.g., the phobia), and the *C* (i.e., intrapersonal, interpersonal, or environmental effects engendered by the *R*). These functional relationships become the basis for the CBT case formulation that helps identify potentially important patient-relevant target variables.

Case Example

To illustrate this SORC chaining, consider the case of "Sally," a patient who was referred by her primary care physician because of suspected depression. Using our model, one possible case formulation might be as follows: Sally becomes sad (*R*) when she is by herself in her apartment and inactive, often feeling fatigued and listless, and ruminates about the lack of serious relationships in her life. She continues to dwell on her past failed relationships and recent breakup with her boyfriend. Such memories trigger thoughts of self-blame and hopelessness (*S*). When she becomes more upset, it becomes increasingly difficult for her to feel motivated to do anything to change her situation and counteract the depressive mood (*C*). Frequently, when her friends call to make her feel better, Sally tends to engage in ruminative thinking, focusing on her feelings of depression and internal state (*O*), generally complains about her situation, and finally refuses to engage in any social activities with such friends. These reactions usually irritate her friends, who then stop calling her (another *C*), which, in turn, reinforces her overall feelings of rejection and isolation (another *C*), and so forth, perpetuating a continual interaction among SORC variables. Note that this is only one possible causal chain—there are likely to be multiple causal chains operating concurrently.

Step 4: Developing a Clinical Pathogenesis Map

We have found that developing a clinical pathogenesis map (CPM) is a useful device when conducting a functional analysis. A CPM is a graphic depiction of the functional relationships among those variables posited to contribute to the initiation and maintenance of a patient's problems (Nezu & Nezu, 1989; Nezu et al., 2004). Using SORC nomenclature, the CPM represents a concrete statement of the therapist's initial causal hypotheses and case formulation. It can also be viewed as a path analysis or causal modeling diagram developed specifically for a particular patient (Nezu et al., 1997). As new information is obtained, and various predictions are confirmed or disconfirmed, the CPM can be altered. The advantage of developing a CPM is to provide a means by which the therapist can "document" his or her hypotheses about the pathogenesis of a client's problems, as well as to share this conceptualization with patients themselves in order to foster increased understanding.

A CPM incorporates the following five elements using SORC nomenclature: (a) distal variables, (b) *s*timulus variables, (c) *o*rganismic variables, (d) *r*esponse variables, and (e) *c*onsequential variables (see Figure 10.1).

Distal Variables

Distal varialbles include those developmental variables that have potential causal influence on a patient's problems via the initial emergence of particular vulnerabilities, as well as for the distressing symptoms themselves. Examples can include

10.1

Clinical pathogenesis map using SORC nomenclature.

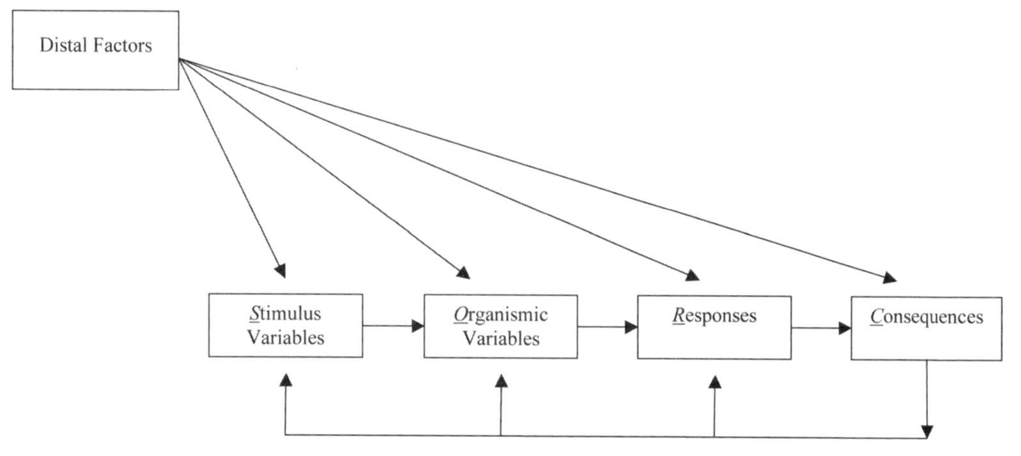

severe trauma (e.g., rape, combat), early learning experiences, poor coping ability, lack of appropriate social models for responsible behavior, and negative life events. Identifying these distal IOs can help to predict various responses to certain more proximal stimuli (e.g., early childhood experiences of being ridiculed in public might predict anxiety responses as an adult in public settings). Note that as indicated in Figure 10.1, distal factors can impact each of the SORC variables (e.g., early learning experiences can influence the saliency of a particular stimulus for a given individual, can lead to a vulnerability of poor problem-solving skills, can lower one's stress threshold, or can negatively reinforce avoidance behavior).

Stimulus Variables

This set of factors includes various patient-related (i.e., behavioral, cognitive, affective, biological, sociocultural) and environment-related (i.e., social and physical environmental) variables that serve as triggers or discriminative stimuli for other IO factors or for the symptoms themselves. For example, social isolation (a social environmental factor) can trigger another IO variable, such as negative thoughts (e.g., "I am such a loser because I am once again home alone on a Saturday night having nothing to do!"), which can then trigger sad affect and feelings of hopelessness. In addition, the social factor of "being rejected" when one's boss makes negative comments can directly trigger distressing symptoms (e.g., depression).

Organismic Variables

This dimension involves a variety of patient-related variables. These can represent response mediators (i.e., variables that help explain why a given response occurs in the presence of certain antecedent variables) or response moderators (i.e., variables that influence the strength and/or direction of the relationship between an antecedent factor and a response). Examples of mediating variables include poor social skills (behavioral variable), cognitive distortions related to mistrust of other people (cognitive variable), heightened arousal and fear (emotional variable), coronary heart disease (biological variable), and ethnic background concerning one's understanding of the meaning of a particular set of symptoms (socio-cultural variable). An example of an organismic moderator variable is problem-solving ability, which has been found to decrease the likelihood of experiencing depression under circumstances of high stress (A. M. Nezu, 2004).

Response Variables

This category refers to either certain patient-related IO variables that are very closely associated with one of the patient's UO goals (e.g., suicide ideation is strongly associated with suicidal behavior), or the set of distressing symptoms that constitute the OUs themselves (e.g., depression, pain, substance abuse, distressed marriage).

Consequential Variables

This group of factors includes the full range of both patient-related and environment-related variables that occur in reaction to a given response. Depending on the nature and strength of the consequence, the response-consequence relationship can serve to either increase or decrease the probability of the response occurring in the future (via operant conditioning). For example, avoidance behavior (*R*) in reaction to a feared object (*S* or antecedent) can serve to decrease a mediating organismic variable (*O*), such as heightened arousal to high places, thus leading to a decrease in fear and anxiety (*C*) via negative reinforcement. Such consequential variables are often a major reason why various maladaptive behaviors continue to persist (e.g., a decrease in phobia-related anxiety that results from avoidance behavior serves to negatively reinforce such a response, thereby increasing the likelihood that such a response will persist in the future).

Step 5: Selecting Initial Treatment Targets

After conducting a functional analysis and developing an initial CPM specific to a given patient, the next step involves narrowing down the list of IO variables in order to specify initial treatment targets or objectives. Here, the CBT practitioner is directed to select those IO variables that, when targeted, can maximize overall treatment success. Applying the problem-solving model to this step involves the use of specific decision-making guidelines. Effective decision making is enhanced when basing choices on an evaluation of the utility of alternatives, which in turn is determined by both (a) the likelihood that an alternative will achieve a particular goal, and (b) the value of that alternative.

Likelihood Estimates

This particular type of prediction involves two probability assessments: (a) that an alternative will achieve a particular goal, and (b) that the person implementing the alternative will be able to do so optimally. With regard to CBT case formulation, this translates into determining the answers to the following types of questions with specific regard to a given patient: Will achieving this IO goal lead to the desired UO either directly or by its impact on an IO variable in the chain? Based on the empirical literature, can this IO goal be achieved successfully? Do I as the CBT practitioner have the competence to implement those types of clinical interventions that have been found to change this target problem? Do I have the necessary resources to achieve this IO goal?

Value Estimates

The "value" of ideas can be estimated by addressing the following four specific dimensions: (a) *personal consequences* (e.g., time, effort, or resources necessary to reach the IO, emotional cost or gain involved in reaching this outcome, consistency of this outcome with one's ethical values, physical or life-threatening effects involved in changing this target problem, effects of changing this problem area on other target problems); (b) *social consequences* (i.e., effects on others, such as a spouse/partner, family members, larger community); (c) *short-term effects* (e.g., immediate consequences); and (d) *long-term effects* (e.g., long-range consequences).

In essence, this step requires the CBT practitioner to conduct a cost-benefit analysis for each potential target problem previously generated using these four criteria. IO variables associated with a high likelihood of maximizing positive effects and minimizing negative effects would be selected as initial target problems. Therefore, the two general sets of decision-making criteria (i.e., likelihood and value estimates) are used to guide the selection of target problems and to prioritize which areas to address early in therapy (Nezu & Nezu, 1993). Once an initial priority list of treatment targets is identified, a formal CPM can be completed; that is, using the format contained in Figure 10.1, the therapist can list those SORC variables and their interrelationships on the CPM that constitute an initial working case formulation. Based on the outcome of the next step, that of evaluating its validity, the CPM can be altered until it appears to capture the client's problems in a meaningful and accurate manner, and can help drive the development of a potentially efficacious treatment plan.

Case Example Revisited

To illustrate how case formulation informs the process of treatment design, returning to Sally, note that various intervention strategies can be identified to address each of the variables within the previously delineated causal chain. For instance: (a) the amount of time she spends in isolation can be decreased (focus on the *S*); (b) Sally can be taught certain self-control skills in order to redirect her focus toward positive events (focus on the *O*); (c) she can be taught to engage in various relaxation exercises as a means of counteracting feelings of depression when alone (focus on the *R*); (d) she can be taught problem-solving skills to facilitate her ability to identify alternative ways to react in response to depressive feelings, such as developing new social relationships (focus on the *C*); and (5) she can be helped to develop new pleasurable activities (focus on the *S*).

Step 6: Evaluating the Validity of the CPM

Given the canon that the practice of CBT should be scientifically informed, this next step is crucial in determining the validity of an initial case formulation for a specific patient. This can be accomplished in two ways—social validation and hypothesis testing.

Social validation involves having the CBT practitioner share the CPM with the patient (and significant others if they are involved). Patient feedback can be sought regarding the relevance, importance, and salience of the selected target problems and goals. We have found that because the CPM provides for a visual representation, this process becomes easier.

Second, testable hypotheses that are based on the original case formulation can also be used to verify the CPM. Specifically, the therapist can evaluate the outcome by attempting to confirm and disconfirm CPM-generated hypotheses. For example, if an initial CPM indicates that a patient's major presenting problem involves depression related to ineffective problem-solving skills, then the CBT therapist can put forth certain predictions. One prediction would suggest that this patient would have scores on a measure of social problem solving that signifies problem-solving deficits or weaknesses. Another hypothesis might suggest that during a structured role play involving a social situation (e.g., meeting new people), this patient would have difficulty identifying multiple ways to cope with such a stressful situation. Confirmations and disconfirmations of such predictions are important aids for the CBT clinician to use when evaluating the validity and relevance of the CPM for a specific patient.

A second set of hypotheses should be posited at a later time. This involves evaluating the effects of treatment strategies that are implemented based on the CPM. This strategy offers a powerful source of feedback about the validity of the CPM. If the hypothesized CPM is valid, changes in IO variables hypothesized to be causally important should be associated with predicted changes in UO goals (e.g., therapy geared to improve this patient's problem-solving ability should lead to such changes, in addition to decreasing depressive symptoms). If successful attainment of IO variables is not associated with changes in UO goals (e.g., improvements in problem solving do not lead to decreases in depression), then the validity of the CPM is questionable and may need to be modified. With more complicated cases, it is likely that the CBT clinician undergoes the process of evaluating and reformulating the case formulation several times throughout the course of treatment.

Developing a Treatment Play

Continuing with the problem-solving nature of our model of CBT case formulation and treatment design, this next major phase involves having the therapist develop the "middle part of a patient's story"; that is, the means by which to reach the "end of the story" that is, successful attainment of a patient's UO goals. The operational definition of this means-end analysis would be an efficacious treatment plan that contains intervention strategies geared to address those treatment targets (i.e., IO goals) previously specified in the CPM. In other words, a treatment plan, to be successful, needs to help the patient overcome those impediments to goal achievement, as delineated in the CPM (Nezu et al., 2004; Nezu, Nezu, Peacock, & Girdwood, 2004).

Although it might seem that designing a treatment plan should be a straightforward process once a CPM is developed, because this process entails multiple clinical decisions, the potential of judgmental errors is ever present (Nezu & Nezu, 1989). For example, the CBT clinician may believe that a certain intervention should be implemented with a given patient primarily on the basis of its successful use with another individual who presented with similar problems. However, failure to consider the unique characteristics of the new patient can result in implementing a treatment strategy that does not take into account various outcome moderating factors, such as differences in the intensity of baseline symptoms, presence of comorbid problems, or various sociocultural factors.

Further, if a patient's presenting problems are thought to be easily amenable to treatment, a therapist may erroneously decide to employ a particular intervention before a proper decision analysis is completed. For example, although an exposure-based treatment strategy may, in theory, be an effective intervention for the patient suffering from a severe medical phobia, it may be necessary for the therapist to first implement a cognitive restructuring protocol in order to decrease a patient's depressive symptoms related to a sense of hopelessness. In such a case, it is possible that feeling depressed and hopeless leads to lowered motivation to engage in the exposure intervention. As such, treatment may be ineffective if conducted prematurely.

Problem Orientation and Treatment Design

In keeping with the planned critical multiplism framework described earlier, we argue that CBT should be viewed in terms of intervention strategies, principles, and general approaches to address various IOs, and not exclusively in terms of specific techniques. For example, anxiety reduction interventions represent one general strategy of treatment methods geared to address various anxiety-related IO variables. Under this general umbrella, a variety of specific treatment tactics or techniques exist, including exposure, systematic desensitization, guided imagery, visualization, covert conditioning, progressive muscle relaxation, autogenic training, and mindful meditation. The efficacy of any of these techniques for a given patient is dependent on his or her unique characteristics, as well as the competence of a given CBT therapist.

In addition, there may be multiple differing ways to implement a given clinical technique. For example, the following can be viewed as a partial list of varying methods that can be used to carry out cognitive restructuring as a means of addressing the IO variable of "decreasing self-defeating thinking related to depression": behavioral experiments to test the validity of one's distorted beliefs, bibliotherapy, modeling more adaptive ways of thinking, mild refutation of the negative thoughts, overt confrontation, didactic explanations, homework assignments, use

10.1 Possible Treatment Strategies for Clinical Targets Involved in Social Anxiety

Treatment Target	Potential Intervention Approaches
Decrease heightened arousal	■ Exposure therapy ■ Flooding ■ Relaxation training
Decrease dysfunctional beliefs	■ Cognitive restructuring ■ Problem-solving therapy
Enhance interpersonal skills	■ Social skills training ■ Social effectiveness training ■ Group therapy

of family members to serve as adjunct therapists, use of friends to serve as adjunct therapists, visualization, and role plays. In addition, although we tend to conceptualize therapy within the context of individual, weekly, 50-minute sessions, alternative ways of conducting overall treatment can include group CBT, computer-enhanced protocols, and the use of the telephone (e.g., Simon, Ludman, Tutty, Operskalski, & Von Korff, 2004).

The specific steps in our model related to treatment design include: (a) identifying potentially efficacious treatment strategies for each IO variable specified in a patient's CPM, (b) conducting a cost-benefit analysis of the potential efficacy of these strategies, (c) developing an overall treatment plan in the form of a "goal attainment map" (GAM), and (d) evaluating the validity of the GAM.

Step 1: Identifying Treatment Strategies

At this point, based on a patient's individualized CPM, the CBT practitioner generates a list of possible treatment ideas for each IO variable that has been identified as an initial treatment target. In keeping with our particular orientation emphasizing critical multiplism, the clinician should consider various treatment strategies, tactics, *and* methods of implementing *each* clinical strategy for *each* clinical target.

For example, as contained in Table 10.1, we previously developed a list of potentially effective intervention strategies for each of three major treatment targets identified in the literature as being causally related to social anxiety (Nezu et al., 2004). Note that we are not advocating that all of these clinical interventions would be relevant and important for all patients suffering from social anxiety. Rather, this list represents a range of empirically derived intervention strategies that are important to consider across all such patients.

Step 2: Conducting a Cost-Benefit Analysis

In this next step, the CBT clinician applies various decision-making guidelines in order to systematically evaluate the various interventions identified. In essence, he or she attempts to determine the utility of each alternative strategy by estimating various likelihood and value estimates, similar to the process described earlier when selecting initial treatment targets. In determining various likelihood estimates, the therapist should ask the following types of questions: What is the likelihood that this particular intervention will achieve the specified goal(s)? What is the likelihood that I can optimally implement this particular treatment approach? What is the likelihood that the patient will be able to carry out a particular strategy in an optimal fashion? If relevant, what is the likelihood that collateral or paraprofessional therapists will be able to implement a particular strategy in an optimal way?

Likelihood of a Particular Intervention Achieving the Specified Goals

In making this estimate, the therapist assesses the effectiveness of a given technique in treating a given problem or set of distressing symptoms based on the empirical literature. In doing so, it is important for the clinician to remain cognizant of the unique characteristics of a particular patient when reviewing the available literature and evaluating a particular strategy or technique. In other words, a given patient may be different from the population on which the outcome literature is based. As such, the effects of a particular strategy with a particular patient may be quite different from those found within the population that was investigated in a given study. Examples of relevant variables that might engender such differential treatment effects include comorbid disorders, age, sex, and ethnic background.

Likelihood of Optimal Implementation

Here, the therapist evaluates his or her own competence in applying the particular approach in question. The effectiveness of the intervention and the likelihood of goal attainment are strongly related to the extent to which the CBT practitioner is able to competently implement the intervention. As such, the efficacy of a given treatment technique in the literature may differ if the therapist in question has less experience or training in that technique, as compared with the protocol therapists included in the research investigation (Nezu & Nezu, 2008).

Likelihood That the Patient Can Optimally Carry Out a Particular Strategy

Patients often play an integral role in their own treatment. As such, patient-related factors need to be considered with regard to the likelihood that he or she will be able to optimally carry out a particular intervention. One dimension involves the level of the individual's motivation to be an active participant. Because this is associated with treatment adherence, it is a factor that requires continued assessment throughout therapy (Nezu, Nezu, & Perri, 2006). Other factors that should be considered include the patient's physical health, financial and social resources, and cognitive ability.

Likelihood That Collateral Therapists Are Able to Implement a Particular Strategy

At times, the ability of adjunct treatment providers may be an important factor to consider when predicting overall treatment outcome. Such providers may include caregivers, spouses, partners, family members, and other health care providers. In addressing the likelihood that these individuals will be able to implement a particular intervention optimally, it is important for the CBT practitioner to assess such individuals' competence. In addition, it is important to assess their level of involvement and the extent to which they are invested in helping the patient achieve his or her treatment goals.

Estimates of Value of a Given Intervention Strategy

In assessing the value of treatment effects, the therapist considers the following four sets of criteria: (a) personal consequences, (b) social consequences, (c) short-term consequences, and (d) long-term consequences.

Personal consequences related to a particular intervention can include: amount of time and resources required of the therapist and/or patient; amount of effort required of the therapist and/or patient; emotional costs or gains that the patient may experience; consistency of an intervention with the values, morals, and ethics of the therapist and/or patient; physical side effects of treatment; and potential positive and negative effects of treatment on other problem areas in the patient's life.

Social consequences include the variety of ways in which a certain strategy will affect the patient's family, friends, and other significant people in his or her life. This dimension also addresses the potential "ripple effects" of therapy, as well as the value of a multivariate approach to patients and treatment. The extent to which the patient's social environment will facilitate or hinder treatment implementation can impact the level of treatment generalization and maintenance.

Short- and long-term consequences also need to be considered. Specifically, it is recommended that short-term and long-term effects be evaluated in terms of each of the specific value criteria with regard to the potential effects of a given treatment strategy.

Step 3: Developing an Overall Treatment Plan

This step entails the CBT clinician developing a treatment plan that is both effective in goal attainment and highly likely to be implemented optimally. Further, such a treatment plan would ideally have few temporal and financial costs, would be consistent with the therapist's and patient's values and ethics, would elicit reinforcement from the individual's social network, and would decrease distressing symptomatology and enhance a patient's quality of life. Whereas the probability of meeting *all* of these criteria with a particular treatment plan is limited, use of formal and systematic decision-making guidelines as espoused by our model can facilitate attainment of these goals. Therefore, after the CBT practitioner evaluates each treatment tactic according to the aforementioned criteria, he or she then selects those treatment alternatives that appear most favorable with regard to the utility for goal attainment. Such criteria will also be helpful in prioritizing which interventions, for which IO variables, should be implemented first, or whether, due to certain circumstances of the patient, several treatment techniques should be conducted simultaneously.

Goal-Attainment Map

Similar to the CPM, we advocate developing a pictorial representation of the treatment plan, called the goal-attainment map (GAM) (Nezu & Nezu, 1989). The GAM graphically depicts where the patient is currently and where he or she wants to go. The GAM should initially include a listing of relevant IO goals (i.e., obstacles to goal attainment, such as deficient social skills, presence of cognitive distortions) and UO goals (i.e., treatment objectives, such as decreasing depression) that were previously selected during the decision-making process. These outcomes are largely based on the patient's unique CPM. As such, the GAM serves as the basis upon which possible intervention strategies can be identified that ultimately lead to goal attainment. In other words, the GAM becomes the "treatment map" or plan that graphically describes: (a) the general treatment goals that have been mutually selected (i.e., UOs); (b) the obstacles that currently exist in reaching such goals (i.e., the targeted IO variables); and (c) the specific means (i.e., intervention strategies) by which to overcome such obstacles. Table 10.1 actually can be viewed as representing aspects of the last two dimensions of the GAM.

Completion of the GAM involves listing the treatment approaches selected as those that function as pathways to attaining goals. As such, the patient can have the opportunity to express concerns that he or she may have with the initial treatment choices. This provides the CBT therapist with data that can be used to revise the treatment plan, if necessary.

Step 4: Evaluating the Validity of the GAM

Now that the GAM has been developed for a given patient, the CBT practitioner, in continuing to apply our problem-solving model, seeks to determine whether the outcome of the problem-solving process thus far (i.e., the development of a GAM) is effective. As noted previously, this can be accomplished in two ways: (a) social validation, and (b) hypothesis testing.

Social validation at this point involves having the clinician share the GAM with the patient (and significant others if they are involved). Patient feedback can be sought regarding the relevance, importance, salience, and potential iatrogenic effects of the selected treatment options. Having the GAM in pictorial form makes this process much easier.

Second, testable hypotheses that are based on the original treatment plan may be used to verify the GAM. This involves beginning to evaluate the actual effects of the treatment plan that is delineated in the GAM. In other words, interventions that successfully achieve a particular IO objective that engender positive movement toward an UO goal would serve to support the validity of the GAM. Conversely, change in a given hypothesized mechanism of action that does *not* effect change in the UO would suggest that that part of the GAM is not valid.

These two methods of evaluation, then, serve to determine whether concerns exist with the most current version of the GAM. If such an evaluation supports the validity and relevance of the GAM for a given patient, the therapist then continues to implement the treatment plan in accord with the GAM. However, if discrepancies do occur, the clinician must then reinitiate the problem-solving process and attempt to determine the source(s) of the "mismatch." In troubleshooting this new problem, the CBT clinician should ask a variety of questions, such as: Is CBT appropriate for this patient? Did I overlook any related problems? Is this patient motivated to change? Is this patient afraid to change? Have I overlooked any negative consequences? Is this treatment generally effective for this problem? Am I implementing this intervention properly? Does the patient understand this treatment? Does the patient agree with the use of this treatment? Is treatment too costly? Is treatment taking too long? Is there adequate social support for this patient? Was the case formulation accurate? Does this treatment incur any negative effects of which I am unaware? Does this treatment conflict with the patient's values? Does the patient have unrealistic goals or expectations concerning therapy? Is the patient completing homework assignments? Is the patient optimally practicing the technique(s) that are part of treatment? Are any of the patient's family members sabotaging this treatment approach? Should I use a different treatment approach? Should I change the method of using this treatment approach? Is the use of this treatment premature? Does this patient view me as invested in his treatment? Does this patient trust me as her therapist? Have I identified the most salient reinforcers for this patient? Are there conflicting problems or variables that serve to maintain the patient's difficulties, thereby blocking a successful outcome? Should I terminate treatment? Should I get opinions from other professionals?

Summary

The path from identifying the presence of a psychological disorder to conducting treatment for a given individual is not straightforward. Even if two patients meet criteria for the same diagnosis, a multitude of moderating variables exist (e.g., age, sex, baseline intensity of symptoms, ethnic background, comorbid illness, religious background) that seriously question the advisability of automatically determining that both such individuals should be treated with the exact same CBT intervention plan. How to design a treatment plan that is uniquely tailored for a given patient, in our opinion, requires first developing a patient-specific case formulation. Note that we are not advocating that the clinician engage in each specific step in our overall model for each primary care patient. However, especially when a given patient deviates from the "textbook research participant" (which is likely to be often), we strongly advocate that our model is one important means of effectively bridging the gap between assessment and treatment.

Our model of CBT case formulation and treatment design is based on three general principles. The first principle advocates the use of a functional analysis as a framework to best understand, describe, and predict human functioning. Second, our model relies heavily on the empirical literature as a means of identifying meaningful clinical targets that are specific to a given psychological problem, as well as clinical interventions geared to impact meaningfully on such problems. Last, we cast the CBT clinician in the role of "problem solver."

The steps we described in developing a CBT case formulation included: (a) delineating patient-specific UOs goals, (b) identifying patient-specific IO variables, (c) conducting a functional analysis, (d) developing a clinical pathogenesis map,

(e) selecting initial treatment targets, and (f) evaluating the validity of the case formulation for a given patient.

Treatment design involved the following series of steps: (a) identifying potentially efficacious treatment strategies for each IO variable specified in a patient's CPM, (b) conducting a cost-benefit analysis of the potential efficacy of these strategies, (c) developing an overall treatment plan in the form of a goal-attainment map, and (d) evaluating the validity of the goal-attainment map.

Acknowledgment

The writing of this chapter was supported in part by Grant Number R34MH080840 from the National Institute of Mental Health awarded to the first author. The content is solely the responsibility of the authors and does not necessarily represent the official views of the National Institute of Mental Health or the National Institutes of Health.

References

Alloy, L. B., Abramson, L.Y., Keyser, J., Gerstein, R. K., & Sylvia, L. G. (2008). Negative cognitive style. In K. S. Dobson & D. J. A. Dozois (Eds.), *Risk factors in depression* (pp. 237–262). New York: Academic Press.

American Psychiatric Association. (2000). *Diagnostic and statistical manual of mental disorders* (4th ed., text rev.). Washington, DC: Author.

Dozois, D. J. A., & Beck, A. T. (2008). Cognitive schemas, beliefs, and assumptions. In K. S. Dobson & D. J. A. Dozois (Eds.), *Risk factors in depression* (pp. 121–143). New York: Academic Press.

Durham, R. C., Swan, J. S., & Fisher, P. L. (2000). Complexity and collaboration in routine practice of CBT: What doesn't work with whom and how might it work better? *Journal of Mental Health, 9*, 429–444.

D'Zurilla, T. J., & Nezu, A. M. (2007). *Problem-solving therapy: A positive approach to clinical intervention* (3rd ed.). New York: Springer Publishing Company.

Eells, T. D. (1997). Psychotherapy case formulation: History and current status. In T. D. Eells (Ed.), *Handbook of psychotherapy case formulation* (pp. 1–25). New York: Guilford.

Freeman, A., Felgoise, S. H., Nezu, A. M., Nezu, C. M., & Reinecke, M. A. (Eds.). (2005). *Encyclopedia of cognitive behavior therapy*. New York: Springer Publishing Company.

Haynes, S. N. (1992). *Models of causality in psychopathology: Toward synthetic, dynamic and nonlinear models of causality in psychopathology*. Boston: Allyn & Bacon.

Haynes, S. N., & O'Brien, W. O. (2000). *Principles of behavioral assessment: A functional approach to psychological assessment*. New York: Plenum/Kluwer.

Hersen, M., Bellack, A. S., & Himmelhoch, I. M. (1980). Treatment of unipolar depression with social skills training. *Behavior Modification, 4*, 547–556.

Hoberman, H. M., & Lewinsohn, P. M. (1985). The behavioral treatment of depression. In E. E. Beckham & W. R. Leber (Eds.), *Handbook of depression: Treatment, assessment, and research* (pp. 39–81). Homewood, IL: Dorsey.

Nezu, A. M. (2004). Problem solving and behavior therapy revisited. *Behavior Therapy, 35*, 1–33.

Nezu, A. M., & Nezu, C. M. (Eds.). (1989). *Clinical decision making in behavior therapy: A problem-solving perspective*. Champaign, IL: Research Press.

Nezu, A. M., & Nezu, C. M. (1993). Identifying and selecting target problems for clinical interventions: A problem-solving model. *Psychological Assessment, 5*, 254–263.

Nezu, A. M., & Nezu, C. M. (2008). Ensuring treatment integrity. In A. M. Nezu & C. M. Nezu (Eds.), *Evidence-based outcome research: A practical guide to conducting randomized clinical trials for psychosocial interventions* (pp. 263–281). New York: Oxford University Press.

Nezu, A. M., Nezu, C. M., & Clark, M. A. (2008). Social problem solving as a risk factor for depression. In K. S. Dobson & D. J. A. Dozois (Eds.), *Risk factors in depression* (pp. 263–286). New York: Academic Press.

Nezu, A. M., Nezu, C. M., & Cos, T. A. (2007). Case formulation for the behavioral and cognitive therapies: A problem-solving perspective. In T. D. Eells (Ed.), *Handbook of psychotherapy case formulation* (2nd ed., pp. 349–378). New York: Guilford.

Nezu, A. M., Nezu, C. M., & D'Zurilla, T. J. (2007). *Solving life's problems: A 5-step guide to enhanced well-being*. New York: Springer Publishing Company.

Nezu, A. M., Nezu, C. M., Friedman, S. H., & Haynes, S. N. (1997). Case formulation in behavior therapy: Problem-solving and functional analytic strategies. In T. D. Eells (Ed.), *Handbook of psychotherapy case formulation* (pp. 368–401). New York: Guilford.

Nezu, A. M., Nezu, C. M., & Lombardo, E. R. (2001). Cognitive-behavior therapy for medically unexplained symptoms: A critical review of the treatment literature. *Behavior Therapy, 32*, 537–583.

Nezu, A. M., Nezu, C. M., & Lombardo, E. R. (2004). *Cognitive-behavioral case formulation and treatment design: A problem-solving approach*. New York: Springer Publishing Company.

Nezu, A. M., Nezu, C. M., Peacock, M. A., & Girdwood, C. P. (2004). Case formulation in cognitive-behavior therapy. In S. N. Haynes & E. M. Heiby (Eds.) & M. Hersen (Series Ed.), *Behavioral assessment* (pp. 402–426).Volume 3 of the *Comprehensive handbook of psychological assessment*. New York: Wiley.

Nezu, A. M., Nezu, C. M., & Perri, M. G. (2006). Problem solving to promote treatment adherence. In W. T. O'Donohue & E. R. Levensky (Eds.), *Promoting treatment adherence: A practical handbook for health care providers* (pp. 135–148). New York: Sage.

Nezu, C. M., Nezu, A. M., & Foster, S. L. (2000). A 10-step guide to selecting assessment measures in clinical and research settings. In A. M. Nezu, G. F. Ronan, E. A. Meadows, & K. S. McClure (Eds.), *Practitioner's guide to empirically based measures of depression* (pp. 17–24). New York: Kluwer Academic/Plenum Publishers.

O'Donohue, W., Fisher, J. E., & Hayes, S. C. (Eds.). (2003). *Cognitive behavior therapy: Applying empirically supported techniques in your practice*. New York: Wiley.

Rosen, A., & Proctor, E. K. (1981). Distinctions between treatment outcomes and their implications for treatment evaluations. *Journal of Consulting and Clinical Psychology, 49*, 418–425.

Shadish, W. R. (1993). Critical multiplism: A research strategy and its attendant tactics. In L. Sechrest (Ed.), *Program evaluation: A pluralistic enterprise* (pp. 13–57). San Francisco: Jossey-Bass.

Simon, G. E., Ludman, E. J., Tutty, S., Operskalski, B., & Von Korff, M. (2004). Telephone psychotherapy and telephone care management for primary care patients starting antidepressant treatment. *Journal of the American Medical Association, 292*, 935–942.

Wisco, B. E., & Nolen-Hoeksema, S. (2008). Ruminative response style. In K. S. Dobson & D. J. A. Dozois (Eds.), *Risk factors in depression* (pp. 221–236). New York: Academic Press.

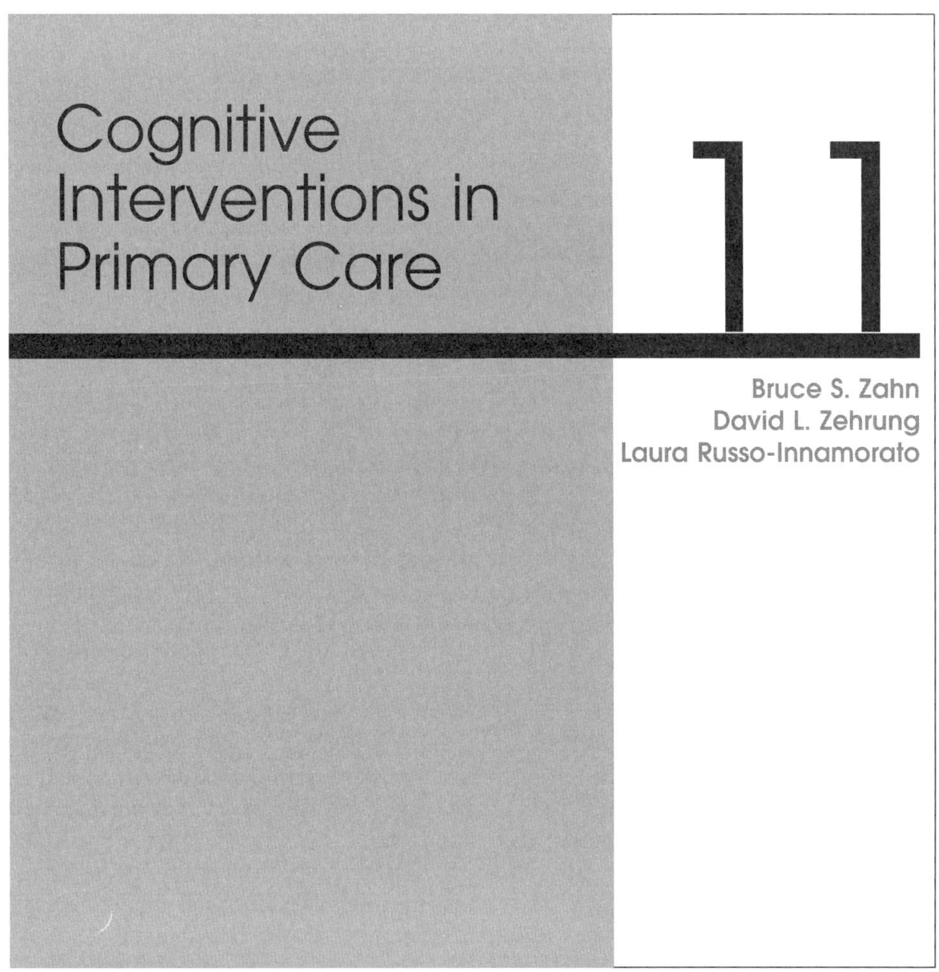

Cognitive Interventions in Primary Care

11

Bruce S. Zahn
David L. Zehrung
Laura Russo-Innamorato

Introduction

For nearly the past 2 decades, leading advocates have envisioned the future of clinical psychology to include integration of psychological services with primary care medical practice. In recognition of the impact of the biopsychosocial model on total health care, the American Psychological Association has recently renewed its call for psychologists to focus their attention to a variety of health-related challenges, including disease management, modification of maladaptive lifestyle behaviors, and promotion of self-care. In January 2009, James H. Bray, PhD, President of the American Psychological Association, called for a Presidential Task Force and Summit on the Future of Psychology Practice, to specifically focus on strategies to promote collaborative opportunities and to facilitate access for psychologists as integral players on the health care team, in recognition of the evidence that over 60% of mental health problems are treated by primary care physicians (PCPs) alone (Bray, 2009).

As psychology begins to assume a more central role in the delivery of total health care, it is important to train psychologists in systematic methods of inquiry, assessment, case conceptualization, and empirically validated intervention. In addition, psychologists need to understand how to use a variety of cognitive and behavioral techniques for behavior change, and become skilled in the strategic and efficient use of these techniques in a variety of health care challenges that present in the primary care setting.

This chapter is devoted to an exploration of some of the common methods for assessment of adult patients in the primary care office or clinic; to review common cognitive-therapy techniques that may be used quickly and efficaciously in the primary care setting, and to examine the application of some of these methods in several case scenarios. It is our hope that having read this chapter, psychologists may have a broader appreciation for how their clinical skills, especially in relation to use of cognitive therapy methods, may be transferred to the primary care setting, thereby advancing psychological practice from aspiration to reality.

Theoretical Issues

Cognitive Theory

The historical roots of cognitive therapy are based in the Socratic tradition, which states that internal realities are unique to the individual's apperceptive process. That is, "truth" is shaped and defined by each person's perception and interpretation of events, be they external events in the world, internal experiences, or events that are anticipated in the future. Modern cognitive therapy is predicated upon the tenets of the mind-body connection. It is postulated that there is a strong interrelationship among thoughts, feelings, and behaviors, and that physical functioning and cognitive processing are inextricably intertwined. Furthermore, it has been advanced that cognitions and perceptions of self, world, and future, otherwise known as the *cognitive triad* (Beck, Kovacs, & Weissman, 1979), are shaped by each person's unique perceptual lens, which is informed by past learning. These historical frameworks and rules, known as *schemas*, form the basis for organizing information, meaning making, prediction, and control. In cognitive therapy, clinicians seek to help patients relieve suffering by teaching them how to be more curious and open to empirical evidence regarding their assumptions, to being as unbiased as possible, and to correct maladaptive schemas, which are the wellspring for distorted cognitions.

Cognitive therapy includes components of psychoeducation, problem solving, relearning with behavioral practice, and conflict resolution. Although it is not to be confused with the power of positive thinking, patients are taught to be more accurate and unbiased in their assumptions, thereby freeing them from negative and pessimistic cognitive sets that influence mood and behavior. In addition, cognitive therapy takes place within the context of an effective working alliance that is framed by agreement on goals and methods (Bordin, 1979), which serves to validate the patient's experiences, yet supportively challenges the patient to examine his or her assumptions from an open and curious perspective, rather than one of biased certainty. Like most other forms of psychotherapy, a strong collaborative working alliance is a quid pro quo of effective cognitive therapy.

A particular challenge for cognitive therapists in the primary care setting relates to the referral process, and how patients are engaged in a process that acknowledges the role of cognitions in physical health and somatic discomfort. The manner in which the physician or other medical practitioner in the primary care office explains the reason for referral for psychological services sets the stage for effective collaboration or disengagement from the therapeutic process. Most patients in the primary care setting are understandably expecting a medical explanation for their symptoms and discomfort. Despite recent advances in public education regarding the mind-body connection, many patients are skeptical about the power of the mind's influence on the soma, and may misinterpret the reason for referral as being invalidating of their physical suffering, as if to say, "It's all in your head." Therefore, considerable attention needs to be given to training medical professionals to explain how behavioral health specialists are used as an integral part of the primary care team, and validating the patient's physical realities, yet opening up the possibility of learning about the power of the mind in influencing one's response to these realities.

Role of Psychologists in Primary Care

Psychologists offer their full range of skills when serving on a primary health care team. Although each provider typically develops specialty areas that suit his or her interests and the needs of the community, the primary care setting also demands the broad clinical foundation of a generalist. A primary care psychologist, like a family physician or general practitioner counterpart, treats problems that range across the lifespan and across the local community's demographics. Because primary care psychologists cannot specialize in every diagnostic category or clinical subgroup, they maintain openness to referral to specialists as needed.

Cognitive Therapy in the Primary Care Setting

The application of cognitive-therapy strategies and techniques in the primary care setting has a limited documented history in the psychological research literature, as most applications of cognitive therapy have been restricted to mental health conditions such as depression, anxiety disorders, psychological adjustment disorders, and so on. Recent studies have even focused on applications of cognitive therapy interventions to chronic mental health problems such as schizophrenia (Beck & Rector, 2000).

Some patients view their symptoms too exclusively as psychological, behavioral, or spiritual in nature. Cognitive therapists are well positioned in the health care team to reframe medical interventions in a more balanced and inclusive manner. For example, a depressed woman, Wanda, who was interested in psychotherapy, avoided seeing her PCP for a physical examination prior to engaging in treatment. Her therapist explored her distorted automatic thoughts, such as, "If I get a medical test, the results will indicate catastrophic medical problems." Cognitive therapy plus psychoeducation about treatable medical aspects of depression encouraged Wanda to see her PCP. Lab tests revealed thyroid dysfunction, and thyroid medicine incrementally improved her mood.

Cognitive therapists offer a sophisticated understanding of psychological and social influences on thoughts, mood, and behavior. Some develop expertise on how a patient's spirituality influences their lives. Cognitive therapists serve their patients best, however, when they also maintain at least a rudimentary understanding of biological influences on thoughts, mood, and behavior. Staying up to date with relevant medical issues promotes physical health by helping the therapist detect cues that prompt referrals for medical care.

Assessment Methods

Biopsychosocial History

Conceptualization of illness using a holistic model, comprising biological, psychological, and social dimensions, arose in response to the reductionistic biomedical model that had dominated industrialized societies since the mid-20th century (Engel, 1977). A growing body of research points out the important role that factors such as psychosocial stress can play in health and illness (Kiecolt-Glaser, McGuire, Robles, & Glaser, 2002; Rozanski, Blumenthal, & Kaplan, 1999; Salovey, Detweiler, Steward, & Rothman, 2000). Although a 2005 National Institutes of Health report emphasized the need for physicians to be trained in the biopsychosocial factors that influence disease and illness (NIH, 2005), and many physicians endorse the importance of this approach for health conditions including insomnia and hypertension, a minority currently do so (Astin, Sierpina, Forys, & Clarridge, 2008).

A psychologist who practices as a member of the primary care team can enhance the use of the biopsychosocial approach through education of the medical staff (Biderman, Yeheskel, & Herman, 2005). Valuing the collaborative role of psychologists in treating medical patients has been increasing, as physicians and other health care professionals embrace the biopsychosocial model of health and illness (Engel, 1977). Psychologists acting in the consultation role in the primary care setting can assist physicians to incorporate the biopsychosocial approach by teaching the BATHE method; this mnemonic stands for **B**ackground (what happened to you?), **A**ffect (and how does that make you feel?), **T**rouble (and what troubles you the most now?), **H**andling (and what helps you handle this the most?), and **E**mpathy (Stuart & Lieberman, 1993).

Belar et al. (2001) offered a model of self-assessment for practice in health care settings by presenting a template consisting of targeted questions that can be used by psychologists who wish to practice in medical settings to assess their readiness to treat patients with medical problems. Kennedy and Llewelyn (2003) describe the targets of assessment by domain of information (biological or physical, affective, cognitive, or behavioral) and unit of assessment (patient, family, health care system, and sociocultural context) when attempting to understand the patient using the biopsychosocial perspective. They note that in each area, the patient's current status, changes since the onset of illness, and past history are also important in order to attain a full understanding of the present condition. For example, effective conceptualization of the pain patient using the biopsychosocial model necessitates an understanding of the reciprocal relationship among the biological (physical), psychological (emotional, cognitive, and behavioral), and social (interactions with other factors) that must be incorporated for assessment, diagnosis, and treatment (Golden, 2002).

The assessments recommended for use by psychologists in health care settings often give information about more than one target in these domains. The type of assessment chosen most obviously depends upon the presenting problem, but includes other factors, such as ease of administration, cost-effectiveness, training required to interpret the results, and appropriateness of the instrument to the setting/individual.

Millon Behavioral Medicine Diagnostic

The Millon Behavioral Medicine Diagnostic (MBMD; Millon, Antoni, Millon, Minor, & Grossman, 2001) is a relatively brief instrument developed to identify psychosocial factors that may support or interfere with a chronically ill patient's course of medical treatment. General medical norms include patients with a wide variety of medical conditions, making it applicable to both the primary care setting and other specialty medical settings. The MBMD consists of 165 items that take approximately 20–25 minutes to complete. Twenty-nine content scales are grouped into five domains (psychiatric indicators, coping styles, stress moderators, treatment prognostics, and management guide). These domains shape the way patients deal with health problems, identifying attitudes that may exacerbate their ailments and interfere with their overall progress (Millon et al.). There are two additional domains, response patterns and negative health habits, which assess response patterns and problematic behavior that will alert the clinician to issues that deserve attention (Millon et al.). Prevalence scores (PS) between 60 and 74 are suggestive, but not sufficiently indicative of a scale's symptom pathology, unless they stand clearly as the highest score in this segment of the profile (Millon et al.). Scores of 75 to 84 (inclusive) suggest the presence of the scale's disorder; scores of 85 and above provide strong support for the prominence of the pathological problem (Millon et al.).

Mood Assessment

It is important to note that PCPs provide the majority of mental health services of the patients with the most common mental illnesses, including depression, anxiety, and alcohol use (e.g., Williams, & Manning, 2008). Primary care psychologists can assist medical personnel in developing and refining screening practices to best inform treatment and referral. Studies have found that during office visits, primary care medical providers missed depression up to two-thirds of the time (Coyne, Schwenk, & Fechner-Bates, 1995). Arguably, this leads to less effective treatment, more office visits, higher overall health care costs, and missed opportunities to reduce risk of self-harm.

The prevalence rates of major depressive disorder in the primary care setting range from 4.8 to 8.6% (Callahan, Bertakis, Azari, Robbins, Helms, & Miller, 1996); when dysthmic disorder and depressive disorder not otherwise specified are included, the prevalence rate rises to 25% (Brantley, Mehan, & Thomas, 2000). It is important to remember that the experience of depression occurs within a social context that is culturally informed; these influences include gender role expectations and conflicts, the nature of relationships with family members and support networks, women's preferences for behavioral and psychological coping (Brown, Abe-Kin, & Barrio, 2003), information that again emphasizes the need to use a biopsychosocial approach in assessment.

It is also important to note that patients presenting with depressive symptoms may be more accurately diagnosed with bipolar disorder. A naturalistic study found that 80% of individuals diagnosed with "treatment-resistant depression" were shown to have evidence of bipolar disorder, resulting in a change from antidepressants to mood stabilizers and significant improvement in functioning, compared with functioning level at intake (Sharma, Khan, & Smith, 2004).

Beck Depression Inventory–II

The Beck Depression Inventory, second edition (BDI-II), is a self-rating inventory designed to assess symptoms consistent with depression as defined by the *Diagnostic and Statistical Manual of Mental Disorders* (*DSM-IV*; American Psychiatric Association, 1994). The BDI-II contains 21 items containing four statements reflecting varying degrees of symptom severity experienced during the past 2 weeks. Individuals are asked to rate symptom severity using a range from 0 (none or no change) to 3 (severe). Scores are totaled to calculate a total BDI-II score, which can range from 0 to 63. Total score ranges between 0–13 are considered "minimal," scores between 14–19 are considered "mild," 20–28 is "moderate," and BDI-II scores between 29–63 are considered "severe."

The BDI-II is one of the most commonly used measurements of depression and possesses excellent reliability and validity (e.g., Storch, Roberti, & Roth, 2004). The BDI-II has performed well in a study of primary care patients (Arnau, Meager, Norris, & Bramson, 2001), including African American patients in an outpatient medical setting (Grothe et al., 2005). It has the added advantage for the clinician of screening for symptoms associated with risk for suicide (hopelessness and thoughts of suicide, questions #2 and #9).

Geriatric Depression Scale

The assessment of depression in elderly patients presenting to primary care providers is crucial for a number of reasons. Severe depression is common among older adults; a large population study of individuals older than 65 years found prevalence of major depression of 4.4% in women and 2.7% in men (Steffens et al., 2000). Most older adults are diagnosed and treated for depression in the primary care setting (Harman, Crystal, Walkup, & Olfson, 2003). In addition, suicide rates are the highest in this age group, making effective screening for depression in older adults essential, as affective disorders and affective illness are a highly powerful risk factor for suicide in later life (Conwell, Duberstein, & Caine, 2002). Depressive disorders in the elderly, independent of other clinical predictors such as physical illness and unexplained somatic complaints, are also associated with increased visits in primary care (Menchetti, Cevenini, De Ronchi, Quartesan, & Berardi, 2005). It is important to note that assessment of depression in older adults is complicated by the overlap in symptomotology such as physical complaints; it is, therefore, important to use mood-screening tools specifically normed on an older adult population.

The Geriatric Depression Scale (GDS; Brink et al., 1982) was designed specifically for older adults and excludes somatic symptoms of depression, which can confound depression diagnosis with physical illnesses common in older adults. The GDS is a 30-item self-report questionnaire that requires the respondent to give a yes/no determination. It uses simple language, can be administered in a written or oral format, and does not require special training for the interviewer. An affirmative response on 20 questions indicates the presence of depression, and responding negatively to 10 items indicates depression. Each depressive item endorsed counts as one point, and zero points are given to each nondepressed answer.

Beck Anxiety Inventory

The Beck Anxiety Inventory (BAI; Beck, Epstein, Brown, & Steer, 1988) is a 21-item self-rating inventory designed to assess symptoms consistent with anxiety. It uses a 4-point rating scale ranging from "not at all" (0) to "severely" (3), and requires the respondent to rate how much they have experienced each symptom for the past week. The BAI consists of 14 items that represent physiological symptoms, and 7 items representing cognitive symptoms. A total score for the BAI is obtained by summing the responses to the 21 items. A total score between 0–7 is considered "minimal," scores of 8–15 are considered "mild," 16–25 are considered "moderate," and scores in the range of 26–63 are considered "severe." The BAI was developed to assess symptoms specific to anxiety and minimizes content overlap with measures of depression (Beck et al., 1988; Beck & Steer, 1993). Because of its apparent discriminative validity, the use of the BAI as a quick and reliable screening tool in primary care seems warranted (Ferguson, 2000).

The reliability, validity, and cultural equivalence of both the Beck Depression Inventory and BAI has been demonstrated for use with Caucasian American and acculturated Latino younger college students (Contreras, Fernandez, Malcarne, Ingram, & Vaccarino, 2004). The BAI has demonstrated good test-retest reliability and good internal consistency (Wilson, de Beurs, Palmer, & Chambless, 1999). The concurrent validity of the BAI has been demonstrated by significant correlations with anxiety diaries and self-report instruments (e.g., Beck et al., 1988; Fydich, Dowdall, & Chambless, 1992). A norm-referenced interpretation of the total BAI score is recommended when trying to identify problematic anxiety in individuals presenting in the primary care setting (Ferguson, 2000).

Beck Hopelessness Scale

Current practice guidelines suggest that hopelessness should be examined when assessing suicide risk (American Psychiatric Association, 2003). Research suggests that the Beck Hopelessness Scale (BHS; Beck, Weissman, Lester, & Trexler, 1974) successfully predicts suicide in a sample of outpatients (Brown, Beck, Steer, & Grisham, 2000).

The BHS is the only widely used standardized measure of hopelessness (Glanz, Haas, & Sweeney, 1995). It is a 20-item scale with a yes/no response format (9 items are keyed false, 11 true); each response is summed to give a severity rating ranging from 0 to 20, with high scores (defined at or above a score of 9) indicating the presence of hopelessness. A total score on the BHS of 0–3 is considered "minimal," 4–8 is considered "mild," 9–14 is considered "moderate," and over 14 is considered "severe."

Beck Scale for Suicide Ideation

The Beck Scale for Suicide Ideation (BSI; Beck, Kovacs, & Weissman, 1979) is a 21-item self-report instrument that can be used to detect and measure suicidal ideation in adults. Patients rate each item on a scale of 0 to 2 (2 being the most severe). Patients complete the first 5 items and are instructed to skip to item 20 if they endorsed a "0" on items 4 and 5 ("no desire to kill self"/"I would try to save my life if I found myself in a life-threatening situation"). If they have endorsed a 1 or 2 in either item 4 or 5, they are instructed to open the booklet and answer all of the remaining items. The last two items address the number of previous suicide attempts and the intention to die at the last attempt; these items are not used in the total BSI score. The maximum score is 38, but scores over 1 may suggest the presence of suicidal ideation and require further investigation. The BSI has been used as a screening tool in emergency room departments and was found to detect suicidal ideation in emergency room patients (Healy, Barry, Blow, Welsh, & Milner, 2006).

Yale-Brown Obsessive-Compulsive Scale

The Yale-Brown Obsessive-Compulsive Scale (YBOCS; Goodman, Price, Rasmussen, Mazure, Delgado, et al., 1989; Goodman, Price, Rasmussen, Mazure, Fleishmann, et al., 1989; Goodman, Rasmussen, et al., 1989) is the most used structured interview developed to assess the severity of the various aspects of obsessive-compulsive disorder, including obsessions, compulsion, avoidance, and insight.

The YBOCS checklist (YBOCS CL) is a clinician-rated inventory that was developed in 1986 to provide a comprehensive list of obsessions and compulsions that comprises 74 items divided into 15 categories (Goodman, Price, Rasmussen, Mazure, Delgado, et al., 1989). The checklist accompanies the YBOCS rating scale, which is a widely used measure of symptom severity (Goodman, Price, Rasmussen, Mazure, Fleishmann, et al., 1989).

Mood Disorder Questionnaire

The Mood Disorder Questionnaire (MDQ; Hirschfeld, Lewis, & Vornik, 2000) was developed to assist in the diagnosis of bipolar disorder. The authors point out that it has been able to identify seven out of ten affected individuals in clinical trials (Hirschfeld et al., 2003). It is a 16-item scale broken down into five sections with a yes/no response format for questions other than Question #3. Research suggests that the MDQ it is also a useful screening tool for milder forms of bipolar spectrum disorder with sensitivity to Bipolar II disorder improved by dropping two questions related to severity of impairment and family history (Twiss, Jones, & Anderson, 2008).

Pain Inventories

Although pain has been a physical phenomenon for centuries, a major breakthrough in our understanding of pain came about as a result of the gate-control theory of pain (Melzack & Wall, 1965), which postulated three interrelated systems are responsible for the processing of painful stimulation: sensory-discriminative, motivational-affective, and cognitive-evaluative (Okifuji & Palmer, 2004). Sensation is not registered as pain until subjected to a higher order psychological and mental processing that involves perception, appraisal, and behavior.

The biopsychosocial conceptualization incorporates the patient's experience of the type, quality, duration, and location of pain, as well as the emotional factors that stem from the pain experience and the overall impact on the patient's life (Golden, 2002). As pain is a multidimensional process, descriptive screening instruments are needed that provide information about the patient's perception, reaction, and cognition of their pain state, of importance when choosing adequate treatment modalities and assessing the impact of interventions (Strand, Ljunggren, Bogen, Ask, & Johnsen, 2008). There is a growing body of research indicating that men and women do not always respond to pain and the treatment of pain in the same way (Fillingim, 2000; Keogh, McCracken, & Eccleston, 2005).

McGill Pain Questionnaire

The McGill Pain Questionnaire (MPQ; Melzack, 1975) is a 21-item instrument designed to obtain quantitative measures of complex qualitative pain experiences including the sensory, affective, and evaluative aspects of pain (Corcoran & Fischer, 2000). It has demonstrated success in distinguishing between chronic migraine and chronic tension-type headache (Mongini, Deregibus, Raviola, & Mongini, 2003). Research also supports the MPQ as a reliable and valid measure for evaluating the qualities of cancer pain inpatients receiving palliative care (Mystakidou et al., 2002). It takes approximately 5–15 minutes to complete, 1–2 minutes to score, and does not require training to score or interpret.

The MPQ includes descriptive words of sensory, affective, and evaluative aspects of pain, and has body diagrams for the patient to indicate pain locations. It consists of 78 adjectives arranged into 20 groups; 10 groups measure the sensory quality of pain (SQ: items 1–10), 5 groups measure the affective quality for pain (AQ: items 11–15), 1 set of adjectives measures the evaluative quality of pain, the overall intensity of the pain experience (EQ: item 16), and 4 groups measure miscellaneous pain (MP: items 17–20); 1 item measures present pain intensity (PPI: item 21).

Substance-Abuse Assessments

CAGE-AID (Altered to Include Drugs)

Evidence for the necessity of screening for alcohol-use disorders in the primary care setting includes its prevalence and high rates of comorbidity with other psychological and medical conditions. It is estimated that from 3 to 20% of patients in the primary care setting are affected by alcohol-use disorders (Johnson et al., 1995), and one study demonstrated that 45% of patients presenting for addiction treatment reported that their physician did not know about their substance abuse (Saitz, Mulvey, Plough, & Samet, 1997). Drinking affects—and is affected by—all of the domains already discussed in the biopsychosocial conceptualization, and is associated with cognitive impairment, medical problems, interpersonal difficulties, and legal and vocational problems. Drinking should be considered as heavy or high risk if a man drinks more than 28 standard drinks in a week, or a woman drinks 21 standard drinks in a week (McCrady, 2008). Increased concern is also warranted if episodes consist of drinking five or more drinks for men, four or more drinks for women, at a frequency of two times or more per month (McCrady, 2008).

The CAGE (Mayfield, McLeod, & Hall, 1974) is a useful screening interview that consists of four questions related to the acronym CAGE:

1. Have you ever felt you should cut (**C**) down on your drinking?
2. Have people annoyed (**A**) you by commenting on your drinking?
3. Have you ever felt bad or guilty (**G**) about your drinking?
4. Have you ever had a drink first thing in the morning (eye-opener [**E**])?

Answering "yes" to two questions suggests a high probability of an alcohol use disorder, and even one affirmative response suggests further examination is necessary.

It is recommended that individuals identified with a highly sensitive initial screen, such as the CAGE, then be further assessed with a more specific measure, such as the Michigan Alcoholism Screening Test (MAST, Selzer, 1971; Tucker, Vuchinich, & Murphy, 2002).

AUDIT-C

The Alcohol Use Disorders Identification Test (AUDIT; Saunders, Aasland, Babor, DeLaFuente, & Grant, 1993) is a 10-item screening measure designed specifically for use in the primary care setting. Questions 1 through 8 require the individual to note how often he/she has experienced the event noted in the question on a scale measuring frequency ("never" to "daily or almost daily"). Question #9 asks whether the patient or someone else has been injured as a result of drinking (responses include "no," "yes but not in the past year," and "yes, during the last year"). Question #10 asks whether a relative, friend or doctor, or other health care worker has been concerned about the patient's drinking (with answer choices parallel to question nine).

Questions 1–8 are scored 0 to 4 (with higher scores reflecting greater drinking or more frequent consequences). Questions 9 and 10 are scored 0, 2, or 4 only. Total scores range from 0 (for nondrinkers) to 40. A score of "8" is strongly suggestive of an alcohol problem. An advantage of the AUDIT over the CAGE is that the former gathers information on quantity and frequency of alcohol consumption, reflecting a greater potential for eliciting indications of a broader range of alcohol use, and therefore, dysfunction or risk.

Cognitive Distortions

Inventory of Cognitive Distortions

The Inventory of Cognitive Distortions (ICD; Yurica & DiTomasso, 2002) is a self-report instrument developed to measure the presence of specific types of cognitive distortions in an adult population with a range of mental disorders. It has 69 items, and takes approximately 15–20 minutes to complete the survey (Uhl, 2007). It includes 11 subscales representative of 11 different types of cognitive distortions. The 10 cognitive subscales include: externalization of self-worth, fortune telling, magnification, labeling, perfectionism, comparison to others, emotional reasoning, arbitrary inference/jumping to conclusions, minimization, and mind reading; the 11th subscale, emotional decision making, loaded as a new subscale. The ICD appears to demonstrate acceptable content validity, as established by factor analysis and evaluation by cognitive-therapy experts, and acceptable levels of criterion validity, through its ability to distinguish between the control and psychiatric outpatient samples (Yurica & DiTomasso, 2001). The total test–retest reliability coefficient for the total ICD scores was .998. The ICD has been demonstrated to be an excellent measure for uncovering relationships between distorted thinking and psychological and behavioral health risks (Uhl). Research supporting the ICD includes evidence that the ICD determined that approximately half of the variance of both the severity and quantity of psychological dysfunctions was accounted for by the frequency of cognitive distortions (Rosenfield, 2004).

Behavioral Observation

ADLs and IADLs

Among self-assessed multidimensional measures of health status in older adults, the OARS Multidimensional Functional Assessment Questionnaire (OMFAQ; George & Fillenbaum, 1985) is most widely used and published, and demonstrates the most evidence despite limited evidence for reliability and responsiveness (Haywood, Garratt, & Fitzpatrick, 2005). The OARS Multidimensional Functional Assessment Questionnaire contains parts A and B and produces score profiles. The activities of daily living (ADLs) domain consists of 14 items (7 representing instrumental activities of daily living [IADLs]), economic resources (15 items), mental health (21 items), physical health (16 items), and social resources (9 items); there are 11 demographic items and 10 informant items.

The Functional Assessment Inventory (FAI; Pfeiffer, Johnson, & Chiofolo, 1981) has 90 fewer items than the OMFAQ, is interview administered, and includes domains related to ADL impairment, economic resources, mental health, life satisfaction, self-esteem, physical health, and social resources.

Locus of Control

The Multidimensional Health Locus of Control Scales (MHLC) was developed by Wallston, Wallston, and DeVellis (1978) to measure locus of control of health-related behavior. This 18-item instrument measures three dimensions of locus of control of reinforcement as it pertains to health. Specifically, the MHLC assesses people's belief that their health is or is not determined by their own behavior. The MHLC looks at three sources of control over health, with each subscale containing six items: internality of health locus of control (IHLC), powerful other locus of control (POLC), and chance locus of control (CHLC).

Problem-Solving Orientation

The Problem-Solving Inventory (PSI; Heppner & Petersen, 1982) was developed to assess individuals' perceptions of their problem-solving behaviors and attitudes (Heppner, 1988). It is a 35-item instrument that measures how individuals perceive their level of effectiveness when confronting personal problems and their overall approach to problem solving. This includes the process by which they respond to personal problems, their ability to address and solve their problems effectively, and their emotional response to problem solving. Individuals are asked to rate responses on a 1 to 6 scale (1 = strongly agree, 6 = strongly disagree). The PSI contains three subscales including problem-solving confidence, approach-avoidance style, and personal control (Heppner & Petersen, 1982). In addition, the total score is viewed as a general index of problem solving.

Treatment Approaches

In the ensuing paragraphs, we will examine a variety of cognitive strategies and techniques that the clinician may use when working in a primary care setting. The first part of this discussion will focus on the use of foundational strategies, which include the development of a problem list with prioritization of problems, case conceptualizations, development of a treatment plan that addresses targeted problems, motivational interviewing, and the instillation of hope. Following this section, we will define and give examples of a variety of cognitive techniques that can be used in the primary care setting, including Socratic questioning, defining idiosyncratic meaning, identifying cognitive errors, reattribution, problem solving, examining the evidence, historical review with reframe, thinking in shades of gray, and therapeutic acceptance.

Foundational Strategies

Problem List With Prioritization

One of the most challenging tasks for the psychologist working in the primary care setting is to rapidly identify and prioritize what are often a complex comingling of medical and somatic problems into a concise, coherent case conceptualization and treatment plan that makes sense to all parties—the patient, the physician, and a psychologist. Input into the problem list may be elicited directly from the patient and collateral reporters, such as family members and the treating physician. However, although the patient may have expertise in reporting symptoms and the physician has expertise in medical diagnosis, the psychologist must quickly identify and prioritize the complex mix of medical and psychological ingredients, in order to be an effective agent of change. This requires the psychologist to not only be an expert in assessment and diagnosis, but also to be highly informed about the realities of medical diagnosis and the complexities of symptom expression and impact on overall health of the patient.

Cognitive Case Conceptualization

Cognitive case conceptualization typically focuses on a careful examination of the number of critical factors, including: the patient's chief complaints, the review of past and recent history of the central problem, critical incidents in childhood that might influence the current problem (such as previous illnesses, or observing significant others who suffered from medical problems), interoceptive (internal) and exteroceptive (external) cues and responses to medical symptoms and illness, a review of past and present coping techniques, consideration of present consequences to the problem, any additional problems or areas of concern (such as effect on family members, financial cost, effect on employment status and ability to work), and resources to cope with the illness, including social support.

Cognitive case conceptualization should also examine hypothesized underlying mechanisms that may impact psychological and physical health, such as dysfunctional beliefs associated with the problem, attributions related to illness, perceived consequences of illness, perceived self-efficacy to control symptoms, interactional-systemic maintenance factors for dysfunctional beliefs and coping strategies, a review of any behavioral, emotional, and/or cognitive skills deficits, and any other vulnerability factors. The reader should be directed to Persons (2008) and Needleman (1999) for further explanation of cognitive case conceptualization models.

Most symptoms psychotherapists encounter can arise from heterogeneous sources. For example, maternal alcohol use, birth complications, lead poisoning, and genetic anomalies may lead to intellectual disability, and often more than one risk factor is present. Understanding probable medical causes of psychological symptoms can lead to more individualized and effective interventions.

Aggression, for example, is a common trigger for a mental health referral. Although psychological and social/behavioral dynamics are usually sufficient to account for the onset and maintenance of aggression, sometimes seizure activity is part of the clinical picture. Listening closely to the details of how aggression manifests can help identify when to generate a neurology or primary care referral. Evidence of petit mal seizures should be routinely inquired as to the possibility of seizure activity as contributing to the aggression. Clues may include skewed looks in the person's eyes and diminished responsiveness during aggression, relative dissociation between provocation and aggression, lack of a pattern that makes behavioral sense, emotional and physical exhaustion after aggression, sometimes followed by tearfulness, expressions of remorse, and a need for sleep, euthymic mood if aggression succeeds in meeting an instrumental goal, and reports of "spells." "Hits" on any of these items do not exclusively indicate that seizures are present, but they should trigger additional questions on the therapist's part.

Targeted Treatment Plan and Agenda Setting

Once the cognitive case conceptualization has been articulated, an initial treatment plan can be drafted. The treatment plan should focus on ameliorating presenting problems in order of prioritization, and should be presented with goals and objectives that are easily achieved within a session or two each. Prior to each session, the clinician should elicit input from the patient regarding progress on homework assignments and refining of the treatment object for that session. Agenda-setting in the primary care setting may differ somewhat from standard outpatient therapy, in that in the latter setting, the patient may bring any number of issues that he or she wishes to work on that are related to the master treatment plan. It is our position that often, the clinician working in the primary care setting needs to take the lead in setting the agenda for the session, and still maintain the collaborative relationship, rather than placing the responsibility for developing the agenda primarily in the hands of the patient.

Because of the limited amount of time for sessions in the primary care office, both the clinician and the patient must work as efficiently as possible in order to accomplish the work before them. Agenda setting should include a brief review of the treatment plan and its rationale, a review of the main learning points from the previous session (bridging), and a course of action with the rationale for the plan in the session at hand.

As part of the first session and periodically thereafter, therapists might ask what area of change will provide the most leverage for overall improvement. Another approach is to consider what area might yield the most change with the least work or resources. One question to ask is what symptom or area is most distressing or life-threatening. Part of the prioritizing process includes assessing collaboratively with the patient what they are most able and motivated to work on. During each session when multiple problem topics arise, ask, "Of these stressors, which would be the most helpful to work on today?" or, "Of these topics, what would be the best use of our time to work on today?"

Cost-Benefit Analysis and Motivational Interviewing

A fundamental error in clinical practice, whether it is in the private practice office or the primary health care setting, is to assume the patients are prepared and motivated to relinquish unhealthy behavioral patterns and adopt healthier choices. The concept of assessing readiness to change arises from the stages of change model (Prochaska & DiClemente, 1983, 1986; DiClemente & Prochaska, 1998), which proposes that a patient's readiness varies along a continuum from "not ready" to acknowledge a problem, to "ready" to not only acknowledge the problem and its importance, but also to take specific action steps geared toward change. Patients who do not believe that behavioral change is important enough, or if they lack confidence in their ability to actually make changes, may be labeled as "unmotivated" or even "resistant," and their behavior will result in noncompliance.

A patient's smoking schema can render the primary care team completely ineffectual in their repeated admonitions to quit smoking. For example, a simple statement like, "You need to quit smoking" may trigger resistance in a patient who thinks, "Hey, I gave up drinking, and then I gave up too much salt, and then I gave up too many sweets, and then I gave up too much red meat, and now you are trying to take away my last remaining pleasure in life. Forget it."

Motivational interviewing takes a patient-centered focus and includes the following components: acknowledging patients' unique cognitions related to disease and illness, and the meaning that they have within the context of the whole person; taking into consideration the meaning of disease and illness within the cultural and spiritual context; establishing goals of medical management with clarity about the role expectations of both the patient and the clinician; and being realistic about the resources the patient has, including time and energy, toward working on health behavior change. This approach requires use of active listening and reflective skills, with negotiation being the cornerstone of consultation relevant to change, rather than using prescriptive advice giving or unilateral goal setting. Motivational interviewing can also be used to reduce the strength and frequency of resistance and noncompliance by emphasizing personal choice and control in making decisions, and taking action toward healthy behavior change.

A cognitive technique used by the clinician to facilitate readiness to change is the cost-benefit analysis. To demonstrate this method, the clinician may make a double column on a sheet of paper, and ask the patient to consider the potential advantages (benefits), as weighed against the potential disadvantages (costs) of adopting a specific healthy behavior. Similar to the scales of justice, the patient can be asked to consider whether or not the value of change outweighs the potential costs of change. Costs may include sacrificing unhealthy lifestyle choices, maintaining compliance despite fluctuations in the mood, motivation, or energy, and persisting with healthy behaviors even though compliance may not be immediately observed as tangible changes in medical pathology. Paradoxically, the patient may be asked to consider the advantages and disadvantages of maintaining the current behavioral patterns; in other words, the costs and benefits of maintaining homeostasis regardless of health consequences. The cost-benefit analysis and paradoxical cost-benefit analysis techniques may be used as a fulcrum in assisting patients to make their own choices about change, with a comprehensive understanding of what sacrifices may be required of them in order to maximize the potential payoff of improved health.

Specific Cognitive Intervention Techniques

Patients' schemas regarding the science of medicine and medical interventions can dramatically affect their medical care and outcomes. Individuals with a history of trauma may initially idealize their medical providers. They may also react intensely to procedures like surgery that render them completely vulnerable to others. One response is for the person to seek needless procedures to fulfill perceived needs for healing or for punishment of the body they feel betrayed them. Another response is for the person to avoid medical care altogether. Somatic hypervigilance may lead to exaggerated reactions to postintervention pain or side effects, which may lead to perceived revictimization, and then to adversarial interactions with the medical team. As idealization of the medical team providers crumbles, the patient may transfer their idealization to the therapist, and engage in splitting behaviors. Dialectical Behavior Therapy and other cognitive-behavioral interventions can be helpful with balanced thinking and distress tolerance, as related to medical issues. The patient's self-efficacy, especially regarding managing chronic medical conditions, can greatly affect how they interact with their medical providers, how well they advocate for themselves, how well they implement treatment regimes, and how resilient their mood is.

Thinking in Shades of Gray

All-or-nothing thinking, or *black-or-white thinking*, is a very common cognitive distortion that is observed in the primary care setting, with potentially lethal consequences. For example, depressed mood with all-or-nothing thinking is one of the most powerful predictors of poor outcome after a cardiac event. Consider the patient who thinks, "I've always been strong, but now this has taken me out in one fell swoop. My life is totally ruined. I'll never be able to work like I did, get excited about anything, or have sex without the fear of death. Yeah, I'm alive, but this heart attack was like the kiss of death for me." This thinking may negatively impact compliance with exercise, medication, and other postoperative recommendations. Without intervention, the patient may remain convinced that restoration of healthy functioning is a fantasy that will permanently elude him, despite repeated reminders for compliance from his medical team and concerned others.

Intervention using the technique, "Thinking in Shades of Gray" (Burns, 1980), can help to counteract polarized thinking ("Either I have perfect health and I am not restricted in my lifestyle in any manner, or else I am doomed to a life of misery and pain all of the time"). The patient can be guided to develop balanced thoughts by empathetically pointing out the extremeness of such thinking. Similarly, the therapist can also suggest that the patient try to think about examples from his network of associations for people who do *not* enjoy perfect health, and yet seem to be living well-adjusted lives.

Distinguishing Thoughts From Facts

When patients receive news about their medical condition, they may be primed to draw conclusions that are based on attributions that are not necessarily based in medical fact. This can be accomplished by demonstrating the connection between activating events (A), beliefs (B), and consequences (C), as both feelings and behaviors. This is known as the A-B-C Technique (Leahy, 2003), which can be useful as a simple technique to demonstrate how our interpretations of events may directly influence or change related feelings and behaviors, whereas facts are resistant to change.

To demonstrate this principle, the clinician may prompt the patient to imagine an alternative interpretation of externalities events, such as the weather. The patient may be invited to imagine how invigorated she might feel on a beautiful, moderately temperate, sunny spring day, which beckons with the promise of pleasure and accomplishment. The patient may then be invited to notice how her feelings might change if she was feeling exhausted after a late night out at a lavish party, and therefore, unable to take full advantage of this same gorgeous day. Alternatively, the patient may then be encouraged to picture a cold, damp, and overcast day, and notice how her feelings and motivation to act might change while entertaining the alternative thoughts that: (a) "This is a horrible day, therefore I'm not likely to accomplish anything," or (b) the thought that "This would be an advantageous time to catch up on some indoor chores," which might result in a sense of accomplishment and increased self-efficacy.

In this manner, patients may begin to understand that although events such as illness or disease states should be taken seriously, catastrophic predictions such as, "This means that I am doomed to suffer," or "I can't stand pain" are actually cognitions that may be altered, with more positive consequences in terms of feelings and behaviors, including motivation to engage in compliance with medical recommendations.

Identifying Cognitive Distortions

Beck (1975) originally identified 10 unique classes of cognitive errors that depressed patients made as part of their inductive reasoning bias, and which were central to the creation and maintenance of their misery. These errors, or cognitive distortions, consisted of: dichotomous thinking, catastrophizing, emotional reasoning, fortune telling, labeling, mental filter, mind reading, overgeneralization, personalization, and "should" statements. Similarly, Ellis (1994) originally identified 11 "irrational beliefs" that were at the root of disturbance and human suffering, which he later distilled into three overall dysfunctional beliefs: "I must be outstandingly competent, or I am worthless"; "Others must treat me considerately, or they are absolutely rotten"; and "The world should always give me happiness, or I will die." Burns (1980) reframed Beck's original list of distortions with his own Checklist of Cognitive Distortions, and Gilson and Freeman (1999) and Leahy (1996) added to the list, including perfectionism, fallacies of change, worrying, control, unfair comparisons, discounting the positive, "what if-ing," regret orientation, inability to disconfirm, and judgment focus.

The primary goal of cognitive therapy is to "correct" these cognitive errors by use of the scientific method, disproving the faulty assumptions that lie at the heart of disturbance and unhealthy negative mood states. Alternatively, patients may also learn to short-cut the method once they learn how to identify the extremeness in their thinking, and quickly catch the distorted cognitions in the moment, without necessarily engaging in scientific investigation to disprove their seeming veracity. Once patients begin to understand the connection between thinking errors and emotional suffering, they may consult the list of cognitive distortions any time they sense an unhealthy negative shift in mood, as a "quality check" for negatively biased assumptions or thoughts.

Reattribution

As patients consider the evidence that supports or disputes automatic thoughts, the cognitive therapist should consider medical status as a critical factor that moderates the presence and intensity of thoughts. For example, a patient processing a panic attack might balance initial catastrophic thoughts with more rational cognitions, such as, "The argument last night with my husband doesn't necessarily mean he is planning to leave me. We have things we need to work on, but one reason he has been discouraged, irritable, and sluggish is that his thyroid levels are still out of whack."

Similarly, a patient who is feeling helplessly and hopelessly depressed might substitute dark and gloomy thoughts with a more balanced argument. "It's true that I'm discouraged by my finances and the decisions my kids are making these days, but it's also true that part of my concentration difficulties and feeling fuzzy-headed may be due to my blood sugar levels running around 275. As I work to normalize my blood sugar levels, I will think and feel better, and this will lead to fewer mistakes when I do my bills. I will more easily think through how to be the parent I want to be for my kids. That will help lower my stress, which will also help my diabetes."

A patient living with cancer might say "The physical yuck and the feeling that I'm trying to think through a dense fog is probably *not* signaling me that my cancer status is deteriorating. In fact, the last time I saw my oncologist, she said treatment is going according to plan. Instead, this is probably the side effects of my chemo. You know, on my better days I'm actually able to smile, because I think *if this is what the chemo is doing to me, just think what it's doing to those cancer cells!*"

Decatastrophizing (Vertical Arrow)

Leahy (2006) identified a core mechanism in anxiety as being uncertainty and unpredictability. Patients seek to predict the future with the reassuring assumption that, "If only I could know the outcome, I wouldn't be so worried." In clinical practice, many patients worry themselves in a downward spiral of panic and "doom and gloom," seeking to disconfirm their worst fears by asking "why me"questions, yet paradoxically sensitizing them to any shred of potential evidence that seems to confirm their nightmare predictions. Decatastrophizing, typically referred to as the *vertical arrow technique* (Leahy, 2006), may be used to demonstrate to patients that many of their fears may be illogical exaggerations of bits of information and "hunches." This technique consists of repeatedly asking, "What if your thought (fear) was actually true? Why would that be so terrible? How would you cope with that if it actually came to pass?" By peeling away each layer of anxiety, patients may come to understand that many of their fears are based on wild speculation, rather than fact. In so doing, they may also remind themselves that they are not helpless sitting ducks, awaiting their inevitable fate of pain and suffering.

Reframing (Viewing Illness as a Challenge, Rather Than Defeat)

Patients vary in their ability to mobilize their coping responses to a crisis. For some, the diagnosis of a disease is taken as a death sentence, whereas for others, it is a wake-up call to mobilize all of one's resources to fight. Many of us know or have read accounts of individuals who have been diagnosed with an illness like non–insulin-dependent diabetes mellitus (NIDDM), only to give in to their dietary indiscretions and reject the advice to self-monitor blood glucose and begin a regimen of regular exercise, and others with the identical diagnosis have taken the news as a "wake-up call" to engage in serious lifestyle changes.

Reframing is a technique for recasting or "putting a more balanced spin" on medical news, and motivating patients to mobilize their coping resources. For many patients, a historical analogy may be in order, by cueing them to reflect on other times in their life when they have fought back in the face of a threat, rather than passively accepting bad news without a whimper. Questions that may be helpful in facilitating reframing may be to ask, "How is this challenge similar to other challenges in your life that you have overcome?" or "How can you use this news to improve the quality of your life and your relationships, regardless of the long-term outcome?"

Case Example #1

Joan was a 43-year-old single mother of two teenage girls. She worked as a paralegal for a high-profile legal firm downtown. She suffered from fibromyalgia for most of her adult life. Despite trying a number of medical and somatic treatments, she rarely enjoyed relief from pain. Recently, she was required to put in more overtime due to cutbacks at the firm. Not only did she notice an exacerbation of her pain, but others in the office and her family commented or her increased irritability, short temper, and negative mood. She sought a consultation with her PCP, who referred her to a psychologist before considering prescribing medications such as opioids or muscle relaxants.

In her sessions with her psychologist, Joan discussed her anger at having to work harder for longer hours, and the stress of raising her children. She had given up exercise in the past two months, even though that had been an important outlet for her. Her automatic thoughts included: "I can't do *anything* anymore without pain," "I have *no* time for myself," and "I *never* get any relief." In cognitive-behavior therapy, she learned about the physical and psychosocial variables associated with pain, and some elementary techniques for improving her coping and quality of life. She also learned to catch her "all-or-nothing thoughts," and understand the connection between extreme thinking, negative mood, and increased perception of pain. Joan also learned to distract herself when she experienced flare-ups of pain, and use structured breathing and relaxation exercises to let go of her anger.

Rather than telling herself, "I can't do anything without pain," Joan learned that by not fighting so hard against pain, she was actually able to accomplish many things with minimal-to-moderate interference. She used a cost-benefit analysis to come to the conclusion that it was not to her advantage to continue to fight against pain. She worked in therapy to accept her pain as a part of life, disciplined herself to focus more on the tasks at hand, allowing the pain sensations to recede into the background whenever possible. She made a structured schedule for herself, carving out time for exercise, and a coping plan for those days when she was not able to get as much time for herself as she would have liked. As she began to engage in greater consistency of self-care, acceptance, and distraction, she noticed her mood improve and her irritability diminish.

Case Example #2

Jake was a 56-year-old underground lineman with the local energy company. He was morbidly obese and suffered from hypertension. His father had died of a heart attack when Jake was 13 years old, and several other family members suffered from cardiovascular disease. In addition, Jake was noncompliant with diet and exercise, and on weekends, he typically went down to the local bar where he had four to six beers while watching sporting events with his friends on the cable TV.

Jake consulted his PCP when he noticed himself suffering from increasing headaches and occasional chest pains when he was stressed. His PCP ordered a consultation with a cardiologist, who had Jake take a stress test and several other cardiovascular tests. In addition, his PCP suggested several sessions with a psychologist for cognitive-behavioral therapy. Initially, Jake was reluctant to see a psychologist, as he argued that he was not "crazy," and that his symptoms were not just "all in my head." However, he was reassured by his PCP and his psychologist that his health care "team," including his physician, his cardiologist, and his psychologist, would make a formidable opponent against cardiovascular disease if they all pulled together and developed a winning "game plan." By reframing the "health care team approach" into a sports metaphor, Jake was encouraged to be an active "player," rather than a "bench player," a bystander to his own health future, with dim prospects of achieving a winning outcome.

In several sessions of brief cognitive therapy, Jake learned how to "coach" himself by developing a positive attitude toward his own health care, and "going into training" by developing behavioral strategies designed to improve his health. He used activity scheduling to make time for light exercise that was recommended by his physician, and he worked with his psychologist to develop a moderation approach toward use of alcohol so he could get into "playing shape." His psychologist also worked with him to identify negative cognitions related to health care, such as, "Nothing I do matters," and "No one in my family lives past 65, so neither will I."

Jake learned to "counterattack" these negative thoughts with the behavioral "game plan" that was constructed with his input and his behavioral health care team. He identified "defeatist" thoughts that supported noncompliance, and developed a list of coping responses that he attached to a clipboard, much as a football coach might do. He consulted his clipboard during moments of weakness, and gave himself a pep talk by identifying cognitive distortions of discounting the positive, overgeneralization, fortune telling, and all-or-nothing thinking. He cued himself to use techniques including reframing, cost-benefit analysis, and the best friend technique (engaging in positive self-talk, using language one would use when encouraging a best friend who had identical negative and self-doubting thoughts as one's own) to encourage himself to remain "in the game" until positive results (stabilization of hypertension, weight loss, exercise, and alcohol moderation) were achieved.

Conclusions

Cognitive therapy techniques are a vital component in the "tools of the trade" for psychologists working in primary care settings, and may be strategically used to improve health outcomes and compliance with medical regimens. In this chapter, we have discussed several techniques and strategies that may be used in cognitive therapy by the psychologist who is part of the primary health care team. Although the list of strategies is by no means exhaustive, it is our hope that the reader will be encouraged to explore creative applications of cognitive techniques that can enhance compliance with medical treatment, reducing further medical risk, and improving quality of life.

References

American Psychiatric Association. (1994). *Diagnostic and statistical manual of mental disorders* (4th ed.) Washington, DC: American Psychiatric Press.

American Psychiatric Association. (2003). *Practice guideline for the assessment and treatment of patients with suicidal behaviors.* Retrieved August 10, 2009, from http//www.psychiatryonline.com/pracguide/loadguidelinepdf.aspx?file=suicidalbehavior_inactivated_04-16-09.

Arnau, R. C., Meager, M. W., Norris, M. P., & Bramson, R. (2001). Psychometric evaluation of the Beck Depression Inventory-II with primary care medical patients. *Health Psychology, 20*, 112–119.

Astin, J. A., Sierpina, V. S., Forys, K. L., & Clarridge, B. (2008). Integration of the biopsychosocial model: Perspectives of medical students and residents. *Academic Medicine, 83*(1), 20–27.

Beck, A. T. (1975). *Cognitive therapy and the emotional disorders.* Madison, CT: International Universities Press.

Beck, A. T., Epstein, N., Brown, G., & Steer, R. A. (1988). An inventory for measuring clinical anxiety: Psychometric properties. *Journal of Consulting and Clinical Psychology, 56*, 893–897.

Beck, A. T., Kovacs, M., & Weissman, A. (1979). Assessment of suicidal intention: The scale for suicide ideation. *Journal of Consulting and Clinical Psychology, 47*(2), 343–352.

Beck, A. T., & Rector, N. (2000). Cognitive therapy of schizophrenia: A new therapy for the new millennium. *American Journal of Psychotherapy, 54*(3), 291–300.

Beck, A. T., & Steer, R. A. (1993). *The Beck Anxiety Inventory Manual.* San Antonio, TX: Psychological Corporation.

Beck, A. T., Weissman, A., Lester, D., & Trexler, L. (1974). The measurement of pessimism: The hopelessness scale. *Journal of Consulting and Clinical Psychology, 42*, 861–865.

Belar, C. D., Hersch, L. E., Rozensky, R. H., Brown, R. T., Brown, R. A., Hornyak, L. M., et al. (2001). Self assessment in clinical health psychology: A model for ethical expansion of practice. *Professional Psychology: Research and Practice, 32*, 135–141.

Biderman, A., Yeheskel, A., & Herman, J. (2005). The biopsychosocial model–Have we made any progress since 1977? *Families, Systems, and Health, 23*(4), 379–386.

Bordin, E. S. (1979). The generalizability of the psychoanalytic concept of the working alliance. *Psychotherapy: Theory, Research, and Practice, 16*, 252–260.

Brantely, P. J., Mehan, D. J., Jr., & Thomas, J. L. (2000). The Beck Depression Inventory (BDI) and the Center for Epidemiologic Studies depression scale (CES-D). In M. E. Maruish (Ed.), *Handbook of psychological assessment in primary care settings*. Mahwah, NJ: Erlbaum.

Bray, J. H. (2009). Future of psychology practice. *Pennsylvania Psychologist, 16*(1), 3–4.

Brink, T. L., Yesavage, J. A., Lum, O., Heersema, P. H., Adey, M., & Rose, T. L. (1982). Screening tests for geriatric depression. *Clinical Gerontology, 1*, 37–43.

Brown, C., Abe-Kin, J. S., & Barrio, C. (2003). Depression in ethnically diverse women: Implications for treatment in primary care settings. *Professional Psychology: Research and Practice, 34*(1), 10–19.

Brown, G. K., Beck, A. T., Steer, R. A., & Grisham, J. R. (2000). Risk factors for suicide in psychiatric outpatients: A 20-year prospective study. *Journal of Consulting and Clinical Psychology, 68*, 371–377.

Burns, D. D. (1980). *Feeling good: The new mood therapy.* New York: HarperCollins.

Callahan, E. J., Bertakis, K. D., Azari, R., Robbins, J., Helms, L. J., & Miller, J. (1996). The influence of depression on physician-patient interaction in primary care. *Family Medicine, 28*(5), 346–351.

Contreras, S., Fernandez, S., Malcarne, V., Ingram, R., & Vaccarino, V. R. (2004). Reliability and validity of the Beck Depression and Anxiety Inventories in Caucasian Americans and Latinos. *Hispanic Journal of Behavioral Sciences, 26*(4), 446–462.

Conwell, Y., Duberstein, P. R., & Caine, E. D. (2002). Risk factors for suicide in later life. *Society of Biological Psychiatry, 52*, 193–204.

Coyne, J. C., Schwenk, T. L., & Fechner-Bates, S. (1995). Non-detection of depression by primary care physicians reconsidered. *General Hospital Psychiatry, 17*, 3–12.

Corcoran, K., & Fischer, J. (2000). *Measures for clinical practice: A sourcebook* (3rd ed.). New York: Free Press.

DiClemente, C., & Prochaska, J. (1998). Toward a comprehensive, transtheoretical model of change: Stages of change and addictive behaviors. In W. R. Miller & N. Heather (Eds.), *Treating addictive behaviors* (2nd ed.). New York: Plenum.

Ellis, A. (1994). *Reason and emotion in pyschotherapy.* New York: Carol Publishing Group.

Engel, G. (1977). The need for a new medical model: A challenge for biomedicine. *Science, 196,* 129–136.

Ferguson, R. J. (2000). Using the Beck Anxiety Inventory in primary care. In M. E. Maruish (Ed.), *Handbook of psychological assessment in primary care.* Mahwah, NJ: Erlbaum Associates.

Fillingim, R. B. (2000). *Sex, gender and pain. Progress in pain research and management.* Seattle, WA: IASP Press.

Fydich, T., Dowdall, D., & Chambless, D. L. (1992). Reliability and validity of the Beck Anxiety Inventory. *Journal of Anxiety Disorders, 6,* 55–61.

George, L. K., & Fillenbaum, G. G. (1985). OARS methodology: A decade of experience in geriatric assessment. *Journal of the American Geriatrics Society, 33,* 607–615.

Gilson, M., & Freeman, A. (1999). *Overcoming depression: A cognitive therapy approach for taming the depression beast.* San Antonio, TX: Psychological Corporation.

Glanz, L. M., Haas, G. L., & Sweeney, J. A. (1995). Assessment of hopelessness in suicidal patients. *Clinical Psychology Review, 15*(1), 49–64.

Golden, B. A. (2002). A multidisciplinary approach to nonpharmacologic pain management. *Journal of the American Osteopathic Association, 102*(9), S1–S5.

Goodman, W. K., Price, L. H., Rasmussen, S. A., Mazure, C., Delgado, P., Heninger, G. R., et al. (1989). The Yale-Brown Obsessive-Compulsive Scale: II. Validity. *Archives of General Psychiatry, 46,* 1012–1016.

Goodman, W. K., Price, L. H., Rasmussen, S. A., Mazure, C., Fleishmann, R. L., Hill, C.L., et al. (1989). The Yale-Brown Obsessive-Compulsive Scale: I. Development, use, and reliability. *Archives of General Psychiatry, 46,* 1006–1011.

Goodman, W. K., Rasmussen, S. A., Price, L. H., Mazure, C., Heninger, G. R., & Charney, D. S. (1989). *Manual for the Yale-Brown Obsessive-Compulsive Scale (revised).* New Haven, CT: Connecticut Mental Health Center.

Grothe, K. B., Dutton, G. R., Jones, G. N., Bodenlos, J., Ancona, M., & Brantley, P. J. (2005). Validation of the Beck Depression Inventory–II in a low-income African American sample of medical outpatients. *Psychological Assessment, 17*(1), 110–114.

Harman, J. S., Crystal, S., Walkup, J., & Olfson, M. (2003). Trends in elderly patients' office visits for treatment of depression according to physician specialty: 1985–1999. *Journal of Behavioral Health Services and Research, 30,* 332–341.

Haywood, K. L., Garratt, A. M., & Fitzpatrick, R. (2005). Older people specific health status and quality of life: A structured review of self-assessed instruments. *Journal of Evaluation in Clinical Practice, 11*(4), 315–327.

Healy, D., Barry, K., Blow, F., Welsh, D., & Milner, K. K. (2006). Routine use of the Beck Scale for Suicide Ideation in a psychiatric emergency department. *General Hospital Psychiatry, 28*(4), 323–329.

Heppner, P. P. (1988). *The problem-solving inventory (PSI): Manual.* Palo Alto, CA: Consulting Psychologists.

Heppner, P. P., & Petersen, C. H. (1982). The development and implications of a personal problem-solving inventory. *Journal of Counseling Psychology, 29,* 66–75.

Hirschfeld, R. M., Lewis, L., & Vornik, L. A. (2003). Perceptions and impact of bipolar disorder: How far have we really come? Results of the National Depressive and Manic Depressive Association 2000 survey of individuals with bipolar disorder. *Journal of Clinical Psychiatry, 64*(2), 161–174.

Johnson, J., Spitzer, R., Williams, J., Kroenke, K., Linzer, M., Brody, D., et al. (1995). Psychiatric comorbidity, health status and functional impairment associated with alcohol abuse and dependence in primary care patients: Finding of the PRME-MD-1000 study. *Journal of Consulting and Clinical Psychology, 63,* 133–140.

Kennedy, P., & Llewelyn, S. (2003). Clinical health psychology assessment. In S. Llewelyn & P. Kennedy (Eds.), *Handbook of clinical health psychology.* New York: John Wiley.

Keogh, E., McCracken, L., & Eccleston, C. (2005). Do men and women differ in their response to interdisciplinary chronic pain management? *Pain, 114*(1), 37–46.

Kiecolt-Glaser, J. K., McGuire, L., Robles, T. F., & Glaser, R. (2002). Psychoneuroimmunology: Psychological influences on immune function and health. *Journal of Consulting Clinical Psychology, 70,* 537–547.

Leahy, R. L. (1996). *Cognitive therapy: Basic principles and applications.* Northvale, NJ: Aaronson.

Leahy, R. L. (2003). *Cognitive therapy techniques: A practitioner's guide*. New York: Guilford.
Leahy, R. L. (2006). *The worry cure*. New York: Three Rivers Press.
Mayfield, D., Mcleod, G., & Hall, P. (1974). The CAGE questionnaire: Validation of a new alcoholism instrument. *American Journal of Psychiatry, 131*, 1121–1123.
McCrady, B. S. (2008). Alcohol use disorders. In D. H. Barlow (Ed.), *Clinical handbook of psychological disorders: A step-by-step treatment manual* (4th ed.). New York: Guilford.
Melzack, R. (1975). The McGill pain questionnaire: Major properties and scoring methods. *Pain, 1*, 277–299.
Melzack, R. (1983). *Pain measurement and assessment*. New York: Raven Press.
Melzack, R., & Wall, P. D. (1965). Pain mechanisms: A new theory. *Science, 150*, 971–979.
Menchetti, M. M., Cevenini, N., De Ronchi, D., Quartesan, R., & Berardi, D. (2005). Depression and frequent attendance in elderly primary care patients. *General Hospital Psychiatry, 28*(2), 119–124.
Millon, T., Antoni, M., Millon, C. M., Minor, S., & Grossman, S. (2001). *Millon Behavioral Medicine Diagnostic manual*. Minneapolis, MN: Pearson.
Mongini, F., Deregibus, A., Raviola, F., & Mongini, T. (2003). Confirmation of the distinction between chronic migraine and chronic tension-type headache by the McGill Pain Questionnaire. *Headache: The Journal of Head and Face Pain, 43*(8), 867–877.
Mystakidou, K., Parpa, E., Tsilika, E., Kalaidopoulou, O., Georgaki, S., Galanos, A., et al. (2002). Greek McGill pain questionnaire: Validation and utility in cancer patients. *Journal of Pain and Symptom Management, 24*(4), 379–387.
National Institutes of Health. (2005). *Strengthening behavioral and social sciences in medical schools*. Retrieved November 20, 2008, from http://www.grants.nih.gov/grants/guide/search_results.htm
Needleman, L. (1999). *Cognitive case conceptualization: A casebook for practitioners*. New York: Routledge.
O'Connor, D. W., Pollitt, P. A., Treasure, F. P., Brook, C. P. B., & Reiss, B. B. (1989). The influence of education, social class and sex on Mini-Mental State scores. *Psychological Medicine, 19*, 771–776.
Okifuji, A., & Palmer, T. (2004). In L. H. Haas (Ed.), *Handbook of primary care psychology*. New York: Oxford University Press.
Persons, J. B. (2008). *The case formulation approach to cognitive-behavior therapy*. New York: Guilford.
Pfeiffer, E., Johnson, T. M., & Chiofolo, R. C. (1981). Functional assessment of elderly subjects in four service settings. *Journal of the American Geriatrics Society, 29*, 433–437.
Prochaska, J., & DiClemente, C. (1983). Stages and processes of self change of smoking: Towards an integrated model of change. *Journal of Consulting and Clinical Psychology, 51*, 390–395.
Prochaska, J., & DiClemente, C. (1986). Towards a comprehensive model of change. In W. R. Miller & N. Heather (Eds.), *Treating addictive behaviors: Processes of change*. New York: Plenum.
Rosenfield, B. M. (2004). *The relationship between cognitive distortions and psychological disorders across diagnostic axes*. Unpublished doctoral dissertation, Philadelphia College of Osteopathic Medicine.
Rozanski, A., Blumenthal, J. A., & Kaplan, J. (1999). Impact of psychological factors on the pathogenesis of cardiovascular disease and implications for therapy. *Circulation, 99*, 2192–2217.
Saitz, R., Mulvey, K. P., Plough, A., & Samet, J. H. (1997). Physician unawareness of serious substance abuse. *American Journal of Drug and Alcohol Abuse, 23*, 343–354.
Salovey, P., Detweiler, J. B., Steward, W. T., & Rothman, A. J. (2000). Emotional states and physical health. *American Psychologist, 55*, 110–121.
Saunders, J. B., Aasland, O. G., Babor, T. F., DeLaFuente, J. F. R., & Grant, M. (1993). Development of the Alcohol Use Disorders Identification Test (AUDIT): WHO collaborative project on early detection of persons with harmful alcohol consumption. *Addiction, 88*, 791–804.
Selzer, M. L. (1971). The Michigan Alcohol Screening Test: The test for a new diagnostic instrument. *American Journal of Psychiatry, 127*, 1653–1658.
Sharma, V., Khan, M., & Smith, A. (2005) A Closer look at treatment resistant depression: is it due to a bipolar diathesis. *Journal of Affective Disorders, 84*(1-2), 251–257.
Steffens, D. C., Skoog, I., Norton, M. C., Hart, A. D., Tschanz, J. T., Plassman, B. L. et al. (2000). Prevalence of depression and its treatment on the elderly population—The Cache County study. *Archives of General Psychiatry, 57*, 601–607.
Storch, E. A., Roberti, J. W., & Roth, D. A. (2004). Factor structure, concurrent validity, and internal consistency of the Beck Depression Inventory-second edition in a sample of college students. *Depression and Anxiety, 19*(3), 187–189.
Strand, L. I., Ljunggren, A. E., Bogen, B., Ask, T., & Johnsen, T. B. (2008). The short-form McGill Pain Questionnaire as an outcome measure: Test-retest reliability and responsiveness to change. *European Journal of Pain, 12*, 917–925.

Stuart, M. R., & Lieberman, J. A. (1993). *The fifteen minute hour: Applied psychotherapy for the primary care physician* (2nd ed.). Westport, CT: Praeger.

Tucker, J. A., Vuchinich, R. E., & Murphy, J. G. (2002). In M. M. Antony & D. H. Barlow (Eds.), *Handbook of assessment and treatment planning for psychological disorders.* New York: Guilford.

Twiss, J., Jones, S., & Anderson, I. (2008). Validation of the Mood Disorder Questionnaire for screening for bipolar disorder in a UK sample. *Journal of Affective Disorders, 110*(1), 180–184.

Uhl, J. K. (2007). *The relationship between cognitive distortions and psychological and behavioral factors in a family medicine outpatient sample.* Unpublished doctoral dissertation, Philadelphia College of Osteopathic Medicine.

Wallston, K. A., Wallston, B. S., & DeVellis, R. (1978). Development of the Multidimensional Health Locus of Control (MHLC) scales. *Health Education Monographs, 6,* 160–170.

Williams, J. W., & Manning, J. S. (2008). Collaborative mental health and primary care for bipolar disorder. *Journal of Psychiatric Practice, 14*(2), 55–64.

Wilson, K. A., de Beurs, E., Palmer, C., & Chambless, D. L. (1999). Beck Anxiety Inventory. In M. L. Maruish (Ed.), *The use of psychological testing for treatment planning and outcome assessment* (2nd ed., pp. 971–992). Mahwah, NJ: Lawrence Erlbaum.

Behavioral Strategies

12

Elizabeth A. Gosch
Robert A. DiTomasso
Amelia G. Findiesen

Introduction

In this chapter, we argue that behavioral models of learning and their inherent principles, constructs, and processes are critical in understanding, explaining, altering, and predicting the onset, development, and maintenance of health and health-related behaviors in the primary care setting. We propose that the persistence and repetitiveness of health-specific behaviors, and their inherent habit strengths, are primarily influenced by the presence of unique environmental stimuli, direct and vicarious learning influences, and environmental contingencies that constitute, shape, and maintain the unique health behavior histories of patients. Across individuals, these differential environmental influences account for individual differences in behavior and health risk patterns. We present a behavioral model of health behavior by reviewing the critical role of learning in human behavior, the importance of behavioral principles in shaping and maintaining health behaviors, and the value of the behavioral model in explaining, predicting, and altering health risks. Our focus will be on important theoretical issues, assessment methods, and the application of behavioral interventions designed to preserve health and reduce health risks. The behavioral model, the core of evidence-based practice, provides a critical technology for providing effective assessment and intervention. Learning theory and principles (Hergenhahn & Olson, 2005) and their applications are the keys to eliminating maladaptive learned habits (Wolpe, 1990). We must first examine the basic definitions of health behaviors and learning.

Learning and Health Behaviors

Health behavior may be considered a deeply embedded constellation of behaviors that set the stage for promoting health or creating risk for health-related problems. In examining health problems in today's society, it is difficult to identify an illness in which behavior is not implicated at some level in the onset or maintenance of problems. These so-called health habits are overlearned patterns of responding that either promote the well-being of an individual or undermine health. Exposure to environmental influences appears to play a powerful role in consolidating behavior patterns, with seemingly endless opportunities for reinforcing behaviors.

"Learning" may be defined as a relatively permanent change in behavior that results from the experience of the individual (Hergenhahn & Olson, 2005). Additionally, learning should not be considered a function of native or instinctual factors, or temporary states such as alertness, fatigue, or drug states. The environment of an individual is thus viewed as the primary mechanism through which health behavior is acquired, sustained, and generalized. In some instances, of course, behavior is a function of central nervous system development, or dysfunction, and there is little reason to expect that learning processes may be the primary causative agent for explaining behaviors. Yet, even in such instances, learning principles are inextricably intertwined with these individual differences, affecting response to environmental stimuli and operant strength.

Theoretical Issues

Behavioral interventions were developed from the theoretical frameworks underlying respondent, operant, and social theories of learning. They are based on an experimental analysis of individual behavior, governed by single-subject methodological approaches to examine individual behavior change. These objective methods ensure that intervention approaches are developed, monitored, evaluated, and recycled to ensure objectivity in problem identification, problem analysis, intervention development and implementation, and intervention evaluation of stages of problem solving, thereby ensuring ecological validity and treatment efficacy (e.g., Skinner, 2002). The focus of intervention is on objective, measurable, target behaviors, with contingencies used to effect behavior change. Single-subject approaches require careful contingency management, which must be individualized to address behavioral variability commonly associated with individualized reinforcer or punisher strength (Powell, 1987). This focus allows clinicians to examine apparently overwhelming and pervasive problem behaviors, breaking these complex rule-governed behaviors and behavior chains into subcomponent parts that are more amenable to behavior change. Advances in functional analytic techniques have allowed for more accurate clinical judgments and effective behavior therapy strategies, but limitations still must be acknowledged (Bellack & Hersen, 1998). Regardless, as the problematic behavioral complex is analyzed and deconstructed, by focusing on one instead of many target behaviors simultaneously, meaningful change becomes apparent, which can serve to document behavior change, not only for the clinician, but the individual as well. As a result, behavioral approaches not only provide us with the functional determinants of behavior, but the technology necessary to effectively reduce, and ultimately eliminate, the maladaptive behavior patterns.

The collection of interventions considered behavioral is fairly broad in scope, but typically shares several qualities: (a) adherence to the scientific model in which treatments are chosen that have empirical support; (b) monitoring of treatment effects through empirical methods over the course of treatment to determine efficacy; (c) basing interventions on a functional analysis of target behaviors, the situational factors maintaining the occurrence of target behaviors, and situational variables that may promote therapeutic change; (d) an emphasis on psychoeducation; (e) direct interventions that target specific areas of concern; and (f) relapse prevention and generalization training at the end of treatment (Compton et al., 2004).

The behavioral model assumes that most behavior is governed by antecedent and consequent events contingent to the behavior. Although typically focusing on overt, observable events, the behavioral model also includes consideration of covert, internal events (thoughts, feelings, physiological changes). Behavioral interventions focus on correcting behavioral excesses (e.g., overeating, panicking during medical procedures) and deficits (lack of exercise, forgetting to take medications as prescribed). The behavioral approach generally follows a series of steps: clarify the patient's problem, describe a specific behavior targeted for change and how that behavior will be measured, identify the antecedents and consequences of the behavior, set specific objectives for behavioral change, devise a treatment plan (specific therapy procedures) to change the maintaining conditions, implement the plan, and evaluate the program (Spiegler & Guevremont, 2003). People may need to learn prerequisite skills (e.g., how to organize their medication-taking regime or communicate effectively with their doctor), as well as experience contingent antecedent events to prompt or elicit adaptive behaviors and contingent consequences to reinforce adaptive behavior and punish undesirable behaviors. To develop behavioral interventions to enact these changes, it is important to first understand the basic principles of respondent, operant, and social learning theories.

Respondent Conditioning

The basic respondent-conditioning paradigm describes a learning process that begins with an environmental stimulus (the unconditioned stimulus) that elicits biologically established reflexes such as salivation, eye blinks, emotional responses, sexual responses, and psychosomatic symptoms (Wolpe & Plaud, 1997). For example, people reflexively respond to food with salivation or to pain-inducing stimuli with bodily responses that help the person adapt to the situation. Stimuli such as the smell of food or the sight of a needle that reliably precede and predict these unconditioned stimuli will come to evoke certain reflexive responses or conditioned responses (e.g., salivation, fear) to help prepare the person for the unconditioned stimulus. Cancer patients receiving chemotherapy that elicits feelings of nausea often find that stimuli predicting the chemotherapy also come to elicit nausea. They may feel nausea as they sit in the chair waiting for the treatment to begin or as they enter the building in which they receive the chemotherapy. If the treatment occurs at a set time each day, the time of day may come to elicit feelings of nausea.

This learning process is thought to have survival benefits, in that cues in the environment could elicit responses that would encourage individuals to approach or avoid certain stimuli. A person could avoid situations associated with pain or harm and seek out situations associated with pleasure or satisfaction of needs. Individuals who have been stung by a bee frequently experience some anxiety when they see bees and often will move away from them. The smell of food cooking will often elicit salivation and approach behaviors. However, at times, individuals do not form the correct associations between predictive cues and reflexes. Cancer patients will tend to have a conditioned reaction of nausea to foods they eat on the days they receive chemotherapy although the food was not the cause of the nausea.

In the medical environment, people may be required to undergo procedures that are painful in the short term but helpful to them in the long term. Individuals receive vaccination shots, ingest unpleasant-tasting medicine, and undergo surgical procedures. Some individuals may come to fear the cues that predict these negative experiences. Patients may avoid medical visits, children may fight staff when told they will be receiving an injection, and individuals may panic during preparations for procedures.

Sometimes the conditioned stimulus is an internal experience, such as feeling a bit out of breath before an asthma attack, a mental image/thought of being ill, or attending to one's heartbeat prior to a panic attack. In these situations, some individuals may experience heightened fear or arousal when later experiencing benign physical sensations, such as a normally beating heart or breathing a little more quickly as one goes up the stairs. Routine bodily sensations come to elicit strong emotional reactions, prompting individuals to overuse health care services.

A variety of respondent-conditioning procedures have been developed to decrease the elicitation of maladaptive responses and increase the elicitation of adaptive responses to the appropriate stimuli. Empirically supported treatments for sleep onset or maintenance problems are based on conditioning the bed to be a stimulus that evokes the sleep response (i.e., sleep hygiene procedures, Bootzin, 1977). Changes in sexual, eating, and needle-phobia responses can also be successfully conditioned using respondent-conditioning procedures (e.g., Fairburn, Cooper, Shafran, & Wilson, 2008; Willemsen, Chowdhury, & Briscall, 2002; Wincze, Bach, & Barlow, 2008). Systematic desensitization can be used to decrease fear, panic, and avoidance in a variety of medical settings. Most of these procedures rely on conditioning a new response to the cue by pairing the cue with another unconditioned stimulus, or exposing the patient to the cue without the unconditioned stimulus until the conditioned response is extinguished.

Operant Conditioning

Operant learning focuses on the environmental conditions, the "three-term contingency," occurring prior to, during, and following the occurrence of a target response that maintain the response (Skinner, 1969). A basic premise of operant conditioning is that behavior is selected by its history of consequences (Cooper, Heron, & Heward, 1987; O'Neill et al., 1997). Individuals learn which behaviors are most adaptive and maladaptive based on the environment's response to their behavior.

The operant model includes three main, interrelated components: antecedent events, conditions, and cues (a) that precede a behavior, (b) the specific behavior targeted for change, and (c) the consequences that follow the target behavior (Spiegler & Guevremont, 2003). Functional analysis allows for direct examination of the antecedent and consequent events that maintain the target behaviors identified for change, thereby providing the impetus for experimental manipulation of either for subsequent behavior change (Schloss & Smith, 1994). Operant-behavioral interventions tend to target the antecedents that set the stage for certain behaviors to occur and the consequences of those behaviors to foster behavior change.

Antecedents strongly influence the occurrence of behavior. Antecedents may be the focus of an intervention when they set the stage for a maladaptive behavior to occur (e.g., having potato chips in the kitchen of someone trying to maintain a low-salt diet), or when they are not present to influence the occurrence of a behavior (e.g., failing to provide a person with written postoperative care instructions). A common example that illustrates the power of antecedents in influencing behavior is the ringing of a phone. The ringing prompts the individual to pick up the phone. Past experience has taught the person that picking up a phone that is ringing will be reinforced by talking with someone, although picking up a nonringing phone will not be reinforced (no one will be on the line). Antecedents like the phone ringing or an alarm signaling that it is time to take one's medication often function as discriminative stimuli, providing information to individuals about what behavior will likely be reinforced or not reinforced in particular situations. Another type of antecedent, setting events, refers to broad contextual variables or conditions that influence the likelihood that certain behaviors will be performed (Spiegler & Guevremont, 2003). External or environmental events such as being at home or in a hospital, having previously had a fight with a coworker, or waiting a long time in a doctor's office will serve to influence behavior. Internal states and events such as being tired or hungry, feeling anxious, or experiencing particular thoughts may also impact behavior. A third type of antecedent, prompts, refers to specific cues that directly guide and facilitate performance of a behavior (Kazdin, 2001). Prompts can be verbal, environmental, physical, and behavioral. Written directions regarding how to prepare for a surgical procedure, asking someone to step on a scale, and setting a pill bottle out where it can be seen are examples of prompts. Spiegler and Guevremont (2003) include the prerequisite knowledge, skills, and resources needed to engage in a behavior (e.g., knowing how to monitor insulin levels and having the appropriate supplies to do so), as another group of antecedents to consider when designing interventions.

In conjunction with antecedents, several types of consequences serve to strengthen or weaken the future likelihood of behavior. Reinforcers are events whose contingent application following a specific behavior strengthens the likelihood that a behavior will occur in the future. Some individuals are more likely to comply with their medication regimes when taking the medication is followed by praise or a preferred food. A negative reinforcer is one whose contingent removal following the behavior strengthens the likelihood of a future response. Negative reinforcers are often considered aversive stimuli. For example, people tend to wear seatbelts more frequently when buckling the belt serves to terminate a loud pinging sound. There are basically three classes of reinforcers: material, social, and activity, all of which have the capacity to influence behavior. Extinction refers to the withholding of a positive reinforcer following the occurrence of a behavior, which decreases the future occurrence of a behavior. Punishment decreases the future frequency of behavior. Punishment refers to the contingent application of undesired stimuli or the removal of desirable stimuli following the occurrence of a behavior.

The operant model proposes that individuals are highly susceptible to the influences of contingencies, especially tangible and social reinforcers (Kazdin & Weisz, 2003). However, it is essential to understand that the effect of a reinforcing or punishing stimulus is not due to the perceived quality of the stimulus itself (e.g., M&M candies are not necessarily a positive reinforcer to all people; likewise, nagging someone may not necessarily serve as a punisher); rather, this relationship must be discovered functionally through observing the effects of consequences on the target behavior for the individual over time and under a variety of circumstances.

Because the behavior of an individual also impacts the environment, it is likely that the individual elicits certain types of responses from important figures in the environment that may serve to sustain the behaviors. It is also likely that certain figures in the individual's environment may come to serve as discriminative stimuli for the occurrence of the behavior in question. Over the course of time, certain behaviors such as maladaptive eating patterns, sedentary behavior (e.g., watching television), or substance abuse may be selectively reinforced and learned to the exclusion of other more adaptive behavior. With extinction of adaptive responding, and maladaptive behaviors maintained on a variable ratio schedule of reinforcement, the likelihood of behavior change becomes improbable. Without intervention, these maladaptive habits continue despite even differential reinforcement of low rates or levels of responding, because the individual seeks the discriminative stimuli—the individuals and situations—that are most likely to reinforce and maintain the maladaptive behavioral repertoire.

The educative approach incorporates skill acquisition and choice making into interventions designed to replace maladaptive health care behaviors with more adaptive responses that fulfill a similar function for the individual. Based on theories of behavioral systems that incorporate principles of response relations, the educative philosophy assumes that behavioral topographies can be functionally related (Vittimberga, Scotti, & Weigle, 1999). Thus, change in one behavior may lead to changes in other related responses. Key to this approach is the identification of the functions served by the maladaptive behavior. Common functions of behavior include: (a) avoidance or escape, (b) sensory stimulation, (c) attention seeking, and (d) positive tangible reinforcement (Kazdin, 2001). Educative treatment approaches entail the learning and reinforcement of coping skills that provide the individual with more adaptive alternatives (e.g., challenging negative self-talk, engaging in relaxation exercises) that replace undesired behaviors (e.g., taking excessive amounts of pain medication) by more effectively achieving a similar function (e.g., avoiding anxiety).

The complexity of environmental-response relations cannot be understated (Cooper et al., 2007). Skinner noted that a single response is often a function of multiple variables, and that these variables impact more than one response (Skinner, 1957). Moreover, changes in one behavior may lead to collateral behavioral change. Eating healthier meals can be accompanied by increased exercise. On the other hand, blocking a problem behavior has been observed, at times, to lead to increases in other problematic behaviors that serve a similar function (Sprague & Horner, 1992). Numerous contingencies often cooccur, making it difficult to decipher which contingencies, and in what combination, serve to maintain a particular behavioral response. Despite these complexities, the models and procedures derived from operant-conditioning learning paradigms have been found extremely useful in impacting heath-related behaviors.

Social Learning Theory

According to social learning theory, individuals learn through observation as well as direct experience. For example, children may learn anxious responses and schema through observing this behavior being modeled by significant others. Seeing role models doubt their own abilities or overestimate the likelihood of threat may influence the child to engage in similar ways. Evidence has accumulated that children seem to learn fear responses from observing these responses in others, including parents, siblings, peers, and the media (Bandura, 1977; Rachman, 1977).

Social learning theory further emphasizes the role that an individual's sense of self-efficacy, their belief that they can cope effectively with a situation, strongly influences their behavior (Bandura, 1977). An individual's sense of self-efficacy regarding a situation derives from personal encounters with the situation, vicarious encounters with the situation, somatovisceral arousal experiences in the situation, and verbal persuasion (Bandura). From this perspective, treatment focuses on increasing an individual's perceived self-efficacy to cope with or control anxiety-provoking stimuli. Self-efficacy expectations may be increased through performance accomplishments, vicarious experiences, emotional arousal techniques, and verbal exhortation (Bandura). Active, real-world performance accomplishments are considered the most effective means of increasing perceptions of self-efficacy. Guided participant modeling has been established as one of the most effective types of modeling procedures in the treatment of phobias (Barrios & O'Dell, 1998).

Assessment Methods

Behavioral assessment, an empirically based assessment paradigm, was derived from the behavioral model of therapy, and fits well within the medical environment in which there is a focus upon identifiable markers. Traditional assessment approaches, which evolved from the trait model, often lack utility for behavioral clinicians and their medical colleagues, who emphasize the necessity of directly observable phenomena and the verifiability of observations. Physicians often rely upon valid and reliable measurement tools to detect the presence of causative factors in disease, to confirm diagnostic hypotheses, to monitor the status of ongoing medical conditions, and to determine the outcomes of medical interventions. In the health and mental health realm, the use of behaviorally based assessment strategies is, then, not unlike tests and assessments typically employed in medical settings.

According to Bellack and Hersen (1998), behavioral assessment is an empirically driven, multimethod, multimodal, multitemporal, and multiinformant process. We posit that this model is quite applicable in primary care. In the primary care environment today, there is significant emphasis upon evidence-based approaches that can yield useful information in the care of patients. Likewise, in facing the challenging problems clinicians often encounter with primary care patients, reliance upon a multitude of methods provides the necessary flexibility to meet the demands of patients suffering from multiple problems. The multimodal nature of behavioral assessment allows for comprehensiveness of care in measuring critical facets of the environment that are likely to affect behavioral change. Because continuity of care is such a critical tenet of primary care medicine, the availability of measuring patients across multiple occasions is easily available. Behavioral assessment requires the delineation of carefully specified measurement of observable behavior and associated temporally related causal variables. Likewise, the availability of family members and significant others provides an additional opportunity to assess behavior. Overall, then, behavioral assessment is a systematic approach designed to facilitate the understanding of behavior and its reliable and valid measurement for clinical purposes. The goal of behavioral assessment is to provide a solid basis for making clinical decisions and developing effective behavior change strategies (Haynes, Leisen, & Blaine, 1997; Haynes & Williams, 2003). Therefore, the emphasis on the environment assists in identifying specific maladaptive behaviors and repertoires, and interventions most likely to result in adaptive behavior change (Gettinger & Stoiber, 2006), practices commonly associated with effective evidence-based programs (Kazdin & Weisz, 2003).

In the clinical context of primary care, behavioral assessment procedures rely upon minimally inferential tools that are applied in a repeated measurement format over a period of time for a given health behavior of interest. These measurements target specific problematic health-related behaviors and associated antecedent and consequential social, physical, and environmental factors as they relate to the development and maintenance of problematic behavior that threaten the patient's health. In the medical setting, it is difficult to find a problem in which behavioral factors do not play an important role in precipitating, exacerbating, or maintaining problems.

Behavioral assessment provides data about what a person does, the circumstances under which the behavior reliably occurs, how often the behavior occurs, whether a behavior should be increased or decreased, how long it lasts, and the consequences of the behavior, that is, its impact regarding what is obtained, escaped, or avoided as a result (Bellack & Hersen, 1998). These data provide a sound basis for implementing a functional analysis of behavior or behavior analysis by specifying critical variables to consider in the development of treatment interventions.

The behavioral-assessment model evolved from the growing dissatisfaction with traditional assessment approaches. These traditional approaches were derived from a trait model of personality and behavior. Inferred enduring characteristics of individuals were employed as a basis for explaining and predicting the behavior of individuals across different contexts and situations. Behaviorists, viewing personality as the totality of a patient's habit repertoire (DiTomasso & Gilman, 2005; Wolpe, 1990), understandably deemed the traditional trait model as deficient in offering the requisite data for developing a conceptualization of a patent's problem, let alone a behavioral intervention. The popularity of behavior therapy required a unique assessment process that was congruent with assumptions about behavior therapy.

The behavioral-assessment model assumes that learning is a primary mechanism for the development of maladaptive behavior. Established and tested principles of learning could, therefore, be helpful in explaining the onset, development, and maintenance of maladaptive behavior. By emphasizing observable phenomena in the here and now, this approach eliminated the need for reliance upon inference. The patient's behavior, instead of an underlying assumed cause, is considered to be the problem that becomes the target of treatment. Behavioral clinicians sought an approach that provided an actual sample of the individual's behavior in the contexts of interest. Therefore, learning principles could be used to assist patients in acquiring new adaptive behaviors that are incompatible with their maladaptive behaviors. The behavioral approach to assessment, therefore, encompassed these assumptions and spawned the development of methods for actively gathering empirical information about maladaptive problems. This information could then quite easily be used to inform a learning-based conceptualization of the patient's problem.

In the primary care setting, given the types of problems that physicians confront, a comprehensive behavioral assessment is critical in focusing upon the emission, reinforcement, and maintenance of behaviors that are directly tied to the health risk experienced by the patient. The identification of occasions that set the stage for the occurrence of problematic behaviors (e.g., overeating) is necessary in attempting to design a model to explain and alter behavior. Previous models, based on psychodynamic approaches, focus on characteristics that are highly theoretical, largely inaccessible, and of questionable relevance in explaining and predicting health behavior.

Characteristics of Behavioral Assessment

Bellack and Hersen (1998), and DiTomasso and Gilman (2005), have elucidated the distinctiveness of behavioral assessment. These characteristics are explicated in detail below and underscore the unique characteristics of this model.

Empirical Basis

Behavioral assessment is an empirically based approach (Bellack & Hersen, 1998). Its empirical underpinnings allow it to be directly observed and, more important, subject to being verified. In the process of behavioral assessment, the criterion behavior and the test situation are essentially identical. Therefore, the clinician can more easily generalize from the observed and recorded behavioral assessment data to the real-life situation of the patient. However, to do so, the clinician must obtain a representative sample of the occasions under which the criterion behavior is likely to occur. To achieve this end, the clinician must systematically schedule and collect observations over a wide array of appropriate situations. DiTomasso and Colameco (1982) have warned clinicians about the risks of limiting observations to a relatively restricted number of situations. Under some circumstances, to obtain relevant data, the clinician may find it necessary to create the situation under which the response occurs. For example, to identify the extent to which a diabetic patient is competent in testing blood glucose and adjusting insulin level, the clinician must arrange a behavioral test in conjunction with a diabetic nurse educator, and that clearly specifies the step-by-step tasks to achieve the goal.

Multiple Methods

In behavioral assessment, there is reliance on a multiplicity of methods (Bellack & Hersen, 1998). These methods are selected and based upon the nature of the problem to be studied. The characteristics of the target behavior chosen for measurement, such as frequency, intensity, latency, duration, or a combination of such, are a direct function of the problem itself. In some instances, multiple aspects of a problem behavior may require observation to provide a full understanding and thorough analysis of the behavior in question. To yield the maximum amount of relevant and usable information for a minimal amount of effort and cost requires a careful balance. Behavioral-assessment tools are tailored to the problem and patient, and are explicitly designed to yield the most critical information. The observations are directly gathered in the patient's natural environment where the behavior is occurring; here the behavior is directly self-monitored by the patient or observed by a person in the patient's environment. For example, in assessing the insomniac, self-reported latency to sleep onset may be supplemented by a spouse who is asked to record sleep onset latency. In the case of a diabetic patient, the behavioral-assessment model would directly sample target behaviors that are known to affect the probability of achieving tight blood glucose control. On occasion, behavioral clinicians may rely on self-reported information. However, even in these situations, where observable behavior may be coded in some fashion, the reliance upon inference is held to a minimum.

Precise Definition of the Target Behavior

The quality of the information obtained from behavioral assessment greatly depends upon explicitly defining the target behavior or complaint in question. Clinicians must carefully and precisely determine and operationalize the critical components of the target behavior. Doing so leaves little room for doubt about clearly discriminating the occurrence and nonoccurrence of the behavior under observation (DiTomasso & Colameco, 1982). The clinician's level of specification of the target behavior permits precise measurement of the phenomena and allows that the behavior of focus is indeed detected and recorded by the observer. The availability of behavioral-rating scales, based on a comprehensive sampling of the universe of behaviors constituting a domain of interest, can be quite useful as they rely upon clearly specified behavioral referents.

Multimodal Focus

Behavioral assessment is also multimodal, meaning that it focuses on more than one aspect of the patient (Bellack & Hersen, 1998). Given the impact of a variety of factors on observed behavior of the patient in the primary care setting, the clinician is interested in more than simply the observable behavior of the patient. Behavior is, then, more broadly defined and may include cognitive, emotional, and physiological variables.

Reliance on Multiple Informants

The behavioral-assessment approach may incorporate observational information from more than one source of information. Possible informants may include not only the patient, but those who share the patient's environment. Informants may include spouses, parents, siblings, and friends.

By using a variety of informants, the clinician is able to gain a fuller understanding of the target behavior from different perspectives. All observers, however, must employ behavioral-assessment tools, be trained to do so, and are asked to record carefully collected observations. For example, when making observations, the data are recorded at the time of the occurrence, and not completed at a later time when memory decay may operate to reduce the validity of the information. Of course, the clinician must determine when much information is really too much. There is a point of diminishing returns and issues of time, convenience, and cost that must be considered.

An important advantage of using multiple informants is that it may ultimately help those in the patient's environment learn how their own behavior may trigger the patient's behavior, and be intimately tied into reinforcing and strengthening the patient's problem behavior. These data may also yield useful information about the consistency and sustainability of change.

Determining Antecedent Conditions

The identification of antecedent conditions is also important in identifying specific situations under which the target problem is emitted (Bellack & Hersen, 1998). Problem behaviors of patients may be more likely to occur under one set of conditions than another. For example, a diabetic may be able to show great restraint in choosing appropriate foods at home, but completely lose control at a wedding buffet. In this sense, certain situations may represent high-risk circumstances. If the target problem is observed to differentially occur across situations, the clinician should explore differences across these situations, and may unearth subtle information about subtle precipitating factors.

Identifying Temporally-Associated Causal Variables

To explain and predict health risk behaviors, behavioral assessment considers time-associated causal variables and comprehensively provides a complete picture (Bellack & Hersen, 1998; DiTomasso & Gilman, 2005). The clinical data derived from behavioral assessment are analyzed to select, design, and implement interventions that have a great likelihood of altering behavior. Once again, data about the frequency of a problem behavior provide an incomplete picture. Behavioral observations often include the situations under which a behavior is most likely to occur or not occur; the target behavior; associated thoughts, images, and feelings; and the consequences in the patient's environment that may serve to reinforce and maintain the problem. The identification of environmental factors that reinforce and maintain problematic behavior is crucial. By analyzing the impact a problem has on the patient's environment, it is possible to identify possible gains mediated through the role of positive reinforcement. The impact of family member attention on the pain behavior of chronic pain patients is a well-known phenomenon. Also, understanding how the patient's problem prevents the patient from contact with an anticipated aversive stimulus (avoidance) or removes the patient from an aversive situation (escape) is also important.

Repeated Measures Gathered Over Time

Behavioral-assessment measures are usually collected across a variety of situations and over the course of time. Data are collected during baseline, treatment, and follow-up periods (Bellack & Hersen, 1998; DiTomasso & Gilman, 2005). The clinician obtains a series of integrated snapshots of the targets by sampling across a variety of relevant situations. The ultimate synthesis of this assessment data provides a comprehensive view of the target problem, yielding clinically useful information for physician, patient, and clinician. Baseline information provides a measure of the severity, frequency, or intensity of the problem, useful information for performing a functional analysis, and a criterion against which to measure treatment effectiveness. Systematic observational data obtained during treatment further informs the case conceptualization, either supporting the continuation of the treatment or requiring a reanalysis of the problem and delivery of another treatment. Data obtained during the treatment phase should support that the problem is improving. Follow-up data provide a measure of the stability of the change in behavior, signify signs of possible relapse, and the extent to which alternative ways of responding have been learned.

Prudent Scheduling of Observations

In the assessment of targets, continuous observation would normally be impossible, let alone highly impractical and costly in terms of time and effort. To provide valid information, behavioral assessments must be gathered under circumstances that guarantee adequate representation of the target problem. Decisions about when and where to collect observations involve selection and planning of observations during samples of time and events that are most likely to be representative of the problem. Otherwise, a biased, invalid, and perhaps inaccurate view of the problem may emerge (Bellack & Hersen, 1998; DiTomasso & Gilman, 2005).

Reliability of Observations

When using an observer in the patient's environment to collect data, an important issue concerns the reliability of the information gathered. This issue has to do with interobserver agreement, that is, the extent to which the observations are replicable by an independent observer (Bellack & Hersen, 1998). The reliability of self-monitored data is just as important. In either case, the use of an independent observer in the patient's environment can enhance the confidence one places in the information obtained. The extent to which two observers agree, for example, on the frequency and duration of a target behavior, provides credibility to the observational process and the information itself.

Reactivity Issues

Reactive effects occur when the process of observation changes the phenomenon being observed. Observations obtained when the patient is aware of the observation will not necessarily generalize to situations when observations are made without this awareness (Bellack & Hersen, 1998). Reactivity produces effects that occur in a direction that is congruent with treatment effects and although transient, and initially confused with treatment effects, may serve to bolster the confidence of the patient that change is possible.

Nonreactive and Random Reliability Checks

Reliability between observers is expected to be higher when observers, even self-observers, are aware that reliability will be determined. The reliability of observations gathered when the observers are aware may not generalize to situations when they are aware they are not being checked (Bellack & Hersen, 1998; DiTomasso & Gilman, 2005). A possible solution here is to inform observers that reliability will be checked, but not let them know when the checking will occur (DiTomasso & Colameco, 1982).

Assessment Tools

In working with medical patients, the behavioral-assessment tools used depends upon the specific types of target problems being assessed. For example, in the case of the obese hypertensive patient attempting to lose weight, behavioral assessment may include home monitoring of blood pressure, a daily weight check, and keeping a food diary. In behavior-modification programs, typical food diaries include the exact foods, amounts, calories consumed, eating situations, thoughts, and associated feelings preceding eating. The tension-headache sufferer may be asked to monitor the day, time of onset of headache, characteristics of the symptoms, length of the headache, and supply a pain-intensity rating.

Case Formulation and Treatment

Behavioral assessment provides the raw data for developing the case formulation (DiTomasso & Gilman, 2005). Through a careful process of integration and synthesis of these data with other relevant information about the patient, the clinician will be able to choose an effective treatment and address obstacles to success. Treatment planning and implementation are critical to successful cognitive-behavioral therapy. Both are linked to the therapist's ability to generate clinical hypotheses and develop, refine, and tailor treatment to the client's needs. Behavioral assessment helps the clinician formulate case-specific treatment plans (Needleman, 1999; Persons, 1989) that are of direct relevance to the client's treatment.

Behavioral assessment enables the clinician to reduce target problems into observable and measurable units. It also informs the treatment process in an ongoing manner. For example, baseline data provide the clinician with important information about the state of the client's problem before an intervention has been made. During the course of treatment, the clinician expects that if treatment is appropriately directed to the critical aspects of the problem then change will occur in the desired direction. Insufficient change in target behaviors also serves to inform intervention decisions, leading to changes in conceptualization and treatment implementation.

Behavioral Strategies

A variety of behavioral strategies are available for clinical application in the primary care setting. The clinician must choose the most appropriate strategy based on a number of factors, including the functional analysis of behavior. These strategies include procedures based on positive reinforcement, negative reinforcement, extinction, stimulus control, and generalization.

Freeman, Pretzer, Fleming, and Simon (1990) have reviewed a number of behavioral strategies employed by therapists in the mental health context. These procedures include: graded task assignments, activity scheduling, behavior rehearsal, relaxation training, assertiveness training, behavioral experiments, and bibliotherapy.

Graded Task Assignments

Patients with chronic medical conditions are frequently asked to change a number of aspects of their behavior as a means of bringing medical conditions under better control. It is easy to imagine patients who when confronted with the enormity of this challenge feel overwhelmed, if not paralyzed. Graded task assignment involves breaking complex behaviors down into smaller components and gradually introducing more and more changes over time. It is prudent under such circumstances to ensure the likelihood of success by introducing changes early on that are easier, and for which the patient is more likely to succeed. This approach provides plenty of opportunities for patients to practice the components of the required behavior, and will likely enhance their self-efficacy.

Activity Scheduling

Many patients who need to learn new habits may report that they have too little time to do what is requested of them. Assuming their observation is accurate, reviewing their activity schedules over the course of a week hour by hour and day by day may help to identify untapped opportunities to more effectively manage time and, as a result, create unforeseen opportunities for change. For example, the patient who complains that he has no time to exercise is a case in point. Activity scheduling may provide specific opportunities on a daily basis to insert lifestyle exercise activities.

Behavior Rehearsal

On a related note, many patients are required to perform a variety of tasks to provide assessment data or to implement an intervention. Take the case of the hypertensive patient for whom the physician requires home monitoring of blood pressure. Having the patient come into the office with the automated blood pressure device can serve as an opportunity to model the use of the equipment and to provide ample opportunity to rehearse the behaviors under guidance. This strategy may also be useful with the diabetic who needs to learn to use a glucometer.

Relaxation Training

Many patients may benefit from relaxation training and breathing exercises as a means of reducing stress, hypertension, and anxiety (e.g., Haaga et al., 1994). Popular relaxation strategies include imagery, body scan techniques, progressive muscle relaxation, meditation, and autogenic training. The behavioral clinician can train patients in any one of a variety of strategies in the office, and audiotape the exercise for home use and practice by the patient.

Assertiveness Training

Assertion training is a useful strategy for the patient for any number of reasons. As a means of the appropriate expression of one's feelings, it may be used as an alternative to aggression or nonassertion, both of which may adversely affect the medical patient. Through a process of education, behavioral rehearsal, feedback, and shaping, patients may learn a more appropriate response that increases the likelihood of having their needs met.

Behavioral Experiments

Having a patient engage in a behavioral experiment can be a powerful method for testing out an unrealistic prediction. Patients who believe that a medication will not help can be asked to experiment for a short period of time, monitor the effects of the medicine and test out their prediction.

Bibliotherapy

Educating patients about their medical conditions, health care behaviors, and treatments remains a cornerstone to effective behavioral interventions. Bibliotherapy may help in educating patients and increasing the likelihood of successfully assimilating the treatment.

Reinforcement

Many studies support the use of direct tangible, social, activity, and choice reinforcers to increase health-related behaviors (e.g., Willemsen, Chowdhury, & Briscall, 2002). For example, Carton and Schweitzer (1996) increased compliance during hemodialysis using a token economy system with a 10-year-old boy. A variety of factors that influence the effectiveness of reinforcement procedures have been summarized by Cooper, Heron, and Heward (1987). Reinforcement that is delivered immediately following the behavior in a consistent manner is more effective than delayed reinforcement applied inconsistently. Setting an achievable criterion for reinforcement as well as using high-quality reinforcers of sufficient magnitude influences behavior change. It is important to vary reinforcers, use generalized reinforcers, or use token systems to guard against satiation and habituation effects. Clarifying the behavior-reinforcement relationship through prompts may increase patient responsiveness. Finally, when establishing a new behavior pattern, a continuous schedule of reinforcement leads to quicker learning, and fading to an intermittent schedule helps with generalization and maintenance of the behavior change. Generalization and maintenance can also be augmented by gradually shifting to increasing the delay between the response to reinforcement and to naturally occurring reinforcers.

Systematic Desensitization and Exposure Procedures

Exposure-based procedures significantly decrease maladaptive fears or fear-related avoidance that interferes with appropriate health-related behavior (e.g., visiting the dentist, needle phobias, pill swallowing, changing certain behavioral habits) (Spiegler & Guevremont, 2003; Wolpe, 1990). In these procedures, the patient is exposed within a structured protocol to the feared stimulus until the fear response undergoes extinction. The exposure is often completed in graduated steps, beginning with low-anxiety-provoking stimuli and gradually moving to high-anxiety-inducing stimuli.

In conclusion, behavioral assessment and treatment strategies are critically important and useful tools for the primary care clinician. The clinical application of behavioral methods is likely to enhance the effectiveness of therapists in the primary care setting and, most importantly, maximize benefits to those patients being served.

References

Bandura, A. (1977). *Social learning theory.* Englewood Cliffs, NJ: Prentice-Hall.

Barrios, B. A., & O'Dell, S. L. (1998). Fears and anxieties. In E. J. Mash & R. A. Barkley (Eds.), *Treatment of childhood disorders* (2nd ed.). New York: Guilford.

Bellack, A. S., & Hersen, M. (1998). *Behavioral assessment: A practical handbook* (4th ed.). Boston: Allyn and Bacon.

Bootzin, R. R. (1977). Effects of self-control procedures for insomnia. In R. B. Stuart (Ed.), *Behavioral self-management* (pp. 176–195). New York: Brunner/Mazel.

Carton, J. S., & Schweitzer, J. B. (1996). Use of a token economy to increase compliance during hemodialysis. *Journal of Applied Behavior Analysis, 29,* 111–113.

Compton, S. N., March, J. S., Brent, D., Albano, A., Weersing, K. R., & Curry, J. (2004). Cognitive-behavioral psychotherapy for anxiety and depressive disorders in childhood and adolescence: An evidence-based medical review. *Journal of the American Academy of Child and Adolescent Psychiatry, 43*(8), 930–959.

Cooper, J. O., Heron, T. E., & Heward, W. L. (1987). *Applied behavior analysis*. Upper Saddle River, NJ: Prentice-Hall.

DiTomasso, R. A., & Colameco, S. (1982). Patient self-monitoring of behavior. *Journal of Family Practice, 15*(1), 79–83.

DiTomasso, R. A., & Gilman, R. (2005). Behavioral assessment. In A. Freeman, S. H. Felgoise, A. M. Nezu, C. M. Nezu, & M. A. Reinecke (Eds.), *Encyclopedia of cognitive behavior therapy* (pp. 61–68). New York: Springer Publishing Company.

Fairburn, C. G., Cooper, Z., Shafran, R., & Wilson, G. T. (2008). Eating disorders: A transdiagnostic protocol. In D. H. Barlow (Ed.), *Clinical handbook of psychological disorders* (4th ed., pp. 578–614). New York: Guilford.

Freeman, A., Pretzer, J., Fleming, B., & Simon, K. M. (1990). *Clinical applications of cognitive therapy.* New York: Plenum.

Gettinger, M., & Stoiber, K.C. (2006). Functional assessment, collaboration, and evidence-based treatment: Analysis of a team approach for addressing challenging behaviors in young children. *Journal of School Psychology, 44*(3), 231–252.

Haaga, D. A., Davison, G. C., Williams, M. E., Dolezal, S. L., Haleblian, J., Rosenbaum, J., et al. (1994). Mode-specific impact of relaxation training for hypertensive men with Type A behavior pattern. *Behavior Therapy, 25*, 209–223.

Haynes, S. N., Leisen, M. B., & Blaine, D. D. (1997). Design of individualized behavioral treatment programs using functional analytical clinical case models. *Psychological Assessment, 9*(4), 334.

Haynes, S. N., & Williams, A. E. (2003). Case formulation and the design of behavioral treatment programs: Matching treatment mechanisms to causal variables for behavior problems. *European Journal of Psychological Assessment, 19*(3), 164.

Hergenhahn, B. R., & Olson, M. H. (2005). *Introduction to theories of learning* (7th ed.). Upper Saddle River, NJ: Pearson Prentice-Hall.

Kazdin, A. E. (2001). *Behavior modification in applied settings* (6th ed.). Belmont, CA: Wadsworth.

Kazdin, A. E., & Weisz, J. R. (2003). *Evidence-based psychotherapies for children and adolescents.* New York: Guilford.

O'Neill, R. E., Horner, R. H., Albin, R. W., Sprague, J. R. Storey, K., & Newton, J. S. (1997). *Functional assessment and program development for problem behavior: A practical handbook.* Pacific Grove, OR: Brooks/Cole.

Needleman, L. D. (1999). *Cognitive case conceptualization: A guidebook for practitioners.* Mahwah, NJ: Lawrence Erlbaum.

Persons, J. B. (1989). *Cognitive therapy in practice: A case formulation approach.* New York: Norton.

Powell, D. A. (1987). Cognitive and affective components of reinforcement. *American Psychologist, 42*, 409–410.

Rachman, S. J. (1977). The conditioning theory of fear-acquisition. A critical examination. *Behaviour Research and Therapy, 15*, 375–387.

Schloss, P. J., & Smith, M. A. (1994). *Applied behavior analysis in the classroom.* Boston, MA: Allyn and Bacon.

Skinner, B. F., (1957). *Verbal behavior.* Acton, MA: Copley Publishing Group.

Skinner, B. F. (1969). *Contingencies of reinforcement: A theoretical analysis.* New York: Appleton-Century-Crofts.

Skinner, C. H. (2002). Inquiry and critical thinking in school-based problem solving: Behavioral psychology in the schools. *Inquiry: Critical Thinking Across the Disciplines, 21*, 5–7.

Spiegler, M. D., & Guevremont, D. C. (2003). *Contemporary behavior therapy* (4th ed.). Belmont, CA: Wadsworth.

Sprague, J. R., & Horner, R. H. (1992). Covariation within functional response classes: Implications for treatment of severe problem behavior. *Journal of Applied Behavioral Analysis, 25*(3), 735–745.

Vittimberga, G. L., Scotti, J. R., & Weigle, K. L. (1999). Standards of practice and critical elements in an educative approach to behavioral intervention. In J. R. Scotti & L. H. Meyer (Eds.), *Behavioral intervention: Principles, models, and practices* (pp. 25–46). Baltimore: Brookes.

Willemsen, H., Chowdhury, U., & Briscall, L. (2002). Needle phobia in children: A discussion of aetiology and treatment options. *Clinical Child Psychology and Psychiatry, 7*(4), 609–619.

Wincze, J. P., Bach, A. K., & Barlow, D. H. (2008). Sexual dysfunction. In D. H. Barlow (Ed.), *Clinical handbook of psychological disorders* (4th ed., pp. 615–661). New York: Guilford.

Wolpe, J. (1990). *The practice of behavior therapy* (4th ed.). New York: Pergamon Press.
Wolpe, J., & Plaud, J. J. (1997). Pavlov's contributions to behavior therapy. *American Psychologist, 52*, 966–972.

Preparation for Stressful Medical Procedures

13

Jeff Baker

Introduction

There are a number of medical procedures that require extensive evaluation of patients, including numerous tests and clinical assessments. Medical procedures can vary widely from mundane to life-saving procedures. Every patient is unique, and has different coping strategies to deal with stressful information. There has been some excellent information written about preparing individuals for stressful medical procedures (Anderson & Masur, 1983; Gil, 1984; Katz, Kellerman, & Siegel, 1980; Peterson, 1989; Williams & Kendall, 1985). Cognitive strategies for managing anxiety have been well documented (A. Beck, 1997; Deacon & Abramowitz, 2008; Walker & Furer, 2008). Much of the literature has focused on children and behavioral strategies for treating common problems in childhood (Christopherson & Mortweet, 2001; Gosch, Flannery-Schroeder, Mauro, & Compton, 2006; Kendall, 2000).

However, there remains a need for additional information to be presented to clinicians, regarding the treatment of patients with medical issues and the stressors associated with considering or going through these procedures. Current literature provides little guidance concerning issues that psychologists face in the medical center, and primary clinical care is typically supported by grant or translational research dollars. However, most medical centers are undergoing major changes in financial well-being and have been struggling to continue clinical services long before the financial crisis of 2008. Over the past 10 years, most medical centers have experienced considerable stress and there continues to be a decreasing patient revenue stream, not to mention support from the federal or state governments regarding training psychologists for health care. Psychological services in medical centers are typically supported by grant-funded research for clinical trials or in the hope that patient revenue can offset significant costs for providing the psychological care of a patient.

These services are still valued, though they face challenges when trying to implement an effective model of intervention, due to financial and time constraints. Most hospitals and outpatient clinics are trying to find ways to reduce costs, and psychological care is not always perceived as a significant money maker or critical to the care of a patient in a medical setting. In reality, appropriate preparation of the patient for stressful medical procedures can help avoid significant medical and psychological complications (Baker, Keenan, & Zwischenberger, 2005). Patients may return to the clinic or to the Emergency Department when they have unforeseen complications, perhaps as a result of poor response to treatment. Many times, patient education or preparation for the medical procedure that includes possible outcome scenarios would likely be reduced with adequate preparation.

Providing the patient with an appropriate cognitive map can help reduce anxiety, reduce stress, and increase adherence to the rehabilitation or recovery process. Complications of stress are easily compounded, and increase secondary conditions that are most likely exacerbated by inadequate preparation for a medical procedure. Patients frequently call panicked about an upcoming medical procedure, especially ones that are less life-threatening, as usually they have more control in those situations. Patients may relinquish control in more serious procedures where they feel they have less of a choice and are focused on survival. In less discrete situations where the patient is provided with several options to consider for their treatment, anxiety is likely to be higher as their self-doubts and anxieties may be more likely to interfere with decision making.

It is quite well known that stress results in many physical and psychological problems, including reduced immunological response, heart disease, cancer, increased ethanol use and abuse, hypertension, loss of concentration and motivation, and, of course, posttraumatic stress disorder (PTSD). Studies consistently report that anxiety disorders can affect health and decrease quality of life by exacerbating physical and psychological problems. Individuals with anxiety and stress are more likely to develop depression. One study indicated that an anxiety disorder is an important predictor of subsequent depressive disorders (Stein et al., 2001). Anxiety is also associated with an increased risk for suicide (Sareen et al., 2005); alcoholism (Brady, Tolliver, & Verduin, 2007); and effects on work, school, and relationships (Stansfeld, Clark, Caldwell, Rodgers, & Power, 2008). Prolonged exposure to stress and anxiety is also highly associated with gastrointestinal disorders, headaches, respiratory problems, obesity, and personality changes, such as obsessive-compulsive disorder that may have a variety of components, including increased hand washing, injuries from repetitive acts, and hair loss from repeated hair pulling.

All of these are major exacerbations of stress and anxiety, and many can be traced to inadequate coping strategies that may be linked directly to some traumatic event, as well as developmental etiology, and even a reaction to what someone says or does not say in preparation for a stressful medical procedure. Appropriate preparation for medical procedures can reduce self-imposed stress and anxiety, and will likely result in higher patient satisfaction with reduced complications for both the patient and the provider.

It could be argued that all medical procedures are stressful. No matter how "minor" the procedure, the individual modulates their response to the stressor, and individuals are equipped differently to respond to an external stimulus. However, as the individual processes the threat of the stimuli and it elevates to significant stress, it is typically in response to the situation and how best the individual is equipped to respond. Life-threatening events are programmed and meant to increase anxiety to get a life-saving (fight or flight) response from the individual. The mind acclimates to the information through cognitions, and the mind/body react with whatever is necessary to "survive" the threat. If the individual is prepared for available options and appropriate information to threats, either through prior experience or educational information, the threat is appropriately modulated and will result in less anxiety.

Whenever a patient is considering a medical procedure or being told he/she needs a medical procedure, the patient will begin assimilating or evaluating what impact this is going to have. The medical procedure may be most perceived as threatening if it has a component of expected pain, possible loss of quality of life, or even the chance encounter with near death or a possibility of death. In these incidences, patients are evaluating that this procedure is going to cause some discomfort and there is a likelihood that their quality of life will be forever changed, or perhaps even a threat to their life. With poor coping resources or inappropriate preparation, the patient is likely to experience an increase in anxiety or stress. Perception can be based on reality, as any medical procedure has risks of infection or threat to well-being.

In addition, patients are exposed to increasing awareness of medical mistakes through what they read in the newspapers regarding medical errors. Also, when they review and sign the presurgical paperwork, it rarely decreases their anxiety, as each and every consequence is usually spelled out in fine detail in the "informed consent" papers required for almost all medical procedures. This in itself can be distressing for the individual, and a good practitioner will be able to identify the patient's distress. Quality health care providers will either spend additional time with the patient or insure the patient spends time with a patient educator or behavioral health care specialist. It is not always a simple matter of noticing stress. Most medical professionals understand that patients are distressed when an invasive procedure is involved, but in busy clinics with waiting patients, the preparation of medical patients may be given less time than necessary. Cognitive preparation may become routine, with the anticipation that the patient will bring it to the attention of the provider if there is a problem with stress or anxiety.

The use of cognitive-behavioral techniques is well documented (Kabat-Zinn et al., 1992) regarding the effectiveness of changing behavior. However, much of the literature has focused on treatment of specific psychiatric disorders, such as anxiety and depression and other major psychiatric disorders (Butler, Chapman,

Forman, & Beck, 2006; Chambless & Ollendick, 2001; Gloaguen, Cottraux, Cucherat, & Blackburn, 1998). The focus of this chapter will identify and review the major strategies, assessment methods, and treatment approaches regarding cognitive-behavioral techniques used to prepare individuals for undergoing a medical procedure. Our physician colleagues are well aware that there are many patients that can benefit from this preparation, and given today's time constraints, are appreciative of having access to a clinical health psychologist. Having this access for most health care providers is somewhat of a luxury, and many times only found in medical centers with teaching and research, but there are more and more doctoral training programs that now provide primary care psychology either with a training emphasis or a practicum experience in preparation for the psychology internship.

There is a clear misunderstanding about the value and efficacy of psychological interventions for the health and well-being of medical patients. It is incumbent on the psychology profession to continue to provide evidence of the efficacy of treatment interventions. Information about psychotherapy has been slow to get out to the public and to our medical colleagues. Psychologists are very much welcome on the majority of medical center campuses and are valued members of the treatment team. Gone are the days when physicians made all the decisions about an individual's care, and gone are the days when the medical center psychologist sits in his or her office and waits for patients to show up for treatment from referrals. These changes have brought about new innovation and, most likely, a closer working relationship with an increased number of medical doctors beyond the original scope of traditional work only with psychiatrists. Adaptation to these changes has been slow and difficult, and economically devastating to many psychologists. However, the survivors of the vast economic and practice changes are typically now seen as members of an integrated health care team that triages patient care, and discusses and recommends treatment interventions as part of a group of health care practitioners. This is true for primary care psychology as well as specialty care psychology.

Primary care psychology is still emerging in health care settings, but continues to grow. Even less recognized are psychologists who provide specialized care to patients in a variety of specialty clinic or hospital settings. Both venues attempt to provide care to the patient as a system, rather than traditional individual treatment care with a hope that the health care providers are consulting and communicating information about the patient for the best outcome. There is much to be said for a team treatment approach, and psychologists need to be a part of that team. Psychologists can no longer afford to wait in their offices for referrals, as most patient care has gone online through electronic medical records, and sharing the patient care, as well as the treatment interventions, is an expectation of everyone on the health care team.

The traditional referral to a psychologist's office may still be the norm in many settings, but there are more and more psychologists who have an office in the middle of the medical care provider's area, especially in a medical center. Psychologists are now located inside many medical providers' offices, and some are directly next to anesthesiology, surgery, or transplant center offices. All that being said, communication is the specialty of the psychologist, and many times, they will emerge as the team leader and are in a good position to coordinate the care of the patient. This puts them in an appropriate leadership position to provide patient education and preparation, as well as help the patient navigate through the health care system. Cognitive-behavioral interventions can be very helpful, as patients are likely to be distressed and confused when trying to navigate through the plethora of responsibilities to maintain their health.

Cognitive behavioral interventions are well documented, and the use of these interventions by qualified professionals will increase patient satisfaction and provide a reduction in costs to third-party payers (Baker, Mancuso, Norris, & Lyons, 2002; Keefe, 1996). Patients will most likely benefit from recent changes, as they will benefit with greater access that is being provided as of January 1, 2010, through the Wellstone-Domenci Mental Health Parity Act of 2008. The new law provides parity for mental health and physical health care provisions provided by employers that meet specific employment criteria (Open Congress for the 111th U.S. Congress, 2008). This is expected to provide greater access for patients seeking mental health care, and may provide more access to psychologists at primary care and medical specialty clinics.

Theoretical Issues

It is important for the clinician to have basic training and understanding of the theoretical issues in the treatment of psychological disorders, along with the use of cognitive-behavioral therapy (CBT). The majority of doctoral training programs in psychology provide training in major theories of psychological intervention. All accredited psychology doctoral programs are required to demonstrate how they integrate science and practice in their training program (American Psychological Association, 1996). Cognitive-behavioral treatment has become one of the most researched treatment procedures and is accepted and recommended as a treatment intervention in a number of situations. Thus, it is difficult to find a doctoral psychology training program that does not provide exposure or a specific class in cognitive-behavioral interventions (Dobson & Dobson, 2009). It is the leading evidence-based treatment intervention for a number of psychological disorders, including depression, eating disorders, anxiety, and PTSD. There are many structured treatment strategies that have incorporated behavior therapy and cognitive therapy to provide a more action-oriented intervention (J. Beck, 1995). There is much evidence on the efficacy of treatment through CBT, and there are considerable resources for clinicians to obtain advanced training through workshops on the latest treatment strategies for major psychological disorders, as there are training institutes in most major cities. CBT has been found to be effective in changing attitudes and behavior by focusing on thoughts, images, beliefs, and attitudes, and how these interact and result in behavior (Leahy, 2006). However, there is little written regarding CBT and preparation for stressful medical procedures, as most of the research focuses on major psychological disorders.

The majority of reactions to medical procedures could possibly fit under anticipatory anxiety, and would probably fit into the acute and chronic anxiety disorders. The clinician would be expected to effectively provide treatment for patients for stress or anxiety reduction, as the majority of major medical procedures would most likely include a component of stress or anticipatory anxiety. Of course, patients are typically focused on survival and less concerned about their anxiety at a time when they are likely thinking about survival and how this procedure is going to disrupt their lives. The patients awaiting a procedure are likely to be focusing less on their stress about a medical procedure versus survival and adjustment. In the scope of developing a problem list of patient issues, anxiety would most likely not be at the top of the list for most patients undergoing a medical procedure. The patient may consider anxiety a natural reaction, one she or he has no control over and he/she hopes will go away with time. However, a trained clinician will be sensitive to these issues and attempt to address them as part of the standard of care in the preparation of the medical procedure.

By understanding the side effects of anesthesiology, patients would be better served and better prepared for the psychological reactions to the anticipation of the procedure and the length of rehabilitation, possible loss of income during the recovery time, physical needs during the recovery time, and their own thoughts and reactions that may or may not be influenced by negative self-concept, previous traumatic experiences, or prior psychological overlay. The anxiety and stress a patient might be experiencing may be a minor irritation, or it may begin to build and eventually interfere with the patient's ability to focus or concentrate, to the point where he/she may become forgetful about the information he/she was given about the preparation for the procedure, and be less adherent to the recommendations of the medical provider. This is a very common outcome when the patient does not have the energy (as a result of feeling ill) or skills and resources to perform due diligence in his/her approach to the medical procedure. Of course, it is still somewhat unusual that a patient would be this well prepared or self-aware and bring this to the physician's attention.

Most medical providers are aware when a patient does have these resources or skills, and understands these patients will most likely be better prepared for the expectations of the recovery process. Patients like this will be unlikely to seek out services from a psychologist or a counselor, and will likely use their own resources to deal with the stressors. However, it is more likely that the majority of patients has a "hope for the best" outcome in mind, and they leave the decisions or imparting of information up to the health care provider. Patients who use this more passive strategy are less likely to have a proactive approach to the procedure, and this is certainly not the norm.

The patient who does seek out assistance from a psychologist may typically have more serious psychological problems, and it may not occur to the patient to seek treatment unless the problem has a major psychological overlay or feels disabling to the patient. By that time, it may be too late to simply participate in anxiety-reduction exercises or other cognitive strategies, and the medical outcome procedure may have less of a chance of success because of poor psychological preparation. Health care providers who continue to spend considerable time with patients given the time constraints are most likely decreasing. A referral to a psychologist or counselor may only occur if significant disabling behaviors are noticed by the medical provider, and even with this encouragement or even a formal referral, most patients are unlikely to follow up on a recommendation to make arrangements to be seen by another specialist in another clinic.

However, one growing option is for clinical health psychologists to work side by side in a primary care setting and/or a specialty medical clinic. Obstetrics clinics, transplant centers, and chronic pain clinics have long employed psychologists. Many medical procedures require a psychological evaluation as part of the standard of care. It sometimes depends on the insurance provider and the region of the country, but procedures such as a spinal cord stimulator, morphine pump implant, or transplant of a major organ usually require a review and assessment of the psychosocial stressors before the procedure can be approved for funding. Many medical centers employ a standard of care that would typically require the involvement of a psychologist, but in many of these cases, the focus is on evaluation of the patient and their ability to respond to or tolerate a medical procedure, or to determine whether the psychological overlay will unduly influence the success or outcome of the medical procedure. This is certainly an important role for a psychologist, but in addition to evaluating the appropriateness of a candidate for a medical procedure, time could also be well spent regarding the preparation of the patient for an upcoming medical procedure.

There are a number of settings where this now routinely occurs (child and adolescent burn treatment, high-risk OB/GYN clinics, transplant centers), although most times, the patient is referred to a psychologist who is familiar with the procedure and can help prepare the patient if there is evidence of major psychological symptoms of anxiety. The following selected examples of medical procedures attempt to illustrate a few traditional medical settings and discusses the expected medical-psychological issues. The issues and dynamics can be applied to a wide variety of procedures, and the selected examples should provide an overview of issues that can be generalized to other medical procedures. Many of the settings in this next section are where medical providers engage in preparation for a medical procedure; the providers would likely benefit from having a psychologist involved in patient treatment for both evaluation and procedure preparation. The section after this brief review of settings will describe a few of these procedures and the psychological impact they have. The next section after that will discuss and present assessment strategies to better inform the cognitive-behavioral therapist; the final section will focus on methods of intervention.

Examples of Procedures That Benefit From CBT

Intrathecal Pump Implant

Sometimes intrathecal pump implants are referred to as "morphine pumps." Pump implants are most often used to control cancer pain, but have been expanded to help those patients who have not done well with conservative treatment of chronic pain and who may have a problem taking oral medications or cannot tolerate oral medications. Sometimes these pumps are also used for other medication delivery, such as delivering large amounts of medication to reduce muscle spasms. The intrathecal pump delivers medication directly to the spinal cord. The most commonly used system is the totally implanted, battery-operated synchronized pump. The pump is about the size of the palm of an adult's hand. It is inserted underneath the skin in the front part of the abdomen just under the rib cage. A tiny catheter is then inserted underneath the skin, tunneled to the back and placed leading into the spinal fluid. For patients with chronic pain, preservative-free morphine is placed in the pump and is delivered continuously in small increments. The total daily dose is regulated by electronics within the pump and is adjusted via a laptop computer by the medical provider. This may seem like a minor procedure to some, but to the typical patient with chronic pain, it is another intervention that takes away his or her freedom and independence. The patient may look for an intervention that frees him/her from medical care so he/she can return to work or his/her previous level of functioning. The majority of patients do experience a decrease in pain and some are able to return to work. The majority of patients receiving this intervention have an increase in quality of life with a concomitant reduction in pain; there are few who are totally pain free. Patients who have their expectations disappointed may feel that their pain cannot be controlled and the procedure was a failure. With appropriate preparation and clarification of expectations and some basic cognitive-intervention strategies, the patient may have a totally different response than those without this preparation.

The patient without appropriate preparation could develop further learned helplessness or depression, depending on the perceived effectiveness of the medical procedure and the proper preparation for the procedure. Patients who are fully informed and are part of the decision-making team appear to have a better response than those who only want a solution to their pain and don't care how they get it. Patients who are insightful, articulate, and assertive may have a better chance of getting their answers before the procedure, but many patients do not have these skills and could benefit from cognitive-behavioral interventions prior to the procedure.

Spinal Cord Stimulator

The spinal cord stimulator, also known as a dorsal cord stimulator, is another implantable device used to control pain. This device is normally used when a patient cannot tolerate oral pain medications and/or has a history of failed conservative interventions. Another common reason for use of this device is a history of failed back surgeries. Many patients believe that only spinal surgery will "fix" their pain, and may wander from surgeon to surgeon to correct their condition. The standard for many years was that if one surgeon did not fix the problem, then maybe the next surgeon will be better skilled and will finally solve the spinal disorder problem. More likely, the additional spinal surgeries add to the complications of the pain as a result of additional scar tissue, or additional nerve endings being cut or traumatized disturbing what was once healthy tissue. Spine surgery, as discussed in the next section, is certainly a viable option, and as techniques improve through microsurgical techniques, this surgery has improved in its outcomes and has reduced the recovery and rehabilitation time. It is also unusual to see a patient undergo an immediate spinal surgery unless there is clear trauma and the surgery is expected to immediately alleviate the compression on the spinal cord. It is more likely that the patient will be provided conservative treatment unless there are clear signs of trauma, including beginning paralysis or bowel and bladder problems. If the only symptom is pain, it is now unlikely there will be an immediate surgical intervention without these other symptoms.

For those patients who have had multiple surgeries or have found no relief from conservative treatment, the spinal cord stimulator is commonly used. Spine surgeons do a good job of repairing the tears, compression, or stenosis, but the side effects or consequences of surgery sometimes outweigh the positive outcomes, and the patient is left with the same or increased pain. The spinal cord stimulator is a small implanted device that generates small electrical pulses expected to replace the pain with a tingling feeling. The physiological explanation relies on the gate theory of pain, where the electrical impulse interrupts the neuropathic pain pathway and the brain registers a lesser degree of pain.

The standard expectation for a spinal cord stimulator, in an ideal world, is for the pain to be decreased by at least 50%. This would typically be expected to improve the quality of life for the patient by restoring the ability to increase movement and possibly return to work, though usually not in a labor-intensive occupation. It is an FDA-approved therapy for chronic pain, and success depends on the proper placement of the electrical leads as well as the psychological health of the patient. In one study, an 84% improvement in the quality of life was reported by those receiving a neurostimulator (Barolat, 2001), and in another, 77% reported they had good or excellent pain relief (Simpson, 2003). Patient preparation for this procedure is essential. Psychological assessment is required by Medicare in most states, and when used in combination with patient preparation, it can improve the surgeon or anesthesiologist's positive outcome results with this procedure. Cognitive strategies and reframing are essential for the majority of patients who have chronic pain. Patients who have been through several surgeries and appear not to be responsive to conservative treatment will typically be diagnosed with failed back syndrome. CBT can be a significant component to appropriate and effective patient preparation.

Spine Surgery

It is not unusual for patients with chronic low back pain to consider spine surgery as a means to eliminate pain and return to work. Most are certainly hesitant to elect this type of surgery, but most individuals with chronic low back pain will seek relief no matter what the risks or possible consequences might be. Anything is often better than having to live with chronic debilitating low back pain. The pain is more than aggravating, and living with it for more than 6 months can have significant consequences such as decrease in quality of life, loss of job and income, loss of family support, and lowered self-esteem. All of these will likely increase the incidence of depression, as there is a strong correlation with chronic low back pain and depressive symptoms. Patients want a quick fix so they can return to their previous level of functioning, and spine surgery seems like the best way to get this problem fixed so the patient can get their "life back." If it were that simple, there would not be enough spine surgeons to perform the number of surgeries that would be requested.

The truth is that spine surgery does not eliminate low back pain in the large majority of the cases. This is especially true when the patient has a psychological overlay. Spine surgery has recently developed minimally invasive procedures, such as a microdiscectomy for a herniated disk. This typically allows for a quicker recovery and less effort in rehabilitation. It is a less invasive surgery that will typically have a shorter recovery time. However, if a patient is not well prepared for this procedure and has a psychological overlay (significant symptoms of depression, anxiety, thought disturbance, and/or poor coping resources) the less likely his/her surgery will be successful. The patient's expectation for the surgery may include complete pain relief and a return to his/her previous life. Those expectations are not always fulfilled, and the preparation for this surgery typically requires psychological assessment in addition to preparation.

Some medical centers provide support groups for patients considering spinal surgery that usually includes cognitive-behavioral intervention, and also includes an education component regarding expectations, coping strategies, family issues, and communication skills. To be considered for this surgery one must have little or no response to pain medications, and a significant amount of time during which the patient is unable to complete basic daily activities. For the majority of patients with chronic low back pain, the amount of time with pain and no effective relief of pain will typically result in psychological symptoms of depression and anxiety. Adding these psychological issues will likely result in a patient that is more vulnerable to a poor outcome. However, with appropriate preparation involving CBT, the patient will likely be in a better frame of mind and will be able to have their expectations addressed. CBT is expected to provided these patients with more effective coping strategies, clarification of expectations, and additional pain and stress management strategies, and thus, increase the success of the outcome of the surgery.

There are a variety of spine surgeries, some more extensive than others. Patient preparation is just as or more important for the more extensive surgeries, which include posterolateral fusion. The primary purpose of low back surgery is to correct an anatomical lesion in individuals whose mobility and quality of life have not improved after more conservative treatment. It is rarely considered acceptable to engage in exploratory surgery to look for the "cause" of the pain. Magnetic resonance imaging (MRI) is now so advanced that it has completely changed spine surgery. If there is no lesion identified on the MRI, there is rarely a reason to seek spine surgery until there are major changes in mobility (paralysis) or bowel or bladder problems.

Psychologists are almost always involved in the assessment of patients with low back problems; indeed many states or regional Medicare-sponsored surgery requires a psychological evaluation. It is proposed that psychological preparation with CBT in conjunction with the evaluation will result in a better surgical outcome. Patients with a significant amount of psychological overlay or trauma do not do as well in this type of surgery, compared with those without a history of psychological overlay (Block, Gatchel, Deardorff, & Guyer, 2003).

General Surgery

Any surgical procedure can be perceived as stressful. From dental extraction to amputation, the patient is going to experience some anxiety. Anxiety is a normal response to help prepare the mind/body to react or acclimate to the stressor (fight or flight). Healthy anxiety can increase the motivation to read more about the procedure or ask questions of the provider. Accurate information can reduce anxiety and make the procedure more tolerable or less surprising to the patient. Higher tolerance for the expected outcomes and increased information can be soothing to the patient. These are critical components to preparation for surgery. In most cases, this information is delivered through informed consent or surgical preparation. The surgical procedure can seem rather mundane for the surgeon as well as for the anesthesiologist, who is typically required to visit with the patient prior to the scheduled surgery. The patients may perceive this dynamic, making them hesitant to ask questions of the health care professionals who appear too busy or uninterested in such a routine procedure.

However, the majority of patients will benefit from a surgeon, anesthesiologist, or psychologist who helps walk them through the procedure, providing a cognitive map that one hopes will lower anxiety. If the patient is prepared by identifying possible outcomes, it is more likely the patient can acclimate or adjust his/her expectations for the procedure. CBT can work very well in this situation, assisting the patient to identify and discuss beliefs that can sometimes be irrational. CBT can also assist with preparing the patient by exposing him/her to expected outcomes as well as unexpected outcomes. Outcomes and expectations need to be discussed that may assist the patient to identify fears or concerns that she/he might be reluctant to discuss with the surgeon or anesthesiologist, given time constraints and concern of overreacting to his/her emotions. The patient may feel more comfortable discussing these issues with a psychologist. The surgeon and anesthesiologist could help the patient identify concerns that can be addressed by the medical provider and appropriately refer patients to the psychologist if they are aware of the psychological resources available. Those medical professionals who do not want to deal with the patient's emotions may or may not be comfortable with a referral for the patient, thinking that the patient needs to deal with this on his/her own. The likely outcome of this thinking by the medical professional will result in the patient not returning or being disappointed with the result, in part because of increased anxiety from poor preparation for the procedure.

Difficult or High-Risk Pregnancies

Even though this is not a specific procedure, there is preparation involved. Every pregnancy has some risks, but patients can manage or reduce their stress and anxiety if the appropriate preparation is provided to them. Many OB/GYN clinics now have psychologists on staff to assist in the management of patients that could benefit from psychological interventions. The role of the psychologist in an obstetrics and gynecology setting is to work with patients who may be experiencing adjustment reactions to the pregnancy, whether high risk or normal. The psychologist works with the patient to address the ongoing issues of demands and the resulting stressors that many patients experience in anticipation of side effects of the pregnancy, as well as expected and unexpected changes in the home environment and possible changes in relationships with family and spouse.

High-risk patients or those with complicated pregnancies can particularly benefit from working with a psychologist. Examples of common conditions that can complicate a pregnancy include: heart disease, high blood pressure, diabetes, cancer, autoimmune disorders, kidney problems, or sexually transmitted diseases. Some patients develop gestational diabetes, and others may develop depression. Psychological adjustment is expected in almost all pregnancies, especially the first one, when having less knowledge or experience may be a factor. It is not uncommon for patients to begin experiencing anxiety or depression in reaction to this wonderful event (wonderful for most).

Acclamation to such a significant change is not always an easy task. Patients with high-risk pregnancies are more likely to develop anxious or depressive reactions, and better preparation will decrease the development of these symptoms. A psychologist working with the patient can offer strategies for managing the stress and depressive feelings, and use self-talk or cognitive reframing to decrease these symptoms. Those left unchecked may be at risk for a more severe postpartum response that can have disastrous results. It is normal to be anxious about a new family or an addition to the family. It is not so normal to experience such high anxiety that thinking, concentration, and quality of life is affected by the stress.

Psychological preparation for the birthing process can be done in a variety of settings. Childbirth classes provide this type of basic preparation and provide the expectant mother with a better idea of the process and the opportunity to plan for the next stage. However, when anxiety is so significant or there is high risk involved, preparation or support from a psychologist can have additional benefits, including developing or accessing coping strategies and stress-management strategies for decreasing anxiety or depressive symptoms.

Summary

For all of these procedures, it is important to recognize that stress may be self-induced and that CBT can assist the patient in reducing this effect. Cognitive strategies, including mapping and controlled exposure, would likely be helpful to the majority of these patients, with the expectation there will be a lowering of the symptoms, thus increasing the success of the medical procedure. Many patients choose other methods of coping when they do not have these resources, or are unaware that it is acceptable to be experiencing a reaction to the medical procedure. Some patients definitely have proactive strategies and can respond with health coping mechanisms. However, other patients are more likely to use denial and poor coping strategies (alcohol, anger, frustration) to manage their anxiety about the situation. These kind of coping strategies are not helpful to the successful outcome of the procedure, and may impair the progress or negatively affect the rehabilitation process. Nor are these negative coping strategies helpful to the family support system, as it may complicate that relationship that may be tenuous anyway. It is helpful to understand that most medical procedures will have some component of stress and anxiety, and an awareness of the degree to which the patient might experience these psychological responses could be helpful in better identification of "at-risk" patients that could benefit from preparation for medical procedures using CBT. The following section addresses assessment methods for identifying coping, depression, and anxiety that would likely improve the outcome of the medical procedure if the patient has these issues addressed at an early stage of the procedure.

Assessment Methods

Psychological assessment in its purest form is the empirical measurement and evaluation relevant to the broad field of clinical psychology. It is an attempt to focus on the diagnosis and evaluation of psychological characteristics or processes using objective and subjective assessment (Groth-Marnat, 2003). In the real world of clinical practice, different assessment instruments are used in a variety of ways, but are more likely to have a focus on how these assessment indicators relate to the patient's problem and what is interfering with their strategy to maintain or improve their quality of life. Basic psychological assessment likely includes a clinical interview to assess for motivation, effort, and the likelihood of the subject providing reliable responses.

The clinical interview will provide this needed information, and provide a foundation that will increase the expected reliability of the psychological measures. Assessment for a patient undergoing a medical procedure, as discussed previously, will have a slightly different focus, and the clinical interview will typically identify what processes or dynamics might be suspect and possibly interfere with the patient's progress in both medical and psychological treatment. Psychiatrists typically rely solely on the clinical interview.

In addition to the clinical interview, psychologists in medical centers typically employ a number of psychological assessment instruments that can be used to help in identifying when a patient would be amenable to a cognitive-behavioral intervention. Patients who are above average in intelligence and highly verbal are typically thought of as good patients for CBT. However, these qualities are not necessarily required for successful outcomes in preparation for medical procedures. Almost all patients can benefit from CBT, even when only applying cognitive strategies or training in relaxation strategies.

CBT can be applied to a wide variety of patients who will benefit from the basic intervention strategies of cognitive reframing and exposure, and using a variety of interventions that will be discussed in more detail in the next section. During the clinical interview, there are a number of assessment strategies that can be employed, including self-report inventories for background and biographical data, as well as a mini mental status exam. The biographical data may or may not be used in the intervention, but it is important to give the clinician a fuller picture of what the patient is managing in his or her life, such as psychosocial stressors that are typically reported on Axis IV of the *Diagnostic and Statistical Manual of Mental Disorders*, 4th edition, text revision (*DSM-IV-TR*; American Psychiatric Association, 2000). A brief history of family and family issues is paramount in the patient's ability to respond with cognitive reframing as well as assessing coping strategies that may or may not be working for the patient. The clinical interview may use this format in gathering data to assess the likelihood the patient is a good candidate for CBT.

Psychological Assessment

Minnesota Multiphasic Personality Inventory-2

The personality assessment most widely used and researched in psychological assessment is most likely the Minnesota Multiphasic Personality Inventory (MMPI-2) (Hathaway et al., 2000). This instrument has 567 true/false questions, though there is a short-form version that only uses the first 370 questions. It is widely used in medical populations, and many ACGME (Accreditation Council for Graduate Medical Education) training programs in anesthesiology, neurology, or spine surgery require the medical fellows to be familiar with the attributes of this instrument to meet competency requirements for the training program. The primary purpose of the MMPI-2 is to identify a psychological overlay of psychopathology, and the instrument does a fair-to-good job of identifying when a patient has extreme psychological distressors, such as a thought disorder, anxiety, depression, somatic concerns, social inhibition, or impulse-control issues. It is important to understand the consistency of the response items, the test-taking attitude of the person responding, the level of distress, and disturbance being experienced by the test taker before drawing conclusions on the assessment. The instrument should not be used as a stand-alone assessment, and is best interpreted in conjunction with the clinical interview.

Elevations on individual scales can indicate stress or distress, but it is more common to use "codetypes" to assist in determining specific issues. Even with elevations on the clinical scales, it is not always an indication of psychopathology that would necessarily interfere with a patient's eligibility to participate in a stressful medical procedure, but it can provide additional insight into the thinking patterns of the patient, which is ideal to help develop cognitive reframing strategies for the patient. It also provides the medical staff with objective data that can assist in understanding the complexities of the patient. The MMPI-2 (Hathaway & McKinley, 1967) was originally normed on psychiatric patients, but much has been published on working with patients who have chronic medical disorders. One of the most respected publications concerning the use of the MMPI-2 with patients being considered for a surgical intervention is by Andrew Block and colleagues (Block et al., 2003). Robert Gatchel has also published a very helpful article on identifying the "MMPI Disability Profile" (Gatchel, Mayer, & Eddington, 2006). Both of these publications and many more are supportive of the use of the MMPI-2.

Using information from the assessment instrument can be helpful in developing effective interventions with the use of CBT by identifying stressors and personality issues of the medical patient. Identifying thinking errors, exacerbated anxiety, or significant depression can be very helpful in developing an intervention plan with the patient. Other elevations on the MMPI-2 profile can also provide additional insight in planning and identifying strategies to assist the patient to cope or show vulnerabilities the patient may have in specific areas. The MMPI-2 was not specifically designed for use with medical patients, and most clinicians are well aware of the "conversion-V" (scales 1, 3, 2) and how it may or may not apply to a patient with a chronic medical condition (Denollet, Nyklicek, & Vingerhoets, 2008).

Beck Depression Inventory Fast Medical Screen

The Beck Depression Inventory Fast Medical Screen (BDI FMS) is a seven-item assessment that requires fewer than 5 minutes to administer, but is specifically designed for work with medical patients. It addresses the concerns of clinicians who have questioned the Beck Depression Inventory II because it includes 8 somatic-related depression questions, and may give artificially high depression scores to patients who have a chronic medical condition. It consists of items taken from the BDI-II and effectively measures the psychological nonsomatic affect of patients with a medical problem.

The BDI-FS was specifically constructed to reduce the number of false positives for depression with medical problems (Beck, Steer, & Brown, 2000). The instrument correlates well with the MMPI-2, but also gives specific responses to a patient's thought processes, especially around suicidal ideation and self-esteem. Several of the items are helpful in identifying the patient's cognitive mindset and can be used in developing a treatment approach with CBT. It is a brief, easy-to-score measure that can be easily understood by all health professionals, and is a widely researched and respected instrument (Poole, Bramwell, & Murphy, 2008).

The Coping Skills Questionnaire

The Coping Skills Questionnaire (CSQ) is a unique instrument that provides eight different categories of coping strategies that a patient may use to deal with their chronic pain (Robinson et al., 1997). Because most troublesome medical conditions have a pain or distress component, this instrument is helpful in identifying which coping strategies and to what degree the patient is using these strategies. Awareness of the level of the strategy can be helpful in identifying cognitive reframing scripts. The eight different strategies identified in this instrument include: reinterpreting pain symptoms, coping self-statements, ignoring pain sensations, catastrophizing, increased behavioral activity, pain behaviors, diverting attention, and praying/hoping.

Using this instrument can provide significant information that can be used to assist a patient to address more specific behaviors related to cognitive framing, restructuring, and mapping (Thorn, 2004). Each category is self-identifiable on what reframing can take place, and will be discussed in further detail in the treatment section.

The Type D Questionnaire

The Type D personality has been associated with unfavorable clinical courses (medical and psychological) and negative health outcomes (including death) in various cardiovascular populations (Denollet, Pedersen, Vrints, & Conraads, 2006; Kupper & Denollet, 2007; Schiffer et al., 2006). Similar findings have been obtained in other populations. Among older adults in primary care, the Type D personality was found to be associated with high rates of medically documented multimorbidity, low subjective health ratings, poor physician-assessed physical functioning, and poor interview-rated psychosocial functioning (Chapman, Duberstein, & Lyness, 2007). The Type D personality has also been associated with negative psychological outcomes following medical procedures. The Type D personality predicted chronic anxiety 1 year after percutaneous coronary intervention using either sirolimus-eluting stent or bare metal stent implantation (Spindler et al., 2007). The Type D personality, and not depression, predicted the severity of anxiety in heart failure patients at 1-year follow-up (Schiffer, Pedersen, Broers, Widdershoven, & Denollet, 2008). Additionally, the Type D personality was identified as a risk factor for depressive symptoms after myocardial infarction (Martens,

Smith, Winter, Denollet, & Pedersen, 2008). Taken together, these studies suggest that the Type D personality is a significant risk factor; thus, it may be worth screening for this variable prior to a variety of procedures.

The Type D Questionnaire (DS-14) instrument is a 14-item questionnaire that takes less than 10 minutes to administer and score. Two scores are achieved by the patient: negative affect and social inhibition. There is a strong relationship between negative emotions, pain, and decreased functioning (Tan, Jensen, Thornby, & Sloan, 2008). Negative emotions, including stress, have been linked to increased pain, disability, mood disturbance, and flare-ups (Potter & Zautra, 1997; Thomason, Brantley, Jones, Dyer, & Morris, 1992; Urrows, Affleck, Tennen, & Higgins, 1994; Zautra, Okun, Robinson, & Lee, 1989). The literature regarding ambivalence over emotional expression supports the notion that social inhibition, the other component of the Type D personality, may be another important variable among chronic pain patients. Ambivalence over emotional expression was related to higher pain levels (Carson et al., 2007), and emotional processing and emotional expression were found to be associated with less pain and depression (Smith, Lumley, & Longo, 2002).

Awareness of these two variables, negative affect and social inhibition, can assist in identifying cognitive strategies for intervention with the patient. This will be further discussed in the next section on treatment.

Treatment Approaches

Numerous research studies have shown that cognitive therapy (CT) or CBT are very effective in the treatment of a number of psychological disorders, including panic, agoraphobia, generalized anxiety, social anxiety/phobia, obsessive-compulsive disorder (OCD), PTSD, specific phobias, chronic anger, and other problems with fear, worry, or stress. Consistent data from repeated studies have shown that CT/CBT are just as effective as medications for these conditions, and have identified that in some ways, they are superior to medications. Patients are hesitant to take medication to decrease their symptoms because of the high number of side effects that are typically found with medications. Some studies suggest that patients receiving CT or CBT do not tend to have as much relapse after treatment is concluded. This outcome may likely be because clients learn coping skills that can be used in the future and are easily generalized to a wide variety of difficult situations. This is likely because they often change underlying dysfunctional beliefs and related patterns of thinking and behaving or thinking errors, such as self-criticism, worry, or avoidance. Patients may thereby be reducing long-standing thinking problems or distortions, and preparing themselves for dealing with stressful situations. Thus, clients who receive CT may become more emotionally healthy, more resistant to life stressors, and less prone to anxiety, depression, or other problem areas in the future.

There are a large number of published studies that identify the effectiveness of CBT/CT, and there are a number of structured interventions sometimes referred to as "manualized treatment." The majority of CBT/CT includes teaching the client techniques of managing cognitive distortions, including cognitive reframing, cognitive restructuring, and cognitive mapping. These techniques address the cognitions of the patient, which many times include distorted thinking, irrational beliefs, and misunderstanding of perceived conflicts. CBT is not a single type of therapy, but is a combination of many procedures and techniques. Intervention includes diagnostic interviewing, functional analysis, direct observation, and self-monitoring. Developing a treatment plan includes collaboration with the patient to identify a problem-solving model targeting the patient's thoughts and beliefs.

There are a number of action-oriented procedures that can help a patient reduce her/his anxiety, and reframe her/his thought patterns using documented best practices while changing behaviors. Many patients spend years developing faulty thinking strategies that may have been effective at one time but are no longer helpful. In addition to addressing a patient's cognitive distortions, the patient is typically trained and guided through techniques of exposure to assist in developing strategies for reducing distortions and to identify techniques of managing the increasing anxiety. Techniques used for reducing stress or anxiety include relaxation training, visualization, systematic desensitization, hypnosis and biofeedback, and a variety of other strategies.

Interventions

Cognitive Strategies

There are a wide variety of cognitive strategies that are specifically tailored for individual issues, concerns, and/or disorders. They typically include in-session strategies that focus on giving the client a plan or strategy for responding to a difficult or confusing situation. The cognitive strategies used in the past may no longer be effective, and the patient is now left with intrusive thoughts, cognitive distortions, and faulty processing of information when trying to understand or assimilate information. The cognitive strategies used for medical procedures are usually used in a number of CBT/CT interventions and are not unique to medical procedures. However, they can be very useful in preparation of the patient for a stressful medical procedure. The following brief review provides a short overview of cognitive strategies and how they might be used to prepare a patient for a stressful medical procedure.

Behavioral Homework Assignments

There are a number of opportunities for the patient to prepare for his/her medical procedure using cognitive-behavioral strategies through the assignment of behavioral homework assignments. There has to be an established relationship, and the previous issues and assessment are essential to identifying an appropriate homework assignment for each patient. There are some general homework assignments that are highly applicable to patients in their preparation for a stressful medical procedure. Cognitive-behavioral therapists frequently request that their patients complete homework assignments between counseling sessions. They are typically designed to assist the patient in increasing success with reduction of stress and anxiety. But too much of a homework assignment given to someone who has a high need to please may interfere with that person's return to counseling, feeling he/she is a failure for not following through on the homework. Enough patients have prior memories of the failure of incomplete assignments from school that it is not helpful to overwhelm the patient with an assignment that is impossible or next to impossible to complete.

These homework exercises may consist of real-life "behavioral experiments," in which patients are encouraged to try out new responses to situations discussed in the interview or a counseling session. Homework assignments for patients considering a medical procedure may simply be to make a list of questions to ask their medical provider. Another assignment might include having the patient make a list of the pros and cons to discuss in counseling. A follow-up to that would be to have the patient discuss the pros and cons of the procedure with both their medical provider and/or significant others. Another assignment might be to have the patient identify the after-care resources he/she will need and to begin contacting them for clarification of needed arrangements for home health care, for example. Each patient will present something a little different, but several of these exercises will be helpful for a patient in developing a cognitive strategy to reduce anxiety and stress, as well as a cognitive map to identify the patient's role in the procedure and how she/he can take more control or direction of the outcome.

Cognitive Rehearsal

In this cognitive exercise, the patient is provided an opportunity to develop a mental strategy for processing ideas, thoughts, and feelings that she/he may have been avoiding and have not wanted to deal with up to this point. The patient imagines how he/she might have a difficult time talking with the medical provider, and the therapist guides the patient through the step-by-step process of facing and successfully dealing with the imagined difficulty. The patient then works on practicing, or rehearsing, these steps mentally. The idea behind this strategy is to have a mental rehearsal of when and how the situation might arise and the patient can then draw on the rehearsed behavior to address it.

Some patients fear freezing up or not being able to think clearly during a stressful situation and they can use this cognitive rehearsal as a way to manage their anticipatory anxiety and call on the script they may have developed during the rehearsal for use in the middle of the actual encounter. This rehearsal is much like the example of a seasoned lecturer who has a set of notes to rely on to ensure he/she has a back-up or memory cue to use during the lecture to ensure that everything is covered and to prevent worry over being unable to remember an important point during the lecture. Medical patients can use this practice to assimilate thoughts and feelings that may surface during the rehearsal, and additional strategies can be provided to address this issue, thus allowing them to feel better prepared when in the middle of the situation. This same technique can be used for both the surgical procedure and the rehabilitation period post procedure.

Keeping a Journal

Patients are sometimes asked to keep a detailed diary recounting their thoughts, feelings, and actions when specific situations arise. In the time period between the interview and follow-up session, the patient may be asked to take time to write down his/her concerns and to identify any thoughts or feelings that he/

she might be experiencing. The patient would also be asked what actions he/she took to deal with the thoughts and feelings, giving him/her some ideas on any pattern that is not working or identifying actions that were helpful to manage the stressful thoughts and feelings. The journal helps to make the patient aware of his or her maladaptive thoughts and to show the consequences of the thoughts on behavior. This information is then reviewed in the follow-up session to identify what additional areas need to be addressed or to reinforce positive responses.

Modeling

The therapist and patient learn to engage in practice rehearsals that include role-playing exercises in which the therapist acts out appropriate behaviors or responses to situations, giving the patient insight on additional options they may consider when faced with a stressful situation. Behaviors patients may consider revising are negative self-talk, irrational beliefs, and ineffective thoughts that may escalate anxiety rather than decrease anxiety. An example of this might be when a patient is awaiting a liver transplant and his/her main thoughts are focused on prior "bad" behavior that makes him/her feel undeserving of a new liver, and he/she may experience thoughts and feelings that were previously part of the precipitating event that led to increased substance abuse or possible negative self-image. The patient can learn from the therapist how to reframe negative thoughts and beliefs into more positive affirmations and positive thoughts and feelings. Patients awaiting a stressful medical procedure may exacerbate their anxiety by engaging in negative self-talk and may benefit from hearing strategies used in modeling to practice more self-affirmation, positive reframing, and thought-stopping.

Conditioning

The therapist uses reinforcement to encourage a particular behavior by identifying a stimulus-response scenario with the patient. If through motivational interviewing a patient identifies that she/he receives relief from anxiety by smoking cigarettes, the therapist can work with the patient to develop a new paired association by substituting positive stress-reduction activities for smoking. The old association may be long held and reinforced over years by having a pleasurable meal, then smoking, pleasant conversations during work breaks while smoking, or another pleasurable activity and then having a cigarette. This paired association has been reinforced over the years and may take additional motivational interviewing to assist the patient in identifying their reasons for smoking, but conditioning is a large part of what keeps smokers smoking. In the preparation for a medical procedure, many patients are required to discontinue smoking and the idea of not receiving a liver for transplant or spine surgery for the relief of pain typically provides strong motivation for a patient to discontinue a habit, at least for a period of time before and after the medical procedure.

Another example is a young patient anticipating an upcoming surgery to remove additional decayed burnt skin tissue. In anticipation of another round of increased pain and discomfort, the patient can be put on a reinforcement schedule to support learning and practicing distraction techniques. The patient can be rewarded by tracking the number of times they are successful at thought-stopping or using a different distraction in order to decrease negative self-talk or pain. A reward schedule can be designed to reinforce positive self-talk with an end reward, such as a movie or a new puzzle book, which are also distractors in and of themselves.

Systematic Desensitization

Patients are instructed to imagine a situation they may fear, while the therapist employs techniques to help them relax. This will help the person to cope with the fear reaction, and likely eliminate the anxiety altogether. For example, a patient who has had a prior trauma may have difficulty in preparing for a medical procedure that involves the task of completing an MRI. This may be a simple procedure for some, but if the patient has a prior traumatic experience such as being trapped under water or in a small enclosure, the thought of going in a small space for an extended period of time may bring on a panic reaction.

Systematic desensitization would first start with the patient in the office, developing relaxation responses through deep breathing, visualization of a calming event, and/or muscle tensing and relaxing. Once a relaxation response is established, the therapist may have the patient begin talking about the trauma and invoking a relaxation exercise as the patient appears to begin to tense up, which can be observed or determined through biofeedback. Biofeedback can identify physiological stressors (increased heart rate, decreased respiration, decreased surface temperature, increased muscular electrical activity) that will assist the therapist to identify when a certain description of the incident begins the anxiety response. As the stressors increase, the discussion is slowed and the relaxation exercise, such as deep breathing, is increased. The patient learns to do these activities on his/her own and to identify when physiological stress is increasing (tightness in the chest, sweaty palms, light-headedness), and can invoke the relaxation exercise whenever needed.

In addition to teaching the relaxation response for discussing or thinking about the stressors, the therapist would then gradually introduce additional shaping behaviors, such as using a box that the patient places over his/her head when he/she is in a safe environment (therapist's office) while engaged in the relaxation exercise. As the patient becomes more and more comfortable with the relaxation exercise and the incremental increase in exposure to an enclosed space, the next step would be to go with the patient to the MRI clinic and work with him/her to continue the relaxation exercise. It may take several sessions to get the patient to this point, but a methodical, systematic decrease in the patient's previous thoughts and fears of closed spaces and being inside the MRI machine for extended periods of time will ease his/her anxiety. Even an open MRI can cause a similar reaction in some patients, although this is certainly an option that should be included for this specific case. The successful patient gains more control over his/her thoughts and feelings and recognizes that when taking deep breaths he/she will experience a reduction in the physiological symptoms when paired with thought-stopping or other strategies the patient has learned.

Validity Testing

Using this strategy, patients are asked to test the validity of the automatic thoughts and scenarios that are playing out in their encounters. The therapist will typically ask the patient to identify or produce evidence that a scenario or thought is likely true or could really happen. If the patient is unable to meet the challenge, the thinking errors of the scenario are exposed, and the patient is asked to explore his/her pattern of negative beliefs or thinking errors and how to use the validity testing whenever she/he encounters future scenarios outside the therapy session. The validity testing is very helpful in preparing for medical procedures, as a common scenario is that the physician will be angry if the patient asks too many questions. The patient may be asked for proof of when this has happened, and most likely that patient is projecting his/her thoughts and beliefs and has no evidence of the health care provider being angry about questions. This scenario can be played out a number of different ways, and humor is usually appreciated in this situation if a trusting relationship exists.

Conclusions

The initial evaluation session is usually spent explaining the reasons for meeting with the psychologist, and if time allows, the basic concepts of CBT are discussed with the patient to help prepare him/her for the follow-up session in which the results of the assessment and the establishment of a positive working relationship between therapist and patient continues. Because CBT is a collaborative, action-oriented therapy effort, patients appreciate the time and effort of the assessment, but also like to get to work to prepare for a medical procedure. As such, it is important the patient is given an active role in the assessment and therapy process and helps to discourage any overdependence on the treatment provider. Follow-up treatment is typically agreed on by both the therapist and the patient. The patient immediately sees the benefit of this preparation time within the first session and will follow up to address anxiety or stress issues. Sometimes patients are reluctant, and if there is a therapeutic alliance in which they have an active part in the assessment and treatment, most will engage and stay engaged through the follow-up session. This should provide a foundation and identify goals of the treatment session (reduce anxiety in preparation for the medical procedure).

Patients may seek therapy independently, but are typically referred for treatment by a primary or specialty physician. Because the patient and therapist work closely together to achieve specific therapeutic objectives, it is important that their working relationship is comfortable and their goals are compatible. Prior to beginning treatment it is important that the patient and therapist meet for a consultation session or mutual interview. This is why location within a medical clinic is helpful in the early establishment of rapport, and the patient's reluctance to attend a session with a psychologist is reduced. The consultation gives the behavioral health provider the opportunity to make an initial assessment of the patient and recommend a course of treatment and goals for therapy. It also gives the patient an opportunity to find out important details about the therapist's approach to treatment, professional credentials, and any other issues of interest.

References

American Psychiatric Association. (2000). *Diagnostic and statistical manual of mental disorders* (4th ed., text rev.). Washington, DC: American Psychiatric Press.

American Psychological Association. (1996). *Guidelines and principles for accreditation of programs in professional psychology*. Retrieved September 15, 2009, from http://www.apa.org/ed/gp2000.html

Anderson, K. O., & Masur, F. T. (1983). Psychological preparation for invasive medical and dental procedures. *Journal of Behavioral Medicine, 6*(1), 1–40.

Baker, J., Keenan, L., & Zwischenberger, J. (2005). A model for primary care psychology with general thoracic surgical patients. *Journal of Clinical Psychology in Medical Settings, 12*(4), 359–366.

Baker, J., Mancuso, M., Norris, M., & Lyons, B. (2002). Treating postpartum depression. *Physician Assistant, 26*(10), 37–44.

Barolat, G. (2001). Epidural spinal cord stimulation with multiple electrode paddle lead is effective in treating intractable low back pain. *Neuromodulation, 4*(2), 59–66.

Beck, A. (1997). The past and future of cognitive therapy. *Journal of Psychotherapy Practice and Research, 6*, 276–284.

Beck, A. T., Steer, R. A., & Brown, G. K. (2000). *Beck Depression Inventory fast screen for medical patients: Manual*. San Antonio, TX: Pearson Publishing.

Beck, J. (1995). *Cognitive therapy: Basics and beyond*. New York: Guilford.

Block, A. R., Gatchel, R. J., Deardorff, W., & Guyer, R. D. (2003). *The psychology of spine surgery*. Washington, DC: American Psychological Association.

Brady, K. T., Tolliver, B. K., & Verduin, M. L. (2007). Alcohol use and anxiety: Diagnostic and management issues. *American Journal of Psychiatry, 164*, 217–221.

Butler, A. C., Chapman, J. E., Forman, E. M., & Beck, A. T. (2006). The empirical status of cognitive-behavioral therapy: A review of meta-analyses. *Clinical Psychology Review, 26*(1), 17–31.

Carson, J., Keefe, F., Lowry, K., Porter, L., Goli, V., & Fras, A. (2007). Conflict about expressing emotions and chronic low back pain: Associations with pain and anger. *Journal of Pain, 8*(5), 405–411.

Chambless, D. L., & Ollendick, T. H. (2001). Empirically supported psychological interventions: Controversies and evidence. *Annual Review of Psychology, 52*, 685–716.

Chapman, B. P., Duberstein, P. R., & Lyness, J. M. (2007). The distressed personality type: Replicability and general health associations. *European Journal of Personality, 21*, 911–929.

Christopherson, E. R., & Mortweet, S. L. (2001). *Treatments that work: Empirically supported strategies for managing childhood problems*. Washington, DC: APA Books.

Deacon, B., & Abramowitz, J. S. (2008). Is hypochondriasis related to obsessive-compulsive disorder, panic disorder or both? An empirical evaluation. *Journal of Cognitive Psychotherapy, 22*(2), 115-127.

Denollet, J., Pedersen, S. S., Vrints, C. J., & Conraads, V. M. (2006). Usefulness of type D personality in predicting five-year cardiac events above and beyond concurrent symptoms of stress in patients with coronary heart disease. *American Journal of Cardiology, 97*, 970–973.

Denollet, J., Nyklicek, I., & Vingerhoets, A. (2008). *Emotion regulation*. New York: Springer Publishing Company.

Dobson, D., & Dobson, K. S. (2009). *Evidence-based practice of cognitive-behavioral therapy*. New York: Guilford.

Gatchel, R. J., Mayer, R. G., & Eddington, A. (2006). MMPI disability profile: The least known, most useful screen for psychopathology in chronic occupational spinal disorders. *Spine, 31*(25), 2973–2978.

Gil, K. M. (1984). Coping effectively with invasive medical procedures: A descriptive model. *Clinical Psychology Review, 4*(4), 339–362.

Gloaguen, V., Cottraux, J., Cucherat, M., & Blackburn, I. (1998). A meta-analysis of the effects of cognitive therapy in depressed patients. *Journal of Affective Disorders, 49*, 59–72.

Gosch, E. A., Flannery-Schroeder, E., Mauro, C. F., & Compton, S. N. (2006). Principles of cognitive-behavioral therapy for anxiety disorders in children. *Journal of Cognitive Psychotherapy, 20*(3), 247–262.

Groth-Marnat, G. (2003). *Handbook of psychological assessment* (4th ed.). New York: John Wiley.

Hathaway, S. R., & McKinley, J. C. (1967). *Minnesota multiphasic personality inventory manual* (rev. ed.). New York: Psychological Corporation.

Hathaway, S. R., McKinley, J. C., Meehl, P. E., Drake, L. E., Welsh, G. S., & MacAndrew, C. (2000). Construction of the original MMPI. In J. N. Butcher (Ed.), *Basic sources on the MMPI-2* (pp. 1–100). Minneapolis, MN: University of Minnesota Press.

Kabat-Zinn, J., Massion, A. O., Kristeller, J., Peterson, L. G., Fletcher, K. E., Pbert, L., et al. (1992). Effectiveness of a meditation-based stress reduction program in the treatment of anxiety disorders. *American Journal of Psychiatry, 149*, 936–943.

Katz, E. R., Kellerman, J., & Siegel, S. E. (1980). Behavioral distress in children with cancer undergoing medical procedures: Developmental considerations. *Journal of Consulting and Clinical Psychology, 48*(3), 356–365.

Keefe, F. J. (1996). Cognitive behavioral therapy for managing pain. *Clinical Psychologist, 49*(3), 4–5.

Kendall, P. C. (2000). *Cognitive-behavioral therapy for anxious children. Therapist's manual* (2nd ed.). Ardmore, PA: Workbook Publishing.

Kupper, N., & Denollet, J. (2007). Type-D personality as a prognostic factor in heart disease: Assessment and mediating mechanisms. *Journal of Personality Assessment, 89*, 265–276.

Leahy, R. L. (2006). *Contemporary cognitive therapy: Theory, research and practice*. New York: Guilford.

Martens, E. J., Smith, O. R. F., Winter, J., Denollet, J., & Pedersen, S. S. (2008). Cardiac history, prior depression and personality predict course of depressive symptoms after myocardial infarction. *Psychological Medicine, 38*, 257–264.

Open Congress for the 111th United States Congress. (2008). *HR 1424 Emergency economic stabilization act of 2008*. Retrieved February 6, 2009, from http://www.opencongress.org/bill/110-h1424/show

Peterson, L. (1989). Coping by children undergoing stressful medical procedures: Some conceptual, methodological, and therapeutic issues. *Journal of Consulting and Clinical Psychology, 57*(3), 380–387.

Poole, H., Bramwell, R., & Murphy, P. (2008). The utility of the Beck Depression Inventory Fast Screen (BDI-FS) in a pain clinic population. *European Journal of Pain, 13*(8), 865–869.

Potter, P. T., & Zautra, A. J. (1997). Stressful life events' effects on rheumatoid arthritis disease activity. *Journal of Consulting and Clinical Psychology, 65*, 319–323.

Robinson, M. E., Riley, J. L., Myers, C. D., Sadler, I. J., Kvaal, S. A., Geisser, M. E., et al. (1997). The coping strategies questionnaire: A large sample, item level factor analysis. *Clinical Journal of Pain, 13*(1), 43–49.

Sareen, J., Cox, B. J., Afifi, T. O., de Graaf, R., Asmundson, G. J. G., ten Have, M., & Stein, M. B. (2005). Anxiety disorders and risk for suicidal indeation and suicide attempts: A population-based longitudinal study of adults. *Archives of General Psychiatry, (62)*, 1249–11257.

Schiffer, A. A., Pavan, A., Pedersen, S. S., Gremigni, P., Sommaruga, M., & Denollet, J. (2006). Type D personality and cardiovascular disease: Evidence and clinical implications. *Minerva Psichiatrica, 47*, 79–87.

Schiffer, A. A., Pedersen, S. S., Broers, H., Widdershoven, J. W., & Denollet, J. (2008). Type-D personality but not depression predicts severity of anxiety in heart failure patients at 1-year follow-up. *Journal of Affective Disorders, 106*, 73–81.

Simpson, B. A. (Ed.). (2003). *Electrical stimulation and the relief of pain*. Boston, MA: Elsevier.

Smith, J. A., Lumley, M. A., & Longo, D. (2002). Contrasting emotional approach coping with passive coping for chronic myofascial pain. *Annals of Behavioral Medicine, 24*(4), 326–335.

Spindler, H., Pedersen, S. S., Serruys, P. W., Erdman, R. A. M., & van Domburg, R. T. (2007). Type-D personality predicts chronic anxiety following percutaneous coronary intervention in the drug-eluting stent era. *Journal of Affective Disorders, 99*, 173–199.

Stansfeld, S. A., Clark, C., Caldwell, T., Rodgers, B., & Power, C. (2008). Psychological work characteristics and anxiety and depressive disorders in midlife: The effects of prior psychological distress. *Occupational and Environmental Medicine, 65*, 634–642.

Stein, M. B., Fuetsch, M., Muller, N., Hofler, M., Lieb, R., & Wittchen, H. (2001). Social anxiety and the risk of depressive disorder. *Archives of General Psychiatry, 58*, 251–256.

Tan, G., Jensen, M. P., Thornby, J., & Sloan, P. A. (2008). Negative emotions, pain, and functioning. *Psychological Services, 5*, 26–35.

Thomason, B. T., Brantley, P. J., Jones, G. N., Dyer, H. R., & Morris, J. L. (1992). The relation between stress and disease activity in rheumatoid arthritis. *Journal of Behavioral Medicine, 15*, 215–220.

Thorn, B. (2004). *Cognitive therapy for pain*. New York: Guilford.

Urrows, S., Affleck, G., Tennen, H., & Higgins, P. (1994). Unique clinical and psychological correlates of fibromyalgia tender points and joint tenderness in rheumatoid arthritis. *Arthritis & Rheumatism, 37*, 1513–1520.

Walker, J. R., & Furer, P. (2008). Interoceptive exposure in the treatment of health anxiety and hypochondriasis. *Journal of Cognitive Psychotherapy, 22*(4), 366–378.

Williams, C. L., & Kendall, P. C. (1985). Psychological aspects of patient education for stressful medical procedures. *Health Education Quarterly, 12*(2), 135–150.

Zautra, A. J., Okun, M. A., Robinson, S. E., & Lee, D. (1989). Life stress and lymphocyte alterations among patients with rheumatoid arthritis. *Health Psychology, 8*, 1–14.

Part III

Clinical Problems I: Common Behavioral Problems in Primary Care

14 Nonadherence in Primary Care

Robert A. DiTomasso
Deborah Chiumento
Marsha S. Singer
Oliver Bullock

Introduction

Adherence to medical advice refers to whether a patient follows the directions offered by his/her physician in regard to performing some behavior, or sequence of behavioral tasks, designed to ultimately improve or maintain the health or mental health of the patient, or prevent the development of illness and disease. A sampling of the typical activities of primary care physicians (PCPs) reveals that they often prescribe a variety of behavioral activities to patients, related to engaging in health-promotion activities and reducing or eliminating health-risk behaviors. Physicians order more than simple pharmacological prescriptions. They frequently provide patients with behavioral prescriptions related to eating, sleeping, smoking, exercising, drinking, and managing stress. In the medical world, the effectiveness of any intervention is essentially a combination of the demonstrated efficacy of the treatment and the extent to which patients appropriately engage in the implementation of the treatment. Simply, the demonstrated evidence of any medication, or any treatment, for that matter, supported through randomized double-blind clinical trials, for example, is virtually worthless, unless the patient takes the proper dosage of the medication for the prescribed length of time. There is much evidence to suggest that patients, even well-intentioned ones, frequently do not adhere to what their physicians ask them to do. Nonadherence may be intentional when a patient chooses not to comply, or unintentional, such as when a patient forgets.

A multitude of factors ranging from the patient, the provider, the physician-patient relationship, the treatment, and the treatment regimen, as well as a host of other related factors, including treatment-setting characteristics, may serve to undermine the extent to which patients remember or choose to follow recommended expert medical advice. The complexities and challenges of effectively addressing nonadherence is evidenced by the domains (patient, provider, treatment, and health care setting) that influence it, the variety of factors within each domain that contribute to it, and the variety of ways in which nonadherence may manifest itself.

In an effort to more fully appreciate the problem of nonaherence, Berlant and Pruitt (2003) have offered the most useful definition of adherence to date as "an acceptable frequency, intensity, and/or accuracy of specific behaviors, given a specific circumstance, that is associated with improved clinical outcomes…a process—a behavioral means to the end point of better health status" (p. 208). Nonadherence, then, refers to a collaborative interaction or series of interactions between a health care provider and patient in which, although there is ideally mutual expectation and responsibility for promoting the patient's health behavior, patients simply fail to follow the advice provided by their physicians. In the primary care setting, where there is a focus on issues of health promotion and disease prevention, few would disagree that ultimately the behavior of the patient is a critical factor in yielding positive health outcomes. The Institute for the Future (2000) reported that the behavior of the patient accounts for about 50% of a person's health status. In light of this finding, enhancing the effectiveness of treatments for nonadherence seems essential. After all, what good are medical treatments if patients do not follow them? Because nonadherence is a common pathway across all medical problems, consideration should be given to those factors that are common across conditions, and those that are specific and unique to each condition. Treatments designed to alter the shared and unique factors that create nonadherence may, then, be more universally applicable and effective.

Efforts to explain, predict, and treat adherence are manifested in a multitude of models, a review of which is beyond the scope of this chapter. These psychological models include the following: the Theory of Interpersonal Behavior (Triandis, 1997); the Health Belief Model (Rosenstock, 1990); Theory of Reasoned Action (Ajzen & Fishbein, 1980); Multiattribute Utility Theory (Carter, 1990); Protection Motivation Theory (Maddux & Rogers, 1983); Social Learning Theory (Bandura, 1986); Attribution Theory (Weiner, 1988); Transtheoretical Theory (Prochaska, DiClemente, & Norcross, 1992); Theory of Information Processing (Glanz, Lewis, & Rimer, 1990); and the Information, Motivation, Behavior Skills Model (Fisher & Fisher, 1992). Berlant and Pruitt (2003) argue that Fisher and Fisher's model supports the importance of information, motivation, and behavioral skills as critical for changing nonadherent behavior.

Failure to comply with recommended advice creates many potential consequences for patients. First, nonadherence may result in the continuation, progression, perpetuation, and exacerbation of medical problems, and places patients at greater risk for more serious medical complications. For example, failure to treat elevated blood pressure is a documented risk factor for the eventual development of cardiovascular disease and death (Rakic, Burke, & Lawrence, 1999). Second, distal effects may be manifested through irreparable end organ damage that sets the stage for further morbidity and mortality. Ignoring elevated blood pressure may result in cardiovascular disease that, in turn, may cause heart attack or stroke. Third, patients may be exposed to more medications and their potentially toxic combinations and effects. Fourth, nonadherent patients may require more frequent need for medical visits and hospitalizations. Cost-related medication nonadherence (CRN), which is defined as skipping or reducing doses, not obtaining prescriptions, and spending less on basic needs to afford medicines, is a persistent problem for individuals, especially the elderly and disabled in the United States. CRN outcomes include increased risk of myocardial infarction, stroke, and preventable hospitalization (Madden et al., 2008). Overall, poorer health outcomes appear to be the direct result of health-risk behaviors that are often embedded within problematic beliefs and behaviors of patients.

The extent to, and manner in, which nonadherence manifests itself is multifaceted, complex, and dependent upon the target behavior. Nonadherence to medication regimens, for example, may take one of a variety of forms, including failure to fill a prescription, not taking the proper dosage of the medication, failing to take the medicine for the recommended period of time, taking someone else's medicine, inconsistent dosing patterns, or even taking too much of a prescribed medication (Burke & Dunbar-Jacob, 1995). Obviously, each of these manifestations may have different causes and require different interventions or combinations of such.

Often, the more that is required on the part of the patient to adhere, the more likely nonadherence may occur. This problem is clearly the case in the realm of lifestyle behavior change. On the surface, adherence to a lifestyle change may appear simpler than it actually is (Burke & Dunbar-Jacob, 1995). Adherence to diet and exercise are cases in point. Dietary change to promote and maintain weight loss involves more than simply eating differently. Rather, it requires changes in a number of critical areas, including basic nutritional choices, increasing exercise, challenging maladaptive attitudes, beliefs and assumptions, negotiating social relationships that affect eating, altering stimulus situations that become occasions for unhealthy eating, reinforcing incompatible habits, extinguishing unhealthy behavior patterns, and coping effectively with high-risk situations.

The application of cognitive-behavioral approaches in treating nonadherence clearly appears to be helpful. Weber et al. (2004) demonstrated that CBT interventions were effective in improving adherence to medications. Crepaz et al. (2008) reported that both individual and group format interventions grounded in theory and aimed at risk reduction increased adherence. Much in line with Sperry's observation (Sperry, 2009), cognitive-behavioral therapy (CBT) has distinguished itself as the psychotherapeutic modality of choice for patients suffering from medical conditions of a chronic nature. Like other problems, however, the effective treatment of nonadherence depends on a thorough assessment and diagnosis of the problem.

Assessment and Diagnostic Issues

Our premise in this chapter is that nonadherence, like many other problems in the primary care setting, is a diagnosable and treatable problem. The *Diagnostic and Statistical Manual of Mental Disorders* (*DSM-IV-TR*; American Psychiatric Association, 2000) includes this problem as an additional condition that may be a focus of clinical attention when the presenting problem is related to failure to comply with one or more aspects of the treatment plan for a physical or mental disorder. However, despite the high incidence of nonadherence, the real question is how often does it truly become a focus of intervention in the primary care setting. We suspect not as frequently as it might and, perhaps, not in ways that are most likely to be helpful. Nonadherence seems to be frequently considered an annoyance by physicians and one that complicates the clinical picture. This view is understandable, as nonadherence interferes with the ability of physicians to maximize treatment delivery. Although it is most certainly a problem about which physicians are well aware, it is often not one which they are well equipped to formally assess, diagnose, and treat. Given that the treatment of any problem necessitates a thorough assessment and conceptualization, there is little wonder why adherence difficulties continue to plague the primary care setting.

Formal assessment requires a thorough consideration of the specific manner or manners in which the problem manifests itself in a specific patient, as well as the consideration of potential hypotheses that account for the problem. The use of cognitive-behavioral assessment (DiTomasso & Esposito, 2005; DiTomasso & Gilman, 2005) has much to offer in this regard, especially because situational variables account for more of the variance in adherence behavior than personality characteristics (Burke & Dunbar-Jacob, 1995). Clinicians must work with physicians and patients to identify the variety of factors that may influence whether patients follow advice. The involvement of the CBT clinician would usually begin with a consultation or referral, whereas the PCP may have a clear picture of the manner in which the patient is not complying, but not necessarily have investigated the myriad of factors accounting for the problem. The CBT clinician would be wise to spend some time discussing the patient with the physician and, if possible, reviewing the medical record for hints about potential causative factors. The clinician must focus on the thoughts, attitudes, beliefs, behaviors, feelings, situational factors, and other relevant considerations. The work of Burke and Dunbar-Jacob (1995), Meichenbaum and Turk (1987), and Belar and Deardorf (2009) will prove most useful, and could form the basis for a thorough and comprehensive cognitive-behavioral interview.

To address the assessment of nonadherence, the clinician must identify factors that may be associated with the onset and maintenance of this challenging problem. A thorough consideration of relevant factors must be conducted. The goal is to comprehensively assess one or more primary or secondary causative factors that account for the problematic behavior and create a conceptual model that elucidates how these factors may account for the behavior. A consideration of variables related to theories of nonadherence may prove to be a useful means of identifying key targets to assess.

Meichenbaum and Turk (1987) have conveniently grouped important factors into several categories. This list includes factors associated with the treatment, treatment regimen, the physician, the patient, the physician-patient relationship, disorder characteristics, and the treatment setting. This myriad of factors essentially constitutes an inventory of testable hypotheses that may be implicated in nonadherence and, as such, require consideration by the clinician. We will mention a few critical variables within each domain and refer the reader to the original sources for a more comprehensive overview.

In their now classic text on facilitating the process of treatment adherence, Meichenbaum and Turk (1987) delineate a number of important domains and variables for clinicians to consider. Their work underscores both the number of factors, alone or in combination, that can potentially impact whether or not patients adhere, as well as the need for a comprehensive assessment. Some relevant patient variables of interest include: psychiatric diagnoses, forgetfulness, problems understanding prescribed advice, conflicting cultural beliefs, competing internal models of illness, prior history of nondherence, dissatisfaction with the health care provider, lack of social support, chaotic living circumstances, and family reinforcement of patient's nonadherent behavior. Disease-specific variables include factors such as chronicity of the disease state, lack of observable symptomatology, and factors specifically related to a disorder that undermine adherence, such as confusion states. Meichenbaum and Turk also report a long list of treatment-related variables such as wait times, referral timing, protracted time between referral and appointment, regimen complexity, regimen duration, treatment recommendations, extent of requisite behavior change, inconvenience, and cost and side effects, real or attributed. Some other relevant treatment-related factors may be less likely to have an impact in primary care settings in which physicians and mental health practitioners work in an integrated manner. These factors are lack of continuity, timing of the referral, and lack of integrated treatment-delivery systems. Finally, provider-patient relationship variables of importance include lack of rapport, communication problems, attitudinal issues, failure to invite feedback about negative problems related to the treatment regimen, and patient dissatisfaction with the provider. The CBT clinician would be wise to use the described domains as templates for assessment, and as a means of providing a comprehensive targeting of potential factors promoting nonadherence that may deserve attention. Each individual patient is likely to display an idiosyncratic profile of nonadherence-related factors, and the likelihood of positively impacting adherence involves adequately addressing factors of relevance. For example, asking the patient questions about the medication regimen and whether it interferes with his/her ability to adhere could provide useful information that would be helpful to both the physician and patient in resolving the problem. The complexity of a medication regimen (Meichenbaum & Turk) has been shown to predict nonadherence, and probing questions related to the number of medications and timing of the doses would be important. If these factors are judged as being primarily implicated in the nonadherent behavior, the intervention may simply involve altering the number of medications and the scheduling of the dosing regimen.

Burke and Dunbar-Jacob (1995) elucidated a number of related factors in three domains, covering most of what Meichenbaum and Turk (1987) discussed, but adding some additional factors in three domains: patient, regimen, and provider. These factors include: the extent to which the patient is educated about the regimen and understands how to implement the plan, self-efficacy to perform the plan, avoidance as a strategy for coping, identifiable obstacles to treatment implementation, provider ability to impart knowledge, provider communication skills, and displaying a nonjudgmental attitude.

Belar and Deardorff's (2009) work offers much to the clinician, as well. This model illustrates the importance of considering the role of biological, cognitive, behavioral, social, psychological, and spiritual factors in understanding patient problems. Belar and Deardorff (2009) have identified a multitude of key clinical questions that are critical in determining possible hypotheses for consideration. These questions are important for determining biopsychosocial factors and hypotheses that may be related to nonadherence.

Another relevant scheme for assessing nonadherence factors and forming the basis for a treatment plan involves a functional analytic strategy (DiTomasso & Gilman, 2005). This model of behavioral observation and assessment is designed to carefully identify causative factors that are functionally related to nonadherent behavior. First, clearly specifying the behavior in question and being able to define and describe it is critical. This helps the clinician and patient identify the target behavior in question and distinguish its occurrence from nonoccurrence. Second, specifying relevant parameters of the behavior in question is extremely important, such as establishing the frequency or infrequency of occurrence, severity, or duration. Providing a means of monitoring the behavior and associated factors is essential. Third, identifying situations under which the problematic behavior is occurring is vital. These circumstances are implicated as setting the stage for the occurrence or nonoccurrence of the behavior. Finally, determining the consequences of nonadherent behavior and their role in reinforcing the behavior are also important. The end result is the development of an empirically based intervention plan that targets causative factors and helps to resolve the problem.

Besides these schemes for identifying causative factors of nonadherence, clinicians must also be aware of specific and available methods for assessing nonadherence. The clinician must choose reliable and valid assessment measures and collect this information at baseline, during treatment, and at follow-up. Clinicians should be aware, however, that a poor therapeutic outcome is not necessarily a measure of treatment nonadherence, just as a positive therapeutic outcome is not always a measure of adherence (Burke & Dunbar-Jacob, 1995). For example, there are many patients who may be adhering to a regimen, but not show clinically significant change on a symptom parameter for any number of physical reasons.

There are a number of means for assessing adherence levels that vary in subjectivity, validity, reliability, convenience, availability, and cost. These factors must be weighed carefully in designing and choosing an assessment strategy, as the quality and accuracy of the yielded information may be undermined. Generally, these methods include: the clinical interview, patient self-report, provider self-report, patient self-monitoring, pill counts, monitoring medication refill rates, behavioral measures, provider ratings of patient behaviors, marker strategies, physiological measures, patient records, and outcomes (Meichenbaum & Turk, 1987). There are advantages and limitations to each method, and clinicians should rarely rely on one method exclusively. Moreover, the more subjective methods should be supplemented by more objective methods, when available and cost-effective. Of course, subjective self-report may be limited by the motivation of the patient to present him/herself in the most positive light, possibly resulting in the tendency to overestimate adherence. Patients may also be more accurate in estimating their nonadherence than adherence. However, there is some literature to support that patients may be capable of predicting, with a fair degree of accuracy, their probability of adhering (Dunbar & Agras, 1980; Morisky, Green, &

Levine, 1986). There is also reason to expect that physicians may actually overestimate adherence in many of their patients. Awareness of the frequency of nonadherence in primary care and the typical manners in which this problem may manifest are essential in bridging the gap between assessment, diagnosis, and treatment.

Incidence and Clinical Manifestations in Primary Care Setting

The incidence of nonadherence is surprisingly high in primary care settings, considering the number of patients suffering from chronic illness. As much as 45% of the general population and 88% of persons over the age of 65 have at least one chronic condition, and 75% of health care dollars are spent on patients with chronic illness (Williams, 2003). Daniel Gerner, Chairman of the Health Care Compliance Packaging Council in Washington, DC, notes that the problem of patient noncompliance is astounding (McCarthy, 1998), with somewhere between $60 billion and $100 billion being spent each year to treat problems caused by noncompliance. Other data reviewed previously point to the same conclusion.

Nonadherence, an extremely common and costly problem in the primary care setting (Williams, 2003), is multidetermined and cuts across all groups regardless of age, socioeconomic status, physical problems, and therapies (Burke & Dunbar-Jacob, 1995). The research in this area is quite alarming, with billions of dollars allocated to the treatment of problems in which nonadherence plays a major role (McCarthy, 1998). Nonadherence to regimens results in 125,000 avoidable deaths every year (McCarthy). The National Heart, Lung, and Blood Institute (1998), for example, reported that between 3 out of 10 and 7 out of 10 patients fail to fully comply with the advice offered by their physicians. About 8 out of 10 patients are unable to sustain behavioral lifestyle changes. Improper prescription medication use is the number one problem in treating illnesses for patients of all ages (American Heart Association, 2009). About half of patients referred for long-term exercise programs drop out between 6 and 12 months (Burke & Dunbar-Jacob, 1995). An overwhelming majority of patients are unable to lose weight and keep themselves from regaining what pounds they have already shed (Brownell & Wadden, 2000). Rates of adherence to dietary recommendations vary widely from as little as 13% to as much as 76% (Dunbar-Jacob, Dwyer, & Dunning, 1991). A consideration of the common problems confronted by PCPs suggests that some of the most preventable causes of disease are intricately intertwined with the behavioral repertoire of the patient. However, a consideration of patient factors alone provides an incomplete picture of the problem. One, therefore, must consider the impact of the provider and the treatment setting characteristics as well.

Case History

Esther V. is a 41-year-old, morbidly obese African American woman with an eighth-grade education who was being treated for type II diabetes, hypertension, obesity, and hypercholesterolemia. She was also manifesting symptoms of peripheral neuropathy, frequent urination, and blurred vision. Esther was being treated by her PCP in a community-based, university-affiliated family medicine residency outpatient center in the Philadelphia area. She was a new patient to the practice who had recently been rushed to the emergency room of a local hospital; Esther was subsequently assigned to the inpatient service for problems stemming from her uncontrolled diabetes. During the course of her brief hospitalization, the patient was highly anxious, fearful, and agitated. She repeatedly denied the seriousness of her condition, refused to eat healthy low-glycemic-index foods, was uncooperative with her treatment plan, expressed the desire to go home, and refused insulin injections. The resident and attending physicians on the service were completely frustrated with her and were at their wit's ends as to what to do with her. They were angry about her "uncooperativeness" and attributed her nonadherence to "pure laziness and ignorance." She was told that she was a "walking time bomb" and was bluntly informed that either she does what she was told to do or "find another doctor." One inexperienced intern physician even told her that she would "do best to learn how to control yourself when it comes to eating." When the hospital psychiatrist was consulted and showed up at her room, Esther became very defensive and hostile, told him that she was "not crazy," and demanded that he leave her room. The next morning, Esther left the hospital against medical advice. A concerned nurse told Esther to follow up with Dr. B., a PCP with over 30 years of experience in treating chronically ill, underserved vulnerable patients and who had a reputation as a caring and compassionate physician with excellent listening skills. Esther had also heard about Dr. B. through her pastor. Two weeks after leaving the hospital, Esther made an appointment to see Dr. B. for an initial office visit.

Cognitive-Behavioral Case Conceptualization

There are a variety of cognitive-behavioral case conceptualizations that may be used in formulating problems in primary care patients. In this instance, we have chosen the model developed by Persons (1989) to elucidate the core beliefs that fueled Esther's behavior in this situation. Persons's approach necessitates a consideration and integration of a variety of factors that are critical for formulating a model of the patient and driving a treatment plan: identifying information, chief complaint, problem list, hypothesized mechanism, relation of mechanism to problems, precipitant of current problems, origins of central problem, treatment plan, and predicted obstacles to treatment. Esther's chief complaint involved physical symptoms associated with her diabetes that were significantly interfering with her life. Her problem list included a primary problem of nonadherence that was seriously threatening her health and intense anxiety at the thought of injecting herself with insulin. In addition, problems included overeating, lack of exercise, poor nutritional choices, diabetes, hypertension, high cholesterol, fatigue, poor understanding of her medical problems, and mistrust and poor relationships with medical personnel. Her feelings included high levels of anxiety associated with injecting insulin, behavioral avoidance of this treatment protocol, hopelessness about her health problems, and frustration with the medical establishment. Her automatic thoughts included: "If I inject insulin, they'll cut off my legs," "My aunt lost her legs from insulin and I will do the same," "My doctors don't really care about me," and "My doctors don't understand me." Her underlying core belief and hypothesized mechanism was as follows: "If I do what the doctors tell me to do, I'll end up just like my aunt." The relationship of the mechanism to the problems was such that her core beliefs related to her vulnerability and fueled her catastrophic automatic thoughts, anxious feelings, and avoidance behaviors that created and maintained a negative cycle of nonadherence. Esther's precipitating events included a variety of situations surrounding her hospitalization and interactions with the physicians, during which she was asked to engage in health-promoting behaviors designed to offset the risk associated with her risky lifestyle habits. Specifically, these triggering events included being asked to inject herself with insulin, being asked to make lifestyle changes, and negative encounters with her physicians. The origins of her central problem stemmed in part from witnessing the long-term illness of her aunt, lack of understanding of her condition, misconceptions about her aunt's treatment, and the terrible outcome her aunt experienced. Another contributory factor resulted from her less-than-satisfactory experiences with the medical establishment. Esther's treatment plan was derived from a thorough assessment and formulation of her problems over a series of visits, including a consultation with her physician from a cognitive-behavioral clinician. Predicted obstacles to Esther's treatment were also considered and included lack of social support, financial problems, possible exacerbation of anxiety and depressed feelings, and transportation to appointments.

Next, we describe Dr. B.'s interactions with Esther and the contributions of Dr. C., a CBT-oriented clinical health psychologist, to her care plan. Esther presented at the health care center in a cautious and guarded manner, and expressed great distress to the medical assistant over her prior experience. Dr. B. spoke to the medical assistant, who briefed him about the situation. Before entering the room, Dr. B. removed his white coat. He introduced himself and welcomed Esther to the practice, spent a few minutes socializing with her, expressed his interest in hearing her concerns, and then in a nonthreatening manner asked her to share with him her reason for coming and her medical history. Dr. B. listened intently and carefully to Esther's story, asked open-ended questions, maintained good eye contact, and expressed his genuine interest, exuding a sense of warmth and caring in helping Esther in a nonjudgmental manner. By doing so, he created a safe environment in which Esther could trust to share her concerns and ask her questions, all the while feeling the support, respect, empathy, and encouragement that come along with good physician-patient rapport. Over several visits, Dr. B. continued to provide this safe atmosphere, all the while encouraging Esther to relay important details about her life, beliefs, customs, perceptions, fears, and concerns, also eliciting her goals and needs, and past medical and psychosocial history. He discussed her medical conditions, always being careful to explain the information at a level that she could appreciate, always checking for comprehension of her understanding, normalizing her concerns, eliciting and answering her questions about her conditions and medical treatments, and comprehensively exploring her reasons for nonadherence. Dr. B. realized that Esther was confronting significant challenges that interfered with her ability to adhere to her medical regimen. He educated her about the mind-body connection and introduced the importance of integrating the biopsychosocial model in patient care, as well as the use of additional resources. Her medical treatment was in stark contrast to what she had experienced in the past. Dr. B. broached the idea of incorporating a clinical health psychologist into her current treatment team as one who could offer specialized assistance in helping them to tackle her current difficulties. He was extremely careful to avoid implying that her problems were all in her head and that he was giving her care up to the mental health clinician. Instead, he emphasized a team approach to her care and that this was a routine part of the manner in which he practiced. After obtaining Esther's permission, Dr. B. arranged to have Dr. C. join their next office visit, and subsequently, Esther agreed to spend a few sessions with the clinician discussing the roots of her nonadherence. The clinician conducted a comprehensive assessment of Esther's nonadherence and discovered important information. Of most importance, Dr. C. found a number of areas of concern that fueled Esther's nonadherence. These included being intimidated and overwhelmed by medical personnel based on her previous experience, as well as a general mistrust of the medical establishment. She also had difficulty comprehending medical information, limited knowledge, and denial of the seriousness of her medical problems. There was also evidence of significant levels of anxiety and depression. Particularly noteworthy, after Dr. C. understood Esther's belief system surrounding insulin, she discovered that Esther's refusal to take insulin injections was completely understandable from her standpoint. Dr. C. elicited Esther's mistaken belief that her aunt's bilateral amputations to the level of her knees were a consequence of injecting insulin, as opposed to her aunt's failure to adhere to medical advice, which ultimately resulted in her need for insulin injections. This case formulation was shared with both Esther and Dr. B. Dr. C. worked with both Esther and Dr. B. to implement a treatment plan that addressed her problems. Over the course of the next several months, these interventions included: (a) health education and psychoeducation designed to teach Esther about her conditions, available treatment options, consequences of nonadherence, her misconceptions and myths about medical treatment, and the relationship between her beliefs and her anxiety and health behavior; (b) instilling hope and self-efficacy training to develop a belief that she could change her situation; (c) motivational interviewing designed to help her to evaluate the costs and benefits of adhering and not adhering; (d) cognitive interventions designed to assist Esther in testing her automatic thoughts and beliefs related to insulin and her belief about being unable to change her situation; (e) training her to administer insulin (using a diabetic educator/nurse) as well as nutritional counseling; (f) behavior rehearsal and feedback in learning to use a glucometer and adjust her levels of insulin; (g) self-monitoring to assist Esther in logging her self-administered insulin injections and nutritional content (this tangible measure assists with meeting daily goals), as well as monitoring her catastrophic thinking; (h) referral to a weight-management program using the LEARN manual (Brownell, 2004); (i) problem-solving training (for anticipated future problems/setbacks) aimed at problem recognition, definition, identifying resources, generating possible solutions, developing plans, and carrying out solutions (Leahy, 2003); (j) relaxation training and stress-management training; (k) assertiveness training to build confidence when interacting with medical personnel and to increase responsible positive assertion in making requests, asking questions, and knowing when to escalate her assertion (Leahy); (l) ongoing assessment of anxiety and depression using the Beck Depression Inventory and Beck Anxiety Inventory; (m) discussing blood work results with her occasionally to show her progress and how it relates to her new behaviors; (n) developing and maintaining a social support network, including family members and close friends in her church, to support her lifestyle changes; and (o) relapse prevention training.

Identifying and Addressing Obstacles to Treatment

Many factors present obstacles to patient adherence. Without addressing such interferences, the likelihood of successfully promoting adherence is small. In this section, we summarize the obstacles to adherence related to patient characteristics, regimen factors, and specific obstacles related to nonadherence to medication and lifestyle changes for a wide range of patients. Cognitive-behavioral clinicians working with primary care patients would be wise to fully assess and effectively address all potential obstacles that may interfere with adherence. It is incumbent upon the clinician to determine what specific factors in a given patient, if any, may threaten the likelihood of adherence. Obstacles vary, and patients are likely to have more than one obstacle confronting them. In this section, we describe some common obstacles clinicians need to consider and suggestions for overcoming obstacles.

Few primary care patients probably take their medication 100% of the time, always avoid unhealthy snacks, or exercise every day. One obstacle is defining adherence/nonadherence in a dichotomous fashion. Doing so creates a situation in which patients may inadvertently be set up for failure. It is more useful to think of a continuum with nonadherence at one end and adherence at the other. The continuum perception of adherence is particularly useful when working with patients on changing lifestyle behaviors. Consistent, gradual behavioral improvements are easier to achieve, are cumulative, and are often more effective than an unrealistic total overhaul.

Wroe (2002) has elucidated the role of patient beliefs as obstacles to adherence. She distinguishes between intentional and unintentional nonadherence, hypothesizing that different factors contribute to each. She defines intentional nonadherence as an active decision (e.g., whether or not to take medications), based on the patients' beliefs and cognitions regarding the condition and the prescribed treatment. Patients in Wroe's study whose health beliefs contributed to nonadherence with asthma maintenance medication made statements such as, "I don't like the taste," "I don't think it helps me," "I don't like taking medicines," and "I don't want to remind myself I am an 'ill' person" (p. 363). Unintentional nonadherence is defined as forgetting to follow the prescribed regimen (e.g., forgetting to take medications), and is more related to regimen complexity, patient age, and clinical variables (e.g., depression, alcohol use) than patient beliefs. Her work underscores the need for clinicians to consider different obstacles under these two circumstances.

Most clinicians realize that patients do not actually need to be told what to do or actually do what they are told. Rollnick, Miller, and Butler (2008) posit that two critical obstacles occur when patients are not given the opportunity to explore the meaning of the situation for them and to determine that the prescribed changes are both important and achievable. The patient's belief that he or she can achieve the behavior change and that the change will make a difference is critical. The notion of importance relates to research on fatalism and hopelessness. Patients who feel that a cancer diagnosis is a death sentence, despite state-of-the-art medical interventions, are less apt to follow through with physician recommendations for screening (Magai, Consedine, Neugut, & Hershman, 2007). The notion of achievability relates to self-efficacy theory, or the patient's perception of how capable he or she is of performing the prescribed behaviors. Self-efficacy has been consistently identified as a key predictor of adherence to prescribed treatments (Burke & Dunbar-Jacob, 1995).

Other patient-related obstacles identified by Burke and Dunbar-Jacob (1995) include: lack of knowledge and understanding of the regimen and what the patient must do to implement the plan; a history of previous nonadherence to physician recommendations; multiple stressors at the time the treatment is being initiated; lack of confidence in the ability to perform the prescribed behavior (i.e., low self-efficacy); use of avoidance as a coping strategy; lack of social support, particularly for changes in diet; dissatisfaction with patient-physician interactions and the medical care received; cost, complexity, duration, and the extent to which patient lifestyle is affected by the change. Burke, Dunbar-Jacob, and Hill (1997) speculate that as the number of behaviors to be changed increases, as the frequency with which the behaviors to be performed increase, and as the length of the prescribed duration increases, the more likely it is that adherence will decrease with time. Of course, patients with cultural, ethnic, or religious backgrounds different from those of their Western physician providers are more likely to hold health beliefs that lead to nonadherence. Fadiman (1997) provides a powerful illustration of this phenomenon, sharing the story of an epileptic Hmong child whose parents' views of how her illness should be treated is in striking contrast to the opinions of her American physicians.

Similarly, patients' perceptions of the severity of their condition presents another potential obstacle (DiMatteo, Haskard, & Williams, 2007). For patients in poor health with serious disease conditions, adherence may seem futile, causing them to feel depressed and hopeless about their futures. These are also the patients who tend to have the most complex treatment regimens and the greatest physical and emotional challenges—they often have the most difficult tasks and the most limited resources. The sickest patients, therefore, are often at high risk for nonadherence. The emotional state of patients may impact both their ability and willingness to adhere to demanding treatment plans. DiMatteo, Lepper, and Croghan (2000) identified depression as a strong predictor of nonadherence to medical advice. A similar analysis of 13 studies addressing anxiety and nonadherence yielded mixed results. In a study of nonadherence to HIV treatment, depression, anxiety, and psychosocial distress were all associated with nonadherence (Van Servellen, Chang, Garcia, & Lombardi, 2002).

Pharmacological nonadherence is most common among elderly patients and patients prescribed multiple medications (Bedell et al., 2000). Nonadherence can be a result of overdosing, underdosing, erratic dosing intervals, failing to fill the prescription, or patient-initiated drug holidays (Burke & Dunbar-Jacob, 1995). The reasons behind the nonadherence include patient forgetfulness, cost factors, medication side effects, and health beliefs reflecting mistrust of modern medicine (e.g., "If I continue to take this hypertension medication, I will become addicted").

A particularly challenging obstacle occurs when the condition for which the patient is being treated has minimal symptoms. Perceived adverse effects of medication can be viewed by the patient as more problematic than the condition, which is often asymptomatic (Hughes, 2004). For example, hypertensive patients often discontinue medication because the side effects of frequent urination, fatigue, and loss of libido seem more problematic than having high blood pressure. As the number of side effects increases, the rate of intentional nonadherence increases (Toyoshima, Takahashi, & Akera, 1997). Asthma patients in asymptomatic phases often become nonadherent, believing that medication is unnecessary unless they feel ill (Wroe, 2002). Kim et al. (2007) found that intentional nonadherence to antihypertensive medication among middle-aged Korean Americans was commonly related to a lack of knowledge regarding hypertension, including the benefits and side effects of the medication.

Bedell et al. (2000) categorized patients' feedback regarding their medications into four areas: (a) a desire for more information (e.g., details about how the prescribed drug would help their symptoms or interact with other medications); (b) concerns about adverse effects (e.g., feeling fatigued, loss of sexual interest, concern about liver toxicity); (c) cost or convenience obstacles; and (d) the influence of multiple physicians (e.g., receiving different messages from the PCP and the specialist caused confusion and left the patient feeling less committed to the prescribed treatment regimen).

Yet another risk factor for medication nonadherence includes lower levels of patient intelligence (Stilley, Sereika, Muldoon, Ryan, & Dunbar-Jacob, 2004). Estimated IQ level was the single most powerful predictor of medication adherence; the higher the intelligence estimate, the higher the adherence level. These findings underscore the potential value of arranging for social support and supervision in certain cases.

Patients who have reading or vision problems also have increased difficulty taking their medications as prescribed. Forgetfulness, resulting from memory problems or daily stressors, remains a major cause of unintentional nonadherence. Sleep difficulties among the elderly can also lead to nonadherence regarding dosing schedules. Hughes (2004) suggests that physicians attempt to simplify the drug regimens of their elderly patients and advocates for dosage scheduling for the elderly, including reminder cues, calendars, and the use of weekly medication boxes. Easy-open packaging reduces problems caused by arthritis or other motor difficulties, and the use of special labeling and color coding of containers may circumvent visual or cognitive impairments.

Patients tend to be most adherent when they are prescribed a short-term medication that has once-daily dosing. But even in this simplest of situations, obstacles exist. Cost is a factor even with those who have prescription plans. Barron, Wahl, Fischer, and Plauschinat (2008) found higher levels of adherence for antidiabetic medications with patients who had copays of less than $10, compared with patients whose copays were $20 or $30, or more. Madden et al. (2008) report that about 10% of current Medicare patients have no prescription coverage. When faced with cost barriers to medications, they posit that the elderly often skip doses, reduce doses, or fail to fill their prescriptions at all. Research on maintaining adherence to medication prescriptions over the long term is limited. There is some evidence that ongoing education by medical providers and long-term monitoring of adherence behavior can improve adherence to long-term medication prescriptions (Burke, Dunbar-Jacob, & Hill, 1997).

Burke et al. (1997) report that adherence to rehabilitative and preventive exercise programs may be lower than adherence to pharmacological therapies. Burke and Dunbar-Jacob (1995) note that exercise nonadherence is high because regular physical exercise requires lifelong alterations to the patients' and families' lifestyles. It can be time-consuming, complex, inconvenient, and costly, as well.

Methods employed in attempts to increase exercise adherence include contracting for 6-month participation and verbal persuasion to enhance self-efficacy related to exercise adherence (Burke et al., 1997). Contracting was found to increase adherence rates. Verbal persuasion paired with psychoeducation with both the patient and spouse led to a 12% increase in attendance (Burke et al.).

Weight-loss programs, heart-healthy eating, and diabetic diets are examples of prescribed regimens in the area of nutrition. Dietary modifications are among the most challenging for patients. Adherence to dietary modification instructions is thought to be lower than for the other medical regimens. Diet adherence is difficult and even those patients who lose weight initially, often gain it back. Burke et al. (1997) evaluated adherence to heart-healthy diets, which generally promote reductions in total calories (if the patient is overweight or obese), less total and saturated fat, less dietary cholesterol, and increase in dietary fiber. Their meta-analysis of 46 studies identified some evidence that providing small educational groups, including opportunity for group discussion, has a positive effect on dietary adherence. They also found that individual or group sessions with a dietitian have positive benefits.

Spouse support related to dietary changes seemed very important. The patients in the highest support quartile had the largest proportion of subjects who successfully attained their goals (Burke et al., 1997). Despite efforts to enhance adherence, a gradual decrease in adherence to prescribed nutrition regimens was noted in the long-term studies that were reviewed (Burke et al.). Burke et al. (1997) also reviewed patients' efforts to quit smoking on the advice of their physicians. They found adherence rates for smoking cessation at 1 year ranging from 35 to 71%. Methods associated with successful smoking cessation included a personalized, unequivocal message from the physician regarding the necessity of quitting, counseling on the benefits of quitting, asking the patient to set a quit date, and offering nicotine replacement therapy. Phone follow-up was not significant in increasing adherence.

In sum, there are a number of obstacles that interfere with promoting and maintaining adherence in patients. A consideration of specific obstacles affecting an individual patient is important in designing effective treatment interventions.

Points of Collaboration With Physicians and Family

CBT clinicians must be aware of methods for collaborating with physicians that have a great likelihood of facilitating adherence. Cognitive-behavioral clinicians should strongly encourage physicians to monitor patient adherence on an ongoing basis. Patel and Davis (2006) posit that a great deal of nonadherence goes unrecognized by physicians. Providing physicians with strategies to enhance the physician-patient relationship and recommending individually tailored educational efforts and behavioral interventions are also important.

Probably the most critical factor in improving nonadherence to medical regimens is the establishment of a nonjudgmental, collaborative therapeutic alliance, sometimes referred to as concordance (Hughes, 2004). Concordance occurs when physician and patient work together, discussing the importance of change, methods for achieving change, and the patient's concerns regarding the prescribed treatment. The goal is to problem solve around the patient's concerns to develop an individualized, collaborative treatment plan. This approach allows the patient to assume responsibility for the prescribed behavior changes, to feel more confident that the changes can be accomplished, and to be an active participant in decision making related to his or her health care (Hughes). As Rollnick et al. (2008) point out, the physician may be the expert on what needs to be done (e.g., regular exercise), but the patient is the expert on how to incorporate the prescribed behavior into his or her daily routine.

Based on evidence that patients have difficulty remembering their physician's instructions after leaving the office (Hughes, 2004), clinicians should encourage physicians to repeat the message over time, review prior discussions, and write down the most important instructions for patients to take with them. This is another reason for physicians to aim to achieve patient behavior changes gradually.

Physicians should also be urged to consider the manner in which information is provided. Wroe (2002) found that the amount of information the physician provides about the pros and cons of the recommended treatment options needs to match the patient's level of interest. Underinforming or overinforming can lead to patient nonadherence. Physicians are encouraged to check in with their patients on a regular basis to gauge whether or not additional discussion or education is desired.

Likewise, as Burke and Dunbar-Jacob (1995) posit, the more effectively the patient is educated, the more likely he or she will follow the prescribed regimen. Educational interventions should be tailored to the patient's current level of understanding regarding the treatment plan, and should take into account the complexity of the treatment, the frequency of contacts between physician and patient, and the patient's view of what is most important to learn. They suggest that it is preferable to provide information and supporting materials in smaller doses over an extended period of time to avoid overwhelming the patient. They caution, however, that educational strategies alone, even under the best of circumstances, are not sufficient in improving nonadherence.

Clinicians also need to provide physicians with a number of strategies that are likely to improve adherence. The following interventions are among those outlined by Burke and Dunbar-Jacob (1995) that physicians and patients can work on collaboratively to improve patient adherence.

Intervention Strategies

Goal setting involves working toward goals that are specific, attainable, and proximal in time. Goals should address the patient's individualized needs in relation to the prescribed treatment (e.g., the patient will walk 30 minutes a day, five times a week, during her lunch hour). If the patient fails to meet her goals, the physician should engage her in nonjudgmental discussion, aimed at understanding the factors that interfered with adherence (Burke & Dunbar-Jacob, 1995).

Problem-solving strategies can be applied to medical nonadherence by examining barriers to behavior change, defining the problem, generating possible solutions, selecting a plan of action from among a list of alternatives, and evaluating the effectiveness of the plan. Problem solving can be particularly useful in helping patients anticipate and prepare for challenging situations (e.g., going into a bar after quitting smoking, maintaining an exercise regimen while traveling for business) (Burke & Dunbar-Jacob, 1995).

Monitoring is used to document behavior related to the prescribed treatment regimen. When physicians ask patients to monitor their behavior, the importance of achieving the prescribed behavior is underscored. Physicians need to reinforce this by asking for and reviewing the patient's records. Self-monitoring can be reinforcing, which can lead to increased self-efficacy. The achievement of progress toward the goal actually makes goal attainment more likely. Research supports the value of monitoring across all aspects of behavior change, but the findings are strongest in the area of weight reduction (Burke & Dunbar-Jacob, 1995).

Modeling involves the patient's observation of another patient or role model demonstrating the prescribed behavior. Patients prefer reference models whose abilities are similar to their own, rather than expert models performing effortlessly and with perfection. Videotapes provide a cost-effective option for physicians who wish to provide modeling interventions (Burke & Dunbar-Jacob, 1995).

Habit-building strategies attempt to modify the patient's behavior by establishing a relationship between the stimulus for the behavior and the prescribed behavior (e.g., placing the medication bottle by the patient's toothbrush). The established habit can serve as a prompt to complete the prescribed behavior. The use of cues for performance (e.g., reminder stickers) also leads to habit building (Burke & Dunbar-Jacob, 1995).

Contracting is a proven strategy for improving adherence. It involves the patient in the development of the prescribed behavior change, provides a written statement of expectations, creates a form of public commitment, and delineates a reward for goal attainment. A contract should be outlined in small steps, be individualized to the patient's particular needs and challenges, and should lead to the attainment of a goal that the patient believes to be important. The reward should also be something the patient views as valuable (Burke & Dunbar-Jacob, 1995).

Evaluation of adherence needs to be an ongoing task for the physician and must be evaluated based on the patient's actual behavior. McQuaid (2008) suggests that if a physician only has a brief amount of time to discuss the prescribed regimen with the patient, that he or she reviews the issues and circumstances that are likely to impede the patient's adherence.

Collaborating with family members is also important in promoting adherence. Social support refers to the involvement of others (e.g., family, friends) in education related to the medical condition, and in the development and implementation of the prescribed treatment plan. The purpose of social support strategies is to "develop an ally" who can help the patient modify required behaviors, reduce obstacles to adherence, and be supportive through both failures and successes (Burke & Dunbar-Jacob, 1995). Developing social support is of critical importance when lifestyle changes are prescribed. It can often be critical to include key family members in treatment planning. For example, the wife of a newly diagnosed diabetic needs to be included in discussions of diet, meal planning, label reading, and eating schedules.

There is considerable research supporting the benefits of family support in improving adherence to a variety of prescribed behaviors. When the prescribed behavior may take the patient away from the family for significant periods of time (e.g., exercise programs, relaxation training), it is vital that the family understand the importance of the behavior change in order to build support for the patient. Otherwise, family members are likely to sabotage the patient's efforts to change.

DiMatteo (2004) reported that social support (cohesive families) is associated with patient adherence to medical regimens. If no viable family member is available, research suggests that coworkers, community resources, and friends can also provide valuable support (Burke & Dunbar-Jacob, 1995).

Vik et al. (2006) found that older patients were more adherent to medication regimens when they had assistance with medication administration. Family members can serve this function if they live with the patient or visit frequently. Burke et al. (1997) described two studies employing educational strategies for insulin-dependent diabetic children targeting the family members and school personnel. The authors reported positive changes in adherence to a diabetic diet when the patients received this form of social support.

Patient knowledge that a loved one has faith in his or her ability to follow through with prescribed medical regimens seems to improve patient adherence. Taylor, Bandura, Ewart, Miller, and DeBusk (as cited in Burke and Dunbar-Jacob, 1995) shared evidence that patients' exercise behavior improved when their spouses demonstrated belief in the patients' ability to maintain their exercise regimens.

In sum, a number of critical factors must be addressed in ensuring the treatment of nonadherence. Perhaps, most important, CBT clinicians must derive treatment plans based on empirically derived evidence.

Development and Implementation of Empirically Based Treatment Plan

The development and implementation of an empirically based treatment plan flows directly from the case conceptualization, targeting specific factors that are determined to have a likely impact on improving adherence. Effective treatments are tailored to the individual patient, and clinicians should choose an empirical treatment that most appropriately applies in the situation. In other words, the clinician should select the treatment or combination of treatments that are most likely to produce the best outcome. As Berlant and Pruitt (2003) have noted, "In general, behavior change strategies that focus on what occurs before and after targeted behaviors have been substantially more effective than other approaches" (p. 210).

The outcome literature on improving nonadherence is an important source of information. Generally, interventions fall into four broad categories: educational, behavioral, affective, and provider interventions. In their meta-analysis on nonadherence interventions, Roter et al. (1998) have defined each treatment approach in operational terms. Educational interventions include either written or verbal activities specifically designed to impart information to the patient through one or more of a variety of means, including one-on-one teaching, groups, written materials, or instruction by telephone. Behavioral strategies are designed to pinpoint specific problematic behaviors and to shape more adaptive behaviors through reinforcement. This category includes strategies such as skill building, behavioral practice, modeling, contingency contracting, modifications in the packaging and dosing of medications, tailoring treatments to the patients, the use of positive reinforcement for appropriate behavior, and mail and phone reminders. Affective strategies are those that capitalize on feelings and emotions through the social network of the patient with support (such as family support for positive behaviors), family counseling, and home visits designed to reinforce compliant behavior. Provider interventions refer to educational strategies designed to enhance the abilities of providers to promote adherence through the use of improved instructional approaches, communication training, and behavioral interventions. Generally, the literature demonstrates that the interventions showed highly significant average small to large effect sizes on all compliance measures such as health outcomes (e.g., blood pressure), direct measures (e.g., tracers on physiological tests), indirect measures (e.g., pill counts), subjective (e.g., patient or other reports), and (e.g., appointment-keeping rates or engaging in preventive services). Overall, interventions demonstrated their strongest effects on indirect measures of compliance, specifically drug use. For example, there was a greater effect on refill behavior than on pill taking. Finally, there were stronger effects on appointment making than appointment-keeping behavior.

Also, programs that incorporated combined educational and behavioral components produced stronger effects than single-focus interventions. Particularly noteworthy, programs that included all three components were especially potent. The effect sizes for behavioral and combined educational/behavioral interventions were apparent on use measures. The advantage of multicomponent interventions was also apparent on indirect measures of adherence. Specifically, behavioral strategies produced stronger effect sizes than educational interventions on prescription refill behavior. There is also evidence that using two or more educational strategies or two or more behavioral strategies produces stronger effects. Adding a second strategy on educational or behavioral programs showed no advantage on the health outcomes or subjective measures.

The empirical evidence has several implications for the treatment of adherence. First, the more comprehensive the program, the greater its impact on improving adherence. Second, multicomponent treatments, particularly educational and behavioral combinations, are more effective than unimodal interventions with a single focus. Third, multicomponent programs incorporating educational, behavioral, and affective components produce the most impact. Fourth, educational and behavioral strategies are about equally effective and better than affective interventions, and combining educational and behavioral combinations are better still. Fifth, written educational materials are less effective than other types of educational approaches. Group educational programs yield the strongest effects on direct measures of adherence, as well as use measures. Telephone education is particularly useful on use measures.

Burke and Dunbar-Jacob (1995) report that although past research has failed to support patient education alone as having an effect on adherence, they provide a number of strategies to enhance the effectiveness of educational interventions.

Given the variety of factors that contribute to adherence, education may be necessary but not sufficient to effect change. In short, patients cannot be expected to effectively implement an adherence strategy unless they know exactly what and how to do it. They suggest imparting small amounts of information relevant to the problem distributed over time and tailored to the educational level of the patient. Written materials should be used to strengthen verbal messages with ample opportunity for patients to ask questions and for providers to assess patient understanding. Education should focus on what the patient needs to do instead of the disease, provide demonstrations, and practice opportunities when relevant. Referral to ancillary resources may also be beneficial. Burke and Dubar-Jacob (1995) also list a number of useful behavioral strategies including modeling, fitting regimens to patient lifestyles and culture, goal setting, self-monitoring, reinforcement strategies, problem solving, cue insertion into patient's environment, pairing adherent behavior with daily habits, contracting, enhancing self-efficacy, and promoting social support.

Given the importance of social support on immune, endocrine, and cardiovascular function, illness recovery and maintenance of health, DiMatteo (2004) conducted a meta-analysis of 122 studies on practical, emotional, and undifferentiated social support and family functioning. Patients receiving practical support, emotional support, and undifferentiated support showed an odds of complying that are 2, 1.35, and 1.53 times higher, respectively, than those patients not receiving such support. The risk of nonadherence is about 1.74 times higher in patients with low levels of family cohesiveness, with a positive correlation between family dysfunction and poor adherence. DiMatteo (2004) concludes that patient adherence is the mediating factor between social support and health, and that social support yields substantial effects on adherent behavior. Finally, functional support yields larger effects than structural support, meaning perhaps that the availability of others in the patient's environment is less important than the quality of the relationships patients have with others.

In describing state-of-the-art interventions designed to foster adherence, Berlant and Pruitt (2003) have pointed out that the most promising methods for treating nonadherence include combinations of a number of strategies, including patient education, behavioral strategies, self-rewards, social support, and telephone follow-up. More recently, Haynes, Ackloo, Sahota, McDonald, and Yao (2008), in the *Cochrane Database of Systematic Reviews* of randomized clinical trials, reported finding that treatment of medication adherence (measuring both adherence and clinical outcome in studies with a minimum of 80% follow-up of each group, and 6 months' follow-up for longer-term interventions) showed beneficial initial findings. In summarizing their findings, Haynes et al. (2008) state, "[A]lmost all of the interventions that were effective for long term care were complex, including combinations of more convenient care, information, reminders, self-monitoring, reinforcement, counseling, family therapy, psychological therapy, crisis intervention, manual telephone follow-up and supportive care" (www.cochrane.org/reviews/en/ab000011.html).

Evaluation of Treatment Outcomes

Assessing treatment outcomes for nonadherence in the clinical setting is undoubtedly important, and the measures chosen to reflect whether or not change has occurred will depend on the problem or problems being treated. Given the complexity and co-morbidities found in many patients in primary care, especially nonadherent patients, a number of suggestions seem warranted. First, the measures chosen must be direct or indirect valid and reliable reflections of the treatment targets. In view of issues such as cost, staff, time, and other resources to achieve this goal, the clinician may need to rely on what measures are already available in the clinical environment, choosing those that provide the best estimates of change. The primary care setting has many possible measures already embedded within the context of patient care that may provide important clues about the effectiveness of the interventions. The clinician must make a balanced choice by selecting the best available measures while avoiding the potential for overburdening the system. Using multiple available measures with an eye toward minimizing cost, effort, and inconvenience for the office staff and physician would be wise. Second, given that nonadherence problems are multifaceted and multicausal in nature, a consideration of the changes on a number of levels or aspects of patient functioning and health status may be useful in comprehending the degree and breadth of meaningful clinical change. A combination of patient beliefs, attitudes, behaviors, feelings, medical outcomes, and report of family members may prove most useful. Third, ultimately, the major question is whether patients are truly demonstrating changes during and after treatment that differ from baseline levels. Available nonreactive measures in the patient's chart may provide convincing evidence in the form of laboratory test results or other more objective measures, such as weight loss and blood pressure. Finally, multimodal sources and informants that are conveniently available may provide socially valid indices of change. CBT clinicians working with primary care patients should consider using multiple outcomes assessments (reactive and nonreactive), from a variety of sources, including the patient, physician, and family, physiological measures, and other valid and reliable instruments when available.

Considerations With Special Populations/Diversity Issues

In assessing and treating nonadherence, it is essential to consider the role of special populations and diversity. Given the host of factors that influence whether and to what extent a patient does or does not adhere to a medical regimen, failure to attend to differences and special characteristics of certain patient populations may undermine the assessment process and implementation of a treatment regimen. Of course, failure on the part of the provider to be aware and sensitive to differences is equally, if not more, important. In this section, we review important considerations in assessing and treatment adherence in four groups: the elderly, cultural/ethnic groups, mentally challenged, and psychiatrically impaired.

Elderly

Problems of nonadherence are common in the elderly population (Le Roux & Fisher, 2006). There are many characteristics associated with the aging patient that present special challenges to the health care provider. Elderly patients are often prescribed multiple medications, which, by definition, make medical regimens more complex and difficult for patients to follow. The use of multiple medications also increases the risk for more adverse side effects and drug interactions that may ultimately undermine adherence. The fact that many elderly patients are living on fixed, limited incomes also complicates the picture even further, especially in today's economic climate. Patients may be unable to afford prescribed medications that are in direct competition with basic needs and necessities. Even if patients could financially afford the cost of medications, there may be challenges related to lack of transportation and other means to accessing and obtaining medical necessities. Elderly patients who are living alone may be at even more risk of nonadherence, secondary to lack of available support and supervision, when needed. Because elderly patients may be more affected by sensory deficits related to vision and hearing loss and motor problems, these factors may also interfere with adherent behaviors. Finally, cognitive impairments such as memory loss and long-term memory issues may contribute to problems. LeRoux and Fisher (2006) have provided an extensive and relatively exhaustive list of risks for nonadherence in the elderly and suggested strategies for overcoming or minimizing the impact of these factors. It is important to consider that patients may be likely to have more than one risk factor that requires attention. In addition, the clinician would be wise to consider common factors across risks, reduce these to a smaller number of contributing issues, target these issues, and determine a limited number of focused interventions that are most likely to yield benefits to the patient. In this manner, the intervention protocol becomes less unwieldy. For example, in the case of an elderly patient on a complex medical regimen, living alone, who is also experiencing mild cognitive decline and visual deficits, assistance in recording and following the prescribed medication schedule, the use of environmental cues, pairing medications with specific activities, the use of a daily medication dispenser, and regularly scheduled visits from supportive family members or friends would likely be helpful.

Cultural Diversity

The consideration of cultural factors is of paramount importance in providing effective culturally sensitive care to patients (Rodriguez-Gomez & Sala-Serrano, 2006). Given the prevalence of diversity in the population of this country, as well as those patients presenting in the primary care setting, the health care provider must be particularly open and astute to soliciting patient beliefs and perceptions in a sensitive and respectful manner. Sperry (2009) has argued that cultural variables manifested in religious, spiritual, and ethnic beliefs significantly impact whether a patient accepts an explanation for illness, engages in treatment, and adheres to important medical advice. Cultural myths and beliefs have a determining influence on patient behavior. The clinician is wise to solicit the beliefs and perceptions of patients about their illness representations (Rodriguez-Gomez & Salas-Serrano, 2006), attributions about causes of disease, beliefs about medication and other treatments, views related to diagnostic tests, and other culture-specific factors that may undermine the assessment and treatment process. Respecting the beliefs and values of patients is critically important, as well. Failure to solicit and address these factors may result in the physician inadvertently placing a patient at odds with strongly held religious and cultural convictions and family values. Health care disparities in vulnerable populations are largely a function of issues of barriers to access that may, in part, be affected by cultural factors that prevent patients from seeking care. Other issues related to trust may also be relevant. For example, among African Americans, the deception and mistreatment imparted through the well-known Tuskegee Experiments has likely contributed to suspicion, mistrust, and anger with the medical community. Among other cultural groups, language barriers may undermine the communication process by contributing to misunderstanding and confusion. In other groups, such as Asian American patients, there may be hesitancy in disclosing personal and family information to a stranger. Still other groups, such as refugees, who have a history of trauma and violence perpetrated against them, may understandably be at high risk for distrust. An assessment of level of acculturation of a patient is also important to consider. Finally, appreciation for the role of traditional designated healers endorsed by a culture and flexibility in incorporating their role into the prescribed treatment regimen by the health care provider may be useful in promoting more positive treatment outcomes.

Mentally Handicapped

Providing care for mentally handicapped patients is greatly affected by the level of severity of the condition and the availability of supervision and support. Intellectual problems may significantly interfere with ability of the patient to fully comprehend and independently implement a self-care plan designed to promote adherence. The skill of the health care provider in tailoring and simplifying treatment recommendations to the level of the patient, as well as incorporating appropriate supports, may serve to enhance the likelihood of compliance. Concrete, as opposed to highly abstract explanations, and avoidance of medical jargon are two practical suggestions. Flexibility and patience, as well as seeking convenient and user-friendly alternatives in treatment implementation, are critical.

Psychiatrically Impaired

The treatment of psychiatrically disturbed patients presents significant challenges to primary care providers who depend very much upon the severity of the condition. A thorough understanding of the patient's condition and associated symptoms are, therefore, important to understand. Symptoms associated with conditions such as depression, paranoia, hallucinations, and delusions may undermine the extent to which patients are willing to engage in adherent behavior. Coordination of care with other mental health professionals would be important here.

Clinical Pearls of Wisdom for Practitioners

1. Consider nonadherence a possible focus of attention whenever patients are struggling with any medical problem.
2. View nonadherence as a problem to be formally assessed, conceptualized, and treated.

3. Conduct a comprehensive assessment of factors associated with nonadherence, incorporating factors related to the patient, patient's home environment, physician, disorder, medical regimen, and treatment setting, and address those factors that are most likely to be affecting the patient's inability to adhere.
4. Identify key target behaviors, broadly defined, for intervention.
5. Employ a combination of subjective and objective measures to ensure reliability, validity, and convenience of data collection.
6. Obtain relevant data on nonadherence at baseline, during treatment, and follow-up.
7. Include the patient and physician in the development of the problem formulation, share the formulation with each of them, and adjust it to ensure accuracy based on their feedback.
8. Use multiple cognitive, behavioral, and educational methods of intervention, especially those for which empirical evidence exists.
9. Select and implement empirically supported strategies that are the most relevant interventions in the given situation.
10. Integrate treatment strategies with the PCP while developing and implementing a system for monitoring change on variables of relevance.

References

Ajzen, I., & Fishbein, M. (1980). *Understanding attitudes and predicting social behaviour.* Englewood Cliffs, NJ: Prentice-Hall.

American Heart Association. (2009, March 23). *Statistics you need to know.* Retrieved September 4, 2009, from http://www.americanheart.org/presenter.jhtml?identifier=107

American Psychiatric Association. (2000). *Diagnostic and statistical manual of mental disorders* (4th ed., text rev.). Washington, DC: Author.

Bandura, A. (1986). *Social foundations of thought and action: A social cognitive theory.* Englewood Cliffs, NJ: Prentice-Hall.

Barron, J., Wahl, P., Fisher, M., & Plauschinat, C. (2008). Effect of prescription copayments on adherence and treatment failure with oral antidiabetic medications. *Pharmacy and Therapeutics, 33*(9), 532–540.

Bedell, S. E., Jabbour, S., Goldberg, R., Glaser, H., Gobble, S., Young-Xu, Y., et al. (2000). Discrepancies in the use of medications: Their extent and predictors in an outpatient practice. *Archives of Internal Medicine, 160,* 2129–2134.

Belar, C. D., & Deardorff, W. W. (2009). *Clinical health psychology in medical settings: A practitioner's guidebook* (2nd ed.). Washington, DC: American Psychological Association.

Berlant, N. E. & Pruitt, S. D. (2003). Adherence to medical recommendations. In L. M. Cohen, D. E. McChargue, & F. L. Collins, Jr. (Eds.), *The health psychology handbook: Practical issues for the behavioural medicine specialist* (pp. 208–223). Thousand Oaks, CA: Sage.

Brownell, K. D. (2004). *The LEARN program for weight management* (10th ed.). Dallas, TX: American Health Publishing.

Brownell, K. D., & Wadden, T. A.(2000). Obesity. In B. J. Sadock & V. A. Sadock (Eds.), *Comprehensive textbook of psychiatry* (7th ed., pp. 1787–1797). Philadelphia: Lippincott, Williams, & Wilkins.

Burke, L. E., & Dunbar-Jacob, J. M. (1995). Adherence to medication, diet, and activity recommendation: From assessment to maintenance. *Journal of Cardiovascular Nursing, 9*(2), 62–79.

Burke, L. E., Dunbar-Jacob, J. M., & Hill, M. N. (1997). Compliance with cardiovascular disease prevention strategies: A review of the research. *Annals of Behavioral Medicine, 19*(3), 239–263.

Carter, W. B. (1990). Health behavior as a rational process: Theory of reasoned action and multiattribute utility theory. In K. Glanz, M. Frances, & B. K. Rimer (Eds.), *Health behavior and health education: Theory, research, and practice* (pp. 63–91). San Francisco, CA: Jossey-Bass.

Crepaz, N., Passin, W. F., Herbst, J. H., Rama, S. M., Malow, R. M., Purcell, D. W., et al. (2008). Meta-analysis of cognitive-behavioral interventions on HIV-positive persons' mental health and immune functioning. *Health Psychology, 27,* 4–14.

DiMatteo, M. R. (2004). Social support and patient adherence to medical treatment: A meta-analysis. *Health Psychology, 23*(2), 207–218.

DiMatteo, M. R., Haskard, K. B., & Williams, S. L. (2007). Health beliefs, disease severity, and patient adherence: A meta-analysis. *Medical Care, 45*(6), 521–528.

DiMatteo, M. R., Lepper, H. S., & Croghan, T. W. (2000). Depression is a risk factor for noncompliance with medical treatment. *Archives of Internal Medicine, 160*, 2101–2107.

DiTomasso, R. A., & Esposito, C. (2005). Primary care therapy. In A. Freeman, S. H. Felgoise, A. M. Nezu, C. M. Nezu, & M. A. Reinecke (Eds.), *International encyclopedia of cognitive and behavioral therapies* (pp. 295–297). New York: Springer Publishing Company.

DiTomasso, R. A., & Gilman, R. (2005). Behavioral assessment. In A. Freeman, S. H. Felgoise, A. M. Nezu, C. M. Nezu, & M. A. Reinecke (Eds.), *International encyclopedia of cognitive and behavioral therapies* (pp. 61–65). New York: Springer Publishing Company.

Dunbar, J. M., & Agras, W. S. (1980). Compliance in medical instructions. In J. M. Ferguson & C. B. Taylor (Eds.), *Comprehensive handbook of behavioural medicine*. New York: Spectrum.

Dunbar-Jacob, J., Dwyer, K., & Dunning, E. J. (1991). Compliance with antihypertensive regimen: A review of the research in the 1980s. *Annals of Behavioral Medicine, 13*, 31–39.

Fadiman, A. (1997). *The spirit catches you and you fall down: A Hmong child, her American doctors, and the collision of two cultures*. New York: Farrar, Straus, Giroux.

Fisher, J. D., & Fisher, W. A. (1992). Changing AIDS-risk behavior. *Psychological Bulletin, 111*(3), 455–474.

Glanz, K., Lewis, F. M., & Rimer, B. K. (1990). *Health behavior and health education: Theory, research, and practice*. San Francisco: Jossey-Bass.

Haynes, R. B., Ackloo, E., Sahota, N., McDonald, H. P., & Yao, X. (2008). Interventions for enhancing medication adherence. *Cochrane Database of Systematic Reviews, 2*, 1–129.

Hughes, C. M. (2004). Medication non-adherence in the elderly: How big is the problem? *Drugs and Aging, 21*(12), 793–811.

The Institute for the Future. (2000). *Health and health care 2010: The forecast, the challenge*. San Francisco: Jossey-Bass.

Kim, E., Han, H., Jeong, S., Kim, K., Park, H., Kang, E., et al. (2007). Does knowledge matter? Intentional medication nonadherence among middle-aged Korean Americans with high blood pressure. *Journal of Cardiovascular Nursing, 22*(5), 397–404.

Leahy, R. L. (2003). *Cognitive therapy techniques: A practitioner's guide*. New York: Guilford.

LeRoux, H., & Fisher, J. E. (2006). Strategies for enhancing medication adherence in the elderly. In W. O'Donohue & E. R. Levensky (Eds.), *Handbook of treatment adherence* (pp. 353–362). New York: John Wiley.

Madden, J. M., Graves, A. J., Zhang, F., Adams, A. S., Briesacher, B. A., Ross-Degnan, D., et al. (2008). Cost-related medication nonadherence and spending on basic needs following implementation of Medicare Part D. *Journal of the American Medical Association, 299*(16), 1922–1928.

Maddux, J. E., & Rogers, R. W. (1983). Protection motivation theory and self-efficacy: A revised theory of fear appeals and attitude change. *Journal of Experimental Social Psychology, 19*, 469–479.

Magai, C., Consedine, N., Neugut, A. I., & Hershman, D. L. (2007). Common psychosocial factors underlying breast cancer screening and breast cancer treatment adherence: A conceptual review and synthesis. *Journal of Women's Health, 16*(1), 11–23.

McCarthy, R. (1998). The price you pay for the drug not taken. *Business and Health, 16*(10), 27–33.

McQuaid, E. L. (2008). Commentary: Integrating lessons from evidence-based assessment of adherence into clinical practice. *Journal of Pediatric Psychology, 33*(9), 937–938.

Meichenbaum, D., & Turk, D. C. (1987). *Facilitating treatment adherence: A practitioner's guidebook*. New York: Plenum Press.

Morisky, D. E., Green, L. W., & Levine, D. M. (1986) Concurrent and predictive validity of a self-report measure of medication adherence. *Medical Care, 24*(1), 67–74.

National Heart, Lung, and Blood Institute. (1998). *Behavioral research in cardiovascular, lung, and blood health and disease*. Washington, DC: U.S. Department of Health and Human Services.

Patel, U. D., & Davis, M. M. (2006). Physicians' attitudes and practices regarding adherence to medical regimens by patients with chronic illness. *Clinical Pediatrics, 45*(5), 439–445.

Persons, J. B. (1989). *Cognitive therapy in practice: A case formulation approach*. New York: W. W. Norton.

Proachaska, J., Norcross, J., & DiClemente, C. (1994). *Changing for good*. New York: William Morrow.

Rakic, V., Burke, V., & Lawrence, J. B. (1999). Effects of coffee on ambulatory blood pressure in older men and women. *Hypertension, 33*, 869–873.

Rodriguez-Gomez, J. R., & Salas-Serrano, C. S. (2006). Treatment adherence in ethnic minorities: Particularities and alternatives. In W. T. O'Donohue & E. R. Levensky (Eds.), *Promoting treatment adherence: A practical handbook for health care providers*. Thousand Oaks, CA: Sage.

Rollnick, S., Miller, W. R., & Butler, C. C. (2008). *Motivational interviewing in health care: Helping patients change behavior.* New York: Guilford.

Rosenstock, I. M. (1990). The health belief model: Explaining health behavior through expectancies. In K. Glanz, F. M. Lewis, & B. K. Rimer (Eds.), *Health behavior and health education: Theory, research, and practice* (pp. 41–59). San Francisco: Jossey-Bass.

Roter, D., Hall, J., Merisca, R., Nordstrom, B., Cretin, D., & Svarstad, B. (1998). *Effectiveness of interventions to improve patient compliance: A meta-analysis. Medical Care, 36*(8), 1138–1161.

Sperry, L. (2009). *Treatment of chronic medical conditions: Cognitive-behavioral therapy strategies and integrative treatment protocols.* Washington, DC: American Psychological Association.

Stilley, C. S., Sereika, S., Muldoon, M. F., Ryan, C. M., & Dunbar-Jacob, J. (2004). Psychological and cognitive function: Predictors of adherence with cholesterol lowering treatment. *Annals of Behavioral Medicine, 27*(2), 117–124.

Toyoshima, H., Takahashi, K., & Akera, T. (1997) The impact of side effects on hypertension management: A Japanese survey. *Clinical Therapeutics, 19,* 1458–1469.

Triandis, H. C. (1997). Cross-cultural perspectives on personality. In R. Hogan, J. Johnson, & S. Briggs (Eds.), *Handbook of personality psychology* (pp. 439–464). San Diego, CA: Academic Press.

Van Servellen, G., Chang, B., Garcia, L., & Lombardi, E. (2002). Individual and system level factors associated with treatment nonadherence in human immunodeficiency virus-infected men and women. *AIDS Patient Care and STDs, 16*(6), 269–281.

Vik, S. A., Hogan, D. B., Patten, S. B., Johnson, J. A., Romonko-Slack, L., & Maxwell, C. J. (2006). Medication nonadherence and subsequent risk of hospitalization and mortality among older adults. *Drugs and Aging, 23*(4), 345–356.

Weber, R., Christen, L., Christen, S., Tschopp, S., Znoj, H., Schneider, C., et al. (2004). Effect of individual cognitive behaviour intervention on adherence to antiretroviral therapy: Prospective randomized trial. *Antiviral Therapy, 9,* 85–95.

Weiner, B. (1988). Attribution theory and attributional therapy: Some theoretical observation and suggestions. *British Journal of Clinical Psychology, 64*(4), 815–835.

Williams, B. C. (2003). Acute-on-chronic care: A new framework for medical education. *Journal of General Internal Medicine, 18*(1), 126–127.

Wroe, A. L. (2002). Intentional and unintentional nonadherence: A study of decision making. *Journal of Behavioral Medicine, 25*(4), 355–372.

15 Problematic Lifestyle Habits

Stephen D. Anton
Kimberly A. Hand
Michael G. Perri

Introduction

In the introduction to the 1979 Surgeon General's Report on Health Promotion and Disease Prevention, Secretary of Health, Education, and Welfare, Joseph Califano, stated "We are killing ourselves by our careless habits. We are killing ourselves by carelessly polluting the environment. We are killing ourselves by permitting harmful social conditions to persist—conditions like poverty, hunger, and ignorance" (U.S. Department of Health, Education, and Welfare, 1979, pp. 1–9). Unfortunately, this message remains as true in 2009 as it was approximately three decades ago. This message may be amplified today because we now have overwhelming evidence that the leading causes of death are directly related to our lifestyle and health behaviors, including tobacco use, dietary intake, physical activity (or inactivity), alcohol consumption, recreational drug use, and sexual behavior (Mokdad, Marks, Stroup, & Gerberding, 2004). For example, in the recently published 25-year update of the Multiple Risk Factor Intervention Trial (MRFIT) (Stamler & Neaton, 2008), a large-scale trial designed to evaluate the effect of a multiple risk factor intervention on mortality from coronary heart disease among middle-age males, Stamler and colleagues state, "The first and foremost of the crucial disturbances (in culture) producing epidemic rates of major coronary heart disease is population-wide adverse dietary patterns, along with cigarette smoking and sedentary lifestyle at work and leisure" (p. 1344).

Today's health threats stand in sharp contrast to the major health challenges of our past, which were primarily infectious and communicable diseases. Appropriately, the focus of past medical approaches was on identification and application of specific treatments for particular diagnoses. Whereas these approaches are very effective in managing infectious and communicable diseases, they are less effective at modifying maladaptive lifestyle behaviors and health habits. Because lifestyle habits are now recognized to have a central role in affecting the health status of every individual, the effectiveness of future treatments may greatly depend on the extent to which patients actively participate in improving their health status by changing their health habits. Although it may be disheartening to realize that our behaviors are directly contributing to today's health problems, it can also be empowering to know that we can significantly improve the health of our patients (and society at large) by encouraging them to engage in healthy lifestyle habits.

Advances in health care over the past few decades, particularly in the area of behavioral medicine, have demonstrated the important role that correctly administered behavioral health treatments can have in improving patients' health and quality of life (Smith, Kendall, & Keefe, 2002). Numerous studies document health improvements when patients follow lifestyle changes recommended in behavioral health interventions (e.g., reductions in dietary intake, increased physical activity, smoking cessation [Cutler & Miller, 2005]). Unfortunately, the majority of patients have difficulty making and sustaining healthy behavior changes. Rates of nonadherence to chronic illness treatment regimens have been reported to be as high as 30–60%, and up to 50–80% for preventive regimens (Christensen, 2004). Findings from the behavioral-therapy literature also suggest most individuals have difficulty maintaining healthy behavior changes, with reports of premature drop-out ranging from 30–60% (Garfield, 1994; Reis & Brown, 1999).

The costs of poor adherence are substantial and can dramatically reduce the effectiveness of treatment, as well as result in no change, or even worsening of health problems (Christensen, 2004; Cleemput, Kesteloot, & DeGeest, 2002). Hundreds of studies now indicate that sustained behavior change, particularly in lifestyle habits, including dietary intake, physical activity, and/or smoking, is very challenging for most individuals. Thus, most patients who desire to make healthy behavior changes will need assistance in initiating and maintaining these changes. Health care professionals can play a key role in facilitating these behavior changes, provided they have training in behavior modification and knowledge about the role that lifestyle behavior can have in contributing to health and disease. In response to this need, and to the recognition of the important role that behavioral and psychosocial factors have in contributing to today's chronic disease conditions, the field of health psychology emerged as a specialty area of clinical psychology in the 1970s.

Health psychology is defined as the application of the discipline of psychology to the promotion and maintenance of health, prevention, and treatment of diseases, and identification of etiological factors for disease and dysfunction (Matarazzo, 1980). In contrast to more biologically oriented approaches, the field of health psychology recognizes the important contribution that behavioral and psychosocial factors make in health and disease. Professionals in this specialty have made substantial contributions to the development and application of psychological and behavioral interventions for reducing disease risk, preventing disease, and encouraging disease management and treatment. Health psychology's advancements in the understanding of health and illness have come through basic and clinical research, education, and service. At the national level, the Division of Health Psychology of the American Psychological Association (APA Division 38) works toward establishing liaisons between legislators, researchers, and clinicians to ensure access to health psychologists as part of quality health care. Because of these efforts, health psychologists have become integrated into an extensive and diverse range of medical care over the past 30 years, including primary care programs, inpatient medical units, and specialized health care programs such as pain management, rehabilitation, women's health, oncology, smoking cessation, and headache management. Although health psychologists are specifically trained to assist individuals in modifying their behavior to promote health and reduce disease, many types of health care providers can be trained to assist patients in changing their health behaviors.

The purpose of this chapter is to provide an overview of the incidence and clinical manifestations of three specific lifestyle behaviors (excessive caloric intake, physical inactivity, and tobacco use) that are known to contribute to chronic health conditions (CHCs), as well as discuss potential treatments deliverable in a primary care setting that may assist patients in modifying their behavior. We will also review potential obstacles to treatment, points of collaboration with physicians, and considerations that apply to special populations. It is our hope that this chapter will provide physicians and other health care professionals with a general overview of the important role that lifestyle behaviors may have in affecting their patients' health status, as well as the important role they can have in improving their patients' health by encouraging healthy lifestyle changes.

Assessment and Diagnostic Issues

In line with the field of health psychology, a new model for understanding the etiology and maintenance of disease conditions was proposed in the mid-1970s, and was termed the biopsychosocial model (Engel, 1977; Schwartz, 1982). As opposed to the traditional medical or biomedical model, which proposes that disease processes can be explained by underlying deviations in normal physiological function, the biopsychosocial model recognizes the contribution of physiological, psychological, and social factors in the etiology and maintenance of chronic disease conditions. The biopsychosocial model thus expands upon the biomedical model by recognizing the contributions of physiological, psychological, and social factors (as well as their interactions) in affecting disease risk and treatment.

An important implication of the biopsychosocial model is that psychological, behavioral, and social factors (including environmental conditions) are viewed as having a significant role in affecting an individual's health status. A number of studies support the biopsychosocial model of health and disease, as well as its potential application to behavioral health interventions. With respect to psychological factors, for example, it has been reported that chronic depression is associated with twice the risk of death among women infected with HIV (Ickovics et al., 2001). Depression has also been found to increase mortality risk among individuals diagnosed with cardiovascular disease (CVD) (Ferketich, Schwartzbaum, Frid, & Moeschberger, 2000), the number-one cause of death in America. Abundant evidence implicates specific lifestyle behaviors, particularly excessive caloric intake, physical inactivity, and tobacco use, as having a central role in affecting health and disease (Prasad & Das, 2009). Social factors, such as perceived positive or negative social support, have also been found to play a key role in affecting an individual's quality of life, mood state, and ability to adhere to an intervention (Coyne & Downey, 1991). Additionally, a number of studies have demonstrated the significant role that environmental conditions can have in affecting an individual's health behavior, particularly engagement in physical activity (Taylor, Repetti, & Seeman, 1997).

In line with the biopsychosocial model, health care professionals should attempt to understand their patients' motivations, their decision-making processes, and the antecedents and consequences of particular behaviors. Because almost all medical and preventive health treatments require some degree of behavior change, health care professionals need to understand the reasons patients choose to engage in specific behaviors (e.g., tobacco use) known to increase risk for chronic disease. This can be a challenging process and requires full cooperation from the patient in exploring topics that may be difficult to discuss. Therefore, health care providers should view patients as active collaborators, rather than passive recipients, in determining the best path toward improving their health.

In the section that follows, we review the role that three specific lifestyle behaviors (i.e., excessive caloric intake, physical inactivity, and tobacco use) have in affecting health and disease processes, as well as the prevalence and economic consequences of these lifestyle behaviors.

Incidence and Clinical Manifestations

Tobacco Use

Prevalence of Tobacco Use

The most recent data indicate that almost 20% of adults in the United States are smokers, with the highest rates among men, working-class adults, and those with less income and formal education. In terms of ethnic differences, among American Indians/Native Alaskans smoking prevalence (36.4%) is higher than in both Caucasians and African Americans (21.4 and 19.8%, respectively); Asians have the lowest prevalence at 9.6% (Center for Disease Control and Prevention, 2008a). Most smokers begin at a young age; 82% of current adult smokers began smoking before the age of 18, and very few individuals begin smoking after the age of 25 (Centers for Disease Control and Prevention, 1994). Young adults between the ages of 18 and 25 are estimated to have the highest rate of current use of tobacco products at 44.3% (Centers for Disease Control and Prevention, 2008a). Campaigns designed to educate the public about the negative health outcomes of smoking and to encourage quitting have apparently made some impact, because almost half of adult smokers attempt to quit each year. Only 4–7% of attempted quitters are likely to be successful, however (Centers for Disease Control and Prevention,

2008a), providing evidence for the challenge involved in terminating this powerful addiction.

Incidence and Clinical Manifestations of Tobacco Use

Each day, approximately 3600 youth between the ages of 12 and 17 years initiate cigarette smoking in the United States, and an estimated 1100 youth become daily cigarette smokers (Centers for Disease Control and Prevention, 2008b). If a patient is suspected of smoking or tobacco use because of smell, cough, shortness of breath, sore throat, or other clinical manifestations of tobacco use, certain screening measures should be taken to properly diagnose potential tobacco use. Clinical screening should begin with a brief smoking history; questions involving current usage, how long the patient has smoked, and whether he or she has ever tried to quit (Babor, Sciamanna, & Pronk, 2004). Self-report measures are reasonably accurate, and physicians should be aware of multiple self-report tests available to diagnose the level of nicotine dependence. These include the Heaviness of Smoking Index, which measures the number of cigarettes smoked per day and the time between waking and the first cigarette of the day to assess heaviness of smoking (Heatherton, Kozlowski, Frecker, Rickert, & Robinson, 1989), and the Fagerstrom Test for Nicotine Dependence (FTND) (Heatherton, Kozlowski, Frecker, & Fagerstrom, 1991; Heatherton et al.). The FTND, one of the most widely used scales for the measurement of nicotine dependence, is a six-item self-report questionnaire assessing various components of smoking behavior, including an estimate of daily intake, difficulty in refraining, and other aspects related to the pattern of intake, in order to measure physiological dependence on nicotine (Heatherton et al., 1991; Heatherton et al., 1989). If denial of nicotine use is suspected, there are several biochemical options to diagnose tobacco use, such as cotinine in saliva and carbon monoxide levels, although self-report measures are generally less expensive and more accurate (Babor et al., 2004).

Health and Economic Consequences of Tobacco Use

The relationship between tobacco use and CVD, chronic obstructive pulmonary disease (COPD), and cancer is well documented. Tobacco use accelerates the progression of CVD, the current leading cause of death in the United States, and increases the odds of a myocardial infarction by three times (Teo et al., 2006). An estimated 30% of total cancer deaths, the second leading cause of death in the United States, including 87% of lung cancer deaths, are attributable to tobacco use (Stewart et al., 2008). Tobacco use is also estimated to be responsible for at least 75% of COPD deaths, a significant number, considering that in 2005, approximately 1 in 20 deaths in the United States had COPD as the underlying cause (Centers for Disease Control and Prevention, 2008c). Recently, studies have also shown a causal relationship between smoking and the development and severity of type 2 diabetes (Radzeviciene & Ostrauskas, 2009), a disease that is reaching epidemic proportions in our society (Koplan & Dietz, 1999; Koplan, Thacker, & Lezin, 1999; Mokdad et al., 1999). Cigarette smoking and tobacco use also increase the risk of infectious diseases including severe influenza, invasive pneumococcal disease, and tuberculosis (Benowitz, 2008). Moreover, the economic costs of nicotine use are astounding. Cigarette smoking in the United States results in an estimated $193 billion in direct health care expenditures and productivity losses each year (Centers for Disease Control and Prevention, 2008e).

Health Benefits of Tobacco Use Cessation

Smoking or tobacco use cessation provides substantial and immediate health and economic benefits across the lifespan, even after 50 years of smoking (Orleans, 2007). Health improvements following smoking cessation occur within a few weeks, and include improved pulmonary function and aerobic tolerance (Anthonisen, Connett, & Murray, 2002). After a year of sustained cessation, the risk of CVD drops to half that of smokers, and within 15 years, it falls to the rate of lifetime nonsmokers (Anthonisen, Connett, Enright, & Manfreda, 2002). The rate of stroke declines in a similar manner (Anthonisen, Connett, Enright, et al.). Smokers of any age benefit from quitting; even smokers who quit at age 65 are estimated to gain up to 4 additional years of life (Ebbert, Burke, Hays, & Hurt, 2009). In addition to increased lifespan, health-related quality of life is improved; for example, patients who have stopped smoking have been found to have greater aerobic capacity and an enhanced ability to complete the daily activities of life (Anthonisen, Connett, Enright, et al., 2002). Because smoking initiation rarely occurs at later ages, the critical time for prevention occurs in adolescence and early adulthood. Given the large number of individuals who begin smoking before the age of 18, primary prevention efforts targeted toward youth could provide an effective intervention for this major public health concern and expense. Encouragingly, new treatments have been reported to have higher success rates than previous methods (Ebbert et al., 2009), which supports the importance of regular assessment of tobacco use.

Physical Inactivity

Prevalence of Physical Inactivity

The 2008 Physical Activity Guidelines for Americans ("Physical Activity Guidelines," 2008) suggest that adults should engage in at least 150 minutes (2 hours and 30 minutes) per week of moderate intensity aerobic activity (i.e., brisk walking), or 75 minutes (1 hour and 15 minutes) of vigorous intensity aerobic activity (i.e., jogging or running), as well as muscle-strengthening activities on 2 or more days a week. For additional and more extensive health benefits, the most recent guidelines recommend adults increase their moderate intensity aerobic physical activity to 300 minutes (5 hours) or engage in 150 minutes (2 hours and 30 minutes) a week of vigorous intensity aerobic physical activity. The guidelines also state that additional health benefits are gained by engaging in physical activity beyond this amount. Unfortunately, physical inactivity is currently the most common behavioral risk factor in the United States, as the majority of individuals do not engage in even the minimum physical activity recommendations, and there is a trend of less activity as individuals age through life (Centers for Disease Control and Prevention, 2003a, 2003b; Pleis, Schiller, & Benson, 2003). According to the most recent report by the Centers for Disease Control and Prevention (2008d), approximately 40% of adults engage in no leisure-time physical activity. The vast decrease of physical activity in our lifestyles is likely attributable to an increase in the use of mechanized transportation, as well as other technological advances that have greatly lessened the need for physical labor (Ludwig & Pollack, 2009). These technological advances have made it possible for physical activity to no longer be naturally part of many people's lifestyles. Rather, many people now have to volitionally schedule exercise or planned physical activity into their daily routine to engage in physical activity.

Incidence and Clinical Manifestations of Physical Inactivity

The percentage of high school students who engage in vigorous intensity physical activity declines with age (Pratt, Macera, & Blanton, 1999). Similarly, older adults tend to be less active than younger adults (Pratt et al.). Potential clinical manifestations of physical inactivity include obesity, reported shortness of breath upon mild exertion, high blood pressure, or high resting heart rate. When seeing patients with any of these conditions, physicians should inquire about the amount of physical activity they are currently engaged in. Many self-report measures may be clinically useful, such as the International Physical Activity Questionnaire, which has shown a high degree of validity, based on a reliability and validity study conducted by 14 centers in 12 countries, and is easily accessible online (http://www.ipaq.ki.se/ipaq.htm; Craig et al., 2003). More objective measures of physical activity levels that are relatively low cost include step counters, accelerometers, and treadmill fitness tests (Babor et al., 2004).

Health and Economic Consequences of Physical Inactivity

A sedentary lifestyle doubles the risk of developing coronary artery disease, and has been identified as one of the most important modifiable risk factors for cardiovascular morbidity and mortality (Prasad & Das, 2009). Physical inactivity is also known to increase the risk of developing Type 2 diabetes mellitus (Hayes & Kriska, 2008). Obesity is a growing problem in our society, and physical inactivity is a major contributor to this epidemic. Moreover, both obesity and physical inactivity may increase insulin resistance and metabolic risk through pathways that are partially independent (Ingelsson et al., 2009). In 2000, physical inactivity and poor dietary intake combined were responsible for 16.6% of the deaths in America (Mokdad et al., 2004). The annual cost directly attributable to physical inactivity in the United States is an estimated \$24 billion–\$76 billion, or 2.4–5.0% of national health care expenditures (Fine, Philogene, Gramling, Coups, & Sinha, 2004).

Health Benefits of Physical Activity

Engagement in regular physical activity leads to improvements in many of the established risk factors for CVD (Thompson et al., 2003; Thompson & Lim, 2003). Specifically, physical activity has been shown to reduce blood pressure, serum triglycerides, LDL and total cholesterol, and glucose intolerance, as well as to increase insulin sensitivity and HDL cholesterol (Thompson et al.). It is well known that more active individuals tend to develop less CVD than their sedentary counterparts. If CVD does develop in active or fit individuals, it occurs at a later age and tends to be less severe (U.S. Public Health Service, 1996). Regular physical activity also leads to improvements in muscular function and strength, as well as enhanced aerobic capacity, leading to overall better physical functioning (Hornig, Maier, & Drexler, 1996). These changes typically improve quality of life for most people, and increase self-confidence, lower stress, and decrease anxiety (Myers, Atwood, & Froelicher, 2003).

Excessive Caloric Intake

Prevalence of Excessive Caloric Intake

Epidemiological studies indicate that per-capita energy intake increased by approximately 300 kcal per day from 1985 to 2000, after having remained fairly constant for the previous 75 years (Finkelstein, Ruhm, & Kosa, 2005). Assuming energy expenditure remained constant during this time, this increase in caloric intake would be expected to lead to a 2- to 3-pound weight gain per month. In line with this, secular trend data suggest that weight tends to increase with age in young and middle-aged adults (Lewis et al., 2000). Factors contributing to the increased energy intake during the past 30 years include a larger percentage of meals being consumed outside the home (particularly in the form of fast food), larger portion sizes of foods and beverages, and an increased consumption of sweetened beverages (Briefel & Johnson, 2004).

Incidence and Clinical Manifestations of Excessive Caloric Intake

Potential clinical manifestations of excessive caloric intake include obesity, high levels of serum LDL and total cholesterol, high levels of serum triglycerides, and high blood pressure. When seeing patients with any of these conditions, physicians and other health care professionals should inquire about the type of diet the patient is following. Many screening measures have been designed to detect specific unhealthy eating patterns and dietary habits (Babor et al., 2004; Briefel & Johnson, 2004). Although no single measure will be acceptable for all clinical uses, self-report scales, such as the *W*eight, *A*ctivity, *V*ariety, and *E*xcess (WAVE) and The Rapid Eating and Activity Assessment for Patients (REAP), may be clinically useful tools. The WAVE is designed to numerically evaluate and provide feedback to patients about their caloric intake and caloric expenditure. The REAP is a brief questionnaire that can evaluate both dietary intake and physical activity levels (Gans et al., 2003). Both the REAP and the WAVE are accompanied by a Physician Key to help facilitate nutrition assessment and counseling in the provider's office. If a more objective measure of dietary intake is desired, serum cholesterol is reasonably accurate in predicting intake of saturated fat and dietary cholesterol (Kendall & Jenkins, 2004).

Health and Economic Consequences of Excessive Caloric Intake

Dietary intake is a major factor influencing patients' health, because it contributes to metabolic disease conditions (e.g., obesity and type 2 diabetes) and other CHCs, such as CVD and cancer (Frazao, 1999). A number of alarming health trends may be linked to dietary intake. For example, the dramatic increase in the rates of obesity and type 2 diabetes during the past few decades appears to be strongly related to increases in caloric intake during this time period (Briefel & Johnson, 2004). These two socially predominant health conditions, in turn, lead to a plethora of other health concerns, causing substantial amounts of unnecessary disability, medical expenses, lost work, and premature deaths (Briefel & Johnson). Moreover, a number of risk factors for CVD, the number-one cause of death in the United States, can be modified through changes in dietary intake, including high blood cholesterol levels, diabetes, overweight, and hypertension (Frazao, 1999). The United States Department of Agriculture has estimated that the total economic cost related to poor diets, concerning conditions related to obesity and type 2 diabetes only, is $70.9 billion dollars a year (Frazao). As the prevalence of overweight and obesity continues to rise in children and adolescents, the chronic diseases that traditionally occur in middle-aged and older adults may begin to appear at an earlier age, an outcome that would likely significantly increase medical costs.

Health Benefits of a Calorically Balanced Diet

For overweight individuals, weight reduction produces a number of health benefits. Reductions in caloric intake can have beneficial effects on established risk factors for CVD, including high blood cholesterol levels, diabetes, overweight, and hypertension. It has been estimated that half of type 2 diabetes cases could be prevented by healthy weight-management practices (Ripsin, Kang, & Urban, 2009). Moreover, studies have also shown a strong relationship between total caloric intake with elevated cholesterol levels and the development of depression (Bonnet et al., 2005). Because it has been estimated that 8.5% of the population is taking antidepressants (Stagnitti, 2008), many of which can cause severe unwanted side effects, it may be advantageous for health care professionals to explore the effectiveness of dietary modifications before prescribing drugs. Beyond the potential health benefits of reducing dietary intake for overweight and obese individuals, studies have demonstrated a strong protective effect of an increased intake of antioxidants and folic acid, both of which are found in many fruits and vegetables, on the risk of developing CVD (Plotnick, Corretti, & Vogel, 1997; Riddell, Chisholm, Williams, & Mann, 2000). An effective approach to reducing caloric intake and improving diet quality is increasing the consumption of fruits and vegetables (Rolls, Ello-Martin, & Tohill, 2004). Fruits and vegetables are low in energy density but high in nutrient density, and may also decrease energy intake by promoting satiety because they are high in fiber, nutrients, and water (Rolls, Roe, & Meengs, 2004).

Obesity

Although obesity is not a "behavior," lifestyle behaviors appear to be the major causal factor behind the increasing obesity epidemic. More specifically, the dramatic rise in the prevalence of obesity (defined as a body mass index [BMI] > 30 kg/m^2) during the past few decades can be directly linked to increased calorie intake combined with higher rates of physical inactivity during this time period (Hedley et al., 2004; Ludwig & Pollack, 2009). A number of factors have likely contributed to these changes in dietary and physical activity patterns, including: (a) the relative rising costs of fruits and vegetables, and the exceptionally inexpensive option of the modern fast-food meal, typically containing low-quality carbohydrates and fats, few essential nutrients, little fiber, high energy density, and poor satiety value; (b) the increased use of the automobile for transportation and rise in sedentary pastimes, particularly television watching and computer use; and (c) the increase in time spent at work and in commuting by parents, who have less time to prepare meals at home (Ludwig & Pollack, 2009). Considerable subgroup variation exist in the prevalence of obesity according to age, gender, and race/ethnicity (Sundquist, Winkleby, & Pudaric, 2001). The highest rates of obesity are observed among non-Hispanic Black women, the majority of whom (50.6%) have BMIs in excess of 30 kg/m^2. Moreover, among women older than 60 years, African Americans have a prevalence (14.0%) of extreme obesity (BMI > 40) that is nearly three times the rate for White women (5.2%) (Sundquist et al., 2001).

The rising prevalence of obesity has heightened concerns about its impact on health. Obesity has been directly linked to CVD, diabetes, hypertension, dyslipidemia, gallbladder disease, respiratory disease, osteoarthritis, and certain forms of cancer (Haslam & James, 2005). Annual deaths attributable to obesity in the United States may be in excess of 300,000 (Allison, Fontaine, Manson, Stevens, & VanItallie, 1999). Moreover, obesity-attributable costs account for 5–7% of annual health care expenditures, currently amounting to more than $100 billion per year (Finkelstein et al., 2005). The direct economic effects of obesity may be twice this figure, when missed workdays and other costs outside the medical care system are considered (Finkelstein et al.). Without significant lifestyle changes, obesity rates are likely to continue to increase among all segments of the population, which will significantly increase risk for chronic disease and health care expenditures. Thus, a major challenge for health care professionals working in primary care settings is to encourage healthy behavior change among their overweight and obese patients so as to facilitate weight loss and/or prevent further weight gain.

Summary

Research indicates that smoking remains the leading behavioral cause of mortality in the United States, but with the increasing prevalence of obesity, poor diet and physical inactivity may soon overtake tobacco use as the leading behavioral cause of death. These findings, along with growing health care costs and an aging population, argue persuasively for the need to focus on the important role behavioral factors have in contributing to CHCs commonly seen in primary care settings. Due to the large number of children and adolescents who begin smoking before the age of 18, primary prevention efforts targeted toward youth could provide the type of intervention needed to reduce this growing public health problem. In addition to the rising prevalence of tobacco use, sedentary lifestyle (or physical inactivity) has become firmly established as part of our society. The majority of the population is overweight and inactive, which dramatically increases risk for many chronic disease conditions. Treatments for many health conditions are less likely to be effective, and may even be ineffective, if patients continue to engage in unhealthy lifestyle behaviors. Thus, early prevention efforts may be critical to improving the health of many patients seen in primary care settings. According to Koplan and Dietz of the Centers for Disease Control and Prevention, "obesity, overweight, and a sedentary lifestyle are serious health issues now and will only worsen without thoughtful and scientifically based interventions that address societal and individual attitudes and behaviors and their environmental context" (Koplan & Dietz, 1999). Thus, it is urgent and important that health care professionals recognize the magnitude of these health care problems and their potential role in treating problematic lifestyle behaviors in primary care settings.

Brief Case History

Mr. Jones is a 38-year-old, married man and the father of two children. He is 6'0" tall and currently weighs 280 lbs. (BMI = 38.1, Class II obesity). Mr. Jones reported that, prior to his marriage at the age of 23, he had never experienced any weight problems and had been a very healthy and active person throughout college. He stated that neither of his parents were overweight and also described his wife as "normal" weight. He reported that he gained approximately 25 pounds within the first year of marriage. Mr. Jones attributed this weight gain primarily to lifestyle changes related to his job as a financial planner; he indicated that he became much less active and ate out much more often as a result of his long work hours. He also explained that as part of his job, he routinely takes clients out to eat; on these occasions, he often consumes alcohol and tends to eat large portions.

Mr. Jones reported that his weight has continued to increase since age 24, when he reportedly weighed 170 pounds (BMI = 23.1). He noted that in the past, he had successfully lost 30 lbs. or more on multiple occasions by reducing his portion sizes, cutting out sweets completely, and increasing his physical activity; however, he reportedly had difficulty maintaining these lifestyle changes and weight losses for more than a few months. Approximately 10 years ago, Mr. Jones indicated that he achieved his largest weight loss of approximately 60 lbs. by exercising six times per week. These gains were not maintained after 8 months, however, because of a loss of motivation to continue exercising, primarily because his exercise partners stopped going to the gym. He noted that he gradually regained the weight he previously lost after he stopped exercising. Mr. Jones stated that he has an "all or none" personality, which he believed has contributed to his difficulties with weight management. He indicated that he is currently not actively trying to lose weight and reported no regular physical activity at present.

Mr. Jones also reported that he began smoking about a pack a day at age 26 as a way to cope with increased stress levels related to marital conflict during this time. He denied use of recreational drugs, but did report regular use of alcohol. In addition to consuming alcohol when he takes clients out to lunch or dinner, Mr. Jones stated that he typically consumes six or more alcoholic drinks each weekend night. Mr. Jones reported that his wife does not smoke or drink and that his use of alcohol and cigarettes is an additional source of conflict.

Mr. Jones indicated he has attempted to quit smoking "cold turkey" on several occasions, but that he has never been able to sustain these attempts for longer than a couple of weeks.

Mr. Jones reported that he has never received professional assistance to help with smoking cessation or weight management. He indicated that he was becoming increasingly concerned about the negative effects his smoking behavior and weight are having on his health. At present, he reported experiencing a number of medical problems, including high blood pressure, high cholesterol, back and joint pain, sleep apnea, and fatigue upon mild physical exertion. At the age of 35, he was diagnosed with insulin resistance and had a BMI of 34.6. As noted above, his current BMI is 38.1, and he has been told that he is at high risk for type 2 diabetes.

Cognitive-Behavioral Case Conceptualization

The factors that can influence each patient's behaviors are highly individualized, and therefore, a case conceptualization should be performed on each patient prior to initiating any form of treatment. When conceptualizing cases, clinicians should think critically about the various psychosocial factors that may be influencing their patient's current behavioral patterns. During this time, multiple hypotheses will be generated for testing during future interactions with the patient. Thus, case conceptualization can be viewed as an ongoing, collaborative activity between the clinician and patient (Kuyken, Padesky, & Dudley, 2009), and clinicians should feel comfortable sharing their formulations with patients. The feedback they receive from patients can inform them whether they are on the right track or should revise the formulation in some way. Although case conceptualization may initially appear to be a daunting task, it is a skill that can be learned through practice and supervision from trained individuals, such as clinical/health psychologists (Kuyken et al., 2009).

Case Example Revisited

Mr. Jones is a morbidly obese man who is currently experiencing health complications related to his excess weight, including hypertension, spine and back problems, back and joint pain, sleep apnea, and fatigue. Many of these health complications are directly related to the lifestyle behaviors he has engaged in for nearly 2 decades. Mr. Jones reports that he has lost and regained weight for almost 15 years, and he has been smoking a pack of cigarettes per day for nearly all of that time. He has attempted to modify his lifestyle behaviors (i.e., dietary intake, physical activity, and tobacco use) before, but has not been able to sustain any behavior change. Mr. Jones has become increasingly concerned about the negative health consequences of his behaviors as his medical problems continue to grow in number and severity. Previous attempts at change have proven unsuccessful and it is only now, as his concerns for his health grow stronger, that he is motivated to seek professional help to make these behavioral changes.

A complex interaction of personal and environmental factors may have led Mr. Jones to begin smoking, as well as contributed to his unhealthy dietary and physical activity practices. First, Mr. Jones described himself as an "all or none" person, so he may have had difficulty balancing the demands of work and family. In an attempt to manage what he perceived as stress related to his work and marital life, Mr. Jones may have turned to smoking cigarettes, which offered an immediate and convenient coping mechanism. As with other unhealthy habits, this behavior became negatively reinforced because it allowed him to temporarily avoid possible conflict. Given his consistent smoking behavior over the past 12 years and the known addictive properties of nicotine, Mr. Jones has likely developed a true physiological addiction to cigarettes. Although Mr. Jones' thought processes and emotional experiences prior to and after smoking may have initiated his smoking behavior, additional physiological processes are likely contributing to the maintenance of this behavior. Therefore, an important component of treatment will involve structuring the intervention so as to minimize the withdrawal symptoms Mr. Jones may experience during smoking cessation. Additionally, a successful treatment program should help Mr. Jones identify alternative behaviors that he can engage in for stress reduction. For example, many forms of routine physical activity can assist with stress management. Mr. Jones would also likely benefit from engaging in marital therapy, because he reported marital conflict being a current significant source of stress. Another important treatment component would be teaching Mr. Jones how to identify and modify some of his thought processes, particularly those that initially contributed to his smoking behavior. For example, he may currently be engaging in erroneous thinking patterns, such as believing that smoking helps to reduce his stress level within his marriage and presumably in other aspects of his life.

In addition to decreasing his smoking behavior, Mr. Jones would likely benefit from engaging in healthier eating and exercise practices. Mr. Jones' recent weight gain appears to be due to his poor eating habits and lack of physical activity that he attributes to the time-demanding nature of his job. He reports eating away from the home frequently due to both his long work hours and the need to take clients out to eat. Mr. Jones' self-proclaimed "all-or-nothing" philosophy has likely contributed to his weight regain following each of his successful weight-loss attempts. He indicated that he has always lost weight by following a very strict eating and exercise regimen. For example, he stated that he exercised before work every day and only consumed very specific portion-controlled food during each of his weight-loss attempts. When he inevitably deviated from his strict routine or failed to meet his unrealistically high expectations of himself, Mr. Jones may have had negative thoughts about himself (e.g., "I'll never be able to follow a diet" or "I'm a failure"). These types of negative thoughts can result in negative emotional states (e.g., depression, apathy) and subsequently decrease his motivation to continue engaging in a strict diet and exercise routine, and ultimately lead him to return to previous eating and exercise behaviors (Elfhag & Rossner, 2005).

Development and Implementation of an Empirically Based Treatment Plan

A treatment plan for behavior modification consists of a set of individualized behavior-change strategies derived from the case conceptualization that are designed to incrementally develop and sustain desirable behaviors or to decrease the frequency of undesirable behaviors. Treatment orientation should provide the patient with a complete understanding of the purpose and goals of behavior change. It is imperative that patients understand that successful behavior modification is a lifetime endeavor that requires long-term lifestyle changes. During initial treatment consultations, health care professionals should assess the patient's current health behavior patterns and psychological factors (e.g., depression) that may be contributing to the patient's presenting problem. Also important in the initial phase of treatment development is the establishment of realistic expectations for treatment, because many individuals have unrealistic expectations with regard to weight loss and smoking cessation that need to be addressed in order to prevent early discouragement.

Behavioral skills training is specifically designed to provide individuals with a tool set to assist them in making healthy lifestyle changes such as smoking cessation, as well as behavior changes required for successful weight management. Common elements of behavioral treatment programs that have demonstrated a long-standing record of success in behaviorally oriented smoking cessation programs and lifestyle obesity treatments include the following: self-monitoring, goal setting, problem solving, stimulus control, cognitive restructuring, stress management, social support, and relapse prevention (Brownell, 2004; Knowler et al., 2002; Perri et al., 2008). This list should be thought of as a *tool set* that health care professionals can use to assist their patients in making healthy behavior changes, particularly related to dietary intake, physical activity, and smoking. Below is a brief description of these eight frequently used empirically supported behavioral components, along with practical strategies for delivering each component within the limited time constraints of a primary care setting.

Behavior-Change Strategies

Self-Monitoring

The systematic observation and recording of target behaviors (e.g., number of cigarettes smoked or days exercised) is one of the single most important tools in behavior modification (Germann, Kirschenbaum, & Rich, 2007). For example, self-monitoring of the types, amounts, and caloric amount of foods consumed increases awareness of eating habits (Pierce & Gunn, 2007).

Role of Health Care Provider

Health care providers can assist patients with self-monitoring by emphasizing the importance of record keeping and encouraging the patient to maintain consistent and detailed records.

Goal Setting

Goals are critical to the success of any behavior change program. To be effective, goals must be specific, achievable, clear, and measurable (Wing, 2002). Setting a limited number of goals can also help increase the patient's confidence that they can make desired behavior changes.

Role of Health Care Provider

Health care providers can assist patients with goal setting by encouraging patients to specify a limited number of goals, and working with patients to ensure goals are specific, clear, and attainable.

Problem Solving

Most individuals have difficulty developing effective solutions to challenges encountered while making healthy lifestyle changes. Fortunately, the ability to solve problems is a process that can be learned and easily applied to any obstacle encountered during the behavior change process (Nezu & Perri, 1989; Nezu & Ronan, 1985; Perri et al., 2001).

Role of Health Care Provider

Health care providers can directly assist patients in developing their problem-solving abilities by encouraging them to come up with potential solutions to identified problems during each office visit.

Cognitive Restructuring

Cognitive restructuring involves identifying and replacing maladaptive thought patterns with more adaptive thoughts (A. T. Beck, Rush, Shaw, & Emery, 1979; J. S. Beck, 1995). Because thoughts can influence emotional states and negative emotional states are associated with unhealthy lifestyle behaviors, negative thought patterns can lead to counterproductive behaviors through their influence on negative emotions (J. S. Beck, 1995).

Role of Health Care Provider

The health care professional can help patients identify maladaptive thinking patterns by having them describe particularly challenging situations and asking them to recall what they were thinking at this time.

Stimulus Control

Stimulus control involves identifying and modifying cues that are associated with either positive or negative health behaviors (Ferster, Nurnberger, & Levitt, 1996). For example, certain foods can be eliminated from the environment (e.g., remove high-fat, calorically dense foods from home) to remove cues for unhealthy eating.

Role of Health Care Provider

Health care providers can encourage their patients to use stimulus control techniques to reduce their smoking behavior, as well as to induce weight loss by encouraging them to limit the environments in which they engage in unhealthy lifestyle habits (e.g., restaurants, bars), as well as modify their home environment to encourage healthy lifestyle behaviors.

Stress Management

Perceived stress is positively associated with food consumption and tobacco use or smoking behavior (Greeno & Wing, 1994; Lattimore, 2001; Oliver & Wardle, 1999; Roemmich, Wright, & Epstein, 2002). Eating or smoking in response to stress may help patients feel better quickly, but in the long term, these are not effective stress-management strategies (Oliver, Wardle, & Gibson, 2000).

Role of Health Care Provider

Health care providers can assist patients with stress management by teaching them simple and quick relaxation exercises, such as diaphragmatic breathing, during office visits. Health care professionals can also encourage patients to engage in healthy stress-management activities, such as exercise, positive self-talk, and/or social support. In some circumstances, a referral to a clinical/health psychologist or other health care professional may be appropriate.

Social Support

Social support can be an important component of both weight loss and smoking cessation programs. Significant others within one's social network can either support or hinder a patient's efforts to change his/her lifestyle (Wing & Jeffery, 1999).

Role of Health Care Provider

Health care professionals can help patients identify sources of positive social support through the use of open-ended questions or statements such as "Most individuals need help when making lifestyle changes. I wonder who you think might be able to assist you if they knew you wanted to lose weight and stop smoking."

Relapse Prevention

Slips or relapses are common occurrences during both weight loss and smoking cessation (Wing, 2002). Most individuals occasionally slip or experience a relapse and temporarily return to their old habits. Therefore, it is important for patients to anticipate the occasional slip, as well as to develop a plan for getting back on track following a relapse.

Role of Health Care Provider

Health care providers should emphasize that successful lifestyle change entails long-term effort, and slips and relapses are to be expected during the change process. Ideally, patients should develop specific plans for their response before a relapse happens.

Identifying and Addressing Obstacles to Treatment

As recently described (Newton, Milsom, Nackers, & Anton, 2009), there are a number of potential barriers to implementation of the behavioral strategies discussed above in primary care settings. Three of the most salient barriers include: (a) lack of time, (b) lack of reimbursement, and (c) patient factors. In the section below, we briefly discuss ways to address these salient barriers.

Lack of Time

Although the interventions described above may be perceived to be time-consuming, recent studies have shown that behavioral interventions can be effectively administered by physicians and other health care providers with minimal training and relatively little time commitment (< 15 minutes per session; Martin et al., 2006). Because unhealthy lifestyle habits and obesity contribute to many of the health problems seen in primary care settings (Bramlage et al., 2004), we believe the time devoted to behavioral interventions will be worth the investment.

Lack of Reimbursement

A potential major challenge to delivering lifestyle-based treatments in primary care settings is lack of reimbursement for time devoted to assisting patients in modifying unhealthy lifestyle behaviors. At present, few insurance providers cover behaviorally oriented weight loss and/or smoking cessation programs when comorbid conditions are not present (Tsai, Asch, & Wadden, 2006). Thus, it is recommended health care providers working in primary care settings provide lifestyle-based treatment programs (e.g., weight loss or smoking cessation) as a means of addressing the comorbid condition, because this treatment should be covered by insurance.

Patient Factors

Many patients may feel embarrassed about their behavioral habits, and thus, may be reluctant to discuss certain behaviors with a health care provider in a primary care setting (Ruelaz et al., 2007). Health care providers can facilitate communication with patients by taking a nonjudgmental, collaborative approach toward their patients. If a patient views the health care provider as a partner who will listen to his/her challenges in a nonjudgmental manner, then the patient is much more likely to communicate in an open and honest manner. When attempting to evaluate patients' readiness for change, motivational interviewing (MI) techniques can be useful for assessing motivations and level of commitment for behavior change, as well as exploring ambivalence that patients may feel about making behavior changes (Miller & Moyers, 2002).

Overcoming Obstacles to Treatment

Mr. Jones is at increased health risk because he has three major behavioral risk factors: regular tobacco use, excessive caloric intake, and physical inactivity; a situation indicating the need for multiple foci of change. Although this situation may at first be overwhelming, it can also be encouraging, as it indicates the potential for significant health benefits to be derived from multiple behavioral changes. A common first obstacle to treatment is in determining which behavior or behaviors to focus on modifying first. Presuming Mr. Jones is sufficiently motivated, it is recommended that treatment first focus on helping him reduce his smoking behavior, because the harmful effects of tobacco are well established. Moreover, his smoking behavior may interfere with his ability to engage in other healthy lifestyle behaviors, such as physical activity. Once the initial focus of treatment has been determined, the next step is in identifying other potential obstacles that will need to be addressed to help Mr. Jones achieve a successful outcome.

When asked why he smokes cigarettes, Mr. Jones reported that he began smoking to deal with marital and work-related stress. His belief that smoking is an effective stress-management strategy has likely contributed to the maintenance of his smoking behavior for the past 12 years, as well as his relapses when he has attempted to quit smoking. A thorough evaluation of Mr. Jones' smoking habits will be critical in developing a plan for him to reduce his nicotine intake and eventually quit by systematically reducing the number of cigarettes he smokes each week. As a first step toward this goal, Mr. Jones will be asked to record each cigarette he smokes as well as rate on a scale of 1 to 10 how much he desired the cigarette and how he felt after the cigarette. This will also be useful in helping Mr. Jones in identifying thought processes that are contributing to his smoking behavior. An important treatment component will then involve teaching Mr. Jones to replace thought processes that may be contributing to his smoking behavior with more adaptive thinking patterns. Additionally, Mr. Jones will be taught alternative stress-management strategies, such as relaxation techniques and/or methods of obtaining support from significant others in his life. Finally, Mr. Jones' belief that smoking assists with stress management in his marriage could be challenged, and a referral for marital therapy may be an important component of treatment.

Another potential obstacle to treatment will be the withdrawal symptoms Mr. Jones may experience while he reduces his tobacco use. Therefore, an important component of treatment will involve structuring the intervention so as to minimize these withdrawal symptoms. To begin treatment, Mr. Jones will be asked to learn as much as possible about his smoking habits, so he can be aware of how often he desires a cigarette and his common triggers. The Fagerstrom Test for Nicotine Dependence (FTND) will be administered as a measure of physiological dependence to nicotine, and this information will help determine Mr. Jones' needs and the appropriate dosage to use when considering the option of nicotine gum or other smoking cessation aids (e.g., the patch).

In addition to smoking cessation, Mr. Jones would benefit from a behaviorally oriented weight-loss program. Once Mr. Jones feels comfortable with the behavioral changes required for smoking cessation, treatment could then focus on modification of his eating and exercise behaviors with the goal of helping him achieve a 5–10% weight loss over a 6-month period. A common obstacle to successful weight-loss treatment is unrealistic weight-loss expectations. Thus, it will be important to assess Mr. Jones's weight-loss expectations both in terms of actual weight loss, as well as the behavior changes he believes are required for weight loss. For example, studies have found that many obese individuals often expect to lose between 25–32% of their initial body weight, but reductions of this magnitude are rarely achieved in behavioral treatment programs (Foster, Wadden, Vogt, & Brewer, 1997). This mismatch between expected and actual health outcomes may lead patients to become discouraged and not fully comply, or even to stop engaging in recommended lifestyle changes (Schulman-Green, Naik, Bradley, McCorkle, & Bogardus, 2006).

To overcome this common obstacle, Mr. Jones could be educated about realistic weight-loss outcomes prior to treatment. He should be informed that he can expect to lose approximately 0.5–1 kg/wk (1–2 lbs./wk) per week by reducing his caloric intake and increasing his energy expenditure through physical activity. Specifically, Mr. Jones should be advised to reduce his energy intake by approximately 500–1000 kcal/day and increase his energy expenditure, through structured exercise and other forms of physical activity, thereby creating an energy deficit of 500–1000 kcal/day. If consistently achieved, this calorie deficit should translate to a weight loss of 1–2 lbs./week and lead to a 5–10% reduction in weight over 24 weeks. Weight losses of this magnitude are considered sufficient to improve many of the health-risk factors associated with obesity (Jakicic et al., 2001).

Another significant potential obstacle to Mr. Jones's treatment is his "all or none" personality and approach to behavior change. This style has previously generated positive short-term but poor long-term results, in regard to weight loss. To overcome this obstacle, Mr. Jones should be provided with a treatment orientation, so that he can understand the purpose and goals of weight loss. It is imperative that he understand that successful weight management is a lifetime endeavor, which requires long-term lifestyle changes. Additionally, treatment should be designed to incorporate a set of healthy, active-living principles that can be integrated more readily into his current lifestyle. Mr. Jones will be instructed to keep a record of his dietary intake, in order to better evaluate his current caloric intake, as well as any problem areas that may need to be addressed in treatment. Cognitive strategies should also be employed to elucidate Mr. Jones' maladaptive thinking patterns regarding what would happen if he were to change his dietary habits.

It is likely that Mr. Jones will have difficulty overcoming some of the obstacles or challenges that he encounters during the behavior change process. Thus, an important role of the health care provider will be to assist Mr. Jones in developing potential solutions to overcome these barriers. By exploring the challenges Mr. Jones has encountered in a collaborative, nonjudgmental manner, Mr. Jones will be more likely to be open and honest in his communication, which will help define any problems encountered as specifically as possible, as well as generate potential solutions. If possible, the health care provider should also praise any positive behavior changes, however minor, that Mr. Jones has made, because positive reinforcement will increase the likelihood he will continue to make positive behavior changes.

Evaluation of Treatment Outcomes

The evaluation of treatment outcomes should first be based on the extent to which Mr. Jones was able to successfully make and sustain healthy lifestyle changes, and then on changes (improvements) in physical markers of health. First, treatment should be considered successful if Mr. Jones was able to stop smoking and modify his eating and exercise behaviors to produce weight loss. To determine whether smoking cessation was achieved, self-report measures can be used. If denial of nicotine use is suspected, more objective measures, such as cotinine in saliva and carbon monoxide levels, can also be used (Babor et al., 2004). To assess changes in dietary intake and physical activity patterns, self-report measures can again be used; however, changes in body weight are likely the best indicator of changes in eating and exercise patterns.

Abundant evidence indicates that smoking cessation is associated with health benefits and reduced risk of disease. Additionally, the efficacy of lifestyle-based weight-loss interventions in improving risk factors for disease (e.g., blood pressure, blood glucose) has been well documented (Stevens et al., 2001). Based on these consistent findings, it is expected that Mr. Jones would derive significant health benefits from the lifestyle changes described previously. Nevertheless, physiological markers of health should also be directly measured at regular intervals, because health concerns were Mr. Jones's primary motivating factor for seeking treatment. Specifically, Mr. Jones's blood pressure, cholesterol, back and joint pain, sleep quality, and fatigue levels should be assessed to provide him with objective feedback about changes over time. If possible, a cardiopulmonary exercise test could also be administered pre- and posttreatment, using a maximal incremental treadmill protocol, as outlined by the American Thoracic Society/American College of Chest Physicians (Ross et al., 2003) to directly assess changes in aerobic capacity. The results of this test are a powerful predictor of mortality among men (Myers et al., 2002); thus, improvements in this parameter may be particularly relevant to Mr. Jones.

Points of Collaboration With Physicians

Primary care physicians (PCPs) can serve as an excellent source for delivering behavioral health interventions because they have frequent contact with patients. However, they may face certain barriers to delivering behaviorally oriented treatments, including lack of training, lack of time, and lack of reimbursement (Newton et al., 2009). Thus, it is optimal for PCPs to work in conjunction with other health care professionals, such as health psychologists, who are trained in delivering behavioral health interventions. Ideally, PCPs would have access to a multidisciplinary team that would include dieticians, exercise physiologists, nurses, and psychologists to assist patients in modifying their lifestyle or maladaptive behavioral patterns.

Research suggests that collaborative interventions delivered in primary care settings are more effective than standard care interventions. For example, a one-year interdisciplinary, collaborative practice intervention for community-dwelling older adults with chronic illnesses was found to reduce health care use rates and helped maintain health status among individuals who received this intervention (Sommers, Marton, Barbaccia, & Randolph, 2000). Of note, the hospitalization rate of participants in the control group, who received standard care, increased significantly (0.34 to 0.52) but did not increase for participants in the intervention group. After accounting for the cost of the intervention, there was a cost savings of $90 per participant, which is in addition to the costs saved from fewer office visits. In another study, patients with chronic depression were found to have better outcomes when the treatment was delivered through a collaborative care approach involving both a physician and a mental health professional than patients whose treatment was provided by a PCP alone (Katon et al., 1999). These and other studies suggest that mental health professionals and other health care providers can work collaboratively with PCPs to enhance treatments for CHCs affected by behavioral and/or psychological factors. In view of the role of the family environment in fostering negative habits, their participation in helping patients is critical.

Considerations With Special Populations

The citizens of rural areas represent one of the largest medically underserved populations in the United States (Eberhardt et al., 2001). Rural communities comprise more health professional shortage areas than nonrural areas (USDHHS, 2002). Rural counties also have higher rates of poverty (U.S. Department of Agriculture, 1993), greater percentages of patients with chronic diseases (Mainous, King, Garr, & Pearson, 2004; Patterson, Moore, Probst, & Shinogle, 2004), and higher proportions of residents without health insurance (Eberhardt et al., 2001; Frenzen, 1993; Schur & Franco, 1999). Moreover, data from the National Center for Health Statistics indicate that the nationwide death rate from ischemic heart disease is higher in rural than in urban areas (Ingram & Gillum, 1989; Murphy, 2000). For both women and men, the disparity is most pronounced in the South (Ingram & Gillum; Murphy).

The urban/rural disparity in heart disease mortality rates may be attributed to several factors, including low socioeconomic status, limited access to medical care and preventive services, and the extended distances many rural residents must travel to receive care (Brown et al., 2000; Findeis et al., 2001; U.S. Department of Agriculture, 1993; Schootman & Fuortes, 1999). Moreover, health promotion activities are often neglected in rural settings due to the need to address more pressing acute care concerns (U.S. Department of Agriculture; Schootman & Fuortes). Compared with their urban counterparts, rural populations have been slower to adopt lifestyle changes that might alter risk factors for chronic disease conditions, such as reductions in saturated fat intake, increases in physical activity, and cessation of smoking (Pearson & Lewis, 1998). Rural families traditionally have consumed high-fat, high-calorie diets (Flora, Flora, & Fey, 2004) that were offset to some extent by high caloric expenditure during the vigorous physical labor necessary for farming, logging, and other activities. Increased mechanization of rural occupations has reduced these levels of caloric expenditure, thereby contributing to higher rates of obesity in rural areas (Pearson & Lewis, 1998). In one recent study (Vitolins et al., 2007), more than half of rural older women and almost half (45%) of rural older men were found to be obese. The urban/rural differences in obesity and sedentary lifestyle appear to contribute to the geographic disparities in health (Brownson et al., 2000; Eberhardt et al., 2001). Older adults who live in rural areas have been found to consume poor diets and to have nutritional deficiencies (Vitolins et al.), as well as have a higher prevalence of CHCs (e.g., coronary artery disease) (Eberhardt et al.; Gamm, Hutchinson, Linnae, Dabney, & Dorsey, 2003; Ramsey & Glenn, 2002).

Among adults over 65 years old in both rural and urban areas, mortality is known to rise when BMI exceeds 30 (Wing, 2002). Additionally, older obese adults may be particularly susceptible to sarcopenia (i.e., the involuntary loss of skeletal muscle), and a vicious cycle between muscle loss and fat gain may act synergistically to increase their risk of physical disability (Villareal, Apovian, Kushner, & Klein, 2005). Few studies have examined the effects of behavioral weight-loss treatment in obese older adults, but the results of initial studies are encouraging. Recent trials have found that the combination of diet-induced weight loss plus exercise can improve frailty (Villareal, Banks, Sinacore, Siener, & Klein, 2006), metabolic disease risk factors (Villareal, Miller, et al., 2006), and pancreatic endocrine function (Villareal, Banks, Patterson, Polonsky, & Klein, 2008) in older obese adults (> 65 years). Other studies have found that a diet-plus-exercise intervention that induced a 10% loss in body weight maintained fat-free mass (FFM) in older obese subjects (ages 65–80), compared with a weight-stable control group (Villareal, Banks, et al., 2006). This suggests that, in older adults, regular exercise may attenuate diet-induced loss of FFM, a potential concern of weight-loss interventions conducted in older individuals.

In terms of ethnic differences, overall age-adjusted mortality from CVD is higher in African Americans than Caucasians (Gillum, 1991, 1996; Rosenberg et al., 1999). A complex interaction of cultural factors with genetic, environmental, and behavioral factors (Stamler, Stamler, & Neaton, 1993; Willett et al., 1995) likely contributes to the increased risk among African Americans. Socioeconomic factors (i.e., income and education) (Guralnik, Land, Blazer, Fillenbaum, & Branch, 1993) and access to health care (Bolen, Rhodes, Powell-Griner, Bland, & Holtzman, 2000) may also contribute to elevated risk among this population. However, health disparities cannot be solely explained by current measures of social class (Winkleby, Kraemer, Ahn, & Varady, 1998). For example, African Americans have the highest prevalence of obesity and a lower prevalence of leisure-time physical activity than other ethnic groups reported (Crespo, Smit, Andersen, Carter-Pokras, & Ainsworth, 2000). Cross-cultural differences in norms pertaining to ideal body image have also been documented, with African American women reporting a larger ideal BMI and body image than Caucasian women (Becker, Yanek, Koffman, & Bronner, 1999). Findings of variations in body image perception may partially explain the disproportionate increase in the prevalence of overweight and obesity among African Americans compared with Caucasians (Must et al., 1999).

Few data exist regarding whether perceptions of health-related factors in relation to actual measures of health-related factors vary by ethnicity and/or socioeconomic status. One recent study found African American women were less likely to perceive themselves as overweight when categorized by actual weight relative to ideal weight (Dawson, 1988). Similarly, Newton and Perri (1997) found African American women perceived themselves to be more susceptible to becoming obese, but perceived the health and psychological consequences of being obese to be less severe than Caucasian women. Another study found that although African Americans were heavier, more obese, less fit, and consumed a greater percentage of fat than Caucasian women, they perceived their weight, physical shape and appearance, physical fitness, and eating habits to be no worse than those of their White counterparts (Duncan, Anton, Newton, & Perri, 2003). Thus, the perceptions of African American women regarding their weight, fitness, and eating habits may represent barriers to change, and an improved understanding of African American patients' perceptions regarding weight control may facilitate successful lifestyle-based interventions.

Clinical Pearls of Wisdom for Practitioners

1. Many chronic diseases are directly related to an individual's health behaviors; thus, health care providers working in primary care settings should consider the potential role that lifestyle or behavior patterns have in affecting their patients' health conditions.
2. Early prevention efforts may be critical to improving the health of many patients seen in primary care settings. Thus, it is recommended that health care providers initiate behaviorally oriented interventions as early as possible, and not wait for overt signs of disease to be present before recommending healthy lifestyle changes to their patients.
3. The majority of patients will have difficulty initiating and sustaining healthy behavior changes and will, therefore, need assistance with the behavior change process. Because patients are most likely to be seen in primary care settings, it is urgent and important that health care providers working in primary care settings recognize the key role they can have in facilitating healthy behavior changes in their patients. For further reading, an excellent guide designed for PCPs regarding behavior change counseling is *Rapid Reference to Lifestyle & Behavior Change: Rapid Reference Series* by Chris Dunn and Stephen Rollnick (2003).
4. Health care providers can facilitate the behavior change process by first attempting to understand the circumstances (or perceptions) that lead their patients to engage in specific behaviors (e.g., tobacco use), and then exploring the perceived costs and benefits of behavior change. The goal is to increase the patients' motivation for behavior change by helping them recognize the importance of benefits and minimize the perceived costs of a healthy lifestyle change. For further information about these strategies, an excellent reference is *Motivational Interviewing in Health Care: Helping Patients Change Behavior*, written by Stephen Rollnick, William R. Miller, and Christopher C. Butler (2007).
5. Patients will be more likely to open up and express concerns, fears, frustrations, and problems they have encountered when health care providers approach them in a friendly, collaborative, and nonjudgmental manner, rather than a hierarchical, coercive manner. Therefore, health care providers should view patients as active collaborators, rather than passive recipients,

in determining the best path toward improving their health. In this regard, a nice guidebook to help patients follow a healthy lifestyle is *The Johns Hopkins Family Health Book*, written by Johns Hopkins University (1999).

6. Patients are more likely to be persuaded by their own arguments (i.e., what they hear themselves say) than by what their health care provider tells them to do. Thus, the role of the health care providers should be to assist patients in developing solutions to their health challenges rather than directly offering solutions. If patients are unable to come up with possible solutions, it is recommended health care providers ask the patient's permission before offering potential solutions. For further reading into how this can be achieved through the technique of MI, a classic reference is *Motivational Interviewing: Preparing People to Change Addictive Behavior*, by William R. Miller and Stephen Rollnick (1991).
7. Collaborative interventions delivered in primary care settings have been found to be more effective than standard care interventions. Therefore, it is recommended that PCPs work collaboratively with other health care providers to enhance treatments for CHCs that are affected by behavioral and/or psychological factors.

References

Allison, D. B., Fontaine, K. R., Manson, J. E., Stevens, J., & VanItallie, T. B. (1999). Annual deaths attributable to obesity in the United States. *Journal of the American Medical Association, 282*(16), 1530–1538.

Anthonisen, N. R., Connett, J. E., Enright, P. L., & Manfreda, J. (2002). Hospitalizations and mortality in the lung health study. *American Journal of Respiratory Critical Care Medicine, 166*(3), 333–339.

Anthonisen, N. R., Connett, J. E., & Murray, R. P. (2002). Smoking and lung function of lung health study participants after 11 years. *American Journal of Respiratory Critical Care Medicine, 166*(5), 675–679.

Babor, T. F., Sciamanna, C. N., & Pronk, N. P. (2004). Assessing multiple risk behaviors in primary care. Screening issues and related concepts. *American Journal of Preventive Medicine, 27*(2 Suppl.), 42–53.

Beck, A. T., Rush, A. J., Shaw, B. F., & Emery, G. (1979). *Cognitive therapy of depression.* New York: Guilford.

Beck, J. S. (1995). *Cognitive therapy: Basics and beyond.* New York: Guilford.

Becker, D. M., Yanek, L. R., Koffman, D. M., & Bronner, Y. C. (1999). Body image preferences among urban African Americans and whites from low income communities. *Ethnicity & Disease, 9*(3), 377–386.

Benowitz, N. L. (2008). Clinical pharmacology of nicotine: Implications for understanding, preventing, and treating tobacco addiction. *Clinical Pharmacology & Therapeutics, 83*(4), 531–541.

Bolen, J. C., Rhodes, L., Powell-Griner, E. E., Bland, S. D., & Holtzman, D. (2000). State-specific prevalence of selected health behaviors, by race and ethnicity—Behavioral Risk Factor Surveillance System, 1997. *MMWR CDC Surveillance Summaries, 49*(2), 1–60.

Bonnet, F., Irving, K., Terra, J. L., Nony, P., Berthezene, F., & Moulin, P. (2005). Depressive symptoms are associated with unhealthy lifestyles in hypertensive patients with the metabolic syndrome. *Journal of Hypertension, 23*(3), 611–617.

Bramlage, P., Wittchen, H. U., Pittrow, D., Kirch, W., Krause, P., Lehnert, H., et al. (2004). Recognition and management of overweight and obesity in primary care in Germany. *International Journal of Obesity and Related Metabolic Disorders, 28*(10), 1299–1308.

Briefel, R. R., & Johnson, C. L. (2004). Secular trends in dietary intake in the United States. *Annual Review of Nutrition, 24*, 401–431.

Brown, C. D., Higgins, M., Donato, K. A., Rohde, F. C., Garrison, R., Obarzanek, E., et al. (2000). Body mass index and the prevalence of hypertension and dyslipidemia. *Obesity Research, 8*(9), 605–619.

Brownell, K. D. (2004). Obesity and managed care: A role for activism and advocacy? *American Journal of Managed Care, 10*(6), 353–354.

Brownson, R. C., Eyler, A. A., King, A. C., Brown, D. R., Shyu, Y. L., & Sallis, J. F. (2000). Patterns and correlates of physical activity among US women 40 years and older. *American Journal of Public Health, 90*(2), 264–270.

Centers for Disease Control and Prevention. (1994). Preventing tobacco use among young people. A report of the Surgeon General. Executive summary. *MMWR Recommendations and Reports, 43*(RR-4), 1–10.

Centers for Disease Control and Prevention. (2003a). Physical activity levels among children aged 9-13 years—United States, 2002. *MMWR Weekly: Morbidity and Mortality Weekly Report, 52*(33), 785–788.

Centers for Disease Control and Prevention. (2003b). Prevalence of physical activity, including lifestyle activities among adults—United States, 2000-2001. *MMWR Weekly: Morbidity and Mortality Weekly Report, 52*(32), 764–769.

Centers for Disease Control and Prevention. (2007). *Best practices for comprehensive tobacco control programs—2007*. Atlanta: US Department of Health and Human Services, Centers for Disease Control and Prevention, National Center for Chronic Disease Prevention and Health Promotion, Office on Smoking and Health.

Centers for Disease Control and Prevention. (2008a). Cigarette smoking among adults—United States, 2007. *MMWR Weekly: Morbidity and Mortality Weekly Report, 57*(45), 1221–1226.

Centers for Disease Control and Prevention. (2008b). Cigarette use among high school students—United States, 1991–2007. *MMWR Weekly: Morbidity and Mortality Weekly Report, 57*(25), 686–688.

Centers for Disease Control and Prevention. (2008c). Deaths from chronic obstructive pulmonary disease—United States, 2000–2005. *MMWR Weekly: Morbidity and Mortality Weekly Report, 57*(45), 1229–1232.

Centers for Disease Control and Prevention. (2008d). Prevalence of self-reported physically active adults—United States, 2007. *MMWR Weekly: Morbidity and Mortality Weekly Report, 57*(48), 1297–1300.

Centers for Disease Control and Prevention. (2008e). Smoking-attributable mortality, years of potential life lost, and productivity losses—United States, 2000–2004. *MMWR Weekly: Morbidity and Mortality Weekly Report, 57*(45), 1226–1228.

Christensen, A. J. (2004). *Patient adherence to medical treatment regimens: Bridging the gap between behavioral science and biomedicine*. New Haven, CT: Yale University Press.

Cleemput, I., Kesteloot, K., & DeGeest, S. (2002). A review of the literature on the economics of noncompliance. Room for methodological improvement. *Health Policy, 59*(1), 65–94.

Coyne, J. C., & Downey, G. (1991). Social factors and psychopathology: Stress, social support, and coping processes. *Annual Review of Psychology, 42*, 401–425.

Craig, C. L., Marshall, A. L., Sjostrom, M., Bauman, A. E., Booth, M. L., Ainsworth, B. E., et al. (2003). International physical activity questionnaire: 12-country reliability and validity. *Medicine & Science in Sports & Exercise, 35*(8), 1381–1395.

Crespo, C. J., Smit, E., Andersen, R. E., Carter-Pokras, O., & Ainsworth, B. E. (2000). Race/ethnicity, social class and their relation to physical inactivity during leisure time: Results from the third national health and nutrition examination survey, 1988-1994. *American Journal of Preventive Medicine, 18*(1), 46–53.

Cutler, D., & Miller, G. (2005). The role of public health improvements in health advances: The twentieth-century United States. *Demography, 42*(1), 1–22.

Dawson, D. A. (1988). Ethnic differences in female overweight: Data from the 1985 national health interview survey. *American Journal of Public Health, 78*(10), 1326–1329.

Duncan, G. E., Anton, S. D., Newton, R. L., Jr., & Perri, M. G. (2003). Comparison of perceived health to physiological measures of health in Black and White women. *Preventive Medicine, 36*(5), 624–628.

Dunn, C., & Rollnick, S. (2003). *Rapid reference to lifestyle & behavior change: Rapid reference series*. Philadelphia: Elsevier.

Ebbert, J. O., Burke, M. V., Hays, J. T., & Hurt, R. D. (2009). Combination treatment with varenicline and nicotine replacement therapy. *Nicotine & Tobacco Research, 11*(5), 572–576.

Eberhardt, M., Ingram, D. D., Makuc, D. M., Pamuk, E. R., Freid, V. M., Harper, S. B. et al. (2001). *Urban and rural health chartbook. Health, United States, 2001*. Hyattsville, MD: National Center for Health Statistics.

Elfhag, K., & Rossner, S. (2005). Who succeeds in maintaining weight loss? A conceptual review of factors associated with weight loss maintenance and weight regain. *Obesity Review, 6*(1), 67–85.

Engel, G. L. (1977). The need for a new medical model: A challenge for biomedicine. *Science, 196*(4286), 129–136.

Ferketich, A. K., Schwartzbaum, J. A., Frid, D. J., & Moeschberger, M. L. (2000). Depression as an antecedent to heart disease among women and men in the NHANES I study. National health and nutrition examination survey. *Archives of Internal Medicine, 160*(9), 1261–1268.

Ferster, C. B., Nurnberger, J. I., & Levitt, E. B. (1996). The control of eating. 1962. *Obesity Research, 4*(4), 401–410.

Findeis, J. L., Henry, M., Hirschl, T. A., Lewis, W., Ortega-Sanchez, I., Peine, E., et al. (2001). *Welfare reform in rural America: A review of current research.* Columbia, MO: Rural Policy Research Institute.

Fine, L. J., Philogene, G. S., Gramling, R., Coups, E. J., & Sinha, S. (2004). Prevalence of multiple chronic disease risk factors. 2001 national health interview survey. *American Journal of Preventive Medicine, 27*(2 Suppl.), 18–24.

Finkelstein, E. A., Ruhm, C. J., & Kosa, K. M. (2005). Economic causes and consequences of obesity. *Annual Review of Public Health, 26*, 239–257.

Flegal, K. M., Carroll, M. D., Kuczmarski, R. J., & Johnson, C. L. (1998). Overweight and obesity in the United States: Prevalence and trends, 1960-1994. *International Journal of Obesity and Related Metabolic Disorders, 22*(1), 39–47.

Flegal, K. M., Carroll, M. D., Ogden, C. L., & Johnson, C. L. (2002). Prevalence and trends in obesity among US adults, 1999-2000. *Journal of the American Medical Association, 288*(14), 1723–1727.

Flora, C. B., Flora, J. L., & Fey, S. (2004). *Rural communities: Legacy and change* (2nd ed.). Boulder, CO: Westview Press.

Foster, G. D., Wadden, T. A., Vogt, R. A., & Brewer, G. (1997). What is a reasonable weight loss? Patients' expectations and evaluations of obesity treatment outcomes. *Journal of Consulting and Clinical Psychology, 65*(1), 79–85.

Frazao, E. (1999). *America's eating habits: Changes and consequences. Agriculture information bulletin no. AIB750.* Retrieved November 29, 2008, from http://www.ers.usda.gov/Publications/AIB750/

Frenzen, P. D. (1993). Health insurance coverage in U.S. urban and rural areas. *Journal of Rural Health, 9*(3), 204–214.

Gamm, L. D., Hutchinson, L. L., Linnae, L., Dabney, B. J., & Dorsey, A. M. (Eds.). (2003). *Rural Healthy People 2010: A companion document to Healthy People 2010.* College Station, TX: The Texas A & M University Health Science Center, School of Rural Public Health, Southwest Rural Health Research Center.

Gans, K. M., Ross, E., Barner, C. W., Wylie-Rosett, J., McMurray, J., & Eaton, C. (2003). REAP and WAVE: New tools to rapidly assess/discuss nutrition with patients. *Journal of Nutrition, 133*(2), 556S–562S.

Garfield, S. L. (1994). Research on client variables in psychotherapy. In A. E. Bergin & S. L. Garfield (Eds.), *Handbook of psychotherapy and behavior change* (4th ed., pp. 190–228). New York: Wiley.

Germann, J. N., Kirschenbaum, D. S., & Rich, B. H. (2007). Child and parental self-monitoring as determinants of success in the treatment of morbid obesity in low-income minority children. *Journal of Pediatric Psychology, 32*(1), 111–121.

Gillum, R. F. (1991). Cardiovascular disease in the United States: An epidemiologic overview. *Cardiovascular Clinician, 21*(3), 3–16.

Gillum, R. F. (1996). Epidemiology of hypertension in African American women. *American Heart Journal, 131*(2), 385–395.

Greeno, C. G., & Wing, R. R. (1994). Stress-induced eating. *Psychological Bulletin, 115*(3), 444–464.

Guralnik, J. M., Land, K. C., Blazer, D., Fillenbaum, G. G., & Branch, L. G. (1993). Educational status and active life expectancy among older blacks and whites. *New England Journal of Medicine, 329*(2), 110–116.

Haslam, D. W., & James, W. P. (2005). Obesity. *Lancet, 366*(9492), 1197–1209.

Hayes, C., & Kriska, A. (2008). Role of physical activity in diabetes management and prevention. *Journal of the American Dietetic Association, 108*(4, Suppl. 1), S19–S23.

Heatherton, T. F., Kozlowski, L. T., Frecker, R. C., & Fagerstrom, K. O. (1991). The Fagerstrom Test for nicotine dependence: A revision of the Fagerstrom Tolerance Questionnaire. *British Journal of Addiction, 86*(9), 1119–1127.

Heatherton, T. F., Kozlowski, L. T., Frecker, R. C., Rickert, W., & Robinson, J. (1989). Measuring the heaviness of smoking: Using self-reported time to the first cigarette of the day and number of cigarettes smoked per day. *British Journal of Addiction, 84*(7), 791–799.

Hedley, A. A., Ogden, C. L., Johnson, C. L., Carroll, M. D., Curtin, L. R., & Flegal, K. M. (2004). Prevalence of overweight and obesity among US children, adolescents, and adults, 1999-2002. *Journal of the American Medical Association, 291*(23), 2847–2850.

Hornig, B., Maier, V., & Drexler, H. (1996). Physical training improves endothelial function in patients with chronic heart failure. *Circulation, 93*(2), 210–214.

Ickovics, J. R., Hamburger, M. E., Vlahov, D., Schoenbaum, E. E., Schuman, P., Boland, R. J., et al. (2001). Mortality, CD4 cell count decline, and depressive symptoms among HIV-seropositive women: Longitudinal analysis from the HIV epidemiology research study. *Journal of the American Medical Association, 285*(11), 1466–1474.

Ingelsson, E., Arnlov, J., Sundstrom, J., Riserus, U., Michaelsson, K., & Byberg, L. (2009). Relative importance and conjoint effects of obesity and physical inactivity for the development of insulin resistance. *European Journal of Cardiovascular Prevention & Rehabilitation, 16*(1), 28–33.

Ingram, D. D., & Gillum, R. F. (1989). Regional and urbanization differentials in coronary heart disease mortality in the United States, 1968-85. *Journal of Clinical Epidemiology, 42*(9), 857–868.

Jakicic, J. M., Clark, K., Coleman, E., Donnelly, J. E., Foreyt, J., Melanson, E., et al. (2001). American College of Sports Medicine position stand. Appropriate intervention strategies for weight loss and prevention of weight regain for adults. *Medicine and Science in Sports and Exercise, 33*(12), 2145–2156.

Johns Hopkins University. (1999). *The Johns Hopkins family health book: The essential home medical reference to help you and your family promote good health and manage illness.* New York: William Morrow.

Katon, W., Von Korff, M., Lin, E., Simon, G., Walker, E., Unutzer, J., et al. (1999). Stepped collaborative care for primary care patients with persistent symptoms of depression: A randomized trial. *Archivves of General Psychiatry, 56*(12), 1109–1115.

Kendall, C. W., & Jenkins, D. J. (2004). A dietary portfolio: Maximal reduction of low-density lipoprotein cholesterol with diet. *Current Atherosclerosis Reports, 6*(6), 492–498.

Knowler, W. C., Barrett-Connor, E., Fowler, S. E., Hamman, R. F., Lachin, J. M., Walker, E. A., et al. (2002). Reduction in the incidence of type 2 diabetes with lifestyle intervention or metformin. *New England Journal of Medicine, 346*(6), 393–403.

Koplan, J. P., & Dietz, W. H. (1999). Caloric imbalance and public health policy. *Journal of the American Medical Association, 282*(16), 1579–1581.

Koplan, J. P., Thacker, S. B., & Lezin, N. A. (1999). Epidemiology in the 21st century: Calculation, communication, and intervention. *American Journal of Public Health, 89*(8), 1153–1155.

Kuyken, W., Padesky, C. A., & Dudley, R. (2009). *Collaborative case conceptualization: Working effectively with clients in cognitive-behavioral therapy.* New York: Guilford.

Lattimore, P. J. (2001). Stress-induced eating: An alternative method for inducing ego-threatening stress. *Appetite, 36*(2), 187–188.

Lewis, C. E., Jacobs, D. R., Jr., McCreath, H., Kiefe, C. I., Schreiner, P. J., Smith, D. E., et al. (2000). Weight gain continues in the 1990s: 10-year trends in weight and overweight from the CARDIA study. Coronary artery risk development in young adults. *American Journal of Epidemiology, 151*(12), 1172–1181.

Ludwig, D. S., & Pollack, H. A. (2009). Obesity and the economy: From crisis to opportunity. *Journal of the American Medical Association, 301*(5), 533–535.

Mainous, A. G. III, King, D. E., Garr, D. R., & Pearson, W. S. (2004). Race, rural residence, and control of diabetes and hypertension. *Annals of Family Medicine, 2*(6), 563–568.

Martin, P. D., Rhode, P. C., Dutton, G. R., Redmann, S. M., Ryan, D. H., & Brantley, P. J. (2006). A primary care weight management intervention for low-income African-American women. *Obesity (Silver Spring), 14*(8), 1412–1420.

Matarazzo, J. D. (1980). Behavioral health and behavioral medicine: Frontiers for a new health psychology. *American Psychologist, 35*(9), 807–817.

Miller, J. H., & Moyers, T. (2002). Motivational interviewing in substance abuse: Applications for occupational medicine. *Occupational Medicine, 17*(1), 51–65, iv.

Miller, W. R. & Rollnick, S. (1991). *Motivational interviewing: Preparing people to change addictive behavior.* New York: Guilford.

Mokdad, A. H., Marks, J. S., Stroup, D. F., & Gerberding, J. L. (2004). Actual causes of death in the United States, 2000. *Journal of the American Medical Association, 291*(10), 1238–1245.

Mokdad, A. H., Serdula, M. K., Dietz, W. H., Bowman, B. A., Marks, J. S., & Koplan, J. P. (1999). The spread of the obesity epidemic in the United States, 1991-1998. *Journal of the American Medical Association, 282*(16), 1519–1522.

Murphy, S. L. (2000). Deaths: Final data for 1998. *National Vital Statistics Report, 48*(11), 1–105.

Must, A., Spadano, J., Coakley, E. H., Field, A. E., Colditz, G., & Dietz, W. H. (1999). The disease burden associated with overweight and obesity. *Journal of the American Medical Association, 282*(16), 1523–1529.

Myers, J. (2003). Cardiology patient pages. Exercise and cardiovascular health. *Circulation, 107*(1), e2–e5.

Myers, J., Atwood, J. E., & Froelicher, V. (2003). Active lifestyle and diabetes. *Circulation, 107*(19), 2392–2394.

Myers, J., Prakash, M., Froelicher, V., Do, D., Partington, S., & Atwood, J. E. (2002). Exercise capacity and mortality among men referred for exercise testing. *New England Journal of Medicine, 346*(11), 793–801.

Newton, R. L., Milsom, V. A., Nackers, L. M., & Anton, S. D. (2009). Supporting behavior change in overweight patients: A guide for the primary care physician. *Journal of Clinical Outcomes Management, 15*(11), 536–544.

Newton, R. L., & Perri, M. G. (1997). Health beliefs and obesity: Effects of race and obesity status. *Annals of Behavioral Medicine, 19*, S105.

Nezu, A. M., & Perri, M. G. (1989). Social problem-solving therapy for unipolar depression: An initial dismantling investigation. *Journal of Consulting and Clinical Psychology, 57*(3), 408–413.

Nezu, A. M., & Ronan, G. F. (1985). Life stress, current problems, problem solving, and depressive symptoms: An integrative model. *Journal of Consulting and Clinical Psychology, 53*(5), 693–697.

Oliver, G., & Wardle, J. (1999). Perceived effects of stress on food choice. *Physiology and Behavior, 66*(3), 511–515.

Oliver, G., Wardle, J., & Gibson, E. L. (2000). Stress and food choice: A laboratory study. *Psychosomatic Medicine, 62*(6), 853–865.

Orleans, C. T. (2007). Increasing the demand for and use of effective smoking-cessation treatments reaping the full health benefits of tobacco-control science and policy gains—in our lifetime. *American Journal of Preventive Medicine, 33*(6 Suppl.), S340–S348.

Patterson, P. D., Moore, C. G., Probst, J. C., & Shinogle, J. A. (2004). Obesity and physical inactivity in rural America. *Journal of Rural Health, 20*(2), 151–159.

Pearson, T. A., & Lewis, C. (1998). Rural epidemiology: Insights from a rural population laboratory. *American Journal of Epidemiology, 148*(10), 949–957.

Perri, M. G., Limacher, M. C., Durning, P. E., Janicke, D. M., Lutes, L. D., Bobroff, L. B., et al. (2008). Extended-care programs for weight management in rural communities: The treatment of obesity in underserved rural settings (TOURS) randomized trial. *Archives of Internal Medicine, 168*(21), 2347–2354.

Perri, M. G., Nezu, A. M., McKelvey, W. F., Shermer, R. L., Renjilian, D. A., & Viegener, B. J. (2001). Relapse prevention training and problem-solving therapy in the long-term management of obesity. *Journal of Consulting and Clininical Psychology, 69*(4), 722–726.

Physical activity guidelines for Americans. (2008). *Oklahoma Nurse, 53*(4), 25.

Pierce, D., & Gunn, J. (2007). GPs' use of problem solving therapy for depression: A qualitative study of barriers to and enablers of evidence based care. *BMC Family Practice, 8*, 24.

Pleis, J. R., Schiller, J. S., & Benson, V. (2003). Summary health statistics for U.S. adults: National health interview survey, 2000. *Vital Health Statistics, 10*(215), 1–132.

Plotnick, G. D., Corretti, M. C., & Vogel, R. A. (1997). Effect of antioxidant vitamins on the transient impairment of endothelium-dependent brachial artery vasoactivity following a single high-fat meal. *Journal of the American Medical Association, 278*(20), 1682–1686.

Prasad, D. S., & Das, B. C. (2009). Physical inactivity: A cardiovascular risk factor. *Indian Journal of Medical Sciences, 63*(1), 33–42.

Pratt, M., Macera, C. A., & Blanton, C. (1999). Levels of physical activity and inactivity in children and adults in the United States: Current evidence and research issues. *Medicine and Science in Sports and Exercise, 31*(11 Suppl.), S526–S533.

Radzeviciene, L., & Ostrauskas, R. (2009). Smoking habits and the risk of type 2 diabetes: A case-control study. *Diabetes and Metabolism*, 35(3), 192–197.

Ramsey, P. W., & Glenn, L. L. (2002). Obesity and health status in rural, urban, and suburban southern women. *Southern Medical Journal, 95*(7), 666–671.

Reis, B. F., & Brown, L. G. (1999). Reducing psychotherapy dropouts: Maximizing perspective convergence in the psychotherapy dyad. *Psychotherapy, 36*, 123–136.

Riddell, L. J., Chisholm, A., Williams, S., & Mann, J. I. (2000). Dietary strategies for lowering homocysteine concentrations. *American Journal of Clinical Nutrition, 71*(6), 1448–1454.

Ripsin, C. M., Kang, H., & Urban, R. J. (2009). Management of blood glucose in type 2 diabetes mellitus. *American Family Physician, 79*(1), 29–36.

Roemmich, J. N., Wright, S. M., & Epstein, L. H. (2002). Dietary restraint and stress-induced snacking in youth. *Obesity Research, 10*(11), 1120–1126.

Rollnick, S., Miller, W. R., & Butler, C. C. (2007). *Motivational interviewing in health care: Helping patients change behavior.* New York: Guilford.

Rolls, B. J., Ello-Martin, J. A., & Tohill, B. C. (2004). What can intervention studies tell us about the relationship between fruit and vegetable consumption and weight management? *Nutrition Reviews, 62*(1), 1–17.

Rolls, B. J., Roe, L. S., & Meengs, J. S. (2004). Salad and satiety: Energy density and portion size of a first-course salad affect energy intake at lunch. *Journal of the American Dietetic Association, 104*(10), 1570–1576.

Rosenberg, H. M., Maurer, J. D., Sorlie, P. D., Johnson, N. J., MacDorman, M. F., Hoyert, D. L., et al. (1999). Quality of death rates by race and Hispanic origin: A summary of current research, 1999. *Vital Health Statistics, 1, 2*(128), 1–13.

Ross, R. M., Beck, K. C., Casaburi, R., Johnson, B. D., Marciniuk, D. D., Wagner, P. D., et al. (2003). ATS/ACCP statement on cardiopulmonary exercise testing. *American Journal of Respiratory Critical Care Medicine, 167*(2), 211–277.

Ruelaz, A. R., Diefenbach, P., Simon, B., Lanto, A., Arterburn, D., & Shekelle, P. G. (2007). Perceived barriers to weight management in primary care—Perspectives of patients and providers. *Journal of General Internal Medicine, 22*(4), 518–522.

Schootman, M., & Fuortes, L. J. (1999). Breast and cervical carcinoma: The correlation of activity limitations and rurality with screening, disease incidence, and mortality. *Cancer, 86*(6), 1087–1094.

Schulman-Green, D. J., Naik, A. D., Bradley, E. H., McCorkle, R., & Bogardus, S. T. (2006). Goal setting as a shared decision making strategy among clinicians and their older patients. *Patient Education and Counseling, 63*(1–2), 145–151.

Schur, C. L., & Franco, S. J. (1999). Access to health care. In T. C. Ricketts (Ed.), *Rural health in the United States* (pp. 25–37). New York: Oxford University Press.

Schwartz, G. E. (1982). Testing the biopsychosocial model: The ultimate challenge facing behavioral medicine? *Journal of Consulting and Clinical Psychology, 50*(6), 1040–1053.

Smith, T. W., Kendall, P. C., & Keefe, F. J. (2002). Behavioral medicine and clinical health psychology: Introduction to the special issue, a view from the decade of behavior. *Journal of Consulting and Clinical Psychology, 70*(3), 459–462.

Sommers, L. S., Marton, K. I., Barbaccia, J. C., & Randolph, J. (2000). Physician, nurse, and social worker collaboration in primary care for chronically ill seniors. *Archives of Internal Medicine, 160*(12), 1825–1833.

Stagnitti, M. N. (2008). *Antidepressants prescribed by medical doctors in office based and outpatient settings by specialty for the U.S. civilian noninstitutionalized population, 2002 and 2005. Statistical brief #206.* Rockville, MD: Agency for Healthcare Research and Quality.

Stamler, J., & Neaton, J. D. (2008). The multiple risk factor intervention trial (MRFIT)—Importance then and now. *Journal of the American Medical Association, 300*(11), 1343–1345.

Stamler, J., Stamler, R., & Neaton, J. D. (1993). Blood pressure, systolic and diastolic, and cardiovascular risks. US population data. *Archives of Internal Medicine, 153*(5), 598–615.

Stevens, V. J., Obarzanek, E., Cook, N. R., Lee, I. M., Appel, L. J., Smith West, D., et al. (2001). Long-term weight loss and changes in blood pressure: Results of the trials of hypertension prevention, phase II. *Annals of Internal Medicine, 134*(1), 1–11.

Stewart, S. L., Cardinez, C. J., Richardson, L. C., Norman, L., Kaufmann, R., Pechacek, T. F., et al. (2008). Surveillance for cancers associated with tobacco use—United States, 1999-2004. *MMWR Surveillance Summaries, 57*(8), 1–33.

Sundquist, J., Winkleby, M. A., & Pudaric, S. (2001). Cardiovascular disease risk factors among older black, Mexican-American, and white women and men: An analysis of NHANES III, 1988–1994. Third national health and nutrition examination survey. *Journal of the American Geriatrics Society, 49*(2), 109–116.

Taylor, S. E., Repetti, R. L., & Seeman, T. (1997). Health psychology: What is an unhealthy environment and how does it get under the skin? *Annual Review of Psychology, 48*, 411–447.

Teo, K. K., Ounpuu, S., Hawken, S., Pandey, M. R., Valentin, V., Hunt, D., et al. (2006). Tobacco use and risk of myocardial infarction in 52 countries in the INTERHEART study: A case-control study. *Lancet, 368*(9536), 647–658.

Thompson, P. D., Buchner, D., Pina, I. L., Balady, G. J., Williams, M. A., Marcus, B. H., et al. (2003). Exercise and physical activity in the prevention and treatment of atherosclerotic cardiovascular disease: A statement from the Council on Clinical Cardiology (Subcommittee on Exercise, Rehabilitation, and Prevention) and the Council on Nutrition, Physical Activity, and Metabolism (Subcommittee on Physical Activity). *Circulation, 107*(24), 3109–3116.

Thompson, P. D., & Lim, V. (2003). Physical activity in the prevention of atherosclerotic coronary heart disease. *Current Treatment Options in Cardiovascular Medicine, 5*(4), 279–285.

Tsai, A. G., Asch, D. A., & Wadden, T. A. (2006). Insurance coverage for obesity treatment. *Journal of the American Dietetic Association, 106*(10), 1651–1655.

U.S. Department of Agriculture. (1993). *Rural conditions and trends*. Washington, DC: Author. Retrieved December 2, 2008, from http://www.usda.gov

U.S. Department of Health, Education, and Welfare. (1979). *Healthy people: The Surgeon General's report on health promotion and disease prevention: 1979.* Washington, DC: Author. Retrieved September 18, 2009, from http://profiles.nlm.nih.gov/NN/B/B/G/K/nnbbgk.pdf

U.S. Public Health Service, Office of the Surgeon General. (1996). *Physical activity and health: A report of the surgeon general.* Atlanta, GA: U.S. Department of Health and Human Services, Centers for Disease Control and Prevention, National Center for Chronic Disease Prevention and Health Promotion.

U.S. Department of Health and Human Services. (2002). *List of designated primary medical care, mental health, and dental health professional shortage areas.* Retrieved November 28, 2008, from http://www.hhs.gov/

Villareal, D. T., Apovian, C. M., Kushner, R. F., & Klein, S. (2005). Obesity in older adults: Technical review and position statement of the American Society for Nutrition and NAASO, the Obesity Society. *Obesity Research, 13*(11), 1849–1863.

Villareal, D. T., Banks, M., Sinacore, D. R., Siener, C., & Klein, S. (2006). Effect of weight loss and exercise on frailty in obese older adults. *Archives of Internal Medicine, 166*(8), 860–866.

Villareal, D. T., Banks, M. R., Patterson, B. W., Polonsky, K. S., & Klein, S. (2008). Weight loss therapy improves pancreatic endocrine function in obese older adults. *Obesity (Silver Spring), 16*(6), 1349–1354.

Villareal, D. T., Miller, B. V. III, Banks, M., Fontana, L., Sinacore, D. R., & Klein, S. (2006). Effect of lifestyle intervention on metabolic coronary heart disease risk factors in obese older adults. *American Journal of Clinical Nutrition, 84*(6), 1317–1323.

Vitolins, M. Z., Tooze, J. A., Golden, S. L., Arcury, T. A., Bell, R. A., Davis, C., et al. (2007). Older adults in the rural South are not meeting healthful eating guidelines. *Journal of the American Dietetic Association, 107*(2), 265–272.

Willett, W. C., Manson, J. E., Stampfer, M. J., Colditz, G. A., Rosner, B., Speizer, F. E., et al. (1995). Weight, weight change, and coronary heart disease in women. Risk within the 'normal' weight range. *Journal of the American Medical Association, 273*(6), 461–465.

Wing, R. R. (2002). Behavioral weight control. In T. A. Wadden & A. J. Stunkard (Eds.), *The handbook of obesity* (pp. 249–275). New York: Guilford.

Wing, R. R., & Jeffery, R. W. (1999). Benefits of recruiting participants with friends and increasing social support for weight loss and maintenance. *Journal of Consulting and Clinical Psychology, 67*(1), 132–138.

Winkleby, M. A., Kraemer, H. C., Ahn, D. K., & Varady, A. N. (1998). Ethnic and socioeconomic differences in cardiovascular disease risk factors: Findings for women from the third national health and nutrition examination survey, 1988–1994. *Journal of the American Medical Association, 280*(4), 356–362.

Treatment of Depression in Primary Care Medical Practice

16

Arthur Freeman
Eileen Lightner
Barbara A. Golden

Introduction

Depression has been called the "common cold" of emotional disorders. It is, therefore, an apt metaphor for a discussion of depression and primary medical care treatment. Like the common cold, depression is an experience or disorder that virtually all people encounter throughout their lives. Some individuals may be more prone to colds and have them as frequent, though unwelcome, occurrences. For others, colds are infrequent, and the individual may claim that diet, exercise, constitutional factors, heredity, or their vitamin regimen help to make them less susceptible to cold viruses. Some people have colds and are debilitated for several days by the severity of the cold symptoms, whereas others are affected by the cold symptoms but manage to experience only a small inconvenience or reduction in their functioning. For some people, cold symptoms are dealt with at home with home/family remedies or techniques (e.g., chest rubs, steam humidifiers, etc.). Others choose to medicate themselves with over-the-counter medications or paraphernalia that might include analgesics, antihistamines, decongestants, or expectorants, all easily and readily available. The common wisdom is that an untreated cold lasts 7 days, a treated cold lasts for a week. Many individuals can feel the cold "coming on" and stock their medicine cabinet with the range of medications (cough drops, tissues, nasal spray, or vitamin C) that they think is necessary to weather the storm. From experience, many individuals know the course of their cold, about how long it will last, what impact it will have on their mood, their bodies, or their energy. The cold can be quite contagious, so that if one family member has it, others who are vulnerable can contract the cold and suffer along with the carrier of the cold virus.

Some individuals immediately seek help from their primary care practitioner (PCP), whereas others nurse their symptoms without formal medical interventions. Colds have many concomitant or comorbid symptoms that can involve every bodily system to a greater or lesser degree. In point of fact, one can have a cold and, in addition, have other physical disorders superimposed upon the cold such as allergies, flu, or sinus and/or throat infections. Depending on the frequency, severity, and amplitude of the constellation of cold symptoms, an individual's reaction may run the range from mild and irritated to severe and disabled. It would be rare that the first course of medical action for a cold would be an allergist, an otolaryngologist, or a pulmonary specialist. The first medical contact for a serious and debilitating cold would be the primary care medical provider.

In any of the preceding statements, the term *depression* can be substituted, and the statements would be accurate. It is clear that depression can run the range of severity from mild and annoying to severe and debilitating. Like the cold, there are a number of depressive manifestations that may be difficult to tease out of a polysymptomatic experience, including dysthymia or anxiety. Too, depression may be nursed at home, chased by a strong shot (or several) of alcohol, treated by old family recipes, ignored, or suffered in silence until the depression lifts. For both the common cold and depressive phenomena, the PCP is most often the first line of treatment. The goal of this chapter is to describe depression and the various depressive phenomena, identify assessment tools that can be used by the clinician, describe treatment possibilities, and discuss concomitant psychological disorders and appropriate referral directions.

Assessment and Diagnostic Issues

In a recent study to examine the underrecognition and undertreatment of depressive disorders in primary care, researchers found that PCPs recognized 79.4% of depression cases, with 40.9% of those cases prescribed antidepressant medication (Berardi et al., 2005). They also found that another 45% of PCPs identified depressed patients did not meet the *International Statistical Classification of Diseases and Related Health Problems* (*ICD-10*; World Health Organization, 2007) criteria, and 26.9% received an antidepressant. Researchers concluded that in more recent years, PCPs may be using a more inclusive diagnostic threshold that may result in excessive antidepressant prescriptions for mild depression. Prior studies have consistently found low recognition rates and underprescription of antidepressants (WHO Study on Psychological Disorders in General Health Care, cited in Berardi et al., 2005). In that study conducted in 14 countries, PCPs on average only recognized 39.1% of *ICD-10* depression, with antidepressant prescriptions limited to 22.2%.

In a national German study, 85% of depression cases were recognized by PCPs, and 44.3% were prescribed an antidepressant. PCPs in Italy recognized 61.7% of depression cases, and prescribed 32.7% with antidepressants. In their study, which examined clinical behavior of physicians in 152 primary care offices in Rochester, New York, and Northern California in the context of patient requests for antidepressant treatment, Feldman, Franks, Epstein, Franz, and Kravitz (2006) found that patient requests for antidepressants were associated with enhanced depression history-taking by PCPs, including inquiries about suicidality. However, for the patients diagnosed with major depression, less than 50% received suicidality inquiries.

Mental health professionals and physicians must be careful and deliberate when evaluating their patients for a diagnosis of clinical depression. It takes more than just unhappiness, negative life experiences, tearfulness, or a feeling of sadness on the part of the patient to indicate and diagnose the presence of some aspect of a depressive phenomenon. The physician should take the time to gather a good deal of information about a person, including his/her behavior, mood, and personal and family history before determining that he or she is clinically depressed. In addition to a medical evaluation, a clinical interview, and possibly additional assessments, a physician must evaluate whether a person has specific symptoms of a mood disorder such as major depression, dysthymia, or bipolar disorder. Each mood disorder is characterized by a unique set of symptoms, or diagnostic criteria, which are listed in the *Diagnostic and Statistical Manual of Mental Disorders-Fourth Edition, Text Revision* (*DSM-IV-TR*; American Psychiatric Association, 2000). The first set of assessment issues and questions relates to the depression per se:

1. What type of depression affects the patient?
2. What is the patient's level of depression (by category: mild, moderate, or severe) and by a score on a standard evaluation instrument, such as the BDI-II (Beck, Steer, & Brown, 1996) or the Hamilton Depression Rating Scale (Hamilton, 1960)?
3. How does the depression phenomena manifest within the patient's life, work, family, or career?
4. How ready is the patient to change his/her life circumstance?
5. What supports does the patient have to make and maintain a change in his/her depressive status?
6. What is the patient's skill set to make and maintain change?
7. What impediments are there to changing?
8. What are the patient's environmental and life circumstances?
9. What is the patient's previous history of depression?
10. What is the patient's history of formal therapy to treat the depression?
11. What disorders are comorbid to the depression?
12. What is the patient's history of informally attempting to cope with the depression?
13. What is the patient's family history of depression?

14. What is the patient's history of suicide attempts, suicidal thoughts, suicidal plans, or self-injurious behavior?
15. What is the patient's history of attempts at pharmacological interventions for their depression?

The second set of assessment issues relates to data sources. This can be the patient's self-monitoring or the report of others. Based on Bellack and Hersen's classic work on behavioral assessment (1998), DiTomasso and Gilman (2005) note that "behavioral assessment is an empirically driven, multimethod, multimodal, and multiinformant process that involves the carefully specified measurement of observable behavior and associated temporally related causal variables" (p. 61). Ultimately, the purpose of this process is to provide a sound basis for clinical decision making and the development of effective behavior-change strategies (Haynes, Leisen, & Blaine, 1997; Haynes & Williams, 2003).

Data sources can include the patient's self-report verbally and on standard self-report measures, data from the initial referral, data derived from family report or significant others, and data from and relevant to the patient's previous therapy. In addition, reports from the patient's medical provider and reports from the patient's psychiatric record, including hospitalizations, should be gathered.

The third area of concern is an evaluation of each of the following areas: biology, emotion, behavior, situation, and thoughts, and a ranking of how each one contributes to the depression and, in a circular manner, also helps to create and maintain the depression. There are many assessment measures that are valid and reliable to diagnose degrees of depression and the many factors that contribute to depression. The diagnosis and management of depression is complex, as the etiology is rooted in biological, psychological, sociological, and cultural variables.

Incidence and Clinical Manifestations in the Primary Care Setting

It has been predicted that by the year 2020, depressive disorders will be a leading global cause of disability (Miedema, Tatemichi, Thomas-Maclean, & Stoppard, 2004). The lifetime rates of a major depressive disorder for males is 5–12%; for females it is 10–25%, with 75% of patients seeking treatment in a primary care setting (Hameed, Schwartz, Malhotra, West, & Bertone, 2005). General practitioners in primary care settings have become more involved in depression diagnosis, treatment, and management during the past two decades (Gaynes et al., 2007; Schwenk, Evans, Laden, & Lewis, 2004). Depressed patients are more likely to use a PCP than a mental health clinician, with an increase in rates for PCP visits for depression from 50% in 1987 to 64% in 2001 (Gaynes et al.). In a recent study of 1,756 patient cases in primary care, 13.2% were diagnosed with a mental health problem, and 86% of those patients were treated solely by the general practitioner (van Rijswijk, Borghuis, van de Lisdonk, Zitman, & van Weel, 2007). Wolf and Hopko (2008) provide a critical review of the psychological and pharmacological interventions for people with depression and primary care medicine.

Over 50% of patients with mental illness receive their treatment solely from primary care providers. Some research suggests that 90% of U.S. PCPs report treating depressed patients at their offices (Carney, Dietrich, Eliassen, Owen, & Badger, 1999). As a result, PCPs need to become actively involved with effective assessment, diagnosis, and treatment for their depressed patients.

The Many Faces of Depression

Many terms are used to describe depression, including, "down," "blue, "blah," "depressed," "under the weather," "low," or "out of sorts." The multiple manifestations of depression can include *emotional manifestations*, such as dejected mood, self-dislike, loss of gratification, loss of attachment, crying spells, and the loss of mirth response. *Vegetative and physical manifestations* include the depths of depression, being easily fatigued, and the experience of sleep disturbance, loss of appetite, or the loss of libido.

Cognitive manifestations are marked by low self-evaluation, negative expectations, self-blame, self-criticism, indecisiveness, distorted self-image, distorted body image, loss of motivation, and suicidal wishes. *Motivational manifestations* may include a paralysis of the will, avoidance, escapist and withdrawal wishes, suicidal wishes, and increased dependency.

Case Conceptualization

In the treatment of depression, the therapist needs to clearly formulate the problem. Without this formulation, therapy is vague or may be ambiguous. The key to effective treatment planning is conceptualization. The key to developing the treatment conceptualization is data collection. Effective assessment provides data about what a person does, the circumstances under which the depressive behavior reliably occurs, how often the depression occurs, where it occurs, with whom it most likely occurs, whether a behavior should be increased or decreased, how long the depression lasts, and the consequences of the behavior, that is, its impact regarding what is obtained, escaped, or avoided as a result of the depression (Bellack & Hersen, 1998). In behavioral assessment, there is reliance on multiple methods that are selected and based upon the nature of the problem to be studied. The characteristics of the target behavior or problem measured, such as frequency, intensity, latency, duration, or a combination of such, depend upon the nature of the problem. In some instances, multiple facets of the problem behavior may require observation (DiTomasso & Gilman, 2005). The intent is for the method to yield the maximum amount of relevant and usable information for the least amount of effort and cost. It is best to avoid employing a measure of some underlying trait upon which to infer the depressive behavior, e.g. abandonment.

Self-Directed Negative Behavior

In conceptualizing the treatment of depression in primary care, it is beneficial to categorize depression along a continuum that varies from a low degree of severity to a higher level of threat or risk. To make treatment planning more focused, a model that divides depressive phenomena into several overlapping areas, each

16.1

A diagram of self-directed negative behavior. (SDNB)

Degree of Severity of Life Threat

LOW **MEDIUM** **HIGH**

Self Denigration /Debasement

Self Punishment

Self Harm

Self Abuse

Self-Disregard for Personal Safety

Self Injury

Self destruction

Larger numbers of patients	**Smaller numbers of patients**
Less lethality	**Greater lethality**
Fewer crises	**Greater numbers of crises**

with a significantly higher level of severity and potential lethality is presented. The term chosen is self-directed negative behavior (SDNB). In Figure 16.1, the range of SDNB is diagrammed.

The numbers of individuals in each group decrease with the severity of the behavior, so that the most frequent behaviors seen in practice are the negative views of self, which include self-denigration and self-debasement. The types are described below.

Self-Denigration

The individual tends to verbally and cognitively demean and debase themselves both internally and externally. They are prone to negative expectations inasmuch as they have a negative perceptual bias. Both episodically and stylistically, this individual is prone to depression. Their view may be stated directly (e.g., "I'm so dumb," or "No one would want to be with me.").

Self-Punishment

The individual will deprive themselves of enjoyable activities or experiences inasmuch as they believe that they should "pay a price" for thoughts, actions, transgressions, or feelings in the present or past. This is related to and is often a sequelae of guilt and/or shame (e.g., "I deserve the bad things that happen to me," or, "I cannot go to the movies with my friends because I did not study enough last night.").

Self-Harm

The individual engages in behaviors or activities that may have a negative impact on his/her life. This would include smoking, avoidance of prescribed medication, potentially life-threatening activities, such as unprotected sex with multiple partners, or the choice of occupation. There is no guarantee that the risk-related behavior will cause self-directed injury. The risk factor may, in fact, be antidepressive in nature (e.g., "I am invulnerable and the risk is worth it," or "There's no sure way of predicting that these things WILL hurt me.").

Self-Abuse

The individual engages in activities that have, or will likely have, a direct negative impact on his/her present life circumstance. This would include extensive and regular use of alcohol, and addictive drugs (both illegal and prescription). Also included would be overeating, bulimia, and anorexia (e.g., "Sure they have a negative effect, but I only do it on weekends and I can stop whenever I want," or "These things reduce my anxiety and that makes it worth the risk.").

Self-Disregard for Danger

The individual places himself/herself in situations, circumstances, and relationships that are, or may be, hurtful, dangerous, or potentially lethal. He or she may be in abusive relationships, involved as a victim of abusive family members, or place himself or herself into situations of high risk (e.g., going to an area of their city at night that is known to be dangerous or, for example, "I cannot get out of this family/relationship. I am helpless to fight back.").

Self-Injury

The individual involves himself or herself in a pattern of bodily damage such as burning, cutting, or ingestion of poisons and may refuse needed and necessary medication. He or she may describe the self-injurious behavior as a distraction from psychic pain, and/or a way of attracting attention or calling for help. Included here would be parasuicidal behavior (e.g., "Look what I have to do to get anyone to notice me," or "I need this as a release.").

Self-Destruction

The individual takes clear and powerful action to end his/her life. The means are not important, and the destruction is sooner rather than later. If he or she survives, it is often a surprise (e.g., "There is no hope for things to get any better so that I will act to end my life," or "Anything is better than living this awful life").

Brief Case History

Richard is a 55-year-old Caucasian male who presented at the primary care office with symptoms of uncontrolled hypertension and insomnia. His spouse of 30 years died 6 months ago from breast cancer. Richard has not worked for the past 2 weeks because of "illness" and is concerned about losing his job. He was referred by the PCP for grief counseling.

Richard's father has been deceased for the past 5 years, and his mother resides with his older married brother whom he visits occasionally. Richard has a 28-year-old married son with two grandchildren and a 26-year-old single daughter who resides nearby. He has a high school education and has worked in manufacturing management for the past 20 years. Subsequent to his spouse's death, Richard experienced a loss of appetite and increased sleep disruption. He also has been feeling fatigued and irritable most days, and has been isolating and withdrawing from family and coworkers. He lost interest in his woodworking hobby and stopped attending events with his grandchildren.

Cognitive-Behavioral Case Conceptualization

This formulation is based on Needleman's (1999) case conceptualization model using a cognitive-behavioral therapy (CBT) approach for the treatment of depression.

Presenting Problem: Richard's children are concerned about his ability to cope with their mother's death and care for himself, as he is not eating well or taking his blood pressure medications consistently. Recently, he stopped going to work.

Precipitants: Loss of spouse, insomnia, increased fatigue, increased irritability, decreased energy, and withdrawal from family and work.

Exhaustive List of Problems, Issues, and Therapy-Relevant Behaviors:

1. Depressed mood and insomnia
2. Passive suicidal ideation (no plans or intentions)
3. Decreased energy and fatigue
4. Ruminations and fears about losing his job
5. Isolation and withdrawal from family and coworkers
6. Loneliness and inability to process his grief
7. Increased arguments with children about his well-being.

Diagnosis:

Axis I: 296.23 Major Depressive Disorder, Single Episode, Severe, Without Psychotic Features

Axis II: 799.9 Deferred

Axis III: Hypertension, insomnia

Axis IV: Death of spouse; threat of job loss

Axis V: 55

Relevant Beliefs:

1. I'm not capable of living alone;
2. I'm so lonely without my wife, I don't know what to do;
3. I can't concentrate on anything at work, so I will probably lose my job;
4. My children shouldn't be burdened with me;
5. I can't talk with anyone about my loss.

Origin of Key Core Beliefs: Richard's family of origin rarely expressed vulnerabilities. A strong belief held by Richard since childhood was that parents do not show weakness around their children. During the course of his spouse's illness, Richard participated in caregiver duties along with his children, but did not discuss his feelings about his wife's pending death with anyone. He harbors resentment toward his mother and brother, whom he believes have never been empathetic toward him about his wife's illness. The resentment is manifested when his children encourage him to spend time with his family to relieve his loneliness. The resentment escalates into arguments with his children followed by sequential withdrawal by him. These interactions with his children appear to trigger resentment fostered by feelings of emotional deprivation from his childhood. The continued isolation from work and others, along with his unexpressed grief and the belief that he cannot express vulnerable feelings around his children, contributes to his depression.

Vicious Cycles/Maintaining Factors: His belief that he should not burden his children, along with his belief that his mother and brother are not empathetic toward him, triggers his overgeneralization that he cannot confide his grief feelings to them. Selective abstraction contributes to his irritability and emotional isolation although he ignores other relevant aspects of adjustment to his loss. Depression is maintained by these cycles, along with his dichotomous thinking and emotional reasoning about the adjustments he will need to make to cope with this loss.

A cognitive-behavioral treatment plan for this patient would include the following goals:

1. Improve mood and quality of life and monitor reductions in depression levels by using the Beck Depression Inventory;
2. Improve connectedness with family and friends to reduce feelings of isolation and increase perceived support;
3. Return to work to reduce worry and fears about job loss and to restore meaningful activity.

Possible Obstacles to Treatment: The loss of his job when Richard is ready to return to work may be an obstacle to treatment. This should be monitored and problem-solving strategies as needed to address this obstacle should be an ongoing part of the treatment. In addition, because the family also is suffering losses of their mother and grandmother, they may struggle with recognizing Richard's depression, and as a result, may withdraw their support for him. Family sessions may be helpful.

Plan:

1. Consult with PCP concerning evaluation for antidepressant medication.
2. Get sleep hygiene education to reduce insomnia difficulties.
3. Take prescribed hypertension medications daily, and monitor results with follow-up appointment with PCP.
4. Use cognitive restructuring of automatic thoughts and relevant beliefs contributing to depressive thought patterns. Use daily thought record and downward arrow technique (Freeman, Pretzer, Fleming, & Simon, 2004).
5. Teach coping skills training to cope with grief and related stressors. Use Coping with Stressors Worksheet (Gilson & Freeman, 1999) and positive problem orientation education (Nezu, Nezu, & Lombardo, 2004).
6. Return to work as soon as feasible.
7. Increase positive interactions with family, including engaging in pleasant activity with children and grandchildren.
8. Resume woodworking activity.
9. Follow-up consultation on patient's progress with PCP.

Points of Collaboration With Physicians and Family

When necessary, referral and collaboration needs to be implemented between the PCP and the psychological care provider. This collaboration is vital, inasmuch as treatment adherence and the other contributing factors to the depression can be dealt with effectively. These factors might include marital discord, family problems, parenting issues, financial stressors, job problems/loss, social stressors, and physical illness. These may take the form of hopelessness and the attendant risk of suicide, low self-esteem and self-denigration, lack of self-care, avoiding support systems, or impaired performance. The team of the cognitive-behavioral therapist and the PCP is an essential collaboration.

Cognitive Vulnerability for Depression

A number of factors can create vulnerability for depression and further fuel the depression, and may require collaboration with the PCP. These factors include the onset of any serious and disabling medical disorder (Krishnan et al., 2002), as well as the top four leading causes of death: cardiovascular disease, cancer, stroke, and chronic obstructive pulmonary disease (COPD).

Other medical conditions include neurologic disorders, such as Parkinson's disease, Alzheimer's disease, and multiple sclerosis; hepatitis C infection and associated liver disease; and chronic insomnia (Galeazzi et al., 2005; Katz & McHorney, 2002; Krishnan et al., 2002; Wessely & Pariante, 2002). Certain medications/drug therapy can induce or exacerbate depression (Patten & Barbui, 2004). Patten and Barbui's (2004) systematic review of controlled and noncontrolled studies did not reveal any drugs causing major depression, but they did find causal effects for depressive symptoms in the following listed drugs, with the exception of the beta blockers propranolol and sotalol, which showed side effects for depressive symptoms.

Evidence has been found linking corticosteroids, interferon-alpha, interleukin-2, propranolol, mefloquine (antimalarial drug), gonadotropin-releasing hormone agonists, and progestin-releasing implanted contraceptives to atypical depressive syndromes (Patten & Barbui, 2004). These drugs are used to treat diseases that may make a biopsychosocial etiological contribution to depression. The depressive symptoms may intermingle with the disease they are being used to treat through processes of psychological adjustment and psychiatric vulnerability that precedes drug exposure. Despite some contradictory results concerning the linkage (i.e., whether the medications exacerbate or induce depression), many studies implicate certain medications used to treat common medical conditions in older adults, such as hypertension, cardiac disease, pulmonary disease, liver disease, and neurologic disorders (Kotlyar, Dysken, & Adson, 2005).

Pathogenesis for the Depression Vulnerability

Functional neuroimaging studies and functional brain-mapping studies indicate that depression involves widespread alteration of the neural network in prefrontal motor, temporal and parietal cortical, limbic, lateral hypothalamic and thalamic areas modulating basal ganglia, midbrain, brainstem, and spinal motor-control mechanisms (Stone, Lin, & Quartermain, 2008; Swanson, 2000). This dysregulation involves hypoactivity in brain regions associated with positively motivated behavior and hyperactivity in brain regions associated with stress responses (Stone et al., 2008).

Cytokines (produced by human blood cells) may impair dopaminergic and serotonergic neurotransmission (Anisman, Hayley, Turrin, & Merali, 2002; Hayley, Poulter, Merail, & Anisman, 2005; Kalivas & Duffy, 1995). These could trigger behavioral responses involved in depression: sickness behavior, malaise, fatigue, and depressed mood. Increased cytokines related to interferon treatment for hepatitis C, multiple sclerosis, cancer, and certain other disorders pose a depression vulnerability risk (Schafer, Wittchen, Seufert, & Kraus, 2007; Wichers et al., 2006).

Interferon Treatment

Interferons are a type of cytokines with antiviral, antiproliferative, and immunomodulatory properties (Raison et al., 2005; Schafer et al., 2007; Wichers et al., 2006). Major depression has been associated with increased concentrations of the pro-inflammatory cytokines with cell-mediated immune activation (Wichers et al.), and significant depressive symptoms have been found in 20–50% of patients receiving interferon treatment for chronic infection with hepatitis C virus (Raison et al.).

Hepatitis C

Hepatitis C is currently the leading cause of end-stage liver failure, and the leading indicator for a prospective liver transplant candidate in the developed world

(Golden, O'Dwyer, & Conroy, 2005). WHO estimates that 3% of the world's population (170 million people) are infected with hepatitis C and are at risk for developing liver cancer and liver cirrhosis. The association with depression is significant, because in addition to the stigma of the disease for individuals with hemophilia and other recipients of blood transfusions, IV drug users can contract hepatitis C, which poses another cognitive vulnerability for this at-risk population (Golden et al.).

COPD

COPD is the fourth leading cause of death and the only leading cause of death for which prevalence rates have not declined over the past 30 years, with the illness afflicting up to 24 million individuals in the U.S. alone (Alexopoulos et al., 2006). There is a high prevalence of depression in older adults with COPD, with rates ranging from 16 to 74% in some studies (Ng et al., 2007) to 20–60% (Ahmed, Kelshiker, & Jenner, 2007).

As the disease progresses with irreversible decline in lung function, corticosteroid treatment is commonly used to reduce inflammation and breathing distress. Depression has also been implicated with the chronic long-term treatment of this disease with glucocorticosteroid therapy. The irreversible physically disabling disease process, related to increased episodes of dyspnea (breathlessness) and an eventual state of oxygen-dependent therapy, has been associated with the high prevalence of depression and hopelessness about prognosis (Wedzicha & Seemungal, 2007).

Beta Blockers

Adrenergic-inhibiting antihypertensive drugs such as beta blockers and alpha-agonists have been associated with depressive symptoms, a relatively common drug side effect. The biobehavioral sequellae associated with these medications frequently result in changes in cognitive, affective, sleep, and sexual function (Rosen & Kostis, 1985). However, a more recent meta-analysis of 15 randomized controlled trials of beta-blocker therapy for hypertension, myocardial infarction, and congestive heart failure found that their use was associated with fatigue and sexual dysfunction, but not depression (Ko et al., 2002; Paulman, Paulman, Huffman, Wulsin, & Stern, 2005).

Cardiovascular Disease

A large body of evidence suggests that depression is a risk factor for morbidity and mortality in patients with coronary heart disease (McConnell, Jacka, Williams, Dodd, & Berk, 2005; Whooley, 2006). Depressed patients who have suffered an acute myocardial infarction have an approximate two- to fourfold risk of mortality in comparison with nondepressed patients (Bush et al., 2001, McConnell et al., 2005). Relatively consistent levels of depression have been reported in recent studies, with prevalence of major depression at 17–18% and minor depression at

16–23% (McConnell et al.). Despite increasing evidence for a link between depression, cardiac disease, and an increase in cardiac morbidity and mortality, the pathogenesis is still debated and remains unclear. Physiological mechanisms that have been hypothesized include cardiac rhythm disruption, inflammatory processes, increased platelet aggregation, and hypothalamic-pituitary-adrenocortical axis (HPA) and sympathoadrenal (SA) hyperactivity (Joynt, Whellan, & O'Connor, 2003).

Development and Implementation of Empirically Based Treatment Plan

Recent trends in the field have made the need for short-term models of therapy an increasing necessity. There have been multiple factors that have driven this increased interest and necessity in short-term models. For example, the nature of patient problems will often dictate a short-term model for treatment of specific disorders. Based on empirical studies, a number of disorders have been clearly demonstrated to be treated in several sessions. Too, patients now seek quick, directive, symptomatic relief. The motivation for extended therapy based on the erroneous but often-quoted adage that problems took a long time to form, so will now need a long time for amelioration, is gone. The wish to quickly feel better, rid oneself of long-standing thoughts, actions, or behaviors is not the result of a pathological need for instant gratification, but is motivated by the need to quickly and reasonably address a specific symptom. Patients have been empowered to ask for what they want without being intimidated by interpretations.

Another factor that has increased the need for short-term models is institutional or administrative constraints. Both inpatient and outpatient programs have shortened lengths of available treatment/services so as to be able to provide services to a broader number of individuals with static or shrinking funding. This phenomenon has also been seen in community mental health centers, where resources are often limited. Sweeping changes in health care reimbursement procedures have also impacted on the need for short-term models. With the proliferation of health maintenance organizations (HMOs) and preferred provider programs (PPOs) has come an increased demand for accountability, and a drive to contain health care costs. Behavioral health benefits were the first to be scrutinized, and were required to demonstrate this accountability. Contrary to some critiques, CBT was not developed as a response or surrender to the demands or directions of managed care organizations or providers. It developed far earlier than and independently of managed care. It has emerged as the treatment of choice for many managed care providers for a variety of reasons, including, but not limited to, the emphasis on evaluation of outcome and resulting accountability.

There is clear evidence for the effectiveness of cognitive-behavioral approaches to the common mental health problems present in primary care. However, the challenge is how to respond to the volume of need present in primary care. Patients with depression comprise 10–30% of patients seeking services in the primary care office (McQuaid, Stein, Laffaye, & McCahill, 1999). Training programs for primary care mental health workers have focused on increasing knowledge of CBT. Incorporation in clinical practice and awareness of key barriers have led to positive changes in patient care (Ekers, Lovell, & Playle, 2006). In treating depression, patients' preferences deserve attention. Although antidepressants are often prescribed, adherence rates are low. Review of the research supports that informed patients prefer the addition of psychotherapy (Digna et al., 2004).

More recent studies evaluating the effectiveness of treating depression in primary care practices have reviewed the design, standardized diagnostic assessment procedures, the use of empirically evaluated treatment manuals, and appropriate comparison conditions for evaluation (Schulberg, Raue, & Rollman, 2002). When used to treat major depression, psychotherapy specifically for the depression produces better clinical outcomes than simply the use of medication alone. Because the majority of patients with depression are treated in primary care alone, it is imperative that PCPs and mental health clinicians work to continue to develop creative and practical programs for care (Feldman, 2007; Walters & Tylee, 2006; Wolf & Hopko, 2008).

CBT and Pharmacotherapy

Major depression is most often treated in primary care settings (Schwenk et al., 2004) and antidepressants are the most common treatment (Dimidjian et al., 2006). Eighty-five percent of psychotropic medications taken by children and adolescents are prescribed by PCPs and pediatricians (Fremont, Nastasi, Newman, & Roizen, 2008).

Although antidepressant medication is highly used as a first-line depression treatment in primary care, only 40–70% of patients with depression adhere to antidepressant medication (Brown et al., 2005). Nonadherence patterns have remained unchanged despite the pervasiveness of SSRIs (Burra et al., 2007). The combination of psychological treatment with antidepressants has been associated with greater improvement than with antidepressants alone for patients in need of longer drug treatment (Pampallona, Bollini, Tibaldi, Kupelnick, & Munizza, 2004). Social mediators and health beliefs, along with education level and practical aspects of daily dosage routines, were found to be significant predictors of nonadherence to antidepressants during the continuation phase of depression treatment (Burra et al.).

Like CBT, pharmacotherapy must be structured, problem-oriented, solution-focused, active, and directive, with the PCP orchestrating the medical regimen with a goal of the greatest possible positive impact with the smallest potential negative impact. Pharmacological interventions need to be based on well-defined theories and strong empirical support for efficacy. Although CBT and psychopharmacology treatments are derived from different theoretical perspectives, they are often used together to offer patients a full range of biological, cognitive, and behavioral therapies for psychiatric disorders (Blackburn & Bishop, 1983; Hollon et al., 1992; Keller et al., 2000; Murphy, Simons, Wetzel, & Lustman, 1984; Wright, 2004; Wright & Casey, 2005).

In their recent study of family medicine and general internal medicine physicians, Robinson, Geske, Prest, and Barnacle (2004) found psychotropic medications were prescribed more frequently than other interventions, such as psychotherapy. These researchers also found that patients who had a combination of psychotherapy and psychotropics had an 85% remission rate, compared with 55% for medication alone, and 52% for psychotherapy alone. Despite these findings and prior research that indicates that combination therapy is the most effective treatment strategy for severely depressed patients, PCPs continue to use pharmacotherapy without psychotherapy as their primary treatment modality. These researchers also note that 25–30% of primary care patients discontinue antidepressant medication within 1 month, with 40–50% discontinuing treatment within 3 months.

The prevalence of antidepressant medication treatment increased more than four times between 1990 and 2003 (Mojtabai, 2008). Sociodemographic disparities have been found to persist over that last decade in the U.S., which has promulgated concern about undertreatment among underserved populations. Compared with middle-aged adults, women, and non-Hispanic Caucasians, younger adults, males, and racial/ethnic minorities were prescribed antidepressants at a lower rate. Mojtabai (2008) found an increase in antidepressant medications prescribed for individuals with more mild depression compared with those with more severe psychopathology, which has raised concerns about the assessment of depression in primary care and possible overmedication of less severely depressed individuals. This study is based on general population surveys; the National Comorbidity Surveys (NCS) conducted between 1990 and 1992, and the National Comorbidity Survey-Replication (NCS-R) conducted between 2001 and 2003. The rate of antidepressant treatment increased in subjects with major depressive disorders, as well as with individuals diagnosed with anxiety disorders, due to those disorders having become approved targets for antidepressant treatment since the mid-1990s.

Regarding the combination of CBT and medication, Wright and Casey (2005) state:

> *The primary reason for combining CBT and pharmacotherapy is the prospect that using the two treatments together will lead to better results than either therapy alone. Several possible scenarios for interaction have been suggested: (1) addition—treatments given together produce results that are greater than the action of either component alone; (2) synergism—result of combined treatment is greater than the sum of the individual components; and (3) inhibition—treatment effects are impaired by the combination of approaches (Wright, 2004). Although the mechanism of potential interactions is still largely unknown, several possibilities exist. For example, CBT has been found to improve medication adherence (Wright, 2004). Also, pharmacotherapy can improve concentration, reduce painful affects and physiological arousal, and decrease distorted or irrational thinking. Positive changes in any of these areas could enhance participation in CBT. (pp. 285–286)*

Wright and Casey (2005) offer a theoretical rationale for an integrative and comprehensive approach to treatment. This includes:

1. Cognitive processes modulate the effects of the external environment on the central nervous system for emotion and behavior.
2. Maladaptive cognitions can be influenced by both psychological and biological processes.
3. Pharmacotherapy and other biological treatments can alter cognitions.
4. Because cognitive and behavioral interventions can change biological processes, psychotherapy can thus be viewed as a biological treatment.
5. Environmental, cognitive, biological, emotional, and behavioral processes should be conceptualized as interacting with one another in a biopsychosocial system.

6. It is worthwhile to develop methods of combining and integrating cognitive and biological therapies with the goal of enhancing treatment outcome.

Evaluation of Treatment Outcomes

The evaluation of treatment outcomes is essential to assess the impact of treatment. Has treatment attended to the frequency, depth (amplitude), and duration of the depression? Has the treatment attended to both main effects and side effects of the depression and the antidepressive medications? Has the impact on the individual and the family been attenuated so that the sequelae are limited in both time and negative effect? The answers to all of these questions are necessary to plan further treatment of the individual, and to apply the treatment(s) to other similar individuals and symptom presentations. The key factor in monitoring treatment and evaluating treatment outcomes is the establishment and documentation of a data base for the individual. This data base will become the background upon which the treatment will be applied. The data base and subsequent evaluations should be made, as much as is possible, with standardized screening measures.

In addition, the patient's report of "feeling better," increased activity, improved sleep, better concentration, or increased libido are all positive markers. The report of significant others also adds to the ongoing evaluation of progress. If, however, there is no change to the level or quality of the depressive report by the patient or by significant others, the clinician must look to other possible contributing factors to the depression and account for them in the treatment protocol.

Consideration With Special Populations/Diversity Issues

The clinical presentation of depression may differ significantly across different populations and cultural backgrounds. Although there are individual differences, sociocultural factors play an important role in the physical and emotional expression of depression (Bhugra & Mastrogianni, 2004). Research suggests there is a global phenomenon of underdetection of depression in primary care, which may be partially explained by the sociocultural influences impacting the variations in symptom presentation (Bhugra & Mastrogianni; Menchetti, Murri, Bertakis, Bortolotti, & Berardi, 2009).

Somatic symptoms represent common clinical presentations of depression worldwide. Many cultures use somatic metaphors to describe psychological distress and their symptoms of depression. Mexican Americans may report "brain ache or brain exploding"; individuals from Nigeria suggest "heat in the head or heaviness sensation in the head"; and colloquial British expressions such as "I feel gutted" have been used to describe depression symptoms (Bhugra & Mastrogianni, 2004). Less acculturated individuals in the United States may express their experience of depression in their more traditional culturally accepted somatic forms such as fatigue, gastrointestinal problems, headaches, or backaches (Lau & Kinoshita, 2006).

Other environmental and contextual factors associated with depression include trauma exposure, low socioeconomic status, poverty and single motherhood, and chronic urban neighborhood stress (Halbreich & Karkum, 2006; Matheson et al., 2006; Rayburn et al., 2005). Recent research suggests that neighborhood residential instability and material deprivation poses a significant risk factor for depression (Matheson et al.).

High rates of postpartum depression have been found among urban African American, Hispanic, and Asian females (Halbreich & Karkum, 2006; Siefert, Williams, Finlayson, & Delva, 2007).

Older Adults

For older adults, depression is often undetected and untreated because of its co-occurrence with physical illness, such as diabetes, cancer, cardiovascular disease, stroke, and chronic pulmonary disease. Other sociodemographic risk factors such as gender and marital status have also been associated with depression in older adults, with higher rates shown for females and lower rates for those who are married (Weyerer et al., 2008). Research has also shown that older African American and Latino populations may be less likely to adhere to antidepressant medication, compared with Caucasian older adults (Ayalon, Arean, & Alvidrez, 2005). Beliefs about the stigma associated with taking antidepressants and concerns about the side-effect profiles were found to influence decisions about nonadherence.

Most older adults with depression present at primary care settings where they are diagnosed and treated with antidepressants (Scogin & Shah, 2006). In one study, only 37% of patients who presented to primary care with a psychiatric diagnosis from a specialist were detected by PCPs (Saarela & Engestrom, 2003). Somatization has been found to reduce the detection of depression and anxiety in primary care. In a study exploring management strategies for geriatric depression in primary care, researchers found that depressive disorders were diagnosed in 9% of the patients (N = 1089) (Dearman, Waheed, Nathoo, & Baldwin, 2006). Of those depressed older adults, 86.8% were managed solely in primary care with 30.6% receiving no medication. Of the 69.7% who received antidepressant medication, 41.1% were prescribed SSRIs, 52.9% received tricyclics, and 5.8% received venlafaxine. Only 13.3% were referred for psychiatric services. These researchers noted that PCPs rarely used the *DSM-IV* or even *ICD-10* criteria in the diagnosis of depression.

Research conducted to review evidence-based treatments for depression in older adults in primary care settings, comparing psychosocial interventions to general primary care, provides evidence for the use of multidisciplinary teams (Skultety & Zeiss, 2006). Treatment models designed to be integrated health care models supported improvement in depressive symptoms. Community-based interventions for older adults have also been effective with depression care management, group and individual therapy, and psychotherapy for caregivers showing positive outcomes (Frederick et al., 2007). Treating older adults involves a multidisciplinary approach to be most effective. Much more research is needed here.

Children and Adolescents

The diagnosis of depression in children and adolescents is often missed in primary care visits. The myth that depression does not exist in children may still prevail. Although this is changing, the rates of detection remain generally low in health care settings due to multiple child, family, clinician, practice, and health care system factors (Wells, Kataoka, & Asarnow 2001). Children and adolescents with depression may also present with frequent physical complaints, which may make it difficult to recognize. In children and adolescents, depression can coexist with attention, learning, and conduct problems or disorders. Aggression and disruptive behaviors have been associated with depression in adolescent males (Paz Pruitt, 2007).

Solutions involve a more systematic approach to care, implementing a case-management approach and the provision of clinical training for pediatric providers. Current trends in electronic technology, consolidation and coordination in practices, and medical care on a more personal level will help to increase the provision of mental health services for children in primary care (Kelleher & Stevens, 2009).

PCPs should consider the stigma associated with mental health disorders among many of these special populations, which may prevent disclosures of depression-relevant information. Greater understanding and recognition of the varied clinical presentations in the primary care setting, along with the sociocultural influences that pose vulnerability for depression, may lead to improved detection, treatment, and referral services.

Clinical Pearls of Wisdom for Practitioners

The PCP is most often the first source of evaluation and treatment of depression, whether directly expressed or "masked" as somatic concerns. In this role, the primary function is the identification of the syndrome and the ability to tease it apart from other comorbid and complicating phenomena. Once the assessment has been made, the primary care professional must then develop a focused and highly structured treatment plan. This may involve medication, lifestyle change recommendations, or psychotherapy. The treatment protocol then needs to be monitored to evaluate the effect of the treatment, the degree to which the patient is adhering to the protocol, and the frequency, duration, and amplitude of the depression.

PCPs are the backbone and mainstay of medical treatment. They are trained and equipped to deal with the broad range of medical problems, and when appropriate, refer a patient for more highly specialized treatment. The PCP is, therefore, the key individual in the treatment of the most common form of emotional distress, depression. Given the direct and indirect costs of depression, it is "wise" for the PCP to work with mental health providers for the most optimal outcomes. The results of this collaboration offer promise for a far more solid and long-lasting treatment for this most common disorder.

References

Ahmed, K., Kelshiker, A., & Jenner, C. (2007). The screening and treatment of undiagnosed depression in patients with chronic obstructive pulmonary disease (COPD) in a general practice. *Primary Care Respiratory Journal, 16*(4), 249–251.

Alexopoulos, G. S., Sirey, J., Raue, P. J., Kanellopoulos, D., Clark, T. E., & Novitch, R. S. (2006). Outcomes of depressed patients undergoing inpatient pulmonary rehabilitation. *American Journal of Geriatric Psychiatry, 14*(5), 466–475.

American Psychiatric Association. (2000). *Diagnostic and statistical manual of mental disorders* (4th ed., text rev.). Washington, DC: Author.

Anisman, H., Hayley, S., Turrin, N., & Merali, Z. (2002). Cytokines as a stressor: Implications for depressive illness. *Neuropsychopharmacology, 5*, 357–373.

Ayalon, L., Arean, P. A., & Alvidrez, J. (2005). Adherence to antidepressant medications in black and Latino elderly patients. *American Journal of Geriatric Psychiatry, 13*(7), 572–580.

Beck, A. T., Steer, R. A., & Brown, G. K. (1996). *Beck Depression Inventory—II.* San Antonio, TX: Pearson Education.

Bellack, A. S., & Hersen, M. (1998). *Behavioral assessment: A practical handbook.* New York: Allyn and Bacon.

Berardi, D., Menchetti, M., Cevenini, N., Scaini, S., Versari, M., & De Ronchi, D. (2005). Increased recognition of depression in primary care: Comparison between primary-care physicians and ICD-10 diagnosis of depression. *Psychotherapy and Psychosomatics, 74*, 225–230.

Bhugra, D., & Mastrogianni, A. (2004). Globalisation and mental disorders: Overview with relation to depression. *British Journal of Psychiatry, 184*, 10–20.

Blackburn, I. M., & Bishop, S. (1983). Changes in cognition with pharmacotherapy and cognitive therapy. *British Journal of Psychiatry, 143*, 609–617.

Brown, C., Battista, D. R., Bruehlman, R., Sereika, S. S., Thase, M. E., & Dunbar-Jacob, J. (2005). Beliefs about antidepressant medications in primary care patients: Relationship to self-reported adherence. *Medical Care, 43*(12), 1203–1207.

Burra, T. A., Chen, E., McIntyre, R. S., Grace, S. L., Blackmore, E. R., & Stewart, D. E. (2007). Predictors of self-reported antidepressant adherence. *Behavioral Medicine, 32*, 127–134.

Bush, D. E., Ziegelstein, R. C., Tayback, M., Richter, D., Stevens, S., Zahalsky, H., et al. (2001). Even minimal symptoms of depression increase mortality risk after acute myocardial infarction. *American Journal of Cardiology, 88*, 337–341.

Carney, P. A., Dietrich, A. J., Eliassen, M. S., Owen, M., & Badger, L. W. (1999). Recognizing and managing depression in primary care: A standardized patient study. *Journal of Family Practice, 48*, 965–972.

Dearman, S. P., Waheed, W., Nathoo, V., & Baldwin, R. C. (2006). Management strategies in geriatric depression by primary care physicians and factors associated with the use of psychiatric services: A naturalistic study. *Aging & Mental Health, 10*(5), 521–524.

Digna, J. F., van Schaik, D. J. F., Klijn, A. F. J., van Hout, H. P. J., van Marwijk, H. W. J., Beekman, A. T. F., et al. (2004). Patients' preferences in the treatment of depressive disorder in primary care. *General Hospital Psychiatry, 26*, 184–189.

Dimidjian, S., Hollon, S. D., Dobson, K. S., Schmaling, K. B., Kohlenberg, R. J., Addis, E., et al. (2006). Randomized trial of behavioral activation, cognitive therapy, and antidepressant medication in the acute treatment of adults with major depression. *Journal of Consulting and Clinical Psychology, 74*(4), 658–670.

DiTomasso, R. A., & Gilman, R. (2005). Behavioral assessment. In A. Freeman, S. H. Felgoise, A. M. Nezu, C. M. Nezu, & M. A. Reinecke (Eds.), *International encyclopedia of cognitive and behavioral therapies.* New York: Springer Publishing Company.

Ekers, D. M., Lovell, K., & Playle, J. F. (2006). The use of CBT based, brief, facilitated self-help interventions in primary care mental health service provision: Evaluation of a 10-day training programme. *Clinical Effectiveness in Nursing, 9*, e88–e96.

Feldman, G. (2007). Cognitive and behavioral therapies for depression: Overview, new directions, and practical recommendations for dissemination. *Psychiatric Clinics of North America, 30*, 39–50.

Feldman, M. D., Franks, P., Epstein, R. M., Franz, C. E., & Kravitz, R. L. (2006). Do patient requests for antidepressants enhance or hinder physicians' evaluation of depression? A randomized controlled trial. *Medical Care, 44*(12), 1107–1113.

Frederick, J. T., Steinman, L. E., Prohaska, T., Satariano, W. A., Bruce, M., Bryant, L., et al. (2007). Community-based treatment of late life depression: An expert panel-informed literature review. *American Journal of Preventive Medicine, 33*, 222–249.

Freeman, A., Pretzer, J., Fleming, B., & Simon, K. M. (2004). *Clinical applications of cognitive therapy* (2nd ed.). New York: Kluwer Academic/Plenum Publishers.

Fremont, W. P., Nastasi, R., Newman, N., & Roizen, N. J. (2008). Comfort level of pediatricians and family medicine physicians diagnosing and treating child and adolescent psychiatric disorders. *International Journal of Psychiatry in Medicine, 38*(2), 153–169.

Galeazzi, G. M., Ferrari, S., Giaroli, G., MacKinnon, A., Merelli, E., Motti, L., et al. (2005). Psychiatric disorders and depression in multiple sclerosis outpatients: Impact of disability and interferon beta therapy. *Neurological Science, 26*, 255–262.

Gaynes, B. N., Rush, A. J., Trivedi, M. H., Wisniewski, S. R., Balasubramani, G. K., Spencer, D. C., et al. (2007). Major depression symptoms in primary care and psychiatric settings: A cross-sectional analysis. *Annals of Family Medicine, 5*(2), 126–134.

Gilson, M., & Freeman, A. (1999). *Overcoming depression: A cognitive therapy approach for taming the depression beast*. New York: Oxford University Press.

Golden, J., O'Dwyer, A. M., & Conroy, R. M. (2005). Depression and anxiety in patients with hepatitis C: Prevalence, detection rates and risk factors. *General Hospital Psychiatry, 27*, 431–438.

Halbreich, U., & Karkum, S. (2006). Cross-cultural and social diversity of prevalence of postpartum depression and depressive symptoms. *Journal of Affective Disorders, 91*, 97–111.

Hamilton, M. A. (1960). A rating scale for depression. *Journal of Neurology, Neurosurgery, and Psychiatry, 23* 56–62.

Hameed, U., Schwartz, T. L., Malhotra, K., West, R. L., & Bertone, F. (2005). Antidepressant treatment in the primary care office: Outcomes for adjustment disorder versus major depression. *Annals of Clinical Psychiatry, 17*(2), 77–81.

Hayley, S., Poulter, M. O., Merail, A., & Anisman, H. (2005). The pathogenesis of clinical depression: Stressor-and cytokine-induced alterations of neuroplasticity. *Neuroscience, 135*, 659–678.

Haynes, S. N., Leisen, M. B., & Blaine, D. D. (1997). Design of individualized behavioral treatment programs using functional analytic clinical case models. *Psychological Assessment, 9*, 334–348.

Haynes, S. N., & Williams, A. E. (2003). Case formulation and the design of behavioral treatment programs: Matching treatment mechanisms to causal variables for behavior problems. *European Journal of Psychological Assessment, 19*, 164.

Hollon, S. D., DeRubeis, R. J., Evans, M. D., Wiemer, J. J., Gravey, M. J., Grove, W. M., et al. (1992). Cognitive therapy and pharmacotherapy for depression: Singly and in combination. *Archives of General Psychiatry, 49*, 774–781.

Joynt, K. E., Whellan, D. J., & O'Connor, C. M. (2003). Depression and cardiovascular disease: Mechanisms of interaction. *Biological Psychiatry, 54*, 248–261.

Kalivas, P. W., & Duffy, P. (1995). Selective activation of dopamine transmission in the shell of the nucleus accumbens by stress. *Brain Research, 675*, 325–328.

Katz, D. A., & McHorney, C. A. (2002). The relationship between insomnia and health-related quality of life in patients with chronic illness. *Journal of Family Practice, 51*(3), 229–235.

Kelleher, K. J., & Stevens, J. (2009). Evolution of child mental health services in primary care. *Academic Pediatrics, 9*, 7–14.

Keller, M. B., McCullough, J. P., Klein, D. N., Arnow, B., Dunner, D. L., Gellenberg, A. J., et al. (2000). A comparison of nefazodone, the cognitive behavioral-analysis system of psychotherapy, and their combination for the treatment of chronic depression. *New England Journal of Medicine, 342*, 1462–1470.

Ko, D. T., Hebert, P. R., Coffey, C. S., Sedrakyan, A., Curtis, J. P., & Krumholz, H. M. (2002). Betablocker therapy and symptoms of depression, fatigue, and sexual dysfunction. *Journal of the American Medical Association, 288*(3), 351–357.

Kotlyar, M., Dysken, M., & Adson, D. E. (2005). Update on drug-induced depression in the elderly. *American Journal of Geriatric Pharmacotherapy, 3*(4), 288–300.

Krishnan, K. R. R., Delong, M., Kraemer, H., Carney, R., Spiegel, D., Gordon, C., et al. (2002). Comorbidity of depression with other medical diseases in the elderly. *Society of Biological Psychiatry, 52*, 559–588.

Lau, A. W., & Kinoshita, L. M. (2006). Cognitive-behavioral therapy with culturally diverse older adults. In P. A. Hays & G. Y. Iwamasa (Eds.), *Culturally responsive cognitive-behavioral therapy* (p. 182). Washington, DC: American Psychological Association.

Matheson, F. I., Moineddin, R., Dunn, J. R., Creatore, M. I., Gozdyra, P., & Glazier, R. H. (2006). Urban neighborhoods, chronic stress, gender and depression. *Social Science and Medicine, 63*, 2604–2616.

McConnell, S., Jacka, F. N., Williams, L. J., Dodd, S., & Berk, M. (2005). The relationship between depression and cardiovascular disease. *International Journal of Psychiatry in Clinical Practice, 9* (3), 157–167.

McQuaid, J. R., Stein, M. B., Laffaye, C., & McCahill, M. E. (1999). Depression in a primary care clinic: The prevalence and impact of an unrecognized disorder. *Journal of Affective Disorders, 55*(1), 1–10.

Menchetti, M., Murri, M. B., Bertakis, K., Bortolotti, B., & Berardi, D. (2009). Recognition and treatment of depression in primary care: Effect of patients' presentation and frequency of consultation. *Journal of Psychosomatic Research, 66*, 335–341.

Miedema, B., Tatemichi, S. Thomas-Maclean, R., & Stoppard, J. (2004). Barriers to treating depression in the family physician's office. *Canadian Journal of Community Mental Health, 23*(1), 37–46.

Mojtabai, R. (2008). Increase in antidepressant medication in the US adult population between 1990 and 2003. *Psychotherapy and Psychosomatics, 77*, 83–92.

Murphy, G. E., Simons, A. D., Wetzel, R. D., & Lustman, P. J. (1984). Cognitive therapy and pharmacotherapy: Singly and together in the treatment of depression. *Archives of General Psychiatry, 41*, 33–41.

Needleman, L. D. (1999). *Cognitive case conceptualization: A guidebook for practitioners*. Mahwah, NJ: Lawrence Erlbaum.

Nezu, A. M., Nezu, C. M., & Lombardo, E. (2004). *Cognitive-behavioral case formulation and treatment design: A problem-solving approach*. New York: Springer Publishing Company.

Ng, T., Miti, M., Tan, W., Cao, Z., Ong, K., & Eng, P. (2007). Depressive symptoms and chronic obstructive pulmonary disease: Effects on mortality, hospital readmission, symptom burden, functional status, and quality of life. *Archives of Internal Medicine, 167*, 60–67.

Pampallona, S., Bollini, P., Tibaldi, G., Kupelnick, B., & Munizza, C. (2004). Combined pharmacotherapy and psychological treatment for depression: A systematic review. *Archives of General Psychiatry, 61*, 714–719.

Patten, S. B., & Barbui, C. (2004). Drug-induced depression: A systematic review to inform clinical practice. *Psychotherapy and Psychosomatics, 73*, 207–215.

Paulman, A., Paulman, P. M., Huffman, J. C., Wulsin, L. R., & Stern, T. A. (2005). *Journal of Family Practice, 54*(1), 39–46.

Paz Pruitt, I. T. (2007). Family treatment approach for depression in adolescent males. *American Journal of Family Therapy, 35*, 69–81.

Raison, C. L., Broadwell, S. D., Borisov, A. S., Manatunga, A. K., Capuron, L., Woolwine, B. J., et al. (2005). Depressive symptoms and viral clearance in patients receiving interferon-α and ribavirin for hepatitis C. *Brain, Behavior, and Immunity, 19*, 23–27.

Rayburn, N. R., Wenzel, S. L., Elliott, M. N., Hambarsoomians, K., Marshall, G. N., & Tucker, J. S. (2005). Trauma, depression, coping, and mental health service seeking among impoverished women. *Journal of Consulting and Clinical Psychology, 73*(4), 667–677.

Robinson, W. D., Geske, J. A., Prest, L. A., & Barnacle, R. (2004). Depression treatment in primary care. *Journal of the American Board of Family Practitioners, 18*(2), 79–86.

Rosen, R. C., & Kostis, J. B. (1985). Biobehavioral sequellae associated with adrenergic-inhibiting antihypertensive agents: A critical review. *Health Psychology, 4*(6), 579–604.

Saarela, T., & Engestrom, R. (2003). Reported differences in management strategies by primary care physicians and psychiatrists in older patients who are depressed. *International Journal of Geriatric Psychiatry, 18*, 161–168.

Schafer, A., Wittchen, H., Seufert, J., & Kraus, M. R. (2007). Methodological approaches in the assessment of interferon-alpha-induced depression in patients with chronic hepatitis C—A critical review. *International Journal of Methods in Psychiatric Research, 16*(4), 186–201.

Schulberg, H. C., Raue, P. J., & Rollman, B. L. (2002). The effectiveness of psychotherapy in treating depressive disorders in primary care practice: Clinical and cost perspective. *General Psychiatry, 24*(4), 203–212.

Schwenk, T. L., Evans, D. L., Laden, S. K., & Lewis, L. (2004). Treatment outcome and physician-patient communication in primary care patients with chronic, recurrent depression. *American Journal of Psychiatry, 161*(10), 1892–1901.

Scogin, F., & Shah, A. (2006). Screening older adults for depression in primary care settings. *Health Psychology, 25*(6), 675–677.

Siefert, K., Williams, D. R., Finlayson, T. L., & Delva, J. (2007). Modifiable risk and protective factors for depressive symptoms in low-income African American mothers. *American Journal of Orthopsychiatry, 77*(1), 113–123.

Skultety, K. M., & Zeiss, A. (2006). The treatment of depression in older adults in the primary care setting: An evidence-based review. *Health Psychology, 25*, 665–674.

Stone, E. A., Lin, Y., & Quartermain, D. (2008). A final common pathway for depression? Progress toward a general conceptual framework. *Neuroscience and Biobehavioral Reviews, 32*, 508–524.

Swanson, L. (2000). Cerebral hemisphere regulation of motivated behavior. *Brain Research, 886*, 113–164.

van Rijswijk, E., Borghuis, M., van de Lisdonk, E., Zitman, F., & van Weel, C. (2007). Treatment of mental health problems in general practice: A survey of psychotropics prescribed and other treatments provided. *International Journal of Clinical Pharmacology and Therapeutics, 45*(1), 23–29.

Walters, P., & Tylee, A. (2006). Mood disorders in primary care. *Psychiatry, 5*, 138–141.

Wedzicha, A. J. A., & Seemungal, T. A. R. (2007). COPD exacerbations: Defining their cause and prevention. *Lancet, 370*, 786–796.

Wells, K. B., Kataoka, S. H., & Asarnow, J. R. (2001). Affective disorders in children and adolescents: Addressing unmet need in primary care settings. *Biological Psychiatry, 49*, 1111–1120.

Wessely, S., & Pariante, C. (2002). Fatigue, depression and chronic hepatitis C infection. *Psychological Medicine, 32*(1), 1–10.

Weyerer, S., Eifflaender-Gorfer, S., Kohler, L., Jessen, F., Maier, W., Fuchs, A., et al. (2008). Prevalence and risk factors for depression in non-demented primary care attenders aged 75 years and older. *Journal of Affective Disorders, 111*, 153–163.

Whooley, M. A. (2006). Depression and cardiovascular disease: Healing the broken-hearted. *Journal of the American Medical Association, 295*, 2874–2881.

Wichers, M. C., Kenis, G., Leue, C., Koek, G., Robaeys, G., & Maes, M. (2006). Baseline immune activation as a risk factor for the onset of depression during a interferon-alpha treatment. *Biological Psychiatry, 60*, 77–79.

Wolf, N. J., & Hopko, D. R. (2008). Psychosocial and pharmacological interventions for depressed adults in primary care: A critical review. *Clinical Psychology Review, 28*, 131–161.

World Health Organization. (2007). *International standard classification of diseases and related health problems* (10th rev., version from 2007). Geneva: Author.

Wright, J. H. (2004) Integrating cognitive therapy and pharmacotherapy. In R. L. Leahy (Ed.), *Contemporary cognitive therapy.* New York: Guilford.

Wright, J. H., & Casey, D. A. (2005). Pharmacotherapy and cognitive therapy: Combined treatment. In A. Freeman, S. H. Felgoise, A. M. Nezu, C. M. Nezu, & M. A. Reinecke (Eds.), *Encyclopedia of cognitive behavior therapy* (pp. 285–288). New York: Springer Publishing Company.

Anxiety Disorders in Primary Care

17

Jesús A. Salas
Erica A. Henninger
Rebecca K. Stern
Maurice F. Prout

Introduction

Anxiety disorders are one of the most common mental health problems seen in the general medical setting, and have devastating effects on both the individual and community level. They cost an estimated $42 billion dollars per year in the United States, with direct and indirect costs Kroenke, Spitzer, Williams, Monahan, & Löwe, 2007. Anxiety disorders are associated with social and vocational impairment (R. C. Kessler, Berglund, Demler, Jin, Merikangas, & Walters, 2005) and overall poor functioning (M. B. Stein et al., 2005). Recent research also suggests that individuals with anxiety disorders tend to be high users of medical services (Kroenke et al., 2007), and report quality-of-life impairment (Rapaport, Clary, Fayyad, & Endicott, 2005; M. B. Stein et al., 2004). Anxiety disorders are also associated with adverse health behaviors, such as smoking and sedentary lifestyle (Bonnet et al., 2005; John, Meyer, Rumpf, & Hapke, 2004).

Most individuals in need of mental health services turn to their primary care physician (PCP) as a first, and sometimes only, source of help (Haas & deGruy, 2004). A minority of patients with anxiety disorders will receive treatment from specialized mental health professionals (Munoz, Hollon, McGrath, Rehm, & VandenBos, 1994; M. B. Stein et al., 2004). For many patients with anxiety disorders, PCPs have become the de facto mental health professionals (Coyne, Thompson, Klinkman, & Nease, 2002; Garcia-Shelton & Vogel, 2002). Research suggests, however, that despite their prevalence and associated disability, anxiety disorders have only begun to receive consideration in the medical setting other than as a comorbidity of depression. Anxiety disorders have been granted less attention than depression in the medical literature, partly because each specific anxiety disorder involves different symptoms and distinct treatment considerations, making them more complicated in terms of accurate diagnosis and treatment planning (Katon & Roy-Byrne, 2007; M. B. Stein et al.).

Anxiety disorders are commonly undetected and untreated in medical populations. In a recent study, Kroenke and colleagues found that a minority of patients (15–36%) with anxiety are recognized in primary care (Kroenke et al., 2007). Several factors have been cited to explain such poor detection rates, including underused screening measures, office visit time constraints, lack of physician education about anxiety, and poor patient disclosure due to mental illness stigma (Arnau, Meagher, Norris, & Bramson, 2001; Culpepper, 2004; Dutton et al., 2004; Katon & Roy-Byrne, 2007; Katzelnick et al., 2001; Kroenke et al., 2007; Mori et al., 2003; Roy-Byrne & Wagner, 2004). Additional research suggests the quality of care for primary care patients diagnosed with anxiety disorders is particularly poor (M. B. Stein et al., 2004; Young, Klap, Sherbourne, & Wells, 2001).

Assessment and Diagnostic Issues

The *Diagnostic and Statistical Manual of Mental Disorders* (*DSM-IV-TR*; American Psychiatric Association, 2000) describes 12 diagnostic categories of anxiety disorders that have overlapping features and some differences. PCPs must recognize essential features of each disorder for accurate diagnosis. Effective screening is the first step to improve quality of care. In mental health settings, structured clinical interviews, such as the Anxiety Disorder Interview Schedule (Brown, DiNardo, & Barlow, 2004) and the Structured Clinical Interview for *DSM-IV-TR* Disorders (First, Spitzer, Gibbon, & Williams, 1997), are commonly used to aid in diagnosis. However, PCPs, nurses, and other health professionals in primary care settings often lack time and training to complete a comprehensive interview of a patient's psychological functioning (Mori et al., 2003). Self-report screening measures have been developed in an effort to identify patients who may be experiencing symptoms of distress and may benefit from a comprehensive evaluation. These screening measures provide a relatively objective glance at a range of symptoms in a fairly brief amount of time, which makes them easy to administer. Commonly used screening measures for various anxiety disorders include the Beck Anxiety Inventory (BAI; Beck, 1993), the State-Trait Anxiety Inventory (Spielberger, Gorusch, & Lushene, 1970), and the Hamilton Anxiety Rating Scale (Hamilton, 1969). Although these measures are valuable in identifying patients with some type of anxiety disorder, little research has been conducted using these measures in the primary care setting (Katon & Roy-Byrne, 2007; Mori et al., 2003). Consequently, a concern with using these inventories is the possibility of falsely identifying patients with anxiety, because many of these scales assess somatic symptoms, which are common to many nonanxious medical patients (Wetherell & Arean, 1997).

At present, three commonly used measures that have been investigated for use in primary care settings include the Beck Anxiety Inventory-Primary Care (BAI-PC; Beck, Guth, Steer, & Ball, 1997), the Primary Care Evaluation of Mental Disorders (PRIME-MD; Spitzer, Kroenke, & Williams, 1999), and the Generalized Anxiety Disorders Scale (GAD-7; Spitzer, Kroenke, Williams, & Löwe, 2006). The BAI-PC (Beck, Steer, Ball, Ciervo, & Kabat, 1997) is a 7-item version of the 21-item BAI, which can be completed in one minute. Research suggests that the BAI-PC is methodologically sound, and may be an effective screening tool for generalized anxiety disorder (GAD), panic disorder (PD), posttraumatic stress disorder (PTSD), and depression. The BAI-PC also demonstrates good sensitivity and specificity rates in differentiating primary care patients with and without anxiety (Mori et al., 2003).

The PRIME-MD (Spitzer et al., 1994) is a brief, rater-administered scale to assist PCPs in diagnosing patients with psychiatric disorders common to primary care settings. It is a 25-item questionnaire which screens for mood, anxiety, somatoform, and eating disorders and alcohol use. There is also a clinician evaluation guide to follow up on positive items. The PRIME-MD can be completed in less than 20 minutes, and can efficiently screen patients with GAD and PD (Rollman et al., 2005). A shorter, self-report version of the PRIME-MD was also developed. This self-report inventory, the Patient Health Questionnaire (PHQ), takes less than three minutes to complete, and shows similar validity and clinical utility to the PRIME-MD (Spitzer et al., 1999).

The GAD-7 (Spitzer et al., 2006) is a 7-item self-report scale with good reliability and validity that is efficient for screening for GADs and assessing severity in primary care settings. A cut point is used to optimize the sensitivity and specificity for the diagnosis of GAD.

Incidence and Clinical Manifestation in the Primary Care Setting

Prevalence in Primary Care

Studies about the prevalence of diagnoses of anxiety disorders in primary care settings suggest the rate of anxiety disorders in the population of patients seeking primary care is higher than in the general population. However, only a few studies are available to precisely quantify their prevalence. A recent study found that 19.5% of the primary care patients had at least one anxiety disorder (Kroenke et al., 2007). Among those anxiety patients, 12.85% had one anxiety disorder, 4.35% had two anxiety disorders, 1.45% had three, and 0.83% had four anxiety disorders. Deacon, Lickel, and Abramowitz (2008) found in a sample of 171 anxiety-disordered primary care patients that 35.7% (61) of the patients had at least one additional Axis I diagnosis, including 16.9% (29) with an additional anxiety disorder, 14.6% (25) with major depression, and 19.8% (34) with other Axis I diagnoses.

Varying 1-year prevalence rates for anxiety disorders have been reported in primary care settings: *Specific phobia*: 6.3% (Nisenson, Pepper, Schwenk, & Coyne, 1998); *social phobia*: 2.6%–6.2% (Kroenke et al., 2007; Nisenson et al.); *posttraumatic stress*: 8.6% (Kroenke et al.); *GAD*: 1.6%–14.8% (Kroenke et al; Nisenson et al.; Olfson et al., 1997, 2000; Parker, May, Maviglia, Petrakis, Sunde, & Gloyd, 1997; Von Korff et al., 1987); *PD*: 0.7–8.3% (Kroenke et al., 2007; Nisenson et al., 1998;

Olfson et al., 1997, 2000; Parker et al., 1997; Von Korff et al., 1987); *obsessive-compulsive*: 0.84%–2.0% (Fireman, Koran, Leventhal, & Jacobson, 2001; Nisenson et al.); *agoraphobia without a history of PD*: 0.7%.

In a sample of 366 primary care patients with one or more anxiety disorders, Stein and colleagues (2004) found the following prevalence of anxiety disorders: 69.7% for PD with and without agoraphobia, 59% for GAD, 48.9% for social phobia, and 33.3% for PTSD. These percentages are not mutually exclusive and evidence high comorbidity: 48.6% of the sample had more than one anxiety disorder. Deacon, Lickel, and Abramowitz (2008) found that in a sample of 171 anxiety-disordered primary care patients, 23.98% (41 patients) had a principal diagnosis of PD, 18.13% (31) had social phobia, 18.13% (31) had obsessive-compulsive disorder, 21.05% (36) had GAD, and 18.13% (31) had specific phobias. Comparisons across studies are complicated by differences in sample characteristics, diagnostic criteria, and assessment procedures. Using the same diagnostic criteria and same evaluation procedures, Kroenke and colleagues (2007) found differences in anxiety disorders prevalence (7.0–32%) among 15 different primary care sites. Overall, studies indicate that PD, GAD, and PTSD may be the most common anxiety disorders in primary care.

Medical Utilization in Anxiety Disorder Patients

For patients who frequently visit general medicine practices, the prevalence of anxiety or depressive disorder is 40–60% higher than for patients with low frequency (McFarland, Freeborn, Mullooly, & Pope, 1985; Neal et al., 1998). A number of studies indicate that the rate of medical use for anxiety disorder patients in a 1-year period is approximately 50% higher than the rate for general medical outpatients (Barsky, Delamater, & Orav, 1999; Deacon et al., 2008; Kennedy & Schwab, 1997; Kroenke et al., 2007; Marciniak, Lage, Landbloom, Dunayevich, & Bowman, 2004; Swinson, Cox, & Woszcyna, 1992). Kroenke and colleagues (2007) found that patients without anxiety disorders averaged 1.6 self-reported physician consultations in the past three months, patients with *one* anxiety disorder averaged 1.9 visits, patients with *two* anxiety disorders averaged 3.2 visits, and patients with *three or four* anxiety disorders averaged 4.1 visits. Deacon and colleagues (2008) found the average anxiety disorder patient reported having 6.2 outpatient medical consultations in the past 12 months; this rate does not include mental health consultations, inpatient, or surgical treatments. Most of the visits were for internal medicine (39.8%), urgent care (39.8%), family medicine (28.7%), and emergency medicine (28.1%). Among different anxiety disorders, patients with PD reported significantly higher rates of emergency medicine, family medicine, and cardiology consultations.

Deacon and colleagues' (2008) findings are consistent with results from studies that indicate that panic-disordered patients have significantly higher rates of medical use than patients with other anxiety disorders and controls (Barsky, Delamater, & Orav, 1999; Kennedy & Schwab, 1997; Rees, Richards, & Smith, 1998). Also, research indicates that the experience of panic attacks, irrespective of diagnosis, is predictive of increased health care use (Boyd, 1986). The disproportionately high medical use of patients with panic attacks is not surprising, given the intensity of somatic correlates of a panic attack (Dattilio & Salas-Auvert, 2000).

Clinical Manifestations of Anxiety

Anxiety is not a singular entity or homogeneous phenomenon; instead, it involves four major response systems: cognitive, affective, behavioral, and biological/physiological. Some features of each response system vary significantly across anxiety disorders and among patients. The essential features for each anxiety disorder are listed in the *DSM-IV-TR* (American Psychiatric Association, 2000). Beyond the anxiety disorders listed in the *DSM-IV-TR*, anxiety is an essential feature of other diagnoses: Adjustment Disorders with Anxiety (*DSM-IV-TR* 309.24), Adjustment Disorder with Mixed Anxiety and Depressed Mood (*DSM-IV-TR* 309.24), some cases of somatic delusions (i.e., delusion of a parasitic infestation), and some somatoform disorders. Hypochondriasis is of particular importance, because 5–9% of primary care patients have this disorder (Barsky et al., 1991; Fallon, Javitch, Hollander, & Liebowitz, 1991; Noyes et al., 1997). People with hypochondriasis show a strong bias toward beliefs that they are sick. They tend to seek out medical information to validate their distorted beliefs, and are prone to consult health care providers.

Implications of the Nature of Anxiety for Consultation and Diagnosis

Primary care patients may directly report feelings of anxiety, but more often complain of somatic symptoms, which often raise the possibility of a serious illness. Because the content of the typical primary care consultation is influenced by what patients choose to disclose and how they present information, if patients focus on their somatic symptoms, the PCP may miss potential psychological distress associated with or concurrent with these symptoms. Research findings consistently demonstrate that diagnosis of an anxiety disorder is more likely when patients report significant subjective complaints (cognitive and emotional symptoms of anxiety) than when they focus primarily on somatic symptoms. In a sample of 1,211 patients from 12 primary care centers, only 83 patients (6.9%) reported psychosocial symptoms as a reason for the consultation (Füredi, Rózsa, Zámbori, & Szadóczky, 2003). When patients consulted with their general practitioner while experiencing acute physical illness there was little chance that comorbid anxiety or mood disorders were diagnosed by the PCP (Füredi et al.). D. Kessler, Lloyd, and Colleagues (1999) had a sample of primary care patients report how they felt on the General Health Questionnaire and to give attributions for 13 common bodily symptoms. General practitioners were blind to patients' scores on both questionnaires. Researchers found that when patients tended to explain somatic sensations as normal, practitioners failed to detect depression and anxiety disorders in 46 (85%) of the 54 patients. In contrast, when patients tended to explain somatic symptoms as an expression of psychological distress, practitioners failed to detect cases of depression and anxiety in only 21 (38%) of 55 patients. Those findings suggest that patients' different attribution styles for physical symptoms are associated with different rates of detection of anxiety and depression. These factors may help to understand research findings indicating that general practitioners fail to diagnose up to half of anxiety and depression cases (Fleet et al., 1996; Füredi et al.; R. C. Kessler, DuPont, Berglund, & Wittchen,

1999a; D. Kessler, Lloyd, Lewis, & Gray, 1999b; Kroenke et al., 2007; Löwe et al., 2003).

Anxiety and Depression Comorbidity

The high comorbidity rates of anxiety and depressive disorders are documented in both epidemiologic and clinical samples. Fifty-eight percent of respondents in the National Comorbidity Study with a lifetime prevalence of major depressive disorder (MDD) also had at least one anxiety disorder in their lifetimes. In addition, 51.2% of participants with 1-year MDD prevalence also had at least one anxiety disorder in the past 12 months. Among anxiety disorders, PD and GAD have the strongest comorbidity with MDD. Large primary care surveys suggest anxiety-depression comorbidity is even higher in primary care patients than in the general population (Nisenson, Pepper, Schwenk, & Coyne, 1998; Olfson, Fireman, & Weissman, 1997. Overall, research findings consistently suggest that the presence of comorbid anxiety-depression is associated with greater severity of symptoms (including more somatic symptoms), an increased risk of suicidality, a more chronic course, greater social and occupational functional impairments, and poor treatment responsiveness, that is, slower progress and higher chances of relapse (Belzer & Schneier, 2004; C. Brown et al., 1996; Durhan, Allan, & Hackett, 1997; Olfson et al., 1997; Pollack, 2005; Roy-Byrne et al., 2000). Typically, epidemiological studies (Epidemiological Catchment Area data; NCS data) indicate that cases of MDD have a later onset than cases of anxiety, which suggests that in a significant proportion of cases, depression is secondary to anxiety. Early detection of anxiety disorders may prevent the future development of a secondary depressive disorder.

Brief Case History

Debra was a 37-year-old Caucasian female, married for 10 years and mother of two girls, ages 8 and 6. She was a college graduate working full time as a health care facility administrator. Her PCP referred Debra for treatment because of her anxiety. Debra presented her complaints as "I suffer from anxiety; I have panic attacks and fear of dying."

Symptoms and Problems

Debra reported a long-standing history of anxiety. Her panic attacks started six months ago, and she is now experiencing weekly mild panic attacks (unexpected and expected). Her panic attacks are marked by palpitations, sweating, hot and cold flashes, abdominal distress, feeling faint, fear of losing emotional control or going crazy, and a fear of dying. The intensity of her panic attacks varies from mild to moderate, and usually last between 10 and 60 minutes. She indicated that her panic attacks were the most disturbing problem, then her constant worries, and then her fear of dying. She also worried about dying a slow and painful death caused by breast cancer, and felt devastated when she thought about leaving her children without her protection and love. In terms of her generalized anxiety, Debra reported she had always anticipated that something bad was about to happen to her or to her family. She found it difficult to control her worries, felt irritable, and had difficulties concentrating at work.

The main consequences of her panic attacks were: (a) avoiding some business meetings through delegating attendance to subordinates, (b) not flying, (c) avoiding travel, (d) avoiding social gatherings, (e) feeling angry because she felt she should be able to control her anxiety; not being able to do so made her feel "crazy and abnormal." Other problems she presented were: (a) fear of heights, and (b) "I don't want my husband to touch my breasts for fear that he might find a lump. I am very afraid of breast cancer. My mother and grandmother had breast cancer."

Diagnosis:

Axis I: 300.21 Panic Disorder with Agoraphobia;
300.02 Generalized Anxiety Disorder;
300.29 Specific Phobias (Acrophobia; Disease phobia: breast cancer).

Axis II: Dependent Personality Disorder traits.

Axis III: None

Axis IV: Job promotion

GAF: Current: 60 Highest level in the past year: 80

Precipitants/Antecedents: Debra indicated that her panic attacks occur in enclosed areas, such as sitting in the middle of a pew in church, the middle of the row in a movie theater, in business meetings, and in a corner at restaurants. She also reported panic attacks in new situations, when away from home, before medical consultations, when having mammograms, and when hearing or watching stories of health problems, especially about breast cancer. Stories of people suffering harm or illness usually triggered worries, and lately, panic attacks.

Relevant History/Predisposing Factors: Debra said that she was a bit anxious as long as she could remember, but her problem was intensifying. She first experienced limited-symptoms panic attacks at age 22, but they were infrequent and did not impair her functioning. Those subclinical panic attacks lasted a short time and ceased without treatment. However, her tendency to worry continued. She had no history of depression or alcohol/substance abuse. She described her family history as good and felt close to her parents. However, her father was overprotective and opinionated. She also indicated her father was very anxious, but only expressed his chronic abdominal distress. She reported talking to her mother daily, and occasionally, sought validation from her father about what she saw as important decisions. Her anxiety exacerbated 6 years ago after her mother had breast cancer, and became out of control about 4 months ago, approximately when she got a job promotion. Her new position involved more meetings and traveling. Other than her anxiety and its consequences, Debra reported that her life was good.

Coping Strategies: Debra's main coping strategies to deal with her anxiety and panic were avoidance and escape from situations she thought would cause panic attacks or worry. Although she was not aware, she also coped by going to most places with her husband, and by demanding that he stay with her. She described her husband as "pleasing, caring, and protective."

Protective Factors: Debra was very intelligent, disciplined, and committed to her treatment. She was compliant with her homework assignments. She had good family support and strong interpersonal skills, she liked her job, and was self-confident in her professional skills.

Underlying Psychosocial Mechanisms: The development of a moderately dependent relationship with her parents for emotional support seems to have contributed to her anxiety vulnerability. Her father's anxious somatizations could have modeled health anxiety behaviors. Also, his mild controlling tendencies seemed to have undermined Debra's confidence to solve problems and make decisions, as it fostered some fear of potential loss of his love and approval. Her mother's history of breast cancer caused a disruption in the security of her attachment bond, producing more separation anxiety. It also led her to worry about developing breast cancer. More recently, her increased work-related social and travel responsibilities exacerbated her separation anxiety. Most of Debra's current worries were about losing her loved ones due to terminal illness or fatal accident. She was prone to catastrophize about others and about herself. Debra's high anxiety sensitivity rendered her prone to panic attacks and social anxiety. Specifically, she was afraid of the emotion of anxiety and associated bodily changes because she believed it could cause her physical or psychological harm. Also, she anticipated that, if as a result of having a panic attack she passed out or showed observable anxiety reactions, she would make a scene and elicit negative evaluations, ridicule, and social rejection from others.

Debra's health anxiety and panic attacks appeared to be maintained through three self-confirmatory mechanisms of her catastrophic beliefs: (a) bodily hypervigilance for potentially dangerous somatic changes, which increased her perception of bodily sensations; (b) distorted information processing that reinforced her inflated perception of danger and inability to cope; and (c) forms of cognitive, affective, and behavioral avoidance. Debra did not use bodily checking or reassurance-seeking behaviors. She tried to avoid those behaviors for fear of facing what she or her health care providers could find. Her generalized anxiety was also maintained by her reluctance to accept the possibility of facing interpersonal loss or harm; her worry served as a magical way of preventing the uncertainty about potential aversive outcomes. In addition, Debra maintained her chronic worry through attempts to suppress negative affect, avoidance of situations that could induce negative mood, and her tendency to conceal her anxiety from others, which contributed to not feeling close to others, except her safety people (parents and husband).

Treatment Plan: Debra reported that she had been taking Effexor (75 mg/day) for two months when she came for psychological treatment. The medication was prescribed by her family physician, and she indicated that it helped to reduce her generalized anxiety. Her last visit to her PCP was a month prior to the psychology consultation.

Her psychological treatment was conducted in 6 phases and delivered in 20 weekly 50-minute sessions. First was the panic control phase, which included the following interventions: education about the nature of anxiety, education about PD with agoraphobia, discussion of treatment rationale, interoceptive exposure, panic-focused cognitive restructuring, diaphragmatic breathing, and homework assignments (four sessions). The second phase focused on agoraphobia control, which included gradual in-vivo exposure, agoraphobia-focused cognitive restructuring, and applied diaphragmatic breathing (four sessions). The third phase targeted her generalized anxiety. This phase included education about GAD and treatment rationale, progressive muscle relaxation (PMR) training, cognitive restructuring, and homework assignments (four sessions). The fourth phase focused on her acrophobia, which included prolonged in-vivo exposure, attention training, focal cognitive restructuring, and applied diaphragmatic breathing (two sessions). The fifth phase (three sessions) focused on her fear of breast cancer and fear of death, and consisted of a treatment rationale, prolonged exposure to a medical education video about breast examination and breast cancer, focused cognitive restructuring, and homework assignment (breast self-examination and participation in a breast cancer support walk during the breast cancer awareness month). The sixth phase (three sessions) targeted relapse prevention and included the following technique: brief assertiveness training regarding her dependent relationship with her parents. The goal of this section was to teach Debra adaptive ways of feeling secure and safe even when her husband or parents were not around. Other goals were to review skills and knowledge learned in therapy, having realistic expectations about the role that anxiety plays in her life, identification of future potential difficult situations, and how to cope with them.

Mechanisms of Change and Assessment of Progress: The combination of different techniques in the treatment phases allowed Debra to better understand the nature of her anxiety problems. Debra also understood how, unintentionally, she was maintaining the panic attacks and worries. Three main change mechanisms facilitated her recovery: (a) habituation to experience fear and associated somatic changes, (b) cognitive reappraisal of anxiety and associated bodily changes, and (c) increased confidence in problem-solving and decision-making skills. In addition to the techniques described in the treatment plan, Debra shared her experience with other coworkers who had expressed suffering from anxiety and depression. As a result, she improved in processing vulnerable emotions with others, which, in turn, helped her to feel independent from her safety people, and to see herself as normal. Regarding problem solving, Debra learned to trust her judgment more and reduced the dependency on her father's approval of her decisions. She improved her self-concept as competent to effectively deal with future life adversities. Measurements of relevant outcome variables were repeatedly administered during the course of treatment. Her medication was titrated, and she was not taking Effexor by the follow-up sessions.

Cognitive-Behavioral Case Formulation

A cognitive-behavioral case formulation consists of biopsychosocial causal and predictive hypotheses that integrate theories about anxiety disorders and research findings with idiosyncratic data obtained for a particular patient (Nezu, Nezu, & Lombardo, 2004; Persons, 2008; Tarrier, 2006). A comprehensive case conceptualization was described in the previous section for the case of Debra and was used in planning her treatment.

Current cognitive-behavioral models of anxiety disorders regard them as being a result of interactions between internal diatheses (creating vulnerability) and exposure to external and/or internal stressors. Individual differences (i.e., in genetics, early learning experiences, dispositional factors) serve as predisposing factors. Precipitants of anxiety disorders include exposure to environmental stressors (i.e., life events) and internal stressors (i.e., bodily sensations, affective or cognitive experiences, biological dysregulation). People develop anxiety disorders when perceived threats become disproportionate to the actual threats. Patients maintain anxiety disorders through patterns of biased attention, distorted information processing, and maladaptive coping behaviors that may be reinforced by environmental contingencies (patients' social system). As part of the case formulation, practitioners create a model about the functional relationship among precipitants, anxiety responses, coping efforts, and their consequences to explain patients' patterns of responding (Haynes, Nelson, Tacher, & Kaholokula, 2001).

Identifying and Addressing Obstacles to Treatment

Cognitive-behavior therapy (CBT) is demanding on patients, and does not work well with patients who are not willing and/or able to take an active role in treatment. A number of potential obstacles to CBT for psychiatric disorders exist (Mancebo, Pinto, Rasmussen, & Eisen, 2008; Wright, Basco, & Thase, 2006). This section will cover three frequent obstacles that occur.

Refusal and Noncompliance With Exposure Practices

An essential component of effective CBT for anxiety disorders is the use of in-session and out-of-session exposure practices. Such interventions involve the activation of patients' fears through the systematic and repetitive confrontation with distressing stimuli. For some patients, the exposure component can be intimidating, and they are reluctant to initiate treatment or to fully engage in the exposure tasks. Such concerns are usually addressed by: (a) explaining to patients how they unintentionally contributed to anxiety maintenance through avoidance; (b) providing patients with the rationale for the exposure (i.e., the modification of dysfunctional associations among stimuli, responses and threatening meaning, testing and correcting false beliefs, and practicing new skills); (c) establishing a trusting relationship and providing encouragement for courage with confronting feared stimuli; (d) using gradual exposure, which allows patients to first confront stimuli that generate manageable levels of anxiety; (e) modeling the desired approach behaviors to feared situations; and (e) conducting a cost-benefit analysis of maintaining and eliminating/reducing anxiety symptoms.

Homework Noncompletion

Homework assignments are another essential component of CBT protocols for anxiety disorders. Homework completion requires patients to clearly understand the purpose and nature of assignments, and also their ability to engage in disciplined practices (e.g., using thoughts records, doing behavioral experiments, reading relevant material, rehearsing coping skills such as relaxation and problem solving). A considerable amount of self-directed work is required to alter stable cognitive and behavioral patterns. Several obstacles may interfere with homework completion because they impair a patient's capacity to do the assignments or take priority over the homework. Examples of such obstacles are patients' cognitive deficits, low motivation and energy to do the assignments, which are usually associated with comorbid depression, patients' comorbid health problems, and lack of discipline. Also, exposure to environmental stressors such as family conflicts, or financial and legal problems, may interfere with homework completion. Assignment noncompliance can be reduced or prevented by: (a) collaborating with patients in designing homework so tasks are not too difficult and patients develop ownership and commitment to them; (b) rehearsing the assignments in-session so patients better understand them, and identifying in advance potential obstacles to the task outside of the office; (c) checking patients' understanding and acceptability of the assignments before they leave; (d) conducting assignment follow-up at the beginning of the next session; (e) discussing reasons for missed homework and, if possible, arranging for the assignment to be completed during the next session before assigning any new homework. Patients' reported obstacles to homework completion must be addressed and the necessary adjustments made to ensure a successful performance.

Family Accommodations

Accommodations refer to modification of daily activities that patient's family members (or romantic partner) perform to adjust to anxiety symptoms. Such accommodations include modifying daily routines, providing excessive reassurance and overprotection, taking over patient's responsibilities, and participating in avoidance or rituals at the patient's request. Usually, adjustments intend to reduce distress; however, they help maintain anxiety symptoms. Accommodations are part of family or couple dynamics, and its members may be resistant to change that pattern of interaction. The maintenance of such patterns throughout the treatment may interfere with progress because they allow maintenance of dysfunctional coping behaviors. Family accommodation can be addressed by: (a) helping the family (partner) become aware of the impact of such adjustments; (b) educating the family (partner) about more helpful ways of dealing with symptoms; (c) helping patients develop awareness so they can modify family patterns that exacerbate or maintain anxiety symptoms; and (d) if necessary, referring for adjunctive family (couples) therapy.

Points of Collaboration With Physician and Family

The Importance of Collaborative Care

PCPs are under great pressure to diagnose and treat a variety of medical and psychosocial problems. As stated earlier, it has been consistently documented that mental health problems such as anxiety are overrepresented, yet poorly detected in the primary care setting (Culpepper, 2004; Katon & Roy-Byrne, 2007; Katzelnick et al., 2001; Kroenke et al., 2007; Roy-Byrne & Wagner, 2004). Cognitive-behavioral therapists are in a unique position to expand their practice to include medical settings, where their expertise in diagnosis and intervention can close the gap that currently exists in quality care. Research suggests that collaborative practice between PCPs and psychologists is one method to meet the multiple needs of primary care patients (Bray & Rogers, 1997).

Collaboration involves a functional interdependency among each party and the notion that each health care provider's point of view is fully recognized and valued. Simply put, psychologists, PCPs, nurses, and physician assistants can work together to treat patients' multifaceted issues (McDaniel & Hepworth, 2004). This shared responsibility may reduce the provider's burnout and the stress felt with complex, challenging cases (Seaburn, Lorenz, Gunn, Gawinski, & Mauksch, 1996). It is essential for clinicians to understand common medical conditions seen in primary care in order to understand the clinical picture and collaborate effectively. Finally, being part of a health care team may increase a therapist's source of referrals and opportunity for long-term follow-up with patients.

The Therapist's Role in Addressing Anxiety in Primary Care

Cognitive-behavioral therapists can assist PCPs in enhancing quality of care for patients with anxiety in several ways, depending on the flexibility of their position and the model of collaboration being implemented. First, they can emphasize the importance of anxiety disorder screening in all patients, given patients' lack of self-disclosure about mental health issues in this setting. Psychologists, for example, are educated about a number of self-report measures for anxiety disorders, and can use this knowledge to identify patients with anxiety. Second, psychologists can provide more comprehensive psychological evaluations when needed. These evaluations are especially valuable, given that patients with a primary anxiety disorder diagnosis frequently present with comorbid conditions, such as depression, somatoform disorders, and secondary anxiety disorders. Thus, psychologists can use their expertise to diagnose any additional conditions, which is essential to treatment planning (Mergl et al., 2007; Sherbourne, Jackson, Meredith, Camp, & Wells, 1996).

Next, cognitive-behavioral therapists can assist in developing treatment plans, which often include both psychopharmacological and psychological interventions. Although PCPs are able to prescribe medications to manage anxiety, they may be unfamiliar with the range of treatment modalities and interventions that are empirically supported within psychology. Psychologists may serve as consultant-educators, enhancing knowledge of psychological treatment strategies and interventions for each type of anxiety disorder. They can also help PCPs to better understand the role of biopsychosocial variables in clinical presentations of anxiety-disordered patients, as well as anxiety's effects on health behaviors and medical conditions. Psychologists can educate PCPs about the importance of the patient-physician relationship when treating patients with mental health conditions. Finally, psychologists may practice individual and group psychotherapy or conduct brief interventions and skill-building strategies for anxiety within primary care settings, eliminating the need for outside referrals.

Patients presenting with anxiety in medical settings may have comorbid health conditions that are affected by anxiety, such as asthma, diabetes, irritable bowel syndrome, and chronic pain. Given the time constraints of primary care practice, psychologists should be direct and expedient in evaluating patients (Haley et al., 1998). Primary care psychologists must obtain information and draw conclusions in limited time, and may need to make decisions with limited data (Gatchel & Oordt, 2003).

Clinical Considerations for Collaborating With Family Members

Research in the area of family CBT for anxiety disorders has mainly focused on the value of it in treating childhood anxiety. Although the literature on family therapy for the treatment of anxiety disorders in adults is scarce, there does appear to be clinical utility to collaborating with family members of primary care patients with anxiety. Research consistently demonstrates the powerful influence of family on health and illness. Collaboration with families may allow for comprehensive treatment of anxiety and other health issues (Campbell & Patterson, 1995; Kendall, Hudson, Gosch, Flannery-Hudson, & Suveg, 2008). By sharing power with patients and family members, psychologists and PCPs may be improving health outcomes (McDaniel & Hepworth, 2004).

Collaborating with patients and families surrounding issues of anxiety may take several forms. Understanding the cultural and health beliefs of each family can assist health care providers in understanding the etiology of the patient's condition, as well as the best approach to care. Therapists can also provide education and support to family members who may not understand how they contribute to anxiety through reinforcement and modeling of maintenance behaviors and beliefs, and through expression of irritation, sadness, or disappointment with the distress and impaired functioning of the patient. In treating anxiety, family support may be needed to carry out aspects of the intervention (i.e., using family for support during in-vivo exposure for phobias). Family CBT may also be appropriate for certain patients with anxiety. This modality of therapy involves the family to a greater extent, and focuses on the anxiety's role in the family's emotional lives. Family CBT may include the following techniques: providing education, recognizing how family dynamics play into the patient's experience, recognizing psychosocial aspects of anxiety that affect the family, drawing on family strengths, improving communication and empathy, and reducing overall family distress. Family members may also be coached on how to reinforce coping efforts of the patient and provide optimal support (Baum, Perry, & Tarbell, 2004).

Development and Implementation of an Empirically Based Treatment Plan

The Notion of Evidence-Based Practice

The health care industry has become more cost-conscious, creating an expectation that psychotherapy should be demonstrably effective. The demand now exists for evidence-based practice in psychotherapy. Evidence-based practice emerges from a mix of psychotherapy research and professional consensus; it suggests that psychotherapy practice should be rooted in empirical findings, however, should not be circumscribed by them (Roth & Fonagy, 2005).

As discussed previously, the category of anxiety disorders describes a group of conditions that share many features, but are also diverse in symptoms and presentations. Given their disparate diagnostic criteria, each anxiety disorder presents different treatment considerations. The interventions discussed for each diagnostic category have been selected given their extensive support in the literature on treatment efficacy. They do not cover every CBT option for psychotherapy, but are a guide for clinicians to base their treatment decisions.

Panic Disorder

CBT for panic disorder (PD) has been shown to be highly effective (Craske & Barlow, 2005). Treatment typically includes three main components: exposure practices, cognitive restructuring, and anxiety-management techniques. Interoceptive exposure aims to lessen the fear of bodily sensations that accompany panic attacks through repeated and systematic exposure to those cues (Barlow & Cerny, 1988; Dattilio & Salas-Auvert, 2000). Training in PMR and diaphragmatic breathing aim to manage the physiological symptoms of anxiety, including hyperventilation (Barlow & Cerny). Cognitive restructuring targets catastrophic misappraisals of bodily sensations, replacing anxiety-provoking thoughts with realistic attributions and coping self-statements (D. M. Clark, 1986, 1993). Exteroceptive exposure is typically added for patients experiencing agoraphobia, and involves gradually exposing patients, in a systematic way, to real-life situations that have triggered panic (Craske & Barlow).

CBT treatment for PD (with and without agoraphobia) can be relatively brief, with research demonstrating effectiveness within 12–15 sessions (Roth & Fonagy, 2005). CBT has been shown to yield panic-free rates of 70%–80% (Barlow, Craske, Cerny, & Klosko, 1989; D. M. Clark et al., 1994). Large clinical trials have shown that CBT's effectiveness is not increased by the use of medications (Barlow, Gorman, Shear, & Woods, 2000). Research also suggests that CBT is a cost-effective treatment, when compared with other treatments alone (McHugh et al., 2007). Selective serotonin reuptake inhibitors (SSRIs) are the drug of choice for PD treatment. There is no research evidence suggesting a reliable differential efficacy within this class of medication (Roy-Byrne, Craske, & Stein, 2006). Research findings also indicate comparable efficacy of the extended-release form of the serotonine/norepinephrine reuptake inhibitor (SNRI) and venlafaxine (Bradwejn et al., 2005). Benzodiazepines are considered a second-line treatment because of tolerance and potential for abuse, failure to target comorbid depression (Weisberg, Dyck, Culpepper, & Keller, 2007), and interference with the learning processes intended in CBT protocols (Otto, Bruce, & Deckersbach, 2005; Westra, Stewart, Teehan, Dufois, & Hill, 2004).

Generalized Anxiety Disorder

Research suggests both CBT and applied relaxation provide the greatest efficacy for generalized anxiety disorder (GAD ; Borkovec & Costello, 1993; Roth & Fonagy,

2005). Two hallmark components of GAD are targeted: (a) excessive, uncontrollable worry, and (b) chronic muscle tension. Standard cognitive therapy, as outlined by Beck and colleagues, is used to modify patients' automatic thoughts and catastrophic beliefs. Emphasis is on helping patients deal with uncertainty (Butler, Fennel, & Hackman, 2008). Worry exposure is also used to address worry directly, and involves identifying a hierarchy of worries and systematic exposure to them (O'Leary, Brown, & Barlow, 1992). Safety-seeking behavior prevention is included in many protocols for GAD. Progressive relaxation training is used to increase one's ability to control arousal and alleviate physiological symptoms, particularly chronic muscle tension, which is the most distinctive somatic symptom of GAD (Pluess, Conrad, & Wilhem, 2009). Time management and problem solving may also be treatment components (T. A. Brown, O'Leary, & Barlow, 2005).

Antianxiety medications, benzodiazepines, and one type of azapirones (buspirone) have demonstrated efficacy to treat GAD, and have been approved by the Food and Drug Administration (FDA). At present, however, the primary drugs of choice to treat GAD are SSRIs and SNRIs, due to their combined anxiolytic and antidepressant properties and sustained long-term efficacy. The use of benzodiazepines is limited due to their decreased long-term effectiveness, poor effectiveness for cognitive symptoms (i.e., worry), risk of abuse, and degradation of patient performance, including cognitive impairment (Culpepper, 2002; Otto et al., 2005). In some cases, benzodiazepines are taken with SSRIs/SNRIs during the first 1–4 weeks of treatment, to provide faster reduction in muscle tension or insomnia, and for exacerbation of worries. Other alternatives include venlafaxine, tricyclic antidepressants, and pregablin (Baldwin & Polkinghorn, 2005; Frampton & Foster, 2006; Ryan, Riddle, Yeung, & Kunz, 2007).

Specific Phobias

Research suggests that specific phobias respond well to exposure treatments. Studies have demonstrated that clinically significant improvement in phobic symptoms is achieved in 70–85% of cases when using exposure treatment (Roth & Fonagy, 2005). Fairly brief interventions can be effective when fears are specific and circumscribed. Exposure treatments involve presenting a patient with anxiety-producing material for a long enough time to decrease the intensity of their emotional reaction. Research also suggests that cognitive interventions can be an effective treatment (McLean & Woody, 2001; Roth & Fonagy, 2005). Through a combination of habituation and cognitive restructuring, the feared stimulus no longer creates anxiety. This is achieved in a graduated format. Patients develop a fear hierarchy and systematically work to full exposure to the feared stimulus. Exposure treatment is done in-vivo or with virtual reality.

Social Phobia

Cognitive-behavioral techniques for social phobia involve cognitive restructuring, relaxation training, exposure, and social skills training. Combined cognitive therapy and exposure treatments are often used (Turk, Heimberg, & Hope, 2005). Both in-session and out-of-session social exposures provide opportunities for clients to test dysfunctional beliefs about social interactions, to experience a natural decrease in anxiety from habituation to a situation, and to practice social skills that have been avoided (Heimberg & Becker, 2002; Hope, Heimberg, Juster, & Turk, 2000). The combination treatment, including exposures and cognitive restructuring, is associated with the largest effect sizes in meta-analytic reviews for social phobia (Roth & Fonagy, 2005; Zaider, Heimberg, Roth, Hope, & Turk, 2003). Researchers suggest that whereas exposure is essential to overcoming fear of social situations, the cognitive component of treatment addresses irrational beliefs. Additional studies support cognitive-behavioral group therapy, showing treatment response rates of 75% (Liebowitz et al., 1999). The group setting provides advantages, such as vicarious learning, normalization, the availability of multiple role-play partners, and feedback from others regarding cognitive distortions (Turk et al., 2005).

SSRIs and the SNRI venlafaxine have demonstrated efficacy treating social anxiety and treating comorbid conditions. Second-line drug treatments include clonazepam, mirtazapine, and gabapentin (Schneier, 2006). Beta-blockers are used for performance anxiety, rather than for generalized social phobia (Davidson, 2006). Overall, research findings suggest pharmacotherapy alone and individual CBT alone are effective for reducing social anxiety symptoms, but combined treatment has no further advantage (Davidson et al., 2004; Haug et al., 2003).

Obsessive-Compulsive Disorder

The efficacy of CBT for obsessive-compulsive disorder (OCD) has been clearly established. The most researched intervention is exposure and response prevention (ERP). This kind of therapy involves gradually exposing patients to situations that trigger patients' obsessions and anxiety. Through in-vivo or imaginal exposure, patients learn to confront the triggers without engaging in rituals. ERP treatment is based on the theory that prolonged exposure to feared thoughts and triggers will provide information that disconfirms erroneous associations, and thus permits habituation to feared stimuli (Foa & Kozak, 1986). Numerous studies suggest that patients treated with ERP make and maintain clinically significant gains, and randomized control trials have found it to be superior to placebo (Marks, Stern, Mawson, Cobb, & MacDonald, 1980), relaxation training (Fals-Stewart, Marks, & Schafer, 1993) and anxiety-management training (Lindsay, Crino, & Andrews, 1997). Also, a review of 12 outcome studies showed that 83% of ERP completers are classified as responders to the treatment (Foa & Kozak, 1986). Additional research suggests that cognitive therapy interventions may be a useful supplement for patients struggling to manage ruminations with ERP treatment alone (D. A. Clark, 2004; Roth & Fonagy, 2005).

Medications that inhibit serotonin reuptake (SSRIs) are the first-line pharmacologic treatment for OCD; sertraline, fluvoxamine maleate, and fluoxetine are the most commonly used drugs. Clomipramine and monoamine oxidase inhibitors are used as a second-line treatment due to their side effects (D. J. Stein, Ipser, Baldwin, & Bandelow, 2007). Although studies have been in conflict, staying on medication is required for treatment effects to last (Barlow, 2008).

Posttraumatic Stress Disorder

There are several empirically supported psychological treatments for posttraumatic stress disorder (PTSD), including prolonged exposure (PE) (Foa & Kozak,

1986; Foa, Hembree, & Rothbaum, 2007), cognitive processing therapy (CPT) (Resick & Schnicke, 1992, 1993), and eye movement desensitization reprocessing (EMDR) (Shapiro, 1989, 1995). It is believed that PTSD symptoms stem from a highly generalized fear network. When the fear network becomes generalized, many situations trigger intense fear and hyperarousal, and thus the PTSD sufferer avoids more thoughts and situations. PE works to extinguish this fear network through extended, in-session exposure to the traumatic memory. PE takes 9–12 sessions, and the patient describes the traumatic event in great detail during sessions. PE involves breathing retraining and exercises outside of the therapy where clients are instructed to confront feared situations for at least 45 minutes a day (Barlow, 2008; Kozak & Foa, 1997). The treatment rationale is that by being in the presence of feared stimuli—both the traumatic memory and real-life triggers—the anxiety will gradually lessen and be extinguished, as the body cannot maintain hyperarousal for a long time. PE has been found to decrease PTSD symptoms by an average of 75%, with over 80% of clients remitting from PTSD diagnosis (Resick, Nishith, Weaver, Astin, & Feuer, 2002). Other studies have found that PE alone is as effective as PE with an added component of stress inoculation training (Foa et al., 1999).

CPT is also highly effective in treating PTSD. CPT also involves intensive revisiting of the traumatic memory, over the course of approximately 12 sessions (Barlow, 2008). As in PE, CPT aims to extinguish the generalized fear network, but also aims at correcting clients' flawed cognitions around the traumatic memory. The client describes cognitions around such topics as self-blame, trust, and safety related to the trauma, and to challenge distorted cognitions with more balanced statements. CPT has been found to be as effective as or more effective than PE, matching the 80% remission rate and addressing other related issues, such as depression and dissociation (Resick et al., 2002).

EMDR is a mode of treating PTSD that combines several elements of the above therapies, including examining the traumatic memory and challenging negative cognitions about the self, as related to the trauma. The unique element in the EMDR protocol, designed by Shapiro (1989, 1995), is that during the treatment, the client is instructed to follow the therapist's finger as it moves back and forth, thus moving the eyes back and forth. The proponents of EMDR assert this lateral movement allows for reprocessing and release of traumatic memories. The research is mixed as to whether the lateral movement adds to the efficacy of the treatment (Barlow, 2008). However, EMDR has been found to be as effective as PE (Rothbaum, Astin, & Marsteller, 2005). Additionally, some therapists pursue CBT treatment with the aid of either of two FDA-approved SSRI drugs for treating PTSD: paroxetine and sertraline.

Evaluation of Treatment Outcomes

Health care costs continued to increase at alarming rates over the last few decades, and are a national concern. Pressure has been placed on health care professionals to provide cost-effective and efficacious treatments. It is important that health care providers monitor treatment outcomes to provide necessary information to third-party payers (Gatchel & Oord, 2003). Psychologists are in a unique position to help PCPs with mental health outcome assessment.

Monitoring Patient Progress

Several aspects of patient functioning should be considered in outcomes assessment for anxiety treatment in the primary care setting, as research has demonstrated that anxiety can cause significant disability and impacts various aspects of functioning (Kroenke et al., 2007; Rapaport et al., 2005; M. B. Stein et al., 2005). These areas of patient functioning may include experience of disorder-specific symptoms, comorbidity, and health-related quality of life.

Evaluating the Course of Anxiety

Self-report measures to assess symptoms of anxiety in the primary care setting, discussed previously in this chapter, can serve as more than screeners. They can be used at follow-up visits to monitor changes in frequency or intensity of patients' anxiety symptoms. Most of these inventories offer quantitative scoring methods, and patient scores can be entered into databases for statistical analysis of their progress. Primary care psychologists familiar with this type of analysis can assist medical staff in the construction of databases and in understanding the parameters of the analysis (Gatchel & Oordt, 2003).

Evaluating Comorbidity

Because anxiety is often comorbid with depression and other psychiatric diagnoses, additional self-report inventories may be valuable in assessing secondary diagnoses. It is essential for all of those involved in the outcomes measurement process to remember that anxiety can be a chronic condition for many patients, as factors outside of treatment often cause relapse or resurgence in symptoms.

Evaluating Quality of Life

Health-related quality of life is an important dimension to assess in treatment outcomes (Kaplan, Patterson, & Groessl, 2004). The phrase "health-related quality of life" encompasses physical health, emotional health, cognitive functioning, sexual functioning, social role performance, and work productivity (Ware & Sherbourne, 1992). One commonly used measure of quality of life in the medical setting is the Medical Outcome Study Short Form-36 (SF-36; Ware & Sherbourne, 1992). This brief inventory assesses eight health concepts: physical functioning, role-physical, bodily pain, general health perceptions, vitality, social functioning, role-emotional, and mental health. The SF-36 can be self-administered or administered by a trained interviewer, and research supports its reliability and validity (Kaplan et al., 2004).

Patient Satisfaction

Research suggests that the quality of care for patients with anxiety disorders in the primary care setting may be substandard (M. B. Stein et al., 2004; Young et al., 2001). These patients often leave appointments feeling dissatisfied as a result of unmet needs (Prins, Verhaak, van der Meer, Pennix, & Bensing, in press; M. B. Stein et al.). The quality of the patient-physician encounter is important to patient satisfaction and treatment outcome. Patients who experience PCPs as genuine, caring, and understanding of their issues are likely to be more satisfied with their care, and more likely to engage in treatment and adhere to recommendations (Frankel & Beckman, 2004). Patient satisfaction can be measured both quantitatively and qualitatively.

Cost-Effectiveness

Cost-effectiveness evaluations help determine whether the inclusion of the psychologist in the primary care team significantly improves the quality of care at a reasonable cost. These analyses assess the investment of time, effort, and money associated with the integration of psychologists to the primary care team, and compare them with the benefits (i.e., increased treatment effectiveness, increased satisfaction in patients of their perceived need for care, improvement of patients' global functioning, reduced use of health care services). In evaluating outcomes for the integration of psychologists in primary care team, it is essential to obtain feedback from PCPs, nurses, physician assistants, and office staff. Such information can identify potential aspects of care and collaboration in need of change and growth.

Considerations With Special Populations

Current biopsychosocial models of anxiety disorders recognize the role of individual differences among anxiety patients. As previously mentioned, such differences (i.e., genetic predispositions, dispositional traits, developmental stages, comorbidity, socioeconomic status, ethnicity) may serve as vulnerability factors that affect some, but not all, patients with the same primary anxiety diagnosis. Case formulations and treatment plans must take into account such differences, as they may interact with other internal diathesis and environmental stressors to generate and maintain anxiety. Also, patients' individual differences include differences in ability to process information and learn from psychotherapy, and in their responsiveness to pharmacotherapy.

Children and Adolescents

Anxiety disorders are the most common type of psychiatric diagnosis in children, constituting the main reason for their referral to specialty mental health services (Albano, Chorpita, & Barlow, 2003; Beidel, 1991). Data from the National Comorbidity Survey Replication (CSN-R; R. C. Kessler, Berglund, et al., 2005; R. C. Kessler, Chiu, et al., 2005) revealed that anxiety disorders can start early in life. The median age of onset for anxiety disorders was the earliest (age 11 years old) compared with other disorders (i.e., 30 years old for mood disorders). Specific phobias and separation anxiety disorder had the earliest median ages of onset (7 years old), followed by social anxiety disorder (13 years old). Children under 12 years old have less generalized anxiety symptoms than preadolescents and adolescent youths (Strauss, Lease, Last, & Francis, 1998; Tracey, Chorpita, Douban, & Barlow, 1997). Retrospective studies have found that up to 40% of adults diagnosed with PD reported their first panic attacks started before age 20 (Moreau & Follet, 1993; Thyer, Parrish, Curtis, Nesse, & Cameron, 1985; Von Korff, Eaton, & Keyl, 1985). Similarly, data indicate that 80% of adults with OCD developed their symptoms before 18 years of age (Pauls, Alsobrook, Goodman, Rasmusen, & Leckamn, 1995). Research has shown that childhood anxiety disorders cause significant impairment in children's lives (e.g., Dweck & Wortman, 1982; Turner, Beidel, & Costello, 1987), frequently continue into adulthood (Albano et al., 2003), demonstrate a worsening of symptoms over time (Kendal, 1994), and often lead to depressive episodes (e.g., Alloy, Kelly, Mineka, & Clements, 1990; Chorpita & Barlow, 1998). Delays in detection and treatment of anxiety disorders leave the affected children and youths vulnerable to debilitating anxiety symptoms, impairing their ability to master life tasks during crucial periods of their development.

Older Adults

Anxiety is also present at the other extreme of the developmental process, the elderly, both as symptoms and as a disorder. Studies show that GAD is more prevalent in the elderly—affecting about 7% of seniors—than depression, which affects approximately 3% of seniors (Lenze, 2006). Recognizing an anxiety disorder in the elderly is difficult given: (a) the frequent coexistence of physical illness and somatic anxiety symptoms, which may resemble specific illnesses; and (b) seniors' realistic concerns about physical problems and medical conditions. Research findings show that experiencing chronic health conditions, self-perception of poor health, and functional limitations are risk factors for anxiety disorders in the elderly (Beckman et al., 2000). If left untreated, anxiety symptoms may lead to depression, and have significant adverse effects on seniors' quality of life and physical health. Anxiety treatments for the elderly include psychotropic medications, psychological treatment, and their combination. Pharmacotherapy must take into account the fact that there are physiological changes associated with aging that cause less efficient metabolization and elimination of medications than in younger patients (von Moltke, Greenblatt, Harmatz, & Shader, 1995). Those changes render seniors more sensitive to side effects of medications (Salzman, Satlin, & Burrows, 1995). Even though benzodiazepines are the first-line treatment for anxiety in the elderly, they are problematic, as their chronic use increases the risk of seniors' cognitive decline and the risk of falls and fractures. The use of SSRIs seems to be more appropriate for this population (Lenze et al., 2003). Similarly, effective cognitive-behavioral treatment of anxiety in older patients must be targeted to the specific disorders, and it should be based on individual case formulations that take into account the biopsychosocial circumstances of each individual patient (e.g., cognitive functioning, health status, social support).

Ethnic Minorities

Ethnicity may have a significant impact in the health care of patients. Immigrants, refugees, or minorities frequently lack access to primary care and mental health services (Bhul, Standfield, Hull, Priebe, Mole, & Feder, 2003; Neighbors et al., 2007; Olfson et al., 2000; Vega et al., 1998). Potential explanations for the lower usage rate include: (a) ethnic differences in acknowledgment of psychological distress, (b) ethnic differences in manifestations of mental disorders, (c) differences in meaning of the patients' anxiety symptoms in relation to the norms of their cultural reference group (subgroup), (d) cultural differences in acceptable ways of coping with psychological distress, (d) language barriers, (e) low socioeconomic level and lack of health insurance coverage, and (e) cultural variations in actual prevalence of the disorders. The PCP's sensitivity to cultural factors is essential to understand patients' distress, to communicate such understanding in an effective way, and to customize treatment strategies that are acceptable to patients (McDaniel, Hargrove, Belar, Schroeder, & Freeman, 2004).

Also, PCPs who treat patients from different ethnic backgrounds are likely to encounter culture-bound syndromes, that is, patterns of aberrant experiences and behaviors that are common to a particular ethnic group (American Psychiatric Association, 1994). Anxiety symptoms are a prominent dimension (i.e., *ataque de nervios* in Latinos, *dhat* and *jiryan* in Hindus, *koro* and *latah* in Malaysians). However, symptoms associated with such syndromes may or may not be linked to a specific *DSM-IV* anxiety diagnosis. The *DSM-IV* Appendix I contains a glossary with a description of some common culture-bound syndromes (American Psychiatric Association, 1994). Health care providers' familiarity with culture-bound syndromes relevant to the ethnic groups they serve will help them to understand their patients' experiences, symptom attributions, and expectations, all of which can have a significant impact on the acceptance of different treatments.

Clinical Pearls of Wisdom for Practitioners

Integrating cognitive-behavioral models and primary care is an opportunity and a challenge. Primary care clinics have a distinct culture, and cognitive-behavioral therapists must adapt to characteristics of this setting to be successful. Therapists need to be flexible and apply specific skills to training and practice models for effective integration. Several skill sets and clinical considerations are described.

1. Don't Wait for Patients to Report Anxiety

Remember that frequently in primary care settings, patients with anxiety disorders may present their somatic symptoms as their reason for the office visit (Katon & Roy-Byrne, 2007). The burden is on the health care provider to consider all of the patient's symptoms, medical and psychological, and pursue the right line of questioning to arrive at an accurate diagnosis.

2. Collaborate With Health Care Providers

Successful collaboration requires a respectful, collegial relationship in which effective communication is essential. Some therapists may find it challenging to work in this setting, given the tendency for physicians to hold the highest status within the primary care clinic (Gatchel & Oordt, 2003).

3. Manage Time Effectively

Primary care office visits often last 15 minutes, which is much shorter than the 50-minute sessions typical in psychological practice. The issue of time is one of the major challenges facing primary care practice, and therapists must be brief, directive, and decisive in their communication with PCPs (Gatchel & Oordt, 2003). Time efficiency involves careful planning to make the most of the time available. Patients present with problems or complaints to which they seek relevant information as well as concrete, immediate solutions, making the primary care setting more outcomes-focused than process-focused (Haley et al., 2004; Prins et al., in press).

4. Primary Care Means Multiple Health Conditions

Working in a primary care clinic requires cognitive-behavioral therapists to understand an array of common medical conditions and their respective treatments. PCPs may also be helpful in providing information about the likely impact of medical problems on psychological functioning; therapists can educate PCPs about the psychosocial impact of various medical diagnoses.

5. Emphasize the Patient-Provider Relationship

Psychologists have extensive training about the importance of the therapeutic relationship in patient satisfaction and outcomes. The culture of medical practice currently puts less emphasis on the patient-provider relationship than on the delivery of efficient health care. Psychologists are in a position to model these skills for PCPs, and demonstrate the benefits of using a collaborative approach with patients. Patients are more likely to engage in treatment and work collaboratively if they view their providers as genuine, interested, understanding, respectful, and helpful.

6. Achieve Cultural Competence

Primary care therapists must understand the social and cultural factors that influence the development of health problems, access to care, help-seeking behavior, and adherence to treatment (McDaniel et al., 2004). Psychologists and PCPs must also consider these cultural influences when diagnosing and treating patients.

7. Refer Out When Necessary

The scope of practice for a primary care psychologist will depend on the model of integration and the structure of the primary care clinic. Psychologists acting as consultants may only be available to conduct assessments and make treatment recommendations, and referrals may be necessary. Other primary care psychologists may be conducting treatment in the clinic. It is essential for primary care psychologists to recognize their boundaries and practice within their functional ability and expertise, and to refer patients when specialized evaluation or treatment is indicated (Haley et al., 2004).

References

Albano, A. M., Chorpita, B. F., & Barlow, D. H. (1996). Childhood anxiety disorders. In E. J. Marsh & A. Barkley (Eds.), *Child psychopathology* (pp. 196–241). New York: Guilford.

Albano, A. M., Chorpita, B. F., & Barlow, D. H. (2003). Childhood anxiety disorders. In E. J. Marsh & A. Barkley (Eds.), *Child psychopathology* (2nd ed., pp. 279–329). New York: Guilford.

Alloy, L. B., Kelly, K. A., Mineka, S., & Clements, C. M. (1990). Comorbidity of anxiety and depressive disorders: A helplessness-hopelessness perspective. In J. D. Maser & C. R. Cloninger (Eds.), *Comorbidity of mood and anxiety disorders* (pp. 499–543). Washington, DC: American Psychiatric Association.

American Psychiatric Association. (1987). *Diagnostic and statistical manual of mental disorders* (3rd ed.). Washington, DC: Author.

American Psychiatric Association. (1994). *Diagnostic and statistical manual of mental disorders* (4th ed.). Washington, DC: Author.

American Psychiatric Association. (2000). *Diagnostic and statistical manual of mental disorders* (4th ed., text rev.). Washington, DC: Author.

Arnau, R., Meagher, M., Norris, M., & Bramson, R. (2001). Psychometric evaluation with the Beck Depression Inventory-II with primary care patients. *Health Psychology, 20*(2), 112–119.

Baldwin, D. S., & Polkinghorn, C. (2005). Evidence-based pharmacotherapy of generalized anxiety disorder. *International Journal of Neuropharmacology, 8*, 293–302.

Barlow, D. H., & Cerny, J. A. (1988). *Psychological treatment of panic: Treatment manuals for psychiatrists.* New York: Guilford.

Barlow, D. H., Craske, M. G., Cerny, J. A., & Klosko, J. S. (1989). Behavioral treatment of panic disorder. *Behavior Therapy, 20*, 261–282.

Barlow, D. H., Gorman, J. M., Shear, M. K., & Woods, S. W. (2000). Cognitive-behavioral therapy, imipramine, or their combination for panic disorder: A randomized controlled trial. *Journal of the American Medical Association, 283*(19), 2529–2536.

Barlow, D. H. (2008). *Clinical handbook of psychological disorders*. New York: Guilford.

Barsky, A. J., Delamater, B. A., & Orav, J. E. (1999). Panic disorder patients and their medical care. *Psychosomatics, 40*, 50–56.

Barsky, A. J., Wyshak, G., Lathman, K. S., et al. (1991). The prevalence of hypochondriasis in medical outpatients. *Society of Psychiatry Epidemiology, 25*, 89–94.

Baum, A., Perry, N. W., & Tarbell, S. (2004). The development of psychology as a health science. In T. Boll, R. G. Frank, A. Baum, & J. L. Wallander (Eds.), *Handbook of health psychology, volume 3: Models and perspectives in health psychology* (pp. 9–28). Washington, DC: American Psychological Association.

Beck, A. T. (1993). *Beck Anxiety Inventory, (BAI).* San Antonio, TX: Pearson.

Beck, A. T., Guth, D., Steer, R. A., & Ball, R. (1997). Screening for major depression disorders in medical inpatients with the Beck Depression Inventory for primary care. *Behaviour Research and Therapy. (35)*, 785–791.

Beck, A. T., Steer, R. A., Ball, R., Ciervo, C. A., & Kabat, M. (1997). Use of the Beck Anxiety and Beck Depression Inventory: Twenty-five years of evaluation. *Clinical Psychology Review, 8*, 77–100.

Beckman, A. T., de Beurs, E., van Balkom, A. J., Deeg, D. J., van Dyck, R., & van Tilburg, W. (2000). Anxiety and depression in later life: Co-occurrence and commonality of risk factors. *American Journal of Psychiatry, 157*, 89–95.

Beidel, D. C. (1991). Social phobia and overanxious disorder in school-age children. *Journal of the American Academy of Child and Adolescent Psychiatry, 30*, 545–552.

Belzer, K., & Schneier, F. R. (2004). Comorbidity of anxiety and depressive disorders: Issues of conceptualization, assessment and treatment. *Journal of Psychiatry Practice, 10*, 296–306.

Bhul, K., Standfield, S., Hull, S., Priebe, S., Mole, F., & Feder, G. (2003). Ethnic variations in pathways to and use of specialist mental health services in the UK. *British Journal of Psychiatry, 182*, 105–116.

Bonnet, F., Irving, K., Terra, J. L., Nony, P., Berthezene, F., & Moulin, P. (2005). Anxiety and depression are associated with unhealthy lifestyle in patients at risk of cardiovascular disease. *Atherosclerosis, 178*, 339–344.

Borkovec, T. D., & Costello, E. (1993). Efficacy of applied relaxation and cognitive-behavioral therapy in the treatment of generalized anxiety disorder. *Journal of Consulting and Clinical Psychology, 61*, 611–619.

Boyd, J. H. (1986). Use of mental health services for the treatment of panic disorder. *American Journal of Psychiatry, 143*, 1569–1574.

Bradwejn, J., Ahokas, A., Stein, D., Salinas, E., Emilien, G., & Whitaker, T. (2005). Venlafaxine extended-release capsules in panic disorder: Flexible-dose, double blind, placebo-controlled study. *British Journal of Psychiatry, 187*, 352–409.

Bray, J. H., & Rogers, J. C. (1997). The linkages project: Training behavioral health professionals for collaborative practice with primary care physicians. *Families, Systems, and Health, 15*, 55–63.

Brown, C., Schulberg, H. C., Madonia, M. J., Shear, M. K., & Houck, P. R. (1996). Treatment outcomes for primary care patients with major depression and lifetime anxiety disorders. *American Journal of Psychiatry, 153*, 1293–1300.

Brown, T. A., DiNardo, P., & Barlow, D. H. (2004). *Anxiety disorders interview schedule adult version (ADIS-IV): Client interview schedule.* New York: Oxford University Press.

Brown, T. A., O'Leary, T. A., & Barlow, D. H. (2005). Generalized anxiety disorder. In D. H. Barlow (Ed.), *Clinical handbook of psychological disorders, third edition* (pp. 154–208). New York: Guilford.

Butler, G., Fennel, M., & Hackman, A. (2008). *Cognitive-behavioral therapy for anxiety disorders.* New York: Guilford.

Campbell, T. L., & Patterson, J. (1995). The effectiveness of family interventions in the treatment of physical illness. *Journal of Marital and Family Therapy, 21*, 545–584.

Chorpita, B. F., & Barlow, D. H. (1998). The development of anxiety: The role of control in the early environment. *Psychological Bulletin, 124*, 3–21.

Clark, D. A. (2004). *Cognitive-behavioral therapy for OCD.* New York: Guilford.

Clark, D. M. (1986). A cognitive approach to panic. *Behaviour Research and Therapy, 24*, 461–470.

Clark, D. M. (1993). Cognitive mediation of panic attacks induced by biological challenge tests. *Advances in Behaviour Research and Therapy, 15*, 75–84.

Clark, D. M., Salkovskis, P. M., Hackmann, A., Middleton, H., Anastasiades, P., & Gelder, M. (1994). A comparison of cognitive therapy, applied relaxation and imipramine in the treatment of panic disorder. *British Journal of Psychiatry, 164*, 759–769.

Coyne, J. C., Thompson, R., Klinkman, M. S., & Nease, D. E. (2002). Emotional disorders in primary care. *Journal of Consulting and Clinical Psychology, 70*(3), 798–809.

Craske, M. G., & Barlow, D. H. (2005). Panic disorder and agoraphobia. In D. H. Barlow (Ed.), *Clinical handbook of psychological disorders, third edition* (pp. 1–59). New York: Guilford.

Culpepper, L. (2002). Generalized anxiety disorder in primary care: Emerging issues in management and treatment. *Journal of Clinical Psychiatry, 63*, 35–42.

Culpepper, L. (2004). Identifying and treating panic disorder in primary care. *Journal of Clinical Psychiatry, 65*, 19–23.

Dattilio, F. M., & Salas-Auvert, J. A. (2000). *Panic disorder. Assessment and treatment through a wide angle lens.* Phoenix, AZ: Zeig, Tucker.

Davidson, J. R. (2006). Pharmacotherapy of social anxiety disorder: What does the evidence tell us? *Journal of Clinical Psychiatry, 67* (Suppl. 12), 20–26.

Davidson, J. R. T., Foa, E. B., Huppert, J. D., Keefe, F. J., Franklin, M. E., Comptom, J. S., et al. (2004). Fluoxetine, comprehensive cognitive behavior therapy, and placebo in generalized social phobia. *Archives of General Psychiatry, 61*, 1005–1013.

Deacon, B., Lickel, J., & Abramowitz, J. S. (2008). Medical utilization across the anxiety disorders. *Journal of Anxiety Disorders, 22*, 344–350.

Dweck, C., & Wortman, C. (1982). Learned helplessness, anxiety and achievement. In H. Krone & L. Laux (Eds.), *Achievement, stress and anxiety* (pp. 93–125). New York: Hemisphere.

Durhan, R. C., Allan, T., & Hackett, C. A. (1997). On predicting improvement and relapse in generalized anxiety disorder following psychotherapy. *British Journal of Psychology, 36*, 101–119.

Dutton, G. R., Grothe, K. B., Jones, G. N., Whitehead, D., Kendra, K., & Brantley, P. J. (2004). Use of the Beck Depression Inventory-II with African American primary care patients. *General Hospital Psychiatry, 26*, 437–442.

Fallon, B. A., Javitch, J. A., Hollander, E., & Liebowitz, M. R. (1991). Hypochondriasis and obsessive-compulsive disorder: Overlaps in diagnosis and treatment. *Journal of Clinical Psychiatry, 52*, 457–460.

Fals-Stewart, W., Marks, A. P., & Schafer, J. (1993). A comparison of behavioral group therapy and individual behavior therapy in treating obsessive compulsive disorder. *Journal of Nervous and Mental Disease, 181*, 189–193.

Fireman, B., Koran, L. M., Leventhal, J. L., & Jacobson, A. (2001). The prevalence of clinically recognized obsessive-compulsive disorder in a large health maintenance organization. *American Journal of Psychiatry, 158*, 1904–1910.

First, M. B., Spitzer, R. I., Gibbon, M., & Williams, J. B. W. (1997). *Structured clinical interview for DSM-IV TR disorders.* Arlington, VA: AmericanPsychiatric Publishing, Inc.

Fleet, R. P., Dupuis, G., Marchand, A., Burelle, D., Arsenault, A., & Beitman, B. D. (1996). Panic disorder in emergency department chest pain patients: Prevalence, comorbidity suicidal ideation, and physician recognition. *American Journal of Medicine, 101*, 371–380.

Foa, E. B., Dancu, C. V., Hembree, E. A., Jaycox, L. H., Meadows, E. A., & Street, G. P. (1999). A comparison of exposure therapy, stress inoculation training, and their combination for reducing posttraumatic stress disorder in female assault victims. *Journal of Consulting and Clinical Psychology, 67*, 194–200.

Foa, E. B., Hembree, E. A., & Rothbaum, B. O. (2007). *Prolonged exposure therapy for PTSD: Emotional processing of traumatic experiences—Therapist guide.* New York: Oxford University Press.

Foa, E. B. & Kozak, N. J. (1986). Emotional processing of fear: Exposure to corrective information. *Psychological Bulletin, 99*, 20–35.

Frampton, J. E., & Foster, R. H. (2006) Pregabalin: In the treatment of generalised anxiety disorder. *CNS Drugs, 20*, 685–693.

Frankel, R., & Beckman, H. (2004). The physician–patient relationship. In R. G. Frank, S. H. McDaniel, J. H. Bray, & M. Heldring (Eds.), *Primary care psychology* (pp. 45–61). Washington, DC: American Psychological Association.

Füredi, J., Rózsa, S., Zámbori, J., & Szádóczky, E. (2003). The role of symptoms in the recognitions of mental health disorders in primary care. *Psychosomatics, 44*, 402–406.

Garcia-Shelton, L., & Vogel, M. E. (2002). Primary care health psychology training: A collaborative model with family practice. *Professional Psychology: Research and Practice, 33*(6), 546–556.

Gatchel, R. J., & Oordt, M. S. (2003). *Clinical health psychology and primary care: Practical advice and clinical guidance for successful collaboration.* Washington, DC: American Psychological Association.

Haas, L., & deGruy, F. (2004). Primary care, psychology, and primary care psychology. In L. Haas (Ed.), *Handbook of primary care psychology.* New York: Oxford University Press.

Haley, W. E., McDaniel, S. H., Bray, J. H., Frank, R. G., Heldring, M., Johnson, S. B., et al. (1998). Psychological practice in primary care settings: Practical tips for clinicians. *Professional Psychology: Research and Practice, 29*, 237–244.

Haley, W. E., McDaniel, S. H., Bray, J. H., Frank, R. G., Heldring, M., Johnson, S. B., et al. (2004). Psychological practice in primary care settings: Practical tips for clinicians. In R. Frank, S. McDaniel, J. Bray, & M. Heldring (Eds.), *Primary care psychology* (pp. 95–112). Washington, DC: American Psychological Association.

Hamilton, A. (1969) Diagnosis and rating of anxiety. *British Journal of Psychiatry: Special Publication 3*, 76–79.

Haug, T. T., Blomhoff, S., Holme, I., Humble, M., Madsbu, H. P., & Wold, J. E. (2003). Exposure therapy and sertraline in social phobia: 1-year follow-up of a randomised controlled trial. *British Journal of Psychiatry, 182*, 312–318.

Haynes, S. N., Nelson, K. G., Tacher, I., & Kaholokula, J. K. (2001). Outpatient behavioral assessment and treatment target selection. In M. Hersen & L. K. Porzelius (Eds.), *Diagnosis, conceptualization, and treatment planning for adults* (pp. 35–70). Mahwah, NJ: Lawrence Erlbaum.

Hays, P. A. (1996). Addressing the complexities of culture and gender in counseling. *Journal of Counseling and Development, 74*, 332–338.

Heimberg, R. G., & Becker, R. E. (2002). *Cognitive-behavioral group therapy for social phobia: Basic mechanisms and clinical strategies.* New York: Guilford.

Hope, D. A., Heimberg, R. G., Juster, H., & Turk, C. L. (2000). *Managing social anxiety: A cognitive-behavioral therapy approach (client workbook).* New York: Oxford University Press.

John, U., Meyer, C., Rumpf, H. J., & Hapke, U. (2004). Smoking, nicotine dependence and psychiatric comorbidity—A population-based study including smoking cessation after three years. *Drug and Alcohol Dependence, 76*, 287–295.

Kaplan, R. M., Patterson, T. L., & Groessl, E. J. (2004). Outcome assessment for resource allocation in primary care. In R. G. Frank, S. H. McDaniel, J. H. Bray, & M. Heldring (Eds.), *Primary care psychology* (pp. 293–315). Washington, DC: American Psychological Association.

Katon, W., & Roy-Byrne, P. (2007). Anxiety disorders: Efficient screening is the first step to improving outcomes. *Annals of Internal Medicine, 146*(5), 390–392.

Katon, W. J., & Roy-Byrne, P. P. (1989). Panic disorder in the medically illness. *Journal of Clinical Psychiatry, 50*, 299–302.

Katzelnick, D. J., Kobak, K. A., DeLeire, T., Henk, H. J., Greist, J. H., Davidson, J. R. T., et al. (2001). Impact of generalized social anxiety disorder in managed care. *American Journal of Psychiatry, 158*(12), 1999–2007.

Kendall, P. C. (1994). Treating anxiety disorders in children: Results of a randomized controlled trial. *Journal of Consulting and Clinical Psychology, 62*, 100–110.

Kendall, P. C., Hudson, J. L., Gosch, E., Flannery-Hudson, E., & Suveg, C. (2008). Cognitive-behavioral therapy for anxiety disordered youth: A randomized clinical trial evaluating child and family modalities. *Journal of Consulting and Clinical Psychology, 76*, 282–297.

Kennedy, B. J., & Schwab, J. J. (1997). Utilization of medical specialties by anxiety disorders patients. *Psychosomatics, 38*, 112–190.

Kessler, D., Lloyd, K., Lewis, G., & Gray, D. P. (1999). Cross sectional study of symptom attribution and recognition of depression and anxiety in primary care. *British Medical Journal, 318*, 436–439.

Kessler, R. C., Berglud, P., Demler, O., Jin, R., & Merikangas, K. R. (2005). Lifetime prevalence and age-of-onset distributions of DSM-IV disorders in the national comorbidity survey replication. *Archives of General Psychiatry, 62*, 593–768.

Kessler, R. C., Berglund, P., Demler, O., Jin, R., Merikangas, K. R., & Walters, E. E. (2005). Lifetime prevalence and age-of-onset distributions of DSM-IV disorders in the national comorbidity survey replication. *Archives of General Psychiatry, 62*, 593–602.

Kessler, R. C., Chiu, W. T., Demler, O., & Walters, E. E. (2005). Prevalence, severity, and comorbidity of twelve-month DSM-IV disorders in the national comorbidity survey replication (NCS-R). *Archives of General Psychiatry, 62*, 617–627.

Kessler, R. C., DuPont, R. L., Berglund, P., & Wittchen, H.-U. (1999). Impairment in pure and comorbid generalized disorder and major depression at 12 months in two national surveys. *American Journal of Psychiatry, 156*, 1915–1923.

Kozak, M. J., & Foa, E. B. (1997). *Therapist guide to mastery of obsessive-compulsive disorder: A cognitive-behavioral approach.* San Antonio, TX: Psychological Corporation.

Kroenke, K., Spitzer, R. L., Williams, J. B. W., Monahan, P. O., & Löwe, B. (2007). Anxiety disorders in primary care: Prevalence, impairment, comorbidity and detection. *Annals of Internal Medicine, 146*, 317–326.

Lenze, E. J. (2006, May). *How to treat in the absence of scientific evidence: A focus on anxiety disorders in the elderly.* Paper presented at the Annual Meeting of the American Psychiatric Association, Toronto, ON, Canada.

Lenze, E. J., Pollock, B. G., Shear, M. K., Mulsant, B. H., Bharucha, A., & Reynolds, Ch. F. (2003). Treatment considerations for anxiety in the elderly. *CNS Spectrums, 12*(Suppl. 3), 6–13.

Liebowitz, M. R., Heimberg, R. G., Schneien, F. R., Hope, D. A., Davies, S., Holt, C. S., et al. (1999). Cognitive-behavioral group therapy versus phenelzine in social phobia: Long term outcome. *Depression and Anxiety, 10*, 89–98.

Lindsay, M., Crino, R., & Andrews, G. (1997). Controlled trial of exposure and response prevention in obsessive compulsive disorder. *British Journal of Psychiatry, 171*, 135–139.

Löwe, B., Gräfe, B., Zipfel, K., Spitzer, R. L., Hermann-Lingen, C., Witte, S., et al. (2003). Detecting panic disorder in medical and psychosomatic outpatients: Comparative validation of the Hospital Anxiety and Depression Scale, the Patient Health Questionnaire, a screening question, and physician's diagnosis. *Journal of Psychosomatic Research, 55*, 515–519.

Mancebo, M. C., Pinto, A., Rasmussen, S. A., & Eisen, J. L. (2008). Development of the treatment adherence survey-patient version (TAS-P) for OCD. *Journal of Anxiety Disorders, 22*, 32–43.

Marciniak, M., Lage, M. J., Landbloom, R. P., Dunayevich, E., & Bowman, L. (2004). Medical and productivity costs of anxiety disorders: Case control study. *Depression and Anxiety, 19*, 112–120.

Marks, I. M., Stern, R. S., Mawson, D., Cobb, J., & McDonald, R. (1980). Clomipramine and exposure for obsessive-compulsive rituals. *British Journal of Psychiatry, 136*, 1–25.

McDaniel, S. H., Hargrove, D. S., Belar, C. D., Schroeder, C. S., & Freeman, E. L. (2004). Recommendations for education and training in primary care psychology. In R. G. Frank, S. H. McDaniel, J. H. Bray, & M. Heldring (Eds.), *Primary care psychology* (pp. 63–92). Washington, DC: American Psychological Association.

McDaniel, S. H., & Hepworth, J. (2004). Family psychology in primary care: Managing issues of power and dependency through collaboration. In R. G. Frank, S. H. McDaniel, J. H. Bray, & M. Heldring (Eds.), *Primary care psychology* (pp. 113–132). Washington, DC: American Psychological Association.

McFarland, B. H., Freeborn, D. K., Mullooly, J. P., & Pope, C. R. (1985). Utilization patterns among long-term enrollees in a pre-paid group practice health maintenance organization. *Medical Care, 23*, 1221–1233.

McHugh, R. K., Otto, M. W., Barlow, D. H., Gorman, J. M, Shear, M. K., & Woods, S. W. (2007). Cost-efficacy of individual and combined treatments for panic disorder. *Journal of Clinical Psychiatry, 68*(7), 1038–1044.

McLean, P., & Woody, S. (2001). *Anxiety disorders in adults. An evidence-based approach to psychological treatment*. New York: Oxford University Press.

Mergl, R., Seidscheck, I., Allgaier, A. K., Möller, H. J., Hegerl, U., & Henkel, V. (2007). Depressive, anxiety, and somatoform disorders in primary care: Prevalence and recognition. *Depression and Anxiety, 24*(3), 185–195.

Moreau, D. L., & Follet, C. (1993). Panic disorder in children and adolescents. *Child and Adolescent Psychiatric Clinics of North America, 2*, 581–602.

Mori, D. L., Lambert, J. F., Niles, B. L., Orlander, J. D., Grace, M., & LoCastro, J. S. (2003). The BAI-PC as a screener for anxiety, depression, and PTSD in primary care. *Journal of Clinical Psychology in Medical Settings, 10*(3), 187–192.

Munoz, R. F., Hollon, S. D., McGrath, E., Rehm, L. P., & VandenBos, G. R. (1994). On the AHCPR depression in primary care guidelines: Further considerations for practitioners. *American Psychologist, 49*(1), 42–61.

Neal, R. D., Heywood, P. L., Morley, S., Clayden, A. D., & Dowell, A. C. (1998). Frequency of patients consulting patterns in general practice and workload generated by frequent attenders: Comparisons between practices. *British Journal of Medical Practice, 48*, 895–898.

Neighbors, H. W., Cadwell, C., Willimas, D. R., Nesse, R., Taylor, R. J., Bullard, K. M. C., et al. (2007). Race, ethnicity, and the use of services for mental disorders. *Archives of General Psychiatry, 64*, 485–494.

Nezu, A. M., Nezu, C. M., & Lombardo, E. (2004). *Cognitive-behavioral case formulation and treatment design*. New York: Springer Publishing Company.

Nisenson, L. G., Pepper, C. M., Schwenk, T., & Coyne, J. (1998). The nature and prevalence of anxiety disorders in primary care. *General Hospital Psychiatry, 20*, 21–28.

Noyes, R., Holt, C. S., Happel, R. L., Kathol, R. G., & Yagla, S. J. (1997). A family study of hypochondriasis. *Journal of Nervous and Mental Disease, 185*, 223–232.

O'Leary, T. A., Brown, T. A., & Barlow, D. H. (1992, November). *The efficacy of worry control treatment in generalized anxiety disorder: A multiple baseline analysis*. Paper presented at the meeting of the Association for Advancement of Behavior Therapy, Boston, MA.

Olfson, M., Fireman, B., & Weissman, M. M. (1997) Mental disorders and disability among patients in a primary care group practice. *Journal of General Internal Medicine, 11*, 9–15.

Olfson, M., Shea, S., Feder, A., Fuentes, M., Nomura, Y., Gameroff, M., et al. (2000). Prevalence of anxiety disorders and substance-use disorders in an urban general medicine practice. *Archives of Family Medicine, 9*, 876–883.

Otto, M. W., Bruce, S. E., & Deckersbach, T. (2005). Benzodiazepine use, cognitive impairment, and cognitive-behavior-therapy for anxiety disorders: Issues in the treatment of patients in need. *Journal of Clinical Psychiatry, 66*(Suppl. 2), 34–38.

Pauls, D. L., Alsobrook, J. P., Goodman, W., Rasmusen, S., & Leckamn, J. F. (1995). A family study of obsessive-compulsive disorder. *American Journal of Psychiatry, 152*, 76–84.

Parker, T., May, P. A., Maviglia, M. A., Petrakis, S., Sunde, S., & Gloyd, S. V. (1997). PRIME-MD: Its utility in detecting mental disorders in American Indians. *International Journal of Psychiatry in Medicine, 27*, 107–128.

Persons, J. B. (2008). *The case formulation approach to cognitive-behavior therapy*. New York: Guilford.

Pluess, M., Conrad, A., & Wilhem, F. H. (2009). Muscle tension in generalized anxiety disorder: A critical review of the literature. *Journal of Anxiety Disorders, 23*, 1–11.

Pollack, M. H. (2005). Comorbid anxiety and depression. *Journal of Clinical Psychiatry, 66*, 22–29.

Prins, M. A., Verhaak, P. F. M., van der Meer, K., Pennix, B. W. J. H., & Bensing J. M. (in press). Primary care patients with anxiety and depression: Need for care from the patient's perspective. *Journal of Affective Disorders*.

Rapaport, M. H., Clary, C., Fayyad, R., & Endicott, J. (2005). Quality-of-life impairment in depressive and anxiety disorders. *American Journal of Psychiatry, 162*(6), 1171–1178.

Rees, C. S., Richards, J. C., & Smith, L. M. (1998). Medical utilization and costs in panic disorder: A comparison with social phobia. *Journal of Anxiety Disorders, 12*, 421–435.

Resick, P. A., Nishith, P., Weaver, T. L., Astin, M. C., & Feuer, C. A. (2002). A comparison of cognitive processing therapy, prolonged exposure and a waiting condition for the treatment of posttraumatic stress disorder in female rape victims. *Journal of Consulting and Clinical Psychology, 70*, 867–879.

Resick, P. A., & Schnicke, M. K. (1992). Cognitive processing therapy for sexual assault victims. *Journal of Consulting and Clinical Psychology, 60*, 748–756.

Resick, P. A., & Schnicke, M. K. (1993). *Cognitive processing therapy for rape victims: A treatment manual.* Newbury Park, CA: Sage.

Rollman, B. L., Herbeck Belnap, B., Hum, B., Mazumdar, S., Zhu, F., Kroenke, K., et al. (2005). Symptomatic severity of Prime-MD diagnosed episodes of panic and generalized anxiety disorder in primary care. *Journal of General Internal Medicine, 20*(7), 623–628.

Roth, A., & Fonagy, P. (2005). *What works for whom? A critical review of psychotherapy research, second edition.* New York: Guilford.

Rothbaum, B. O., Astin, M. C., & Marsteller, F. (2005). Prolonged exposure versus eye movement desensitization and reprocessing (EMDR) for PTSD rape victims. *Journal of Traumatic Stress, 18*, 607–616.

Roy-Byrne, P. P., Craske, M. G., & Stein, M. B. (2006). Panic disorder. *Lancet, 368*, 1023–1032.

Roy-Byrne, P. P., Stang, P., Wittchen, H.-U., Ustun, B., Walters, E., & Kessler, R. C. (2000). Lifetime panic-depression comorbidity in the national comorbidity survey. Association with symptoms, impairment, course, and help-seeking.*British Journal of Psychiatry, 176*, 229–235.

Roy-Byrne, P. P., & Wagner, A. (2004). Primary care perspectives on generalized anxiety disorder. *Journal of Clinical Psychiatry, 65*, 20–26.

Ryan, M. A., Riddle, M. A., Yeung, P. P., & Kunz, N. (2007). Efficacy and safety of extended-release venlafaxine in the treatment of generalized anxiety disorder in children and adolescents: Two placebo-controlled trials. *American Journal of Psychiatry, 164*, 290–300.

Salzman, C., Satlin, A., & Burrows, A. B. (1995). Geriatric psychopharmacology. In A.F. Schatzberg & C. B. Nemeroff (Eds.), *The American Psychiatric Press text book of pharmacology* (pp. 803–821). Washington, DC: American Psychiatric Press.

Schneier, F. R. (2006). Clinical practice. Social anxiety disorder. *New England Journal of Medicine, 355*, 1029–1036.

Seaburn, D. B., Lorenz, A. D., Gunn, W. B., Gawinski, B. A., & Mauksch, L. B. (1996). *Models of collaboration: A guide for mental health professionals working with health care practitioners.* New York: Basic Books.

Sherbourne, C. D., Jackson, C. A., Meredith, L. S., Camp, P., & Wells, K. B. (1996). Prevalence of comorbid anxiety disorders in primary care outpatients. *Archives of Family Medicine, 5*(1), 27–34.

Shapiro, F. (1989). Eye movement desensitization: A new treatment for post-traumatic stress disorder. *Journal of Behavior Therapy and Experimental Psychiatry, 20*, 211–217.

Shapiro, F. (1995). *Eye movement desensitization and reprocessing: Basic principles, protocols, and procedures.* New York: Guilford.

Spielberger, C. D., Gorusch, R. L., & Lushene, R. E. (1970). *State-trait anxiety inventory.* MEnlo Park, CA: Mind Garden.

Spitzer, R. L., Kroenke, K., & Williams, J. B. W. (1999). Validation and utility of a self-report version of the PRIME-MD: The PHQ primary care study. *Journal of the American Medical Association, 282*(18), 1737–1744.

Spitzer, R. L., Kroenke, K., Williams, J. B. W., & Löwe, B. (2006). A brief measure for assessing generalized anxiety disorder. The GAD-7. *Archives of Internal Medicine, 166*, 1092–1097.

Spitzer, R. L., Williams, J. B. W., Kroenke, K., Linzer, M., deGruy, F. V., Hahn, S. R., et al. (1994). Utility of a new procedure for diagnosing mental disorders in primary care. The PRIME-MD 1000 Study. *Journal of the American Medical Association, 272*(22), 1749–1756.

Stein, D. J., Ipser, J. C., Baldwin, D. S., & Bandelow, B. (2007). Treatment of obsessive-compulsive disorder. *CNS Spectrums, 12*(Suppl. 3), 28–35.

Stein, M. B., Roy-Byrne, P. P., Craske, M. G., Bystritsky, A., Sullivan, G., Pyne, J. M., et al. (2005). Functional impact and health utility of anxiety disorders in primary care outpatients. *Medical Care, 43*, 1164–1170.

Stein, M. B., Sherbourne, C. D., Craske, M. G., Means-Christensen, A., Bystrytsky, A., Katon, W., et al. (2004). Quality of care for primary care patients with anxiety disorders. *American Journal of Psychiatry, 161*, 2230–2236.

Strauss, C. C., Lease, C. A., Last, C. G., & Francis, G. (1998). Overanxious disorder: An examination of developmental differences. *Journal of Abnormal Child Psychology, 16*, 433–443.

Swinson, R. P., Cox, B. J., & Woszcyna, C. B. (1992). Use of medical services and treatment for panic disorder with agoraphobia and for social phobia. *Canadian Medical Association Journal, 147*, 878–883.
Tarrier, N. (2006). An introduction to case formulation and its challenges. In N. Tarrier (Ed.), *Case formulation in cognitive behavior therapy* (pp. 1–11). New York: Routledge.
Thyer, B. A., Parrish, R. T., Curtis, G. C., Nesse, R. M., & Cameron, O. G. (1985). Age of onset of DSM-III anxiety disorders. *Comprehensive Psychiatry, 26*, 113–122.
Tracey, S. A., Chorpita, B. F., Douban, J., & Barlow, D. H. (1997). Empirical evaluation of DSM-IV generalized anxiety disorder criteria in children and adolescents. *Journal of Clinical Child Psychology, 26*, 404–414.
Turk, C. L., Heimberg, R. G., & Hope, D. A. (2005). In D. H. Barlow (Ed.), *Clinical handbook of psychological disorders, third edition* (pp. 114–153). New York: Guilford.
Turner, S. M., Beidel, D. C., & Costello, A. (1987). Psychopathology in the offspring of anxiety disordered patients. *Journal of Consulting and Clinical Psychology, 55*, 229–235.
Ware, J. E., & Sherbourne, C. D. (1992). The MOS 36-item short-form health survey (SF-36): Conceptual framework and item selection. *Medical Care, 30*, 473–483.
Weisberg, R. B., Dyck, I., Culpepper, L., & Keller, M. B. (2007). Psychiatric treatment in primary care patients with anxiety disorders: A comparison of care received from primary care providers and psychiatrists. *American Journal of Psychiatry, 164*, 276–282.
Westra, H. A., Stewart, S. H., Teehan, K. J., Dozois, D. J. A., & Hill, T. (2004). Benzodiazepine use associated with decreased memory for psychoeducation material in cognitive-behavior therapy for panic disorder. *Cognitive Therapy and Research, 28*, 193–208.
Wetherell, J. L., & Arean, P. A. (1997). Psychometric evaluation of the Beck Anxiety Inventory with older medical patients. *Psychological Assessment, 9*(2), 136–144.
Wright, J. H., Basco, M. R., & Thase, M. E. (2006). *Learning cognitive behavior therapy. An illustrated guide*. Washington, DC: American Psychiatric Association.
van Zest, W. H., de Beurs, E., Beckman, A. T., Deeg, D. J., & van Dyck, R. (2003). Prevalence and risk factors of post-traumatic stress disorder in older adults. *Psychotherapy and Psychosomatics, 72*, 333–342.
Vega, W. A., Kolody, B., Aguilar-Gaxiola, S., Alderete, E., Catalano, R., & Caraveo-Anduaga, J. (1998). Lifetime prevalence of DSM-III-R psychiatric disorders among urban and rural Mexican Americans in California. *Archives of General Psychiatry, 55*, 771–778.
Von Korff, M., Eaton, W., & Keyl, P. (1985). The epidemiology of panic attacks and panic disorder: Results of three community surveys. *American Journal of Epidemiology, 122*, 970–981.
Von Korff, M., Shapiro, S., Burke, J. D., Teitlebaum, M., Skinner, E. A., German, P., et al. (1987). Anxiety and depression in a primary care clinic. *Archives of General Psychiatry, 44*, 152–156.
von Moltke, L. L., Greenblatt, D. J., Harmatz, J. S., & Shader, R. I. (1995). Psychotropic drug metabolism in old age: Principles and problems of assessment. In F.E. Bloom & D. J. Kupfer (Eds.), *Psychopharmacology: The fourth generation of progress* (pp. 1461–1469). New York: Raven Press.
Young, A. S., Klap, R., Sherbourne, C. D., & Wells, K. B. (2001). The quality of care for depressive and anxiety disorders in the United States. *Archives of General Psychiatry, 58*, 55–61.
Zaider, T. I., Heimberg, R. G., Roth, D. A., Hope, D., & Turk, C. L. (2003, November). *Individual cognitive-behavioral therapy for social anxiety disorder: Preliminary findings*. Paper presented at the Annual Meeting of the Association for the Advancement of Behavioral Therapy, Boston, MA.

A CBT Approach to Assessing and Managing Suicide Risk in Primary Care: Recommendations for Clinical Practice

18

M. David Rudd
Craig J. Bryan[1]

Introduction

Several factors have converged to raise the profile of suicide risk assessment in primary care settings. First, increasing numbers of psychologists and other mental health care providers are positioned in primary care clinics in an effort to improve both the ease of access to mental health care and the efficiency of service provision (Blount et al., 2007). Second, as many as 45% of those that die by suicide present to a primary care clinic the month prior to their death (Luoma, Martin, & Pearson, 2002), and almost 20% contact their primary care provider (PCP) within a day of their suicide (Pirkis & Burgess, 1998). Finally, public health campaigns targeting suicide have identified primary care clinics as crucial sites for front-line intervention, recognizing that many individuals that would never acquiesce to mental health care are willing to see a PCP (Blount et al., 2007). The net result is recognition that there is a substantial need for straightforward, clinically applicable, and

[1]The views expressed in this chapter are those of the authors, and do not necessarily reflect the official position or policy of the Department of the Air Force, the Department of Defense, or the U.S. government.

flexible approaches to assessing and managing suicide risk in primary care environments. In particular, there is a need for approaches that acknowledge the unique clinical constraints of the primary care setting.

Assessment and Diagnostic Issues

Few would argue with the claim that the assessment, management, and treatment of suicidality are among the most challenging and stressful clinical tasks facing practitioners, regardless of setting (Jobes, Eyman, & Yufit, 1995). The unique constraints of the primary care setting (e.g., brief appointments, high patient volumes, comorbid medical conditions, limited follow-up schedules, and restricted management/treatment options) serve to complicate further an already complex task. Among the most prominent questions for mental health clinicians practicing in primary care settings (and primary care physicians) are the following:

- Given the time limitations, what is the most appropriate, efficient, and effective approach to suicide risk assessment?
- Should I screen every patient referred by the PCP?
- How can I document the risk assessment in thorough but efficient fashion?
- What levels of risk can be managed safely and effectively in a primary care setting?
- How do I make the decision to refer to a mental health specialist (i.e., working in a traditional outpatient setting)?
- Are there identifiable "groups" of suicidal patients that always need to be referred to specialty mental health?
- What are some straightforward and short-term management/treatment strategies for primary care? Do they have an empirical foundation?
- How long do I continue to follow up with a suicidal patient (before I refer to a mental health specialist in a traditional outpatient or inpatient setting)?
- Is the standard of care different in a primary care clinic?
- What are the risks of working in a primary care setting?

We hope this chapter will offer some clarity, both in terms of a conceptual understanding of suicidality and direct clinical application in primary care. All of the above questions will be addressed to some degree. The last decade, in particular, has witnessed some impressive scientific advances in the area of clinical suicidology, many with direct implications for day-to-day clinical practice across a range of settings. What is clear, though, is that each and every practitioner in a primary care clinic will face the challenge of assessing and responding to suicide risk, and likely be doing so not only with great frequency but with patients at imminent risk for suicide.

Incidence and Clinical Manifestations in Primary Care Settings

It is widely recognized that psychosocial and behavioral issues are at the heart of many primary care clinical appointments; it is estimated that up to 70% of all appointments involve psychological symptoms of some sort (Gatchel & Oordt, 2003). It is also recognized that the last clinician seen by many patients who take their own lives is the PCP (Luoma et al., 2002). In the primary care setting, psychosocial and behavioral issues present in a number of forms, including clearly identifiable psychiatric diagnoses, such as major depression or a host of anxiety disorders, as well as health-compromising behaviors such as smoking, physical inactivity, and poor dietary habits. Olfson et al. (2002) found high rates of psychiatric illness in a sample of consecutively scheduled adult primary care patients. More specifically, they found that 19% met criteria for major depression, 15% for generalized anxiety, 8% for panic, and 8% for substance abuse. As evidence of the diagnostic complexity often seen in primary care clinics, up to 77% were identified as having comorbid disorders. Indeed, the mental health landscape has changed dramatically over the last few decades, with primary care clinics becoming the predominant source of mental health care in the United States (Wang et al., 2006). Regier et al. (1993) has actually argued that primary care is the de facto mental health system in the United States.

Patients presenting with suicidality in primary care are a challenge due, in part, to the complexity of the symptom picture. Patients reporting suicidal thoughts tend to have a greater number of general health complaints as well, including difficulty sleeping, general and diffuse pain, and low energy levels, all of which lead to more frequent visits to the PCPs (Goldney, Fisher, & Wilson, 2001). Chronic pain is an established risk factor for suicide ideation in primary care, with estimates that up to 13% of chronic pain patients report suicidal thoughts, and another 19% report nonsuicidal morbid ruminations common in major depression (Smith, Edwards, Robinson, & Dworkin, 2004). Researchers found that many symptoms reported by suicidal patients in primary care are not always specific in nature, including diffuse claims of gastrointestinal problems, cardiac and chest pain, hypertension, depression, and generalized anxiety (Jurrlink, Herrma, Szalai, Kopp, & Rodelmeier, 2004).

As mentioned previously, it is estimated that almost half of individuals who take their own lives had contact with a primary care clinician in the month prior to their death (Luoma et al., 2002). Pirkis and Burgess (1998) estimated that 20% of those committing suicide had contact with the PCP within one day of their death. The numbers are even higher among the elderly, with 73% having an appointment with their PCP in the month prior to their suicide and 45% within a week of their death (Jurrlink et al., 2004). There is little doubt that PCPs will interact with suicidal patients on a regular basis and, as the data clearly indicate, many will be at imminent risk for suicide. Central among the concerns is the need to be able to evaluate and respond to suicide risk in a thorough, efficient, and effective fashion.

Brief Case History: John

John, a 42-year-old, recently divorced African American male, is typical for a primary care clinic presentation. He reported a range of symptoms on his initial visit to the clinic, not mentioning suicidal thinking as part of the primary complaint. Among the symptoms reported as the primary complaint were difficulty sleeping, general worry, diffuse body pain, and occasional chest pains. John was approximately 40 pounds over ideal body weight and reported being "worried that he might be having a heart attack," particularly given that his father had died of a heart attack at 55 years of age. He quickly disclosed a recent divorce, with the onset of symptoms shortly thereafter, and described himself as "incredibly stressed out and lonely" and "kind of down." Symptoms have persisted for the past 3 months, with a gradual escalation in severity, with John noting considerable difficulty at both work and home. He described problems in functioning as "trouble getting things done," noting a lack of both motivation and energy. He added that he "will just drink to get through the evening," acknowledging daily alcohol abuse.

Although a bit hesitant early on in the interview, John eventually endorsed the full range of depressive symptoms when queried thoroughly by the PCP. As with most primary care patients, it is unlikely that John would have spontaneously reported the full range of depressive symptoms. Careful questioning was important in clarifying both John's symptom profile, as well as the most effective clinical response. Among the reported symptoms were the following: depressed mood, initial and terminal insomnia, weight gain (15 pounds), poor energy, difficulty concentrating, marked anhedonia, as well as morbid ruminations. John also reported some limited anxiety symptoms including ruminative worry, some gastrointestinal discomfort, and feeling "agitated." Although John did not acknowledge suicidal ideation initially, follow-up questioning revealed escalating hopelessness, along with frequent and specific suicidal thoughts (i.e., "I've thought about shooting myself"). John went on to describe himself as "worthless" and a "burden on my family and friends," stating several times that "everyone would be better off if I were dead." John also reported the emergence of episodic suicide intent, noting that "right now I'm not going to act on my thoughts." When queried, John denied current access to a weapon, noting that he had "given the gun to his brother because he got scared." John's case is an excellent example of the need for specific questioning about suicidality, including not only the presence of suicidal thoughts, but also issues of intent and access to method.

The PCP was careful and methodical in his approach, querying not just about the current episode, but also transitioning to questions about any past history of suicidal behavior. John quickly endorsed two previous episodes of depression, both characterized by suicidal thoughts (i.e., similar thoughts about shooting himself). John denied any previous suicide attempts, and also noted no preparation or rehearsal behaviors of any kind, either currently or with the previous episodes. He reported that previous treatments, primarily a course of antidepressants and supportive follow-up, have been helpful in the past, with symptoms remitting in a few months. Each depressive episode was followed by several years without any prominent symptoms, but clearly John has struggled with several relapses. John also noted a family history of depression, reporting that both his father and brother suffered multiple depressive episodes. Treatment with antidepressants was also effective for his father and brother. He did, however, deny any family history of suicidal behavior.

John's case highlights a number of concerns for the primary care context, with the central issues revolving around a thorough, accurate, and efficient assessment of suicide risk, along with immediate management questions. Can John be safely and effectively treated in the primary care clinic? Even though previous treatment with medications has proven effective, John has relapsed several times now. Does that indicate the need for a referral to a mental health specialist? Would supplemental care such as brief psychotherapy also be of benefit? If so, what therapeutic approach is indicated and for what duration? We will return to John's case again later when discussing case conceptualization, specific assessment issues, and different management strategies.

Cognitive-Behavioral Case Conceptualization

Regardless of setting, day-to-day clinical practice needs to be guided by understandable and empirically supported conceptual models. This is particularly true for suicide risk. Cognitive theory and clinical practice have experienced considerable evolution, particularly over the last decade (Rudd, 2006). Before discussing the primary care context, it is important to keep in mind some basic realities about suicide risk. First, suicidal states are time-limited. Suicide risk comes and goes, with risk sometimes enduring for far longer periods of time than clinicians anticipate or recognize. The easiest way to conceptualize suicide risk is as fluid, consistent with the notion of fluid vulnerability theory (FVT; Rudd). FVT theory states that not only is an individual's vulnerability to suicidal crises variable, but some experience chronic (or enduring) suicidality in addition to acute episodes of risk. In short, some individuals (e.g., multiple suicide attempters) are at heightened risk even after resolution of an acute episode. In other words, multiple suicide attempters have a low threshold for suicidal crises in contrast to others. These individuals are not amenable to management or treatment in primary care settings. Even though FVT recognizes the great variability in suicide risk across individuals, it also appreciates the scientific advances over the last decade that help us effectively differentiate those at chronic risk and in need of specialty (and most likely long-term) mental health care.

FVT is based on recent advances in general cognitive theory; more specifically, the theory of modes (Beck, 1996). In short, the theory of modes states that there is an identifiable mode for every distinguishable emotional state, with an applicable belief system, associated physiological-affective signs or symptoms, along with related behaviors and motivations. For example, we all have an anxious mode, a fear mode, a happy mode, among many others. Beck (1996) defined modes as "specific suborganizations within the personality organization and incorporate the relevant components of the basic systems of personality: cognitive (or information processing), affective, behavioral, and motivational" (p. 4). He went on to describe the mode as, "an integrated cognitive-affective-behavioral network that produces a synchronous response to external demands and provides a mechanism for implementing internal dictates and goals" (p. 4).

The suicidal mode is (as all modes are) comprised of four domains: the suicidal belief (cognitive) system, the affective system, the physiological system, and the behavioral (motivational) system. The four systems work in synchrony, not simple linear fashion (as was presumed in earlier cognitive theory), when triggered by either an external precipitant (e.g., the dissolution of a treasured relationship, in John's case, his divorce) or an internal state (e.g., thought, feeling, image). The end result is a suicidal crisis that is characterized by specific or identifiable core cognitive themes to the patient's hopelessness (i.e., unlovability [including guilt and shame], helplessness, poor distress tolerance, and perceived burdensomeness), acute dysphoria and related physiological upset/arousal (i.e., Axis I symptoms), and suicide-related behaviors (preparation or rehearsal behaviors, suicide attempts). John's suicidal belief system was characterized by both unlovability ("I'm worthless") and perceived burdensomeness ("Everyone would be better off if I were dead").

In very simple terms, if a suicidal mode is activated, the individual will experience a suicidal crisis characterized by certain beliefs (in accordance with the hopelessness themes identified above), symptoms (affective and physiological symptoms consistent with Axis I disorders), and behaviors. Consistent with FVT, every individual has a different threshold value for activation of the suicidal mode. Some, such as those that have made repeated suicide attempts, have a very low threshold for activation, whereas others may never experience a suicidal crisis, even during periods of incredible and enduring stress. In John's case, his previous depressive episodes, accompanied by suicidal thoughts, make him more vulnerable to future episodes. In other words, he has a lower threshold for activation of his suicidal mode. The loneliness and isolation since his divorce clearly have served as a precipitant, activating John's suicidal mode. For those interested, a far more detailed discussion of cognitive theory and FVT is available in Rudd (2006).

This brief summary should provide an adequate foundation for more detailed discussion of actual clinical application in the primary care setting. The cognitive-behavioral therapy (CBT) approach to suicidality has a number of important implications for those practicing in primary care settings:

1. Recognize that suicidal crises are time-limited, that is, acute in nature. Despite the acute nature of suicidal crises, some individuals with heightened vulnerability will manifest enduring or chronic risk, as well (i.e., they have a low threshold for subsequent suicidal crises), and are likely to experience repeated suicidal crises. These individuals are not appropriate for ongoing management or treatment in a primary care setting. They will need a referral to a mental health specialist. It is most efficient (and empirically supported) to identify multiple suicide attempters (i.e., two or more lifetime suicide attempts) as at chronic risk for suicide and refer accordingly (Rudd, Joiner, & Rajab, 1996).
2. Suicidal crises are characterized by certain beliefs (i.e., hopelessness themes), affective and physiological symptoms (Axis I symptoms), and behaviors and motivations. Accordingly, these domains comprise much of the assessment and management process discussed in the following. It is important to consider the complete symptom picture, in addition to suicide-specific information, when formulating risk and making management decisions.
3. Clarity is important in understanding the targeted problem (in this case, suicidality), assessing risk, ongoing management, and documentation in the clinical record. Clarity translates to asking specific questions about suicide, associated symptoms, along with clearly differentiating between suicidal behaviors (i.e., motivation is death), morbid thoughts (i.e., thoughts

about death and dying, but not about taking one's own life), self-harm behaviors (i.e., motivation is something other than death, such as "emotional relief").

Screening for Suicide Risk in Primary Care Settings

This chapter targets the behavioral health care consultant (BHC) working in the primary care setting, although it is clearly applicable to any clinician operating in primary care, including the PCP (Neal-Walden, Bryan, Corso, & Rudd, 2009). Accordingly, it is assumed the mental health clinician is working in the primary care clinic alongside PCPs, with the PCP making referrals. Additionally, this means they are working under the routine constraints of high volume, brief appointment pressures, and rapid clinical dispositions. In simple terms, each and every patient referred to the BHC should be screened for suicidality. Screening can be accomplished in effective and efficient fashion in primary care clinics by using psychometric instruments, or with a few questions during the clinical interview. If there is any doubt about the importance of screening for suicidality, simply revisit the numbers shared at the beginning of this chapter. This is actually one of the primary tasks of the BHC, that is, to help the PCP recognize (assess) suicide risk and respond (manage) accordingly.

Among the most frequently used psychometric instruments are the Behavioral Health Measure-20 (BHM-20; Kopta & Lowry, 2002) and the Patient Health Questionnaire (PHQ-9; Kroenke, Spitzer, & Williams, 2001). Both are brief, but thorough, and easily administered within the primary care context. If a suicide-specific instrument is needed, one that is both comprehensive and reasonable in length is the Beck Scale for Suicide Ideation (BSS; Beck & Steer, 1993). The BSS addresses the full range of issues relevant to the clinical assessment of suicide risk, including the nature of suicidal thinking (e.g., wish to live, wish to die, reasons for living, reasons for dying, frequency and specificity of thoughts), previous suicide attempts, and related motivation and intent (e.g., planning, capability to carry out attempt, access to method, expectancy of attempt, final acts). The Beck Depression Inventory-II (BDI-II; Beck, Steer, & Brown, 1996) can also be used for screening purposes. In addition to providing comprehensive coverage of depressive symptoms in accordance with the *Diagnostic and Statistical Manual of Mental Disorders* (*DSM-IV;* American Psychiatric Association, 1994), the BDI-II includes a suicide item that is useful in identifying those with active ideation and intent. It is important to mention, though, that the single item only serves as a self-report screener, and by no means should be considered a thorough assessment.

It is perhaps easiest to simply screen during the clinical interview. There are a number of variants of screening questions, but most include a hierarchical approach, transitioning from the patient's current symptom picture, to hopelessness, and then to suicidality. The transitional approach not only normalizes or contextualizes the patient's hopelessness and suicidality, but it also reduces associated anxiety and apprehension about revealing this information. This is the sort of approach that was used with John, helping to reduce his anxiety and apprehension about acknowledging the presence of hopelessness and suicidal thoughts. The net result was his acknowledgment of active suicidal thoughts and noticeable risk. Here is an example of this transitional approach to screening:

1. It's not unusual for someone who is feeling depressed and anxious to feel hopeless. Do you ever feel hopeless about life, that is, that things won't change or get any better?
2. Do things ever get so bad that you have thoughts about suicide?

For positive screenings (either through interview or assessment instruments), it is critical to transition to a more thorough and detailed assessment of suicidality. As a first step, though, it is important to differentiate morbid thoughts/ruminations from suicidal ones. One can do this simply by asking the patient to elaborate on his/her initial response (e.g., "Tell me the thoughts that you've had, specifically, what goes through your head?"). Morbid thoughts do not include suicide intent, that is, the idea of "active motivation to die," "killing oneself," or "taking one's life"; rather, they are more consistent with the idea of "what it would be like if I weren't here" or "what it would be like if I were dead." The reason this distinction is so important is because a large percentage of depressed patients will experience morbid thoughts/ruminations during the course of the depression. Those with morbid ruminations alone do not require a detailed suicide risk assessment unless they report a previous history of suicidality. Similarly, it is important to differentiate self-harm behaviors (no intent to die) from suicidal behaviors. One can do this by asking patients about the intent of the behavior. For example, "What did you want to happen when you took the overdose, did you want to die?" A more detailed discussion of differentiating self-harm and suicidal behaviors will follow.

Making Assessment Easy: Five Steps to Suicide Risk Assessment in Primary Care

A thorough suicide risk assessment can be accomplished within the unique constraints of the primary care setting. It is important to keep in mind that expectations in the primary care setting are different from those in a specialty clinic. At the heart of the issue is the need to differentiate those who can be managed in a primary care setting versus those who need to be referred for more intensive specialty mental health care, a task wholly in line with what PCPs do on a daily basis. Attention to empirical research is critical, tailoring the approach to include variables with demonstrated value in predicting suicidal crises, to include both attempts and death by suicide.

In an effort to be efficient and effective, it is important for the clinician to sequence questions. As mentioned above, this decreases the patient's anxiety, general discomfort, and potential resistance to honest responses about suicidality (e.g., Rudd, 2006). The total time dedicated to this assessment should be in the range of 15–18 minutes. The recommended domains and order for sequencing questions included the following:

- **Step 1: Understand the Patient's General Symptom Constellation.** This routinely includes a collection of depressive and anxiety symptoms. After briefly reviewing reported symptoms, it is important to have the patient "rate" the severity of current symptoms.
  - Could you rate how depressed (or anxious) you feel on a scale of 1 to 10, with 1 being the best you've ever felt and 10 being so depressed

(or anxious) that you've had difficulty or were unable to take care of daily responsibilities?

- **Step 2: Identify the Presence of Hopelessness (Transition From Depressive/Anxiety Spectrum Symptoms).**
    - It's not unusual for someone who has been as depressed (or anxious) as you've been to start to feel hopeless about things, that is, that things might not improve and life won't get any better. Do you feel that way now?
    - Could you rate on a scale of 1 to 10 how hopeless you feel, with 1 being hopeful and 10 being completely hopeless?
- **Step 3: Identify Current Suicidality and Explore Any Previous History of Suicidal Behavior (If Hopelessness Is Endorsed).**
    - It's not unusual for someone who's been depressed (or anxious) and feeling hopeless, to think about suicide. Have you had thoughts about suicide? Tell me exactly what you've been thinking (always get a direct quote to use with subsequent questions and in clinical chart).
    - Have you ever made a suicide attempt? Did you want to die at the time (screening for intent in an effort to differentiate self-harm from suicidal behaviors)?
    - If a previous attempt(s) is endorsed, you will need some basic details. The following questions are recommended:
    - How many times have you tried to kill yourself? If there are more than two attempts, always ask for the "first" and "worst" attempts.
    - Ok, let's start with the first one.
    - When did you make the attempt?
    - What did you do?
    - Did you want to die at the time (always assess intent)? If not, what did you want to happen? Did you think [method] would kill you? This question targets intent via the construct of "perceived lethality." It is important to keep in mind the difference between perceived and actual medical lethality.
    - Where did you make the attempt?
    - What was the outcome? It is important to identify the nature and extent of any required medical care. This will provide information to assess the potential medical lethality (or seriousness) of the attempt.
    - How did you get help? This question provides additional information to understand/assess intent. When there is considerable opportunity for discovery or rescue, or whether the patient took immediate steps to make sure his/her life was not in danger, it raises questions about the actual intent associated with the behavior (and raises questions about self-harm rather than suicidality).

- How did you feel about surviving? Were you glad to be alive, disappointed? Most often, those with persistent intent following an attempt will report feeling "upset" about surviving.
- Ok, how about the worst attempt? (Repeat the same questions above.)

- **Step 4: Explore the Current Episode of Suicidality.**
  - Ok, let's talk about how you're feeling right now. What exactly are the thoughts you're having now? (A direct quote is important and helpful).
  - Have you thought about how you might kill yourself?
  - Have you thought about any other method?
  - Do you have access to (identified method)?
  - How often do you think about suicide? Daily? Weekly? Monthly?
  - How much total time in a typical day do you think about suicide (duration)? A few seconds, minutes, hours?
  - How intense are the thoughts? That is, on a scale of one to ten, how likely is it that you'll act on the thoughts, with 1 being in complete control and won't act and 10 being that you feel out of control and will most likely act (indirect intent)? This is a marker of indirect intent, and provides information that can be compared with direct questions regarding intent.
  - Have you prepared in any way for your death (e.g., will, finances, letters to loved ones, research on the internet)?
  - Have your rehearsed or practiced your suicide?
- **Step 5: Explore Accessible and Available Protective Factors.**
  - What is keeping you alive right now?
  - What helps when you're feeling hopeless?
  - What are your reasons for wanting to die?
  - What are your reasons for living?

The sequence of questions offered above will give the clinician ample information to assess acute suicide risk and, accordingly, make immediate management decisions. The sequential nature of the questions provides the opportunity to transition from remote to more recent information, and allowing the patient to become more comfortable with the process and lower resistance. The net result is a more detailed and accurate picture of the patient's suicide risk. A few points in this brief interview need to be emphasized. In particular, asking about "multiple methods" for suicide is important. Occasionally, patients will withhold the preferred method unless queried again (Have you thought about any other method for suicide?) (Rudd et al., 2001). Similarly, the importance of understanding a patient's suicide attempt history is critical. As demonstrated previously, this can be accomplished in a manageable timeframe by asking about the "first" and "worst" attempts. The most robust predictor of a future suicide attempt or death by suicide is a previous attempt (Clark, Gibbons, Fawcett, & Scheftner, 1989; Joiner et al., 2005; Ostamo & Lonnqvist, 2001). This is particularly true for multiple suicide attempters (i.e., those with two or more previous suicide attempts) (Rudd, 2006). As will be described shortly, this information is balanced against additional information, including symptom type and severity, along with mental status, when formulating overall risk and subsequent management decisions. As is evident with John, the transitional and sequential approach worked well. It reduced John's anxiety and apprehension, allowing him a safe and comfortable environment for him to share the fact that he was indeed hopeless and actively suicidal.

The issue of multiple-attempter status warrants special attention. As a general guideline, multiple attempters cannot be managed effectively in a primary care setting. A detailed understanding of a multiple attempter's suicidal history is not a realistic goal for primary care assessment. Rather, the previous sequence provides the opportunity to identify multiple attempters in an efficient and effective fashion. As mentioned, it is important to address issues of "intent" in order to differentiate suicidal from self-harm behaviors. Ordinarily, multiple attempters will report a mixture of both. Although there are clearly limitations to simple interview questions to identify intent, in the primary care setting, it is the most efficient approach (e.g., Did you hope you would die when you [attempt method]?). Subjective patient statements can be compared and contrasted to objective behavioral markers of intent, such as preparation (e.g., writing letters to loved ones, organizing financial matters, updating a will), rehearsal behaviors (e.g., research on the internet, "practicing" with the chosen method), selection of a medically lethal method, refusal to give up access to method, previous near-lethal attempts, and poor compliance with treatment (including both therapy and medications).

Putting It All Together: Formulating Risk in Primary Care

Regardless of the model, approaches to suicide risk formulation routinely differentiate risk levels in accordance with expressed and/or observed suicidal intent (Rudd, Joiner, & Rajab, 2004). As mentioned earlier, it is important for the BHC to consider the current symptom constellation (including type and severity), along with mental status and the suicide-specific assessment in making management/treatment decisions. Because care is being coordinated in the primary care setting, all clinical recommendations need to be coordinated with the PCP. As has been stated previously, multiple attempters with active suicidality cannot be managed effectively in primary care and need to be referred to specialty mental health care. Similarly, patients with elevated intent (either by self-report or observed behaviors), impaired mental status, and heightened symptom severity need to be considered at least moderate risk and referred to specialty mental health care. Patients well suited for management in primary care clinics are those evidencing no (or low) intent, with mild-to-moderate symptom severity, and limited impairment in mental status. As a general rule (although not always the case), symptom severity, mental status, and suicide intent tend to increase in parallel fashion. Table 18.1 provides a summary of all variables that can be addressed during the suicide risk assessment. As discussed in the following, the form will prove particularly useful for documentation purposes.

John's case is a good example of someone that can be managed in a primary care setting, if that is the treatment vehicle he wants. John did not express active intent, despite the presence of moderate to severe symptoms. It would be critical for him to abstain from alcohol use, and it would be important to share with him that his multiple relapses would suggest the need for a specialty mental health referral, with both psychotherapy and medication indicated. If he resisted, he could initially be managed with medication and time-limited therapy in the primary care clinic. His level of risk is in the moderate range and certainly manageable, however, his likelihood of relapse is considerable and would be the primary indicator for referral to a specialty mental health setting.

Identifying and Addressing Obstacles to Treatment

As mentioned previously, the primary care context has a number of unique constraints, most revolving around limited time for not only assessment but also follow-up treatment. In John's case, the potential for relapse is a significant concern. Identifying obstacles to treatment would be critical. Asking John about what did not work in previous treatments would be vital. In John's case, he identified multiple obstacles to treatment, all of which likely played a role in his relapses. He mentioned difficulty in scheduling routine follow-up appointments, variability in the providers, and difficulty getting his prescriptions refilled. Although he readily endorsed previous treatment as effective, he acknowledged that after "a few" supportive follow-up appointments and initial symptom remission, he, "stopped taking his medication."

Anticipating these simple but critical barriers to care for John is critical to an effective management and treatment response. In his case, it would be important to not only schedule regular follow up for medication management, but allow for brief psychotherapy with the BHC. Once symptom recovery was evidenced, it would be important to work with John on continuing medication use, as well as scheduling less frequent (but predictable) booster sessions, recognizing John's vulnerability for relapse.

Points of Collaboration With Physicians and Family

The opportunities for collaboration with the PCP and family are considerable. John's case provides a nice example of how such collaboration might work. John's case would be an ideal one to have assigned to a BHC, with the BHC tracking his response to his medications, along with providing brief psychotherapy. Integrated into John's medication checks and brief psychotherapy would be continuing suicide risk assessment. It would be critical to track John's suicide risk carefully over the first several months, particularly given the need for him to abstain from alcohol use. Once symptom improvement is achieved, the frequency of follow-up could be reduced.

18.1 Brief Monitoring of Suicide Risk

1. **Nature of Suicidal Thinking: Is suicidal ideation continuing?**
   Yes
   No, suicidal thinking has remitted.
   If yes, is there evidence of intent (if ideation is continuing)?

a. Subjective statements? Y N Example: ______
b. Any preparation or rehearsal behaviors? Y N Example: ______
c. Any observed changes in stated reasons for dying or living (describe):

______

______

2. **Daily Symptom Severity Ratings:**

Depression: Rating (1–10)______
Anxiety: Rating (1–10)______
Anger: Rating (1–10)______
Agitation: Rating (1–10)______
Sleep: Rating (1–10)______
Perceived Burdensomeness: Rating (1–10)______
Impulsivity: Rating (1–10)______
Hopelessness: Rating (1–10)______

3. **Observed Changes in Mental Status:**

Alertness:	alert . . . . . drowsy . . . . . lethargic . . . . . stuporous . . . . . other:
Oriented to:	person, place, time, reason for evaluation
Mood:	euthymic, elevated, dysphoric, agitated, angry
Affect:	flat, blunted, constricted, appropriate, labile
Thought continuity:	clear and coherent, goal-directed, tangential, circumstantial, other:
Thought content:	Within normal limits (WNL), obsessions, delusions, ideas of reference, bizarreness Morbidity, other:
Abstraction:	WNL, notably concrete, other:
Speech:	WNL, rapid, slow, slurred, impoverished, incoherent, other:
Memory:	grossly intact, other:
Reality testing:	WNL, other:

Notable behavioral observations: ______

4. **Current treatment compliance, participation rating:**
   Is the patient showing evidence of commitment to treatment and actively participating in care?
   No participation——Minimal——Average——Good——Excellent______

Daily Rating of Acute Suicide Risk (circle appropriate category)*
None: no active suicidal thinking
Mild: infrequent, nonspecific suicidal thinking (no plan) with no intent
Moderate: specific suicidal thinking (plan) with no intent
Severe: specific suicidal thinking (plan) with active intent (observed or stated)

*In addition to current suicidal thinking, always consider symptom type/severity and mental status in assigning category.

In addition to working directly with John, it would be important to consider the role of family in tracking John's risk and watching for warning signs. Naturally, John would need to be agreeable to integrating family into his care. Given his reported loneliness and perceived burdensomeness, integrating family into his care can help diffuse these feelings (i.e., assuming it is a healthy family environment). As will be mentioned later, it would be important to help available family members (in this case, John's brother) recognize applicable warning signs, as well as what steps need to be taken if a warning sign emerges. It is important to note that the clinician needs to be very concrete with family. Identified warning signs need to "personalized," targeting those with relevance to the individual being treated. An example of a warning-signs card (including the national helpline) is available at http://mentalhealth.samhsa.gov/publications/allpubs/walletcard/engwalletcard.asp.

We would recommend writing down all suggestions on a 3x5 card that can be carried in a wallet or purse. John had already taken the step of removing access to his weapon. It would be important to reiterate for John's brother the need to eliminate access to methods, with perhaps even the goal of permanently discarding the weapon.

As mentioned previously, the integration of family members assumes a healthy family system. If family members are integrated into the treatment process, the need to be concrete and specific cannot be emphasized enough. We would strongly suggest writing down all requests (and related instructions) for family members, along with appropriate contact numbers and identified resources.

Development and Implementation of Empirically Based Treatment: Management Issues in Primary Care

Naturally, the use of antidepressants for symptom management is frequent in primary care settings. It is recommended that all BHCs working in primary care familiarize themselves with the use of antidepressants, along with some common misunderstandings about potential risks, particularly following the Food & Drug Administration's black box warning label (Rudd, Cordero, & Bryan, 2009). Antidepressants appear to be a particularly effective management and treatment approach in primary care clinics (Simon & Savarino, 2007). If antidepressants are used, it is important to keep in mind that the first month following initiation of the medication is an extremely important time, given that risk can be elevated in a small subgroup of depressed patients (Bostwick, 2006). Close monitoring, with periodic follow-up, is important during the first 4–8 weeks.

It is suggested that BHC working in primary care clinics consider the utility of creating a "high-interest log" or a related system that helps track suicidal patients. A high-interest log can help facilitate better care because it provides a system for categorizing patients by their level of risk, with clear procedures for no-shows and related treatment compliance problems (Wingate, Joiner, Walker, Rudd, & Jobes, 2004). Regardless of whether a high-interest log is used, some form of continuous tracking of high-risk patients is recommended. When referrals are made to specialty mental health care, it is recommended that the BHC facilitate

18.2 Example CRP

My CRP

- When I find myself making plans to suicide, I agree to do the following:

1. Do things that help me feel better for about 30 minutes, including taking a bath, listening to music, and going for a walk.
2. Talk to friends who I know are supportive, including XXXX at the following phone number: XXX-XXXX.
3. If the thoughts continue [get specific] and I find myself preparing to do something, I call the emergency number 1-800-273-TALK for help.
4. If I'm still feeling suicidal and don't feel like I can control my behavior, I go to the emergency room at [provide specific hospital emergency room, phone number and address].

the referral by getting a specific appointment day and time for the patient. It is also strongly indicated that some agreement be reached with the mental health provider to keep the clinic informed as to whether or not the patient actually kept the appointment. Patients identified as being at high risk for suicide (i.e., those with active intent to die) should be considered for hospitalization and referred for immediate evaluation. The primary care clinic should have clear procedures for access to emergent evaluations for hospitalization, as well as appropriate referral to a mental health specialist if the patient is not admitted to the hospital.

There are a range of management strategies that can be used in day-to-day practice in primary care. If mild-to-moderate risk individuals are going to be managed, it is recommended that all have an individualized crisis response plan (CRP) in place and clearly understand its use. For a number of reasons, the use of "no-suicide contracts" is not recommended (Rudd, Mandrusiak, & Joiner, 2006). The CRP can be written on a 3 x 5 card so the patient can carry it in his/her wallet or purse. The CRP simply articulates what steps the patient needs to take should another crisis emerge in the future. The CRP needs to be simple and include behaviors for which the patient has demonstrated competence. Ideally, the CRP includes a transition from self-management at the beginning to external intervention at the end. Table 18.2 provides an example of a CRP. In addition to traditional follow-up appointments in primary care, it is recommended that the BHC consider the use of phone follow-up monitoring. Telephone monitoring provides a flexible and useful approach to management, and can be accomplished in only a few minutes per day.

Rudd, Joiner, Trotter, Williams, and Cordero (2009) recently provided an exhaustive review of empirically supported treatments for suicidality, with an eye toward identifying common elements of treatments that work. Naturally, the approaches included in the review are not ones amenable to the primary care context, primarily because of the intensity and duration of care. However, there are a number of common elements that have relevance to the brief care (both in intensity and duration) characteristic of primary care settings. All of the treatment approaches proven effective for suicidality (i.e., those that reduce subsequent suicide attempt rates) are cognitive-behavioral in orientation. Among the techniques proven effective that have relevance in the primary care setting are the use of a CRP and a tracking system for high-risk patients (referred to as the high-interest log). An additional technique that has evidence of empirical support and is applicable in the primary care context is providing the patient a clear and understandable model of their suicidality, essentially explaining to the patient why they are suicidal.

In John's case, this would be fairly straightforward. John has a genetic predisposition for depression, given both his family history and multiple episodes. In addition, he has experienced previous suicidal episodes, evidencing a vulnerability to experience periods characterized by hopelessness. It would be important to identify the precipitants to those previous episodes, with an eye toward similarities across episodes. The most recent episode was triggered by John's divorce, leading to feelings of "worthlessness" and burdensomeness. Clarifying for John that hopelessness and, in some cases, suicidality are not uncommon in the midst of a major depression will help diffuse some of the shame and guilt associated with his suicidality. Empirical evidence suggests that providing a clear and understandable model of suicidality for the patient, one that clarifies how treatment works, will facilitate not only hope but the recovery process.

Evaluation of Treatment Outcomes

Rudd (2000) has provided a detailed discussion of treatment outcomes and suicidality, along with a conceptual model. In brief, though, treatment outcome in cases of suicidality is fairly simple. Direct markers of suicidality can be tracked via thoughts as well as behaviors (i.e., suicide attempts and death by suicide). As mentioned previously, it is critical to differentiate morbid ruminations from suicidal thinking. Morbid ruminations are common with moderate-to-severe depression. Although suicidal ideation is not a particularly good marker of treatment outcome (because some people will experience chronic suicidal ideation), it is important to be careful in tracking. In order for suicidal ideation to have salience as a direct marker of treatment outcome, the clinician needs to track the following characteristics: frequency (how often do you think about suicide?), intensity (how intense are the thoughts on a scale of 1–10?), and duration (how long do the thoughts last?). A couple of additional points are important. When asking about intensity, patients will often request clarification. The easiest clarifying question is to ask, "On a scale of 1–10, how likely is it you'll act on your thoughts?" This is an indirect marker of suicide intent and, accordingly, a very useful question. Similarly, it is best to ask for total duration of time consumed thinking about suicide, either daily (for high-frequency ideators) or weekly (for less-frequent ideators). For example, "How much time do you spend each day thinking about suicide?" The clinician will quickly discover that total time consumed with ideation is related to specificity (where, when, how), rehearsal, and any preparation, as well as intent to act on the thoughts.

Suicide attempts are clearly a direct marker of treatment outcome. If a suicide attempt occurs, it is important to document a range of features, including medical lethality, presence of injury, need for medical care, and compliance with medical care, along with perceived lethality (did the patient believe the attempt would result in death?). It is also important for the practitioner to be aware of tracking indirect markers of treatment outcome. This includes the full range of associated symptoms (and warning signs), including depression, anxiety, hopelessness, anger, agitation, sleep disturbance, substance abuse, among a host of others.

Considerations With Special Populations/ Diversity Issues

Issues of diversity and suicide are considerable (Trepper & Leach, 2006) and beyond the scope of this chapter, although clearly important for the clinician in any setting. Of particular concern in the primary care setting is an awareness of the considerable increase in risk with age, as well as a sensitivity and responsiveness to issues of sexual orientation/identity, culture (and cultural buffers), and religion. There is a clear increase in risk among adolescents struggling with sexual orientation and sexual identity issues. Clinicians need to be sensitive to the need to query about this when appropriate. Similarly, there are considerable differences in suicide rates across various religious groups, as well as marked differences in how various religious groups view (and respond) to suicide. There are also some identifiable cultural buffers that practitioners need to be aware of, such as in John's case. His close family ties (particularly his brother) provide a considerable and important protective factor.

Clinical Pearls of Wisdom for Practitioners

Screening in Primary Care Settings

1. Screen all patients (referred to the BHC) for suicide risk during the initial contact and as clinically indicated for all follow-up appointments.
2. Always differentiate between morbid thoughts/ruminations and suicidality. For those with no previous history of suicidality and morbid thoughts only, no additional suicide risk assessment is necessary.
3. For those that screen positive, a more detailed suicide risk assessment is warranted (see the following).

Assessing Suicidality in Primary Care Settings

1. All referrals to the BHC should be screened for suicidality.
2. Positive screens should be assessed with the five-step hierarchical approach, targeting current symptom constellation, hopelessness, past suicidality, the current episode, and protective factors.
3. Those identified as multiple suicide attempters should be referred to specialty mental health care for management and treatment.

Management of Suicidal Patients in Primary Care

1. BHCs need to familiarize themselves with the use of antidepressants for symptom management, along with an accurate understanding of efficacy and associated risks.

2. Use of a high-interest log is recommended for the BHC to track high-risk patients in primary care settings.
3. When referrals are made to specialty mental health care, it is recommended that the BHC facilitate the referral by getting a specific appointment day and time for the patient. Notification procedures are also recommended.
4. Patients identified as being at high risk for suicide should be considered for hospitalization and referred for immediate evaluation. Procedures need to be in place for accessing emergent care, along with specialty mental health follow-up should the patient not be hospitalized.

Suicide Risk Formulation in Primary Care

1. Always notify the PCP about patient suicide risk, regardless of whether high or low. Keeping the PCP informed as to patient clinical status is critical to a well-functioning clinic.
2. Those at high risk should be referred to specialty mental health care. This includes multiple suicide attempters with a current suicidal crisis, as well as those reporting active suicide intent (or observed intent), coupled with serious symptoms and associated mental status impairment.
3. As a general rule, suicide intent, symptom severity (particularly in the depressive-anxiety spectrum), and mental status impairment all increase in parallel fashion.

Documenting Risk Assessment in Primary Care

The issue of clinical documentation, particularly in settings with considerable time constraints, can be difficult. Table 18.1 includes a one-page form that can be used in primary care clinics, one that encapsulates the essential elements to address during the brief interview in efficient fashion. The recommendations for documentation are fairly simple and straightforward:

1. BHCs need to always document the results of screenings, whether positive or negative. The form provided in Table 18.1 can be updated at each assessment point, allowing the BHC to track changes (both positive and negative) during follow up.
2. Similarly, interventions, consultations, and management/treatment plans need to be documented, as do all phone contacts. It is important to document the outcome of referrals (i.e., the patient's compliance with treatment recommendations).

References

American Academy of Pediatrics Committee on Adolescents. (2000). Suicide and suicide attempts in adolescents. *Pediatrics, 105*, 871–874.

American Medical Association. (1997). *Guidelines for adolescent preventive services (GAPS) recommendations monograph.* Retrieved July 15, 2007, from http://www.ama-assn.org/ama/upload/mm/39/gapsmono.pdf

American Psychiatric Association. (1994). *Diagnostic and statistical manual of mental disorders* (4th ed.). Washington, DC: American Psychiatric Press.

Beck, A. T. (1996). Beyond belief: A thepry of modes, personality, and psychopathology. In P. Salkovkis (Ed.), *Frontiers of cognitive therapy* (p. 4). New York: Guilford.

Beck, A. T., Brown, G. K., & Steer, R. A. (1996). *BDI-II manual*. San Antonio, TX: Psychological Corp.

Beck, A. T., & Steer, R. A. (1993). *Beck Scale for Suicide Ideation manual*. San Antonio, TX: Psychological Corp.

Berman, A. L. (2006). Risk management with suicidal patients. *Journal of Clinical Psychology: In Session, 62*, 171–184.

Beck, A. T., Steer, R. A., & Brown, G. K. (1996). *BDI-II, Beck Depression Inventory: Manual* (2nd ed.). Boston: Harcourt Brace.

Blount, A., Schoenbaum, M., Kathol, R., Rollman, B. L., Thomas, M., O'Donohue, W., et al. (2007). The economics of behavioral health services in medical settings: A summary of the evidence. *Professional Psychology: Research and Practice, 38*, 290–297.

Bostwick, J. M. (2006). Do SSRI's cause suicide in children? The evidence is underwhelming. *Journal of Clinical Psychology: In Session, 62*, 235–241.

Bryan, C. J., Corso, K. A., Neal-Walden, T. A., & Rudd, M. D. (2009). Managing suicide risk in primary care: Practice recommendations for behavioral health consultants. *Professional Psychology: Research and Practice, 40*(2), 148–155.

Clark, D. C., Gibbons, R. D., Fawcett, J., & Scheftner, W. A. (1989). What is the mechanism by which suicide attempts predispose to later suicide attempts? A mathematical model. *Journal of Abnormal Psychology, 98*, 42–49.

Gatchel, R. J., & Oordt, M. S. (2003). *Clinical health psychology and primary care: Practical advice and clinical guidance for successful collaboration*. Washington, DC: American Psychological Association.

Goldney, R. D., Fisher, L. J., & Wilson, D. H. (2001). Mental health literacy: An impediment to the optimum treatment of major depression. *Journal of Affective Disorders, 64*(2), 277–284.

Jobes, D. A., Eyman, J. R., & Yufit, R. I. (1995). How clinicians assess suicide risk in adolescents and adults. *Crisis Intervention & Time-Limited Treatment, 2*(1) 1–12.

Joiner, T. E., Conwell, Y., Fitzpatrick, K. K., Witte, T. K., Schmidt, N. B., Berlim, M. T., et al. (2005). Four studies on how past and current suicidality relate even when "everything but the kitchen sink" is covaried. *Journal of Abnormal Psychology, 114*, 291–303.

Jurrlink, D. N., Herrmann, N., Szalai, J. P., Kopp, A., & Redelmeier, D. A. (2004). Medical illness and the risk for suicide in the elderly. *Archives of Internal Medicine, 164*(11), 1179–1184.

Kopta, S. M., & Lowry, J. L. (2002). Psychometric evaluation of the behavioral health questionnaire-20: A brief instrument for assessing global mental health and the three phases of psychotherapy outcome. *Psychotherapy Research, 12*, 413–426.

Kroenke, K., Spitzer, R. L., & Williams, J. B. (2001). The PHQ-9: Validity of a brief depression severity measure. *Journal of General Internal Medicine, 16*, 606–613.

Luoma, J. B., Martin, C. E., & Pearson, J. L. (2002). Contact with mental health and primary care providers before suicide: A review of the evidence. *American Journal of Psychiatry, 159*, 909–916.

Olfson, M., Marcus, S. C., Druss, B., Elinson, L., Tanielian, T., & Pincus, H. A. (2002). National trends in the outpatient treatment of depression. *Journal of the American Medical Association, 287*(2), 203–209.

Ostamo, A., & Lonnqvist, J. (2001). Excess mortality of suicide attempters. *Social Psychiatry and Psychiatric Epidemiology, 36*, 29–35.

Pirkis, J., & Burgess, P. (1998). Suicide and recency of health care contacts: A systematic review. *British Journal of Psychiatry, 173*, 462–474.

Regier, D. A., Farmer, M. E., Rae, D. S., Myers, J. K., Kramer, M., Robins, L. N., et al. (1993). One-month prevalence of mental disorders in the United States and sociodemographic characteristics: The epidemiological catchment area study. *Acta Psychiatrica Scandinavica, 88*(1), 35–47.

Rudd, M. D. (2000). A conceptual scheme for assessing treatment outcome in suicidality. In T. Joiner & M. Rudd (Eds.), *Suicide science: Expanding the boundaries*. Norwell, MA: Kluwer Academic Publishers.

Rudd, M. D. (2006). Fluid vulnerability theory: A cognitive approach to understanding the process of acute and chronic risk. In T. E. Ellis (Ed.), *Cognition and suicide: Theory, research, and therapy* (pp. 355–367). Washington, DC: American Psychological Association.

Rudd, M. D., Cordero, K., & Bryan, C. J. (2009). What every psychologist should know about the Food and Drug Administration's black box warning label for antidepressants. *Professional Psychology: Research and Practice, 40*(4), 321–326.

Rudd, M. D., Joiner, T. E., & Rajab, M. H. (2004). *Treatment of suicidal behavior: An effective, time-limited approach*. New York: Guilford.

Rudd, M. D., Mandrusiak, M., & Joiner, T. E. (2006). The commitment to treatment statement as a practice alternative. *Journal of Clinical Psychology: In Session, 62*, 243–251.

Rudd, M. D., Mandrusiak, M., & Joiner T. E. (2006). The case against no-suicide contracts: The commitment to treatment statement as a practice alternative. *Journal of Clinical Psychology, 62*(2), 243–251.

Rudd, M. D., Joiner, T. E., Trotter, D., Williams, B., & Cordero, I. (2009). The psychological and behavioral treatment of suicidal behavior: A critique of what we know (and don't know). In P. Kleespies (Ed.), *Evaluating and managing behavioral emergencies: An evidence-based resource for the mental health practitioner* (pp. 339–350). Washington, DC: American Psychological Association.

Simon, G. E., & Savarino, J. (2007). Suicide attempts among patients starting depression treatment with medications or psychotherapy. *American Journal of Psychiatry, 164*, 1029–1034.

Smith, M. T., Edwards, R. R., Robinson, R. C., & Dworkin, R. H. (2004). Suicidal ideation, plans, and attempts in chronic pain patients: Factors associated with increased risk. *Pain, 111*, 201–208.

Trepper, T. S., & Leach, M. M. (2006). *Cultural diversity and suicide*. New York: Routledge.

Wang, P. S., Demler, O., Olfson, M., Pincus, H. A., Wells, K. B., & Kessler, R. C. (2006). Changing profiles of service sectors used for mental health care in the United States. *American Journal of Psychiatry, 163*(7), 1187–1198.

Wingate, L. R., Joiner, T. E., Walker, R. L., Rudd, M. D., & Jobes, D. A. (2004). Empirically informed approaches to topics in suicide risk assessment. *Behavioral Sciences and the Law, 22*, 651–665.

19 Substance Abuse

Michael Dolan
Margaret Nam

Introduction

Substance use affects countless Americans every year. According to a 2007 national survey, up to 46% of the population (114 million Americans over age 12) have used an illicit drug at least once in their lifetime (U.S. Department of Justice, 2009), and it is estimated that over 28 million children under 18 live with one or more parent who abuses substances (B. F. Grant, 2000). Illicit drug abuse costs society approximately $181 billion annually, and the addition of alcohol and tobacco raises the cost of substance use to over $500 billion in lost productivity, health care, and criminal justice (U.S. Department of Health and Human Services, National Institute of Health, National Institute on Drug Abuse, 2008a). Despite the pervasiveness and significant impact of substance abuse, it is estimated that only 10.8% of the 23.6 million individuals over age 12 who need treatment actually receive treatment (U.S. Department of Health and Human Services, National Institutes of Health, National Institute on Drug Abuse, 2008b). Cognitive-behavioral therapists and primary care physicians (PCPs) are at the forefront of dealing with this national problem.

Assessment and Diagnostic Issues

Assessment and diagnosis are the cornerstones of good treatment for any medical problem. Substance abuse and dependence are no exception. However, unlike other disorders, considerable controversy surrounds the assessment and diagnostic process, as well as the definition of the criteria that are used to define the disorder. The terms *addiction, dependence, abuse*, and *disease* are among the most controversial terms in the field.

The assessment process for substance problems is "more than a one time paperwork procedure conducted at the onset of treatment to simply gather minimal facts and secure a...diagnosis" (Juhnke, 2002, p. vii). It is actually the beginning of an ongoing process that includes not only the collection of demographic information, but also the initiation of the therapeutic relationship. Unfortunately, however, there is no one universally accepted assessment tool for the detection of alcohol and drug use problems (Fleming & Graham, 2001). The field, as stated earlier, has not even agreed upon a definition of addiction (Peele, 2000).

The assessment of substance abuse is often quite complex, involving many aspects of the patient's life. A useful approach is one that views the problem as a scientific dilemma and employs the experimental method as a means of diagnosing. In this manner, one may avoid the more subjective means of defining addiction, as well as methods that have no basis in science. This process comprises a step-by-step approach. The first step is to gather information and form a hypothesis about what potential issues exists. One must next use the data received to test this hypothesis. As in any scientific inquiry, it is necessary to gather more information or data in order to further refine the hypothesis and rule out alternative hypotheses until a firm conclusion supported by the facts has been reached.

During the assessment process, one critical factor is the ability of the patient to be a good historian. A major compromising issue in this context may be patient's need to protect his/her "use" and, in some instances, to hide the shame that is sometimes associated with a substance abuse problem. As a result, the patient may withhold important information. To achieve an optimum history of the process and current state of the substance use, it may be necessary to rely on a family member or other persons close to the patient. These outside collateral sources, along with the patient and any medical or psychological evaluations, will frequently provide the most accurate picture of the patient.

In assessing for substance problems, there are several brief screenings that may prove useful. In a primary care setting, time constraints and access to patients may be limited. The assessment process may, therefore, need to be very brief and consistent with the needs of the facility (i.e., bedside evaluations., brief consults with physicians). Nonetheless, the quality of the assessment process is absolutely vital, in that it sets the stage for all other aspects within the continuum of care. Depending on a number of factors, the process from screening to intervention may only take 20 minutes.

Traditional screens in medical practice have included the CAGE Questionnaire, named for its questions regarding *cutting* down, *annoying* people with drinking, having *guilty* feelings, and depending on an *eye*-opener or drink first thing in the morning (Ewing, 1984), and its latest edition for drugs, the CAGE-AID (CAGE adapted to include drugs). To date, the CAGE-AID is the only tool that has actually been tested with primary care patients (Brown & Rounds, 1995).

Like the CAGE, the CAGE-AID, which is explained in more detail below, focuses on lifetime use.

Because the questions were originally developed for alcohol, the CAGE-AID does not apply to every illicit drug or drug user. It is, however, a useful starting point. As with the CAGE, it is recommended that one positive answer prompt further evaluation.

The CAGE Questionnaire Adapted to Include Drugs (CAGE-AID)

1. Have you felt you ought to cut down on your drinking or drug use?
2. Have people annoyed you by criticizing your drinking or drug use?
3. Have you felt bad or guilty about your drinking or drug use?
4. Have you ever had a drink or used drugs first thing in the morning to steady your nerves or to get rid of a hangover (eye-opener) (R. L. Brown & Rounds, 1995)?

The use of *urine screening* is another popular tool available in the primary care setting. However, although those patients who are drug-dependent may screen positive, many will possibly be missed. It takes only a brief foray into the Internet to discover the myriad of methods designed to "fool" the urine screen. For this reason, the urine screen should only be considered as one part of a more comprehensive screening process. Nonetheless, even a negative test, of course, does not indicate the absence of a substance use problem. It is also important to bear in mind that adolescents, and those who have not yet experienced the negative sequellae associated with drug use, may not initially present as having a substance-use problem. For this reason, to identify the more subtle indications of a problem, careful listening and exploring all of the available evidence is important. These subtle signs serve as "red flags," often suggesting the need for in-depth screening and possibly assessment.

The most commonly accepted diagnostic criteria for substance difficulties are those listed in the *Diagnostic and Statistical Manual of Mental Disorders* (*DSM-IV-TR*), as presented by the American Psychiatric Association (APA) (2000). These criteria for abuse and dependence are summarized in the following.

Substance abuse is the maladaptive use of substances causing clinical dysfunction. Diagnostic criteria include one or more of the following within the period of a year: use causing inability to perform a familial, vocational, or academic role; use in the face of physical harm or legal complications; or use causing ongoing social problems. Substance dependence includes the criteria for substance abuse as well as additional features reflecting a more severe disorder. Substance dependence includes three or more of the following: tolerance, withdrawal, use of more of a substance than intended, desire to control use, use of significant time to obtain substance, abandonment or reduction of important activities because of a substance, and ongoing use despite acknowledged problems caused by substance (APA, 2000).

Although diagnosis appears relatively straightforward, it does present some unique challenges for the clinician. Working in a medical setting necessitates awareness and recognition of medical conditions that can mimic substance use disorders. Ruling out medical conditions is a vital part of the communication between the therapist and the physician. The assessment process must include a review of any current and past medical records, ongoing discussions with the primary physician, and any other relevant health care professionals. In addition to demographic information, a complete substance-use history is important, as well as the impact of the use on the patient's life. Any medical conditions that are or may be exacerbated by the substance use must be noted, as well as conditions that could give the false impression of substance use, such as the smell of ketoacidosis on a diabetic's breath. This odor is caused by acetone, a direct byproduct of the spontaneous decomposition of acetoacetic acid, and is often described as smelling like fruit or nail polish remover. This smell can, at times, be confused with alcohol use.

Because no single screening instrument can be used with all primary care patients, clinicians may want to select those options that best meet the needs of their patient population. For patients with low literacy skills, face-to-face interviews during which the clinician asks the questions and documents answers will best elicit information. Regardless of the information-gathering technique, however, clinicians are often relying on self-reports with no assurance that answers are truthful. At this time, there is no viable alternative to self-reports in the primary care setting (Institute of Medicine, 1990).

To screen for alcohol problems, using a self-administered written questionnaire, such as the Alcohol Use Disorders Identification Test (AUDIT; Babor, de la Fuente, Saunders, & Grant, 1992), is appropriate, particularly when the expected reading level and comprehension of written English are not likely to be problematic. The AUDIT takes about 2 minutes to answer (Hays, Hill & Gillogly, 1993), and about 15 seconds to score. The CAGE or CAGE-AID, supplemented by the first three quantity/frequency questions from the AUDIT, are recommended. This combination will increase sensitivity for detection of both problem drinking and alcohol dependence, because it includes questions about both alcohol consumption and its consequences. Self-administering the CAGE or CAGE-AID alone takes about 30 seconds (Hays et al.).

Although screening for drug use in the primary care setting can make patients and clinicians uncomfortable, asking about substance use is as important as asking about other personal practices that can affect a patient's health. Laboratory tests, however, may be useful during the assessment process to confirm a diagnosis, to establish a baseline, and later, to monitor progress (Schuckit & Irwin, 1988). Positive test results can be a powerful incentive for changing behavior or motivating patients to accept referrals for treatment.

Certain screening instruments may work better for different age, gender, racial, and ethnic groups. There is some concern that cultural, gender, and age issues are not adequately addressed by the currently available instruments, and that the instruments cannot detect the particular problems that may occur within different populations. No instrument has been shown to be consistently culturally sensitive with all ethnic populations (Cherpitel & Clark, 1995), although some instruments work better with some populations and are less culturally biased than others.

The CAGE has been found to have a higher sensitivity for identifying alcohol dependence in African Americans compared with Whites, whereas the AUDIT identifies alcohol dependence at roughly the same rate of sensitivity in both races (Cherpitel & Clark, 1995).

To assess the effectiveness of a given screening instrument with a given population, a clinician must evaluate, among other factors, a patient's understanding of the questions, the emotional responses to them, and the instrument's psychometric properties in the given patient population. There is insufficient evidence at this time to support a recommendation for specific alternative screening instruments for different cultural groups. Nor do existing data suggest that special tools are necessary to screen different populations (Samet, Friedmann, & Saitz, 2001).

Incidence and Clinical Manifestation in Primary Care

The Institute of Medicine has called for a new health system for the 21st century with primary care teams playing a central role. The quantum leap in the complexity of tasks prevents physicians alone from coping with the scope of practice (Grumbach & Bodenheimer, 2004). This call for a new health system places psychologists, nurse practitioners, therapists, and substance abuse specialists in unique positions as active and vital members of this team.

With this increasing complexity and demand today's health care teams need to be aware of the role that substance abuse plays in the lives of patients. Effectively treating a primary care patient's substance abuse problem is actually addressing a significant personal health care need. Alcohol-related disorders present in up to 26% of patients in general medical clinics, comparable to rates of chronic diseases such as hypertension and diabetes (Fleming & Barry, 1992).

Although not unique to the primary care office, the most recent National Household Survey on Drug Abuse provides compelling estimates that 19.1 million Americans, or 8% of the population age 12 and older, currently use illicit drugs. Also about 57.8 million Americans (23.3% of the population) had engaged in binge drinking (five or more drinks on the same occasion at least once in the previous month), and 6.9%, or 17 million, engaged in heavy drinking. Examining only the 18- to 25-year-olds, the binge drinking rate is 41.8%, and 14.7% for heavy drinking (Substance Abuse and Mental Health Services Administration, 2008). Because more Americans will be involved in substance use, the PCP will encounter increasingly more patients with substance use disorders, as well as all the comorbid illnesses associated with it. As the gatekeeper, the PCP is charged with ensuring the provision of comprehensive care. Therapists in primary care clinics will almost certainly be in the position of encountering the initial stages of a substance use problems. Basic skills in identifying and diagnosing patients who are chemically dependent will become essential. Clinicians in areas with limited substance abuse resources may be responsible for assessments, whereas those trained in addiction medicine may be providing a range of treatment services. Regardless of how extensively involved clinicians become, those who are familiar with the medical complications of substance abuse and are able to relate them to other comorbid illnesses will be better equipped to deliver adequate care.

Although most individuals who consume alcoholic beverages do not experience problems related to their use, primary care clinicians can expect that 15–20% of their male patients and 5–10% of their female patients will be at risk for, or are already experiencing, related medical, legal, or psychosocial problems. These problems include unresponsive diabetes, arrests for driving under the influence (DUI), problems with job or school, or family or marital difficulties (Manwell, Fleming, Barry, & Johnson,1998).

Parthasarathy, Mertens, Moore, and Weisner (2003) provide a list of acute and chronic physiologic or behavioral conditions related to drug and alcohol abuse in those patients diagnosed with a substance use disorder. Almost 73% had at least one of the following conditions in order of prevalence: depression, injury and poisonings/overdoses, anxiety and nervous disorders, hypertension, asthma, psychoses, acid-peptic disorders, ischemic heart disease, pneumonia, chronic obstructive pulmonary disease, cirrhosis, hepatitis C, diseases of the pancreas, alcoholic gastritis, toxic effects of alcohol, alcoholic neuropathy, alcoholic cardiomyopathy, excess blood alcohol level, and perinatal alcohol and drug dependence. As a result of these medical conditions, primary care is the de facto mental health and addictive disorders service system for 70% of the population (Regier et al., 1993).

This state of affairs places primary care physicians and primary care therapists directly on the front line of addictive services, as they are usually the first health care professional to come in contact with patients in the early stages of a substance use disorder. However, alcohol misuse and illicit drug use screening and recognition are often inadequate in primary care settings. A national survey of practicing PCPs (The National Center on Addiction and Substance Abuse, Columbia University, 2000) found that in their study of 648 nationally represented primary care

> *physicians (excluding pediatricians), 94% failed to include substance abuse among the five diagnoses they offered when presented with early symptoms of alcohol abuse in an adult patient. A total of 40.8% of pediatricians failed to diagnose drug abuse when presented with a classic description of an adolescent patient with symptoms of drug abuse. Most patients (53.7%) said their primary care physician did nothing about their substance abuse: 43.5% said their physician never diagnosed it, and 10.7% believed their physician knew about their addiction and did nothing about it. Less than one third of primary care physicians (32.1%) carefully screened for substance abuse. Three out of four patients (74.1%) said their primary care physician was not involved in their decision to seek treatment and 16.7% said the physician was involved only "a little." (The National Center on Addiction and Substance Abuse at Columbia University, 2000, p. ii)*

The typical PCP in the United States today is responsible for 2,500 patients. The size of this caseload makes it impossible for PCPs to spend sufficient time providing preventive and screening services. Today, as in the past, there are two parallel systems of care for patients with drug dependence—general medical care and substance use problems. If we are to successfully stem the current trends in substance use disorders and the comorbid medical complications, these two parallel systems will need to work in collaboration to address this critical need.

Brief Case History

The following is a typical case seen in a primary care setting. Frank is a 32-year-old male seeing his primary physician at the urging of his wife, after he had missed work several times because of nonspecific stomach distress, irritability, and difficulty sleeping. His physician completed an initial review of symptoms as well as a physical exam, and found no immediate cause for the patients' complaints. He ordered blood work and tests and sought a consult from a therapist. The reason for the consult was that during the initial history taking, the use of alcohol and methamphetamines was reported as occurring in the past. The physician asked the therapist to help determine whether there is a substance-use disorder and, if present, to recommend a course of treatment. During history taking, the patient reported significant relationship problems with his spouse as well as coworkers. He was initially reluctant to discuss his substance use, but eventually admitted to nightly alcohol use and occasional methamphetamine use to get through the day. He stated that his use began at age 12 when he stole beer from his parents' refrigerator. He continued to drink in high school and had several incidents of intoxication "just like all of my friends." He reported that he had two arrests for underage drinking and had two driving-under-the-influence (DUI) arrests in the past 5 years, the last one with a blood alcohol content (BAC) of .28. He was placed on house arrest for 2 months and on probation for 6 months. He further reported that he continues to drink, but does not drink and drive. He is somewhat concerned as he has been experiencing abdominal pain as well as nausea and vomiting. In addition, he seems to be bruising more easily and that these bruises seem to persist for long periods of time. His history is significant for family problems with alcohol. His father and paternal grandfather were both heavy drinkers. He has seen a counselor in the past for marital problems and anger management, but the issue of substance use was not discussed.

Cognitive and Behavioral Case Conceptualization

This patient has a family history of substance use. He reported that he was angry with his dad when his dad was drunk, but still looked up to him. Frank's mother was very critical of him, telling him he was acting "just like your father." His core beliefs suggested that he felt inadequate and unable to be anything other than what he saw in his dad. He believed that he could not succeed, and that any attempts to change his lot in life would be failures. He also was very uncomfortable with any type of conflict. He would, therefore, do everything he could to avoid conflict or do anything that could compromise his success. He found early in life that when he used alcohol, he did not have to think about his problems or where his life was going. Alcohol, and later, drugs became the primary methods for him to cope with his fears and anxieties, and became the one thing in the view of his peers at which he was successful. His attempts to quit were always short lived due to the increasing anxiety and lack of effective methods for dealing with his problems.

The first step in treatment was for him to identify the amount of substance use and the consequences of his use in his life. This included his arrest for underage drinking that was met with mixed messages from his parents. His mother was upset and wanted to punish him for the incident, although his father took the "boys will be boys" attitude. A similar response occurred when Frank received the DUIs. His father showed a passive pride in his son's behavior; his mother was ashamed. Frank would routinely turn to his father for approval of his behavior, and subsequently for ways to avoid the consequences, although his mother would repeatedly try to instill responsibility and acceptance of his consequences and passively display her shame and disapproval. These contradictory schemas caused Frank to seek out a middle ground of no discomfort, finding that the use of alcohol and other substances provided that relief.

The next step was to develop and teach the resources necessary to deal with that assessment. This step is the stage of treatment where Frank was required to learn to increase his tolerance for the discomfort he experienced, and identify his own "healthy" schema for dealing with his anxiety and mixed messages. He needed to establish appropriate behaviors toward alcohol, and recognize that the medical consequences of his choices might result in permanent injury or death. One way to achieve this goal was to have Frank identify his cognitive distortions, dispute them, and replace them with a more appropriate cognitive belief system.

Identifying and Addressing Obstacles to Treatment

Many obstacles to substance use treatment exist, including ambiguity toward or fear of treatment, concern about negative social consequences, inadequate time or treatment options (Rapp et al., 2006), the lack of a supportive peer group, and poor coping skills. Research has indicated that individuals who are in the precontemplation or contemplation stages of change, according to the Prochaska and DiClemente model (1983), are less likely to enter treatment, suggesting that an individual's readiness for change can be a significant barrier to treatment (V. B. Brown, Melchoir, Panter, Slaughter, & Huba, 2000).

The difficulty of effective communication between mental health care providers and physicians hinders substance use treatment in primary care settings, as often physicians and therapists speak different languages. Therapists must be clear and concise, recognizing that attempts to explain the psychological basis of health concerns may cause a disconnect between the therapist and physician, who primarily seek information required to treat the patient. The therapist must stay up-to-date on any current medical conditions or medical history that will influence diagnosis or assessment, and collaborate with physicians to rule out unrelated medical conditions.

Time constraints pose the most significant obstacles to treatment in primary care. Adequate time to conduct quality assessments, such as a 50-minute consultation, is rarely available in the health care setting. Appropriate advance planning, training, and communication can mitigate these obstacles.

Point of Collaboration With Physicians and Family

There are several points worth consideration in collaboration. It is not only helpful, but imperative, to collaborate with family and other external sources in order to achieve an accurate picture of the nature and scope of the problem, but also for ongoing collaboration. As an extra set of eyes and ears, these resources help to provide a perspective on the effects of treatment and the veracity of the patients. During the referral and initial screening process, the patient is usually experiencing some sort of distress and crisis. The patient may be most open to suggestions for help, as they are often at a point when they are also more likely to be open and honest about what is going on. Physicians are in a unique position, because they are usually dealing with objective test results, physical symptoms, or disorders that are directly or indirectly exacerbated or caused by the patient's substance use. During the evaluation process, the physician can play the role of fact giver and provide the therapist with areas in which the medical data are suggestive or exclusionary of a substance use diagnosis. The use of the medical record, which the physician most likely has, can be invaluable in providing a long-term history of the patient's various physical complaints that when taken as a whole, will provide a clear picture of the physical results of the substance use as well as a possible time line to the start of the problem and any subsequent exacerbations. Finally, these records can provide the motivation for the patient to stop. For example, a steady decline in liver function or continued use of amphetamine can place the patient at higher risk for stroke or cardiac conditions. Long-term needle use can increase the likelihood of HIV infection or AIDS. The physician can be a source of collaboration during the treatment phase by monitoring drug levels in urine and reporting on any changes in health that are indicative of a return to drug use. Most importantly, the physician can serve as a powerful source of positive reinforcement and motivation for the patient's continued success.

The collaboration with the family usually starts from the first phone call. The family usually is the first contact with the treatment provider, especially for adolescents. This initial history provides a picture of the immediate crisis and, in most cases, a fairly extensive history from their perspective. The family is also a source of information on previous treatments, problems, and physicians who may be aware of the patient and his/her condition. Families can provide a list of the consequences of the use that can be helpful in identifying a proper diagnosis. The family is also in the best position to provide ongoing support during the recovery process, and will be especially tuned to identifying those changes that they suspect are the result of continued problem use or a relapse.

Development and Implementation of Empirically Based Treatment Plan

For short-term and brief therapies, the National Institute on Drug Abuse (NIDA) found that no one treatment was effective for every patient, but some treatment and evaluation processes have been and continue to be effective in the drug and alcohol field. The MATCH Project Research Study (1993, 1997) compared motivational enhancement therapy, 12-step facilitation treatment, and cognitive-behavioral therapy (CBT). This study suggested that certain basics are important, including treatment planning. Effective treatment planning is essential, and provides therapists with the access route to create client change. As practitioners, planning for the change process with patients is the single most important skill therapists bring to the therapeutic table. More recently, Kendall and Chambless (1998) and Nathan and Gorman (1998) have documented this important process.

Understanding the change process elevates therapists from mere technicians to professional practitioners. It also allows therapists to view clients where they are, not where we want them to be, and to see resistance as a part of change processes, not an avoidance of change (Dolan, Seay, & Vellela, 2006). However, studies in which the internal mechanism creating change can be inferred are rare (Kazdin, 2000). Consequently, the use of theory-dependent models and transtheoretical models, such as the Prochaska and DiClemente (1983) stages of change, can be applied to determine a client's readiness for change. Change is part of a dynamic therapeutic process and, therefore, is open to revisions as clinical experience and research provides more specificity.

Freeman and Dolan (2001) have provided such a revision of the Prochaska/DiClemente model. Their revision added new stages that increase the specificity of change and more appropriately reflect the actual therapeutic process. The Freeman/Dolan model takes into account that some people may be unaware of the existence of a problem or the need to change (noncontemplation). The first two stages demonstrate this understanding. Freeman and Dolan recognized that a therapist could encounter patients who are forced to, or required to, enter treatment for a number of reasons (i.e., courts, medical conditions). These individuals are placed in a situation where they must decide between therapy and some threat (i.e., jail, medical illness). At the present time, they are not willing to engage in the change process. In some instances, they may oppose (anticontemplation) the whole therapeutic process (Dolan, 2005).

The next two Freeman/Dolan stages (precontemplation and contemplation) are not tied to commitment, as described in Prochaska and DiClemente (1983). Instead, they are the metacognitive and cognitive functions of the change process. For Freeman/Dolan, the precontemplation stage occurs when the patient begins to consider the consequences, purpose, and the possibility of change; whereas in the contemplation stage, the patient is actively considering and is ready to engage change. The three stages after action are new, and reflect the complex cognitive processes of upsetting the homeostasis of a person through the change process. This is consistent with the work of Miller and Rollnick (2002), in which the value of developing discrepancy acts as a motivator for change. The first of these stages is prelapse, in which the client is evaluating whether the change made in the action stage is beneficial or even needed. This is a cognitive process with no behavioral components. The concept of prelapse is needed to explain that once changes are made, the client initially goes through a rejection process similar to a body going through the rejection of transplanted parts. The lapse stage is the behavioral manifestation of the unsuccessful resolution of the prelapse stage. This is usually characterized by a single behavioral event, and if therapeutic redirection occurs (putting the change process back on track), the patient returns to the change state. If the resolution of the prelapse stage is unsuccessful or if redirection is ineffective, then the process will move to relapse (a return to old behaviors). Relapse includes a reemergence of the behavioral problems and the cognitive patterns that induce or reinforce the problem behavior.

The treatment-planning process starts with identifying what to change, which is established by the problem list, then when to implement the process or the stage of change as identified previously, and, finally, the "how," which are the specific treatments that will be most effective for the patient. The collaboration with the physician is important for all three of these phases of treatment planning.

Open communication is necessary to ensure that everyone is working on the issues that are within their specialty, but are also informed as to what everyone else is doing. Second, having the treatment team aware of the timing of certain treatments is essential, and finally, the selection of the treatment approach must be coordinated, whether that be therapy, medication management, psychopharmacological interventions, or support services. This type of integrative approach to treatment planning offers the patient the best chance at a successful recovery.

Evaluation of Treatment Outcomes

NIDA has listed several components for effective treatment. Among its findings is that no single treatment is effective for everyone. Length of treatment must be sufficient for it to work effectively. Also, counseling and other behavioral therapies are critical components of virtually all effective treatments for addiction. For certain types of disorders, medications are an important element of treatment, especially when combined with counseling and other behavioral therapies. Drug addiction treatment can be a long-term process, and it may typically require multiple episodes of treatment. Medication, behavioral therapy, and support groups, alone or in combination, are all aspects of an overall therapeutic process (Anton et al., 2006; Project MATCH Research Group, 1993).

Medications can be used to help with different aspects of the treatment process, from withdrawal to maintenance. Medication for treatment can be used to help reestablish normal brain function and to prevent relapse and diminish cravings throughout the treatment process. Currently, there are medications for opioid (heroin, morphine) and tobacco (nicotine) addiction. Others for treating stimulants (cocaine, methamphetamine), cannabis (marijuana), and alcohol addiction are being developed.

Methadone and buprenorphine, for example, are effective medications for the treatment of opiate addiction. Buprenorphine is a relatively new and important treatment medication. NIDA-supported basic and clinical research led to its development (Subutex, or in combination with naloxone, Suboxone), and demonstrated it to be a safe and acceptable addiction treatment (Mendelson, Flower, Pletcher, & Galloway, 2008). Congress passed the Drug Addiction Treatment Act (DATA, 2000), permitting qualified physicians to prescribe narcotic medications (Schedules III to V) for the treatment of opioid addiction. This legislation created a major paradigm shift by allowing access to opiate treatment in a medical setting, rather than limiting it to specialized drug treatment clinics. A study by Garbutt, West, Carey, Lohr, and Crews (1999) evaluated 375 articles and abstracted and analyzed data from 41 studies and 11 follow-up or subgroup studies. Naltrexone seemed to reduce the risk of relapse to heavy drinking and the frequency of drinking compared with placebo, but does not substantially enhance abstinence. Acamprasate reduced drinking frequency, although its effects on enhancing abstinence or reducing time to first drink are less clear. There are several other drugs that showed promising results, but the data are inconclusive.

Behavioral treatments help patients to change by focusing on behaviors, attitudes, and cognitions that support or maintain the addictive process. Behavioral treatments can also be used collaboratively with medications to increase their effectiveness and assist people to stay in treatment. A number of treatments are listed and described below:

1. CBT, which seeks to help patients recognize, avoid, and cope with the situations in which they are most likely to abuse drugs (Kadden et al, 1992);
2. Multidimensional Family Therapy, which addresses a range of influences on the drug abuse patterns of adolescents, and is designed for them and their families (Liddle et al., 2001);
3. Motivational interviewing, which capitalizes on the readiness of individuals to change their behavior and enter treatment (Miller & Rollnick, 2002);
4. Motivational incentives (contingency management), which uses positive reinforcement to encourage abstinence from drugs;
5. Twelve-step facilitation groups whose goal is to facilitate patients' active participation in the fellowship of Alcoholics Anonymous. The therapy regards such active involvement as the primary factor responsible for sustained sobriety ("recovery"), and therefore, as the desired outcome of participation in this treatment program. This therapy is grounded in the concept of alcoholism as a spiritual and medical disease (Nowinski, Baker, & Carroll, 1994). Numerous studies related to outcome in substance use treatment have been conducted. The COMBINE study (Anton et al., 2006), Project MATCH Research Group (1993, 1997), and Walsh et al. (1991) all support the NIDA statement that no one treatment worked for all; however, the treatments listed here are the ones that to date have the most evidence-based data.

Considerations With Special Populations/Diversity

Disparities in health care across demographic groups have surfaced at a time when minority populations are increasing, leading health care providers to consider the role of ethnicity and other factors on primary care provision (Paez, Allen, Carson, & Cooper, 2008). The interactions of race, gender, socioeconomic status, and age on substance use prevalence and treatment have been explored, although the research is equivocal. For example, research on the role of socioeconomic status in adolescent substance use suggests that there is no difference in adolescent substance use across socioeconomic groups, whereas other research suggests a positive correlation between low socioeconomic factors, such as parent education, and substance abuse (Bolland et al., 2007). Additional research suggests that African American adolescents have higher rates of relapse (Ciesla, Valle, & Spear, 2008). Providing effective substance-use treatment in primary care settings depends on a comprehensive understanding of the complexities of these factors and the needs of these specific communities.

Race and Ethnicity

Studies have confirmed that the *DSM-IV* diagnostic criteria for substance use disorders do not vary across African American and Caucasian patients (Horton, Compton, & Cottler, 2000), and that American Indian adolescents have similar diagnostic patterns as other adolescents (Novins, Fickenscher, & Manson, 2006). However, in terms of course of substance use, Alvarez, Olson, Jason, Davis, and Ferrari (2004) found significant differences based on ethnicity and gender after controlling for age, vocation, education, and biopsychosocial issues. Although equitable substance use treatment options in low-income and African American communities were observed by Archibald (2007), the author also identified disparities in communities with larger Hispanic populations, younger people, and female-run families.

Treatment outcomes have been shown to vary by race and cultural competency of clinicians. Campbell, Weisner, and Sterling (2006) reviewed treatment initiation and retention in African American, Native American, Latino, Asian American, and Caucasian adolescents, and found that Native Americans had lower rates of initiation and African Americans remained in treatment for shorter time periods. Although Asian Americans are less likely to have substance use disorders, those who do have drug or alcohol dependence have been shown to be less likely to receive treatment (Sakai, Ho, Shore, Risk, & Price, 2005).

The cultural competency of treatment programs has been associated with efficacy of treatment (Howard, 2003). One study found that African American women who participated in a treatment program with African American mentors, in addition to standard treatment, had higher retention, were more satisfied, and showed greater decreases in drug use than those receiving only standard treatment (Stahler et al., 2005). Exploration of the role of Spanish language and social networks in Latino adolescent substance use suggests that clinic- or community-based treatments incorporating aspects of Latino social networks may be more effective than standard treatments (Allen et al., 2008). Guidelines and frameworks for culturally responsive treatments have been outlined (Gil, Tubman, & Wagner, 2001; Liddle, Jackson-Gilfort, & Marvel, 2006). These tailored treatment practices remain uncommon, and have potentially become less frequently used in treatment programs over the past decade (Alexander, Nahra, Lemak, Pollack, & Campbell, 2008).

Gender

Women may be less likely to enter treatment than men. However, gender is not a predictor of outcome in those who do initiate treatment (Greenfield et al., 2007). Research suggests that women in specialized female-only treatment programs have higher retention rates and improved outcomes, although these specialized programs are relatively uncommon (Claus et al., 2007).

Socioeconomic Status

Social, behavioral, and economic factors can also influence substance use and are important to consider for treatment in primary care. Tucker et al. (2005) found that alcohol, marijuana, and crack use were associated with lower levels of social support, lack of economic resources, and avoidant rather than active coping with homeless women. Another study suggested that two years after completion of substance use treatment, having a lower income, being single, and having lower self-efficacy are associated with alcohol use directly and drug use indirectly (Walton, Blow, Bingham, & Chermack, 2003).

Age

Recent trends reflect a growing number of older adults who abuse substances including prescription drugs. Treatments addressing specific concerns of elder populations can be beneficial in relapse prevention (Blow, Brockmann, & Barry, 2007). Older patients (aged 65 and older) who received personalized reports and education from their PCPs reflected a greater decrease in drinking quantity and frequency than those who received usual treatment (Fink, Elliot, Tsai, & Beck, 2005).

Specific barriers to treatment of adolescents have also been explored. Stern, Meredith, Gholson, Gore, and D'Amico (2007) note that social pressures and confidentiality concerns prohibit teens from pursuing treatment. However, the authors found that adolescents are likely willing to discuss their substance use in primary care settings, suggesting that PCPs should strongly consider their role in treating substance use in adolescents.

Physical disabilities and medical complications may also influence treatment of substance use in primary care, increasing the risk of substance use disorders (Krahn, Farrell, Gabriel, & Deck, 2006). Individuals with physical disabilities are likely to experience increased stress, in turn elevating the risk of substance disorders (Turner, Lloyd, & Taylor, 2006). Additionally, increased alcohol intake can provoke earlier onset of heart disease, stroke, or cancers (Schuckit, 2009). The synergistic relationship between substance use and medical problems compels clinicians to understand the role of medical problems in treatment.

Physical disabilities, such as paralysis or wheelchair use, may serve as a logistical barrier to treatment in environments unequipped to accommodate such needs. Health care professionals need to identify these barriers in their offices and make the necessary adjustments so as to not add to the obstacles of accessing treatment.

The importance of medical support in primary services treating chemical dependence was highlighted by Mertens, Flisher, Satre, and Weisner (2008), who advocate for a disease-management model approach to substance-use treatment that uses primary care. A study based in the United Arab Emirates suggests that PCPs can play an effective role in treating substance-use disorders along with the medical complications that often present with substance use (Abou-Saleh, 2006). The integration of medical history with mental history, and the collaboration between medical providers and mental health and substance abuse professionals, is an important component of treatment (Stein, 1999).

Treatments that address medical concerns have been shown to be effective, and can serve as the proverbial "foot in the door" for the PCP to initiate a dialogue in the sometimes uncomfortable area of substance use. Nutrition education can also enhance positive outcomes in substance-use treatment (L. P. Grant, Haughton, & Sachan, 2004).

Clinical Pearls of Wisdom for Practitioners

Working in collaboration with PCPs can be an invaluable and rewarding experience for the therapist or psychologist. Here are some caveats to keep in mind:

1. Cognitive-behavioral clinicians are typically not physicians, and must defer to physicians in areas that are not within the scope of their license and education.
2. Establishing a relationship with individual physicians can be a most effective way to avoid problems or miscommunication. This relationship is very much a two-way street, because therapists possess an expertise the physician does not have, and physicians possess an expertise that therapists do not have. Opening the door to their knowledge and skill will only serve to make for better and more effective collaborative therapy.
3. In the behavioral health field, the tendency is to present very long and detailed histories and assessments. However, physicians tend to focus on the critical information needed to make a medical diagnosis. The moral is that time is a major constraint in the medical field, and keeping the conversations brief and to the point will be appreciated by the physicians.
4. Keep up-to-date on current research and methodologies in the treatment of substance-use disorders.
5. Learn the language of medicine and use it in conversations and reports. Statements like "rule out" mean more to a physician than asking them to find out what is wrong. It allows for more specification.
6. Seek consultation with the physician on the importance of certain lab values and test results that are contained in their charts and reports.
7. Cognitive-behavioral therapists are an equal member of the health care team and should strive to value their own input if they expect physicians to do so.

References

Abou-Saleh, M. T. (2006). Substance use disorders: Recent advances in treatment and models of care. *Journal of Psychosomatic Research, 61*, 305–310.

Alexander, J. A., Nahra, T. A., Lemak, C. H., Pollack, H., & Campbell, C. I. (2008). Tailored treatment in the outpatient substance abuse treatment sector: 1995–2005. *Journal of Substance Abuse Treatment, 34*, 282–292.

Allen, M. L., Elliott, M. N., Fuligni, A. J., Morales, L. S., Hambarsoomian, K., & Schuster, M. A. (2008). Relationship between Spanish language use and substance use behaviors among Latino youth: A social network approach. *Journal of Adolescent Health, 43*, 372–379.

Alvarez, J., Olson, B. D., Jason, L. A., Davis, M. I., & Ferrari, J. R. (2004). Heterogeneity among Latinas and Latinos entering substance abuse treatment: Findings from a national database. *Journal of Substance Abuse Treatment, 26*, 277–284.

American Psychiatric Association. (2000). *Diagnostic and statistical manual of mental disorders* (4th ed., text rev.). Washington, DC: Author.

Anton, R. F., O'Malley, S. S., Ciraulo, D. A., Cister, R. A., Couper, D., Donovan, D. M. (2006). Combined pharmacotherapies and behavioral interventions for alcohol dependence: The COMBINE study: A randomized controlled trial. *Journal of the American Medical Association, 295*, 2003–2017.

Archibald, M. E. (2007). Socioeconomic and racial/ethnic disparities in substance abuse treatment provision, treatment needs and utilization. *Research in the Sociology of Health Care, 25*, 171–200.

Babor, T. F., de la Fuente, J. R., Saunders, J., & Grant, M. (1992). *AUDIT: The alcohol use disorders identification test: Guidelines for use in primary health care*. Geneva, Switzerland: World Health Organization.

Blow, F. C., Brockmann, L. M., & Barry, K. L. (2007). Relapse prevention with older adults. In K. Witkiewitz & G.A. Marlatt (Eds.), *Therapist's guide to evidence-based relapse prevention* (pp. 313–337). Burlington, MA: Elsevier.

Bolland, J. M., Bryant, C. M., Lian, B. E., McCallum, D. M., Vazsonyi, A. T., & Barth, J. M. (2007). Development and risk behavior among African American, Caucasian, and mixed-race adolescents living in high poverty inner-city neighborhoods. *American Journal of Community Psychology, 40*, 230–249.

Brown, R. L., & Rounds, L. A. (1995). Conjoint screening questionnaires for alcohol and other drug abuse: Criterion validity in a primary care practice. *Wisconsin Medical Journal, 94*, 135–140.

Brown, V. B., Melchior, L. A., Panter, A. T., Slaughter, R., & Huba, G. J. (2000). Women's steps of change and entry into drug abuse treatment: A multidimensional stages of change model. *Journal of Substance Abuse Treatment, 18*, 231–240.

Campbell, C. I., Weisner, C., & Sterling, S. (2006). Adolescents entering chemical dependency treatment in private managed care: Ethnic differences in treatment initiation and retention. *Journal of Adolescent Health, 38*, 343–350.

Cherpitel, C. J., & Clark, W. B. (1995). Ethnic differences in screening instruments for identifying harmful drinking and alcohol dependence in the emergency room. *Alcoholism: Clinical and Experimental Research, 19*, 628–634.

Ciesla, J. R., Valle, M., & Spear, S. F. (2008). Measuring relapse after adolescent substance abuse treatment: A proportional hazard approach. *Addictive Disorders & Their Treatment, 7*, 87–97.

Claus, R. E., Orwin, R. G., Kissin, W., Krupski, A., Campbell, K., & Stark, K. (2007). Does gender-specific substance abuse treatment for women promote continuity of care? *Journal of Substance Abuse Treatment, 32*, 27–39.

Dolan, M. J. (2005). Stages of change. In A. Freeman (Ed.), *Encyclopedia of cognitive behavior therapy* (pp. 387–390). New York: Springer Science and Business.

Dolan, M. J., Seay, T. A., & Vellela, T. C. (2006). The revised stage of change model and the treatment planning process. In G. R. Walz, J. C. Bleuer, & R. K. Yep (Eds.), *Vistas, compelling perspectives on counseling 2006* (pp. 129–132), Alexandria, VA: American Counseling Association.

Drug Addiction Treatment Act of 2000. (2000). Retrieved August 10, 2009, from http://www.naabt.org/documents/DATA2000LAWTEXT.pdf

Ewing, J. A. (1984). Detecting alcoholism: The CAGE Questionnaire. *Journal of the American Medical Association, 252*(14), 1905–1907.

Fink, A., Elliott, M. N., Tsai, M., & Beck, J. C. (2005). An evaluation of an intervention to assist primary care physicians in screening and educating older patients who use alcohol. *Journal of the American Geriatrics Society, 53*, 1937–1943.

Fleming, M., & Graham, A. (2001). Screening and brief interventions for alcohol use disorders in managed care settings. *Recent Developments in Alcoholism, 15*, 393–416.

Fleming, M. F., & Barry, K. L. (1992). Clinical overview of alcohol and drug disorders. In M. F. Fleming & K. L. Barry (Eds.), *Addictive disorders* (pp. 3–21). Chicago: Mosby Yearbook.

Freeman, A., & Dolan, M. (2001). Revisiting Prochaska and DiClemente's stages of change theory: An expansion and specification to aid in treatment planning and outcome evaluation. *Cognitive and Behavioral Practice, 8*, 224–234.

Garbutt, J. C., West, S. L., Carey, T. S, Lohr, K. N., & Crews, F. T. (1999) Pharmacological treatment of alcohol dependence: A review of the evidence. *Journal of the American Medical Association, 281*, 1318–1325.

Gil, A. G., Tubman, J. G., & Wagner, E. F. (2001). Substance abuse interventions with Latino adolescents: A cultural framework. In E. F. Wagner & H. B. Waldron (Eds.), *Innovations in adolescent substance abuse interventions* (pp. 353–378). Oxford, UK: Elsevier.

Grant, B. F. (2000). Estimates of US children exposed to alcohol abuse and dependence in the family. *American Journal of Public Health, 90*, 112–115.

Grant, L. P., Haughton, B., & Sachan, D. S. (2004). Nutrition education is positively associated with substance abuse treatment program outcomes. *Journal of the American Dietetic Association, 104*, 604–610.

Greenfield, S. F., Brooks, A. J., Gordon, S. M., Green, C. A., Kropp, F., McHugh, R. K., et al. (2007). Substance abuse treatment entry, retention, and outcome in women: A review of the literature. *Drug and Alcohol Dependence, 86*, 1–21.

Grumbach, K., & Bodenheimer, T. (2004). Can health care teams improve primary care practice? *Journal of the American Medical Association, 291*, 1246–1251.

Hays, R. D., Hill, L., & Gillogly, J. J. (1993). Response times for the CAGE, Short-MAST, AUDIT, and JELLINEK alcohol scales. *Behavioral Research Methods, Instruments, and Computers, 25*, 304–307.

Horton, J., Compton, W., & Cottler, L. B. (2000). Reliability of substance use disorder diagnoses among African-Americans and Caucasians. *Drug and Alcohol Dependence, 57*, 203–209.

Howard, D. L. (2003a). Culturally competent treatment of African American clients among a national sample of outpatient substance abuse treatment units. *Journal of Substance Abuse Treatment, 24*, 89–102.

Institute on Drug Abuse. (2008a). *Treatment approaches for drug addictions*. Retrieved June 18, 2009, from http://www.drugabuse.gov/PDF/InfoFactsTreatment08.pdf

Institute on Drug Abuse. (2008b). *NIDA InfoFacts: Treatment statistics*. Retrieved June 18, 2009, from http://www.drugabuse.gov/infofacts/treatmenttrends.htm

Institute of Medicine. (1990). *Broadening the base of treatment of alcohol problems*. Washington, DC: National Press.

Juhnke, G. A. (2002). *Substance abuse assessment: A handbook for mental health professionals*. New York: Brunner-Routledge.

Kadden, R., Carroll, K. M., Donovan, D., Cooney, N., Monti, P., Abrams, D., et al. (1992). *Cognitive-behavioral coping skills therapy manual: A clinical research guide for therapists treating individuals with alcohol abuse and dependence* (NIAAA Project MATCH Monograph Series, Vol. 3. DHHS Pub. No. [ADM] 92-1895). Rockville, MD: National Institute on Alcohol Abuse and Alcoholism.

Kazdin, A. E. (2000). *Psychotherapy for children and adolescents: Directions for research and practice*. New York: Oxford University Press.

Kendall, P. C., & Chambless, D. L. (Eds.). (1998). Empirically supported psychological therapies (special section). *Journal of Counseling and Clinical Psychology, 66*, 3–167.

Krahn, G., Farrell, N., Gabriel, R., & Deck, D. (2006). Access barriers to substance abuse treatment for persons with disabilities: An exploratory study. *Journal of Substance Abuse Treatment, 31*, 375–384.

Liddle, H. A., Dakof, G. A., Parker, K., Diamond, G. S., Barrett, K., & Tejeda, M. (2001). Multidimensional family therapy for adolescent drug abuse: Results of a randomized clinical trial. *American Journal of Drug and Alcohol Abuse, 27*, 651–688.

Liddle, H. A., Jackson-Gilfort, A., & Marvel, F. A. (2006). An empirically supported and culturally specific engagement and intervention strategy for African American adolescent males. *American Journal of Orthopsychiatry, 76*, 215–225.

Manwell, L., Fleming, M. F., Barry, K., & Johnson, K. (1998). Tobacco, alcohol, and drug use in a primary care sample: 90-day prevalence and associated factors. *Journal of Addictive Diseases, 17*, 67–81.

Mendelson, J., Flower, K., Pletcher, M. J., & Galloway, G. P. (2008). Addiction to prescription opioids: Characteristics of the emerging epidemic and treatment with buprenorphine. *Experimental and Clinical Psychopharmacology, 16*(5), 435–441.

Mertens, J. R., Flisher, A. J., Satre, D. D., & Weisner, C. M. (2008). The role of medical conditions and primary care services in 5-year substance use outcomes among chemical dependency treatment patients. *Drug and Alcohol Dependence, 98*, 45–53.

Miller, W. R., & Rollnick, S. (2002). *Motivational interviewing: Preparing people for change*. New York: Guilford.

Nathan, P. E., & Gorman, J. M. (Eds.). (1998). *Treatments that work*. New York: Oxford University Press.

The National Center on Addiction and Substance Abuse (CASA) at Columbia University. (2000). *Missed opportunity: National survey of primary care physicians and patients on substance abuse*. New York: The National Center on Addiction and Substance Abuse (CASA) at Columbia University. Retrieved June 18, 2009, from http://www.casacolumbia.org/absolutenm/articlefiles/380MissedOpportunityPhysiciansandPatients.pdf18

Nowinski, J., Baker, S., & Carroll, K. (1994). *Twelve-step facilitation therapy manual: A clinical research guide for therapists treating individuals with alcohol abuse and dependence* (National Institute on Alcohol Abuse and Alcoholism, Project MATCH monograph series, Vol. 1. NIH Publication No. 94–3722). Washington, DC: U.S. Government Printing Office.

Novins, D. K., Fickenscher, A., & Manson, S. M. (2006). American Indian adolescents in substance abuse treatment: Diagnostic status. *Journal of Substance Abuse Treatment, 30*, 275–284.

Paez, K. A., Allen, J. K., Carson, K. A., & Cooper, L. A. (2008). Provider and clinic cultural competence in a primary care setting. *Social Science & Medicine, 66*, 1204–1216.

Parthasarathy, S., Mertens, J., Moore, C., & Weisner, C. (2003). Utilization and cost impact of integrating substance abuse treatment and primary care. *Medical Care, 41*, 357–367.

Peele, S. (2000). What addiction is and is not: The impact of mistaken notions of addiction. *Addiction Research, 8*, 599–607.

Prochaska, J. O., & DiClemente, C. C. (1983). Stages and processes of self-change of smoking: Toward an integrative model of change. *Journal of Consulting and Clinical Psychology, 51*, 390–395.

Project MATCH Research Group. (1993). Project MATCH: Rationale and methods for a multisite clinical trial matching patients to alcoholism treatment. *Alcoholism: Clinical and Experimental Research, 17*, 1130–1145.

Project MATCH Research Group. (1997). Project MATCH secondary a priori hypotheses (clinical trial, journal article, randomized controlled trial). *Addiction, 92*, 1671–1698.

Rapp, R. C., Xu, J., Carr, C. A., Lane, D. T., Wang, J., & Carlson, R. (2006). Treatment barriers identified by substance abusers assessed at a centralized intake unit. *Journal of Substance Abuse Treatment, 30*, 227–235.

Regier, D., Narrow, W., Rae, D., Manderscheid, R., Locke, B., & Goodwin, F. (1993). The de facto mental health and addictive disorders service system. *Archives of General Psychiatry, 50*, 85–94.

Schuckit, M. A. (2009). Alcohol-use disorders. *Lancet, 373*, 492–501.

Schuckit, M. A., & Irwin, M. (1988). Diagnosis of alcoholism. *Medical Clinics of North America, 72*, 1133–1153.

Sakai, J. T., Ho, P. M., Shore, J. H., Risk, N. K., & Price, R. K. (2005). Asians in the United States: Substance dependence and use of substance-dependence treatment. *Journal of Substance Abuse Treatment, 29*, 75–84.

Samet, J. H., Friedmann, P., & Saitz, R. (2001). Benefits of linking primary medical care and substance abuse services. *Archives of Internal Medicine, 161*, 85–91.

Stahler, G. J., Shipley, T. E., Jr., Kirby, K. C., Godboldte, C., Kerwin, M. E., & Shandler, I. (2005). Development and initial demonstration of a community-based intervention for homeless, cocaine-using, African-American women. *Journal of Substance Abuse Treatment, 28*, 171–179.

Stein, M. D. (1999). Medical consequences of substance abuse. *Psychiatric Clinics of North America, 22*, 351–370.

Stern, S. A., Meredith, L. S., Gholson, J., Gore, P., & D'Amico, E. J. (2007). Project CHAT: A brief motivational substance abuse intervention for teens in primary care. *Journal of Substance Abuse Treatment, 32*, 153–165.

Substance Abuse and Mental Health Services Administration. (2008). *Results from the 2007 national survey on drug use and health: National findings* (Office of Applied Studies, NSDUH Series H-34, DHHS Publication No. SMA 08-4343). Rockville, MD. Retrieved June 18, 2009, from http://oas.samhsa.gov

Tucker, J. S., D'Amico, E. J., Wenzel, S. L., Golinelli, D., Elliott, M. N. & Williamson, S. (2005). A prospective study of risk and protective factors for substance use among impoverished women living in temporary shelter settings in Los Angeles County. *Drug and Alcohol Dependence, 80*, 35–43.

Turner, R. J., Lloyd, D. A., & Taylor, J. (2006). Stress burden, drug dependence and the Hispanic paradox. *Drug and Alcohol Dependence, 83*, 79–89.

U.S. Department of Health and Human Services, National Institutes of Health, National Institute on Drug Abuse. (2008a). *Treatment approaches for drug addiction*. Retrieved June 18, 2009, from http://www.drugabuse.gov/PDF/InfoFacts/Treatment08.pdf.

U.S. Department of Justice. (2009). *Drugs and crime facts*. Retrieved October 30, 2009, from http://www.jp.gov/bjs/dcf/du.htm#general

Walsh, D. C., Hingson, R. W., Merrigan, D. M., Levenson, S. M., Cupples, L. A., Heeren, T., et al. (1991). A randomized trial of treatment options for alcohol-abusing workers. *New England Journal of Medicine, 325*, 775–782.

Walton, M. A., Blow, F. C., Bingham, C. R., & Chermack, S. T. (2003). Individual and social/environmental predictors of alcohol and drug use two years following treatment. *Addictive Behaviors, 28*, 627–642.

Somatoform Disorders

20

Barbara A. Golden
Clint C. Stankiewicz
Jeanne R. Kestel

Introduction

As you begin to read this chapter, please pause and respond to these questions: Over the last 7 days, have you experienced any feeling of physical discomfort? Have you had any headaches, fatigue, musculoskeletal pain, gastrointestinal discomfort? If the answer is "yes," is there any organic basis for this discomfort? It is likely that most of you answered "yes "to the first two questions and "no" to the last question. Community studies have reported that at least 80% of people experience a medically unexplained physical symptom (UPS) each week (Pennebaker, 1982). In fact, UPSs are part of the human condition. However, statistics for primary care medicine estimate that 25–50% of all visits have no medical basis. In addition, patients with somatization complaints also have more specialist visits, emergency department visits, hospital admissions, ambulatory procedures, and higher inpatient and outpatient costs. By far, this imposes the most staggering costs to individuals, families, employers, physicians, health care facilities and overall health care costs (Barsky, Orav, & Bates, 2005). These patients can be very frustrating for physicians who are trained to look for symptoms, identify the problem, diagnose, and treat appropriately. Patients, as well, may experience significant frustration with the physician who is unable to find a problem and who may suggest, even in nonverbal communication, that the problem is "all in your head." Patients who do experience physical symptoms may not admit to psychosocial stressors that may be exacerbating the physical symptoms, and they may become quite disheartened with the medical community. The need to identify these patients early on and to offer multidisciplinary treatment are key elements in reducing personal distress, minimizing functional impairment, and decreasing significant health care costs.

Assessment and Diagnostic Issues

According to the *Diagnostic and Statistical Manual of Mental Disorders* (*DSM-IV-TR;* American Psychiatric Association [APA], 2000) the common thread running throughout somatoform disorders (SD) is the presence of a constellation of symptoms that implies a medical condition, yet is not fully explained by a general medical condition, by the effects of a substance, or by another mental disorder. In addition, the symptoms must cause clinically significant distress or impairment in social, occupational, or other areas of functioning. The diagnosis of a somatoform disorder must rule out the following: (a) an underlying, but as yet undetected, general medical condition that is causing the symptoms; (b) another mental disorder that is responsible for the somatic symptoms (e.g., anxiety or mood disorder that often present with somatic symptoms); or (c) symptoms that are intentionally produced or feigned, as in malingering or factitious disorder (Frances & Ross, 2004).

Patients suffering from SD experience and report bodily symptoms that have no physiological basis, and thus, they have a tendency to misattribute their condition to disease and seek medical treatment. Individuals with these disorders tend to be resistant to a psychological explanation of their condition, and become fixated on discovering a biological basis. In some instances, this becomes a pattern of behavior similar to a chronic illness, where the patient tends to adopt the "sick" role, and this pattern affects his/her world view (Calabrese & Stern, 2004).

The tautological dilemma inherent in treating SD makes working with this population an exasperating enterprise for physicians and primary health care staff. Physicians often report that somatizing patients are among the most frustrating to treat (Dowrick et al., 2008; Linn et al., 1991). Such patients are often described as "doctor shoppers," "problem patients," "neurotics," "hypochondriacs," "hysterics," and "med seekers," among others. Physicians may feel anxious, frustrated, overwhelmed, and even resentful when working with these patients. Physicians may lack expertise in this area due to diagnostic, conceptual, and classificatory difficulty. Therefore, there is a strong need for interdisciplinary collaboration between primary care physicians (PCPs) and psychologists. An assessment and treatment approach that allows for active multidisciplinary consultation is going to be well suited to effectively managing such a complex health care problem.

The different types of SD include: somatization disorder, hypochondriasis, conversion disorder, pain disorder, body dysmorphic disorder, undifferentiated somatoform disorder, and somatoform disorder not otherwise specified (APA, 2000). The diagnosis of SD is exclusionary in nature, as they are often made after a lengthy process of ruling out all possible physiological causes to the symptoms

(Servan-Schreiber, Tabas, Kolb, & Haas, 2004). Somatization is often conceptualized as being a process with expression occurring on a spectrum (Katon et al., 1991). At one end of the spectrum, a mild somatoform disorder may manifest itself as a stress-related exacerbation of stress-related symptoms (e.g., headache, back pain, lightheadedness, etc.) that occur in the context of a psychosocial stressor such as loss of job, separation or divorce, or a new family member. At the other end of this spectrum, a severe somatoform disorder may express itself in such a way that completely debilitates the patient, leaving the patient unable to fulfill responsibilities of daily living (Servan-Schreiber et al.; Servan-Schreiber, Kolb, & Tabas, 2000a).

In the assessment process, PCPs are careful to note the frequently occurring and overlapping symptoms and syndromes that may be of organic origin. This process can be quite lengthy, as it includes a plethora of gastrointestinal symptoms, pain symptoms, pseudoneurological symptoms, cardiorespiratory symptoms, and reproductive organ symptoms (Blackwell & De Morgan, 1996). In addition, functional somatic syndromes, which have medically unexplained co-occurring symptoms, including irritable bowel syndrome (IBS), chronic fatigue syndrome (CFS), and fibromyalgia, add to the difficulty of specific diagnostic impressions. Consideration must be made for actual medical disorders that present multiple, vague symptoms. These may include thyroid and parathyroid illnesses, multiple sclerosis, lupus, Lyme disease, temporomandibular joint syndrome, and others.

The assessment of SD is difficult, due to the high degree of overlap between psychiatric disorders and SD. The identification of these conditions may, in fact, help a clinician discern the diagnosis (Servan-Schreiber et al., 2004). Psychiatric comorbidity and differential diagnoses include, but are not limited to anxiety disorders, mood and affective disorders with multiple somatic complaints, substance abuse disorders, personality disorders, factious disorder, malingering, and the "worried well." The reported concordance rate for somatization disorder is estimated to be near 60% for depression, 50% for anxiety-based disorders, and nearly 60% for personality disorders (Kroenke et al., 1994). Lowe et al. (2008), in a major primary care study, suggest several explanations for the overlap between depression, anxiety, and somatization. These include the presence of overlapping diagnostic criteria, the presence of one syndrome may be a risk factor for another, and the three disorders may share psychosocial and biological diatheses. There is some suggestion that SD are caused by a cluster of psychiatric disorders that present in an atypical or incomplete fashion. Some of the nonspecific somatic symptoms, that is, sweating, nausea, heart palpitations, fatigue, and other bodily pains, are commonly reported in patients suffering from anxiety and depression (Rief & Barsky, 2005). There is an interesting relationship between physical disorders and psychiatric disorders, which results in potential for greater disability. According to Escobar (as cited in Lamberg, 2005), the more physical symptoms a patient reports, the more likely he or she has a psychiatric disorder. Escobar states "just counting physical symptoms is a good way to screen for psychopathology" (p. 2152).

The comorbidity and overlap of symptoms between somatic and psychological disorders is great, and makes an accurate diagnosis of a somatoform disorder a challenging one for clinicians. In many ways, SD are shrouded in mystery, as the exact pathophysiology underlying these disorders is not well understood at this time. Notwithstanding, four psychological mechanisms are cited frequently in the literature as playing a role in SD (Servan-Schreiber et al., 2000a). These four mechanisms include the following: amplification of body sensations, the "identified patient," sick role or "need to be sick," and dissociation.

Patients suffering from SD often experience and report bodily symptoms, and therefore, misattribute their condition to disease. This excessive concern with physical illness may lead one to focus disproportionately on normal variation in bodily sensations. An individual may amplify a bodily sensation like dizziness, thus developing a heightened sensitivity to this disturbance. This heightened sensation may cause the individual to become preoccupied with the idea that the new symptom may be a signal of a cardiovascular problem. For these patients, this phenomenon becomes confirmation of the presence of a physiological illness, which increases their concern and anxiety, and, in turn, amplifies their sensations. Closely related to this is the discovery that complaints and subjective experience of symptoms tend to fluctuate in response to stressful life situations. In this way, somatizing has been viewed as an expression of psychological pain in individuals that lack the ability to express their distress in any other manner (Barsky, 1992).

Having an "identified patient" serves a stabilizing function by allaying anxiety within the family context, particularly when a family is under duress. The illness becomes a context in which family members interact with one another. As the illness becomes more prolonged, behavior patterns within the family become entrenched and rules and roles begin to develop, governing behavior and interaction among family members. When we apply this to a patient with somatic complaints, we may see the patterns become more dysfunctional as the individual takes on the role of being weak or defective. This reaction can be reinforced inadvertently by physicians as they focus medical attention and resources in attempts to treat their patient's illness. In this way, the system can become increasingly ingrained and resistant to change despite the family's genuine concern for the well-being of the identified patient (Servan-Schreiber et al., 2000a).

When examining SD on an individual level, it becomes clear that the behavior may serve a function that encourages the patient to adopt a "sick role." For example, somatizing may afford a patient temporary relief from stressful, unpleasant, or demanding interpersonal expectation, known as "primary gain." "Secondary gain" may result from the increase in care, attention, and even monetary gain related to their illness. It should be noted that secondary-gain issues should be evaluated and treated in a biopsychosocial model, to target and eliminate the patient factors and environmental factors maintaining these behaviors. This dynamic should be differentiated from a conscious faking of symptoms, as in malingering.

An interesting finding is that somatizing patients tend to experience dissociative symptoms with more frequency than do patients with other psychiatric conditions (von der Kolk et al., 1996). It is hypothesized that some somatic symptoms may be a product of the dissociative process. Researchers have likened it to phantom limb pain, where the central nervous system behaves as if there were tissue damage, despite the lack of observable damage. In this way, symptoms may be a product of somatic representations of pain or other physical sensation in the absence of stimulation (Servan-Schreiber et al., 2004).

A strength of the biopsychosocial model in treating SD is that it considers a more holistic approach that enables both the PCP and mental health providers to conceptualize problems in an integrative manner. This is an important notion, as physical and psychological problems tend to occur and increase together, making collaboration among professionals necessary (Gatchel, 2004). A biopsychosocial approach is in accord with cognitive-behavioral therapy (CBT). Indeed, the psychological factors, cognitions, affect, and behavior are all addressed in CBT, making such an approach well suited to manage SD. A similar model designed for use in primary care is the BATHE technique, proposed by Lieberman (1997). This technique addresses the *background* of the issue, the *affect* associated with it, the related *troubling* aspects, ways the patient is *handling* it, and providing *empathy* on the part of the therapist.

Clinical Interview

Given the complicated picture of the person with a possible somatoform disorder, the clinical interview is a significant priority. Clarity on the specific presenting problem, with a thorough assessment of medical issues and possible psychopathology, is the goal. As in any clinical interview, the discussion should include current and past history of medical, psychological, occupational, social, and physical functioning. It is most helpful to include family members and the PCP's information in completion of this interview.

The Structured Clinical Interview for DSM-IV Disorders (SCID; First, Spitzer, Gibbon, & Williams, 1997) may help to focus the interview. The *SCID* includes questions that review diagnostic criteria for all the SD and other major psychiatric disorders. This may initially be overwhelming to the clinician and the patient, but it may help to increase the therapeutic alliance. The patient may experience, for the first time, a feeling that the clinician is listening and attending to the significant presentation of symptoms, as well as the frequency, duration, and intensity of these issues over time. Additional structured clinical interviews for the assessment of SD include the Composite International Diagnostic Interview (CIDI; World Health Organization, 1994a), the Schedules for Clinical Assessment in Neuropsychiatry (SCAN; World Health Organization, 1994b) and the Somatoform Disorders Schedule (SDS; World Health Organization, 1994c). These measures may prove to be excessive in a clinical setting. The use of brief screening measures may be more effective for the PCP or clinician who has a limited time to assess.

Measures

Screening instruments have been developed to assess medical symptoms that are unexplained. The Screening for Somatoform Symptoms (SOMS, Rief, Hiller, Geissner, & Fichter, 1995; Rief, Hiller, & Heuser, 1997) is a self-report questionnaire that lists 53 symptoms from the somatoform sections of the *DSM-IV* and the *International Statistical Classification of Diseases* (*ICD-10*; World Health Organization, 2007).

The Patient Health Questionnaire (PHQ-15) (Spitzer, Kroenke, Williams, & Patient Health Questionnaire Primary Care Study Group, 1999) is a brief, three-page, self-administered tool that assesses 15 somatic symptoms, 10 of which are included in diagnostic criteria for somatization disorder in the *DSM-IV.* Although the questionnaire can be helpful in assessing the experience of somatic symptoms, it is unable to detect differences between medically explained or unexplained symptoms (Kroenke, Spitzer, & Williams, 2002). Therefore, it cannot be used independent of clinical judgment to diagnose SD. The *Medical Outcomes Study Short-Form General Health Survey* (*SF-20*; Stewart, Hays, & Ware, 1988) is a 20-item assessment that is organized into six subscales, including physical functioning, role functioning, social functioning, mental health, health perceptions, and pain. With these subscales, the total survey, *SF-36*, is inclusive and is also highly practical. The Somatic Symptoms Inventory (SSI; Barsky & Wyshak, 1990) assesses 13 somatic symptoms that are common to the hypochondriasis subscale of the *Minnesota Multiphasic Personality Inventory* (Hathaway et al., 2000) and the somatization subscale of the *Hopkins Symptom Checklist-90* (Derogatis, Lipman, Rickels, Uhlenhuth, & Covi, 1974). Given that it is a self-report measure, medical examinations must be taken into account in order to rule out a medical explanation for each symptom.

There are other measures to assess specific SD, including the Whiteley Index of Hypochondriasis (WI; Pilowsky, 1967). The WI is a self-reported 14-item questionnaire that measures physical, cognitive, and emotional aspects of hypochondriasis. The WI also measures change in response to treatment, and includes items addressing fear of disease, reactions to reports of disease in the media, and reactions to reassurance. The WI is often used to screen for hyphocondriasis, and is frequently used in primary care settings, given its short length.

The Somatic Symptom Amplification Scale (SSAS; Barsky, Wyshak, & Klerman, 1990) assesses a patient's cognitive style, sometimes associated with patients with hypochondriasis and other SD. As previously discussed, somatosensory amplification may play a role in the causes of these disorders.

Additional screening should be completed for other concomitant mental health disorders, especially anxiety and depression. The Beck Depression Scales (Beck, Ward, Mendelson, Mock, & Erbaugh, 1961), Hamilton Rating Scales for Depression (Hamilton, 1960, 1967), and the Zung Self-rating Scale for Depression (Zung, 1965) are useful and common measures of depression. The State-Trait Anxiety Inventory (*STAI*; Spielberger, Gorsuch, & Lushene, 1970), the Beck Anxiety Inventory (Beck, Epstein, Brown, & Steer, 1988), and the Hamilton Rating Scales for Anxiety (Hamilton, 1959) are also used frequently to assess for psychological distress.

Incidence and Clinical Manifestations in Primary Care

The primary care setting is often the first point of contact for patients suffering from SD. Researchers note that SDs are among the most common psychiatric disorders in primary care (Barsky et al., 2005; Hansen, Fink, Sondergaard, & Frydenberg, 2005; Spitzer et al., 1994). This sets up an interesting and frustrating dynamic, as patients are intent on substantiating a physiological basis for their condition, although physicians trained in the medical model can find no such grounds for an illness that, in reality, is a psychiatric condition. It comes as no surprise that these patients use a disproportionate amount of health care resources and expenditure. In fact, Ross, Kashner, and Smith (1994) note that 91% of annual health care costs of treating somatoform patients was due to treatment of a physical symptom, with the remaining 9% for psychiatric services. Further, it has been estimated that the cost of treating patients suffering from somatization disorder is nine times higher than those of the average medical patient, with some estimates approaching 14 times higher (Allen, Woolfolk, Escobar, Gara, & Hamer, 2006; Smith, Monson, & Ray, 1986a). These costs soar when we take into account lost time from work and other lost productivity expenses.

These patients tend to report high levels of disability and subjective level of suffering, despite receiving large amounts of medical attention (Escobar et al., 1987). "Inadequately high medical costs result when patients visit physicians frequently, consult numerous specialists, demand costly diagnostic tests, insist on inpatient care and undergo operations without clear medical indication" (Hiller, Fichter, & Rief, 2003, p. 369). Therefore, the medical management of SD can be as particularly deleterious as ineffective. Inaccurate diagnosis and management leads to frustrating, costly, and potentially dangerous treatment strategies that do not reduce suffering (Servan-Schreiber, Kolb, & Tabas, 2000b).

Brief Case History

The following is a case summary and cognitive-behavioral case conceptualization of a patient suffering from somatization disorder. Somatization disorder may be considered on the more severe spectrum of SD, due to the history of physical complaints over time.

Additional diagnostic criteria are detailed in the following; each is adapted from the *DSM-IV-TR* (APA, 2000).

Somatization Disorder

1. A history of many physical complaints beginning before age 30 that occur over a period of several years, and result in seeking treatment or significant impairment in functioning;
2. Each of the criteria must be met with symptoms occurring at any time over the course of the disturbance: four pain symptoms, two gastrointestinal symptoms, one sexual symptom, and one pseudoneurological symptom;
3. After investigation, the symptoms may not be fully explained by a known medical condition or the direct effects of a substance. Or, when there is a related general medical condition, the physical complaints or impairment are in excess of what would be expected;
4. The symptoms are not intentionally produced or feigned.

Michelle is a 52-year-old Caucasian female presenting to a PCP with multiple unexplained medical symptoms. She has a 25-year history of medical complaints, most of which have been unsubstantiated, based on reports from previous physicians and family members. Michelle is presently married with no children, and has previously been divorced three times. She completed high school and works intermittently as a school secretary. Currently, she is "not feeling well enough to work," and this feeling has been a part of her history since completing high school. Michelle reports multiple vague medical diagnoses involving all required body systems to meet criteria for SD (irritable bowel syndrome; sexual dysfunction; neuorogenic pain; overactive bladder; "bad joints"; chronic pain in limbs, wrists, knees; "severe consequences from inhaling asbestos"). Michelle carries a small calendar she calls her "doctor calendar," which holds several years' of specialist appointments. She averages 1–2 emergency room visits per month for "severe" symptoms that could not wait until the next office hours. Michelle was rarely admitted to the hospital, often only for severe chest pains and for observation only. She is usually released with a clean bill of health, and with recommendations to check with her PCP. Michelle is well known to her PCP and the staff as she frequently visits the office.

Case Conceptualization

The case conceptualization for Michelle will follow the guidelines suggested by Needleman (1999). The goal for any case conceptualization is to facilitate treatment by the selection of appropriate interventions. The conceptualization should be a collaborative working document. It is essential that the conceptualization help patients to understand the presenting problem and the rationale for interventions, help therapists predict potential obstacles to treatment, encourage patients in motivation for therapy, and help therapists and patients establish an effective working relationship.

Identifying Information

A 52-year-old woman, presently married after three divorces, no children and living with husband, intermittently employed, and suffering from UPSs for approximately 25 years.

Presenting Problem

Michelle complains of SD, depression, and anxiety.

Precipitant: During her step-daughter's wedding, patient is not feeling well and complains throughout the day to husband. Husband is angry and threatens to leave her.

Exhaustive List of Problems, Issues, and Therapy-Relevant Behaviors:

- Generally depressed and unable to physically function on a consistent basis because of health
- Seeks continued assurance from doctors and medical personnel for physical diagnoses and the expectation that appropriate physical intervention will cure all ills

- Socially isolated with poor marital, familial, and social relationships
- Intermittently employed with financial stress and concerns with unstable housing.

Diagnosis (Axis I): SD, dysthymia

Relevant Beliefs: If I stop going to doctors, my illnesses will get worse. If I don't have access to support systems at all times, I may get sick and be alone. If I don't continue to tell others how ill I am feeling, they won't take my problems seriously. If the doctors really can't find anything wrong, they must be incompetent.

Origins of Key Core Beliefs: Michelle was raised by both parents in a stable household. Her mother also had "many illnesses," and was cared for by a doting husband. Michelle's father was also very attentive to Michelle and as a result she was very socially isolated from others. She was an average student, but was absent from school often, due to her not feeling well. Michelle first married at 21 years of age. The marriage lasted less than 1 year because of her complaints about her illnesses. This cycle of the need to be cared for and the core belief that she is helpless and will always be sick contributes to her inability to maintain healthy relationships and enjoy others. This results in daily depression with little motivation to change.

Vicious Cycles/Maintaining Factors: Her belief that she is helpless contributes to her self-focus. This, in turn, results in some secondary gain that provides short-term relief. When she is abandoned by others—three failed marriages and another failure pending—she is unable to see how she contributes to these failures. This is exceptionally difficult for Michelle to recognize, due to her childhood experience of an attentive father.

Michelle resorts to going to doctors and other specialists with the belief that if she finds the right physician, all of this will be cured. Her inactivity and continued need for attention results in feelings of sadness, fear, loneliness, and anger when others do not fulfill these needs.

Treatment

Goals: (a) To improve her daily activities and increase general levels of functioning, (b) to coordinate care with her primary physician to develop a realistic plan for treatment, (c) to improve communication with her husband and others thereby limiting social isolation.

Possible Treatment Obstacles: The unrealistic expectation that all symptoms would improve and a cure would be 100% effective. Feelings of continued helplessness, lack of energy, and minimal motivation to change due to secondary gain. Michelle has minimal problem-solving skills as a result of always being cared for by others.

Plan: (a) Work to establish scheduled activities that the patient finds enjoyable and that may provide social contact. Complete this activity schedule with small tasks and rate mastery and pleasure ratings. (b) Teach Michelle appropriate strategies to communicate with her physician, including direct questioning without complaining, regularly schedule appointments to avoid repeated phone contact, and a plan to engage in some physical activity to increase her mobility. (c) Include

Michelle's husband in some therapy sessions to establish mutually pleasurable activities that may enhance their relationship, and thus reduce marital discord.

Identifying and Addressing Obstacles to Treatment

A multitude of obstacles and challenges can arise that may impede successful management of SD, and can be a source of frustration for clinician and patient alike. A common problem in both medical and psychological treatment approaches is the establishment of unrealistic goals. Having unrealistic goals and expectations for treatment can short-circuit the efforts of the clinicians and treatment team, especially when the unspoken goal is to "cure" or "fix" the illness. This often results in the treatment team redoubling efforts and engaging in costly and invasive medical procedures in an attempt to uncover the root of the problem (Servan-Schreiber et al., 2000b). As in the case of Michelle, because she has suffered from UPS since her mid-20s, it is important for her to reconsider her thought that functional restoration would be 100%. It is most helpful to encourage patients to consider how daily living might be different if they were feeling better more times during the day than not. For example, what would life be like if you could go to a movie with friends as opposed to going every day to the gym? Although the goal is to increase physical activity, the step-wise approach is best to avoid failure.

A more appropriate course of action is to focus efforts on helping patients effectively cope with their symptoms and improve functioning. According to Servan-Schreiber et al. (2004), "treatment is successful if it keeps the patient out of the hospital and the emergency room and if it reduces exposure to iatrogenic complications" (p. 558). Treatment goals should work to help patients tolerate uncertainty surrounding their condition and lack of a clear etiology for the basis of their suffering. An integrative, interdisciplinary treatment approach is well suited to handle such a challenge. As medical staff are often overburdened and are focused on more acute medical problems, a mental health clinician can be an asset to the treatment team as he/she can help patients manage the psychosocial correlates of their illness. For Michelle, it would be helpful in therapy to help reach an understanding that there may be limitations to a cure of all physical symptoms, but for many other areas of suffering, including her feelings of depression and social isolation, there are many ways to solve these problems. Recall that Michelle has very little skill in problem solving, and has been dependent on others to take care of her problems over her lifetime. She may welcome the ability to make some independent choices with the assurance that this does not lead to abandonment by others; rather, this often leads to admiration and praise from others.

Another difficulty arises with comorbid medical and psychological conditions that can often confound effective management. Because a patient's SD has no organic basis, this does not preclude them from developing a bona fide organic condition. Especially as patients age, they are as likely as any other group to develop chronic medical illnesses such as osteoarthritis, coronary disease, and cancer. The patient's subjective level of distress may appear exaggerated in relation to the actual level of organic pathology. Accordingly, treatment of an organic problem should be guided by laboratory results, physical examinations, and objective test findings (Servan-Schreiber et al., 2004). For patients like Michelle, it is critical for all providers to evaluate presenting symptoms appropriately, despite that in the past, they have not been of organic origin. This is an excellent opportunity for multidisciplinary teams to work to ensure the patient's overall good health. This collaboration on the part of physicians, mental health clinicians, and family members and patients will enhance the therapeutic interventions and progress on the treatment plan.

Points of Collaboration With Physicians and Families

The management of SD is made more complicated by the high degree of overlap between psychiatric disorders and SD. Therefore, it is critical to provide multidisciplinary treatment throughout the course of the illness. A mental health clinician working on the treatment team is in position to help clarify whether the patient has developed another condition, and to help the patient cope with the psychological aspects of that condition. The mental health clinician always should practice within one's range of competency. This would require the clinician, patient, and family members to seek medical consult as needed. Regular screenings and preventative health measures should be encouraged and worked into the treatment plan.

Given that patients often experience a high level of subjective distress, and become fixated on discovering a biological basis to their condition, their approach to the PCP may be inappropriate. Patients may visit physicians and specialists frequently, demand costly diagnostic tests, insist on inpatient care, and undergo operations and other medical care that is not medically indicated. The insistence on performing medical procedures becomes a process designed to enhance trust between the patient and medical health provider, and provide the patient with a sense of control. However, if the PCP continues to provide these medical procedures, this is reinforcing the patient's belief that an illness may exist. Frequent phone calls from patients may threaten the physician-patient relationship as physicians become frustrated, angry, and experience feelings of helplessness. This is where an established relationship with a PCP may help limit these demands and provide a more realistic and practical level of care. By setting an established plan for regular screenings, office visits, phone call schedule, and resources for questions, the patient is assured that his/her condition will be monitored closely, and thus, experience a sense of relief. It is imperative that the PCP works with the patient on a regular basis to minimize responding in an impulsive or dismissive manner. These types of responses actually reinforce the behavior the team is trying to extinguish.

Another obstacle to treatment may be inappropriate pain management. Complaints of pain are common in patients suffering from SD. Providing patients with pain medication may minimize immediate distress, but does not help the patient to use other psychosocial strategies to reduce overall dysfunction. There are well-documented risks associated with opiates such as constipation, sedation, impaired cognition, and potential for addiction. In addition to nonsteroidal anti-inflammatory and nonopiate drugs, psychological techniques can be helpful in pain management (see chapter 28 on chronic pain).

In attempts to relieve suffering, somatizing patients frequently make visits to the emergency room (ER). The problem is that ER physicians and teams are set up to manage acute problems and restore stability, and are often not in contact with a patient's outpatient treatment team. This lack of communication can result in unclear messages and inconsistent care. The efforts of ER staff to look for undiagnosed medical conditions may reinforce the patient's perception that there is the presence of a life-threatening medical condition yet to be discovered (Servan-Schreiber et al., 2000b). There should be clear lines of communication among medical staff to prevent repetition of costly diagnostic tests. Decreasing intervals between visits and educating patients about proper use of medical services may be necessary.

Finally, it is important to understand that many patients suffering with SD have a long history of negative and unfruitful interactions with physicians and medical care staff. Power struggles, having feelings dismissed, and being told "it's all in your head" and "you're in denial" all too often characterize patient interactions with physicians and health care staff. Clinicians and medical staff who fail to recognize their own negative transference are more likely to dismiss the complaints of patients, and consequently, create feelings of rejection in the patients that exacerbate their symptoms (Servan-Schreiber et al., 2004).

A multidisciplinary treatment approach that emphasizes empathy, communication, and active collaboration among health care professionals, patients, and families will maximize the likelihood of a positive outcome, and prevent many of these obstacles to treatment.

Development and Implementation of Empirically Based Treatment Plan

In the development of an empirically based treatment plan for a patient with an SD, professionals, family members, and patients must work together to ensure that the patient feels supported throughout the process. General principles to be considered are recognition that physical symptoms are distressing, identification of concomitant psychiatric disorders. review of the psychosocial stressors, education about the biopsychosocial model, presentation to the family and patient of opportunities to discuss worries, and the design of a practical plan with the patient to ensure the patient feels some control. Calabrese and Stern (2004) discuss the importance of a trusting and empathetic relationship between the patient and the PCP. Typical goals for treatment working from a medical standpoint include care for the patient, not necessarily "cure" of the somatization; rule out concurrent physical disorders; remove any conversion, or pseudoneurological symptoms; maintain goals to improve the patients overall functioning (p. 276).

Multidisciplinary teams would benefit from these general treatment recommendations for SD:

1. Schedule regular, brief appointments.
2. Explain and discuss the diagnosis.
3. Inquire about symptoms and beliefs about the patient's illness.
4. Perform physical examinations, but conserve diagnostic workups, that is, investigate objective findings.

5. Provide explanations and information.
6. Identify prosocial cues or precipitants to new symptom complaints.
7. Make benign and lifestyle recommendations, for example, suggest physical exercise and offer dietary recommendations.
8. Prepare/socialize the patient for psychiatric consultation/treatment (Calabrese & Stern, 2004; Servan-Schreiber et al., 2000b).

As discussed, SDs are concomitant with a number of other psychiatric illnesses. The reported concordance rate for somatization is estimated to be near 60% for depression, and 50% for anxiety-based disorders (Kroenke et al., 1994). Therefore, a psychopharmacological consult may be an appropriate part of treatment. A very effective intervention for SD is the psychiatric consult intervention (Smith, Monson, & Ray, 1986b). This psychiatric consult requires a letter to be sent to the patient's PCP with the recommendations that the patient receive regularly scheduled office visits with limited additional diagnostic procedures and treatments.

Psychological interventions are critical in the treatment and management of SD. The mental health clinician works to help the patient identify, understand, and accept the biopsychosocial aspects of an SD. In numerous studies, CBT has been shown to decrease subjective distress in patients; decreases the frequency, duration, and intensity of overall somatic complaints; has shown reductions in health care costs in clinical trials; and dramatically improves overall functioning (Allen et al., 2006; Arnold, De Waal, Eckhoft, & Van Hemert, 2006); Servan-Schreiber et al., 2000b).

Treatment using these cognitive-behavioral interventions has been repeatedly successful for patients suffering from various SDs (Allen et al., Taylor & Asmundson, 2004; Turk, 2002):

- Liaison with other clinicians to ensure consistent, appropriate care
- Psychoeducation, skill building
- Goal setting
- Reduce physiological arousal through relaxation/stress-management techniques
- Enhance activity regulation through increasing exercise and pleasurable and meaningful activities, and pacing activities
- Increase awareness of emotions
- Modify dysfunctional beliefs
- Enhance communication of thoughts and emotions
- Reconceptualize patients' views of their problems from overwhelming to manageable (combat demoralization)
- Reconceptualize patients' view of themselves, from being passive, reactive, and helpless to active, resourceful, and competent (foster self-efficacy)
- Reduce spousal reinforcement of illness behavior
- Relapse prevention, anticipate problems, and discuss.

For all patients in psychotherapy, it is crucial to instill a sense of hope. In particular, the patient suffering from an SD may report little hope of any improvement. Thus, caution is recommended to monitor hopelessness and assess for suicidal ideation throughout the course of treatment. Treatment sessions should also include goals to decrease health-related worries and strengthen more adaptive beliefs about health and illnesses (Taylor & Asmundson, 2004). The clinician should provide opportunities for "booster sessions," for the client to return to therapy when experiencing distress or the thoughts that another illness may be looming in the near future.

Turk (2002) recommends several strategies to help prevent relapse in patients suffering from chronic pain. These are applicable to SD. Patients are reminded that continued practice of strategies and self-monitoring is important for success. Review with patients to be proactive and when a problem is anticipated, work on problem solving to prevent obstacles from becoming insurmountable. Patients should rely on all social supports and access as needed.

Given the involvement and investment by clinicians across disciplines in the treatment of SD, all should maintain a multidisciplinary treatment approach and facilitate communication to maintain and enhance a collaborative relationship. This will ultimately provide the most efficacious patient care.

Evaluation of Treatment Outcomes

Cognitive-behavioral approaches target dysfunctional thinking in a collaborative manner, helping clients to discard dysfunctional thoughts and beliefs in favor of more adaptive ways of thinking about their condition. More specifically, clinicians work with clients to help them identify, evaluate, and correct maladaptive conceptualizations thoughts and beliefs. For patients with SD, the clinician should use the client's most distressing symptoms and help the patient to recognize the misperceptions that may be present. In the case of Michelle, her distorted automatic thoughts often lead to exacerbation of physical symptoms, increased depression, and anxiety. She often *jumps to conclusions,* thinking "no one ever cares about me." She *selectively attends* to information from her physicians she may/may not want to hear. She *catastrophizes* that this marriage will also end in divorce, and she will be alone. If she is alone, she resorts to *all-or-nothing thinking,* "I cannot survive without someone to help me with all my illnesses." Once Michelle was able to recognize these connections between thoughts, feelings, and behaviors, she gradually was able to change these distortions, and consequently, her behavior. By monitoring the effects of her negative thoughts, feelings, and beliefs, she was able to see how these thoughts would exacerbate her physical symptoms. When she did not worry so much about her illnesses, she was able to control feelings of depression and anxiety. Michelle was able to increase her activities of daily functioning. She was able to travel from her home without the company of her husband, engage in some social activities with her friends, and also seemed to begin to enjoy spending time with her husband's children.

The use of motivational interviewing for patients with SD may enhance the treatment process. Motivational interviewing applied to health care settings, as it is in other settings, is designed to meet each patient at his or her stage of readiness to change (Rollnick, Miller, & Butler, 2008). It is a patient-centered approach where the patient exercises greater control over the process than in traditional advice-giving. This approach holds promise for health behavior change. For the patient with an SD, evaluating health care changes and thinking that psychosocial stressors may exacerbate physical symptoms can be overwhelming. With motivational interviewing, it would be helpful to identify and normalize basic sources of stress. All people experience stress. The difference for the patient with somatoform illness is that psychosocial stressors may render them functionally impaired. Attempting to guide the patient to understand and explore their own motivations for change is the next step. General principles include listening with empathy and empowering the patient with hope and optimism, which lead to successful changes in health beliefs and conditions. Motivational interviewing has been applied to many health conditions, and has shown successful outcomes (Brodie, Inoue, & Shaw, 2008; Kreman et al., 2006; Martins & McNeil, 2009). Although initial review of motivational interviewing for health behaviors seems promising, more research is needed for specific illnesses and how the model may be adapted.

Self-management techniques, such as relaxation training or progressive muscle relaxation and guided imagery, biofeedback, and diversion of attention help to regulate physiological responses that may be involved in pain and discomfort. Mindfulness-based interventions have been used for many years to help manage stress and reduce pain associated with various illness (see chapter 9, Mindfulness). These techniques have been applied to individuals suffering from depression and anxiety, which are often aspects of the clinical picture of SD patients (Germer, Siegel, & Fulton, 2005). Mindfulness-based stress reduction (MBSR) can be effective for reducing the stress that is part of daily living and chronic health conditions (Praissman, 2008). These interventions develop a behavioral coping strategy, helping patients to believe they are able to exert some control over the situation and to reduce a sense of helplessness. MBSR has alleviated suffering for a variety of medical conditions. In a meta-analysis review, positive outcomes were reported for clinical populations with pain, cancer, heart disease, depression, and anxiety (Grossman, Niemann, Schmidt, & Walach, 2004). Research has also attributed MBSR techniques for better functioning for chronic pain patients with reductions in depression, pain-related anxiety, physical and psychosocial disability (McCracken, Gauntlett-Gilbert, & Vowles, 2007; Rosenzweig et al., 2009). Although the literature does not address the somatoform patient specifically, there is promise for this population, due to general studies on MBSR showing positive results for the improvement of health-related quality of life and physical and psychological symptoms in heterogeneous populations (Reibel, Greeson, Brainard, & Rosenzweig, 2001).

Patients suffering from SD often undergo a multitude of medical tests, procedures, and visits to various health care professionals before receiving a diagnosis. The longer it takes to appropriately diagnosis and treat the problem, the greater the patient's level of distress. Effective problem solving can minimize the effects of stress associated with managing their conditions. The problem-solving model (D'Zurilla & Goldfried, 1971) has been effective for patients in a variety of medical settings. These include patients with noncardiac chest pain (Nezu, Nezu, & Jain, 2008), chronic low back pain (Smeets et al., 2008), and hypochondriasis (Buwalda, Bouman, & van Duijn, 2007). Preliminary studies suggest that this treatment is feasible for patients in primary care settings with UPS (Wilkinson & Mynors-Wallis, 1994). Further research with a variety of medical problems is needed.

Considerations With Special Populations/Diversity Issues

A thorough understanding of gender, age, and cultural differences is synonymous with providing competent health care. In anticipation of the dramatic demographic changes expected over the next few decades, the Centers for Disease Control and Prevention created the Office of Minority Health and Health Disparities (OMHD) to help eliminate racial and ethnic health disparities (Office of Minority Health and Health Disparities, 2009).

According to the *DSM-IV-TR* (APA, 2000), women generally experience these disorders at higher prevalence rates than men. SD rates range from 0.2 to 2% in women, and less than 0.2% in men. UPS occurs with the highest frequency in young women of low socioeconomic status. Conversion disorder appears to be more frequent in women than in men, ranging from ratios of 2:1 to 10:1. Females seem to experience certain chronic pain conditions, migraines, tension headaches, and musculoskeletal pain more than males. PCPs and clinicians are cautioned to consider these statistics, recognize gender differences, and strive to assess, diagnose, and treat women in a holistic manner.

Children may report UPS, including abdominal pain and headaches. Lipsitz et al. (as cited in Lamberg, 2005) reports that up to 5% of visits to PCPs with children and adolescents include these complaints. Often, children with these problems miss school and develop concomitant anxiety and depressive disorders. According to another study by Libsitz et al., children with noncardiac chest pain show higher rates of depression and anxiety (as cited in Lamberg, 2005). In addition, parents worry that an illness may have been missed. Children can be taught to monitor their thoughts and modify their beliefs about illnesses. Activity scheduling, confidence building, and coping-skills development will help children improve daily functioning.

Hispanics in the United States, currently the largest minority group in the country, face significant barriers in health care (Fiscella, Franks, Doescher, & Saver, 2002; U.S. Census Bureau, 2003). Findings from a national sample indicate disparities in health care by race, ethnicity, and language among the uninsured. Reports that depression is underrecognized in adult Hispanic Americans may be related to language differences, somatic presentations, and cultural idioms of distress (Lewis-Fernandez, Das, Alfonso, Weissman, & Olfson, 2005). Studies on the *ataque de nervios* describe episodes with symptoms of uncontrolled shouting, falling to the ground, crying, trembling, heat in the chest rising into the head, heart palpitations, dizziness, and others (APA, 2000). These attacks frequently occur in response to a stressful event, such as bad news, death of a loved one, or an accident of a family member. Patients are often diagnosed with panic disorder and SD. Clinicians should be conscious of differences in clinical presentations and meaning of the symptoms between Hispanic Americans and European Americans (Interian et al., 2005).

Clinical Pearls of Wisdom for Practitioners

Patients with SD are often misunderstood, dismissed as faking symptoms, hopeless for an improvement in quality of life, and generally suffering from depression, anxiety, and social isolation. Physicians and family members also are frustrated and often discouraged when they are unable to help the patient improve. People may give up and see these conditions as a part of the individual's life course. With these difficulties, several "pearls of wisdom" are offered to encourage hope and optimize a course toward change.

1. The complicated nature of SD necessitates a thorough assessment, which will allow for an accurate diagnosis and efficacious treatment. A multidisciplinary team should include the PCP, family members, patient, allied health professionals, and any other social support person who may enhance the team.
2. A biopsychosocial understanding of SD is crucial. Patients will progress, and limitations of exclusively treating physical symptoms will be avoided, when this comprehensive model is applied.
3. Establish realistic goals. This may be very difficult, as the patient may struggle to recognize that this illness is greater than a physiological problem. Work with motivational interviewing and approach the treatment in a step-wise fashion to achieve viable success and minimize failures and hopelessness.
4. Be aware of the frustration that may present with all team members. Patients may see change as impossible, given the length of time they have, "been ill." PCPs may feel that patients are not compliant with recommendations. Family members may be tired of always caring for the patient. Mental health clinicians may be at a loss for strategies to help encourage change. Continue to confront these obstacles and problem-solve solutions.
5. Focus efforts on helping patients effectively cope with their symptoms and improve functioning. Often, patients have minimal coping skills for daily living. Take small steps to recognize present coping styles and increase active coping styles.
6. Regular screenings and preventative health measures should be encouraged and worked into the treatment plan. This will limit the patient's fear of missing an impending illness.
7. Be aware of comorbid medical and psychological conditions that can often confound effective management. These should be always before the treatment team to avert any potential for future impairment in functioning.
8. Develop an adequate understanding of the role of gender, age, culture, and relevant beliefs and conceptions of disease and illness. Practitioners sensitive to these differences will see far more successful outcomes.
9. A multidisciplinary treatment approach that emphasizes empathy, communication, and active collaboration among health care professionals and patients is likely to maximize a positive outcome and encourage hope.

References

Allen, L. A., Woolfolk, R. L., Escobar, J. I., Gara, M. A., & Hamer, R. M. (2006). Cognitive-behavioral therapy for somatization disorder: A randomized controlled trial. *Archives of Internal Medicine, 166*(14), 1512–1518.

American Psychiatric Association. (2000). *Diagnostic and statistical manual of mental disorders* (4th ed., text rev.). Washington, DC: Author.

Arnold, I. A., De Waal, M. W., Eekhof, J. A., & Van Hemert, A. M. (2006). Somatoform disorder in primary care: Course and the need for cognitive-behavioral treatment. *Psychosomatics, 47*(6), 498–503.

Barsky, A. J. (1992). Amplification, somatization, and the somatoform disorders. *Psychosomatics, 33*, 28–34.

Barsky, A. J., Orav, E. J., & Bates, D. W. (2005). Somatization increases medical utilization and costs independent of psychiatric and medical comorbity. *Archives of General Psychiatry, 62*, 903–910.

Barsky, A. J., & Wyshak, G. (1990). Hypochondriasis and somatosensory amplification. *British Journal of Psychiatry: Journal of Mental Science, 157*, 404–409.

Barsky, A. J., Wyshak, G., & Klerman, G. L. (1990). The somatosensory amplification scale and its relationship to hypochondriasis. *Journal of Psychiatric Research, 24*, 323–334.

Beck, A. T., Epstein, M., Brown, G., & Steer, R. A. (1988). An inventory for measuring clinical anxiety: Psychometic properties. *Journal of Consulting and Clinical Psychology, 56*, 893–897.

Beck, A. T., Ward, C. H., Mendelson, M., Mock, J., & Erbaugh, J. (1961). An inventory for measuring depression. *Archives of General Psychiatry, 4*, 561–571.

Blackwell, B., & De Morgan, N. P. (1996). The primary care of patients who have bodily concerns. *Archives of Family Medicine, 5*, 457–463.

Brodie, D. A., Inoue, A., & Shaw, D. G. (2008). Motivational interviewing to change quality of life for people with chronic heart failure: A randomised controlled trial. *International Journal of Nursing Studies, 45*, 489–500.

Buwalda, F. M., Bouman, T. K., & van Duijn, M. A. J. (2007). Psychoeducation for hypochondriasis: A comparison of a cognitive-behavioural approach and a problem-solving approach. *Behaviour Research and Therapy, 45*, 887–899.

Calabrese, L., & Stern, T. A. (2004). The patient with multiple medical complaints. In T. A. Stern, J. B. Herman, & P. L. Salvin (Eds.), *Guide to primary care psychiatry* (pp. 269–278). New York: McGraw-Hill.

Dowrick, C., Gask, L., Hughes, J. G., Charles-Jones, H., Hogg, J. A., Peters, S., et al. (2008). General practitioners' views on reattribution for patients with medically unexplained symptoms: A questionnaire and qualitative study. *BMC Family Practice, 9*, 1471–2296.

D'Zurilla, T. J., & Goldfried, M. R. (1971). Problem solving and behavior modification. *Journal of Abnormal Psychology, 78*, 107–126.

Escobar, J. I., Golding, J. M., Hough, R. L., Karno, M., Burnam, M. A., & Wells, K. B. (1987). *Handbook of primary care psychology* (pp. 551–562). Oxford, UK: Oxford University Press.

Fiscella, K., Franks, P., Doescher, M., & Saver, B. (2002). Disparities in health care by race, ethnicity, and language among the uninsured: Findings from a national sample. *Medical Care, 40*, 52–59.

Frances, A., & Ross, R. (2004). *DSM-IV-TR case studies: A clinical guide to differential diagnosis.* Washington, DC: American Psychiatric Publishing.

Gatchel, R. J. (2004). Comorbidity of chronic pain and mental health disorders: The biopsychosocial perspective. *American Psychologist, 12*, 795–804.

Germer, C. K., Siegel, R. D., & Fulton, P. R. (Eds.). (2005). *Mindfulness and psychotherapy.* New York: Guilford.

Grossman, P., Niemann, L., Schmidt, S., & Walach, H. (2004). Mindfulness-based stress reduction and health benefits: A meta-analysis. *Journal of Psychosomatic Research, 57*, 35–43.

Hamilton, M. A. (1959). The assessment of anxiety states by rating. *British Journal of Medical Psychology, 32*, 50–55.

Hamilton, M. A. (1960). A rating scale for depression. *Journal of Neurology, Neurosurgery, and Psychiatry, 23*, 56–62.

Hamilton, M. A. (1967). Development of a rating scale for primary depressive illness. *British Journal of Social and Clinical Psychology, 6*, 278–296.

Hansen, M. S., Fink, P., Sondergaard, L., & Frydenberg, M. (2005). Mental illness and health care use: A study among new neurological patients. *General Hospital Psychiatry, 27*, 119–124.

Hiller, W., Fichter, M. M., & Rief, W. (2003). A controlled treatment study of somatoform disorders including analysis of health care utilization and cost-effectiveness. *Journal of Psychosomatic Research, 54*, 369–380.

Interian, E. A., Guarnaccia, P. J., Vega, W. A., Gara, M. A., Like, R. C., Escobar, J. I., et al. (2005). The relationship between ataque de nervios and unexplained neurological symptoms: A preliminary analysis. *Journal of Nervous and Mental Disease, 193*, 32–39.

Katon, W., Lin, E., Von Korff, M., Russo, J., Lipscomb, P., & Bush, T. (1991). Somatization: A spectrum of severity. *American Journal of Psychiatry, 148*, 34–40.

Kreman, R., Yates, B. C., Agrawal, S., Fiandt, K., Briner, W., & Shurmur, S. (2006). The effects of motivational interviewing on physiological outcomes. *Applied Nursing Research, 19*, 167–170.

Kroenke, K., Spitzer, R. L., & Williams, J. B. W. (2002). The PHQ-15: Validity of a new measure for evaluating the severity of somatic symptoms. *Psychosomatic Medicine, 64*, 258–266.

Kroenke, K., Spitzer, R. L., Williams, J. B., Linzer, M., Hahn, S. R., deGruy, F. V. 3rd., et al. (1994). Physical symptoms in primary care. Predictors of psychiatric disorders and functional impairment. In L. J. Haas (Ed.), *Handbook of primary care psychology* (pp. 551–562). Oxford, UK: Oxford University Press.

Lamberg, L. (2005). New mind/body tactics target medically unexplained physical symptoms and fears. *Journal of the American Medical Association, 294*, 2152–2154.

Lewis-Fernandez, R., Das, A. K., Alfonso, C., Weissman, M. M., & Olfson, M. (2005). Depression in U.S. Hispanics: Diagnostic and management considerations in family practice. *Journal of the American Board of Family Medicine, 18*, 282–296.

Lieberman, J. A. R. (1997). BATHE: An approach to the interview process in the primary care setting. *Journal of Clinical Psychiatry, 58*, 3–6.

Linn, E. H., Katon, W., Von Korff, M., Bush, T., Lipscomb, P., Russo, J., et al. (1991). Frustrating patients: Physician and patient perspectives among distressed high users of medical services. In L. J. Haas (Ed.), *Handbook of primary care psychology* (pp. 551–562). Oxford, UK: Oxford University Press.

Lowe, B., Spitzer, R. L., Williams, J. B. W., Mussell, M., Schellberg, D., & Kroenke, K. (2008). Depression, anxiety, and somatization in primary care: Syndrome overlap and functional impairment. *General Hospital Psychiatry, 30*, 191–199.

Martins, R. K., & McNeil, D. W. (2009). Review of motivational interviewing in promoting health behaviors. *Clinical Psychology Review.*

McCracken, L. M., Gauntlett-Gilbert, J., & Vowles, K. E. (2007). The role of mindfulness in a contextual cognitive-behavioral analysis of chronic pain-related suffering and disability. *Pain, 131*, 63–69.

Needleman, L. D. (1999). *Cognitive case conceptualization: A guidebook for practitioners.* Lawrenceville, NJ: Lawrence Erlbaum.

Nezu, A. M., Nezu, C. M., & Jain, D. (2008). Social problem solving as a mediator of the stress-pain relationship among individuals with noncardiac chest pain. *Health Psychology, 27*, 829–832.

Office of Minority Health and Health Disparities. (n.d.) Retrieved May 1, 2009, from http://www.cdc.gov/omhd/About/about.htm

Pennebaker, J. W. (1982). *The psychology of physical symptoms.* New York: Springer-Verlag.

Pilowsky, I. (1967). Dimensions of hypochondriasis. *British Journal of Psychiatry: Journal of Mental Science, 113*, 89–93.

Praissman, S. (2008). Mindfulness-based stress reduction: A literature review and clinician's guide. *Journal of the American Academy of Nurse Practitioners, 20*, 212–216.

Reibel, D. K., Greeson, J. M., Brainard, G. C., & Rosenzweig, S. (2001). Mindfulness-based stress reduction and health-related quality of life in a heterogeneous patient population. *General Hospital Psychiatry, 23*, 183–192.

Rief, W., & Barsky, A. J. (2005). Psychobiological perspectives on somatoform disorders. *Psychoneuroendocrinology, 30*, 996–1002.

Rief, W., Hiller, W., & Heuser, J. (1997). *SOMS—Screening fur somatoforme storungen. Manual zum fragebogen* [SOMS—Screening for somatoform symptoms—Manual]. Berne, Switzerland: Huber.

Rief, W., Hiller, W., Geissner, E., & Fichter, M. M. (1995). A two-year follow-up study of patients with somatoform disorders. *Psychosomatics, 44*, 492–498.

Rollnick, S., Miller, W. R., & Butler, C. C. (2008). *Motivational interviewing in health care.* New York: Guilford.

Rosenzweig, S., Greeson, J. M., Reibel, D. K., Green, J. S., Jasser, S. A., & Beasley, D. (2009). Mindfulness-based stress reduction for chronic pain conditions: Variation in treatment outcomes and role of home meditation practice. *Journal of Psychosomatic Research.*

Ross, K., Kashner, T. M., & Smith, G. R. (1994). Effectiveness of psychiatric intervention with somatization disorder patients: Improved outcome and reduced costs. *General Hospital Psychiatry, 16*, 381–387.

Servan-Schreiber, D., Kolb, N. R., & Tabas, G. (2000a). Somatizing patients: Part I. practical diagnosis. *American Family Physician, 61*(4), 1073–1078.

Servan-Schreiber, D., Kolb, N.R., & Tabas, G. (2000b). Somatizing patients: Part II. practical management. *American Family Physician, 61*(5), 1423–1432.

Servan-Schreiber, D., Tabas, G., Kolb, R. E., & Haas, L. J. (2004). Somatoform disorders. In L. J. Haas (Ed.), *Handbook of primary care psychology* (pp. 551–562). Oxford, UK: Oxford University Press.

Smeets, R. J. E. M., Vlaeyen, J. W. S., Hidding, A., Kester, A. D. M., van der Heijden, G. J. M. G. J., & Knottnerus, A. (2008). Chronic low back pain: Physical training, graded activity with problem solving training, or both. The one-year post-treatment results of a randomized controlled trial. *Pain, 134*, 263–276.

Smith, G. R., Monson, R. A., & Ray, D. C. (1986a). Patients with multiple unexplained symptoms. Their characteristics, functional health, and health care utilization. *Archives of Internal Medicine, 146*, 69–72.

Smith, G. R., Monson, R. A., & Ray, D. C. (1986b). Psychiatric consultation letter in somatization disorder. *New England Journal of Medicine, 314*, 1407–1413.

Spielberger, C., Gorsuch, R., & Lushene, R. (1970). *STAI manual*. Palo Alto, CA: Consulting Psychologists Press.

Spitzer, R. L., Kroenke, K., Williams, J. B., & Patient Health Questionnaire Primary Care Study Group. (1999). Validation and utility of a self-report version of PRIME-MD: The PHQ primary care study. *Journal of the American Medical Association, 282*, 1737–1744.

Spitzer, R. L., Williams, J. B., Kroenke, K., Linzer, M., deGruy, F.V., Hahn, S.R., et al. (1994). Utility of a new procedure for diagnosing mental disorders in primary care. The PRIME-MD 1000 case study. *Journal of the American Medical Association, 272*, 1749–1756.

Stewart, A. L., Hays, R. D., & Ware, J. E. (1988). The MOS short-form general health survey. *Medical Care, 26*, 723–735.

Taylor, S., & Asmundson, G. J. G. (2004). *Treating health anxiety: A cognitive-behavioral approach*. New York: Guilford.

Turk, D. C. (2002). A cognitive-behavioral perspective on treatment of chronic pain patients. In D. C. Turk & R. J. Gatchel (Eds.), *Psychological approaches to pain management: A practitioner's handbook* (2nd ed., pp. 138–158). New York: Guilford.

U. S. Census Bureau. (2003). *The Hispanic population in the United States: Population characteristics: March 2002*. Retrieved May 1, 2009, from http://www.census.gov/prod/2003pubs/p20-545.pdf

Von der Kolk, B. A., Pelcovitz, D., Roth, S., Mandel, F. S., McFarlane, A., & Herman, J. L. (1996). Dissociation, somatization, and affect dysregulation: The complexity of adaptation of trauma. *American Journal of Psychiatry, 153*, 83–93.

Wilkinson, P., & Mynors-Wallis, L. (1994). Problem-solving therapy in the treatment of unexplained physical symptoms in primary care: A preliminary study. *Journal of Psychosomatic Research, 38*(6), 591–598.

Woolfolk, R. L., Allen, L. A., Gara, M. A., & Escobar, J. I. (1998). *The somatic symptom questionnaire*. Unpublished manual.

World Health Organization. (1994a). *Composite international diagnostic interview (CIDI)*. Washington, DC: American Psychiatric Press.

World Health Organization. (1994b). *Schedules for clinical assessment in neuropsychiatry (SCAN)*. Washington, DC: American Psychiatric Press.

World Health Organization. (1994c). *Somatoform disorders schedule*. Geneva, Switzerland: Author.

World Health Organization. (2007). *International statistical classification of diseases and related health problems* (10th rev. version for 2007). Geneva: Author.

Zung, W. W. (1965). A self-rating depression scale. *Archives of General Psychiatry, 12*, 63–70.

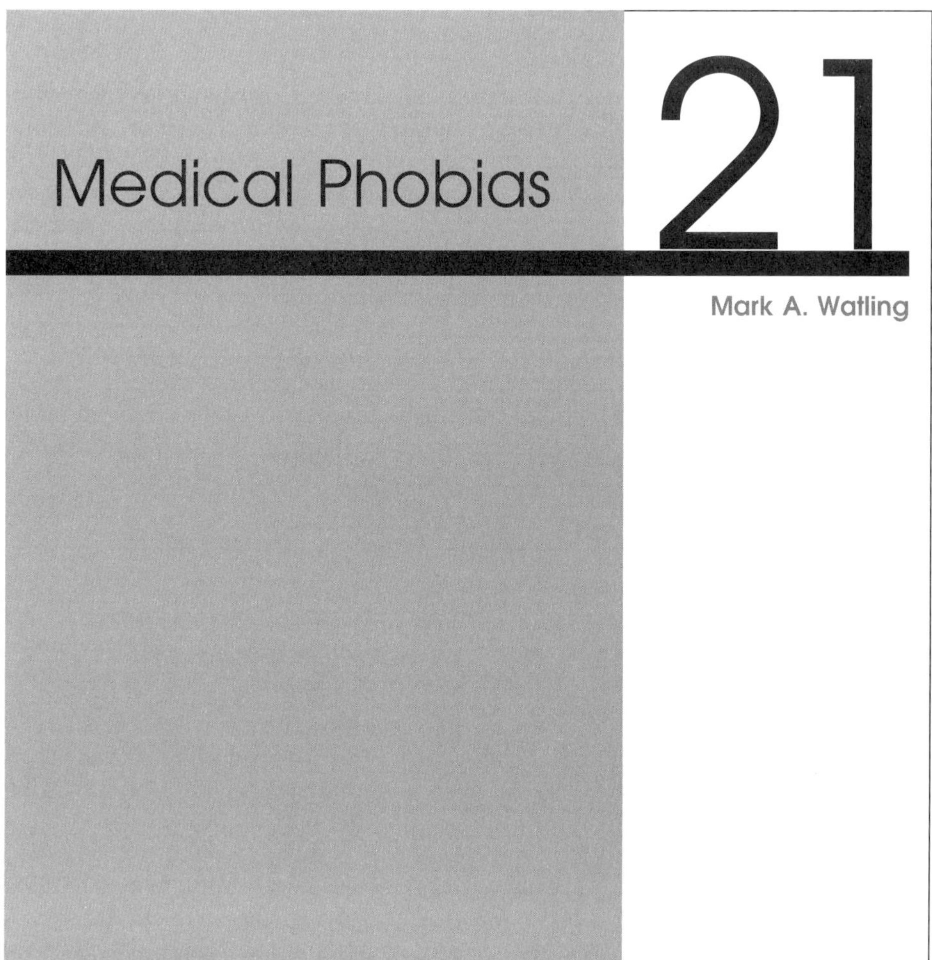

Medical Phobias

21

Mark A. Watling

Introduction

Imagine you have just been diagnosed with cancer. Your physician has told you that with appropriate treatment, you could be cured; without it, death is certain within months. The life-saving treatment involves receiving a medication through an intravenous line, which will require the insertion of a needle into a vein. As you consider what you have been told, your fear rises. You are filled with dread; not about the cancer, but dread about the treatment. Your fear of needles is far greater than your fear of cancer. The idea of a needle going into your body is so terrifying that you seriously consider forgoing the treatment. You have an excessive, unreasonable fear of needles; a medical phobia that is getting in the way of your making good, rational decisions. Your fear is putting your life at risk. This chapter details the assessment and treatment of medical phobias.

Assessment and Diagnostic Issues

A specific phobia is an irrational fear of some singular object or situation, resulting in distress and impairment for the phobic person (American Psychiatric Association, 2000). Exposure to the feared object or situation results in an anxiety response.

The phobic person recognizes that the fear is excessive, yet tends to cope with the anxiety of anticipated exposure by avoiding the fearful object or situation. The term *medical phobia* refers to a specific phobia in which the feared object or situation is medical in nature. Medical locations (e.g., hospitals, waiting rooms), medical personnel (e.g., physicians, nurses, dentists, lab technicians), medical instruments (e.g., needles, syringes, blood pressure cuffs), medical procedures (e.g., blood taking, sutures, immunizations, surgeries, X-rays, MRIs), or medical images in the media (e.g., pictures, movies, advertisements containing blood, injuries, wounds) are examples of feared objects or situations for those with a medical phobia. These are, therefore, the very things that a medically phobic person avoids. Such phobias are often described under the *Diagnostic and Statistical Manual of Mental Disorders* (*DSM-IV-TR*) specific phobia subcategory of "blood-injection-injury" (BII) phobia (American Psychiatric Association, 2000).

When assessing a person with a suspected medical phobia, there are a number of areas to address, in order to ensure the proper diagnosis and, in turn, develop the proper treatment strategy. These areas include the following:

DSM-IV-TR Diagnostic Criteria for Specific Phobia

The *DSM-IV-TR* diagnostic criteria should be confirmed by way of a semistructured interview. Because fear and avoidance of medical procedures may occur for a number of reasons, it is important to differentiate medical phobias from other disorders that may resemble a medical phobia on the surface.

For example, a person with depression may refuse medical treatment or medical procedures based on a sense of hopelessness and futility, rather than on an irrational fear of the medical procedure itself. Likewise, a person with obsessive-compulsive disorder and a fear of germs, dirt, or contamination may avoid hospitals or doctors because of a more widespread obsession about contamination in general. A person with hypochondriasis, who worries about having certain illnesses based on a misinterpretation of bodily symptoms, may also avoid doctors or hospitals for fear of contracting some illness or because going to such places increases their worry about their own imagined illnesses. A person with generalized anxiety disorder, who worries about a number of things, may have as one of his/her many worries a concern about health, and therefore, may avoid medical venues or items. People with other specific phobias may at first appear to have a medical phobia. For example, a person with a fear of vomiting may avoid anything that might induce sickness (hospitals, doctor's offices, etc.) for fear that a contracted illness may result in vomiting. A person who has intrusive unwanted memories of a horrific motor vehicle accident she was involved in years ago, and therefore, avoids all things blood-related because they remind her of that very accident, may be suffering from posttraumatic stress disorder rather than a specific medical phobia. A person with severe social anxiety disorder may avoid seeing the doctor because of a fear of undressing in front of a stranger. A delusional person may avoid needles, injections, and doctors for fear of some sinister plot on the part of the medical community. Clearly, there are many reasons why someone may avoid medical settings, images, or objects. The diagnosis of a specific medical phobia, therefore, requires confirmation that the focus of the fear is singular to a medical procedure, situation, or object, that the patient recognizes that the fear is excessive, and that the fear is not better explained by some other condition.

Course of the Problem, Including Onset, Development, and Current Impact on Functioning

Gathering this information can help to solidify the diagnosis and to rule out other possible reasons for excessive anxiety or avoidance. This information may also give some clues that will be helpful when designing a treatment program. It is very important for the cognitive-behavioral clinician to understand how the fear is affecting the person day to day. What things can they do and what can they not do? What do they avoid? What do they endure with great anxiety? What is the impact on their work, education, and relationships? What things have they passed up because of their phobia? What are some of the goals they would want to accomplish if the phobia did not interfere so much? The answers to these questions will not only provide a greater understanding of the patient, but will also help to give some idea of the direction of treatment.

Patterns of Beliefs and Cognitions

This line of questioning is helpful, as it provides more of an understanding of the fear itself and how it plays out in the person's day-to-day life. It also is helpful in understanding any information-processing biases the person may have. For example, people with needle phobias commonly believe that injections are always painful, that the nurse will think less of them if they get dizzy or faint, or that the needle will break off in their arm (Antony & Swinson, 2000). It is important to be aware of these beliefs early in treatment so they can be addressed and corrected. Inquiries that address these underlying beliefs are helpful. Examples of such questions include, "When you think about getting a needle, what is your most frightening worry?" "Fainting would be scary because?" "Seeing blood makes you feel dizzy...what is so horrible to you about feeling dizzy?"

Patterns of Avoidance

The clinician should determine what the patient is avoiding. Is it medical procedures, dentists' offices, sights, sounds, and smells of blood or illness? What is avoided in more subtle ways? Does the patient close his/her eyes when a medical news story comes on the TV? Does the patient always make sure a friend is with him/her when they go to a hospital? Does he/she pass up opportunities to travel in order to avoid the necessary immunizations? There are a variety of ways that people with medical phobias avoid subtly. It is important to be aware of both overt and subtle avoidance, and to address and eliminate such behavior for treatment to be successful.

Variables Affecting the Fear

An exhaustive consideration all of the variables that affect the intensity of fear that is experienced must be conducted. Is it the gender of the doctor, the size of the needle, the size of the hospital, the smell or sounds of the waiting room, or the dentist's office? Is the patient able to look at someone else's blood but not his/her own? Is the patient able to give blood only while lying down, but not while sitting up? Answers to these questions will be invaluable when designing exposure tasks.

Social Supports

This factor is important, especially when considering treatment. Cognitive-behavioral therapy (CBT) can be anxiety provoking, and can leave the patient wondering whether he/she has taken on too much at times. It can seem quite intimidating at the outset. The presence of a good social network can go a long way to ease the anxiety of the treatment itself. Does the patient have a supportive family who understands the nature of the problem and wants to help? On the other hand, are there family members who, over the years, have become enablers of the patient's avoidance?

Previous Treatment

Investigating the types of treatment the patient has sought previously is a must. What has worked in the past? What hasn't and why? How can those factors be modified to make the present treatment as effective as possible?

Medical History

Are there physical conditions that would make certain exposure exercises risky? For example, certain cardiac conditions may make fainting dangerous.

Taking a detailed history that touches on each of these areas is important for correct diagnosis and treatment design. In order that none of these important areas are missed, use of a structured or semistructured interview is recommended. As well, a number of assessment tools have been developed that may be helpful. They aid in measuring various aspects of the phobia, including symptoms of fear, distress, interference, and avoidance. For example, the Blood-Injection Symptom Scale (Page, Bennett, Carter, Smith, & Woodmore, 1997) is a 17-item, yes/no, self-report scale that measures symptoms on three subscales: faintness, anxiety, and tension. Alternatively, the Medical Fear Survey (Kleinknecht, Thorndike, & Walls, 1996) examines situations that are avoided by a phobic individual, by way of a 50-item, self-report scale that assesses the severity of various medical fears. The Mutilation Questionnaire (Klorman, Hastings, Weerts, Melamed, & Lang, 1974) is a 30-item self-report tool that measures the verbal-cognitive component of mutilation and blood/injury phobias. It takes only 5 minutes to administer, and has been shown to be predictive of fainting in medical-related situations (Kleinknecht & Thorndike, 1990), predictive of tendency to avoid phobic situations (Kleinknecht & Lenz, 1989), and sensitive to treatment effects (Ost, Lindahl, Sterner, & Jerremalm, 1984).

A number of questionnaires specific to dental phobias have also been developed. One such assessment tool is the Dental Fear Survey (Kleinknecht, Klepac, &

Alexander, 1973), which assesses avoidance, physiological symptoms, and fear of specific dental stimuli, using a 20-item, self-report scale, in which higher scores (range 20–100) reflect more severe fear. Other dental fear assessment tools include the Dental Anxiety Inventory (Stouthard, Mellenbergh, & Hoogstraten, 1993), the Dental Cognitions Questionnaire (De Jongh, Muris, Schoenmakers. & Horst, 1995), the Dental Anxiety Scale-Revised (Ronis, 1994), and the Corah Dental Anxiety Scale (Corah, 1969) These assessment tools can be used to evaluate patients at baseline (pretreatment status), as therapy progresses to completion, and can be used periodically (e.g., every five sessions and on completion) for more objective measures of treatment progress and response.

Incidence and Clinical Manifestations in Primary Care Setting

All types of phobias are thought to affect approximately 3.5% of the population (Bienvenu, & Eaton, 1998). A large U.S. study found almost 14% of people reported an extreme fear of blood, with about one third of those meeting full criteria for a phobia (Curtis et al., 1998). A European study reported that almost 2% of people surveyed had an injection phobia, whereas 2.1% reported a dental phobia, and 3.3% reported a phobia of injuries (Fredrikson, Annas, Fischer, & Wik, 1996). There is some question regarding the gender ratio in the prevalence of medical phobias, with some studies suggesting no differences in prevalence between men and women (Fredrickson et al., 1996), and others suggesting that medical phobias are more common in women (Bienvenu & Eaton). Medical fears usually have their onset in childhood (Bienvenu & Eaton), but often do not cause significant impairment or distress until midadolescence (Antony, Brown, & Barlow, 1997). Family physicians have only recently started to note the importance of identifying and addressing medical phobias (Hamilton, 1995). For every patient who presents with a medical phobia, though, there are, no doubt, countless others who never will, for the simple fact that people with medical phobias often avoid doctor's offices altogether out of fear. Indeed, people with medical phobias have increased rates of morbidity and mortality, because of the avoidance associated with the condition (Marks, 1988).

Because medical phobias result in avoidance of a wide range of medical situations, instruments, personnel, images, or objects, the ways in which such a fear might manifest itself in the day-to-day life of someone with a medical phobia is varied, indeed. Blood work, lab tests, and other necessary medical procedures are avoided. Other investigations, including X-rays, MRIs, and CT (computed tomography) scans are shunned. Necessary treatments, including surgeries, dental work, and chemotherapy may be refused, all because of an irrational fear. A teenager with diabetes may have poorly controlled blood sugar because he fears injecting insulin. A young woman who wants to become a medical doctor may choose a different profession because she fears the sight of blood. A retired man who had always dreamed of traveling the world may be restricted because of his fear of the necessary travel immunizations. A woman may decide against having children because doing so would necessitate visits to doctors, hospitals, and blood work. A needle-phobic woman who does become pregnant may put the pregnancy at risk by avoiding recommended prenatal exams. Needed surgeries may be refused, dental work ignored, treatment and investigations avoided, all to the detriment of the person's health and well-being, and all because of an irrational fear.

Case Examples

Lisa

Lisa is a 52-year-old woman who has felt run down for the past few months. She looks pale and finds she just doesn't have the energy she used to have. She sees her family doctor about these symptoms. Her family doctor takes an extensive history that reveals that Lisa has had two bouts of bloody diarrhea over the past few weeks. Based on the history and physical examination, her family doctor determines that Lisa requires further investigations, including a colonoscopy, to try to identify the source of the bleeding. Lisa has a family history of colon cancer and her physician is obviously concerned that this bleeding may represent a malignancy. Her family physician also knows that time is of the essence, and the sooner they can get to the bottom of this, the better. Lisa, however, has always been terrified of medical procedures. In childhood she recalls seeing her father faint once when donating blood and hearing him afterward voice his belief that "doctors are butchers," and should be avoided whenever possible. As an adult, she has heard "nightmare" stories from others who had colonoscopies, and she is so frightened that she refuses to have the procedure. Her family doctor is obviously concerned and insists she have the procedure, but Lisa still refuses, saying she knows it may be the wrong decision, but that the prospect of a colonoscopy frightens her so much that she'd rather "take her chances," hoping that things will resolve on their own.

Brian

Brian is 32 years old. For as long as he can remember Brian has been frightened of all things medical. He thinks it may be related to a very early memory of having received a needle in his family doctor's office as a child. He can recall being held down against his will and surprised by the sharp pain of the needle going into his skin. He recalls feeling extremely lightheaded and generally unwell for days afterward. During his adolescence, he fainted at the sight of blood on many occasions and began to avoid anything he thought might trigger that awful lightheaded feeling. Currently, he avoids any movies, books, pictures, or images that have to do with blood, injury, sickness, or hospitals. He plans his driving route to work so as to avoid having to drive by the large hospital in his city. It takes him 30 minutes out of his way, but to him, it is worth it. His wife previews any new magazine that is bought to make sure stories or images about medicine, hospitals, or injections are removed before he reads the magazine. Brian is suddenly faced with a situation he had long feared. His mother, who is 65 years old, has been admitted to the hospital with a serious illness. She may not survive. Brian wants to visit her in the hospital, but is very frightened. He has spent the last 20 years of his life avoiding hospitals. His family insists that he see his mother. She has been asking for him, but whenever he drives to the hospital, he begins to get lightheaded, and feels too sick to continue. On one occasion, he managed to get in the front doors of the hospital with the help of his wife, but when he saw the doctors, nurses, wheelchairs, patients, and smelled the hospital air, he felt faint and insisted on leaving, not making it beyond the lobby. He wants to see his mother, but cannot. He knows his fear is irrational, but does not know what to do about it.

Cognitive-Behavioral Case Conceptualization

According to learning theory (Rachman, 1977), phobias develop through one of two means: direct learning and/or vicarious learning. In the case of direct learning, the person has a traumatic experience with the medical object or situation that results in an anxiety response. Perhaps the person felt nauseated, scared, or lightheaded. Perhaps the person even fainted on exposure to the object or situation. Because of that reaction, a fear of future encounters with the phobic stimulus develops, and a life of fear-solidifying avoidance begins. This is seen in the case history of Brian, who had a traumatic needle-related experience very early in life, the memory of which is still very much with him and continues to drive his fear even as an adult. The single childhood incident has expanded to encompass a number of related medical settings.

In the case of vicarious learning, the person is either told directly (through education, media, from others in casual conversation, etc.) to be afraid of some medical object or situation, or learns to be afraid, indirectly, usually by watching someone else respond to a medical situation with anxiety or fright. An example of this is seen in the case history of Lisa, who witnessed with horror a fear response of her father to having blood drawn and then listened to him equate doctors with butchers. Lisa then continued to focus on the negative and frightening stories of others who discuss their medical procedures freely.

Between 50–75% of people with medical phobias seem to develop them through direct experience with the phobic object/situation, while 15–20% seem to develop the phobia through observation. Fewer than 10% of people develop a medical phobia through information alone. There are some people (about 40%) for whom the onset of the phobia cannot be traced back to any specific learning experience, either direct or indirect (Kendler, Myers, & Prescott, 2002; Kleinknecht, 1994; Ost, 1991; Townend, Dimigen, & Fung 2000). The person with the phobia cannot identify any traumatic episode that precipitated the phobia, nor can they recall any vicarious learning situation that may have lead to the development of the fear

Avoidance and the Maintenance of the Phobia

Once set into motion, the phobia is then maintained because the phobia itself leads to avoidance, which means that corrective, nonfearful encounters with that phobic object will never occur, and therefore, the fear persists. There are two main types of avoidance, as mentioned briefly in the section on assessment. Overt avoidance is the first and most obvious. The phobic person avoids dentists, hospitals, doctors, blood, needles, and so on, altogether. The second type of avoidance, subtle avoidance, is less obvious, and may be more difficult to identify. The person who uses subtle avoidance finds ways around fully exposing himself/herself to the phobic stimulus. Examples of subtle avoidance would include the person who looks away while getting an injection, or who withholds medical concerns from a doctor for fear of possible associated blood work, or the person who insists on lying down when blood is drawn, or always attends medical or dental appointments with a friend or family member. Through understanding how avoidance serves to maintain a fear, one can then understand how exposure therapy combats the fear (Antony & Barlow, 2002). Exposure therapy allows for new learning to occur by overcoming the fear-sustaining power of avoidance. Through creating opportunities for neutral, or even positive, experiences with phobic objects or situations, the person habituates to the fear as new learning occurs, learning that serves to correct the anxious belief system that has fueled the phobia. Even though some phobias have no clear cause or precipitating event, exposure therapy will still be effective because it does not rely on answering how a phobia developed, just that it did. Just as an orthopedic surgeon does not have to know *how* a broken leg became broken to fix it, a therapist does not have to know *how* a phobia came to be to help.

Identifying and Addressing Obstacles to Treatment

One of the greatest obstacles to treatment may actually be getting the patient into the office for an initial assessment, because of the very nature of the phobia and the resultant tendency to avoid any object or place having to do with medical procedures, including the doctor's office. Encouraging the patient to attend appointments with a family member or friend may be helpful. A phone call to reassure the patient ahead of the initial assessment may be useful, as well. The patient may be comforted to know that you will ensure no needles or other medical devices will be in sight during the assessment stage of treatment. The clinician may consider seeing the patient outside of the office setting, in a more neutral location, for the initial assessment. That could be a home visit, or just some less threatening area outside of your office. At our clinic, we have agreed to do assessments in a park area close to the office for patients who have specific phobias about entering clinics or hospitals.

Patient embarrassment can also be a barrier to treatment. Because patients with phobias recognize their irrationality and excessiveness, shame can limit the full disclosure of a medical phobia. The patient may fear ridicule, misunderstanding, or being labeled as "crazy." Reassurance can go a long way to help overcome the obstacle of embarrassment. Reviewing the statistics regarding the high prevalence of phobias may help the patient to normalize medical phobias.

Fear about treatment itself can also often get in the way of patients seeking help. There are many misunderstandings about treatment, in part because of popular culture's false or exaggerated images of people facing their fears on TV reality shows, on talk shows, or in movies, where phobias are often exaggerated and the lines between entertainment and treatment are blurred. Again, reassurance and education that dispel these myths can make treatment much more palatable and less frightening.

Previous, failed treatments may deter a patient from wanting to face another attempt at overcoming his/her phobia. It is, therefore, important to review previous treatment trials, and to try to assess how and why things did not work out. A collaborative plan to avoid past pitfalls, to learn from past experiences, and to make the present treatment experience a more positive one, can then be designed with the patient.

Points of Collaboration With Physicians and Family

When treating a patient with a medical phobia, collaboration between the therapist and the rest of the medical community will be very important. Practically speaking, such collaboration may be necessary to gain access to medical settings and medical equipment for exposure tasks. For example, in overcoming a medical phobia, a patient may be asked to take home a needle, syringe, or other medical instrument. Or the patient may require access to a doctor's waiting room where he/she may sit for an entire afternoon as part of an exposure exercise. Or the patient may need to have a series of blood tests ordered to allow habituation to blood-taking. Having the physician onboard as an informed, active participant in the treatment will help facilitate access to needed materials and venues for optimal treatment. The same may be said of patients with phobias of other health care settings, such as dental offices. If a collaborative relationship is fostered with dentists or dental hygienists, more exposure options will be available, and treatment outcomes can be maximized.

Physicians and dentists who are able to take the time, and be patient with those with medical phobias, will also be a great resource. This is particularly important when addressing graduated exposure tasks with the patient. A dentist, doctor, or phlebotomist, for example, who understands exposure therapy may be more inclined to allow a patient to have a series of visits, with the first visit being a nonthreatening, procedure-free experience, with plans to gradually build up to more anxiety-provoking visits. Such a health care provider will also be more inclined to explain procedures to patients ahead of time, to answer any questions, to correct misperceptions that may be maintaining the patient's fears, and to be sympathetic to the patient's anxiety.

Collaboration with the patient's family will also be very important, in both the assessment and the treatment processes. It is often quite helpful to get a collateral history from family or friends who know the patient well, in order to get a more complete understanding of the impact the phobia is having on the patient's life. Embarrassment may occasionally keep the patient from being completely honest, in which case, collateral history may be even more important. It is also important to identify family members who may inadvertently be enabling avoidance on the part of the patient.

Throughout the treatment process, the presence of supportive friends or family members will be invaluable. They can be helpful as screeners, evaluating the appropriateness and feasibility of possible exposure materials or locations (i.e., collecting and previewing exposure images for at-home exposure exercises, as discussed in the treatment section of this chapter). They can also be helpful in accompanying the patient to various exposure locations as part of the graduated hierarchy process. Their encouragement will also serve a useful purpose as the patient encounters the normal frustrations and occasional setbacks of treatment. It may be beneficial for a friend or family member helper to accompany the patient to one or two of the earlier office treatment sessions, so that they can understand the rationale for, and the process of, exposure therapy.

Development and Implementation of Empirically Based Treatment Plan

Exposure therapy is the most proven treatment for helping people overcome a medical phobia. Its usefulness has been reviewed in depth elsewhere (Antony & Barlow, 2002; Antony & Swinson, 2000). Various studies have shown that in general, in vivo exposure is a more effective treatment method than is imaginal exposure (Emmelkamp & Wessels, 1975; Mannion & Levine, 1984). Indeed, over the past 4 decades, in vivo exposure to feared situations or objects has shown itself to be an extremely effective treatment for many specific phobias, including medical-related phobias (Moore & Brodsgaard, 1994; Ost, Fellenius, & Sterner, 1991), often resulting in significant, sustained clinical response in as little as a single session for up to 90% of patients (Gitin, Herbert, & Schmidt, 1996). Regardless of whether treatment is therapist-directed or is self-help in nature (Antony & Watling, 2006), the treatment of medical phobias focuses on these four key areas:

1. The education of the patient about the phobia and the nature of the treatment;
2. The behavioral component of treatment;
3. The cognitive component of treatment;
4. The skills-based component of treatment.

Educational Component

The treatment of medical phobias begins with educating the phobic person. Providing information about the reality of medical procedures, tests, investigations, and so forth, can often dispel myths that the person believed to be true. Often, fears are based on misinformation, and education that dispels these myths can help alleviate fear. A person with a medical phobia will often be embarrassed about the phobia itself. He/she has insight into the irrationality of the fear, and therefore realizes that the fears may sound ridiculous. For that reason, he/she may withhold vital details that could be important in treatment, because of shame and embarrassment. Therefore, it is important to let the patient know that no matter how silly some aspect of the phobia may sound, it is important to share. Reassure the patient that you will not think any less of him/her, you understand that phobias are irrational, and you understand that he/she may be embarrassed or reluctant to reveal aspects of the fears or his/her techniques of avoidance. Educate the patient about the symptoms experienced during a phobic reaction: that the vaso-vagal reaction (lightheadedness, feeling faint) experienced on exposure is not caused by something he/she is doing, but instead is a physiological response mediated at the level of the central nervous system; this physiologic response is probably inherited to some degree (Page & Martin, 1998).

The person who begins a course of CBT for a specific medical phobia also needs to be educated about CBT itself (e.g., what it is and what it is not). Many people will have preconceived ideas about therapy. The patient should be informed that exposure exercises will be in her/his control. They will be pre-planned and designed by the patient in collaboration with the therapist, so that the patient is in charge every step of the way. There will be no surprises during exposure therapy. The therapist needs to reassure the patient that at no time will an exposure ever be "sprung" on them. At no time will he/she be forced to remain in an exposure situation if it becomes too anxiety provoking. At no time will he/she be made to do anything he/she is not agreeable to ahead of time. A collaborative atmosphere is essential; one in which the therapist and patient work together as a team, with the common goal of defeating their shared enemy, the phobia.

Behavioral Component

Exposure therapy is the key to treating any phobia and medical phobias are no different. Exposure is the opposite of avoidance. Although avoidance maintains a fear, exposure defeats it. If someone wishes to overcome a fear of dogs, that person needs to be exposed to dogs in a gradual way. Likewise, if someone wishes to overcome a fear of blood, that person needs to be exposed to blood in a gradual way. Exposure has two effects. First, it results in habituation. With repeated exposures to a stimulus, the body and brain respond with less intensity over time. Second, exposure results in new learning. The phobic person begins to have new, positive learning experiences that could never have been achieved with continued avoidance. The feared situation begins to be seen differently, as something less terrifying. As symptoms of anxiety are experienced and endured successfully, they too, will become more manageable and less frightening.

Designing an Exposure Treatment Program With a Phobic Patient

The key to designing an effective exposure program is to have the patient on board from the very beginning. This means having the patient involved in setting up the exposure plan with the guidance of a therapist, using the following rules (the "5 P's") of effective exposure design. Effective exposures are:

1. *Predictable*. This means that exposures are designed by the patient and agreed to ahead of time. There are no surprises. The therapist does not try to scare patients with an unexpected exposure opportunity by springing a needle on them out of the blue, or by hiding a gruesome bloody image amongst a stack of more benign images.

2. *Planned.* At each step of the exposure, the patient knows what is expected of him/her. The patient does not simply wait for exposure opportunities to present themselves, but instead sets out deliberately to confront the feared object or situation in an organized and planned manner. A hierarchy is designed (see the following), and agreed to ahead of time. Any changes to the hierarchy are discussed and agreed to. The patient must set time aside each day to do an exposure in a deliberate fashion, and commitment is key. Success is measured according to whether the patient attempts what is planned, and not according to how much anxiety the patient experiences (the patient is expected to experience anxiety, and is expected to stay in the exposure situation despite the anxiety, as this is the only way habituation can occur).
3. *Prolonged.* A helpful exposure exercise is one in which the patient remains until the anxiety reduces by at least half of its peak level. Anxiety ratings are often spoken of in terms of a "SUDS rating," which stands for "subjective unit of distress." This is simply a number between 0 and 100 that represents the total amount of fear, discomfort, distress, or disgust that a patient feels at some specific time during the exposure exercise. So, if on entering a hospital with a plan to walk its corridors induces a SUDS of 80, the person should continue walking the hospital hallways until the SUDS drops to 40. Leaving an exposure during the peak of anxiety will only serve to strengthen the phobia, as it reinforces the false notion that avoidance is the key controlling the anxiety.
4. *Practiced frequently.* The more frequently a patient confronts the feared object or situation through exposure, the greater the effect at overcoming the phobia. For best results, exposures should be practiced at least daily. Foa and her colleagues showed that 10 daily exposure sessions were significantly more effective at reducing fear in agoraphobic subjects than were 10 sessions spaced at 1-week intervals (Foa, Jameson, Turner, & Payne, 1980). Based on this study and others (Rowe & Craske, 1998), the general rule of using closely spaced exposures is seen as the most effective type of exposure schedule.
5. *Paced.* The exposures should be confronted in a paced manner. This is achieved by ordering the exposures according to the SUDS rating that the patient would assign to each exposure exercise if he/she were to do it today. Doing this creates a gradual exposure hierarchy; a list of different exposure situations according to their capacity to cause fear and anxiety. The least anxiety-provoking objects or situations will be at the bottom of the hierarchy (and tackled first), and the most anxiety-inducing ones will be at the top (to be attempted later in treatment). An exposure hierarchy should have 10–15 exposures on it, and should have a good range of SUDS scores, from about 30 at the low end to 100 at the high end. The top item will usually represent the patient's ultimate goal of treatment.

Recall the case of Brian from earlier in this chapter. He is a man with a lifelong fear of hospitals, as well as other medically related situations and items. He tends to feel faint in these situations. He wants to visit his ill mother in the hospital, but his fear is getting in the way. An exposure-to-hospitals hierarchy for him might look something like this:

Situation	SUDS
Going to mother's hospital room	100
Going to a sitting area on mother's hospital floor	90
Going to sitting area in hospital lobby area	75
Going to outdoor sitting area at mother's hospital	60
Going to mother's hospital parking lot and sitting in car	50
Going to neighborhood of mother's hospital and sitting in car	40
Looking at photos of mother in hospital bed	35
Looking at photos of mother's hospital	30

How to Use the Exposure Hierarchy for Treatment

If the rules of the 5 Ps are followed, Brian will be involved in constructing this hierarchy from the beginning, and he will know ahead of each exposure exactly what is expected of him (predictable and planned). Given that he has a tendency to feel faint in his feared situations, it may make sense, in his case, to start treatment by teaching the skill of applied muscle tension (see Skills Training in the following section). He should practice this skill in nonfearful situations until mastered, and then can incorporate it easily into the exposure situations outlined above. It may be useful for him to do the first exposure exercise in the presence of the therapist, so that the rules of good exposures can be reviewed. When doing this, the therapist must be careful to not give reassurance that could lessen the experience of anxiety. Words of encouragement, though, should be given freely. Brian should start with an exposure item that is anxiety provoking, but felt to be do-able (patients should usually start with something in the 30 SUDS range), thereby increasing the chance of success and supplying motivation to move up the hierarchy. He must be willing and able to stay in each situation until he sees his anxiety reduced significantly (prolonged). Usually, it is suggested that a person stay in an exposure situation until the SUDS reduces to half of its starting point. For example, when sitting in his car in the parking lot of his mother's hospital (a SUDS of 50), he should remain there until he experiences a significant drop (to a SUDS of 25) in fear rating. This may take minutes or hours. He should then repeat this same step (practiced frequently) daily (if not more) until he no longer experiences significant initial anxiety in the situation. At that point, he moves on to getting out of his car at the hospital, moving closer to the hospital itself and sitting in an outdoor seating area until his anxiety reduces, as he moves up his hierarchy (paced), eventually reaching and conquering his goal of visiting his mother in her hospital room.

Now is the time you may have to work collaboratively with other health care professionals. It is also obviously helpful if you can get access to many of the exposure objects or situations that may be required for the therapy to work properly. Many images of needles, injections, blood taking, and so on, are available on the Internet, in still image (e.g., Google® images) and movie (e.g., YouTube®) form. For in-session exposures, the therapist should preview all images ahead of time to assess appropriateness. The patient could enlist a trusted family member or friend to preview images for at-home-exposure exercises. Exposure to medical situations and locations will also have to be arranged. This is where it can really be helpful to know doctors, dentists, nursing staff, or lab technicians who are understanding and would be willing to help, either by allowing access to hospital or lab locations, by allowing viewing of procedures (e.g., watching someone else (i.e., the therapist) have blood drawn), or by sourcing various pieces of medical equipment for exposure.

To maximize the value of the exposure exercises, it is imperative to understand the nuances of the patient's phobia. What things can be adjusted to make an exposure more anxiety provoking versus less anxiety provoking? Are there scents that could be added to the exposure (such as the scent of rubbing alcohol, often associated with hospitals)? Does the size of the hospital matter? Would it be easier to walk through a small rural hospital than it would be to walk through the corridors of a large, fast-paced city hospital? Would having a friend along make an exposure a little easier? Does the size of the needle matter, or the gender of the doctor or nurse make a difference to SUDS ratings? By adjusting these variables, exposure tasks with varying SUDS ratings can be constructed with more precision

Some exposure situations will be impossible to stay in until anxiety diminishes because of the inherent brevity of the exposure. For example, watching a video of a person having blood drawn may last only seconds, which may not be enough time for the patient to experience a decline in the SUDS rating during a single viewing of the scene in question. For exposures like this, the person must reexpose him/herself to that image repeatedly during the same session until a drop in SUDS is experienced. Also, one could consider freeze-framing the video on a particularly anxiety-provoking image (i.e., the moment the needle penetrates the skin), and have the patient sit with that single image until the SUDS rating declines. So, when the rule of "prolonged" exposure is impossible because of the nature of the exposure, then the rule of "practiced frequently" becomes even more important. The key is to be creative.

Cognitive Component

Treatment of a medical phobia may also include some element of cognitive therapy, although the effectiveness of this as a treatment modality has not been studied on a large scale, and certainly has not been shown to be nearly as important as exposure therapy (Antony & Swinson, 2000). Nonetheless, for some patients, challenging anxious beliefs can be an important tool, prior to, during, or following an exposure exercise. Cognitive therapy may have to be used as the initial therapeutic tool for severely phobic individuals who have difficulty engaging in exposure-based treatment from the outset. Through cognitive therapy, automatic beliefs that underlie the phobia are made conscious and are actively challenged for authenticity. The usefulness of this technique is found in the fact that the fear response is mediated through the patient's *perception* of the object or situation, rather than through the *actual* object or situation. Perception hinges on beliefs and thoughts. All situations are filtered through a person's belief system. If that set of anxious beliefs can be challenged, then theoretically, the anxiety response that follows can be modified. The first step is to have the patient discover what his/her beliefs are with relation to the feared object or situation. This can sometimes be difficult, because many people find it challenging to know exactly what they are thinking when anticipating or when confronting the phobic stimulus. Asking the following question may be helpful: "If you were to face your feared situation right now, what would be your number-one worry or concern?" Having the patient complete this sentence may be helpful: "If I were to receive an injection right now, I would worry that...." This can then be followed up on by inserting his/her answer to that question into a new statement, and so on, until a list of fearful thoughts is generated. For example, if the patient says he/she would fear the pain of getting an injection, then this follow-up question would be asked: "And if you were to experience pain, you would worry that...?" The person may then state that he/she worries about fainting because of the pain, or that the pain would be unbearable or too much to handle. These deeper beliefs can then be recorded and challenged for accuracy.

Challenging Anxious Beliefs

Once a set of fear-inducing anxious beliefs is brought into consciousness, the next step is a systematic questioning of the accuracy of those beliefs through a process called cognitive challenging. The goal of cognitive challenging is to allow for consideration of all options of viewing a situation. In the process, one's thinking is broadened by treating a belief as a guess, rather than as a fact. This is accomplished mainly through education and by addressing the specific cognitive distortions of probability overestimation and catastrophization (see the text that follows).

Educating the Patient

Providing education can often be the first step in breaking down these exaggerated beliefs about medical phobias. Education will separate fact from belief. Is the pain of a needle really as intense as it is feared to be? How big is the needle really? What is actually involved in the medical procedure? What are all of the steps that might be encountered in having investigations done? How small is an MRI machine? How does a colonoscope actually work? What steps would the doctor normally take to make sure there is as little discomfort as possible? How much discomfort does the average patient actually experience for some specific medical procedure? Helping a patient get the facts may go a long way in dispelling false beliefs that may be driving the phobia.

Addressing Probability Overestimation

People with anxiety disorders commonly exaggerate the probability of certain, negative outcomes when they imagine a phobic situation. The patient who tends to do this should be encouraged to examine the evidence that supports his/her belief versus the evidence that refutes it. What is the evidence that the feared outcome actually occurs as often as believed? Once all the evidence is considered, it may become more obvious that the feared negative outcome is less likely than first believed. For example, a person may believe, "There is no way I can get a needle without fainting...I always faint when I get needles." Having the patient examine the evidence for the accuracy of this statement may reveal that he/she has fainted once, yet has received an injection 10 times over his/her life. In reality, then, the chance of fainting for any given injection is closer to 10% than the initially imagined 100%.

Addressing Catastrophization

People with phobias often catastrophize when imagining a feared object or situation. In other words, they tend to imagine the worst-case scenario occurring and believe that if it did, it would be unmanageable. Challenging catastrophic thinking is done by encouraging the patient to try to put things into perspective. What if the feared prediction were to come true? What if you really were to faint upon getting a needle, or were to panic in the MRI machine? What would it really matter? Are needles as awful as believed? Is a colonoscopy really unbearably painful or simply uncomfortable? Are symptoms of nausea and lightheadedness unmanageable or just unpleasant? What is the worst thing that will happen if you see blood, enter a hospital, or have an MRI done? Can you handle the worst-case scenario? Would it be a disaster, or would it simply be mildly embarrassing, uncomfortable, or unpleasant?

Skills Training

Applied muscle tension is the most helpful skill for those with a medical phobia who also have a tendency to faint. Besides case reports that point to the importance of training in applied muscle tension (Ost & Sterner, 1987), a number of controlled studies (Hellstrom, Fellenius, & Ost, 1996; Ost et al., 1991) have demonstrated that educating such patients in applied muscle tension helps the patient to maintain blood pressure, avoid fainting, and ultimately to overcome his/her phobia. To understand why it is so helpful it is first useful to understand fainting from a physiological perspective.

Background on Fainting

Fainting occurs in perhaps 50–70% of people with a medical phobia when exposed to a feared object or situation (Ost, 1992). Often, the fear of fainting and/or the fear of the related embarrassment can be just as significant as the fear of the original object or situation. Fainting occurs because of stimulation of the vagus nerve, a major component of the nervous system, with multiple connections. The vagus nerve is stimulated by any intense emotion, including fright and disgust, the two main emotions seen in medical phobias. Some people seem to have a much more sensitive vagus nerve than others, and therefore, experience a more intense vagal reaction than others. There may be hereditary reasons for this, which might explain the tendency for medical phobias (and related fainting) to run in families (Page & Martin, 1998). Stimulation of the vagus nerve results in two main cardiovascular effects; slowing of the heart rate and dilating of peripheral blood vessels (through relaxation of smooth muscles in the walls of the blood vessels themselves). These two effects combined result in lowering of blood pressure and, in turn, result in underperfusion of the brain, which subsequently can result in fainting, known medically as vaso-vagal syncope.

The fear of fainting can be combatted by putting control back in the hands of the patient. The main method for doing this is with a technique called applied muscle tension (Ost & Sterner, 1987), through which a patient can learn to avert a fainting episode. The theory here is that although the tone of the small smooth muscles in the walls of one's blood vessels cannot be controlled consciously, the tone of the larger skeletal muscles of the body that surround the blood vessels can be consciously controlled. A person can choose to flex (increase the tone in) a muscle or to relax (decrease the tone in) a muscle. It is through this conscious control of skeletal muscle tone that pressure can be applied to the walls of the body's blood vessels, counteracting any smooth muscle relaxation within the blood vessel walls. This will help to prevent dramatic dilatation of the blood vessels, which, in turn, will serve to maintain a blood pressure great enough to perfuse the brain, thereby averting a fainting episode. A brief description of applied muscle tension instruction is found in the following section. A more complete description can be found elsewhere (Ost & Sterner, 1987).

Instruction in Applied Muscle Tension

1. Have the patient sit comfortably;
2. Instruct the patient to tense the muscles of the body. Demonstrate what this will look like. Sit with clenched fists, flexed elbows, and tightened legs, face, and torso muscles;
3. Hold the muscle tension for a count of 15, until a warm rush is felt;
4. Release the tension. Relax the muscles. Allow 20–30 seconds of relaxation of all muscles;
5. Repeat the tensing/flexing of all muscles. Focus on getting the larger muscles of the body (legs, back, torso, buttocks) into a tensed state. Hold again for 15 seconds and then relax. Repeat at least five times in any one practice session. Do five practice sessions per day, spaced throughout the day.

If the patient's main fear has to do with having blood drawn, he/she should practice the tensing procedure described above, but should also practice keeping one arm relaxed (the arm from which the blood will be drawn).

The patient will initially be taught to use the applied tension exercises in the absence of the phobic stimulus, until the technique has been mastered and is able to be used effectively and automatically. Most patients will be able to master this technique within a week of starting the practice sessions (Antony & Swinson, 2000). Once mastery has been achieved in the absence of the phobic stimulus, applied tension exercises should then be combined with exposure to the feared stimulus. The patient should be encouraged to use the applied tension prior to and during exposure to the feared situations, according to their exposure hierarchy. Once the fear upon exposure reduces, the person may no longer need to use the tension exercises, because reduced fear will result in less stimulation of the vagus nerve, which, in turn, will decrease the likelihood of fainting. This technique can be kept at the ready if needed again in the future.

Maintaining the Gains

If a patient falls back into his or her old habits of overt or subtle avoidance, fear can regain a foothold, and the medical phobia may reoccur. To prevent this, a number of steps should be taken. First, the patient should be encouraged to continue to practice exposure exercises even after the phobia is treated. He/she should be encouraged to look for everyday opportunities to confront the feared object or situation. For example, a needle phobic could become a regular blood donor, or a person with a fear of hospitals could become a volunteer in a hospital. The person could use a feared image from his or her exposure hierarchy as a computer screensaver, or could tape the image to the bathroom mirror. The patient should be on the alert for subtle avoidance. Family members who have become accustomed to helping the patient avoid fearful images, objects, or situations, may continue their habits even after the phobia is conquered. The patient needs to inform family and friends that this "help" is no longer needed, and remind them instead that encouragement to continue to face the fear is what is needed. Because phobias can recur at times of increased stress, anything that can lessen stress will, in turn, lessen the chance of the phobia returning. Therefore, the patient should be encouraged to incorporate relaxation into day-to-day life. This might be done through exercise, meditation, music, mindfulness, yoga, or any other form of relaxation the patient finds helpful.

Evaluation of Treatment Outcomes

When treating medical phobias, success of treatment is usually based on assessing real-life clinical improvement (Antony & Swinson, 2000). Often, when the person comes for treatment, he/she will have a very specific goal in mind: to be able to do something that fear currently makes impossible. The patient may have very clear ideas about what is important to be able to do and what is not personally important. For example, a patient with severe arthritis might be prescribed a self-injectable medication, but may be unable to take it because of a needle phobia; a phobia that generalizes to all sorts of needles and all sorts of invasive medical procedures. For that particular person, being able to inject the antiinflammatory medication may be the goal. This person may not be interested in combating the fear of getting an IV or having blood drawn. It is imperative to let the patient guide the treatment according to his/her desired outcome. If this is the guiding principle, if this is how the goal of treatment is defined, then outcome measurement is simple: upon completion of treatment, can the person do the thing, encounter the object, or enter the situation that was feared prior to treatment? If the answer is "yes," then treatment was successful. The specific questionnaires and assessment tools, mentioned earlier in the section on assessment, may also be used at this stage to provide a more objective measurement of treatment progress and success.

It should be noted that for some, getting to the point of having no anxiety when confronting the feared object or situation may be unrealistic; after all, even nonphobic people may be a little anxious in certain medical settings. Such anxiety may be normal. Therefore, stressing the importance of facing a fear *despite* anxiety (rather than *without* anxiety) may be a more helpful approach.

Considerations With Special Populations

Children with medical phobias are a particular population that requires special mention. More in-depth descriptions of CBT interventions for children facing medical procedures have been reported elsewhere (Graziano, DeGiovanni, & Garcia,1979; Jay et al., 1985), and much has been written about children and medical phobias (Duff, 2003). For example, it is estimated that more than 50% of primary school children have a needle phobia (Humphrey et al., 1992). Children's cognitive abilities affect their pain perception, as well as their understanding and recall of painful medical experiences (Duff, 2003). We know from learning theory that when a child encounters a painful or distressing experience in a medical setting, a medical phobia can develop later in life. The more negative the childhood experience, when it comes to venepuncture, for example, the higher the resultant anxiety, distress, and noncooperation (Bijitter & Vertommen, 1998). Therefore, in the medical setting, it is important to treat children in a way that reduces the chance of their having a phobia-inducing experience. For the same reason, it is imperative to treat any medical phobia that arises in the pediatric setting in a timely manner, so as to reduce the morbidity of that phobia in later years. Generally, it is suggested that when treating medically anxious children, the prevention of phobia development should be the main aim. This is done by assessing the child's previous experience and by preparing him or her properly for the present medical intervention. Specifically, previous responses to medical procedures, previous interventions, and their outcomes should be clearly assessed. Past "mistakes" should be avoided, and past "successes" should obviously be repeated. For example, some children respond positively to the use of EMLA cream (topical anesthetic) with a noted reduction in pain and distress, whereas for others, the use of EMLA may be an early warning of pain to come, and therefore, its use may simply prolong the anticipatory anxiety and subsequent distress. In fact, it is suggested that in the case of venepuncture, the procedure should occur as close to the beginning of the doctor's visit as possible, so as to reduce the number of anticipatory cues given (Duff, 2003).

Proper preparation for a painful or frightening medical procedure should include a thorough explanation of the procedure, including expectations in terms of pain or discomfort. Such explanations may also help to correct any misconceptions about the procedure itself. Appropriate education has anxiety-reducing power. Demonstrating equipment to the pediatric patient ahead of time can allow the child to become familiar with it, and can help reduce anticipatory anxiety. Showing a video of the procedure can be helpful. It is thought that a child who watches a video depiction of another child experiencing some anxiety, but still successfully coping with the distress of a medical procedure, is more likely to use similar, successful coping skills (Jay et al., 1985). Such videos can also serve an educational purpose, with their ability to demonstrate to the patient exactly what can be expected during the medical procedure.

Parents should be active participants. Children experience less distress from venepuncture, for example, if a parent is present (Graziano et al., 1979). Of course, the presence of a needle-phobic parent, who is likely to react with distress, may be more harmful than helpful, according to vicarious learning theory, and should be avoided. The nonphobic parent's role is to comfort and to distract the child during the medical procedure. If restraint is required, the parent should not be involved, but should remain in the room for comfort and reassurance. False reassurance, though (e.g., saying, "the needle won't hurt" when, truthfully, it might), should be avoided.

The child should be encouraged to participate in the procedure as much as possible. In the case of venepuncture, a child who is allowed to unwrap syringes, to select the arm to be punctured, or to choose the position to be in (lying vs. sitting) during the procedure gains a sense of control. This, in turn, lessens distress. Children who are given permission to cry or scream experience less distress than those who are told to "be strong" (Fernold & Corry, 1981). It may be helpful to plan with the child what loud noise he or she would like to make upon venepuncture, for example.

During the procedure itself, there should be an office environment of calm and tranquility (turn off pagers, put a do-not-disturb sign on the door, etc.). The child should be reminded to relax, breathe slowly, and to use distraction (or for younger children, parents should be instructed to do the distracting).

Despite all of these suggestions, there may still be a child who exhibits so much distress that performing a medical procedure is impossible. In this case, a decision needs to be made as to the importance of the procedure itself. Does it really need to be done? Does it really need to be done now? If there is an opportunity, it may be worthwhile to allow the child to take a break for 30–60 minutes, and then retry. If the entire procedure could be delayed, the appointment may be turned into a type of exposure, allowing for a "practice session." If these options are ineffective or not possible and the medical procedure cannot be completed, a specific program of CBT, as discussed in this chapter, may have to be undertaken. In that case, the focus should be on desensitization through gradual exposure, using an exposure hierarchy, education of the child regarding the procedure itself, and skills acquisition (e.g., applied muscle tension). The one-time use of a sedating medication may also be appropriate.

A Word on Medication

There are some situations in which the use of medication in the treatment of a medical phobia may be very appropriate. If the patient requires an immediate medical procedure or investigation and there is not time or opportunity to do exposure therapy, then use of a benzodiazepine would be warranted. Likewise, if the medical procedure is an isolated, one-off event (like having an MRI) and the fear is quite specific to that one, isolated procedure, and not generalized to a large number of medical situations or procedures, then an argument could easily be made for use of a benzodiazepine. The use of a topical anesthetic, like EMLA, may also be quite reasonable for children and adults alike. If there is an option to give a medication (particularly to a child) in a less painful form (e.g., intranasal spray vs. injection), then the less-painful form should be chosen.

Clinical Pearls of Wisdom for Practitioners of CBT

1. The clinician needs to invest time in developing a good exposure hierarchy. Spending time in collaboration with the patient to design exposure items that really target the fullest aspect of the fears will pay off.

2. Personify the fear. Make the fear a real entity, against whom this fight is waged. This will help with motivation. The patient can visualize standing up to fear and not giving in to its demands of avoidance. Think of exposure therapy as a battle, with you and the patient on one side, and the phobia on the other. The phobia has held the patient hostage for long enough. Exposure therapy is your way of calling fear's bluff and escaping fear's control.
3. Be prepared to modify the exposure hierarchy as treatment progresses. This is a fluid process. Nothing is written in stone. The patient will find that some items originally rated with low SUDS may actually cause more anxiety and vice versa. Do not hesitate to modify as the need emerges.
4. Make exposure therapy an enjoyable experience. Make sure the patient is involved in designing the exposures from the beginning. Be creative. Demonstrate exposures for your patient and become actively involved in the process.

Suggested Readings

Antony, M. M., & Barlow, D. H. (2002). Specific phobia. In D. H. Barlow (Ed.), *Anxiety and its disorders: The nature and treatment of anxiety and panic* (2nd ed., pp. 380–417). New York: Guilford.

Antony, M. M., & Watling, M. A. (2006). *Overcoming medical phobias; How to conquer fear of blood, needles, doctors, and dentists.* Oakland, CA: New Harbinger.

Marks, I. (1988). Blood-injury phobia: A review. *American Journal of Psychiatry, 145*, 1207–1213.

References

American Psychiatric Association. (2000). *Diagnostic and statistical manual of mental disorders* (4th ed., text rev.). Washington, DC: American Psychiatric Press.

Antony, M. M., & Barlow, D. H. (2002). Specific phobia. In D. H. Barlow (Ed.), *Anxiety and its disorders: The nature and treatment of anxiety and panic* (2nd ed., 380–417). New York: Guilford.

Antony, M. M., Brown, T. A., & Barlow, D. H. (1997). Heterogeneity among specific phobia types in DSM-IV. *Behaviour Research and Therapy, 35*, 1089–1100.

Antony, M. M., & Swinson, R. P. (2000). *Phobic disorders and panic in adults: A guide to assessment and treatment.* Washington, DC: American Psychological Association.

Antony, M. M., & Watling, M. A. (2006). *Overcoming medical phobias; How to conquer fear of blood, needles, doctors, and dentists.* Oakland, CA: New Harbinger.

Bienvenu, O. J., & Eaton, W. W. (1998). The epidemiology of blood-injection-injury phobia. *Psychological Medicine, 28*, 1129–1136.

Bijitter, P., & Vertommen, H. (1998). The impact of previous experience on children's reactions to venepunctures. *Journal of Health Psychology, 3*, 39–46.

Corah, N. L. (1969). Development of a dental anxiety scale. *Journal of Dental Research, 48*, 596.

Curtis, G. C., Magee, W. J., Easton, W. W., Wittchen, H. U., & Kessler, R. C. (1998). Specific fears and phobias: Epidemiology and classification. *British Journal of Psychiatry, 173*, 212–217.

De Jongh, A., Muris, P., Schoenmakers, N., & Horst, G. T. (1995). Negative cognitions of dental phobics: Reliability and validity of the Dental Cognitions Questionnaire. *Behaviour Research and Therapy, 33*, 507–515.

Duff, A. J. A. (2003). Incorporating psychological approaches into routine paediatric venepuncture. *Archives of Disease in Childhood, 88*, 931–937.

Emmelkamp, P. M. G., & Wessels, H. (1975). Flooding in imagination vs. flooding in vivo: A comparison with agoraphobics. *Behaviour Research and Therapy, 13*, 7–15.

Fernold, C., & Corry, J. (1981). Emphatic versus directive preparation of children for needles. *Child Health Care Development, 10*, 44–47.

Foa, E. B., Jameson, J. S., Turner, R. M., & Payne, L. (1980). Massed vs. spaced exposure sessions in the treatment of agoraphobia. *Behaviour Research and Therapy, 18*, 333–338.

Fredrikson, M., Annas, P., Fischer, H., & Wik, G. (1996). Gender and age differences in the prevalence of specific fears and phobias. *Behaviour Research and Therapy, 26*, 241–244.

Gitin, N. M., Herbert, J. D., & Schmidt, C. (1996, November). *One session in vivo exposure for odontophobia.* Paper presented at the 30th Annual Convention of the Association for the Advancement of Behavior Therapy, New York.

Graziano, A. M., DeGiovanni, I. S., & Garcia, K. A. (1979). Behavioral treatment of children's fears: A review. *Psychological Bulletin, 86*, 804–830.

Hamilton, J. G. (1995). Needle phobia: A neglected diagnosis. *Journal of Family Practice, 41*(2), 169–175.

Hellstrom, K., Fellenius, J., & Ost, L. G. (1996). One versus five sessions of applied tension in the treatment of blood phobia. *Behaviour Research and Therapy, 34*, 101–112.

Humphrey, G. B., Boon, C. M. J., Chiquit van Linden van den Heuvell, G. F. E, & van de Wiel, H. B. M. (1992). The occurrence of high levels of acute behavioural distress in children and adolescents undergoing routine venipuncture. *Paediatrics, 90*, 87–91.

Jay, S. M., Elliot, C. H., Ozolins, M., Olson, R. A., & Pruitt, S. D. (1985). Behavioral management of children's distress during painful medical procedures. *Behavior Research and Therapy, 23*, 513–520.

Kendler, K. S, Myers, J., & Prescott, C. A. (2002). The etiology of phobias: An evaluation of the stress-diathesis model. *Archives of General Psychiatry, 59*, 242–248.

Kleinknecht, R. A. (1994). Acquisition of blood, injury and needle fears and phobias. *Behaviour Research and Therapy, 32*, 817–823.

Kleinknecht, R. A., Klepac, R. K., & Alexander, L. D. (1973). Origins and characteristics of fear of dentistry. *Journal of American Dental Association, 86*, 842–848.

Kleinknecht, R. A., & Lenz, J. (1989). Blood/injury fear, fainting and avoidance of medically related situations. A family correspondence study. *Behaviour Research and Therapy, 27*, 537–547.

Kleinknecht, R. A., & Thorndike, R. M. (1990). The mutilation questionnaire as a predictor of blood/injury fear and fainting. *Behaviour Research and Therapy, 28*, 429–437.

Kleinknecht, R. A., Thorndike, R. M., & Walls, M. M. (1996). Factorial dimensions and correlates of blood, injury, injection and related medical fears: Cross validation of the Medical Fear Survey. *Behaviour Research and Therapy, 34*, 323–331.

Klorman, R., Hastings, J. E., Weerts, T. C., Melamed, B. G., & Lang, P. J. (1974). Psychometric description of some specific fear questionnaires. *Behavior Therapy, 5*, 401–409.

Mannion, N. E., & Levine, B. A. (1984). Effects of stimulus representation and cue category level on exposure (flooding) therapy. *British Journal of Clinical Psychology, 23*, 1–7.

Marks, I. (1988). Blood-injury phobia: A review. *American Journal of Psychiatry, 145*, 1207–1213.

Moore, R., & Brodsgaard, I. (1994). Group therapy compared with individual desensitization for dental anxiety. *Community Dentistry and Oral Epidemiology, 22*, 258–262.

Ost, L. G. (1991). Aquisition of blood and injection phobia and anxiety response patterns in clinical patients. *Behaviour Research and Therapy, 29*, 323–332.

Ost, L. G. (1992). Blood and injection phobia: Background and cognitive, physiological and behavioral variables. *Journal of Abnormal Psychology, 101*, 68–74.

Ost, L. G., Fellenius, J., & Sterner, U. (1991). Applied tension, exposure in vivo, and tension-only in the treatment of blood phobia. *Behaviour Research and Therapy, 29*, 561–574.

Ost, L. G., Lindahl, I. L., Sterner, U., & Jerremalm, A. (1984). Exposure in vivo vs. applied relaxation in the treatment of blood phobia. *Behaviour Research and Therapy, 22*, 205–216.

Ost, L. G., & Sterner, U. (1987). Applied tension: A specific behavioral method for treatment of blood phobia. *Behaviour Research and Therapy, 25*, 25–29.

Page, A. C., Bennett, K. S., Carter, O., Smith, J., & Woodmore, K. (1997). The Blood Injection Symptom Scale (BISS). Assessing a structure of phobic symptoms elicited by blood and injections. *Behaviour Research and Therapy, 35*, 457–464.

Page, A. C., & Martin, N. G. (1998). Testing a genetic structure of blood-injury-injection fears. *American Journal of Medical Genetics, 81*, 377–384.

Rachman, S. (1977). The conditioning theory of fear acquisition: A critical examination. *Behaviour Research and Therapy, 15*, 375–387.

Ronis, D. L. (1994). Updating a measure of dental anxiety: Reliability, validity and norms. *Journal of Dental Hygiene, 68*, 228–233.

Rowe, M. K., & Craske, M. G. (1998). Effects of an expanding-spaced vs. massed exposure schedule on fear reduction and return of fear. *Behaviour Research and Therapy, 36*, 701–717.

Stouthard, M. E., Mellenbergh, J. G., & Hoogstraten, J. (1993). Assessment of dental anxiety: A facet approach. *Anxiety, Stress and Coping, 6*, 89–105.

Townend, E., Dimigen, G., & Fung, D. (2000). A clinical study of childhood dental anxiety. *Behaviour Research and Therapy, 38*, 31–46.

Pediatric Problems in Primary Care

22

Paul M. Robins
Meghan L. Marsac

Introduction

Pediatric primary care clinics are a main source of service delivery for behavioral health services to children in the United States (Cooper, Valleley, Polaha, Begeny, & Evans, 2006). In recent years, primary care physicians (PCPs) have been encouraged to shift their assessment of patients' health to encompass each patient's global functioning, including physical health and behavioral and emotional functioning (American Academy of Pediatrics, 2001). Children and adolescents present at primary care centers with a wide range of behavioral and emotional functioning. Although some problems or symptoms that children or adolescents present can be a part of a normative, developmental process (e.g., toileting, mild oppositional behaviors, mild separation difficulties), others can be symptoms or red flags for longer term problems (e.g., diagnosable disorders such as attention-deficit/ hyperactivity disorder, depression, or anxiety).

Primary care provides an ideal setting for detection and assessment of behavioral health concerns (Black, 2002; National Association of Pediatric Nurse Practitioners, 2007; U.S. Department of Health and Human Services, 1999, 2003). PCPs are often the first to develop an ongoing relationship with parents and their children. Regular follow-up appointments with patients allow physicians to monitor and evaluate development and behavior over time, while developing trusted relationships with the family. Additionally, multiple appointments over time also allow physicians to observe changes in the family environment or structure (i.e., divorce, new siblings, relocation) (Roberts & Brown, 2004).

Parents frequently face challenges throughout the duration of their child's normative developmental processes and often present their PCP with these challenges. Examples of concerns include noncompliant behavior (Schmitt, 1999), toileting (Taubman, Blum, & Nemeth, 2003), feeding problems (Manikam & Perman, 2000), sleep problems (Stein, Mendelsohn, Obermeyer, Amromin, & Benca, 2001), developmental lags (Blackman, 1999), and school problems (Sandler & Huff, 1999). It is important to note that each of these normative difficulties can also be signals of other more serious problems that require assessment by the PCP and possible referrals to specialists. Assessment of these issues should include awareness of the behaviors of both parent and child, child environment, child physical health, and child emotional health. The range of assessments can include an interview, administration of standardized measures, and/or referrals to specialists (Perrin, 1999).

In addition to guiding parents through normative developmental challenges in their children, PCPs also frequently face other, more severe presentations of psychological symptoms or disorders. In cases in which symptoms are more severe, early detection, assessment, and treatment can greatly improve a child's functioning and outcomes (Roberts & Brown, 2004). However, research suggests that PCPs have some difficulty identifying children who have mental health disorders. Only 17–50% of children presenting with significant behavior problems are identified by their pediatrician; internalizing disorders, such as anxiety and depression, are among the most common missed diagnoses (Costello et al., 1988; Lavigne et al., 1993; Wildman, Kizilbash, & Smucker, 1999). Of those identified, a substantial number of children do not receive treatment (estimated at 50%; Lavigne et al.).

Tolan and Dodge (2005) advocate a central role for behavioral health services within the provision of comprehensive pediatric primary care. They stress four components to an integrated health system: easy access to services; use of sound prevention principles for high-risk youths; access to short-term intervention; and greater promotion of mental health issues across settings. The need to incorporate family-focused, culturally competent, evidence-based, and developmentally appropriate services is stressed. These components are further discussed in the following section.

Assessment and Diagnostic Issues

Types of Assessments Conducted in Primary Care Settings

Efforts have been made to facilitate providers' skills and ability to adequately assess and diagnosis psychological disorders in a primary care setting. Assessment strategies vary, including using manuals for assessment and diagnoses (Drotar,

1999), using screening tools to aid in assessment, including computerized screening systems (Stevens et al., 2008), and collaborating with behavioral health staff to develop and use behavioral screening services (Riekert, Stancin, Palermo, & Drotar, 1999).

One example of a manualized assessment available to PCPs is the *Diagnostic and Statistical Manual for Primary Care, Child and Adolescent Version* (DSM-PC; Wolraich, Felice, & Drotar, 1996). This manual was developed by a panel of experts, with input from a number of individuals in primary care and behavioral health care. The manual guides pediatricians to consider children's severity of symptoms, developmental stage, and environmental situation and stressors when making assessments and diagnoses. The purpose of the manual is to help physicians describe the symptoms they are observing in their patients (Drotar, 1999).

In addition to manualized assessments or interviews based on a manual, screening tools are also frequently used to aid in PCPs' assessment of behavioral health symptomatology (Sandler & Huff, 1999). Brief, standardized screening tools allow pediatricians to quickly assess for any outstanding behavioral concerns. Some screening tools, such as the Child Behavior Checklist (Achenbach & Rescorla, 2000, 2001) or the Pediatric Symptom Checklist (Jellinek, Murphy, & Burns, 1986), provide an overview of a number of possible behaviors or symptoms, including both internalizing and externalizing symptoms, whereas others, such as the Vanderbilt Attention Deficit/Hyperactivity Disorder Parent Rating Scale (Wolraich et al., 2003) or the Children's Depression Inventory (Kovacs, 1985), are more targeted to specific symptoms. Although screeners can be helpful in identifying concerns, they do not take the place of a thorough diagnostic assessment. Thus, screeners can help medical professionals determine when to refer for additional mental health assessment or treatment. See Table 22.1 for examples of commonly used behavioral screening measures in primary care settings.

Computerized screening methods are now being assessed to determine their effectiveness in assisting medical providers in identifying behavioral health needs. For example, Stevens and colleagues (2008) developed a computerized behavioral screening assessment tool for adolescents focused on behaviors related to injury risk, depression, and substance use, which was completed in the waiting room prior to the appointment. The screening took an average of 12.5 minutes to complete. Fifty-nine percent of adolescents screened positive for at least one behavioral concern. Researchers compared the rates of PCP identification of problem behaviors when immediately provided with results from the computerized screening with delayed results. Initial findings suggested that physicians' rate of recognition of a psychosocial problem was higher when immediately provided with the results of the screening, compared with recognition of problem behaviors without the results (68 vs. 52% recognition, respectively).

Some primary care settings have offered a more thorough assessment for youth with emotional or behavioral health concerns by developing a collaborative screening protocol with a behavioral health team. For example, Riekert et al. (1999) developed and implemented a screening service that is initiated when a physician identifies a child about whom he or she has concerns and distributes behavioral screening measures to the parents and teachers. Next, the screening team collects behavioral rating scales from the parent and teachers and obtains data from the medical charts regarding concerns presented to the PCP. The behavioral health staff then scores, interprets, and provides a summary of results and

22.1 Examples of Commonly Used Behavioral/Emotional Screening Assessment Tools Used in Primary Care

Assessment Tool	Age (in years)	Number of Items	Format
Child Behavior Checklist (CBCL; Achenbach & Rescorla, 2000, 2001)	1.5–5; 6–18	118	Parent report
Teacher Report Form (TRF: Achenbach & Rescorla, 2000, 2001)	1.5–5; 6–18	118	Teacher report
Youth Self-Report (YSR; Achenbach, 1991)	11–18	118	Child report
Pediatric Symptom Checklist (PSC; Jellinek et al., 1986)	3–16	35	Parent report
Youth Pediatric Symptom Checklist (PSC-Y; Gall, Pagano, Desmond, Perrin, & Murphy, 2000)	11–18	35	Child report
Vanderbilt Attention Deficit/Hyperactivity Disorder Parent Rating Scale (VADPRS; Wolraich et al., 2003)	6–12	47	Parent report
Vanderbilt ADHD Diagnostic Teacher Rating Scale (VADTRS; Wolraich, Feurer, Hannah, Pinnock, & Baumgaertel, 1998)	6–12	35	Teacher report
Children's Depression Inventory (CDI; Kovacs, 1985)	7–13	27	Child report

recommendations to the PCP. Results indicated that the behavioral health screening service was most helpful in influencing physicians' decisions specific to prescribing psychotropic medication; physicians did not use the screening service information to determine whether or not a referral for behavioral health treatment was indicated.

In assessing children, physicians tend to depend on parental reports in order to identify behavioral health symptoms in children, and are more likely to focus on psychosocial problems in the child when parents are also reporting psychosocial problems themselves. However, parent and child reports of symptoms frequently are not consistent. Thus, PCPs should also consider using child self-report measures or soliciting information from the child regarding psychosocial impairment when appropriate (Wildman et al., 2000), based on the child's developmental age. In addition to parent and child reports, obtaining information from the child's school can provide an additional perspective on child behaviors, and facilitates symptom identification and severity (Sandler & Huff, 1999).

Assessment of Specific Symptoms/Disorders

Specific recommendations have been developed for medical providers to provide the best possible assessment of symptoms for a number of disorders. For example, guidelines for assessment in primary care settings have been developed for both depression and attention-deficit/hyperactivity disorder (ADHD; Cheung et al., 2008; Committee on Quality Improvement, 2000). Specific to depression, physician and behavioral health work groups created guidelines by reviewing current empirical evidence, conducting focus groups, distributing and collecting a survey, holding a workshop to obtain expert opinions, and revising final guidelines through a steering committee. Recommendations for PCPs include identifying youth who are at increased risk for depression, using a combination of rating scales and interviews to obtain information, and using the criteria in the *Diagnostic and Statistical Manual of Mental Disorders* (*DSM-IV-TR*; American Psychiatric Association, 2000) when making a diagnosis (Zuckerbrot et al., 2007). In assessing ADHD, the American Academy of Pediatrics (2000) developed guidelines for physicians' evaluations, including initiating an assessment of every child between the ages of 6–12 who presents with inattention, hyperactive or impulsive behaviors, school difficulties, or behavior problems. The guidelines specify that physicians should obtain information from both the child's caregivers and classroom teacher; comorbidity should be screened as well. Additionally, a child must meet the diagnostic criteria for ADHD as described in the *DSM-IV-TR* (Committee on Quality Improvement, 2000).

In sum, PCPs have demonstrated success with integrating behavioral health assessments into their practices by using manuals, screening tools, and collaborative screening services. Importantly, each of these methods suggests the use of multiple informants in assessing a child's behaviors or symptoms. Although recommendations for assessment of behavioral symptoms are not yet established for all disorders, a growing list of guidelines is being developed to facilitate assessment by PCPs.

Incidence and Clinical Manifestations in Primary Care Setting

Though frequently normative, a number of children present to their PCP's office with parental complaints of noncompliant behavior (Schmitt, 1999), toileting (Taubman et al., 2003), feeding (Manikam & Perman, 2000), sleeping (Stein, Mendelsohn, Obermeyer, Amronin, & Benca, 2001), and somatic pain concerns (Campo, Jansen-McWilliams, Comer, & Kelleher, 1999). Furthermore, 10–15% of behavioral problems in children are of sufficient intensity to create significant impairment in functioning (Schmitt, 1999). In addition to typical toileting challenges, PCPs frequently face more severe toileting problems that present as encopresis or enuresis. Encopresis is the primary presenting problem for approximately 3% of general pediatric appointments (Doleys, 1983). Enuresis is even more common, developing in approximately 7% of 4- to 6-year-olds, 5% of 7- to 10-year-olds, and 3% of 11- to 12-year-olds (Stein et al., 2001).

Estimates of feeding problems in typically developing children are around 25% (Manikam & Perman, 2000). Although many feeding problems resolve as the child enters new phases of development, caregiver understanding and reactions can affect feeding problems, as well as contribute to ongoing feeding challenges (Linscheid, Budd, & Rasnake, 2003).

Sleep difficulties during childhood are one of the most common behavior problems presented to PCPs (Streisand & Efron, 2003). Current estimates of sleep difficulties in typically developing children are between 10–20%. Children who have chronic sleep difficulties often have other challenges, including being hospitalized for physical illness (Stein et al., 2001). Of particular importance to behavioral health, poor sleep is related to increased irritability and acting out in children. Additionally, poor sleep can be a symptom of a number of physiological or psychological disorders (Streisand & Efron, 2003). In adolescence, the sleep problems increase, with 25% of adolescents presenting with symptoms of insomnia that persist overtime. Insomnia in adolescents is related to somatic symptoms, social problems, psychological symptoms, and impaired functioning in daily activities (Roberts, Roberts, & Duong, 2008). Adolescents with symptoms of chronic insomnia are more likely to seek medical attention at their primary care clinic; thus, it is essential that primary care clinicians assess and adequately treat insomnia in youth (Roberts et al.).

Chronic abdominal pain (CAP), an example of a persistent pain concern, is a common problem affecting 10–15% of school-age children (Apley, 1975). Day-to-day functioning is affected in numerous ways, including school attendance (Wasserman, Whitington, & Rivara, 1988), academic productivity (Kusche, Cook, & Greenberg, 1993), and participation in physical activities (Walker & Greene, 1991). Ongoing health-related difficulties associated with pain complaints are often reported as well, leading to increased visits to primary care offices.

In addition to more normative-based concerns, approximately 17–22% of children meet criteria for a diagnosis of a psychological disorder (Briggs-Gowen et al., 2003; Costello et al., 1988; U.S. Department of Health and Human Services, 1999), with 5% experiencing "extreme" impairment. Services for youth in need are underutilized (U.S. Department of Health and Human Services, 1999) with estimates that less than one-third of youth with significantly impairing disorders receive mental health treatment (Leaf et al., 1996; Riekert et al., 1999). More specifically, estimates suggest that about 7% of children presenting at primary care centers meet criteria for an internalizing disorder, whereas 12% meet criteria for an externalizing disorder (Briggs-Gowen et al.). Another 5% of children present with multiple disorders (Briggs-Gowen et al.). However, it is likely that the rate of internalizing disorders is underestimated, given that 25% of youth have experienced major depression and 2% have experienced a manic episode by the end of adolescence (Briggs-Gowen et al.).

Long-Term Impact of Behavioral Health Symptoms

Youth who present with diagnosable disorders are more likely to continue to have significantly impairing symptoms as adults (Briggs-Gowen et al., 2003). For example, it is estimated that 50% of individuals who have major depression, and 90% of individuals who experience a manic episode as a youth, will continue to meet criteria for a mood disorder as an adult (Briggs-Gowen et al.). In addition, studies have demonstrated links between child onset abdominal pain and adult functional gastrointestinal disorders, such as irritable bowel syndrome (Blanchard & Scharff, 2002; Walker, 1999). Unfortunately, a reliable method of predicting which children with disorders will continue to have difficulties in adulthood has not yet been established (Kessler, Avenevoi, & Merikangas, 2001).

Case Example

Mark is an 8-year-old boy who presents with a 3-year history of concerns at school, including not completing schoolwork or homework, not turning in completed homework, losing books and papers, and having few friends. He lives with his single-parent mother, who works full time, as well as two older siblings. He lived with his maternal grandmother until age 5. His mother has a history of substance abuse; he has sporadic contact with his biological father. There are no significant health concerns. Mark's mother is receiving messages from the third-grade teacher that Mark is in danger of failing because of incomplete and inconsistent work. At home, Mark tends to stay by himself, enjoying few neighborhood friends or activities. Rather, over the past year, he often prefers to watch television or play with action figures. He has not previously received any school or mental-health-based services.

Mark was initially seen for these concerns during a well-child visit. His pediatrician has known Mark since infancy, but appointments have been very sporadic, with large gaps between sick-child visits over the years. Based on today's appointment, including a clinical interview, it appeared that Mark was experiencing school-performance concerns related to difficulties completing tasks and organizing materials. Examination of group achievement test scores, supplied by his mother, indicated average/low-average skills, but his report card suggested poor grades as a result of incomplete homework assignments and difficulties completing in-class work. Mark has difficulties with board-to-page copying tasks, including recording homework assignments in his homework journal, as well as copying math problems for in-class completion. Much of his written outcome is sloppy and poorly organized on the page.

Cognitive-Behavioral Case Conceptualization

The cognitive-behavioral clinician in this case was able to quickly obtain and integrate data across multiple informants (teacher, parent, and child) as well as environments (classroom and home), which is essential to develop a cognitive-behavioral conceptualization. This clinical presentation suggested attentional difficulties without significant learning concerns. In addition, Mark's psychosocial history was involved; he did not live with his mother during his first 5 years, and their reunion has been challenging, with Mark exhibiting alternating negative and withdrawn behaviors. Mark's mother would frequently become quite frustrated with both his "laziness" while completing homework, as well as his irritable and often negative behaviors. When Mark's mother repeatedly reminded him to do his homework, he often stated, "I will," or "in a minute," but then did not follow through. He was isolated at school and home, and his mood during today's medical examination was irritable and sad. Thus, concerns about his mood included possible depression. The development and implementation of an empirically based treatment plan was pursued after identification and consideration of barriers to treatment.

Identifying and Addressing Obstacles to Treatment

Challenges for PCPs in Addressing Behavioral Health in Youth

Whereas PCPs have regular contact with their patients and can be helpful in identifying emerging mental health symptoms or behavior problems, there are a number of barriers in assessing and treating behavioral health problems in a primary care setting. For example, due to the vast number of patients who PCPs are required to see each day, it is difficult to allocate enough time to adequately assess behavioral health symptoms or to put prevention efforts in place. In addition, reimbursement for services often will not cover behavioral health assessment or treatment, particularly for prevention of future problems (Roberts & Brown, 2004).

Aside from time and reimbursement limitations, PCPs also typically have limited training in screening/prevention or in assessing behavioral/mental health (Roberts & Brown, 2004; U.S. Department of Health and Human Services, 1999, 2003). Further complicating the situation, children with behavioral disorders or difficulties in school that are requesting assessment through primary care settings often present with a complex picture of comorbid disorders, even when children are being assessed for a specific disorder such as ADHD. Thus, even with specific training to better enhance physicians' diagnostic skills pertaining to ADHD, the comorbid diagnoses provide a challenge. Additionally, PCPs often have limited information about available community resources and lack of time for assessment of psychosocial issues, including communicating with schools (Leslie, Weckerly, Plemmons, Landsverk, & Eastman, 2004). Pediatricians' level of training in psychosocial problems is related to the identification and treatment of youth psychological symptoms and disorders. For example, whereas pediatricians with a moderate amount of training demonstrated the ability to recognize psychological disorders in youth, only pediatricians with advanced training in children's psychosocial issues were able to both identify and to use multiple strategies to manage psychological symptoms in their patients (Leaf et al., 2004).

Another barrier encountered by pediatricians is the amount of behavioral or mental health information parents are willing to share at appointments. In one study, approximately half of parents (55%) who noted significant behavioral or emotional symptoms in their children during a psychiatric evaluation reported that they had not shared their concerns with their pediatricians (Briggs-Gowen et al., 2000). Similarly, over half of parents who indicated that their children had sleep difficulties did not inform their PCP (Stein et al., 2001). When families do decide to discuss concerns with a pediatrician, they are also more likely to seek services from a mental health provider, suggesting that pediatricians play an important role and facilitate services for families in need of services (Briggs-Gowen et al., 2000). At times, physicians may discourage discussions related to psychosocial stressors or problems by ignoring parental concerns, challenging the reality of the problem, or responding in a helpless manner. In a recent study, 43% of psychosocial problems were discouraged from being pursued by residents, either actively or passively (Wissow, Larson, Anderson, & Hadjiiksy, 2005). However, patient and family trust in PCPs aids in the referral process for mental health services (Roberts & Brown, 2004); it is important that physicians encourage rather than discourage patients' expression of mental health concerns.

The American Academy of Pediatrics (2001) acknowledges significant barriers in pediatric primary care practice, including difficulties managing time, economic pressures, and educational deficits that interfere with providing increased psychosocial care in primary care practices. Although acknowledging these barriers, the Academy has made recommendations for overcoming barriers, including: (a) the expansion of residency training and continuing education to include more education on behavioral, developmental, and mental health issues; (b) the use of the *Diagnostic and Statistical Manual for Primary Care, Child and Adolescent Version* by each pediatrician to assist in making accurate diagnoses and to learn about how to be reimbursed for developmental or behavioral services; (c) the identification of the need to focus on improving physicians' interviewing and counseling skills, with an emphasis on empathy and patient-physician relationships; (d) the allocation of realistic time to assess psychosocial issues within their practice; and (e) the collaboration between physicians and mental health providers.

In summary, obstacles interfering with the PCP's ability to adequately assess and treat behavioral health symptoms in youth consists of numerous factors such as time constraints, reimbursement difficulties, education limitations specific to behavioral or mental health, and challenging physician-family relationships. As PCPs increasingly address these barriers, patients benefit by receiving services or referrals from a trusted resource, and by identifying and addressing symptoms early in their development.

Points of Collaboration With Physicians and Family

The role of the primary care pediatrician has undergone significant expansion over the past 20 years. Behavioral health collaboration, in a primary care context, traditionally refers to a mental health professional located within the practice, along with the pediatrician, whose responsibility includes screening, assessment, and intervention of children's psychosocial development and well-being (Perrin, 1999). Increasingly, however, pediatric practice encompasses care to not only the child, but also parents and families, and recognizes child health and development within the context of the school and even community (American Academic of Pediatrics, 2001; Kelleher & Stevens, 2009). There are expanding opportunities to provide effective pediatric care within multiple contexts and models, and collaboration between psychologists and primary care pediatricians can include clinical care, training and education, community liaison, and research domains.

Various collaborative practice models in pediatric settings have been described (Drotar, 1995). In the *independent functions model*, the psychologist provides clinical services of patients referred by the pediatric practice. In the *indirect consultation model*, the psychologist provides teaching, advice, or protocols for patient management, but the pediatrician retains responsibility for clinical management. In the *collaborative team model*, there is shared responsibility and decision making among the health care providers. Expertise between disciplines is represented on the team in clinical management, teaching, or research roles. Finally, the *systems approach model* considers the broader context in which these collaborative relationships occur, such as the family, health care team, school, community, and culture. For example, in establishing local preventive health care services, using local high school wellness centers or community centers, psychologists collaborate with other professionals at different levels and in several contexts.

The models vary with respect to pediatrician/mental health professional proximity, direct patient care responsibility, and the broader context in which collaborative relations occur. Each has its own benefits and drawbacks involving time, amount of contact between professionals, outcomes desired, and accountability for patient care (Drotar, 1995). In addition, the location of services provided is important; in general, colocated health and behavior health services support greater rates of cross-discipline referral and consultation (Guevara, Greenbaum, Shera, Bauer, & Schwarz, 2009).

There are generally three major types of collaborative activities between cognitive-behavioral clinicians and pediatricians within primary care settings, discussed in the following section, including clinical collaboration, teaching/training collaboration, and research collaboration.

Clinical Collaboration

There are numerous ways that behavioral and physical health PCPs can collaborate in order to improve clinical care within the models described above, including screening, assessing, and treating children and families both within and outside of the primary care clinic. Outcome studies strongly suggest that behavioral health services based within primary care help improve children's behavioral functioning. For example, in an early study, children ages 1–15 received psychological treatment for common behavior, toilet, school, and psychosomatic concerns within a primary care-based psychological consultation service. Improvement was noted in 74% of children, and use of medical services was reduced during the year after treatment (Finney, Riley, & Cataldo, 1991). In a later outcome study, brief treatment services (between one and five sessions) delivered within a medical center primary care setting helped improve concerns related to school problems, behavior problems, anger, attention problems, depression, and temper tantrums, as rated by parents and therapists (Sobel, Roberts, Rayfield, Barnard, & Rapoff, 2001). Thus, the direct provision of mental health services to children and families is an effective collaborative role within a primary care setting, and can address not only symptoms, but also use of medical services.

Teaching/Training Collaboration

Within primary care academic medical settings, pediatric residents see children with a wide range of developmental, learning, and behavioral problems. Psychologists often have significant roles in teaching and training in the behavioral and development facets of pediatric practice (Drotar, 1999). Pediatricians-in-training are often uncomfortable with or not adequately prepared to address psychosocial concerns, and additional training that combines communication and clinical tools is suggested (Wissow et al., 2005). Psychologists within a collaborative team model might be involved in teaching pediatricians about effective provider-patient relationships, as there is much research describing the correlations between parent-provider communication and parental satisfaction with care. For example, Hart, Kelleher, Drotar, and Scholle (2007), in a study of 804 parents of children with psychosocial concerns, concluded that parent-provider communication (empathy, concern, and collaboration) was strongly related to parental reports of satisfaction as well as quality of care. Likewise, a review of the correlates of effective pediatric care indicates that more effective pediatrician-parent communication was associated with greater satisfaction with care, increased treatment adherence, and enhanced discussion of psychosocial care (Nobile & Drotar, 2003). Efforts devoted to improving the provider-patient relationship is, thus, an example of effective training collaboration with pediatricians.

It is generally seen that parental disclosure of child psychosocial concerns increases physician identification of psychosocial problems. In fact, parent-initiated communication, and not the presence of child behavior problems, was a significant predictor of physician identification (Wildman, Kizilbash, & Smucker, 1999). Thus, psychologist teaching with patients regarding communication with physician providers is an important point of collaboration. In a review of randomized trials, improved patient-directed communication with PCPs was associated with improved medical outcome, functional status, and adherence to treatment (Post, Cegala, & Miser, 2002). Meeting with parents during a "drop-in" hour (Schroeder, 2004) can facilitate psychologist-parent collaboration around psychosocial issues.

Research Collaboration

A history of effective collaborative clinical care within an academic medical setting can lead to collaborative research efforts that have strong clinical utility for practice. Research-related collaboration within pediatric primary care can take many different forms and provide a number of mutually satisfying paths. For example, Schroeder's early collaborative practice at Chapel Hill Pediatrics in 1973 led to a number of clinical research questions and studies around children's knowledge of sexuality, factors that influence the accuracy of children's testimony, and treatment effectiveness for child noncompliance (Schroeder, 2004). Clinical collaboration within a primary care practice associated with an academic medical center likewise led to an examination of the construct validity of a well-known screening instrument, the Pediatric Symptom Checklist (Jellinek, Murphy, & Burns, 1986) for use as a screening measure within an urban setting (Kostanecka et al., 2008). These collaborations, among others, illustrate the transition from consultation to liaison within health care teams, promoting clinical practice that informs research, and research that, in turn, impacts clinical practice.

Development and Implementation of an Empirically Based Treatment Plan

In returning to the case of Mark, presented previously, we now consider the treatment plan that was developed and implemented. Mark's primary care clinic performed routine behavioral health screenings of all children presenting for well-child visits between the ages of 4–12, using the Pediatric Symptom Checklist-17 (Gardner et al., 1999). The office assistant scored the checklist and entered Mark's results within the electronic medical record for his visit. Screening scores revealed two areas of concern. One, symptoms consistent with ADHD, predominantly inattentive type, moderate, were suggested, evidenced by elevated scores on the inattention factor score. In addition, a moderately elevated score on the internalizing PSC-17 factor score suggested mood concerns.

Following the physical exam, Mark's pediatrician spoke with Mark about his school performance and mood. Mark stated that he wanted to do well in school and often completed his homework, but sometimes he received poor homework grades. His book bag, which he carried into his visit, consisted of one large pocket, with papers and books scattered and crumpled. He stated upon direct questioning that he often played video games by himself because there were not many other kids in the neighborhood. He also stated that he often slept after school and sometimes was not hungry for dinner.

Mark's mother completed the Vanderbilt ADHD Diagnostic Parent Rating Scale (Wolraich et al., 2003), and Mark's pediatrician sent the Vanderbilt ADHD Diagnostic Teacher Rating Scale (Wolraich, Feurer, Hannah, Pinnock, & Baumgaertel, 1998), along with a computer-generated cover letter, to Mark's teacher. Mark's mother also completed the Child Depression Inventory (CDI; Kovacs, 1985) while in the office. A 2-week follow-up visit was scheduled to discuss the results of the assessment. Following receipt of these checklists, Mark's pediatrician next worked with the consulting clinic psychologist to help interpret the results and suggested diagnoses. Integration of the clinical material (i.e., interview with Mark and his mother, rating forms from Mark's teacher and mother, history, and behavioral observations during appointments) suggested signs and symptoms consistent with ADHD, Predominantly Inattentive Type. That is, Mark demonstrated symptoms of inattention, including difficulties sustaining attention to schoolwork, failing to finish schoolwork, difficulties organizing tasks and activities, often losing his completed homework, and making careless mistakes in schoolwork. These symptoms were at or above the 95th percentile compared with same-age peers, and were thought to be significantly affecting Mark's school success. In addition, mild to moderate symptoms of depression were evident, including low energy, low self-esteem, difficulties with sleep onset, and poor sustained attention. These symptoms were generally at the 90th percentile, compared with same-age peers. Mark's mother noted concern about these symptoms for the past year. Finally, there were some fairly complex family issues present; Mark only recently came to live with his biological mother and he had very sporadic and inconsistent contact with his biological father.

The pediatrician saw Mark and his mother at 2-week follow-up. With respect to the depression concerns, she reviewed symptom-appropriate tip sheets contained within "Bright Futures in Practice: Mental Health" (Jellinek, Patel, & Froehle, 2002), and problem-solved situation stressors to better understand Mark's symptoms in the context of school and home. With respect to the ADHD symptoms, a medication trial was initiated, due to the strong empirical support for use of psychostimulant treatment in addressing ADHD symptoms (Jensen et al., 2001).

An ADHD symptom checklist was completed over each level of the trial by Mark's teacher. In addition, parent and patient education was provided using published tip sheets. As a result of ADHD and internalizing comorbidity, as well as psychosocial complexity, an additional follow-up office visit for 1 month was scheduled. At this 1-month follow-up, improvement with respect to attention and work completion was noted via the teacher-completed symptom checklist. However, only mild improvement in depression symptoms was noted, and a referral to the community mental health center was made for parent–child therapy, with ongoing primary care office visits every 2–3 months. There is increasing empirical evidence that psychotherapies are effective in addressing child depression, although the effect sizes are small to moderate (Weisz, McCarty, & Valeri, 2006).

This treatment plan illustrates the use of well-validated assessment tools, combined with a multiinformant (child, parent, and teacher) and multimodal (interview and use of standardized measures) assessment strategy. In addition, the medication trial was based on reduction of the primary symptoms associated with ADHD, assessed via a daily, completed teacher checklist. Finally, increased follow-up was instituted in order to better assess the response to interventions and the need for modification of the treatment plan.

Evaluation of Treatment Outcomes

Interventions can be implemented at multiple stages of a child's or family's development or symptoms. Different types of interventions (i.e., universal, selected, indicated) have been developed with the goal of improving child developmental, emotional, and behavioral outcomes. For example, universal interventions are developed to serve a larger population in improving a specific outcome, such as improved child-parent interactions. Whereas universal interventions can be helpful for a number of families in promoting healthy development for children, these interventions are less likely to be successful for more severe, specific problems. Selective interventions have been developed for at-risk populations (e.g., families with lower socioeconomic status, fewer resources, or chronic illness), and are designed to prevent progression of undesired symptoms. Indicated interventions target significant interfering symptoms and problems that the child is already experiencing, such as depression or encopresis (Black, 2002).

Universal Interventions: Targeting Overall Parenting Techniques/Child Behaviors

As mentioned previously, parents often seek guidance from PCPs for common concerns such as child noncompliance, questions specific to discipline, and managing the stress of parenting. In an effort to address these frequent developmental questions for all parents, Minkovitz and colleagues (2003) developed a universal primary care intervention program to improve care for children ages 0–3 years old. The intervention program trained Healthy Steps Specialists (nurses, nurse practitioners, early childhood educators, and social workers) to implement seven services, including meeting with a Healthy Steps specialist during well visits in addition to their PCP, six home visits by a Healthy Steps specialist, access to a phone line for developmental questions, developmental assessments, provision of written materials to educate parents on child development, parenting groups, and provision of appropriate referrals for families, as needed. Primary care offices participating in the Healthy Steps programs showed improvements in effectiveness, patient-centeredness, timeliness, and efficiency of care. More specifically, preventative care was delivered on time more frequently (e.g., immunizations, developmentally appropriate interventions) and families reported lower levels of negative discipline techniques (i.e., corporal punishment, yelling). Further, parents in the intervention group were more likely to report problematic child behaviors and concerns about their own depressive symptoms, indicating they felt more comfortable discussing difficulties with primary care clinicians. Changes were maintained 2.5 years later when children were 5.5 years old, suggesting that lower level interventions delivered by trained specialists in primary care offices can significantly improve quality of care for children and improve parenting behaviors across time (Minkovitz et al, 2007).

An example of a less intensive, but still helpful, universal service is the call-in service developed by Polaha, Volkmer, and Valleley (2007). The purpose of the service was to enhance pediatric care by providing parents with the opportunity to call the clinic with questions specific to their child's behavior, emotional functioning, or development. Over a period of 70 weeks (during a 4-hour block each week), the service received 81 calls, which averaged 21 minutes in length. Questions were primarily comprised of conduct problems, enuresis, anxiety, sleep, and repetitive behaviors. At follow-up, parents reported high satisfaction with the service and positive outcomes in their children. Of note, these clinics also had collaborative behavioral health teams at their site in which patients could receive ongoing psychotherapy services, if indicated (Polaha et al., 2007). Thus, current studies indicate that enhanced universal programs can help guide families through typical developmental challenges.

Selective Interventions: Targeting Parenting Techniques/Child Behaviors in At-Risk Groups

When universal programs are not available or are not sufficient, often parents request assistance from their PCP in managing their child's behaviors and managing their own parenting stress. Several programs have been developed, and have shown promising outcomes. For example, Hayes, Matthews, Copley, and Welsch (2008) conducted a randomized controlled trial for a one-time intervention for management of infant/toddler behaviors. Participants included mothers who were self-referred due to concerns about their ability to manage their children's behaviors. The intervention was carried out by a nurse and two early-childhood workers, and consisted of a single, 6-hour program with individual and group components. Each mother worked individually with a facilitator to develop a care plan for her child that included components such as establishing daily routines, providing appropriate child play time, learning child-development education, engaging in positive parent–child interactions, and implementing child-safety techniques. In addition to meeting individually with a facilitator, mothers also participated in a group session. Examples of group topics included sleep problems/hygiene, feeding challenges, interpreting child cues, and self-care for the parent. The outcomes of the interventions showed improvement in child behavior, mothers' symptoms of depression, anxiety, and stress level, and parenting efficacy and competency. Follow-up 6 weeks later showed that changes were maintained without additional intervention.

Another example of a brief intervention is the behavioral family intervention program developed by Turner and Sanders (2006). The program (Primary Care Triple P-Positive Parenting Program) consists of 3–4 sessions, was designed for parents of children requesting assistance with managing behavior problems in their children, and was carried out by nursing staff at a primary care center. After completing the program, parents reported less dysfunctional parenting, reduced parental stress and anxiety, and a lower level of targeted child behaviors than those of the control group. Results were maintained at 6-month follow-up. Both of the studies by Hayes et al. (2008) and Turner and Sanders (2006) provide examples of integrating evidence-based care into primary care, by training staff to provide minimally intensive interventions for parents requesting additional parenting assistance.

Indicated Interventions: Targeting Parenting Techniques/Child Behaviors in Clinical Populations

A number of studies have assessed outcomes for treatments carried out in a primary care setting with children diagnosed with specific behavioral health disorders. A review conducted by Bower, Garralda, Kramer, Harrington, and Sibbald (2001) concluded that behavioral health services in primary care centers provided by mental health or behavioral health specialists were generally effective. In addition, they found that educational programs for health care workers increased their skills and knowledge, but evidence was not available as to how the knowledge and skills changed providers' professional behavior or affected patient outcomes. The cost-effectiveness of having specialists work within primary care settings was likewise unclear (Bower et al). See Table 22.2 for a nonexhaustive list of examples of interventions that have been implemented and found effective in primary care settings.

Evaluation of Treatment Outcomes: Summary

All three types of interventions (universal, selected, and indicated) have shown promising results when implemented in a primary care setting by trained clinicians. Even lower intensity interventions have shown significant improvements in parenting and child behaviors. However, while many programs have shown to be effective in improving children's outcomes, the cost benefit of implementing such programs has yet to be determined. Whereas the American Academy of Pediatrics (2001) has made a commitment "to prevention, early detection, and

22.2 Examples of Interventions Implemented Via Primary Care

Indicated Diagnosis	Treatment	Youth Age (in years)	Interventionist	Outcomes
Oppositional Defiant Disorder (Lavigne et al., 2008)	Parent training: The Incredible Years	3–6	1. Nurse 2. Psychologist 3. Parent (Bibliotherapy only)	All groups improved equally, but greater improvements for families attending more than seven sessions
Depression (Asarnow et al., 2005)	Trained primary care providers + four sessions of CBT	13–21	Care managers (graduate degrees in nursing or mental health)	Significant decrease in depressive symptoms compared with usual care group
Encopresis (Ritterband et al., 2003)	Behaviorally based Web program + usual care by PCP	6–12	Research assistant to answer Web questions	Significant improvement in symptoms compared with usual care group

management of behavioral, developmental, and social problems as a focus in pediatric practice" (p. 1227), empirically validated practice standards addressing a wider range of psychosocial issues, problematic behaviors, and emerging mental health concerns in primary care have yet to be established. Additionally, the type of ongoing support of primary care clinicians by trained mental health providers necessary to carry out interventions over time remains less clear.

Considerations With Special Populations/ Diversity Issues

There remain significant barriers to accessing medical and mental health services for children of low-income families (Power, DuPaul, Shapiro, & Kazak, 2003). Although considerable effort and money have been expended to develop a health care system in this country that is adequate for all citizens, substantial health disparities persist. The people most at risk for chronic health problems, including disabilities, are often those with the poorest access to adequate care. These persons include children, particularly very young children residing in single-parent, low-income families who are members of a racial or ethnic minority group, or who reside in rural areas (*Healthy People 2010*; U.S. Department of Health and Human Services, 2000). In addition, there are cultural differences that affect access to primary care services for some ethnic groups. For example, help-seeking patterns are influenced by racial and ethnic group membership, including a reluctance to seek out help from professionals within formal networks, such as a pediatric office vs. reliance on informal networks, including neighborhood or faith-based organizations (McMiller & Weisz, 1996). Culturally determined differences may also impact concerns about being stigmatized by labels, taking medication, and being hospitalized, contributing to a mistrust of professionals and poor treatment adherence (Sue, Fujino, & Takeuchi, 1991).

Children and families dealing with chronic illness represent a special population within pediatric primary care. Although health care reform has gradually shifted responsibility from hospital- and specialty-based care to primary care, PCPs' capacity to address medical conditions requiring complex treatment programs is limited. In addition, two plus decades of research indicate a heightened incidence of mental health concerns among children with chronic illnesses. Pediatricians often underrefer patients with mental health concerns, and this is particularly true in children with a chronic illness. Finally, the additional collaborative care demands for providers treating a chronic illness population often obscures the need to integrate mental health care as well (Drotar, 1995).

Additional training and resources are often required when addressing the health care needs of patients at risk for or exhibiting more significant concerns. Partnerships with community-based resources, such as community health care centers, churches, or other faith-based organizations, can help address some of the barriers to health care for low-income or medically underserved families. Children living within rural settings are also underserved with respect to mental health services. Colocating behavioral health within primary care (Valleley et al., 2007), as well as Web-based intervention, such as the intervention programs for encopresis developed by the National Institutes of Health and the University of Virginia Center for Behavioral Medicine Research (Ritterband et al., 2003, 2005) can help deliver care to geographically diverse populations with specialized behavioral and physical health care needs.

Clinical Pearls of Wisdom for Practitioners

1. PCPs are increasingly charged with the challenging task of evaluating physical, emotional, and behavioral symptoms in children, adolescents, and families.

   - Cognitive-behavioral therapists should understand the culture of the particular primary care clinic, and work toward addressing mutually defined goals prior to delivering services.

- Therapists need to recognize and integrate the realistic barriers physical health providers face carrying out this charge, including time, cost, and training.
- Behavioral health providers can help health providers use manuals, screening tools, and collaborative screening services to aid in the rapid assessment of a child's behavioral/emotional health.
- The use of multiple informants (i.e., child, caregiver, teacher) is recommended when assessing behavioral health concerns.

2. Early identification of behavioral symptoms by medical providers can improve long-term outcomes by facilitating access to behavioral health treatment when indicated.

   - Routine screening during well-child visits, using reliable and valid measures, can be effective.
   - Group drop-in and other no-cost/low-cost services can be effective in addressing larger groups of parents with commonly occurring child behavioral or developmental concerns, and can be delivered by a variety of PCPs, including nurses, physicians, psychologists, and social workers.

3. Slowly building a collaborative relationship (through direct treatment of patients, consultation, training, and research) with behavioral health specialists can help build upon successes, begin to address obstacles, and improve overall patient care.
4. Effective and successful consultation relationships between pediatric primary care behavioral and physical health providers are bi-directional; we have much to share and learn from one another. Being respectful and patient are key attributes to successful collaborative care.

References

Achenbach, T. M. (1991). *Manual for the child behavior checklist/4-18 and 1991 profile*. Burlington, VT: University of Vermont, Research Center for Children, Youth, & Families.

Achenbach, T. M., & Rescorla, L. A. (2000). *Manual for ASEBA preschool forms & profiles*. Burlington, VT: University of Vermont, Research Center for Children, Youth, & Families.

Achenbach, T. M., & Rescorla, L. A. (2001). *Manual for ASEBA school-age forms & profiles*. Burlington, VT: University of Vermont, Research Center for Children, Youth, & Families.

American Academy of Pediatrics. (2000). Clinical practice guideline: Diagnosis and evaluation of the child with attention-deficit/hyperactivity disorder. *Pediatrics, 105*, 1158–1170.

American Academy of Pediatrics. (2001). The new morbidity revisited: A renewed commitment to the psychosocial aspects of pediatric care. *Pediatrics, 108*, 1227–1230.

American Psychiatric Association. (2000). *Diagnostic and statistical manual of mental disorders* (4th ed., text rev.). Washington, DC: American Psychiatric Press.

Apley, J. (1975). *The child with abdominal pain*. Oxford, UK: Blackwell.

Asarnow, J. R., Jaycox, L. H., Duan, N., LaBorde, A. P., Rea, M. M., Murray, P., et al. (2005). Effectiveness of a quality improvement intervention for adolescent depression in primary care clinics. *Journal of the American Medical Association, 293*, 311–319.

Black, M. M. (2002). Society of Pediatric Psychology presidential address: Opportunities for health promotion in primary care. *Journal of Pediatric Psychology, 27*, 637–646.

Blackman, J. A. (1999). Developmental screening: Infants, toddlers, and preschoolers. In M. D. Levine, W. B. Carey, & A. C. Crocker (Eds.), *Developmental-behavioral pediatrics* (3rd ed., pp. 689–695). Philadelphia: W. B. Saunders.

Blanchard, E. B., & Scharff, L. (2002). Psychosocial aspects of assessment and treatment of irritable bowel syndrome in adults and recurrent abdominal pain in children. *Journal of Consulting and Clinical Psychology, 70*, 725–738.

Bower, P., Garralda, E., Kramer, T., Harrington, R., & Sibbald, B. (2001). The treatment of child and adolescent mental health problems in primary care: A systematic review. *Family Practice, 18*, 373–382.

Briggs-Gowen, M. J., Horwitz, S., McCue, S., Schwab-Stone, M. E., Leventhal, J., & Leaf, P. J. (2000). Mental health in pediatric settings: Distribution of disorders and factors related to service use. *Journal of the American Academy of Child & Adolescent Psychiatry, 39*, 841–849.

Briggs-Gowen, M. J., Owens, P. L., Schwab-Stone, M. E., Leventhal, J. M., Leaf, P. J., & Horwitz, S. M. (2003). Persistence of psychiatric disorders in pediatric settings. *Journal of the American Academy of Child and Adolescent Psychiatry, 42*, 1360–1369.

Campo, J. V., Jansen-McWilliams, L., Comer, D. M., & Kelleher, K. J. (1999). Somatization in pediatric primary care: Association with psychopathology, functional impairment, and use of services. *American Academy of Child and Adolescent Psychiatry, 38*, 1093–1101.

Cheung, A.H., Zuckerbrot, R. A., Jensen, P. S., Ghalib, K., Laraque, D., Stein, R. E. K., et al. (2008). Guidelines for adolescent depression in primary care (GLAD-PC): II. Treatment and ongoing management. *Pediatrics, 120,* e1313–31326.

Committee on Quality Improvement, Subcommittee on Attention-Deficit/Hyperactivity Disorder. (2000). Clinical practice guideline: Diagnosis and evaluation of the child with attention-deficit/hyperactivity disorder. *Pediatrics, 5*, 1158–1170.

Cooper, S., Valleley, R. J., Polaha, J., Begeny, J., & Evans, J. H. (2006). Running out of time: Physician management of behavioral health concerns in rural pediatric primary care. *Pediatrics, 118*, 132–138.

Costello, E. J., Edelbrock, C., Costello, A. J., Dulcan, M. K., Burns, B. J., & Brent, D. (1988). Psychopathology in pediatric primary care: The new hidden morbidity. *Pediatrics, 82*, 415–424.

Doleys, D. M. (1983). Enuresis and encopresis. In T. H. Olendick & M. Hersen (Eds.), *Handbook of child psychopathology* (pp. 201–226). New York: Plenum.

Drotar, D. (1995). *Consulting with pediatricians. Psychological perspectives*. New York: Plenum.

Drotar, D. (1999). The diagnostic and statistical manual for primary care (DSM-PC), child and adolescent version: What pediatric psychologists need to know. *Journal of Pediatric Psychology, 24*, 369–380.

Finney, J. W., Riley, A. W., & Cataldo, M. F. (1991). Psychology in primary health care: Effects on brief targeted therapy on children's medical care utilization. *Journal of Pediatric Psychology, 16*, 447–461.

Gall, G., Pagano, M. E., Desmond, M. S., Perrin, J. M., & Murphy, J. M. (2000). Utility of psychosocial screening at a school-based health center. *Journal of School Health, 70*, 292–298.

Gardner, W., Murphy, J. M., Childs, G., Kelleher, K., Pagano, M. E., Jellinek, M. S., et al. (1999). The PSC-17: A brief pediatric symptom checklist with psychosocial problem subscales. *Ambulatory Child Health, 5*, 225–236.

Guevara, J. P., Greenbaum, P. E., Shera, D., Bauer, L., & Schwarz, D. F. (2009). Survey of mental health consultation and referral among primary care pediatricians. *Academic Pediatrics, 9*, 123–127.

Hart, C. N., Kelleher, K. J., Drotar, D., & Scholle, S. H. (2007). Parent-provider communication and parental satisfaction with care of children with psychosocial problems. *Patient Education and Counseling, 68*, 179–185.

Hayes, L., Matthews, J., Copley, A., & Welsch, D. (2008). A randomized controlled trial of a mother-infant or toddler parenting program: Demonstrating effectiveness in practice. *Journal of Pediatric Psychology, 33*, 473–486.

Jellinek, M. S., Murphy, J. M., & Burns, B. J. (1986). Brief psychosocial screening in outpatient pediatric practice. *Journal of Pediatrics, 109*, 371–378.

Jellinke, M., Patel, B. P., & Froehle, M. C. (Eds.). (2002). *Bright futures in practice: Mental health—Volume II. Tool kit*. Arlington, VA: National Center for Education in Maternal and Child Health.

Jensen, P. S., Hinshaw, S. P., Swanson, J. M., Greenhill, L. L., Conners, C. K., Arnold, L. E., et al. (2001). Findings from the NIMH multimodal treatment study of ADHD (MATA): Implications and applications for primary care providers. *Journal of Developmental & Behavioral Pediatrics, 22*, 60–73.

Kelleher, K. J., & Stevens, J. (2009). Evolution of child mental health services in primary care. *Academic Pediatrics, 9*, 7–14.

Kessler, R. C., Avenevoli, S., & Merikangas, K. R. (2001). Mood disorders in children and adolescents: An epidemiologic perspective. *Society of Biological Psychiatry, 49*, 1002–1014.

Kostanecka, A., Power, T., Clarke, A., Watkins, M., Hausman, C. L., & Blum, N. J. (2008). Behavioral health screening in urban primary care settings: Construct validity of the PSC-17. *Journal of Developmental Behavioral Pediatrics, 29*, 124–128.

Kovacs, M. (1985). The children's depression inventory (CDI). *Psychopharmacology Bulletin, 21*, 995–998.

Kusche, C. A., Cook, E. T., & Greenberg, M. (1993). Neuropsychologic and cognitive functioning in children with anxiety, externalizing, and comorbid psychopathology. *Journal of Clinical Child Psychology, 22*, 72–93.

Lavigne, J. V., Binns, J. H., Christoffel, K. K., Rosenbaum, D. L., Arendt, R., Smith, K., et al. (1993). Behavioral and emotional problems among preschool children in pediatric primary care: Prevalence and pediatricians' recognition. *Pediatrics, 91*, 649–655.

Lavigne, J. V., LeBailly, S. A., Gouze, K. R., Cicchetti, C., Pochyly, J., Arend, R., et al. (2008). Treating oppositional defiant disorder in primary care: A comparison of three models. *Journal of Pediatric Psychology, 33*, 449–461.

Leaf, P. J., Alegria, M., Cohen, P., Goodman, S. H., Horwitz, S. M., Hoven, C. W., et al. (1996). Mental health service use in the community and schools: Results from the four-community. MECA study. *Journal of the American Academy of Child & Adolescent Psychiatry, 35*(7), 889–897.

Leaf, P. J., Owens, P. L., Leventhal, J. M., Forsyth, B. W. C., Vaden-Kiernan, M., Epstein, L. D., et al. (2004). Pediatricians' training and identification and management of psychosocial problems. *Clinical Pediatrics, 43*, 355–365.

Leslie, L. K., Weckerly, J., Plemmons, D., Landsverk, J., & Eastman, S. (2004). Implementing the American Academy of Pediatrics attention-deficit/hyperactivity disorder diagnostic guidelines in primary care settings. *Pediatrics, 114*, 129–140.

Linscheid, T. R., Budd, K. S., & Rasnake, L. K. (2003). Pediatric feeding problems. In M. Roberts (Ed.), *Handbook of pediatric psychology* (3rd ed., pp. 481–498). New York: Guilford.

Manikam, R., & Perman, J. A. (2000). Pediatric feeding disorders. *Journal of Clinical Gastroenterology, 30*, 34–46.

McMiller, W., & Weisz, J. (19960. Help-seeking preceding mental health clinic intake among African American, Latino, and Caucasian youths. *Journal of the American Academy of Child & Adolescent Psychiatry, 35*(8), 1086–1094.

Minkovitz, C. S., Hughart, N., Strobino, D., Scharfstein, D., Grason, H., Hou, W., et al. (2003). A practice-based intervention to enhance quality of care in the first 3 years of life. *Journal of the American Medical Association, 290*, 3081–3091.

Minkovitz, C. S., Strobino, D., Mistry, K. B., Scharfstein, D. O., Grason, H., Hou, W., et al. (2007). Healthy steps for young children: Sustained results at 5.5 years. *Pediatrics, 120*, e658–e668.

National Association of Pediatric Nurse Practitioners. (2007). NAPNAP position statement on integration of mental health care in pediatric primary care settings. *Journal of Pediatric Health Care, 21*, A29–A30.

Nobile, C., & Drotar, D. (2003). Research on the quality of parent-provider communication in pediatric care: Implications and recommendations. *Journal of Developmental and Behavioral Pediatrics, 24*(4), 279–290.

Perrin, E. C. (1999). Commentary: Collaboration in pediatric primary care: A pediatrician's view. *Journal of Pediatric Psychology, 24*, 453–458.

Polaha, J., Volkmer, A., & Valleley, R. J. (2007). A call-in service to address parent concerns about child behavior in rural primary care. *Families, Systems, & Health, 25*, 333–343.

Post, D. M., Cegala, D. J., & Miser, W. F. (2002). The other half of the whole: Teaching patients to communicate with physicians. *Family Medicine, 34*, 344–352.

Power, T. J., DuPaul, G. J., Shapiro, E. S., & Kazak, A. E. (2003). *Promoting children's health. Integrating school, family, and community.* New York: Guilford.

Riekert, K. A., Stancin, T., Palermo, T. M., & Drotar, D. (1999). A psychological behavioral screening service: Use, feasibility, and impact in a primary care setting. *Journal of Pediatric Psychology, 24*, 405–414.

Ritterband, L. M., Borowitz, S., Cox, D. J., Kovatchev, B., Walker, L. S., Lucas, V., & Sutphen, J. (2005). Using the internet to provide information prescriptions. *Pediatrics, 116*, e643–e647.

Ritterband, L. M., Cox, D. J., Walker, L. S., Kovatchev, B., McKnight, L., Patel, K., et al. (2003). An Internet intervention as adjunctive therapy for pediatric encopresis. *Journal of Consulting and Clinical Psychology, 71*, 910–917.

Roberts, M. C., & Brown, K. J. (2004). Primary care, prevention, and pediatric psychology. In B. G. Wildman & T. Stancin (Eds.), *Treating children's psychosocial problems in primary care* (pp. 35–60). Greenwich, CT: Information Age Publishing.

Roberts, R. E., Roberts, C. R., & Duong, H. T. (2008). Chronic insomnia and its negative consequences for health and functioning of adolescents: A 12-month prospective study. *Journal of Adolescent Health, 42*, 294–302.

Sandler, A. D., & Huff, O. H. (1999). Developmental assessment of the school-aged child. In M. D. Levine, W. B. Carey, & A. C. Crocker (Eds.), *Developmental-behavioral pediatrics* ((3rd ed., pp. 696–705). Philadelphia: W. B. Saunders.

Schroeder, C. S. (2004). A collaborative practice in primary care. In B. G. Wildman & T. Stancin (Eds.), *Treating children's psychosocial problems in primary care* (pp. 1–32). Greenwich, CT: Information Age Publishing.

Schmitt, B. D. (1999). The enhancement of development and adaptation. In M. D. Levine, W. B. Carey, & A. C. Crocker (Eds.), *Developmental-behavioral pediatrics* (3rd ed., pp. 748–755). Philadelphia: W. B. Saunders.

Sobel, A. B., Roberts, M. C., Rayfield, A. D., Barnard, M. U., & Rapoff, M. A. (2001). Evaluating outpatient pediatric psychology services in a primary care setting. *Journal of Pediatric Psychology, 26*, 395–405.

Stein, M. A., Mendelsohn, J., Obermeyer, W. H., Amromin, J., & Benca, R. (2001). Sleep and behavior problems in school-aged children. *Pediatrics, 107*, e60.

Stevens, J., Kelleher, K. J., Gardner, W., Chisolm, D., McGeehan, J., Pajer, K., et al. (2008). Trial of computerized screening for adolescent behavioral concerns. *Pediatrics, 121*, 1099–1105.

Streisand, R., & Efron, L. A. (2003). Pediatric sleep disorders. In M. Roberts (Ed.), *Handbook of pediatric psychology* (3rd ed., pp. 599–616). New York: Guilford.

Sue, S., Fujino, H., & Takeuchi, D. (1991). Community mental health services for ethnic minority groups: A test of the community responsiveness hypothesis. *Journal of Community and Clinical Psychology, 59*, 533–538.

Taubman, B., Blum, N., & Nemeth, N. (2003). Stool toileting refusal: A prospective intervention targeting parental behavior. *Archives of Pediatric Adolescent Medicine, 157*, 1193–1196.

Tolan, P. H., & Dodge, K. A. (2005). Children's mental health as a primary care and concern: A system for comprehensive support and service. *American Psychologist, 60*, 601–614.

Turner, K. M. T., & Sanders, M. R. (2006). Help when it's needed first: A controlled evaluation of brief, preventative behavioral family intervention in a primary care setting. *Behavior Therapy, 37*, 131–142.

U.S. Department of Health and Human Services. (1999). *Mental Health: A Report of the Surgeon General.* Rockville, MD: U.S. Department of Health and Human Services.

U.S. Department of Health and Human Services. (2000). *Healthy People 2010: Understanding and improving health*. Washington, DC: U.S. Government Printing Office.

U.S. Department of Health and Human Services. (2003). Prevention makes common cents. In *Integrating mental health into primary care: A global perspective*. Washington, DC: Department of Health & Human Services.

Valleley, R. J., Kosse, S., Schemm, A., Foster, N., Polaha, J., & Evans, J. H. (2007). Integrated primary care for children in rural communities: An examination of patient attendance at collaborative behavioral health services. *Families, Systems & Health, 25*, 323–332.

Walker, L. S. (1999). Pathways between recurrent abdominal pain and adult functional gastrointestinal disorders. *Journal of Development and Behavioral Pediatrics, 20*, 320–322.

Walker, L. S., & Greene, J. W. (1991). The functional disability inventory: Measuring a neglected dimension of child health status. *Journal of Pediatric Psychology, 132*, 1010–1015.

Wasserman, A. L., Whitington, P. F., & Rivara, F. P. (1988). Psychogenic basis for abdominal pain in children and adolescents. *Journal of the American Academy of Child and Adolescent Psychiatry, 27*, 179–184.

Weisz, J. R., McCarty, C. A., & Valeri, S. M. (2006). Effects of psychotherapy for depression in children and adolescents: A meta-analysis. *Psychological Bulletin, 132*, 132–149.

Wildman, B. G., Kinsman, A. M., & Smucker, W. D. (2000). Use of child reports of daily functioning to facilitate identification of psychosocial problems in children. *Archives of Family Medicine, 9*, 612–616.

Wildman, B. G., Kizilbash, A. H., & Smucker, W. D. (1999). Physicians' attention to parents' concerns about the psychosocial functioning of their children. *Archives of Family Medicine, 8*, 440–444.

Wissow, L. S., Larson, S., Anderson, J., & Hadjiisky, E. (2005). Pediatric residents' responses that discourage discussion of psychosocial problems in primary care. *Pediatrics, 115*, 1569–1578.

Wolraich, M. L., Felice, M. E., & Drotar, D. (Eds.). (1996). *The classification of child and adolescent mental diagnoses in primary care: Diagnostic and statistical manual for primary care (DSM-PC) child and adolescent version.* Elk Grove Village, IL: American Academy of Pediatrics.

Wolraich, M. L., Feurer, I., Hannah, J. N., Pinnock, T. Y., & Baumgaertel, A. (1998). Obtaining systematic teacher reports of disruptive behavior disorders utilizing DSM-IV. *Journal of Abnormal Child Psychology, 26*, 141–152.

Wolraich, M. L., Lambert, W., Doffing, M. A., Bickman, L., Simmons, T., & Worley (2003). Psychometric properties of the Vanderbilt ADHD diagnostic parent rating scale in a referred population. *Journal Pediatric Psychology, 28*, 559–568.

Zuckerbrot, R. A., Cheung, A. H., Jensen, P. S., Stein, R. E. K., Laraque, D., & the GLAD-PC Steering Group. (2007). Guidelines for adolescent depression in primary care (GLAD-PC): I. Identification, assessment, and initial management. *Pediatrics, 120*(5), e1299–e1312.

Eating Disorders

23

Stacey C. Cahn
Roger K. McFillin

Introduction

Eating disorders (EDs) are among the most deadly of mental illnesses. EDs follow only depression and anxiety disorders in prevalence (Hudson, Hiripi, Pope, & Kessler, 2007), and are associated with high morbidity and mortality, particularly among young women (Keel et al., 2003). Anorexia nervosa (AN), for example, has the highest mortality rate of any mental health disorder (Steinhausen, 2002), with sufferers exhibiting a 12-fold increased mortality compared with the normal population (Keel et al.); over 5% of those suffering from AN die per year (Steinhausen, 2002). In addition to being one the most deadly mental health conditions, EDs are also among the most common, with the lifetime prevalence estimated at .5–1.0% for AN, 3% for bulimia nervosa (BN), and 3.3% for binge eating disorder (BED; Hudson et al.). Primary care physicians (PCPs) (including pediatricians) are on the frontlines for detection, as most cases of EDs are first identified in primary care (Striegel-Moore et al., 2008). It is important to note that early diagnosis of EDs has been associated with improved outcomes (Eisler et al. 1997; Fairburn, Walsh, Agras, Wilson, & Stice, 2004). In this chapter, we provide an overview of the diagnosis and cognitive-behavioral treatment of EDs relevant to evidence-based practice in primary care.

Assessment and Diagnostic Issues

Although PCPs are perhaps uniquely positioned to first identify EDs, detection of disordered eating in the primary care setting is poor, and fully half of all cases go undetected in this setting (Becker, Burwell, Gilman, Herzog, & Hamburg, 2002). The respective diagnostic criteria for AN, BN, and eating disorder not otherwise specified (EDNOS) are detailed in the following (each adapted from American Psychiatric Association [APA], 2000):

Diagnostic Criteria

Anorexia Nervosa

1. Refusal to maintain body weight at or above a minimally normal weight for age and height (e.g., weight loss [or failure to gain weight during growth period], leading to body weight less than 85% of that expected);
2. Intense fear of gaining weight or becoming fat, despite being underweight;
3. Disturbance in the experience of body weight or shape, undue influence of body weight or shape on self-evaluation, or denial of the seriousness of the current low body weight;
4. Absence of at least three consecutive cycles in postmenarchal females.

The specifier of *restricting* or *binge-eating/purging* type is added to the diagnosis:

Bulimia Nervosa

Recurrent episodes of binge eating, with binge eating characterized by both of the following: (a) eating within any 2-hour period an amount of food clearly larger than most people would eat during a similar period of time and under similar circumstances and (b) a perceived lack of control over eating during the episode (e.g., a feeling that one cannot stop or control the eating):

1. Recurrent, inappropriate compensatory behavior to prevent weight gain, including self-induced vomiting, laxative abuse, diuretics, enemas, or other medications, fasting or excessive exercise;
2. The binge eating and inappropriate compensatory behaviors both occur, on average, at least twice weekly for 3 months;
3. Self-evaluation is unduly influenced by body shape and weight;
4. These symptoms do not occur exclusively during episodes of AN.

The specifier of *nonpurging* or *purging* type is added to the diagnosis.

Eating Disorder Not Otherwise Specified

This category includes disordered eating that does not meet the criteria for any specific ED, including:

1. For females, all of the criteria for AN are met except that menstruation is unaffected, or that despite significant weight loss, the individual's current weight is still in the normal range;
2. All the symptoms of BN are met except inappropriate compensatory behavior (binge eating disorder [BED], approximately);
3. All of the criteria for BN are met except that the binge eating and inappropriate compensatory mechanisms occur less than twice a week or for duration of less than 3 months (see APA, 2000).

Note that although BED is currently classified under eating disorder not otherwise specified (EDNOS), it is under consideration for inclusion in the DSM-V as its own diagnosis independent from EDNOS (Walsh, 2007).

Incidence and Clinical Manifestations in Primary Care

One of the challenges in the assessment of EDs in this setting is that most sufferers, particularly in the case of AN, do not commonly present with a complaint of disordered eating, and may even deny eating-disordered symptomatology (Pritts & Susman, 2003). Individuals with anorexia may deny symptoms in an effort to protect or maintain the disorder, whereas others with BN or BED may not voice or even deny concerns out of shame. Thus, the clinician must be alert to suspect such a diagnosis in the face of vehement denials in at-risk patients when he or she observes specific symptoms or complaints. Presenting symptoms can include "fatigue, dizziness, low energy, amenorrhea, weight loss or gain, constipation, bloating, abdominal discomfort, heartburn, sore throat, palpitations, polyuria, polydipsia, and insomnia" (Williams, Goodie, & Motsinger, 2008, p. 187).

When AN is diagnosed or suspected by PCPs (particularly pediatricians), it is often due to weight loss or extremely low body mass index (BMI). When chronic purging is implicated in the case of BN or AN, dentists may be the first professionals to suspect an ED because of dental enamel erosion (Milosevic, 1999). If AN is suspected because of low weight, the clinician should undertake a detailed history from the patient and, ideally, from family members and/or significant others. The clinician should assess for excessive caloric and dietary restriction (avoidance of certain classes of foods or food groups), food rituals, excessive exercise, preoccupation with body image and weight, vomiting, and laxative abuse (Kondo & Sokol, 2006). Social withdrawal and impairment in academic or work functioning should also be evaluated when applicable. Physicians may want to initiate the discussion by simply asking the patient, "Would it be okay if we discussed your eating habits?" or, "I'm concerned about your eating. May we discuss how you typically eat?" (Williams et al., 2008, p. 193). If an ED is suspected, the patient should be screened for other psychological disorders (and suicidality), given that comorbidity is the rule rather than the exception in this population (see Hudson et al., 2007). When comorbid major depression is diagnosed, treatment of the depression before the ED (unless medically urgent) has been recommended (Fairburn, 2008). Obsessive-compulsive disorder (OCD), in particular, should also be assessed, given the high concordance rate (40%) of these two disorders (Matsunaga et al., 1999). Given that a thorough psychiatric evaluation for mental disorders, including EDs, may be impractical in primary care, referring to a specialist for evaluation may be appropriate, in addition to informing parents or guardians of one's concern (in the case of minors) and providing them with specialist referrals directly.

Brief screening measures are available for use in primary care for clinicians who suspect an ED and may be completed in the waiting room. The *Eating Attitudes Test* (EAT-26) has been widely used, is empirically supported, and assesses for underlying eating-disordered psychopathology (Garner, Olmsted, Bohr, & Garfinkel, 1982). Additionally, the *SCOFF* is a screening tool for EDs designed for primary care and an acronym for the following five questions (Morgan, Reid, & Lacey, 1999):

> *Do you make yourself* **S***ick because you feel uncomfortably full? Do you worry you have lost* **C***ontrol over how much you eat? Have you recently lost more than* **O***ne stone [14 pounds] in a 3-month period? Do you believe yourself to be* **F***at when others say you are too thin? Would you say that* **F***ood dominates your life? (p. 1467)*

Should There Be Routine Screening for EDs in Primary Care?

Although the establishment of routine screening would appear to have obvious public health advantages and clinical benefits, it would appear that such a system may not yet be feasible, even if such screening could be parsimonious. Notably, in a recent U.K. study that examined the feasibility of screening for EDs in primary care, only 46% of female patients age 16–35 even agreed to complete the screen. Among those patients who did complete the assessment, the screen yielded a positive screen rate of 16% (Johnston, Fornai, Cabrini, & Kendrick, 2007). Obviously, it is unclear to what degree eating-disordered individuals would be differentially more or less likely to agree to be screened given the nature of EDs, particularly AN. Interestingly, the authors of the feasibility study concluded that at this time, systematically screening for EDs in primary care is unfeasible without ready access to available specialty treatment, given the shortage of clinicians adequately trained and experienced in treating this specialized, high-risk population. It appeared that for physicians, screening for EDs in primary care became akin to the opening of Pandora's Box: *Now that I have identified a possible ED (and presumably subjected myself to the associated liability), what do I do, given that there is no system in place for me to easily refer these patients?* In fact, Johnston and colleagues (2007) found that a positive screen for EDs was often not even noted on the medical chart. According to one health professional surveyed in the feasibility study (when the patient has not spontaneously complained about an ED), "If the patient's quite happy, are you going to do any harm leaving it?" (Johnston et al., 2007, p. 514). To what degree is it the patient's responsibility to share the medical concern with the health care provider; to what degree is it the physician's responsibility to detect it? Whereas this study was conducted in the U.K. in the context of nationalized medicine, it seems that these findings regarding the feasibility of routine screening for EDs in primary care would be more, rather than less, applicable to the United States, where patients overall generally have less access to care. Although there are no easy solutions to this dilemma, one answer may be that routine screening is desirable within at-risk patient groups and special populations (see the text that follows).

Incidence and Clinical Manifestations in Primary Care Setting

Incidence rates of identified EDs among adult primary care patients is low, yet as compared with matched controls, health care utilization rates are inordinately high (Striegel-Moore et al., 2008). Utilization rates across ED diagnoses (e.g., AN, BN, EDNOS), however, appear comparable (Striegel-Moore et al., 2008).

Determining Level of Care

When considering a patient's initial level of care, it is the expert consensus among treatment professionals that weight should not be considered as the sole criterion, rather, the patient's overall clinical and social picture should be thoroughly examined (APA, 2006). The available levels of care from least restrictive to most restrictive include outpatient care, intensive outpatient, partial hospitalization day programs, residential treatment centers, and inpatient hospitalization. The following factors should be thoroughly assessed when determining the appropriate level of care: medical stability, suicidality, weight as a percentage of healthy body weight, motivation to recover, co-occurring disorders, structure needed for eating/weight gain, ability to control compulsive exercising, severity of purging behavior, environmental stress, and geographic availability (APA). Practice guidelines also establish recommended criteria for inpatient hospitalization (see APA).

Brief Case History

To better illustrate the chronicity, diagnostic migration, and cognitive schemata common in EDs, we provide the following case study, which also details a course of cognitive-behavioral treatment (adapted from Cahn, 2006):

Sally is a 26-year-old investment banker who is currently separated from her husband, she presented to her PCP requesting a referral to a psychologist specializing in EDs. Sally also admitted she had been experiencing chronic symptoms consistent with major depression, including subjective feelings of low mood, anhedonia, insomnia, psychomotor agitation, feelings of worthlessness and guilt, low self-esteem, and diminished concentration. Sally stated that a close friend from work had recently committed suicide, and she had suddenly realized that she "would be next" if she did not seek help. Sally's physician admitted her for inpatient care based upon weight alone.

Upon admission to the inpatient unit, Sally weighed 78 lbs. (35.5 kg). At 5′5″ (165.1 cm), this put her at 62.4% of ideal body weight (IBW) for her height, sex, and age. In the 2 months prior to admission, Sally had been restricting food intake and was consuming only clear liquids and coffee. She reported a history of binging, but only "very rarely" in the past 2 years, and admitted to vomiting up to 12 times per day. She had also exercised over an hour daily (excessive for her physical condition), but had recently discontinued because of her continued physical deterioration. Sally weighed herself multiple times daily and though she had abused diet pills in the past, had not done so in the months preceding admission. This was Sally's first inpatient hospitalization for an ED, but the culmination of many years of intensifying ED symptoms.

Background: Sally first purged at the age of 7 after eating one box of Girl Scout cookies. At age 8, Sally began dieting and competing in beauty pageants (in which she continued to compete until age 20). Sally reported purging again at age 15 when her weight was 125 lbs. (56.8 kg), and then continued to binge and purge throughout high school. In college, her weight increased, reaching 170 lbs. (77.3 kg) by age 20. She then saw a college health services physician for depressed mood and was placed on antidepressants, though Sally believed they had only made her feel worse. Sally's weight increased to 190 lbs. (86.4 kg) at age 22, and reached a high of 194 lbs. (88.2 kg) when she passed the CPA exam. When Sally got engaged to be married, she exercised and restricted her food intake and weighed 135 lbs. (61.4 kg) at her wedding. After Sally married, she immediately began severely purging and restricting, and her weight eventually plummeted to a low of 76 lbs. (34.5 kg).

Family and social history: Sally stated that she grew up "poor" in Arkansas. She had been with her husband for a total of 10 years (married for 2), and had recently decided to separate from him. Sally believed they had begun "to want different things" and described her marriage as a failure. She pointed to her husband's decision to drop out of medical school as the "final blow" to their relationship, and admitted feeling anger toward him for doing so. She stated that her husband believed the marital problems were simply a natural side effect of her ED. Sally, however, insisted that, "the marriage never worked" and that marrying Kyle had only served to significantly accelerate her underlying ED.

Sally had experienced an unstable and traumatic childhood, beginning with the divorce of her parents when she was age five. Sally's father did not visit her often, and Sally admitted feeling abandoned by him. She changed households when her parents divorced and her mother married Scott, a man who was addicted to drugs and physically and emotionally abusive to Sally's mother. At one point, the physical abuse had resulted in her mother's hospitalization, and Sally's mother attempted suicide soon thereafter. Sally reported feeling traumatized from witnessing the abuse and had lived in fear for her mother's safety. During this period of her childhood, Sally's two babysitters, who were brother and sister, would walk around naked and make Sally touch them. Sally further reported that when she was aged 5–10, her cousins would "play doctor" with her, touching her inappropriately over her clothes. She had never told anyone about these episodes and child protective services was never involved. Sally reported feeling "contaminated" ever since these childhood sexual incidents.

Sally was uprooted again when her mother divorced Scott to marry for a third time. Bob, the new husband was a man to whom Sally never felt close. After 10 years, Sally's mother divorced Bob to remarry Scott, her second husband, the man who had been physically abusive to her. Sally reported that her step-father Scott is a "different person" now that he is off drugs, and she has slowly learned to trust him again.

Cognitive-Behavioral Case Conceptualization

Fairburn, Cooper, and Shafran (2003) have advocated for a "transdiagnostic" conception of EDs, emphasizing the common cognitive features of each ED diagnosis, rather than a strict categorical view of the EDs as distinct entities meriting separate psychological treatments. The authors argue that EDs should be considered in this manner, given the similar core psychopathology and the common diagnostic migration of individuals from one ED diagnosis to another. In this model, predicated upon the authors' earlier work in BN (e.g., Fairburn, 1995), Fairburn and colleagues (2003) have hypothesized the processes that serve to perpetuate an ED, including distorted and maladaptive schema for self-evaluation. Whereas most individuals' self-concepts are multidimensional, those suffering from BN or AN appraise themselves primarily or solely on their perceived weight and body image.

Sally believed that her weight and perceived body shape were a reflection of her worth as a person. Her success in pageants and high academic and professional achievement were outward signs of, "success," that predictably elicited approbation from those around her, and Sally relied on others' approval and praise as an external substitute for her lack of internal self-worth. Such efforts at outward success are consistent with a compensatory behavioral coping response to the schema of worthlessness (Young & Klosko, 1994; Young, Klosko, & Weishaar, 2003).

Sally's efforts at lowering her body weight were, in reality, attempts to improve her internal self-worth by changing her external self. At first, Sally received considerable external positive reinforcement following her initial weight loss, as she received positive attention and compliments on her appearance from those around her. Sally's weight-loss efforts were also intrinsically reinforcing because she experienced a positive feeling of achievement when she watched the numbers on the scale decline. Of course, such attempts to improve her self-esteem through her weight loss were ultimately futile, as they were attempts at an external solution to an internal problem. No matter how low, no weight was ever low enough for Sally. Despite the internal positive reinforcement she experienced from restricting her food intake and observing her weight decrease, it failed to alter her core belief that she was fundamentally defective. Moreover, Sally had grown up in an unpredictable environment in which she had minimal control; manipulating her weight and food intake gave her the perception of control over her life. This false perception of control was also internally reinforcing, as it momentarily improved her self-esteem and mood.

This cognitive schema of overevaluation of shape and weight in turn influences behaviors such as severe restriction of food intake, a tendency common to all EDs. Starvation is strongly associated with social withdrawal for a number of reasons, and as Fairburn and colleagues (Fairburn, Cooper, Shafran, & Wilson, 2008) point out, this "encourages self-absorption while isolating patients from external influences that might diminish their overconcern with eating, shape, and weight" (p. 584). Self-induced starvation is strongly associated with subsequent binges in BN and BED, as well as in many cases of AN. Binging is then consequently associated with compensatory behavior in both AN and BN (though typically not BED), including self-induced vomiting, laxative abuse, and overexercising.

When Sally experienced negative automatic thoughts influenced by her core schema of worthlessness, she felt intense shame. She then attempted to behaviorally cope with the shame by restricting calories and purging. In the moment, her ED symptoms were an effective distraction from her aversive feelings, but given that Sally was ashamed of her ED, particularly the purging, she subsequently experienced even more shame and thoughts of worthlessness. Sally's ED symptoms were thus self-perpetuating. Moreover, as Sally's purging behavior had become more and more incapacitating as she purged up to 12 times per day, Sally had become physically unable to work. The loss of opportunity for professional achievement only served to further reinforce her underlying belief that she was worthless.

Cognitive-Behavioral Therapy

Sally's course of treatment consisted of a 7-week stay in an inpatient ED program. The primary goal of therapy was to work collaboratively with Sally on identifying, challenging, and modifying her dysfunctional core beliefs and associated maladaptive behavioral patterns (e.g., severely restricting caloric intake and purging).

The first phase of treatment focused on assessment, developing the therapeutic alliance, and creating a treatment plan. The initial goal in Sally's treatment was to work with Sally on identifying the thoughts and beliefs that were underlying and perpetuating her self-destructive behaviors. At first, Sally had minimal awareness of her thoughts, feelings, and behaviors, and seemed somewhat detached from her cognitive and emotional experience. After some psychoeducation on how to identify feelings and thoughts and some self-monitoring assignments, including journaling, Sally was able to recognize that she believed she needed to be "perfect" and that it was only through "being thin" and achieving that she believed that she could accept herself. In fact, Sally stated that "If I did not have my intelligence, I wouldn't want to live." Sally had long been praised for her intellect by teachers and peers, and she was proud of being admitted into business school for her MBA on full scholarship. When her therapist explored with Sally how well this accurately reflected her value system, she acknowledged that she did not evaluate others solely on the basis of their professional achievements or appearance.

In individual cognitive-behavioral therapy (CBT), Sally reviewed any disconfirming evidence to her implicit belief that her weight and achievements equaled worth. Sally was immediately able to point to her sister Jennifer, whom she admired greatly and with whom she was very close. Sally's sister had chosen not to go to college and was not particularly thin. Yet, Sally greatly admired Jennifer for, "following her own path and not caring what anyone else thinks," and for obviously not living her life to please their father. Furthermore, Sally realized that despite achieving professional success and reaching a weight she rationally knew to be dangerously low, she still did not accept herself. In fact, she acknowledged that she still hated her reflection in the mirror, and that no weight had ever been low enough for her. Sally had the unremitting conviction that if she "just lost one more pound" she would feel better about herself.

Through therapy, and without the ED symptoms accessible to insulate her from her negative feelings and thoughts, Sally realized for the first time that deep down, she believed she was actually worthless. After she understood that her tangible successes and seemingly bright mood belied a fundamental self-rejection, Sally was able to successfully challenge her core schema: "I am worthless." To do so, Sally first examined confirming and disconfirming evidence. Yet, Sally could only support the idea that she was worthless by her subjective feeling that she was worthless. In exploring disconfirming evidence, Sally was able to acknowledge positive aspects of her personality unassociated with her weight and intelligence, citing that she was kind to others, had functioned as a "Big Sister" to an inner city youth, and had mentored a female business student. Sally also reflected that she herself did not judge others by their weight and she thought to do so would be petty and shallow; Sally adamantly believed that she was not a superficial person. When her therapist asked her what she would tell a friend in her situation, Sally became tearful and stated, "Of course I would tell her 'You're worthwhile. God loves you and you deserve happiness. Your life is a gift.' " Through cognitive restructuring, Sally was able to replace her maladaptive belief, "I am worthless," with the alternate thought, "I am a kind, good person who deserves to be happy."

As treatment progressed, Sally was increasingly able to identify and tolerate her negative feelings. As Sally continued to give herself permission to have her own needs and feelings, she was able to recognize how resentful she felt toward her father for abandoning her after the divorce. Sally stated that she never realized how much it had continued to affect her until therapy, and agreed to address this issue in a family session. Family sessions were conducted to educate family members about anorexia and offer recommendations on how family members could support Sally in her recovery.

Sally continued to practice acknowledging her own thoughts and feelings and expressing her own needs, however, she continued to experience negative body image. Sally began self-monitoring her body image and noting antecedent events, thoughts, and feelings. In doing so, Sally realized that her body image varied throughout the day, sometimes dramatically. Yet, Sally recognized that, realistically, her actual weight could not possibly fluctuate so much in the course of just one day. Through her self-monitoring, Sally was able to challenge and modify her original assumption that her body image was an accurate reflection of her weight. Instead, Sally realized that her body image was distorted and more accurately reflected her thoughts and feelings about *herself* in any given moment or situation. This realization allowed Sally to be less affected by her negative body image and, as a result, less compelled to use her ED behaviors in an attempt to change her body image.

Identifying and Addressing Obstacles to Treatment

Motivation to Change

Health care providers often work under the premise that a patient shares the physician's treatment plan and is generally motivated to improve his or her physical well-being. Accordingly, assessing motivation for treatment can be easily overlooked. It is important to keep in mind, however, that EDs, particularly AN, may be egosyntonic. These maladaptive behaviors that pose a significant risk to the patient's physical health may also be positively reinforced by family and friends, particularly through increased attention. The initial weight loss is often rewarded with increased positive attention, and often, later in the progression of the disease, with negative attention. Clearly, ambivalence about change should be identified early in the assessment phase as a significant obstacle for treatment.

Identifying Stages of Change

The transtheoretical stages of change model (Prochaska & DiClemente, 1983, 1986; Prochaska, DiClemente, & Norcross, 1992) provides a theoretical framework to assist clinicians in identifying a patient's current stage in the change process. Identifying motivation to change, and tailoring interventions designed to increase the patient's motivation, have been successfully applied to predict treatment adherence and behavioral change across a variety of health-related behaviors (e.g., Biddle & Fox, 1998; Derisley & Reynolds, 2000; Prochaska, DiClemente, Velicer, & Rossi, 1993). The proposed stages have been operationalized as: *precontemplation* (not actively thinking about changing the problem), *contemplation* (currently thinking about changing), *preparation* (planning changes), *action* (making health-relevant changes in behavior), and *maintenance* (having made significant health-related behaviors with the goal of maintaining the changes). Implementing an intervention that is incongruent with the patient's stage of change will likely increase resistance and undermine a positive therapeutic outcome (Prochaska, Redding, & Evers, 2002). It is imperative for clinicians to identify and communicate an understanding of the ambivalence most ED patients experience. The sensitive clinician must communicate empathy for the patient's circumstances, including the very real benefits and maintaining factors of the disorder. Collaboration is considered the hallmark of a CBT approach to treatment and an important mechanism for change (Vitousek, Watson, & Wilson, 1998).

Motivational Interviewing

Motivational interviewing (MI) is a client-centered treatment approach that is designed to enhance intrinsic motivation by exploring and resolving ambivalence (Miller & Rollnick, 2002). MI was initially developed as an alternative treatment for alcohol-dependent individuals, but has since been successfully applied as an effective intervention across a wide range of health-related behaviors (Burke, Arkowitz, & Dunn, 2002; Burke, Arkowitz, & Menchola, 2003). This approach can be seen as an expansion of the Socratic method and guided discovery techniques integral to CBT (Beck, 1976). The four general principles of MI (Miller & Rollnick, 2002) that should be considered invaluable when treating patient's with ED include: (a) expressing empathy through skillful, reflective listening and normalizing ambivalence; (b) identifying discrepancies between patients' present behavior and their stated personal goals or values; (c) "rolling with resistance" and avoiding arguing for change; and (d) supporting self-efficacy by instilling hope and confidence that the client has the ability to make changes. MI provides a skillful approach to working with ED patients that encourages collaboration and empathic understanding.

Addressing Active Resistance

It is important to keep in mind that many ED patients have developed a strong identity with their ED. The ED has often served important functions within their lives (e.g., managing distressing emotions, shifting family dynamics, signifying discipline/achievement, improving self-image), and facing the potential loss of ED symptoms can evoke an intense emotional reaction directed at the clinician. It is not uncommon for patients to blame and vilify their therapist/physician for the consequences the ED has produced (e.g., "You are taking my gymnastics away from me; that is the only thing I care about in my life!"). In the face of such attacks, it is important for clinicians to resist both defending themselves or backpedaling on the contingencies or consequences imposed by the parents or treatment team. Rather, a more effective intervention would be to externalize the problem and break the associated identity between the patient and ED. For example, acknowledge the pain the patient is experiencing, but communicate: "It is, in fact, the ED that is getting in the way of your gymnastics."

Adolescent patients often present in, "healthy opposition" to their parents as a means of asserting independence. Recovery from an ED can be considered developmentally counterintuitive for the patient who is actively resisting parental authority. It is important to first recognize this potential dynamic in order to address the negative impact of authoritarian parental styles, and using motivational strategies to encourage the adolescent patient to assert healthy control and independence.

Family Dynamics

Evidence-based approaches emphasize family commitment and collaboration as essential for the treatment of EDs, especially for children and adolescents (Lock & le Grange, 2005). Unfortunately, the resistance to treatment many patients experience is also evident within their extended families, through the minimization and/or denial of the illness. Children and adolescents with EDs are often seen as "great kids," who value achievement and are sensitive to the expectations of others. They have often gone to great lengths to protect the secrecy of their ED, contributing to the shock and disbelief many family members experience when they are first confronted with the illness or its diagnosis. The nature of the disease itself can be difficult for people to truly understand, often eliciting strong reactions from the casual observer. It is not unusual for friends and family members to minimize the true suffering inherent in the ED and condemn the patient. There is also evidence that suggests the families of patients with EDs may be overly concerned with social presentation (Davis, Shuster, Blockmore, & Fox, 2004), with the patient internalizing the expectations to conform to the family's values. This dynamic can contribute to a volatile environment when the family is asked not only to commit to being active treatment participants, but to accept the possibility that the family environment may have contributed to the maintenance, if not development of the illness.

Third-Party Payers

Unfortunately, a discussion of obstacles to treatment for EDs would not be complete without mention of third-party payers. PCPs and clinicians must be aware that problems with third-party payment for EDs can pose a significant barrier to treatment. Many states' laws, such as New Jersey, specifically exclude EDs as biologically based, or "serious mental illness." This distinction is important, as it can permit insurance companies to legally exclude EDs from mental health parity when it comes to coverage. For example, many insurance plans limit inpatient mental health coverage to 30 days per calendar year, despite the absence of comparable limits for hospitalization due to "physical" illnesses. For many patients with severe anorexia, 30 days of inpatient treatment would not be long enough to safely reach their treatment goal weight, much less achieve other therapeutic goals. Given that inpatient treatment guidelines recommend that patients gain no more than approximately 3.5 lbs. (1.6 kg) per week to avoid serious medical complications such as "refeeding syndrome" (APA, 2006), 30 days would only enable an individual to gain approximately 15 lbs. (6.8 kg). Note that this calculation does not include the possibility of a relapse within the same year requiring hospitalization, nor the necessity of "partial hospitalization" (full-day treatment) which may be covered from patients' inpatient hospitalization benefit. Providers should be aware that there has been recent progress on this issue, however; parents of ED sufferers successfully sued Horizon Blue Cross Blue Shield of New Jersey for denied claims worth $3.7 million, including legal fees, in a class-action lawsuit (Sterling, 2008). The plaintiffs successfully argued that AN should have been covered under medical benefits. The Academy for Eating Disorders has recently issued a statement paper advancing the scientific evidence that EDs are biologically based and should be classified as "serious mental illnesses" (Klump, Bulik, Kaye, Treasure, & Tyson, 2009). Clinicians may wish to encourage patients and family members to use this consensus statement in advocating for expanded coverage of psychological treatment for EDs.

Points of Collaboration With Physicians and Family

Clinicians are placed in the difficult position of having to acknowledge the ambivalence many family members experience, while at the same time conveying the seriousness of the disorder and need for treatment. Clinicians must be careful not to inadvertently blame family members for the disorder, as doing so will ultimately undermine a collaborative treatment plan. Joining with the family and communicating a mutual concern for the patient's health, and acknowledging family members' own fears, confusion, and self-blame, can improve rapport and minimize resistance. Families must receive proper education about the illness and treatment rationale. Including family members as an important part of the treatment team will help build and maintain the alliance necessary for success. This alliance is critical, given that an important element of a treatment plan may be affecting change in the home environment (such as addressing and modifying rules, boundaries, and contingencies). For adult patients with EDs, addressing marital/partner issues may be more relevant than focusing upon issues of family of origin.

Development and Implementation of Empirically Based Treatment Plan

Although the majority of sufferers of EDs are adolescents, and early treatment renders a better prognosis, the majority of treatment outcome studies on EDs have focused on adults (Wilson, Grilo, & Vitousek, 2007). Lock and le Grange (2005) are a notable exception, having focused on family-based treatment for adolescents with anorexia, also known as the *Maudsley Model*. Until better treatment data are available, adult-based approaches have to be extrapolated to adolescent populations.

Anorexia Nervosa

There is a striking paucity of treatment outcome studies in AN. Only 15 comparative clinical trials have been completed and published (Wilson et al., 2007). The dearth of empirical studies is due to the unique clinical features of AN, including its egosyntonic nature (patients often avoid treatment and actively strive to maintain, and indeed protect, the disorder) that leads to recruitment difficulties, participation based on parental influence rather than true motivation for recovery, attrition, and follow-up challenges. Additionally, the medical seriousness of the disorder often necessitates inpatient treatment, rendering randomized controlled outpatient studies problematic. The treatment modality that has been most studied for anorexia has been the Maudsley Model, a type of family therapy for adolescent patients (Eisler et al., 1997; Lock & le Grange, 2005). Treatment consists of 10–20 family sessions over a period of 6–12 months. The Maudsley Model supports parents in initially exerting authority and control over the patient's eating, and gradually returning control to the adolescent as eating improves. Results have been promising, but it is unclear whether such positive outcomes reflect specific treatment effects, or merely the recent onset of disease among these young adolescents with anorexia (see Wilson et al., 2007); the Maudsley Method has not been shown to be effective with patients who are older or have a longer illness history (G. F. M. Russell, Szmukler, Dare, & Eisler, 1987).

Empirical support for CBT for AN has been scarce due to the limited available research, however, this approach has been recommended largely as a result of the clear success of CBT in treating BN (e.g., Fairburn et al., 2004). Importantly, because of the significant treatment resistance and medical morbidity associated with AN, referral to a specialist in EDs for both medical management and psychological treatment is recommended. This is particularly important for patients with BMIs below 17.5 and chronic or recurrent disease (Fairburn et al., 2008). Moreover, a coordinated, multidisciplinary outpatient treatment team is advised; such a team should include a therapist, physician, and often nutritionist, all of whom specialize in EDs (APA, 2006).

Bulimia Nervosa

CBT has been hailed by the United Kingdom's National Institute of Clinical Excellence (NICE) as the gold standard treatment for BN (NICE, 2004). Guided self-help (GSH), however, may be appropriate and effective in some cases of BN (Banasiak, Paxton, & Hay, 2005) as it is cost-effective and ostensibly more easily implemented within primary care settings. However, this type of primary-care-based treatment should only be implemented by therapists who are experienced and/or supervised (Walsh, Fairburn, Mickley, Sysko, & Parides, 2004). Individual CBT for BN has also been delivered by teletherapy (therapy conducted through video), with mixed results and significant technical and (re)scheduling difficulties noted (Mitchell et al., 2008).

Binge Eating Disorders

Pharmacotherapy for obesity, a medical sequelae of BED, has frequently been conducted in primary care, with many of the controlled drug trials occurring in these settings (Davidson et al., 1999; Hauner et al., 2004). For the treatment of the underlying ED, however, there is no empirical basis to support successful psychological treatment administered by therapists who do not specialize in EDs.

Self-help manuals for BED exist (e.g., Fairburn, 1995), and initial evidence suggests that GSH for BED has comparable efficacy to individual psychotherapy (Grilo & Maseheb, 2005). Such treatment would be more easily disseminated and less expensive than individual psychotherapy, with ostensibly higher treatment fidelity, and would thus be a potentially attractive option in primary care in the future. Having treatment available for patients suffering from BED in primary care would be pragmatic, given that these patients are high users of medical resources, yet low users of psychotherapy (Striegel-Moore et al., 2008).

Typically, such cognitive-behavioral treatment modalities all involve the establishment of observable and measurable treatment goals. Such goals could include pounds/kilograms gained per week, number of days without binging or purging, eating "feared foods" (e.g., pizza), dining in restaurants or engaging in activities that are typically "triggering" for that individual. That patients vary in what specifically triggers their eating-disordered behavior (binging, restricting, purging) speaks to the necessity of individualizing treatment plans.

Transdiagnostic Model

A CBT protocol has also been developed for application across the EDs, including EDNOS. After an extensive initial evaluation, treatment consists of four stages (Fairburn et al., 2008):

Stage 1

This stage includes orientation to treatment, psychoeducation, the introduction of weekly weigh-ins, and scheduled eating, and the collaborative creation of a diagram that depicts a hypothesized formulation of the maintaining processes of the ED. Self-monitoring of events, behaviors, thoughts, and feelings is introduced and continued throughout treatment. In this stage, treatment sessions are twice weekly. Significant others, including family members or partners, are included in up to three treatment sessions (Fairburn et al., 2008).

Stage 2

The goal of this phase of treatment is for the therapist and patient to recognize pros and cons of the disorder, identify barriers to change, assess progress, and alter the theorized formulation. An individualized plan for Stage 3 is designed. Sessions in this phase consist of two weekly sessions.

Stage 3

The focus of this stage is targeting the maintaining mechanisms of the disorder, consisting of eight weekly sessions. Depending on the individualized treatment plan, goals include targeting dietary restriction, binge eating, being underweight, and the overevaluation of shape and weight, using interventions such as self-monitoring, cognitive restructuring, and problem solving (Fairburn et al., 2008).

Stage 4

In this final stage, treatment focuses on maintenance and long-term relapse prevention, consisting of three biweekly sessions across 6 weeks.

Evaluation of Treatment Outcomes

EDs are often egosyntonic, with patients experiencing ambivalence about recovery. These individuals often present as lacking in assertiveness and experience shame about their symptoms and/or their lack of desire for recovery, which can both lead to inaccurate reporting on the part of the patient. Therefore, it is crucial that clinicians not rely on self-reports alone in evaluating treatment outcomes. Other obvious data sources include reports from significant others such as parents or significant others, change in global functioning, and objective markers such as weight and lab work. Evaluating a patient's treatment outcome is predicated upon the previously established treatment goals and time lines. Such evaluation should not only include ED symptomology, but the patient's level of functioning across social and academic/professional domains. Given the high relapse rate for EDs, long-term follow-up is essential. Even when initial treatment goals are achieved, routine monitoring by the treatment team is essential in achieving the goal of relapse prevention. Some experts have included a posttreatment review appointment several months after treatment to review progress and assess current functioning (e.g., Fairburn et al., 2008).

Considerations With Special Populations

Children

Because of distinct developmental and ethical considerations, it is important to differentiate the assessment and treatment of EDs in children and adolescents from their adult counterparts. The examination of young children with EDs has received less attention in the clinical literature because its presentation in pediatric settings is less common than older youth. Because children present with a wide range of eating disturbance (Bryant-Waugh, 2000), linking disordered eating with both body image disturbance and fear of weight gain becomes complicated. AN has been described in patients as young as 7 years old (Bostic, Muriel, Hack, Weinstein, & Herzog, 1997), and although a clear diagnostic presentation of anorexia or bulimia is rare in pediatric settings (Rosen, 2003), a preoccupation with weight, body image, and eating is not (Ambrosi-Randic, 2000; Dohnt & Tiggeman, 2005; Kotler, Cohen, Davies, Pine, & Walsh, 2001).

When children present with eating and weight disturbance, a clinician must first consider a wide range of both physical and emotional conditions. Medical and mental health clinicians working in primary care settings must be alert for evidence of abuse or trauma that suggests the eating disturbance represents a child's reaction to acute stress. Gathering information critical toward an accurate diagnosis can be complicated in children. Cognitively, children present with formal operations thinking that inhibits their level of self-awareness and abstract thinking. Although an adolescent may have insight into her thoughts, emotions, and behaviors, and thus be able to provide essential information for diagnosis, such self-report in children may be severely limited. Consequently, conceptualization of the presenting problem depends greatly on parent observation. The astute clinician pays particular attention to any discrepancies that arise among self-report, family report, and clinical observation. That such patients are often characterized as "great kids" who are polite, hardworking, conscientious, perfectionistic, and high achieving may further complicate assessment. Food avoidance may be inconspicuous to family members, as these individuals often take great measures to hide and dispose of their food. Such features, although important in understanding the disposition of these patients, contribute to family ambivalence toward diagnosis and treatment.

Childhood-onset anorexia includes weight loss, food avoidance, and a preoccupation with weight (Bryant-Waugh & Lask, 2002). In rare cases, vomiting and laxative abuse are also evident (Peebles, Wilson, & Lock, 2006). Presenting symptoms generally include nausea, abdominal pain, poor appetite, loss of energy, and even difficulty swallowing (Nicholls & Stanhope, 2000). The development of lanugo, hypotension, bradycardia, poor peripheral circulation with skin discoloration, and cold extremities may also be evident (Nicholls & Stanhope).

Children do not precisely fit into the ED diagnostic categories established by the *Diagnostic and Statistical Manual of Mental Disorders* (*DSM-IV-TR*; APA, 2000). For example, determining a patient's expected weight is challenging for the developing child. For those children who do present as significantly underweight, identifying body dissatisfaction and fear of weight gain as the core pathological feature can be tenuous. Additionally, the absence of menses obviously cannot be considered as pathological in children. Because of these complex features, EDs in children are often misdiagnosed (Rosen, 2003). In contrast to older ED patients, young ED patients are more likely to be male (20–25% of referrals; Bryant-Waugh & Lask, 2002) with a higher rate of comorbid psychiatric diagnoses (5–10% of cases; Rosen). Compared with adolescents, younger patients are less likely to report binging, purging, and laxative use; more likely to be diagnosed with EDNOS; weigh less in percentage of IBW; and lose weight more rapidly (Peebles et al., 2006).

Adolescents

The onset of puberty in adolescent girls results in dramatic changes in body shape and composition, adding an average of 24 lbs. (10.9 kg) of body fat (Warren, 1983). This *fat spurt* in adolescence, combined with a media-driven and body-conscious culture, has been shown to influence the development of unhealthy dieting, body-image disturbance, negative social comparison, and low self-esteem (Tiggeman & Slater, 2004). In fact, adolescence is considered a critical time for the development of disordered eating, and recent research has focused on identifying specific biological, social, and psychological risk factors. For example, girls who mature earlier are at greater risk to report body dissatisfaction and eating problems (Graber, Brooks-Gunn, Paikoff, & Warren, 1994). Having family members and peers who exhibit disordered eating behavior (modeling) has been associated with concurrent bulimic symptoms, and is predictive of later onset of binge eating and purging (Stice, 1998). High externalized self-perceptions, self-reported teasing, and the perceived importance of weight and shape for popularity have been shown to predict body esteem and eating behavior (Lieberman, Gauvin, Bukowski, & White, 2001). EDs have been associated with chaotic home environments with low perceived parental caring, poor family communication, and high parental expectations (Polivy & Herman, 2002). Patients with EDs generally describe a critical home environment with coercive parental control (Haworth-Hoeppner, 2000). Thorough conceptualization and treatment of an adolescent with an ED must consider relevant biological, social, familial, and psychological features.

Current trends toward evidence-based treatments emphasize family involvement as a fundamental instrument for behavioral change. Surprisingly, there is a dearth of quality research regarding the effectiveness of psychosocial interventions for children and adolescents with EDs. In the absence of established research, current treatment approaches extrapolate from adult findings. The Society for Adolescent Medicine has published a position paper on EDs in adolescents, recommending that psychological interventions for EDs include the mastery of the developmental tasks of adolescence (Kreipe et al., 1995). With that in mind, all treatment approaches should consider helping the patient strengthen developmentally appropriate coping skills. Family therapy for AN currently represents a well-established intervention for adolescents (Keel & Haedt, 2008), and CBT represents a well-established treatment for BN in late adolescent/young adult females (Keel & Haedt). Regardless of current differences in theory-based psychotherapy, best practice for the treatment of ED in adolescents calls for a multidisciplinary approach that uses medical management, nutrition counseling, and individual and family psychotherapy (Rome & Ammerman, 2003).

Males

Males generally account for only 5–10% of those diagnosed with anorexia (Sharp, Clark, Dunan, Blackwood, & Shapiro, 1994) and 10–15% of those diagnosed with bulimia (Carlat, Carmago, & Herzog, 1997; Garfinkel et al., 1995). Such data may underestimate the prevalence of EDs in males, and it has been speculated that EDs in males are only considered when significant psychiatric comorbidity is present (Bramon-Bosch, Troop, & Treasure, 2000). Males may be less likely to disclose insecurities about their own bodies and are significantly less likely to seek treatment (Olivardia, Pope, Mangweth, & Hudson, 1995). The challenge for clinicians is to create a safe environment and normalize the presence of body image concerns in males.

The general clinical presentation of men and women with EDs is similar (Bramon-Bosch et al., 2000). Men, however, generally present in clinical settings as less concerned with attaining a specific goal weight or clothing size, and are more concerned with attaining an idealized masculine shape with large shoulders, muscular chest, and narrow hips and waist (Anderson, 1984). Current research now suggests that clinicians should not only look to rule out EDs in male patients, but body dysmorphic disorder, as well (Harvey & Robinson, 2003). Available evidence also suggests that males involved in sports or occupations that value weight control and/or body shape display an increased risk for the development of disordered eating (Braun, Sunday, Huang, & Halmi, 1999). Additionally, clinicians should be aware that approximately 3–5% of men in the general population are homosexual, and there appears to be a higher prevalence of EDs among men who are homosexual (20%; Andersen, 1999). Bi/homosexuality has been suggested as a specific risk factor for BN and EDNOS, though such data are preliminary and largely correlational (e.g., C. J. Russell & Keel, 2002).

Athletes

The Academy of Pediatrics has urged physicians to educate their patients about the dangers of overexercising, prolonged fasting, vomiting, and illicit drug use in sports such as body building, distance running, diving, figure skating, gymnastics, horse racing, swimming, and wrestling (American Academy of Pediatrics, Committee on Sports Medicine Fitness, 1996). The current athletic culture has been implicated as a risk factor for the development of disordered eating and unhealthy weight practices (Petrie & Rogers, 2001). This proclamation is supported by many coaches' often erroneous belief that weight loss improves performance (Griffin & Harris, 1996). Also, the tremendous pressure for victory and high standards for competition sends a distinct message that achievement is valued above health (Petrie & Rogers). The current sports culture reinforces symptoms synonymous with an ED, reframing them as positive attributes essential for success. For example, excessive exercise, denial of pain, and rigid pursuit of perfection define a, "great athlete" (Thompson & Sherman, 1999). With this in mind, clinicians responsible for the treatment of ED in athletes must consider coaches and athletic trainers as integral members of the multidisciplinary team. Five critical suggestions for collaboration with the patient's coaches and trainers have been recommended (Thompson & Sherman). Coaches and trainers should: (a) deemphasize weight as essential for success; (b) avoid publicly weighing athletes; (c) eliminate commonly accepted, but unhealthy sports practices (e.g., "cutting weight" in wrestling); (d) develop individualized training programs for athletes that emphasize health, not weight; and (e) control competiveness regarding weight and size.

Cultural Considerations

EDs have been commonly characterized as illnesses that are largely influenced by cultural norms that emphasize appearance and achievement, occurring predominantly in affluent White/European women. Research clearly indicates that EDs occur across ethnically and socio-economically diverse populations (Crago, Shisslak, & Estes, 1996), including undeveloped countries (e.g., Becker et al., 2002). Therefore, culturally competent assessment and intervention should acknowledge differences in symptom presentation and expression of distress within a cultural context. Examining all the potential differences among various cultures is beyond the scope of this chapter. However, it is important for clinicians to incorporate skilled diagnostic questions that consider individual cultural differences. A thorough cognitive-behavioral case conceptualization incorporates the culturally based origins of core beliefs about food, body image, and achievement, and their impact on functioning.

Clinical Pearls of Wisdom for Practitioners

This chapter should serve as a valuable resource for multidisciplinary clinicians in primary care interested in the screening, evaluation, conceptualization, and cognitive-behavioral treatment of EDs. To that end, the following "clinical pearls of wisdom" are offered.

1. Ask for patients' permission to speak with family members, given the unreliability of self-report of ED symptomology (e.g., "I'm fine!").
2. Consider weighing patients with anorexia in a hospital gown, as patients may attempt to artificially inflate weight (placing heavy items in bras and underwear, etc.). Similarly, clinicians may need to be alert to "water loading" in patients with AN in order to artificially inflate their weight. For those patients who purge, dramatic swings in weight may be due to fluid shifts. Clinicians may consider unscheduled or "pop" weigh-ins as appropriate.
3. Clinically, it is helpful to examine maintaining environmental factors of the disorder. For example, is the ED serving to keep divorced parents closer and more attentive, or does the disorder allow the patient to indirectly communicate anger toward parents or punish them?
4. Maintaining rapport and a therapeutic alliance is challenging with patients who may be characterized, at best, as ambivalent about recovery. One clinical technique that is often useful is to separate the patient from the ED. The clinician then strongly aligns with the patient while giving the ED its own (malevolent) identity (e.g., "The ED is telling you that you are nothing without him, but the ED is a liar. Look at all the ED has taken away from you"). The ED can be likened to a "bad boyfriend" who is hard to leave. This "bad boyfriend" has even been personified as "Ed" (acronym of "Eating Disorder") in a popular account of recovery from an ED, *Life Without Ed* (Schaefer & Rutledge, 2003).
5. Providers treating patients with serious AN and/or BN would be wise to be informed about guardian law in the states in which they practice, as such

action may be ethically necessary in treating those patients who are no longer minors but are too incapacitated to make their own medical decisions.

6. Treatment of EDs often involves working with family members to alter contingencies around eating-disordered behaviors. Clinicians are well advised to prepare family members to anticipate an, "extinction burst" (an expected temporary increase in frequency of behaviors before extinction) after they institute such modifications. Otherwise, family members may perceive that treatment is only making the individual's ED worse and prematurely terminate treatment.
7. On a final note, we urge practitioners to strive to maintain not just compassion, but empathy for these patients. Individuals with EDs often believe that their eating disorder is actually the one thing that is going well in their lives. The disorder provides a refuge from aversive emotional states and overwhelming developmental challenges; it never abandons them. Truly appreciating how and why the patient would not want to willingly let go of the eating disorder is invaluable in establishing and maintaining the therapeutic alliance essential to successful treatment.

References

Ambrosi-Randic, N. (2000). Perception of current and ideal body size in preschool age children. *Perceptual and Motor Skills, 90*, 885–889.

American Psychiatric Association. (2000). *Diagnostic and statistical manual of mental disorders* (4th ed., text rev.). Washington, DC: Author.

American Psychiatric Association (2006). *American Psychiatric Association practice guidelines for the treatment of patients with eating disorders* (3rd ed.). Washington, DC: American Psychiatric Association.

American Academy of Pediatrics, Committee on Sports Medicine and Fitness. (1996). Promotion of healthy weight-control practices in young athletes. *Pediatrics, 97*, 752–753.

Anderson, A. E. (1999). Gender-releated aspects of eating disorders: A guide to practice, *Journal of Gender Specific Medicine, 2*(1), 47–54.

Anderson, E. A. (1984). Anorexia nervosa and bulimia in adolescent males. *Pediatric Annals, 13*, 901–907.

Banasiak, S. J., Paxton, S. J., & Hay, P. J. (2005). Guided self-help for bulimia nervosa in primary care: A randomized controlled trial. *Psychological Medicine, 35*, 1283–1294.

Beck, A. T. (1976). *Cognitive therapy and the emotional disorders*. New York: International Universities Press.

Becker, A. E., Burwell, R. A., Gilman, S. E., Herzog, D. B., & Hamburg, P. (2002). Eating behaviours and attitudes following prolonged exposure to television among ethnic Fijian adolescent girls. *British Journal of Psychiatry, 180*, 509–514.

Biddle, S. J., & Fox, K. R. (1998). Motivation for physical activity and weight management. *International Journal of Obesity and Related Metabolic Disorders, 22*, 39–47.

Bostic, J. Q., Muriel, A. C., Hack, S., Weinstein, S., & Herzog, D. (1997). Anorexia nervosa in a 7-year-old girl. *Developmental and Behavioral Pediatrics, 18*, 331–333.

Bramon-Bosch, E., Troop, N. A., & Treasure, J. L. (2000). Eating disorders in males: A comparison with female patients. *European Eating Disorders Review, 8*, 321–328.

Braun, D. L., Sunday, S. R., Huang, A., & Halmi, K. A. (1999). More males seek treatment for eating disorders. *International Journal of Eating Disorders, 25*, 415–424.

Bryant-Waugh, R. (2000). Overview of the eating disorders. In B. Lask & R. Bryant-Waugh (Eds.), *Anorexia nervosa and related eating disorders in childhood and adolescence* (2nd ed., pp. 27–40). East Sussex, UK: Psychology Press.

Bryant-Waugh, R., & Lask, B. (2002). Childhood-onset eating disorders. In C. G. Fairburn & K. D. Brownell (Eds.), *Eating disorders and obesity: A comprehensive handbook* (2nd ed., pp. 210–214). New York: Guilford.

Burke, B. L., Arkowitz, H., & Dunn, C. (2002). The efficacy of motivational interviewing and its adaptations: What we know so far. In W. R. Miller & S. Rollnick (Eds.), *Motivational interviewing: Preparing people for change* (2nd ed., pp. 217–250). New York: Guilford.

Burke, B. L., Arkowitz, H., & Menchola, M. (2003). The efficacy of motivational interviewing: A meta-analysis of controlled clinical trials. *Journal of Consulting and Clinical Psychology, 71*, 843–861.
Cahn, S. C. (2006). *Case example.* Unpublished manuscript.
Carlat, D. J., Camargo, C. A., & Herzog, D. B. (1997). Eating disorders in males: A report on 135 patients. *American Journal of Psychiatry, 154*, 1127–1132.
Crago, M., Shisslak, C. M., & Estes, L. S. (1996). Eating disturbances among American minority groups: A review. *International Journal of Eating Disorders, 19*, 239–248.
Davidson, M. H., Hauptman, J., DiGiorolamo, M., Foreyt, J. P., Halsted, C. H., Heber, et al. (1999). Weight control and risk factor reduction in obese subjects treated for 2 years with orlistat: A Randomized controlled trial. *Journal of the American Medical Association, 281*(3), 235–242.
Davis, C., Shuster, B., Blackmore, E., & Fox, J. (2004). Looking good: Family focus on appearance and the risk for eating disorders. *International Journal of Eating Disorders, 35*, 136–144.
Derisley, J., & Reynolds, S. (2000). The transtheoretical stages of change as a predictor of premature, attendance and alliance in psychotherapy. *British Journal of Clinical Psychology, 39*, 371–382.
Dohnt, H., & Tiggeman, M. (2005). Peer influences on body image and dieting awareness in young girls. *British Journal of Developmental Psychology, 23*, 103–116.
Eisler, I., Dare, C., Russell, G. F. M., Szmukler, G. I., le Grange, D., & Dodge, E. (1997). Family and individual therapy in anorexia nervosa: A 5-year follow-up. *Archives of General Psychiatry, 54*, 1025–1030.
Fairburn, C. G. (1995). *Overcoming binge eating.* New York: Guilford.
Fairburn, C. G. (2008). *Cognitive behavior therapy and eating disorders.* New York: Guilford.
Fairburn, C. G., Cooper, Z., & Shafran, R. (2003). Cognitive behaviour therapy for eating disorders: A "transdiagnostic" theory and treatement. *Behaviour Research and Therapy, 41*(5), 509–528.
Fairburn, C. G., Cooper, Z., Shafran, R., & Wilson, G. T. (2008). Eating disorders: A transdiagnostic protocol. In D. H. Barlow (Ed.), *Clinical handbook of psychological disorders: A step-by-step treatment manual* (pp. 578–614). New York: Guilford.
Fairburn, C. G., Walsh, B. T., Agras, W. S., Wilson, G. T., & Stice, E. (2004). Early change in treatment predicts outcome in bulimia nervosa. *American Journal of Psychiatry, 161*, 2322–2324.
Garfinkel, P. R., Lin, E., Goering, P., Spegg, C., Goldbloom, D. S., Kennedy, S., et al. (1995). Bulimia nervosa in a Canadian community sample: Prevalence and comparison of subgroups. *American Journal of Psychiatry, 152*, 1052–1058.
Garner, D. M., Olmsted, M. P., Bohr, Y., & Garfinkel, P. E. (1982). The eating attitudes test: Psychometric features and clinical correlates. *Psychological Medicine, 12*, 871–878.
Graber, J. A., Brooks-Gunn, J., Paikoff, R. L., & Warren, M. P. (1994). Prediction of eating problems: An 8-year study of adolescent girls. *Developmental Psychology, 30*, 823–834.
Griffin, J., & Harris, M. B. (1996). Coaches' attitudes, knowledge, experiences, and recommendations regarding weight control. *Sport Psychologists, 10*, 180–194.
Grilo, C. M., & Masheb, R. M. (2005). A randomized controlled comparison of guided self-help cognitive behavioral therapy and behavioral weight loss for binge eating disorder. *Behaviour Research and Therapy, 43*, 1509–1525.
Harvey, J. A., & Robinson, J. D. (2003). Eating disorders in men: Current considerations. *Journal of Clinical Psychology in Medical Settings, 10*, 297–305.
Hauner, H., Meier, M., Wendland, G., Kurscheid, T., Lauterbach, K., & The S.A.T. Study Group. (2004). Weight reduction by sibutramine in obese subjects in primary care medicine: The S.A.T. study. *Experimental and Clinical Endocrinology & Diabetes, 112*, 201–207.
Haworth-Hoeppner, S. (2000). The critical shapes of body image: The role of culture and family in the production of eating disorders. *Journal of Marriage and Family, 62*, 212–227.
Hudson, J. I., Hiripi, E., Pope, H. G., Jr., & Kessler, R. C. (2007). The prevalence and correlates of eating disorders in the National Comorbidity Survey Replication. *Biological Psychiatry, 61*, 348–358.
Johnston, O., Fornae, G., Cabrini, S., & Kendrick, T. (2007). Feasibility and acceptability of screening for eating disorders in primary care. *Family Practice, 24*(5), 511–517.
Keel, P. K., Dorer, D. J., Eddy, K. T., Franko, D., Charatan, D. L., & Herzog, D. B. (2003). Predictors of mortality in eating disorders. *Archives of General Psychiatry, 60*, 179–183.
Keel, P. K., & Haedt, A. (2008). Evidence-based psychosocial treatments for eating problems and eating disorders. *Journal of Clinical Child & Adolescent Psychology, 37*, 39–61.
Klump K. L., Bulik, C. M., Kaye, W. H., Treasure, J., & Tyson, E. (2009). Academy for eating disorders position paper: Eating disorders are serious mental illnesses. *International Journal of Eating Disorders, 42*(2), 97–103.

Kondo, D. G., & Sokol, M. S. (2006). Eating disorders in primary care: A guide to identification and treatment. *Postgraduate Medicine, 119*(3), 59–65.

Kotler, L. A., Cohen, P., Davies, M., Pine, D. S., & Walsh, T. B. (2001). Longitudinal relationships between childhood, adolescent, and adult eating disorders. *Journal of the American Academy of Child and Adolescent Psychiatry, 40*, 1434–1440.

Kreipe, R. E., Golden, N. H., Katzman D. K., Fisher, M., Rees, J., Tonkin, R. S., et al. (1995). Eating disorders in adolescents: A position paper of the Society for Adolescent Medicine. *Journal of Adolescent Health, 16*, 476–479.

le Grange, D., Louw, J., Breen, A., & Katzman, M. A. (2004). The meaning of 'self-starvation' in impoverished black adolescents in South Africa. *Culture, Medicine & Psychiatry, 28*, 439–461.

Lieberman, M., Gauvin, L., Bukowski, W. M., & White, D. R. (2001). Interpersonal influence and disordered eating behaviors in adolescent girls: The role of peer modeling, social reinforcement, and body-related teasing. *Easting Behaviours, 2*(3), 215–236.

Lock, J., & le Grange, D. (2005). Family-based treatment of eating disorders. *International Journal of Eating Disorders, 37*, 64–67.

Matsunaga, H., Kiriike, N., Iwasaki, Y., Miyata, A., Yamagami, S., & Kaye, W. H. (1999). Clinical characteristics in patients with anorexia nervosa and obsessive compulsive disorder. *Psychological Medicine, 29*, 407–414.

Miller, W. R., & Rollnick, S. (2002). *Motivational interviewing: Preparing people for change* (2nd ed.). New York: Guilford.

Milosevic, A. (1999). Tooth surface loss: Eating disorders and the dentist. *British Dental Journal, 186*, 109–113.

Mitchell, J. E., Crosby, R. D., Wonderlich, S. A., Crow, S., Lancaster, K., Simonich, H., et al. (2008). A randomized trial comparing the efficacy of cognitive–behavioral therapy for bulimia nervosa delivered via telemedicine versus face-to-face. *Behaviour Research and Therapy, 46*, 581–592.

Morgan, J. F., Reid, F., & Lacey, J. H. (1999). The SCOFF questionnaire: Assessment of a new screening tool for eating disorders. *BMJ, 319*, 1467–1468.

National Institute for Clinical Excellence. (2004). *Eating disorders: Core interventions in the treatment and management of anorexia nervosa, bulimia nervosa and related eating disorders* (clinical guideline no. 9). London, U.K.: Author. Available at www.nice.org.uk/guidance/CG9

Nicholls, D., & Stanhope, R. (2000). Medical complication of anorexia nervosa in children and young adults. *European Eating Disorders Review, 39*, 800–805.

Olivardia, R., Pope, H. G., Jr., Mangweth, B., & Hudson, J. I. (1995). Eating disorders in college men. *American Journal of Psychiatry, 152*, 1279–1285.

Peebles, R., Wilson, J. L., & Lock, J. D. (2006). How do children with eating disorders differ from adolescents with eating disorders at initial evaluation. *Journal of Adolescent Health, 39*, 800–805.

Petrie, T. P., & Rogers, R. (2001). Extending the discussion of eating disorders to include men and athletes. *Counseling Psychologist, 29*, 743–753.

Polivy, J., & Herman, C. P. (2002). Causes of eating disorders. *Annual Review of Psychology, 53*,187–214.

Pritts, S. D., & Susman, J. (2003). Diagnosis of eating disorders in primary care. *American Family Physician, 67*(2), 297–304.

Prochaska, J. O., & DiClemente, C. C. (1983). Stages and processes of self-change of smoking: Toward and integrative model of change. *Journal of Consulting and Clinical Psychology, 51*, 390–395.

Prochaska, J. O., & DiClemente, C. C. (1986). Toward a comprehensive model of change. In W. R. Miller & H. Nick (Eds.), *Treating addictive behaviors: Process of change* (pp. 3–27). New York: Plenum Press.

Prochaska, J. O., DiClemente, C. C., & Norcross, J. C. (1992). In search of how people change: Applications to the addictive behaviors. *American Psychologist, 47*, 1102–1114.

Prochaska, J. O., DiClemente, C. C., Velicer, W. F., & Rossi, J. S. (1993). Standardized, individualized, interactive and personalized self-help programs for smoking cessation. *Health Psychology, 12*, 399–405.

Prochaska, J. O., Redding, C. A., & Evers, K. E. (2002). The transtheoretical model and stages of change. In K. Glanz, B. K. Rimer, & F. M. Lewis (Eds.), *Health behavior and health education: Theory, research, and practice* (pp. 60–84). San Francisco: Jossey-Bass.

Rome, E. S., & Ammerman, S. (2003). Medical complications of eating disorders: An update. *Journal of Adolescent Health, 33*, 418–426.

Rosen, D. S. (2003). Eating disorders in children and young adolescents: Etiology, classification, clinical features, and treatment. *Adolescent Medicine, 14*, 49–59.

Russell, C. J., & Keel, P. K. (2002). Homosexuality as a specific risk factor for eating disorders in men. *International Journal of Eating Disorders, 31*(3), 300–306.

Russell, G. F. M., Szmukler, G. I., Dare, C., & Eisler, I. (1987). An evaluation of family therapy in anorexia nervosa and bulimia nervosa. *Archives of General Psychiatry, 44*, 1047–1056.

Schaefer, J., & Rutledge, T. (2003). *Life without Ed: How one woman declared independence from her eating disorder and how you can too.* New York: McGraw-Hill.

Sharp, C., Clark, S., Dunan, J., Blackwood, D., & Shapiro, C. (1994). Clinical presentation of anorexia nervosa in males: 24 new cases. *International Journal of Eating Disorders, 15*, 125–134.

Steinhausen, H.-C. (2002). The outcome of anorexia nervosa in the 20th century. *American Journal of Psychiatry, 159*, 1284–1293.

Sterling, G. (2008). Insurer agrees to $1.2M settlement in anorexia lawsuit. *Newark Star-Ledger.* Retrieved April 15, 2009, from http://www.nj.com/news/index.ssf/2008/11/insurer_agrees_to_12m_settleme.html

Stice, E. (1998). Modeling of eating pathology and social reinforcement of the thin-ideal predict onset of bulimic symptoms. *Behaviour Research and Therapy, 36*, 931–944.

Striegel-Moore, R. H., DeBar, L., Wilson, G. T., Dickerson, J., Rosselli, F., Perrin, N. F., et al. (2008). Health services use in eating disorders. *Psychological Medicine, 38*(10), 1465–1474.

Thompson, R., & Sherman, R. T. (1999). Athletes, athletic performance, and eating disorders: Healthier alternatives. *Journal of Social Issues, 55*, 317–337.

Tiggeman, M., & Slater, A. (2004). Thin ideals in music television: A source of social comparison and body dissatisfaction. *International Journal of Eating Disorders, 35*, 48–58.

Vitousek, K., Watson, S., & Wilson, G. T. (1998). Enhancing motivation to change in treatment resistant eating disorders. *Clinical Psychology Review, 18*, 391–420.

Walsh, B. T. (2007). DSM-V from the perspective of the DSM-IV experience. *International Journal of Eating Disorders, 40*(S3), S3–S7.

Walsh, B. T., Fairburn, C. G., Mickley, D., Sysko, R., & Parides, M. K. (2004). Treatement of bulimia nervosa in a primary care setting. *American Journal of Psychiatry, 161*, 556–561.

Warren, M. P. (1983). Physical and biological aspects of puberty. In J. Brooks-Gunn & A. C. Peterson (Eds.), *Girls at puberty: Biological and psychosocial perspectives* (pp. 3–28). New York: Plenum Press.

Williams, P. M., Goodie, J., & Motsinger, C. D. (2008). Treating eating disorders in primary care. *American Family Physician, 77*(2), 187–195, 196–197.

Wilson, G. T., Grilo, C. M., & Vitousek, K. M. (2007). Psychological treatment of eating disorders. *American Psychologist, 62*(3), 199–216.

Young, J. E., & Klosko, J. S. (1994). *Reinventing your life.* New York: Penguin.

Young, J. E., Klosko, J. S., & Weishaar, M. E. (2003). *Schema therapy: A practitioner's guide.* New York: Guilford.

Part IV

Clinical Problems II: Common Medical Problems in Primary Care

Essential Hypertension

24

Robert A. DiTomasso
Deborah Chiumento
Harry J. Morris

Introduction

Hypertension, the silent killer, is a serious, asymptomatic, prevalent, and major public health problem commonly found in the primary care setting. The number of affected individuals is expected to increase over the next several years. Worldwide, hypertension is the third leading risk factor contributing to death (Campbell et al., 1999). The Joint National Committee on Prevention, Detection, Evaluation, and Treatment of High Blood Pressure (1997) recently reported that hypertension impacts 50 million people in the United States alone, with about a billion individuals affected worldwide. The American Heart Association (2006) found that hypertension was a primary or contributing disease in over a quarter of a million deaths in the year 2003. It is also one of the most robust predictors of cardiovascular status and events (Messerli, 2003).

Hypertension, or high blood pressure, is defined as having chronically elevated systolic blood pressure (SBP) of 140 mmHg or greater, diastolic blood pressure (DBP) of 90 mmHg or greater, or taking antihypertensive medication (Blumenthal, Sherwood, Gullette, Georgiades, & Tweedy, 2002). Systolic blood pressure, or SBP, the top number, reflects the peak pressure in the arteries during the cardiac cycle. Diastolic blood pressure, or DBP, the bottom number, is the lowest pressure measured at the resting phase of the cardiac cycle. The cardiac cycle is the sequence of events that occurs as the heart works to pump blood through the body. An individual's DBP increases only until about age 60, but SBP continues to increase with age (Campbell et al., 1999). Hypertension is associated with serious health consequences (Kochaneck, Smith, & Anderson, 2001).

The exact etiology of essential hypertension has been cause for speculation for many years and, to date, remains unknown. Hypertension is categorized as either primary (unknown etiology) or secondary (resulting from a number of causes). A myriad of factors contribute to the onset of this condition. Genetic and environmental factors, specifically psychosocial factors such as stress, personality, and behavior have been shown to play a role in the development of hypertension (Schwartz, Pickering, & Landsbergis, 1996), and in individual cases, may constitute risk factors for hypertension. Although pharmacologic interventions are the treatment of choice, there is reason to believe that these are not always effective in all cases, and problems related to cost and side effects may undermine adherence (Blumenthal, Sherwood, LaCaille, Georgiades, & Goyal, 2005).

The treatment of hypertension is usually initiated with a medication from one of the following classes: diuretics, beta blockers, angiotensin-converting enzyme inhibitors, angiotensin II receptor blockers, renin blockers, calcium channel blockers, alpha-adrenergic antagonists, or peripheral adrenergic antagonists. If the blood pressure goal is not met with the use of the primary medication, then a combination of drugs is commonly used, taking into consideration which agents are compatible and the degree of the patient's hypertension, age, race, and medical comorbidities, such as diabetes or ischemic heart disease.

The complications of uncontrolled hypertension can be serious, and may lead to death or disability due to myocardial infarction, coronary artery disease, heart failure, cerebrovascular accident, cerebral hemorrhage, left ventricular hypertrophy, transient ischemic attacks, peripheral vascular disease, aortic regurgitation, atrial flutter, and atrial fibrillation (Kochanek, Smith, & Anderson, 2001).

Hypertension is related to serious health problems, such as diabetes and obesity. Coupling hypertension with these problems results in an increased risk for morbidity. The incidence in hypertension appears to be rising, and is cause for alarm. Medical treatments and management of psychosocial factors may be helpful in warding off the onset of the condition or controlling it once a diagnosis is made.

The prevalence of hypertension is related to age, gender, and ethnicity (Blumenthal et al., 2002). The incidence of hypertension increases with age. In young adults, the diagnosis of hypertension is much greater in men than in women; however, this trend reverses at around 50 years of age to a greater prevalence in women than in men (Burt et al., 1995). Hypertension is also seen more commonly among the Black population as compared with Americans of European heritage (Hall, Brands, Dixon, & Smith, 1993).

Given the morbidity and mortality associated with hypertension (Hall et al., 1997), more research is needed to clarify the relationship between biopsychosocial factors and this serious disease. The biopsychosocial model (Engel, 1977) provides a comprehensive approach for addressing important factors that may be related to hypertension. Understanding the relationship between lifestyle habits, social support, and biological factors in hypertension may, then, help to provide important information related to its assessment and treatment in three critical spheres of patient functioning. The biopsychosocial model provides a useful vehicle for gaining valuable information in relevant domains of the patient's functioning.

Assessment and Diagnostic Issues

In assessing the hypertensive patient, the cognitive-behavioral therapy (CBT) clinician must work collaboratively with the primary care physician (PCP). A thorough consideration of a number of important factors of relevance to the measurement of blood pressure and related lifestyle characteristics that are likely to impact the patient's blood pressure must be addressed. In this section, we carefully review a number of areas of consideration for assessment.

The measurement, assessment, and diagnosis of essential hypertension are obviously within the purview of the PCP. Therefore, patients being seen in conjunction with the cognitive-behavioral clinician will typically have already been diagnosed at the time of referral or consultation. The physician will have already taken the steps necessary to ensure ruling out possible secondary causes for hypertension and establishing the accuracy of the diagnosis.

Physicians employ a standard protocol for conducting this process, including an extensive medical and family history, averaging blood pressure readings across a number of occasions, and assessment of blood pressure using an acceptable method. The JNC 7 recommends that blood pressure be assessed with the patient quietly seated in a chair with feet on the floor having rested for at least five minutes. The patient should refrain from caffeine, tobacco, and exercise at least 30 minutes before BP assessment. The sphygmomanometer must be properly calibrated, and the cuff must be sized to properly fit the arm of the patient. The BP should be determined at least twice and the results averaged.

The blood pressure measurement consists of two numbers: the systolic (upper) number and the diastolic (lower) number. The BP cuff is inflated to a pressure at least 20 mmHg above the systolic pressure in the arm, which effectively occludes arterial blood flow below the cuff. The pressure in the cuff is slowly decreased (2 mmHg/second) and the SBP is determined to be the point at which two or more pulses are heard (Korotkoff sounds). The disappearance of sound is the DBP.

Office assessment by clinical staff may overestimate blood pressure. This phenomenon of "white coat" hypertension may be corrected by the use of an ambulatory blood pressure monitoring device, assessing blood pressure over a 24-hour period and averaging the results. This has been shown to be a better assessment of blood pressure (Franklin, Sutton-Tyrell, Belle, Weber, & Kuller, 1997). However, a more practical approach may be to have the patient intermittently self-monitor BP at home and work using a traditional syphgmomanometer.

The role of the CBT clinician will involve an assessment of the patient from a biopsychosocial perspective. Although the medical standard of treatment for these patients is pharmacotherapy, the CBT provider will focus on those factors that contribute to and maintain the problem. A thorough assessment much in line with what Belar and Deardorff (2009) have proposed is indicated, including the physical, cognitive, social, psychological, affective, and behavioral components.

For hypertensive patients, the clinician would be wise to focus on specific, important areas within each domain. In the physical realm, the clinician should consider factors such as the age, gender, race, and weight of the patient. Because the incidence of hypertension is higher in certain demographic populations, a consideration of such factors may prove helpful in identifying patients at higher risk for hypertension. In the cognitive realm, the clinician should examine variables related to patient knowledge and understanding of the disease, health beliefs and conceptions, and self-efficacy. In the social arena, the availability and degree of social support is important to consider, as well as specific cultural factors that may contribute to the patient's understanding and beliefs about hypertension and dietary considerations. Habits including diet, physical activity, eating patterns, and sodium, alcohol, caffeine, nicotine, and coping strategies are also important to consider. In the psychological and affective areas, a review of potential issues such as anxiety, depression, anger, hostility, dysfunctional thinking, and stress levels should be examined. To gather these assessment data, the clinician should conduct a clinical interview and supplement this information with self-monitored data about critical lifestyle habits from the patient. The use of standardized measures within each domain, such as the Millon Behavior Medicine Diagnostic (MBMD; Millon, 1982), the Beck Depression Inventory (Beck, Steer, & Brown, 1996), the Beck Anxiety Inventory (Beck & Steer, 1993), the CAGE Questionnaire for alcohol screening (Ewing, 1984), and the RAGS drug use screening questions followed (Levin et al., 1999), when indicated, by the ASSIST (Newcombe, Humeniuk, & Ali, 2005), can be very useful. Excess alcohol consumption may be related to hypertension, as regular daily consumption of 1 or 2 drinks per day increases risk in women. In hypertensives, there is a relatively modest effect on blood pressure when consumption is decreased (Al'Absi & Hoffman, 2003). In general, hypertensives who consume alcohol should limit their drinking; hypertensives who are not already drinking should refrain from beginning to do so (Al'Absi & Hoffman).

Anxiety

Anxiety appears to be more common in patients with cardiovascular disorders than in the general population (Rozanski et al., 1999). These cardiovascular disorders include coronary artery disease, hypertension, and chronic obstructive pulmonary disorder, which, in turn, can lead to stroke and heart attack (myocardial infarction), which can ultimately lead to death. According to Wei and Wang (2006), patients with anxiety may have an increased incidence of cardiovascular disease, such as hypertension. However, it is difficult to ascertain whether anxiety symptoms make blood pressure worse, or if blood pressure makes anxiety symptoms worse for hypertensive patients. Wei and Wang (2006) have postulated that individuals with anxiety disorders are prone to unhealthy lifestyle behaviors such as smoking, which may adversely influence the medication for hypertension. Because anxiety is such a common problem in this population, anxiety should be assessed in these individuals and monitored and managed as well.

Social Support

There are some other factors associated with hypertension to consider. Social support plays a critical role in the development or prevention of hypertension.

Social support refers to a network of individuals, for example, family, friends, and neighbors who are available for help in times of psychological, physical, or financial distress. Social support is a psychosocial factor that may be viewed as a buffer to development of hypertension. Research from Carels, Blumenthal, and Sherwood (1998) indicates that the presence of social support and the perceived satisfaction with social support is associated with lower blood pressure. Individuals who have a social support network upon which they can depend in times of stress tend to have lower blood pressure, and are better equipped to handle stress in a positive way. Individuals who do not have such a social support network tend to internalize their stress and cope negatively with life situations. Possibly, this internalizing coping mechanism may prevent the individual from expressing the stress, and therefore, he/she is left to deal with it alone. This tendency can exacerbate a negative physiological reaction, such as an increase in blood pressure that perhaps, over time, may develop into hypertension. For example, one way in which increased social support is beneficial against the development of coronary heart disease and hypertension is through the ability to reduce cardiovascular arousal associated with psychological stress (Carels et al.). The threat of being alone is not present for those with social support networks and they perceive their stressful situations as less threatening because of the network on which they can depend. These individuals feel that if they "share" their stress with others they are able to reduce it.

Caffeine

Caffeine is another variable of potential importance for assessment. Because elevated blood pressure is a risk factor for the development of cardiovascular disease and may be exacerbated by regular consumption of coffee (caffeine) (Rakic, Burke, & Lawrence, 1999), patients who consume high levels of caffeine should be evaluated. Caffeine grows naturally in the leaves of plants *and* is a central nervous system stimulant that causes arousal, alertness, increased heart rate, and wards off drowsiness temporarily. Over 90% of Americans consume caffeine products every day; caffeine is frequently found in tea, coffee, cola, energy drinks, chocolate, and over-the-counter medications. In moderate amounts, caffeine can ward off drowsiness and increase mental alertness, but in higher doses caffeine can cause anxiety and jitters, and can interfere with normal sleep patterns. Caffeine can be so highly addictive that withdrawal symptoms can be experienced in those who abruptly stop caffeine consumption. The American Psychiatric Association's *Diagnostic and Statistical Manual of Mental Disorders (DSM-IV-TR*; American Psychiatric Association, 2000) includes four caffeine-related disorders: *caffeine intoxication, caffeine-induced anxiety disorder, caffeine-induced sleep disorder*, and *caffeine-related disorder not otherwise specified*. Included within the *caffeine intoxication* category is a sign that relates to the physiological response of caffeine: tachycardia or cardiac arrhythmia. Tachycardia occurs when the heart beats too quickly at rest. Tachycardia usually only occurs during exercise or physical exertion as a response, but this is considered physiologically normal. One can understand how caffeine intoxication can cause tachycardia, and the implications this may have on one's blood pressure and onset of hypertension.

Rakic et al. (1999) studied the effects of caffeinated coffee on blood pressure in older men and women. Their findings, consistent with other research on caffeine intake and blood pressure, showed increased ambulatory blood pressure in hypertensive patients drinking five cups of coffee per day, compared with abstainers. They found a significant effect of coffee drinking relative to abstinence in hypertensive individuals, with a decrease in blood pressure during abstinence and an increase during coffee drinking. Ambulatory SBP and DBP were affected, both of which decreased when abstaining from coffee and increased when consuming coffee. It was also noted that switching to decaffeinated coffee equaled the same benefit as abstaining from caffeinated coffee altogether. This study concluded that some restriction of regular coffee intake may be an effective way to prevent and/or manage hypertension and blood pressure.

Smoking

Blood pressure and heart rate increase during smoking, and these effects are specifically associated with nicotine (Journath et al., 2005). According to Cryer, Haymond, Santiago, and Shah (1976), smoking has been shown to induce an acute rise in blood pressure in normotensive smokers. Sorensen et al. (2004) studied the effects of smoking on blood pressure in hypertensive smokers and hypertensive nonsmokers. They found a significant difference in ambulatory SBP and DBP between smokers and nonsmokers. The hypertensive smokers' blood pressures were significantly higher than those of the hypertensive nonsmokers. Along with elevated blood pressure, there was increased heart rate, both of which are risk factors for cardiovascular disease, specifically hypertension.

A study conducted by Journath et al. (2005) examined whether hypertensive smokers exhibit a worse cardiovascular risk profile, including higher SBP and DBP, than nonsmokers. One of their assumptions is that smoking (nicotine intake) may negatively interact with the pharmacological actions of antihypertensive medications, making them less potent. Another assumption, psychological in nature, is that smokers may differ from nonsmokers in general attitude, behavior, and personality, which may affect blood pressure. The researchers argue that smokers may be less compliant with drug treatment, and recommended smoking cessation for hypertensive and normotensive patients.

Anger and Hostility

Anger and hostility expression have also been viewed as factors in cardiovascular disease. Siegler, Peterson, Barfoot, and Williams (1992) reported that hostility as measured by the Minnesota Multiphasic Personality Inventory (MPPI; Hathaway et al., 2000) has been found to predict elevated rates of coronary heart disease and mortality from all causes. In regard to hypertension, Ricci Britti, Gremigni, Bertolotti, and Zotti (1995) have noted, "Anger and hostility have long been noted important factors in the etiology of essential hypertension and coronary heart disease" (p. 162). In their study of essential hypertensives, coronary heart disease patients, and controls, in which they examined the effects of anger and hostility, the results underscore the need to assess components of anger and hostility in these patient groups. Work by Eng, Fitzmaurice, Kubansky, Rimm, and Kawachi (2003) and Everson, Goldberg, Kaplan, Julkunen, and Salonen (1998) support the relationship between the construct of anger and hypertension. The data support the need to assess these constructs in hypertensive patients.

Adherence

Although the standard medical treatment for hypertension is medication, in view of the potential side effect profile of these drugs, the question of adherence must always be considered. Adherence to medication regimens constitutes only one aspect of this assessment.

Lifestyle Habits

Other important factors that can contribute to hypertension involve lifestyle habits, such as dietary habits (including nutritional choices, sodium intake), physical activity, and weight, all of which must be addressed. Diet can be easily assessed through a food and caloric self-monitoring intake form, similar to that used in the LEARN program (Brownell, 2004), with a focus on high-caloric, fatty, and empty-calorie foods. Chart reviews of weight and calculations of body mass index (BMI) are readily available from patient charts if the CBT clinician is working on site. The assessment of diet and weight is supported by Al'Absi and Hoffman (2003), who report that weight reductions ranging from 3 to 9% of body weight yield SBP and DBP reductions of 3.0 to 6.8 mmHg and 2.9 to 5.7 mmHg, respectively. Further, Oparil (2000) found that in weight-loss studies that permitted medication adjustments in hypertensives, greater weight loss was associated with need for lower dosages and use of fewer blood pressure medications.

Sodium

Another area for assessment is sodium intake, as certain patients, specifically older adults, African Americans, and type 2 diabetics may be sensitive to the effects of salt. Excess sodium may exert its negative influence on blood pressure by expanding blood volume, increasing the workload on the heart muscle, and accumulating in cells. Although some individuals are sensitive to sodium (salt) intake, it is generally accepted that reducing sodium intake is appropriate for most individuals, especially those needing antihypertensive medication (Sacks et al., 2001).

The Dietary Approaches to Stop Hypertension (DASH) diet has been shown to have a positive influence on blood pressure. The DASH diet is high in dietary fiber, moderate in total fat and protein, and low in saturated fat, dietary cholesterol, and sodium. It emphasizes increased fruits, vegetables, whole grains, low-fat dairy products, legumes, nuts, seeds, and lean meats (Appel et al., 1997).

Psychiatric Comorbidities

Finally, assessment of hypertensive patients for psychiatric comorbidities may also be important for a number of reasons. First, psychological problems may interfere with adherence to medication regimens. Second, problems such as depression may undermine a patient's motivation to engage in prescribed lifestyle habit changes. Third, there is an association between anxiety and hypertension (Wei & Wang, 2006). It is conceivable in certain cases that the physiological arousal associated with anxiety states may complicate and exacerbate hypertension and its treatment.

In summary, whereas there is no identifiable marker for hypertensive patients in the office, there are a number of associated characteristics that may set the stage for identifying potential patients. These individuals include the obese, the physically inactive, salt-sensitive people with high sodium intake, consumers of large quantities of caffeine, smokers, and patients who are either anxious or hostile. Assessment data from these measures can be used as a basis for supporting diagnostic determinations and formulating a case conceptualization, but most importantly, for identifying key target areas for treatment planning.

Incidence and Clinical Manifestations in Primary Care Setting

In addressing the incidence of hypertension, over 43 million Americans are hypertensive, with less than one third of them attaining adequate control (Al'Absi & Hoffman, 2003). Hypertension is particularly common among those individuals who are obese, consume alcohol, and are of African American descent (Al'Absi & Hoffman). The prevalence of hypertension is related to age, gender, and ethnicity (Blumenthal et al., 2002). The incidence of hypertension also increases with age. In young adults, the diagnosis of hypertension is much greater in males than females; however, this reverses at about 50 years of age, with a greater prevalence observed in women (Burt et al., 1995). Hypertension is also seen more frequently among the Black population as compared with Americans of European heritage (Hall et al., 1997).

In terms of common clinical presentations, there is no identifiable indicator per se. Hypertensive patients do not typically walk into their PCP's office complaining of hypertension. The asymptomatic nature of this problem is unlike many other medical problems in which a complaint of the patient may trigger him/her to seek medical care. For example, in diabetic patients, increased urination and thirst may signal the patient that something is wrong. There are no such clues with hypertension, which is, in large part, why many patients never seek medical care, and as a result, go untreated. Many hypertensives are identified through routine screenings by their physicians during office visits. Of course, when one considers the risk factors for hypertension, including weight and physical inactivity, it is these problems that may be indirect signs of patients at risk. Therefore, the clinician should be vigilant for possible factors that are highly associated with hypertension.

Brief Case History

John is a 45-year-old divorced African American male who presented for treatment at a primary care center. He is the father of three young teenage children and is currently in a relationship with a divorced attorney who has one small child of her own. He is a regional manager for a large auto manufacturer, who has recently been under increased stress because of the current financial and economic downturn. His job stress has increased, as well as has his demand for additional travel and increased work hours, which have negatively affected his relationship with his children and girlfriend. John recently was forced to fire several of his subordinate coworkers because their required monthly numbers for production were not met. This has caused further stress for John, because these subordinates were friends as well as colleagues.

The usual lifestyle to which John has been accustomed is now threatened. The private gated community has become too expensive to afford because of cutbacks within his company's infrastructure. His work expense account has been substantially reduced, which no longer allows for the extra perks and lavish luxuries to which he was accustomed. He is now questioned about his weekly expense reports and receipts by his superiors, which previously had never been an issue. John has become angry and resentful because of the increased job stress and threat to his personal lifestyle. Recent dismal sales have markedly reduced his income and perpetuated both personal and professional stress.

Historically, John has had significant problems with anger, both in his personal and professional relationships. The increased pressure from the corporate executives at his company to increase demands on dealers to ultimately produce higher numbers and profits have led to extra stress for John and has increased his anger. During a recent performance management evaluation, the National Vice President for Sales criticized John openly at a meeting. John verbally retaliated at the Vice President and was subsequently formally reprimanded by a letter placed in his personnel file.

After this episode and months of unbearable stress, John increased negative health behaviors and decreased positive and established health habits. He has been diagnosed with hypertension for the past 12 years, and has always been adherent to the prescribed medication regimen, as well as the prescribed exercise and nutrition. He had always been physically active and used the gym within his gated community. John usually ate very healthy foods and shopped in expensive organic food stores, rarely eating fast food or eating on the run. His alcohol use had always been moderate, usually only social drinking—wine with colleagues at national business meetings, dinners, and the like. He always kept his doctor appointments, wellness visits, obtained all prescribed medications promptly, and scheduled any diagnostic tests or blood/lab work when indicated by his physician to do so.

More recently, John has been less adherent to his prescribed medication, exercise, and nutrition regimens because of his increased stress and demands at work. John has been spending his time after work at the local bar to "blow off steam," rather than at the gym. Instead of his usual preference for wine, he is consuming four to five beers at the bar, more often than not during the week. His usual hefty work expense allotment has been cut, which has thwarted his efforts for purchasing healthful foods at the grocery store. Now, in an attempt to save money and keep within his new budget, he eats fast food on the run. This not only saves him money, but saves time too, as he needs to travel more often and further away from home as as result of increased work demand for higher production numbers dictated by corporate. In addition, he has been late on alimony payments to his ex-wife and has been threatened by her with an attorney if he does not pay in a more timely manner. This has ignited his anger even more, causing him to be short-fused with colleagues, his children, and his girlfriend, all of whom are already strained in their relationship with him.

These negative lifestyle changes have caused John to gain 10 pounds over the past 3 months. His most recent visit to his physician indicated not only the unhealthy weight gain, but also a blood pressure reading that is in the Stage II category. The physician inquired about the recent unhealthy changes. John admitted to his recent stressors and anger resulting in his consumption of more alcohol, reduced physical activity, and eating fast foods. The physician stated that John needs to manage his stress, reduce anger, cut back on the fast foods and beer, and reinitiate his previous healthy habits. However, John feels angered and frustrated by this suggestion because his increased work demands and salary cutback inhibit both of these recommendations.

Cognitive-Behavioral Case Conceptualization

In conducting the cognitive-behavioral case conceptualization of this patient, we have used Persons' cognitive-behavioral approach (2008). John's chief complaint centers around his hypertension, which had previously been better controlled by medication alone. He had always had a positive relationship with his children and fiancée, who served as a source of social support. He also had a reputation as a team player and positive force with corporate management. Much of the reinforcement he obtained in his life was derived from his job. In the past, he had a strong investment in self-preservation by engaging in a strict exercise regimen and diet.

John's problem list includes uncontrolled hypertension, weight gain, poor diet, excessive use of alcohol, increased job and family stressors, and decreased social support. His problematic feelings include anger outbursts, irritability, anxiety over work-related problems, low frustration tolerance, guilt over having to terminate loyal subordinates, depression, and hopeless feelings. Socially, he is experiencing increasing conflicts with his fiancée and supervisors, which has heightened his level of stress and anxiety. From a health behavior standpoint, he is nonadherent with his diet and exercise regimen, is consuming a high volume of caffeinated beverages and alcohol, and has been consuming foods high in fat, calories, and sodium.

A sample of John's automatic thought list reveals a variety of themes related to loss, threat, pessimism, unjust treatment, catastrophization, and negative attributions. His thoughts include, "My boss is trying to get rid of me; they have no right to cut my expense allowance; I can't take any more of this; this treatment isn't fair and I don't deserve it; things will never get any better for me; I'll lose my job, my kids, & my fiancée." These thoughts fueled his negative feelings and behavior, increased his unhealthy lifestyle habits, and contributed to his medical problems. His automatic thoughts emerged from several underlying assumptions and core beliefs. These schema centered around threat, perfection, and poor self-efficacy. Samples of these schema include, "When things don't go the way I expect,

I must defend myself at all costs; if things don't go perfectly for me, my life will spin out of control; when bad things happen, they'll continue to happen; there's nothing I can do to solve my problems; and, If I don't defend myself, I'll lose everything I have."

The relationship of the mechanism to John's problems reveals several interesting points. A number of profound triggering events precipitated his strongly held underlying beliefs about perfectionism, injustice, vulnerability, and threat that set into motion a number of related automatic thoughts that essentially fueled his anger and anxiety, sense of urgency, and his defensive acting out behavior. Concurrently, his underlying pessimistic beliefs created hopeless feelings and depression, which undermined his adherence to health-promoting behaviors, increased negative coping behaviors, and increased his arousal, all of which may have contributed to his uncontrolled hypertension. Precipitating events were volatile changes in the financial markets that have adversely affected sales, increased unrealistic expectations from his superiors, criticisms of his current performance, cutbacks on his expense accounts and bonuses, and the need to terminate coworkers.

The origins of the central problem appear to include having grown up in a household where he learned hard work pays off and is rewarded. John's parents were both successful professionals who were driven and valued a strong work ethic; they expected nothing less than perfection in him. He learned that he had to stand up for himself and defend himself to secure his position and to achieve his goals.

Potential predicted obstacles to treatment include John maintaining his pessimistic stance in the face of an unstable economy. Also, because hypertension is not visible, there is the risk that John will continue to dismiss the fact that his condition is worsening and place himself at risk for serious medical consequences. Other factors include the continuing time pressures and increased demands at work and traveling, which undermine his diet and exercise regimen. Without proper coping strategies, there is the risk that his self-medication with alcohol will continue.

Based on the above conceptualization, a multifaceted, cognitive-behavioral treatment plan was developed for John:

1. Assess stages of change to identify John's readiness for making the substantial changes required to help himself.
2. Conduct motivational interviewing as a means to motivate him to address these problems and to help him progress to the planning, action, and maintenance stages.
3. Ask John to purchase a home blood pressure monitoring kit and contract with him to measure his blood pressure twice per day at the same time each day under ideal conditions.
4. Train John in the use of his blood pressure kit.
5. Educate him about the need to address key target areas related to his hypertension, including weight, diet, exercise, sodium, alcohol, and management of stressors.
6. Teach self-monitoring strategies for his diet, weight, exercise, alcohol intake, dysfunctional thoughts, stressors, and stress levels.
7. Institute a behavioral program (LEARN) to foster weight loss.
8. Develop an exercise plan and gradually titrate his level of physical activity.

9. Restrict sodium intake through implementation of the DASH program.
10. Obtain a commitment from John to reduce alcohol consumption.
11. Institute graduated additions to physical activity (LEARN—30 minutes of moderate-intensity physical activity at least 5 days/week).
12. Employ specific behavioral strategies to reduce his drinking to acceptable recommended levels;
13. Implement a multicomponent cognitive-behavioral stress management intervention, including cognitive restructuring, communication training and problem solving, awareness of high-risk situations and associated somatic responses, anger management, and relaxation strategies.

Identifying and Addressing Obstacles to Treatment

In working with hypertensives there are a variety of potential barriers to treatment. Al'Absi and Hoffman (2003) has recommended consideration of a number of factors that require attention, including the silent nature of hypertension, medication side effects, unique characteristics of patients, contributory lifestyle habits, complexity of the medication regimen, and lack of social support. First, the asymptomatic nature of hypertension creates a challenge, in that, unless systematically measured in the home environment, the patient's level of blood pressure remains unknown, and therefore cannot provide a focal point for adherence. Patients may not, then, benefit from recognizing the relationship between their efforts and the outcomes of their efforts to manage this disease. Patients should consequently have regular follow-up with their physician and be encouraged to monitor, record, and provide their physician with an on-going log of their blood pressures. Second, negative side effects of hypertensive medication may thwart efforts on the part of the patient to follow the prescribed medication regimen. Clinicians should inquire about known side effects of medication, and be prepared to discuss these with the patient's physician, when indicated. Third, the level of severity of the disease, stage 1, 2, or 3, dictates the importance of immediate intervention and the possible severe consequences of nonadherence. The more advanced the stage, the more imminent the treatment needs to be. The CBT clinician must, therefore, be prepared to recognize and act to access immediate medical care, when indicated. Fourth, the identification and treatment of lifestyle habits that impact blood pressure must be considered. Treatment with medication alone may not be adequate to offset the health risks associated with hypertension, as many of these factors necessitate cognitive and behavioral intervention. Fifth, the complexity of the medication regimen may undermine the effective implementation of the treatment. The CBT clinician should inquire about the possible negative impact of number, dosages, and timing of medications as potential contributors to nonadherence. Finally, the absence of or inadequate level of available social support must be examined. Given the nature, type, and breadth of behavioral changes that hypertensive patients often need to make in their lives, social support can be a critical ingredient in successful management.

Points of Collaboration With Physician and Family

CBT clinicians must work effectively and collaboratively with PCPs to coordinate effective care of hypertensive patients. Helping the physician understand the value of proactively addressing the obstacles and potential barriers reinforces the necessity of planning beforehand, as opposed to dealing with failure afterward. To do this effectively, requires that the clinician be thoroughly aware of specific issues related to assessment, monitoring, and ongoing treatment of this problem. Whereas PCPs routinely obtain blood pressure measurements during patient visits, what happens during and after the patient visit may affect whether the patient engages in the requisite behaviors to manage the problem. Working with the medical provider to reinforce the attitudinal and behavioral changes being made by the patient are important, as a partial means of sustaining positive health behaviors. For example, getting a patient to lose weight involves more than just giving the patient a diet to follow. However, there is evidence to suggest that simply employing an organized approach to review and follow-up of patients coupled with antihypertensive medication seems to be a useful method of controlling elevated blood pressure (Fahey, Schroeder, & Ebrahim, 2006). Working closely with physicians to educate them about the complex nature of promoting and maintaining changes in diet and weight, and offering empirically based options for patient care, have a more positive likelihood of success. The CBT clinician must also be aware that using these adjunctive treatments may decrease the need for medication.

Physicians routinely prescribe antihypertensive medications to control high blood pressure. The clinician should, therefore, be on the alert for adverse effects, as well as patient attributions about side effects of medicines. As experts in pharmacotherapy, PCPs are in a better position to evaluate the likelihood that a side effect reported by a patient is valid. Keeping the physician in the information loop is essential in this regard. Likewise, a patient may be less inclined to report an actual and embarrassing side effect of a medication (e.g., impotence), and may need systematic encouragement to do so.

Identifying patients in whom stress might play a significant role should be considered. Patients who are high in trait and state anxiety, coupled with poor coping skills, as well as angry and hostile patients, are ideal candidates for referral to the CBT clinician. Finally, for the nonadherent patient, a review of suggestions offered by DiTomasso, Chiumento, Singer, and Bullock (see chapter 14) in this volume may be very helpful in this regard.

Collaborating with family members is also important in the treatment of hypertension. The CBT clinician must be aware of and assess the level, if any, of involvement of the patient's family in his/her life and habits. This is especially important in regard to the necessary behavior change required after a diagnosis of hypertension is made. An examination of factors that contribute to hypertension reveals that there are many areas in which the family typically has involvement. The family and support system of the newly diagnosed patient can be influential and integral to the patient's new behavior changes. Emphasizing the need for social support is essential, and will likely assist in fostering better adherence and relieve distress in the patient. The family can also serve to support and reinforce health-promoting behaviors such as diet, nutrition, and meal planning, with regard to types of foods served, eating out at restaurants, and limiting salt in food preparation. Family members may also serve an important role in encouraging physical activity and exercise by partnering with the hypertensive patient. The concept of teaming up with the patient by engaging in exercise together may help to establish motivation, consistency, and show support.

The notion of using family members for involvement and support may serve to create a healthier and more adherence-friendly environment. Education on the value of family involvement should be provided by the CBT clinician. In this vein, it would be helpful to arrange for the patient to log current nutrition, meals, and physical activity, as well as that of the family, to determine where changes are necessary. Resources and a rationale for reducing alcohol consumption, sodium, fat, excess calories, and helpful cooking ideas can be provided here. Families may also be helpful in establishing a newly prescribed regimen, maintaining an already established regimen, assisting in providing reminder cues to the patient about taking prescribed medication, refilling prescriptions, keeping and making appointments, and daily self-monitoring of blood pressure levels.

Development and Implementation of Empirically Based Treatment Plan

To develop an effective treatment plan for the hypertensive requires careful review of published, available outcome research in this area. Cognitive-behavioral approaches clearly have a place in the treatment of the hypertensive. In summarizing interventions for hypertensives, Sperry (2009) has emphasized relevant findings of the Seventh Report of the Joint National Committee on Prevention, Detection, Evaluation, and Treatment of High Blood Pressure (Chobanian et al., 2003) in this way: "It is noteworthy that the committee emphasized the role of psychological interventions, including lifestyle change, as a significant component of combined or integrated hypertension treatment and prevention...Exercise, relaxation exercises and diet modifications are standard elements of these protocols" (p. 211).

For patients who are overweight, there is a vast literature in behavior therapy focusing on weight loss and maintenance. One primary example is Brownell's LEARN program (2004), which is a multicomponent program focusing on assisting patients in changing lifestyle habits, exercise patterns, attitudes about food and relevant matters, relationships, and nutrition. This 12-session group program incorporates education, self-monitoring strategies, monitoring caloric intake and weight, the use of stimulus-control strategies, techniques to increase and maintain physical activity, the use of social supports, reinforcement of habits that are incompatible with problematic behaviors, dealing with high-risk situations, coping with emotional eating triggers, the association of food with cultural beliefs, techniques for increasing physical activity and programmed exercise, increasing positive attitudes, dealing with dysfunctional attitudes, and relapse prevention. This program yields on average a 1–2-pound weight loss per week throughout the program. Brownell (2004) reports a decrease in blood pressure associated with a 10% overall decrease in body weight.

Al'Absi and Hoffman (2003) describe findings from several weight-loss studies of hypertensive patients supporting associated declines in blood pressure. For example, they indicate that weight loss ranging from 3 to 9% of body weight with medication dosages held stable, yield approximately a 3.0–6.8 mmHg decline in SBP, accompanied by DBP decreases between 2.9–5.7 mmHg. Oparil (2000) reported weight reduction may be associated with the need for lower dosages and less antihypertensive medications in patients who lost weight, compared with those who did not. In an exhaustive review of the literature years earlier, DiTomasso (1987) reported a similar phenomenon related to the use of relaxation-based interventions in hypertensives, suggesting overall that psychological interventions may be associated with a decreased need for medication.

Exercise is recommended several times per week, for a period ranging from half to three fourths of an hour as a means of lowering blood pressure (Al'Absi & Hoffman, 2003). Eisenberg and colleagues (1993) evaluated the impact of cognitive-behavioral therapies including biofeedback, meditation, the relaxation response, progressive muscle relaxation, and stress management in 26 studies, comparing it with a no-treatment control group, wait list control group, regular monitoring, or placebo. They concluded that CBT interventions are superior to no therapy, but were no different than sham therapy or self-monitoring. A relevant report from the *Cochrane Database of Systematic Reviews* provided by Dickinson and colleagues (2008) provides useful information related to the utility of progressive muscle relaxation, cognitive-behavioral therapies, and biofeedback in reducing blood pressure, although they could not rule out the effect of frequent professional helpers for the relaxation treatment. They also reported that meta-analytic findings demonstrated small, statistically significant average decreases of 5.5 mmHg systolic and 3.5 mmHg diastolic. Others (DiTomasso, 1987) have claimed that multicomponent stress-management protocols are more effective in decreasing blood pressure than unimodel relaxation treatments. Multicomponent treatment protocols have standard cognitive-behavioral strategies, including becoming mindful of stressors, recognizing signs of arousal, strategies designed to alter mood, cognitive restructuring, relaxation, anger interventions, and problem solving (Spence, Barnett, Linden, Ramsden, & Taenzer, 1999).

Studies aimed at evaluating the impact of reduced salt intake/sodium intake to approximately 90–130 millimoles daily by helping hypertensives to make better food choices, such as foods that are low in salt, and to avoid those that are high in salt, dietary approaches to stop hypertension (DASH), are encouraging. Vollmer et al. (2001) found that patients who limited salt intake and used the DASH diet benefitted by SBP decreases between 7–12 mmHg, and about 5-mmHg declines in DBP.

Promoting reduced alcohol intake in hypertensives appears to yield smaller effects. Al'Absi and Hoffman (2003) concluded the following in this regard: "Although these effects are modest, a dose response relationship was observed between mean percentage of alcohol reduction and mean BP reduction. Regardless of the modest reductions in BP with concomitant alcohol reduction, available guidelines suggest that hypertensive nondrinkers should continue to abstain from consuming alcohol"(p. 260). They further recommend that hypertensives should limit alcohol intake to a maximum of 1 ounce daily.

In sum, combining a number of cognitive-behavioral strategies aimed at specific targets may prove beneficial in the treatment of the hypertensive patient.

Evaluation of Treatment Outcomes

The evaluation of treatment outcomes is inherently tied to the target areas selected for intervention. Most important, the major question here revolves around whether, and the extent to which, the patient's level of blood pressure has been reduced by a clinically significant amount. Support for the continuation of a treatment plan, and a measure of success, is seen when the patient exhibits change on the primary target, in this instance, blood pressure, as evidenced by a change in level or stage. Improvement on other secondary measures may also be considered in the outcome of treatment. For example, changes in weight, cholesterol level, BMI, self-monitored changes in lifestyle habits and risk behaviors, and daily levels of arousal are important to consider. The need for a reduction in medication may also provide evidence, albeit indirect, that the treatment plan is working. The validity, reliability, standardization, timing, and related self-monitored information may also be useful in determining the effectiveness of the treatment plan. Collecting relevant information over time from baseline, during treatment, and follow up is indicated.

Considerations With Special Populations/ Diversity Issues

Special consideration should be given to identifying hypertension in selected groups. Hajjar and Kotchen (2003) have reported that the highest rates of hypertension are evident in older people, females, and Blacks of non-Hispanic heritage. About 33% of African American patients are afflicted with this condition (Burt et al., 1995). It is also seen more frequently among the Black population as compared with Americans of European heritage (Hall et al., 1993). Furthermore, evidence also suggests that hypertension begins at a younger age in African Americans and that overall, it is more severe when it does occur (Al'Absi & Hoffman, 2003). For these reasons, the CBT clinician should be especially aware of the possibility of hypertension in these patient groups, and approach patients in these groups accordingly, with careful screening and coordination of care with the PCP. The relationship between culture and certain foods, and the meanings surrounding food in given cultures, must be carefully considered, as well.

Clinical Pearls of Wisdom for Practitioners

1. Hypertension is a silent killer and very serious problem that should be approached with care and caution, and requires careful and effective collaboration with a PCP.
2. All hypertensive patients should receive a complete education about this condition, including its risks and the necessity of treatment and consideration for pharmacotherapy, when indicated by the PCP.

3. Given the variety of factors that contribute to and exacerbate hypertension, the CBT clinician should conduct a broad and through assessment in areas known to affect hypertension, such as diet, weight, sodium intake, stress, alcohol use, smoking, caffeine use, psychopathology, and level of physical activity.
4. Hypertensive patients should be followed regularly and closely, with a special focus on target areas and adherence.
5. Hypertensive patients should be trained to regularly monitor and record blood pressures outside of the office.
6. The CBT clinician should consider using multicomponent treatment packages including relevant components that are tailored for the individual patient.

References

Al'Absi, M., & Hoffman, R. G. (2003). Hypertension. In L. M. Cohen, D. E. McChargue, & F. L. Collins (Eds.) *The health psychology handbook: Practical issues for the behavioral medicine specialist* (pp. 252–278). Thousand Oaks, CA: Sage.

American Heart Association. (2006). *Heart disease and stroke statistics-2006 update.* Retrieved September 15, 2009, from http://www.americanheart.org/downloadable/heart/1140534985281Statsupdate06book.pdf

American Psychiatric Association. (2000). *Diagnostic and statistical manual of mental disorders* (4th ed., text revision). Washington, DC: Author.

Appel, L. J., Moore, T. J., Obarzanek, E., Vollmer, W. M., Svetkey, L. P., Sacks, F. M., et al. (1997) A clinical trial of the effects of dietary patterns on blood pressure. *New England Journal of Medicine, 336* (16), 1117–1124.

Beck, A. T., & Steeer, R. A. (1993). *Beck Anxiety Inventory Manual.* San Antonio, TX: Psychological Corporation.

Beck, A. T., Steer, R. A., & Brown, G. K. (1996). *Beck Depression Inventory II Manual.* San Antonio, TX: Psychological Corporation.

Belar, C. D., & Deardorff, W. W. (2009). *Clinical health psychology in medical settings: A practitioner's guidebook* (2nd ed.). Washington, DC: American Psychological Association.

Blumenthal, J., Sherwood, A., Gullette, E. C. D., Georgiades, A., & Tweedy, D. (2002). Biobehavioral approaches to the treatment of essential hypertension. *Journal of Consulting and Clinical Psychology, 70*(3), 569–589.

Blumenthal, J. A., Sherwood, A., LaCaille, L., Georgiades, A., & Goyal, T. (2005). Lifestyle approaches to the treatment of hypertension. In N. A. Cummings, W. T. O'Donohue, & E. V. Naylor (Eds.), *Psychological approaches to chronic disease management.* Reno, NV: Context Press.

Brownell, K. D. (2004). *The LEARN program for weight management* (10th ed.). Dallas, TX: American Health Publishing.

Burt, V. L., Cutler, J. A., Higgins, M., Horan, M. J., Labarthe, D., Whelton, P., et al. (1995). Trends in the prevalence, awareness, treatment, and control of hypertension in the adult US population. *Hypertension, 26*, 60–69.

Campbell, N. R. C., Burgess, E., Taylor, G., Wilson, E., Cleroux, J., Fodor, J. G., et al. (1999). Lifestyle changes to prevent and control hypertension: Do they work? *Canadian Medical Association Journal, 160*(9), 1341–1344.

Carels, R. A., Blumenthal, J. A., & Sherwood, A. (1998). Effect of satisfaction with social support on blood pressure in normotensive and borderline hypertensive men and women. *International Journal of Behavioral Medicine, 5*(1), 76–85.

Chonabian, A. V., Bakris, G. L., Black, H. R. , Cushman, W. L., Green, L. A. Izzo, J. L., et al. (2003). Committee on Prevention, Detection, Evaluation and Treatment of High Blood Pressure. *Journal of the American Medical Association, 289*(19), 2560.

Cryer, P. E., Haymend, M. W., Santiago, J. V., & Shsam, S. D. (1976). Norepinephrine and epinephrine release and adrenergic medication of smoking associated haemodynamic and metabolic events. *New England Journal of Medicine, 295*, 573–577.

Dickinson, H. O., Campbell, F., Beyer, F. R., Nicolson, D. J., Cook, J. V., Ford, G. A., et al. (2008). Relaxation therapies for the management of primary hypertension in adults. *Cochrane Database of Systematic Reviews*, 1Art. No.: CD004935. DOI: 10.1002/14651858.CD004935.pub2

DiTomasso, R. A. (1987). Essential hypertension: A methodological review. In L. Michaelson & L. M. Ascher (Eds.), *Anxiety and stress-related disorders*. New York: Guilford.

DiTomasso, R. A., Chiumento, D., Singer, M. S., & Bullock, O. (2010). Nonadherence in primary care. In R. D. DiTomasso, B. A. Golden, & H. J. Morris (Eds.) *Handbook of cognitive-behavioral approaches in primary care* (pp. 291–315). New York: Springer Publishing Company.

Eisenberg, D. M., Delbanco, T. L., Berkey, C. S., Kaptchuk, T. J., Kupelnick, B., Kuhl, J., et al. (1993). Cognitive behavioral techniques for hypertension: Are they effective? *Annals of Internal Medicine, 118*, 964–972.

Eng, P. M., Fitsmaurice, G., Kubansky, L. D., Rimm, E. B., & Kawachi, I. (2003). Anger expression and risk of stroke and coronary disease among male health professionals. *Psychosomatic Medicine, 65*, 100–110.

Engel, G. L. (1977). The need for a new medical model: A challenge for biomedicine. *Science, 186*, 129–136.

Everson, S. A., Goldberg, D. E., Kaplan, G. A., Julkunen, J., & Salonen, J. T. (1998). Anger expression and incident hypertension. *Psychosomatic Medicine, 60*, 6, 730–735.

Ewing, J. A. (1984). Detecting alcoholism: The CAGE Questionnaire. *Journal of the American Medical Association, 252*(14), 1905–1907.

Fahey, T., Schroeder, K., & Ebrahim, S. (2006). Interventions used to improve control of blood pressure in patients with hypertension. *Cochrane Database of Systematic Reviews*, 4 Art. No.: CD005182. DOI: 10.1002/14651858.CD005182.pub3.

Franklin, S. S., Sutton-Tyrrell, K., Belle, S. H., Weber, M. A., & Kuller, l. H. (1997). The imporatance of pulsatile components of hypertension in predicting carotid stenosis in older adults. *Journal of Hypertension, 15*(10), 1143–1150.

Hajjar, I., & Kotchen, T. (2003). Tends in prevalence, awareness, treatment and control of hypertension in the United States, 1998-2000. *Journal of the American Medical Association, 289*, 2560–2572.

Hall, J. E., Brands, M. W., Dixon, W. N., & Smith, M. J. (1993). Obesity-induced hypertension. *Hypertension, 22*, 292–299.

Hathaway, S. R., McKinley, J. C., Meehl, P. E., Drake, L. E., Welsh, G. S., & MacAndrew, C. (2000). Construction of the original MMPI. In J. N. Butcher (Ed.), *Basic sources on the MMPI-2* (pp. 1–100). Minneapolis, MN: University of Minnesota Press.

Joint National Committee on Detection, Evaluation, and Treatment of High Blood Pressure. (1997). The sixth report of the Joint National Committee on Prevention, Detection, Evaluation, and Treatment of High Blood Pressure. *Archives of Internal Medicine, 157*, 2413–2446.

Journath, G., Nilsson, P. M., Petersson, U., Paradis, B., Theobald, H., & Erhardt, L. (2005). Hypertensive smokers have a worse cardiovascular risk profile than non-smokers in spite of treatment—A national study in Sweden. *Blood Pressure, 14*, 144–150.

Kochanek, K. D., Smith, B. L., & Anderson, R. N. (2001). Deaths: Preliminary data for 1999. *National Vital Statistics Reports, 49*(3), 32–33.

Levin, C., Sobell, L. Cleland, P., Ellingstad, T., Sobell, M., Toll, B., et al. (1999). *RAGS: A new brief drug abuse screening instrument*. Poster session presented at the annual convention of the Association for Advancement of Behavior Therapy.

Messerli, F. H. (2003). Hypertension. In R. E. Rakel & E. T. Bope (Eds.), *Conn's current therapy, 2003* (pp. 353–372). New York: Elsevier Science.

Millon, T. (1982). *Millon Behavioral Health Inventory Manual.* Minneapolis, MN: National Computer Systems.

Newcombe, D. I., Humeniuk, R. E., & Ali, R. (2005). Validation of the World Health Organization Alcohol, Smoking, and Substance Involvemenet Screening Test (ASSIST): Report of results from the Australian site. *Drug Alcohol Review, 24*, 217–226.

Oparil, S. (2000). Arterial hypertension. In R. L. Cecil, J. C. Bennett, & L. Goldman (Eds.), *Cecil textbook of medicine* (21st ed., pp. 258–273). Philadelphia: W. B. Saunders.

Persons, J.B. (2008). *The case formulation approach to cognitive-behavior therapy: Guides to individualized evidence-based treatment.* New York: Guilford.

Rakic, V., Burke, V., & Lawrence, J. B. (1999). Effects of coffee on ambulatory blood pressure in older men and women. *Hypertension, 33*(3), 869–873.

Ricci Bitti, P. E., Gremigni, P., Bertolotti, G., & Zotti, A. M. (1995). Dimensions of anger and hostility in cardiac patients, hypertensive patients, and controls. *Psychotherapy and Psychosomatics, 64*(3-4), 162–172.

Rozanski, A., Blumenthal, J. A., & Kaplan, J. (1999). Impact of psychological factors on the pathogenesis of cardiovascular disease and implications for therapy. *Circulation, 99*, 2192–2217.

Sacks, F. M., Svetkey, L. P., Vollmer, W. M., Appel, L. J., Bray, G. A., Harsha, D., et al. (2001). Effects on blood pressure of reduced dietary sodium and the Dietary Approaches to Stop Hypertension (DASH) diet. *New England Journal of Medicine, 344* (1), 53–55.

Schwartz, J. E., Pickering, T. G., & Landsbergis, P. A. (1996). Work-related stress and blood pressure: Current theoretical models and considerations from a behavioral medicine perspective. *Journal of Occupational Health Psychology, 1*(3), 287–310.

Siegler, I. C., Peterson, B. L., Barfoot, J. C., & Williams, R. B. (1992). Hostility during late adolescence predicts coronary risk factors at midlife. *American Journal of Epidemiology, 138* (2), 146–154.

Sorensen, K., Kristensen, K. S., Bang, L. E., Svendsen, T. L., Wiinberg, N., Buttenschon, L., et al. (2004). Increased systolic ambulatory blood pressure and microalbuminuria in treated and non-treated hypertensive smokers. *Blood Pressure, 13*, 362–368.

Spence, J. D., Barnett, P. A., Linden, W., Ramsden, V., & Taenzer, P. (1999). Recommendations on stress management. *Canadian Medical Association, 160*, (9), S46–S50.

Sperry, L. (2009). *Treatment of chronic medical conditions: Cognitive-behavioral therapy strategies and integrative treatment protocols*. Washington, DC: American Psychological Association.

Vollmer, W. M., Sacks, F. M., Ard, J., Appel, L. J., Bray, G. A., Simons-Morton, D. G., et al. (2001). Effects of diet and sodium intake on blood pressure: Subgroup analysis of the DASH-sodium trial. *Annals of Internal Medicine, 135*, 1019–1028.

Wei, T., & Wang, L. (2006). Anxiety symptoms in patients with hypertension: A community based study. *International Journal Psychiatry in Medicine, 36*(3), 315–322.

25 Cognitive-Behavioral Treatment of Asthma

Anu Kotay
Paul Lehrer

Introduction

Asthma is a chronic inflammatory disorder of the airways, characterized by intermittent airflow obstruction and bronchial hyperresponsivity, which can be exacerbated by environmental, physiological, and emotional triggers. Common symptoms are cough, tightness in chest, difficulty breathing, and wheezing, which are worsened by exposure to certain allergens or situations. Psychosocial meanings attributed to asthma symptoms and to treatment can disrupt appropriate asthma management. Poor symptom perception, symptom confusion, and stress physiology can complicate a patient's ability to recognize symptoms, and can lead to misuse (underuse or overuse) of medications. Asthma education is critical to enhancing pharmacological treatment. Cognitive-behavioral management of asthma includes educating the patient about the disease and use of medications, moderating cognitive distortions about illness and medication, differentiating asthma from anxiety symptoms, identifying and addressing asthma triggers, improving stress-management techniques, and encouraging desired activity level and quality of life.

25.1 Asthma Classification*

		Persistent		
	Intermittent	Mild	Moderate	Severe
Activity limited	Not at all	Minor limitations	Some limitations	Extremely limited
Symptoms	=2 x/week	>2 x/week	Daily	Throughout day
Nighttime awakenings	=2 x/month	=3-4 x/month	>1 x/week	Often 7 x/week
Use of short-acting bronchodilator for symptom control (w/o controller medication)	=2 x/week	>2 x/week	Daily	Several x/day

*Adapted from NHLBI Guidelines (NHLBI-NAEPP, 2007, p. 74).

Assessment and Diagnostic Issues

A diagnosis of asthma is established by a medical clinician, and based on recurrence of episodes of airflow obstruction or airway hyperresponsiveness. Key symptoms or signs of asthma include wheezing (a high-pitched whistling sound on exhalation), coughing (worse at night time), recurrent difficulty breathing, and recurrent chest tightness. These symptoms may occur or worsen with exercise, viral infection, inhalant allergens (i.e., animals with fur, house dust mites, mold, pollen), changes in weather, strong emotional expression, stress, or menstrual cycles. Along with a detailed medical history and physical examination, lung function testing is used to objectively assess level of obstruction. Based on the symptoms and findings, asthma is often classified in four categories: intermittent, mild persistent, moderate persistent, and severe persistent (see Table 25.1) (National Heart Lung and Blood Institute and the National Asthma Education and Prevention Program. Expert panel report 3 [NHLBI-NAEPP], 2007; Kwok, Walsh-Kelly, Gorelick, Grabowski, & Kelly, 2006).

Medical Treatment

Understanding medical treatment is an essential aspect of improving self-management among asthma patients. The primary goal of asthma therapy is to prevent potentially life-threatening asthma exacerbations. Additional goals include facilitating normal activities (including exercise and sports activities), and allowing a generally good quality of life (NHLBI-NAEPP, 2007). Current asthma medications have been shown to be highly efficacious and effective at eliminating or reducing asthma episodes; however, noncompliance is very common, with some estimated rates as high as 80% (Bauman et al., 2002; Ivanoa et al., 2008; Kaiser, 2007). Asthma medications can be roughly broken into two categories: controller medications,

25.2 Examples of Long-Acting Controller Medications

Inhaled Corticosteroids	Long-Acting Beta-2 Agonists	Leukotriene Modifiers	Combination	Other
■ Fluticasone (Flovent) ■ Budesonide (Pulmicort) ■ Triamcinolone (Azmacort) ■ Flunisolide (Aerobid) ■ Beclomethasone (Qvar) ■ Mometasone (Asmanex)	■ Salmeterol (Serevent Diskus) ■ Formoterol (Foradil Aerolizer)	■ Fluticasone (Flovent) ■ Budesonide (Pulmicort) ■ Triamcinolone (Azmacort) ■ Flunisolide (Aerobid) ■ Beclomethasone (Qvar) ■ Mometasone (Asmanex)	■ Fluticasone and salmeterol (Advair Diskus) ■ Budesonide and formoterol (Symbicort)	■ Cromolyn (Intal) ■ Nedocromil (Tilade) ■ Theophylline (Theo-24, Theochron, Uniphyl, others)

which control inflammation, and short-acting bronchodilators (e.g., albuterol), which respond quickly to relieve symptoms of an acute asthma exacerbation. The firstline antiinflammatory medications are primarily inhaled steroids, although other antiinflammatory agents, such as leukotriene inhibitors (e.g., monteleukast), also are used. Longer acting bronchodilators, such as the beta-2 sympathetic agonist salmeterol and the parasympathetic blocking agent ipratroprium, are used for longer term symptom relief, but reliance on them without the use of antiinflammatory medications can leave the patient vulnerable to severe asthma exacerbations and sometimes cardiac complications (Lazarus et al., 2001; Salpeter, 1998). In very severe exacerbations, these medications are often supplemented with oral steroids (e.g., prednisone and/or atropine). Examples of each type of medication are listed in Table 25.2.

Psychological Factors and Comorbidities

Because a primary goal of asthma treatment is to maintain normal activity with minimal interruption from asthma episodes, the role of psychological intervention is to address any and all concerns that disrupt achievement of this goal. Adherence to asthma medications is poor, with some estimates of use of long-acting medications among those with persistent asthma as low as 26.2% (Adams, Fuhlbrigge, Guilbert, Lozano, & Martinez, 2002; Kaiser, 2007; Rand et al., 2007). Common barriers to optimal treatment include poor knowledge of asthma (Williams et al., 2004), poor perception of symptoms (Meng & McConnell, 2003; Kikuchi et al., 1994), improper use of medications (Buston & Wood, 2000), poor control of asthma triggers in environment (Brandt et al., 2008; U.S. Environmental Protection Agency, 2003), and comorbid psychological conditions (Cluley & Cochrane, 2001; Robinson et al., 2003).

Psychological Comorbidities

The presence of certain psychiatric conditions in asthma patients appears to be greater compared with nonasthmatic populations (Afari, Schmaling, Barnhart, & Buchwald, 2001; Currie, Douglas, & Heaney, 2009). The strongest link observed is with panic disorder and other anxiety disorders (Goodwin, Jacobi, & Thefeld, 2003). It is likely that a cyclic process maintains the strong relationship between anxiety/panic and asthma. Panic symptoms, such as hyperventilation, can be a potent trigger for airway obstruction (Nardi, Freire, & Zin, 2009), whereas respiratory resistance can be frightening and exacerbate anxiety-provoking cognitions, leading to further hyperventilation. This overlap of symptoms in anxiety and asthma can lead to confusion and improper management (Deshmukh, Toelle, Usherwood, O'Grady, & Jenkins, 2007). Asthma medications, such as albuterol, have anxiogenic properties that can further exacerbate panic (Hasler et al., 2005). There is conflicting evidence for higher incidence of social anxiety or generalized anxiety disorder among asthma patients (Afari, Schmaling, Barnhart, & Buchwald, 2001; Nascimento et al., 2002).

Several studies have also found a greater incidence of mood disorders, particularly depressive disorder, in asthma patients (Afari et al., 2001; Feldman et al., 2005; Nejtek et al., 2001; Nascimento et al., 2002). The relationship between asthma and depression appears to also be bidirectional (Lehrer, Song, Feldman, Giardino, & Schmaling, 2002). Negative affect and depression symptoms have been shown to increase asthma symptoms, both directly through physiology and indirectly through behavior, whereas asthma can exacerbate depression symptoms through fatigue and illness-centered self-concepts (Lehrer et al., 2002). The impact of depression on health care visits and quality of life in asthma patients remains substantial when anxiety is controlled for (Kullowatz, Kanniess, Dahme, Magnussen, & Ritz, 2007).

Psychological Assessment

Psychological assessments most commonly used in asthma care explore multiple factors of the patient's experience of the disease and of treatment: emotional responses to asthma symptoms, health-related quality of life, difficulties associated with self-management, and mental health comorbidities. Examples of self-report psychological assessment tools include:

- **Asthma Symptom Checklist:** This questionnaire measures the nature and severity of various symptoms generally seen in asthma, and the patient's emotional reactions to these asthma symptoms. It has 16 items, with severity to be measured on a 4-point scale. Higher score indicates more severity of symptoms (Kinsman, Luparello, O'Bannion, & Spector, 1973).
- **Asthma Quality of Life Questionnaire:** Patients respond to 32 items on a 7-point Likert scale categorized in four domains: activities domain, asthma symptoms domain, emotional functions domain, and environmental exposure domain. Lower score indicates greater impairment in quality of life (Juniper et al., 1992).
- **Asthma Bother Profile:** Patients respond to 15 items on a 6-point scale, with a higher number indicating being more bothered by asthma

symptoms. This scale also includes seven items that assess the patient's ability to manage asthma, in which a higher score means low confidence of asthma knowledge, perception of poor quality of care, and low confidence in their ability to manage an asthma exacerbation (Hyland, Ley, Fisher, & Woodward, 1995).

- **Brief Patient Health Questionnaire:** Patients respond to multiple items based on eight questions about depression, anxiety, and other psychiatric symptoms commonly seen in primary care settings. Both English and Spanish versions have demonstrated good sensitivity and specificity in detecting mental health disorders (Martin, Rief, Klaiberg, & Braehler, 2006).

Incidence and Clinical Manifestations in Primary Care Settings

The prevalence of asthma in the United States was recently estimated at 7.5% (Centers for Disease Control and Prevention, 2004), accounting for 5.7% of total visits to a primary care office (Cherry, Woodwell, & Rechtsteiner, 2007). It is one of the most common chronic diseases of childhood, affecting nearly 6 million children. The burden of asthma on health care costs can be evidenced by nearly 2 million emergency department events, nearly 730,000 by children and adolescents (Centers for Disease Control and Prevention, 2002). This high number does not reflect the cost to quality of life for millions of children, families, and adults. Uncontrolled asthma is responsible for an estimated 14 million days of missed school and 100 million days of restricted activity yearly (Centers for Disease Control and Prevention, 2001).

Brief Case History[1]

This patient was treated as part of a demonstration project evaluating a treatment strategy for patients with comorbid asthma and panic disorder (Lehrer et al., 2008). The treatment protocol combined elements of D. H. Barlow and Craske's (1994) well-validated procedure of, "panic control therapy" with various asthma education procedures, principally from Reynolds, Kotses, and Creer (1988), but also including various patient education materials published by the American Lung Association (www.lungusa.org) and the National Heart Lung and Blood Institute (www.nhlbi.nih.gov/health/public/lung/index.htm#asthma). The protocol begins with patient education about the two disorders, emphasizing ways that the individual can distinguish symptoms of the two, both by symptom pattern (e.g., cough is common in asthma, but rare in panic) and by peak-flow readings. Patients are given an asthma action plan

[1]From "Case study: Treatment of a woman with co-morbid asthma and panic disorder," by Lehrer, P., 1999, *Biofeedback, 27*(1), 31–32. Copyright © 1999 by *Biofeedback* magazine and the Association of Applied Psychophysiology and Biofeedback. Reprinted with permission.

that includes peak-flow criteria for determining the presence of an asthma flare (primarily 80% of personal best peak-flow readings from the past two weeks), and action plans for managing both disorders (for asthma, taking a bronchodilator, escalating to a physician call or emergency room visit if symptoms do not abate and peak flow readings do not improve; for panic, doing slow breathing and relaxation maneuvers, and decatastrophizing self-talk). Patients are educated about how certain symptoms could occur in both disorders (including breathlessness and chest tightness) due to different mechanisms (for asthma, airways obstruction; for panic, simple hyperventilation), and how hyperventilation may even occur in asthma, as an overcompensation for breathing through obstructed airways, perhaps compounded by anxiety about breathing difficulties. Panic control procedures also include exposure to panicogenic body sensations (dizziness, breathing through resistance, etc.), although the specific panic trigger of deliberate hyperventilation is not used for comorbid panic and asthma patients, because, at least theoretically, it could trigger an asthma exacerbation, due to increased exposure to cold and dry air (that characterizes room air, compared with moist warm air in the airways). An uncontrolled clinical trial of this procedure found significant decreases in both panic symptoms and albuterol use, suggesting more appropriate self-management of asthma, as well as panic (Lehrer et al., 2008).

Presenting problem: A 41-year-old woman with three children (18- and 19-year-olds from a previous marriage, and a 6-year-old from her current marriage) was referred for recurrent panic symptoms. She also had mild asthma and experienced constant discomfort that was disruptive to her life. Her pulmonologist felt that she was overusing her bronchodilator (albuterol, a Beta-2 sympathetic stimulant used typically for immediate relief of an asthma exacerbation), and that the side effects of overuse were triggering her panic symptoms. From her perspective, some of her panic symptoms were similar to her asthma symptoms, which prompted her to take additional albuterol, unintentionally compounding the problem. She reported constant worry and fear of recurring panic exacerbations, and periodically also took a low dose of alprazolam (Xanax, an anxiolytic medication) to manage her anxiety. She had a past medical history of chronic bronchitis, chronic sinus infection, sciatica, and frequent gastrointestinal problems.

Psychosocial history: The patient reported that her symptoms had initially begun three years prior, shortly after sinus surgery due to chronic sinusitis. Around the time, she recalled having significant difficulty managing the behavior of her adolescent daughter. At the onset of psychological treatment, her exacerbations were frequent, occurring several times a week, triggered by milder everyday stress. She had a history of two domestically violent relationships (her prior marriage, ending 15 years ago, and a brief relationship before her current marriage). Her current marriage is stable, with no incidences of abuse, and she described her current lifestyle as, comparatively "calm and easy." Later in therapy, she reported considerable dissension in the family regarding her older, unwed daughter's unexpected pregnancy and her undetermined plans to continue or terminate the pregnancy. The patient had previously worked as a medical administrator, but, at time of treatment, is a full-time housewife and mother doing some occasional professional cake decorating from home.

Symptoms: The patient experienced exacerbations of dry throat, pounding heart, chest tightness, dyspnea, rapid breathing, dizziness, nausea, feelings of unreality, numbness in her lips, trembling, shaking, and fear of dying or going crazy. Each attack would last 10–15 minutes, after which she would feel, "washed out" for the remainder of the day. Sometimes, she thought she was having a heart attack or a stroke, and was taken to the emergency room by ambulance. She was referred to a cardiologist, who found no abnormalities. At the beginning of treatment, she endorsed some signs of agoraphobia, stating that she felt somewhat uncomfortable leaving home for fear of having a panic attack and felt very uncomfortable to travel far from home. Her asthma symptoms included chest tightness, dyspnea, and rapid breathing, leaving her unsure of how to respond.

Cognitive-Behavioral Case Conceptualization and Treatment

The patient began experiencing symptoms of confusion during a time of acute distress, when she was presumably physically weaker, recovering from surgery. Feeling unsure of the meaning of her symptoms, she began feeling anxious about her physical symptoms and misused her asthma medications. Overuse of albuterol, as well as increased worry and increased attentiveness to physical symptoms, exacerbated her physical symptoms. This, in turn, led to more anxiety, albuterol overuse, and physical symptoms. Over time, mild changes in physical sensations brought on by minor daily stressors (e.g., making time to go to the store) triggered the cycle of anxiety, physical symptoms, confusion, and improper management, leading to more physical and cognitive symptoms. Places that she associated with physical discomfort also became places to fear and eventually avoid.

When she came to treatment, her symptoms had already begun to improve, due to reassurance from her pulmonologist that her asthma was not as severe as she had suspected. Initial treatment focused on differentiating panic from asthma symptoms. The patient was taught how to properly use a peak-flow meter, and was asked to track her peak flows daily to estimate her personal best. A formal asthma action plan was devised. She began recognizing that if her full-effort peak flow reading is greater than 80% of her personal best, her symptoms of chest tightness and dyspnea were not related to an asthma exacerbation. Her treatment also included muscle relaxation and heart rate variability (HRV) biofeedback to reduce anxiety-related physical symptoms and improve autonomic reflexes. Fear of body sensations were also discussed, along with the mechanisms of how these physical symptoms can be precipitated by anxiety and mild hyperventilation. The patient was exposed to resistance breathing by breathing through a straw. She was also instructed on how to use breathing and relaxation techniques to decrease the hyperventilation symptoms.

After five sessions, the patient reported successfully blocking several panic exacerbations at home, and had experienced no panic for 3 weeks. She expressed understanding of anxiety, hyperventilation symptoms, and asthma symptoms. She had dramatically reduced her use of asthma medications, and stated that she no longer feared changes in her body sensations. She reported that she continued to be satisfied with her personal and family situation despite continued disagreement about her daughter's pregnancy. She expressed a preference to discontinue therapy.

Identifying and Addressing Obstacles to Treatment

The biggest obstacle to treatment in a case of comorbid asthma and anxiety is that the focus on physical symptoms renders it less likely that the patient would seek mental health assistance. In this case, the patient's symptoms began improving when she spoke with the pulmonologist, who educated her on the disparity between her level of asthma and her medication use. The physician is often the first line of care for asthma patients, and their ability to ascertain mental health disorder is critical to the patient's access to proper care. Ongoing collaboration of mental health services at primary care sites improves patients' access to and outcomes in mental health care (Katon et al., 1999; Rollman et al., 2005; Roy-Byrne, Katon, Cowley, & Russo, 2001).

Points of Collaboration With Physicians and Family

Mental health services on site at primary care offices may increase the likelihood of recognition and early treatment of psychiatric comorbidities. For asthma-specific care, it is important to facilitate and promote regular review of the patient's asthma action plan by multiple health care providers (nurses, school health staff, pharmacists, primary care providers, specialists, etc.) in various settings (NHLBI-NAEPP, 2007). Encouraging communication with medical providers allows the patient to test the reality of symptoms, from consistent reports by various providers.

Chronic conditions such as asthma are managed better when there is a strong partnership between the doctor and patient in treating the condition (Holman & Lorig, 2000). Though poor provider compliance to asthma guidelines has been cited as a factor that can undermine optimal asthma control (Doerschug, Peterson, Dayton, & Kline, 1999), most problems arise from poor patient adherence to medication and avoidance of asthma triggers. Wilson et al. (as cited in NHLBI-NAEPP, 2007, p. 123) compared guideline-based asthma care to the shared decision-making model, where the doctor negotiates with the patient to create a treatment plan, and found that, although both groups had better adherence compared with the usual care group, adherence to asthma medications was significantly better in the shared decision-making model than with guideline-based care.

Fostering a close relationship with the patient's family is particularly important for pediatric asthma, but is also recommended for adult asthma (Chernoff, Ireyes, DeVet, & Kim, 2002; NHLBI-NAEPP, 2007). Family members can often provide additional information about difficulties of daily living, allergen exposures, financial limitations, and other family strains that could impede optimal asthma control if not addressed. A randomized control trial found that including family in doctor's visits improved symptoms, activity level, and self-management confidence among Latino and African American patients (Bonner et al., 2002).

A consistent message from multiple providers in various settings about self-management tools, a strong relationship between the patient and the provider, and inclusion of the patient's family provides a strong foundation to effective asthma treatment (NHLBI-NAEPP, 2007).

Development and Implementation of Empirically Based Treatment Plan Self-Management

The National Health for Heart, Blood, and Lung Institute's published guidelines state that "asthma self-management education is essential to patients with the skills necessary to control asthma and improve outcomes" (Evidence A, NHLBI-NAEPP, 2007, p. 93). Self-management in asthma treatment refers to a variety of intervention programs that includes the following aspects:

- basic facts about asthma
- definition of well-controlled asthma
- patient's current level of control
- roles of controller and rescue medications
- skills to use medication properly
- how to handle signs and symptoms of worsening asthma
- when and where to seek care
- environmental exposure control.

Enhancing self-management skills in patients can be accomplished by using various methods, from providing an individualized written plan to conducting multiple sessions of cognitive-behavioral therapy (CBT) enhanced with asthma-specific educational components. There has not been consistent evidence that written individualized plans by themselves have improved patient outcomes (Toelle & Ram, 2004). Adding regular review by all health providers to a written action plan has been found to improve clinically important outcomes, including reduced hospitalizations, ER visits, unscheduled doctor appointments, days off of work or school, nocturnal asthma, and improved quality of life (Gibson et al., 2002). However, regular review of self-management programs has not demonstrated significant improvement in lung function.

Psychoeducational Interventions

Psychoeducational care adds another layer to self-management interventions, by encouraging use of behavioral and cognitive skills to manage symptoms of asthma, or by providing additional counseling support. A meta-analysis of psychoeducational care of asthma observed improvement in asthma exacerbations, dynamic respiratory volume, peak flow, functional status, adherence, health care utilization, use of "rescue" medications, psychological well-being, and knowledge of medication use. This analysis also did not find any change in lung function (Devine, 1996). Lack of changes in lung function may reflect the episodic nature of asthma; between exacerbations, lung function may be normal or nearly so (Martinez, 2009).

Reduced frequency of exacerbations, therefore, is a more relevant criterion by which effectiveness of these interventions should be evaluated. Patients with severe or difficult-to-control asthma have also benefited from psychoeducational interventions. A systematic review of interventions targeting this complicated population noted improvement in hospitalizations, asthma, quality of life, and psychological comorbidity after psychoeducational interventions.' (Smith, Mugford, Holland, Noble, & Harrison, 2007)

Cognitive-Behavioral Treatment

Cognitive-behavioral interventions further boost the effectiveness of self-management and psychoeducational interventions by directing care toward asthma-specific cognitive errors, and targeting behavioral interventions toward psychophysiological resiliency. In a meta-analysis (Yorke, Fleming, & Shuldham, 2006), the authors demonstrated that CBT was related to significant improvement in asthma quality of life, asthma symptoms, emergency room visits, and absenteeism. Behavioral interventions explored in this study observed that relaxation treatment decreased the use of asthma medications, and biofeedback improved lung functioning, as measured by peak expiratory flow.

Recently, Creer (2008) published a review article that highlights particular cognitive and behavioral processes engaged during asthma self-management, such as goal setting, information interpretation, decision making, action, and self-efficacy. The following section will explore particular cognitive errors and behavioral approaches that have been shown to be relevant for behavioral treatment of asthma.

Cognitive Strategies

Symptom Perception

Leventhal et al. have found, in multiple studies, that subjective interpretation of physical symptoms engages specific coping strategies (Leventhal, Leventhal, & Contrada, 1998; Leventhal, Weinman, Leventhal, & Phillips, 2008) that may or may not correspond with actual symptoms or appropriate management. People often rely on personal experience of symptoms to determine when, how, and what treatment to use more readily than objective factors (Janssens, Verleden, De Peuter, Van Diest, & Van den Bergh, 2009). Major discrepancies between perception of respiratory symptoms and actual airway obstruction have been described previously (Kendrick, Higgs, Whitfield, & Laszlo, 1993; Nguyen, Wilson, & German, 1996; Rietveld, Prins, & Kolk, 1996; Rushford, Tiller, & Pain, 1998). For example, one study presented children with false sounds of wheezing, and found increased reports of breathlessness among children with asthma (Rietveld, Kolk, Prins, & Colland, 1997). Fritz, McQuaid, Spirito, and Klein (1996) explored symptoms perception among children 8–15 years old, and found that poor perceptual accuracy of symptoms was significantly related to more missed days from school and more emergency room visits. In fact, another study that looked at adult and child patients who have had near-fatal asthma exacerbations observed that these patients had significant impaired perception of dyspnea when breathing through an inspiratory-resistive load (Kifle, Seng, & Davenport, 1997; Kikuchi et al., 1994). The inability to accurately recognize asthma symptoms leads to poor management. A couple of studies have shown improved symptom perception of airway obstruction after training. Absolute and difference threshold training with resistive loads and feedback has been used successfully to improve perception accuracy (Harver, 1994; Stout, Kotses, & Creer, 1997).

Symptom Confusion

Asthma and panic disorder is a common comorbidity, with some estimates indicating that adults with asthma from a community sample were five times more likely to have panic symptoms than nonasthmatic persons (Goodwin & Eaton, 2003). There is substantial overlap in symptoms (e.g., dyspnea, chest tightness) that can lead to frequent symptoms confusion and errors in self-care management by both patients and their physicians (Afari et al., 2001). Treatment for the two conditions can also be incompatible, such that beta-sympathetic agents used in asthma treatment can exacerbate anxiety symptoms, and relaxation treatments for anxiety could lead to bronchoconstriction. Likewise, exposure to physical symptoms is suggested for panic disorder (J. H. Barlow, Ellard, Hainsworth, Jones, & Fischer, 2005), whereas avoidance of triggers is recommended for asthma conditions (NHLBI-NAEPP, 2007). Symptom confusion and resulting inappropriate treatment has been implicated in deaths or near-deaths for asthma (Tietz, Kahlstom, & Cardiff, 1975).

The primary strategy to improve symptom confusion is through education and self-monitoring. The incorporation of an asthma action plan is viewed as necessary in cognitive-behavioral interventions of asthma (Deshmukh, Toelle, Usherwood, O'Grady, & Jenkins, 2007; Lehrer et al., 2008). Symptom confusion should be regarded as normal and expected, requiring the use of an objective measure, such as a peak-flow meter, to differentiate between disorders. To create an action plan, the patient is taught and asked to demonstrate how to use a peak-flow meter. The patient is asked to keep logs of peak-flow readings from the beginning of and the end of each day for one week. These values are used to estimate the individual's personal best, which can be inserted into an asthma action plan delineating what steps are necessary in three different situations: >80%, <80% and >50%, and <50% of one's personal best peak-flow value. The use of the action plan is most effective when reviewed by multiple health providers (the patient's physician, school nurse, etc.) (Gibson et al., 2002; NHLBI-NAEPP, 2007).

Behavioral Strategies

Stimulus Control

Changes in lifestyles and housing conditions over the past half-century are thought to have contributed to increased exposure to allergens that have counteracted some of the progress made by improved asthma care and development of effective controller medications. People spend more time indoors in temperature-controlled environments that decrease air-exchange rates, creating more favorable conditions for reservoir dust mite population, fungus growth, and indoor pollutants, such as tobacco smoke. At the same time, there has been an increase in the number of indoor pets, the use of synthetic fillings in pillows that build up mite allergens faster (Custovic et al., 2000), and the neighborhood populations, escalating problems with cockroaches and other insects.

Common allergens associated with asthma include dust mites, cats, dogs, cockroaches, several fungi, grass, and ragweed, although there is significant variation by geographic location, housing conditions, and population lifestyles (NHLBI-NAEPP, 2007). Many of these, such as pet allergens, have been shown to be associated with severity of asthma (Gent et al., in press) and, in some cases, exposure to certain allergens has been connected with fatal exacerbations of asthma (Targonski, Perksky, Kelleher, & Addington, 1995).

Determining a particular patient's allergen sensitivity requires the classic behavioral principle of symptom monitoring and stimulus control. Careful history and observation of increased asthma symptoms during certain activities provide the most useful information for asthma management, as positive allergy testing does not discriminate allergens specifically responsible for asthma symptoms (NHLBI-NAEPP, 2007). Management of allergens involves eliminating or limiting exposure to the extent possible. Selected examples from the NHLBI-NAEPP guidelines (2007) include:

- keeping pets out of patient's bedroom
- limiting upholstered furniture in home with pets
- vacuuming regularly
- using high-efficiency particulate air (HEPA) cleaners
- encasing mattress and pillows with allergen-impermeable covers
- washing sheets and stuffed toys in hot water (>130°F) weekly
- keeping humidity between 30–50%
- removing carpets from bedroom
- cleaning garbage and food promptly to minimize cockroaches
- staying indoors during peak allergy seasons when spore counts are high
- addressing workplace and school exposure as well as home exposures
- exploring exposure to irritants, such as environmental tobacco smoke or other pollutants.

Another likely trigger for asthma is exercise or vigorous activity. Increased ventilation during exercise and the adaptations in the airway mechanisms that follow are likely the cause of exercise-induced asthma (Weiler et al., 2007). Exercise-induced bronchospasm has been found to occur in up to 45.1% of children who were diagnosed with mild-to-moderate asthma, but not treated with long-acting inhaled steroids (Sano, Sole, & Naspitz, 1998). Exercise-induced bronchospasm typically occurs during or immediately after vigorous activity. Treatment for exercise-induced bronchospasm or asthma typically involves taking a short-acting bronchodilator before starting exercise activity (Anderson, 1993). However, there is significant evidence suggesting that daily long-term controller medication can reduce frequency and severity of exercise-induced bronchospasm (Vathenen, Knox, Wisiniewski, & Tattersfield, 1991; Vidal, Fernandez-Ovide, Pinero, Nunez, & Gonzalez-Quintela,, 2001).

Stress Management

In response to laboratory and daily stressors, asthma patients reliably demonstrate stronger bronchoconstriction, compared with healthy controls (Affleck et al., 2000; Ritz, Steptoe, DeWilde, & Costa, 2000; Schmaling, McKnight, & Afari, 2002). Physiological changes related to stress are often mediated through autonomic activity. Although some mild types of stressors, such as mental arithmetic, activate the beta sympathetic response of bronchodilation among healthy individuals and asthma patients, and thus, should not be expected to have adverse effects on asthma (Lehrer et al., 1996; Smyth, Stone, Hurewitz, & Kaell, 1999), other types of stressors, such as embarrassing situations, have caused bronchoconstriction in up to 40% of asthma patients (Isenberg, Lehrer, & Hochron, 1992). Lehrer (1999) proposes that a strong parasympathetic rebound following a stress-induced sympathetic activation may account for stress-induced asthma, as well as nocturnal asthma symptoms.

Various relaxation training interventions have been tested in asthma patients with mixed positive results. A recent meta-analysis (Huntley, White, & Ernst, 2002) identified nine randomized controlled trials (RCTs) that met their criteria (RCTs with relaxation without specific suggestions aimed at asthma, excluding patients with comorbid conditions), and concluded that there is some evidence to support improvement in lung function of asthma patients with Jacobsonian muscle relaxation, and no current evidence in favor of hypnosis, facial muscle biofeedback, or autogenic training.

Heart Rate Variability Biofeedback and Breathing Exercises

HRV biofeedback, a psychophysiological training technique used to improve autonomic function, has been cited in the National Asthma Education and Prevention Program Expert Panel Report (NHLBI-NAEPP, 2007) as evidencing positive effects on lung function in asthma patients. HRV biofeedback trains people to breathe at their resonant frequency, known as resonant breathing, which has been shown to not only increase HRV, but also chronically increase baroreflex gain and peak expiratory flow (Lehrer et al., 2003). A randomized controlled study of HRV biofeedback for the treatment of asthma demonstrated reduced medication use, decreased symptoms, and improved pulmonary function independent of age (Lehrer et al., 2004). Another controlled study demonstrated that symptom of the HRV biofeedback group did not increase when steroid treatments were decreased (Scardella et al., 2004). The mechanism of HRV biofeedback on asthma and lung function are not yet fully understood, and possibly pathways could include antiinflammatory and/or bronchodilator effects of autonomic regulation, as well as stress-management effects of reduced autonomic labiality (Lehrer et al., 2004). Biofeedback procedures are becoming cheaper and easier to use, with reports of clinical effectiveness in as little as a single session, with use of a nominally priced home trainer biofeedback unit (McCraty, Atkinson, & Tomasino, 2003).

A breathing method advocated by Butekyo, involving increasing CO_2 through hypoventilation or slow breathing (Cooper et al., 2003), significantly reduced the use of inhaled corticosteroids and emergency visits and improved lung function, compared with a control group (Cowie, Conley, Underwood, & Reader, 2008). More generic breathing exercises may have similar effects (M. Thomas et al., 2009), although one study suggests that these effects may be more on symptoms of asthma than on underlying physiology (Holloway & West, 2007). The effects of other breathing techniques are promising and comparable to those found in HRV biofeedback, perhaps because the breathing methods produced by the various techniques may be quite similar. Though there is not clear evidence as to which breathing technique is most effective, it appears that the degree of benefit depends on the extent to which the breathing practice approximates the individual's resonant breathing.

Summary of Empirically Based Treatment

Asthma education and teaching self-management principles are essential to all asthma treatment (NHLBI-NAEEP, 2007). In a recent meta-analytic review of psychological treatments for asthma, cognitive-behavioral interventions were noted to improve asthma quality of life, symptoms, emergency room visits, and absenteeism, whereas relaxation treatment was found to decrease the use of asthma medications, and biofeedback has demonstrated improvement in lung functioning (Yorke, Fleming, & Shuldham, 2006). Cognitive processes of particular concern to asthma care include symptom perception, or the level at which an individual can accurately detect respiratory restriction, and symptom confusion, the ability of the patient to accurately attribute a cause for the symptom. Behavioral strategies that have been shown to be most effective for asthma treatment are management of allergens, progressive muscle relaxation, and HRV biofeedback.

Evaluation of Treatment Outcomes

A daily events or symptom record completed by the patient on a weekly basis can provide essential information about changes in number and frequency of asthma exacerbations, frequency of rescue inhaler usage, and changes in mood (Bheekie, Syce, & Weinberg, 2001). Behavioral assessments described previously, such as the Asthma Quality of Life Questionnaire (Juniper, 1997; Leidy, Chan, & Coughlin, 1998; Leidy & Coughlin, 1998; Rowe & Oxman, 1993), the Asthma Symptom Checklist (Belloch, Perpiña, Pascual, Martinez, & De Diego, 1997; Ritz, Bobb, Edwards, & Steptoe, 2001), the Asthma Bother Profile (Lewith, Hyland, & Shaw, 2002; Nishimura et al., 2005), and the Brief Patient Health Questionnaire (Schneider et al., 2008) are widely used in clinical research, and have all been validated in diverse populations. These measures can be used to detect changes in quality of life, ability to manage symptoms, level of disturbance by asthma symptoms, and depression/anxiety symptoms associated with treatment effects.

Objective measures should also be assessed to validate and reinforce the patient's efforts. Peak expiratory flow rate and spirometry measures are used in most asthma outcome studies (i.e., Boushey et al., 2005; Lazarus et al., 2001; Lehrer et al., 2004), and can easily be performed during the final session.

Considerations With Special Populations/Diversity Issues

Minority Populations

The incidence of asthma morbidity and mortality is higher among minority, low-income, and urban populations. From 1980 to 2002, the ratio of Black to White children who had asthma increased 50%, indicating a widening gap with Black children being more likely to have asthma than White children (Gupta, Carrion-Carire, & Weiss, 2006). Asthma hospitalization and death rates have been found to be nearly 3–5 times higher among New York Blacks and Hispanics compared with Whites (Carr, Zeitel, & Weiss, 1992). Among Hispanics, the rates of asthma are highest among Puerto Rican children (13.2%), compared with 5% of Cuban and 3% of Mexican American children (Ledogar, Penchaszadeh, Garden, & Iglesias, 2000).

Minorities are more likely to live in low-quality housing, in inner cities, in overcrowded homes, and in homes lacking proper heat and air-conditioning, increasing the likelihood of exposure to common indoor asthma triggers (Brandt et al., 2008; Litonjua, Carey, Burge, Weiss, & Gold, 2001). Some of these factors also encourage children to spend more time outdoors, where they can be exposed to inner-city smog or other pollutants common in low-income neighborhoods (Asthma and Allergy Foundation of America and the National Pharmaceutical Council, 2005; Cabana, Lara, & Shannon, 2007).

A recent study in the United Kingdom observed an increased incidence in U.K.-born children from minority backgrounds (South African or South Asian), compared with White U.K.-born children, and compared with non-U.K.-born South Africans or South Asians (Netuveli, Hurwitz, & Sheikh, 2005). Both ethnicity and migration status are considered to change the risk of asthma events, although the reasons for this discrepancy, perhaps including stress, have not been identified. There are several possible types of explanations, including genetic, immunity from early exposures in native country, lack of exposure to factors in the host country, and selection through the healthy migrant effect (S. L.Thomas & Thomas, 2004).

Barriers to optimal care include poor access to health care services (Sobo, Seid, & Gelhard, 2006), difficulty connecting with and/or trusting provider (Sobo, Seid, & Gelhard), level of parental acculturation (Mainous et al., 2006), and lack of adequate insurance coverage (Lozano et al., 2003). The high cost of asthma medications has also been cited as a barrier to adequate asthma management, with 20–36% of one survey's respondents indicating cost-related reasons for underusing asthma treatment (Piette, Heisler, & Wagner, 2004). In addition, many asthmatics don't understand the primary action of corticosteriods, and even more fear the side effects of corticosteroids (Boulet, 1998). A cross-sectional study found that 73% of surveyed Medicaid participants were underusers of controller therapy (Finkelstein, Lozano, Faber, Miroshnik, & Lieu, 2002). These factors, in addition to the aforementioned effects of psychological comorbidities, poor symptom perception, and symptom confusion, negatively impact the initialization of and adherence to asthma treatment.

Cultural competency and explicit regard for sociocultural influences have been linked to improved health outcomes. Direct application of cultural sensitivity includes prescribing generic medication, educating patients about prescription company discount programs, partnering with community organizations to increase access, advocating for more medical services in underserved areas, promoting evidence-based treatment and increased compliance to NIH guidelines in community health programs, and development and promotion of culturally relevant educational materials. Outreach programs targeting populations at increased risk for asthma have demonstrated decreased asthma symptoms, hospitalizations, ER visits, and dependence on oral corticosteroids (Federico & Liu, 2003; Quinn, Shalowitz, Berry, Mijanovich, & Wolf, 2006).

Pregnancy and Asthma

It should be noted that asthma control is particularly important during pregnancy, as asthma can increase the risk for perinatal mortality, preeclampsia, preterm birth, and low-birth-weight infants. It is considered "safer that a pregnant woman be treated with asthma medications than to have asthma symptoms and exacerbations" (NHLBI-NAEEP, 2007, p. 365).

Adolescents

Adolescents experience an immense amount of change biologically, emotionally, and socially, which adds another layer of considerations to address when managing asthma. Asthma is a visible condition that can interrupt important social activities, including sports and dancing events, which can negatively affect the developing identity of a teenager (Couriel, 2003). For these reasons, adolescents are less likely to seek help at emergency rooms or at a physician's office than other age groups (Bruzzese et al., 2004). Recommendations for care with adolescents include allowing adolescents to take ownership of their asthma treatment, including meeting with them without parents at times (de Benedictis & Bush, 2007), as well as using peer groups to lead health educational programs (Shah et al., 2001). Asthma goals should be connected to personal goals of the teenager, and active participation in physical activities should be encouraged (NHLBI-NAEEP, 2007).

Clinical Pearls of Wisdom for Practitioners

Adequate asthma management in primary care settings faces multiple challenges, many of which can be addressed by psychosocial and behavioral interventions. The goal of asthma treatment is to improve a patient's ability to manage illness in a manner that minimizes risk and maximizes functioning. In this chapter, a review of the disease, the pharmacological treatment, and psychological comorbidities (particularly panic and anxiety) has been presented. Educating patients about these concepts is an essential part of asthma self-management. Furthermore, it has been determined that poor symptom perception, symptom confusion (with panic and anxiety symptoms), the physiological effect of stress responses, poor management of environmental triggers, distrust of medications and providers, limited access to proper and culturally relevant care, and developmental challenges presented diminish an individual's desire and ability to optimally self-manage asthma. To address these barriers to optimal management, the following "pearls of wisdom" are proposed:

- Explore and address the patient's misunderstanding of the disease and treatment.
- Educate patients on differences between the two types of asthma medications (controller medications and short-acting bronchodilators).
- Teach them proper use of the peak-flow meter to discriminate whether symptoms are asthma-related rather than panic or anxiety symptoms.

- Work with the primary care provider and other health care providers (i.e., nurses, school staff) to consistently review an individualized asthma action plan.
- Use biofeedback techniques to improve autonomic function.
- Identify and address environmental and exercise triggers.

Many of the previous psychosocial or behavioral interventions have been found to not only reduce asthma symptoms and improve quality of life (Smith, Mugford, Holland, Noble, & Harrison, 2007; Yorke, Fleming, & Shuldham, 2006), but also improve pulmonary function (Huntley, White, & Ernst, 2002; Lehrer et al., 2004). Additional cognitive-behavioral interventions for panic, anxiety, depression, or other comorbid conditions should be incorporated as appropriate.

The following Web sites are excellent resources for providers interested in enhancing asthma care:

National Heart, Lung, and Blood Institute: http://www.nhlbi.nih.gov/guidelines/asthma/asthgdln.pdf

Asthma and Allergy Foundation of America: http://www.aafa.org/

American Lung Association: http://www.lungusa.org/

US Environmental Protection Agency: www.epa.gov/asthma

References

Adams, R. J., Fuhlbrigge, A. L., Guilbert, T. W., Lozano, P., & Martinez, F. (2002). Inadequate use of asthma medication in the United States: Results of the asthma in America national population survey. *Journal of Allergy and Clinical Immunology, 110*, 58–64.

Afari, N., Schmaling, K. B., Barnhart, S., & Buchwald, D. (2001). Psychiatric comorbidity and functional status in adult patients with asthma. *Clinical Psychology in Medical Settings, 8*(4), 245–252.

Affleck, G., Apter, A., Tennen, H., Reisine, S., Barrows, E., Willard, A., et al. (2000.) Mood states associated with transitory changes in asthma symptoms and peak expiratory flow. *Psychosomatic Medicine, 62*(1), 61–68.

Anderson, S. D. (1993). Diagnosis and management of exercise-induced asthma. In M. E. Gershwin & G. M. Halpern (Eds.), *Bronchial asthma: Principles of diagnosis and practice* (3rd ed., pp. 513–547). Clifton, NJ: Humana Press.

Asthma and Allergy Foundation of America and the National Pharmaceutical Council. (2005). *Ethnic disparities in the burden and treatment of asthma*. Retrieved September 21, 2009, from http://www.aafa.org

Barlow, D .H., & Craske, M. G. (1994). *Mastery of your anxiety and panic* (2nd ed.). San Antonio, TX: Harcourt Brace.

Barlow, J. H., Ellard, D. R., Hainsworth, J. M., Jones, F. R., & Fischer, A. (2005). A review of self-management interventions for panic disorders, phobias and obsessive-compulsive disorders. *Acta psychiatrica Scandinavica, 111*(4), 272–285.

Bauman, L. J., Wright, E., Leickly, F. E., Crain, E., Kruszon-Moran, D., Wade, S. L., et al. (2002). Relationship of adherence to pediatric asthma morbidity among inner-city children. *Pediatrics, 110*(1), c6.

Belloch, A., Perpiña, M. J., Pascual, L. M., Martinez, M., & De Diego, A. (1997). Subjective symptomatology of asthma: Validation of the asthma symptom checklist in an outpatient Spanish population. *Journal of Asthma, 34*(6), 509–519.

Bheekie, A., Syce, J. A., & Weinberg, E. G. (2001). Peak expiratory flow rate and symptom self-monitoring of asthma initiated from community pharmacies. *Journal of Clinical Pharmacy and Therapeutics, 26*(4), 287–296.

Bonner, S., Zimmerman, B. J., Evans, D., Irigoyen, M., Resnick, D., & Mellins, R. B. (2002). An individualized intervention to improve asthma management among urban Latino and African-American families. *Journal of Asthma, 39*(2), 167–179.

Boulet, L. P. (1998). Perception of the role and potential side effects of inhaled corticosteroids among asthmatic patients. *Chest, 113*(3), 587–592.

Boushey, H. A., Sorkness, C. A., King, T. S., Sullivan, S. D., Fahy, J. V., Lazarus, S. C., et al. and National Heart, Lung, and Blood Institute Asthma Clinical Research Network. (2005). Daily versus as-needed corticosteroids for mild persistent asthma. *New England Journal of Medicine, 352*(15),1519–1528.

Brandt, D. M., Levin, L., Matsui, E., Phipatanakul, W., Smith, A. M., Bernstein, J. A., & American Academy of Allergy, Asthma, & Immunology-Indoor Allergen Committee. (2008). Allergists' attitudes toward environmental control. *Journal of Allergy and Clinical Immunology, 121*(4), 1053–1054.

Bruzzese, J., Bonner, S., Vincent, E. J., Sheares, B. J., Mellins, R. B., Levison, M. J., et al. (2004). Asthma education: The adolescent experience. *Patient Education and Counseling, 55*, 396–406.

Buston, K. M., & Wood, S. F. (2000). Non-compliance amongst adolescents with asthma: Listening to what they tell us about self-management. *Family Practice, 17*, 134–138.

Cabana, M. D., Lara, M., & Shannon, J. (2007). Racial and ethnic disparities in the quality of asthma care. *Chest, 132*(5), 810S–817S.

Carr, W., Zeitel, L., & Weiss, K. (1992). Variations in asthma hospitalizations and deaths in New York City. *American Journal of Public Health, 82*, 59–65.

Centers for Disease Control and Prevention. (2001). Self-reported asthma prevalence and control among adults-United States. *Morbidity and Mortality Weekly Report, 52*, 381–384.

Centers for Disease Control and Prevention. (2002.) *Asthma prevalence, health care use and mortality, 2002*. Retrieved May 2009 from www.cdc.gov/nchs/products/pubs/pubd/hestats/asthma/asthma.htm

Centers for Disease Control and Prevention. (2004). Asthma prevalence and control characteristics by race/ethnicity—United States, 2002. *Morbidity and Mortality Weekly Report, 53*, 145–148.

Chernoff, R. G., Ireys, H. T., DeVet, K. A., & Kim, Y. J. (2002). A randomized, controlled trial of a community-based support program for families of children with chronic illness: Pediatric outcomes. *Archives of Pediatric & Adolescent Medicine, 156*(6), 533–539.

Cherry, D. K., Woodwell, D. A., & Rechtsteiner, E. A. (2007). National ambulatory medical care survey: 2005 summary. *Advance Data, 387*, 1–39.

Cluley, S., & Cochrane, G. M. (2001). Psychological disorder in asthma is associated with poor control and poor adherence to inhaled steroids. *Respiratory Medicine, 95*(1), 37–39.

Cooper, S., Oborne, J., Newton, S., Harrison, V., Thompson, C. J., Lewis, S., et al. (2003). Effect of two breathing exercises (Buteyko and pranayama) in asthma: A randomized controlled trial. *Thorax, 58*(8), 674–679.

Couriel, J. (2003). Asthma in adolescence. *Paediatric Respiratory Reviews, 4*, 47–54.

Cowie, R. L., Conley, D. P., Underwood, M. F., & Reader, P. G. (2008). A randomized controlled trail of the Buteyko technique as an adjunct to conventional management of asthma. *Respiratory Medicine, 102*, 726–732.

Creer, T. L. (2008). Behavioral and cognitive processes in the self-management of asthma. *Journal of Asthma, 45*, 81–94.

Currie, G. P., Douglas, J. G., & Heaney, L. G. (2009). Difficult to treat asthma in adults. *British Medical Journal, 338*, b494.

Custovic, A., Hallam, C., Woodcock, H., Simpson, B., Houghton, N., Simpson, A., et al. (2000). Synthetic pillows contain higher levels of cat and dog allergen than feather pillows. *Pediatric Allergy and Immunology, 11*, 71–73.

de Benedictis, D., & Bush, A. (2007). The challenge of asthma in adolescence. *Pediatric Pulmonology, 42*, 683–692.

Deshmukh, V. M., Toelle, B. G., Usherwood, T., O'Grady, B., & Jenkins, C. R. (2007). Anxiety, panic, and adult asthma: A cognitive-behavioral perspective. *Respiratory Medicine, 101*(2), 194–202.

Devine, E. C. (1996). Meta-analysis of the effects of psychoeducational care in adults with asthma. *Research in Nursing & Health, 19*, 367–376.

Doerschug, K. C., Peterson, M. W., Dayton, C. S., & Kline, J. N. (1999). Asthma guidelines: An assessment of physician understanding and practice. *American Journal of Respiratory and Critical Care Medicine, 159*, 1735–1741.

Federico, M. J., & Liu, A. H. (2003). Overcoming childhood asthma disparities of the inner city poor. *Pediatric Clinics of North America, 50*, 655–675.

Feldman, J. M., Siddique, M. I., Morales, E., Kaminski, B., Lu, S., & Lehrer, P. M. (2005). Psychiatric disorders and asthma outcomes among high-risk inner-city patients. *Psychosomatic Medicine, 67*, 989–996.

Finkelstein, J. A., Lozano, P., Faber, H. J., Miroshnik, I., & Lieu, T. A. (2002). Underuse of controller medication among Medicaid insured children with asthma. *Archives of Pediatric and Adolescent Medicine, 156*, 562–567.

Fritz, G. K., McQuaid, E. L., Spirito, A., & Klein, R. B. (1996). Symptom perception in pediatric asthma: Relationship to functional morbidity and psychological factors. *Journal of American Academy of Child and Adolescent Psychiatry, 35*(8), 1033–1041.

Gent, J. F., Belanger, K., Triche, E. W., Bracken, M. B., Beckett, W. S., & Leaderer, B. P. (in press). Association of pediatric asthma severity with exposure to common household dust allergens. *Environmental Research.*

Gibson, P. G., Powell, H., Coughlan, J., Wilson, A. J., Abramson, M., Haywood, P., et al. (2002). Self-management education and regular practitioner review for adults with asthma. *Cochrane Database of Systematic Reviews*, (3). Article No.: CD001117. DOI: 10.1002/14651858.CD001117.

Goodwin, R. D., & Eaton, W. W. (2003). Asthma and the risk of panic exacerbations among adults in the community. *Psychological Medicine, 33*, 879–885.

Goodwin, R. D., Jacobi, F., & Thefeld, W. (2003). Mental disorders and asthma in the community. *Archives of General Psychiatry, 60*, 1125–1130.

Gupta, R. S., Carrion-Carire, V., & Weiss, K. B. (2006). The widening black/white gap in asthma hospitalizations and mortality. *Journal of Allergy and Clinical Immunology, 117*, 351–358.

Harver, A. (1994). Effects of feedback on the ability of asthmatic subjects to detect increases in the flow-resistive component to breathing. *Health Psychology, 13* (1), 52–62.

Hasler, G., Gergen, P. J., Kleinbaum, D. G., Ajdacic, V., Gamma, A., Elch, D., et al. (2005). Asthma and panic in young adults: A 20-year prospective community study. *American Journal of Respiratory and Critical Care, 171*, 1224–1230.

Holloway, E. A., & West, R. J. (2007). Integrated breathing and relaxation training (the Papworth method) for adults with asthma in primary care: A randomized controlled trial. *Thorax, 62*, 1039–1042.

Holman, H., & Lorig, K. (2000). Patients as partners in managing chronic disease. Partnership is a prerequisite for effective and efficient health care. *British Medical Journal, 320*, 526–527.

Huntley, A., White, A. R., & Ernst, E. (2002). Relaxation therapies for asthma: A systematic review. *Thorax, 57*(2), 127–131.

Hyland, M. E., Ley, A., Fisher, D. W., & Woodward, V. (1995). Measurement of psychological distress in asthma and asthma management programmes. *British Journal of Clinical Psychology, 34*, 601–611.

Isenberg, S. A., Lehrer, P. M., & Hochron, S. (1992). The effects of suggestion and emotional arousal on pulmonary function in asthma: A review. *Psychosomatic Medicine, 54*(2), 192–216.

Ivanoa, J. I., Birnbaum, H. G., Hsieh, M., Yu, A. P., Seal, B., van der Molen, T., et al. (2008). Adherence to inhaled corticosteroid use and local adverse events in persistent asthma. *American Journal of Managed Care, 14*, 801–809.

Janssens, T., Verleden, G., De Peuter, S., Van Diest, I., & Van den Bergh, O. (2009). Inaccurate perception of asthma symptoms: A cognitive-affective framework and implications for asthma treatment. *Clinical Psychology Review, 29*, 317–327.

Juniper, E. F. (1997). Quality of life in adults and children with asthma and rhinitis. *Allergy, 52*(10), 971–977.

Juniper, E. F., Guyatt, G. H., Epstein, R. S., Ferrie, P. J., Jaeschke, R., & Hiller, T. K. (1992). Evaluation of impairment of health-related quality of life in asthma: Development of a questionnaire for use in clinical trials. *Thorax, 47*, 76–83.

Kaiser, H. B. (2007). Compliance and noncompliance in asthma. *Allergy and Asthma Proceedings, 28*(5), 514–516.

Katon, W., Von Korff, M., Lin, E., Simon, G., Walker, E., Unützer, J., et al. (1999). Stepped collaborative care for primary care patients with persistent symptoms of depression: A randomized trial. *Archives of General Psychiatry, 56*, 1109–1115.

Kendrick, A. H., Higgs, C. M., Whitfield, M. J., & Laszlo, G. (1993). Accuracy of perception of severity of asthma: Patients treated in general practice. *British Medical Journal, 307*(6901), 422–424.

Kifle, Y., Seng, V., & Davenport, P. W. (1997). Magnitude estimation of inspiratory resistive loads in children with life-threatening asthma. *American Journal of Respiratory and Critical Care Medicine, 156*(5), 1530–1535.

Kikuchi, Y., Okabe, S., Tamura, G., Hida, W., Homma, M., Shirato, K., & Takishima, T. (1994). Chemosensitivity and perception of dyspnea in patients with a history of near-fatal asthma. *New England Journal of Medicine, 330*(19), 1383–1384.

Kinsman, R. A., Luparello, T., O'Bannion, K., & Spector, S. (1973). Multidimensional analysis of the subjective symptomatology of asthma. *Psychosomatic Medicine, 35*, 250–267.

Kullowatz, A., Kanniess, F., Dahme, B., Magnussen, H., & Ritz, T. (2007). Association of depression and anxiety with health care use and quality of life in asthma patients. *Respiratory Medicine, 101*, 638–644.

Kwok, M. Y., Walsh-Kelly, C. M., Gorelick, M. H., Grabowski, L., & Kelly, K. J. (2006). National Asthma Education and Prevention Program severity classification as a measure of disease burden in children with acute asthma. *Pediatrics, 117*, S71–S77.

Lazarus, S. C., Boushey, H. A., Fahy, J. V., Chinchilli, V. M., Lemanske, R. F., Jr., Sorkness, C. A., et al. (2001). Long-acting beta2-agonist monotherapy vs. continued therapy with inhaled corticosteroids in patients with persistent asthma: A randomized controlled trial. *Journal of the American Medical Association, 285*, 2583–2593.

Ledogar, R. J., Penchaszadeh, A., Garden, C. C., & Iglesias, G. (2000). Asthma and Latino cultures: Different prevalence reported among groups sharing the same environment. *American Journal of Public Health, 90*, 929–935.

Lehrer, P. (1999). Case study: Treatment of a woman with co-morbid asthma and panic disorder. *Biofeedback, 27*(1), 31–32.

Lehrer, P., Song, H., Feldman, J., Giardino, N., & Schmaling, K. (2002). Psychological aspects of asthma. *Journal of Consulting and Clinical Psychology, 70*, 691–711.

Lehrer, P. M., Hochran, S., Carr, R., Edelberg, R., Hamer, R., Jackson, A., et al. (1996). Behavioral task-induced bronchodilation in asthma during active and passive tasks: A possible cholinergic link to psychologically induced airway changes. *Psychosomatic Medicine, 58* (5), 413–422.

Lehrer, P. M., Karavidas, M. K., Lu, S., Feldman, J., Kranitz, L., Abraham, S., et al. (2008). Psychological treatment of comorbid asthma and panic disorder: A pilot study. *Journal of Anxiety Disorders, 22*(4), 671–683.

Lehrer, P. M., Vaschillo, E., Vaschillo, B., Lu, S. E, Eckberg, D. L., Edelberg, R., et al. (2003). Heart rate variability biofeedback increases baroreflex gain and peak expiratory flow. *Psychosomatic Medicine, 651*, 796–805.

Lehrer, P. M., Vaschillo, E., Vaschillo, B., Lu, S. E., Scardella, A., Siddique, M., et al. (2004). Biofeedback treatment for asthma. *Chest, 126*(2), 352–361.

Leidy, N. K., Chan, K. S., & Coughlin, C. (1998). Is the asthma quality of life questionnaire a useful measure for low-income asthmatics? *American Journal of Respiratory and Critical Care Medicine, 158*, 1082–1090

Leidy, N. K., & Coughlin, C. (1998). Psychometric performance of the Asthma Quality of Life Questionnaire in a U.S. sample. *Quality of Life Research, 7*, 127–134.

Leventhal, H., Leventhal, E. A., & Contrada, R. J. (1998). Self-regulation, health, and behavior: A perceptual-cognitive approach. *Psychology and Health, 13*, 717–734.

Leventhal, H. Weinman, J., Leventhal, E. A., & Phillips, L. A. (2008). Health psychology: The search for pathways between behavior and health. *Annual Review of Psychology, 59*, 477–505.

Lewith, G. T., Hyland, M. E., & Shaw, S. (2002). Do attitudes toward and beliefs about complementary medicine affect treatment outcomes? *American Journal of Public Health, 92*(10), 1604–1606.

Litonjua, A. A., Carey, V. J., Burge, H. A., Weiss, S. T., & Gold, D. R. (2001). Exposure to cockroach allergen in the home is associated with incident doctor-diagnosed asthma and recurrent wheezing. *Journal of Allergy and Clinical Immunology, 107*(1), 41–47.

Lozano, P., Grothaus, L., Finkelstein, J., Hecht, J., Farber, H., & Lieu, T. (2003). Variability in asthma care and services for low income populations among practice sites in managed Medicaid system. *Health Service Research, 38*(6), 1563–1578.

Mainous, A. G., Majeed, A., Koopman, R. J., Baker, R., Everett, C. J., Tilley, B. C., & Diaz, V. A. (2006). Acculturation and diabetes among Hispanics: Evidence from the 1999-2002 national health and nutrition examination survey. *Public Health Reports, 121*, 60–66.

Martin, A., Rief, W., Klaiberg, A., & Braehler, E. (2006). Validity of the brief patient health questionnaire mood scale (PHQ-9) in the general population. *General Hospital Psychiatry, 28*(1), 71–77.

Martinez, F. D. (2009). Managing childhood asthma: Challenge of preventing exacerbations. *Pediatrics, 123*, s146–s150.

McCraty, R., Atkinson, M., & Tomasino, D. (2003). Impact of a workplace stress reduction program on blood pressure and emotional health in hypertensive employees. *Journal of Alternative & Complementary Medicine, 9*(3), 355–369.

Meng, A., & McConnell, S. (2003). Symptom perception and respiratory sensation: Clinical applications. *Nursing Clinics of North America, 38*, 737–748.

Nascimento, I., Nardi, A. E., Valença, A. M., Lopes, F. L., Mezzasalma, M. A., Nascentes, R., et al. (2002). Psychiatric disorders in asthmatic outpatients. *Psychiatry Research, 110*, 73–80.

Nardi, A. E., Freire, R. C., & Zin, W. A. (2009). Panic disorder and control of breathing. *Respiratory Physiology & Neurobiology, 167*, 133–143.

National Heart Lung and Blood Institute and the National Asthma Education and Prevention Program (NHLBI-NAEPP). (2007). *Expert panel report 3: Guidelines for the diagnosis and management of asthma.* Retrieved April 12, 2009, from http://www.nhlbi.nih.gov/guidelines/asthma/asthgdln.pdf

Nejtek, V. A., Brown, E. S., Khan, D. A., Moore, J. J., Van Wagner, J., & Perantic, D. C. (2001). Prevalence of mood disorders and relationship to asthma severity in patients at an inner-city asthma clinic. *Annals of Allergy, Asthma, and Immunology, 87*, 129–133.

Netuveli, G., Hurwitz, B., & Sheikh, A. (2005). Ethnic variations in incidence of asthma episodes in England & Wales: National study of 502,482 patients in primary care. *Respiratory Research, 6*, 120–125.

Nguyen, B. P., Wilson, S. R., & German, D. F. (1996). Patients' perceptions compared with objective ratings of asthma severity. *Annals of Allergy, Asthma, and Immunology, 77*(3), 209–215.

Nishimura, K., Hajiro, T., Oga, T., Tsukino, M., Sato, S., & Ikeda, A. (2005). A comparison of two simple measures to evaluate the health status of asthmatics: The asthma bother profile and the airways questionnaire 20. *Journal of Asthma, 41*(2), 141–146.

Piette, J. D., Heisler, M., & Wagner, T. H. (2004). Cost-related medication underuse among chronically ill adults: The treatment people forgo, how often, and who is at risk. *Research and Practice, 94*, 1782–1787.

Quinn, K., Shalowitz, M. U., Berry, C. A., Mijanovich, T., & Wolf, R. L. (2006). Racial and ethnic disparities in diagnosed and possible undiagnosed asthma among public-school children in Chicago. *American Journal of Public Health, 96*, 1599–1603.

Rand, C., Bilderback, A., Schiller, K., Edelman, J., Hustand, C., & Zeiger, R. (2007). Adherence with montelukast or fluticasone in a long-term clinical trial: Results from the mild asthma montelukast versus inhaled corticosteroid trial. *Journal of Allergy and Clinical Immunology, 119*(4), 916–923.

Reynolds, R. V., Kotses, H., & Creer, T. L. (1988). *Living with asthma: Help for adults.* Unpublished manuscript, Ohio University, Athens, OH.

Rietveld, S., Kolk, A. M., Prins, P. J., & Colland, V. T. (1997). The influence of respiratory sounds on breathlessness in children with asthma: A symptom-perception approach. *Health Psychology, 16*(6), 547–553.

Rietveld, S., Prins, P. J., & Kolk, A. M. (1996). The capacity of children with and without asthma to detect external resistive loads on breathing. *Journal of Asthma, 33*(4), 221–230.

Ritz, T., Bobb, C., Edwards, M., & Steptoe, A. (2001). The structure of symptom report in asthma A reevaluation. *Journal of Psychosomatic Research, 51*(5), 639–645.

Ritz, T., Steptoe, A., DeWilde, S. & Costa, M. (2000). Emotions and stress increase respiratory resistance in asthma. *Psychosomatic Medicine, 62*, 401–412.

Robinson, D. S., Campbell, D. A., Durham, S. R., Pfeffer, J., Barnes, P. J., Chung, K. F., & Asthma and Allergy Research Group of the National Heart and Lung Institute. (2003). Systematic assessment of difficult-to-treat asthma. *European Respiratory Journal, 22*(3), 478–483.

Rollman, B. L., Belnap, B. H., Mazumdar, S., Houck, P. R., Zhu, F., Gardner, W., et al. (2005). A randomized trial to improve the quality of treatment for panic and generalized anxiety disorders in primary care. *Archives of General Psychiatry, 62*, 1332–1341.

Rowe, B. H., & Oxman, A. D. (1993). Performance of an asthma quality life questionnaire in an outpatient setting. *American Review of Respiratory Disease, 148*(3), 675–681.

Roy-Byrne, P. P., Katon, W., Cowley, D. S., & Russo, J. (2001). A randomized effectiveness trial of collaborative care for patients with panic disorder in primary care. *Archives of General Psychiatry, 58*, 869–876.

Rushford, N., Tiller, J. W., & Pain, M. C. (1998). Perception of natural fluctuations in peak flow in asthma: Clinical severity and psychological correlates. *Journal of Asthma, 35*(3), 251–259.

Salpeter, S. R. (1998). Cardiovascular safety of beta2-adrenoceptor agonist use in patients with obstructive airway disease: A systematic review. *Drugs and Aging, 21*, 405–414.

Sano, F., Sole, D., & Naspitz, C. K. (1998). Prevalence and characteristics of exercise-induced asthma. *Pediatric, Allergy, and Immunology, 9*(4), 181–185.

Scardella, A., Siddique, M., Habib, R. H., Lehrer, P. M., Vaschillo, E., Vaschillo, B., & Lu, S. (2004). Biofeedback treatment for asthma. *Chest, 126*, 352–361.

Schmaling, K., McKnight, P., & Afari, N. (2002). A prospective study of the relationship of mood and stress to pulmonary function among patients with asthma. *Journal of Asthma, 39*, 501–520.

Schneider, A., Lowe, B., Meyer, F. J., Biessecker, K., Joos, S., & Szecsenyi, J. (2008). Depression and panic disorder as predictors of health outcomes for patients with asthma in primary care. *Respiratory Medicine, 102*(3), 359–366.

Shah, S., Peat, J. K., Mazurski, E. J., Wang, H., Sindusake, D., Bruce, C., et al. (2001). Effect of peer led programme for asthma education in adolscents: Cluster randomized controlled trial. *British Medical Journal, 322*, 583–585.

Smith, J. R., Mugford, M., Holland, R., Noble, M. J., & Harrison, B. D. W. (2007). Psycho-educational interventions for adults with severe or difficult asthma: A systematic review. *Journal of Asthma, 44*, 219–241.

Smyth, J. M., Stone, A. A., Hurewitz, A., & Kaell, A. (1999). Effects of writing about stressful experiences on symptom reduction in patients with asthma or rheumatoid arthritis. *Journal of the American Medical Association, 281*, 1304–1309.

Sobo, E., Seid, M., & Gelhard, L. (2006). Parent identified barriers to pediatric health care: A process oriented model. *Health Service Research, 41*(1), 148–172.

Stout, C., Kotses, H., & Creer, T. L. (1997). Improving perception of air flow obstruction in asthma patients. *Psychosomatic Medicine, 59*, 201–206.

Targonski, P. V., Perksky, V. W., Kelleher, P., & Addington, W. (1995). Characteristics of hospitalization for asthma among persons less than 35 years of age in Chicago. *Journal of Asthma, 32*(5), 365–372.

Thomas, M., McKinley, R. K., Mellor, S., Watkin, G., Holloway, E., Scullion, J., et al. (2009). Breathing exercises for asthma: A randomized controlled trial. *Thorax, 64*, 55–61.

Thomas, S. L., & Thomas, S. D. M. (2004). Displacement and health. *British Medical Bulletin, 69*, 115–127.

Tietz, W., Kahlstom, E., & Cardiff, M. (1975). Relationship of psychopathology to death in asthmatic adolescents. *Journal of Asthma Research, 12*(4), 199–206.

Toelle, B. G., & Ram, F. S. F. (2004). Written individualised management plans for asthma in children and adults. *Cochrane Database of Systematic Reviews*, (2). Article CD002171.

U.S. Environmental Protection Agency. (2003). *National survey on environmental management of asthma and children's exposure to environmental tobacco smoke.* Retrieved September 21, 2009, from http://www.epa.gov/asthma/pdfs/survey_fact_sheet.pdf

Vathenen, A. S., Knox, A. J., Wisiniewski, A., & Tattersfield, A. E. (1991). Time course of change in bronchial reactivity with an inhaled corticosteroid in asthma. *American Review of Respiratory Disease, 143*(6), 1317–1321.

Vidal, C., Fernandez-Ovide, E., Pinero, J., Nunez, R., & Gonzalez-Quintela, A. (2001). Comparison of montelukast versus budesonide in the treatment of exercise-induced bronchoconstriction. *Annals of Allergy, Asthma, & Immunology, 86*(6), 655–658.

Weiler, J. M., Bonini, S., Coifman, R., Craig, T., Delgado, L., Capão-Filipe, M., et al. (2007). *Journal of Allergy and Clinical Immunology, 119*, 1349–1358.

Williams, L. K., Pladevall, M., Xi, H., Peterson, E. L., Joseph, C., Lafata, J. E., et al. (2004). Relationship between adherence to inhaled corticosteroids and poor outcomes among adults with asthma. *Journal of Allergy and Clinical Immunology, 114*(6), 1288–1293.

Yorke, J., Fleming, S. L., & Shuldham, C. M. (2006). Psychological interventions for adults with asthma. *Cochrane Database of Systematic Reviews, 1,* Article CD002982. Retrieved September 26, 2009, from http://www.ncbi.nlm.nih.gov/pubmed/16437449

Type 2 Diabetes

26

Robert A. DiTomasso
Patrick D. Boyle
Larry H. Finkelstein
Harry J. Morris

Introduction

Diabetes mellitus (DM), a common, chronic disorder of the endocrine system, is distinguished by hyperglycemia, abnormally elevated glucose levels in the blood stream. Diabetics experience glucose metabolism abnormalities tied to alterations in the production and/or use of insulin by the body. Insulin, a critical hormone produced by the beta cells in the pancreas, impacts the manner in which glucose is used and stored by the body (Gonder-Frederick, Cox, & Ritterband, 2002). According to the National Diabetes Data Group (Harris et al., 1995), type 1 DM, insulin-dependent diabetes, is the most common disorder of childhood. The overwhelming majority of diabetics, 9 out of 10 patients diagnosed, however, suffer from type 2, noninsulin-dependent DM, which is highly related to age and obesity.

Diabetes type 1 was formerly called juvenile diabetes, occurring mainly in children to young adults, resulting from a lack of insulin produced from beta cells in the pancreas and from an autoimmune process. Diabetes type 2, formerly called adult-onset diabetes, the most common form, can occur at any age, including children, and occurs from impaired metabolism of insulin, primarily insulin resistance.

Type 2 diabetes, the fifth leading cause of death in the United States, is one of the most common chronic illnesses diagnosed today in the primary care setting (Ciechanowski, Katon, Russo, & Walker, 2001;; Hoff, Wagner, Mullins, & Chaney, 2003; Ismail, Winkley, & Rabe-Hesketh, 2004; Jenkins, 2004; Williams & Pickup, 2004; Zazworsky, Bolin, & Gaubeca, 2006). It affects nearly 20.8 million children and adults in the United States, and at least 150 million people worldwide. The United States is currently witnessing an epidemic of type 2 diabetes, and the number of people diagnosed is expected to double by 2025 (Williams & Pickup).

Type 2 diabetes is caused by both impaired insulin secretion and resistance to the action of insulin on its target cells. Insulin is a hormone that is needed to convert sugar, starches, and other food into energy needed for daily life (Williams & Pickup, 2004; Zazworsky et al., 2006). As a result of the insulin defect, glucose does not enter the body's cells where it can be used as fuel, and instead, remains in the blood stream. Early in the course of the disease, the body tries to counteract the high levels of blood glucose by producing more insulin. Although the pancreas continues to produce a sufficient amount of insulin, the body loses its ability to maintain euglycemia, a normal glucose level (Williams & Pickup; Zazworsky et al.). As the disease progresses, the pancreas loses its ability to produce insulin and insulin levels drop off. The overall goal of diabetic management is "tight" glucose control, keeping blood glucose levels with the normal range. Normal fasting glucose is 99 milligrams per deciliter or less; impaired fasting glucose is 100–125 mg/dL. Diabetes diagnosis is equal to or greater than 126 mg/dL on 2 separate *fasting* specimens. Normal nonfasting glucose is less than or equal to 139 mg/dL, and impaired glucose tolerance is 140–199 mg/dL. Diabetes diagnosis is at greater than or equal to 200 mg/dL, again with two separate *nonfasting* specimens.

Maintaining tight blood glucose control requires considerable and consistent efforts on the part of the patient, including dietary restrictions, weight management, physical exercise, blood glucose monitoring and recording, close medical follow-up, periodic diagnostic testing, medication adherence, foot care, visual follow-up, and a number of other psychological and behavioral factors that may adversely impact glucose levels (Gonder-Frederick et al., 2002; Ismail et al., 2004). Although no small challenge, the benefits of achieving and maintaining good control in both type 1 and type 2 diabetics is compelling. Good monitoring and tight control delay the inception of and prevents the occurrence of serious, long-term consequences to the visual and renal systems (DCCT Research Group, 1993). Standard medical care also dictates management of blood pressure and cholesterol levels as a means of preventing cardiovascular complications. A consideration of the requisite behavioral changes for attaining and maintaining control coupled with the numerous potential factors that can undermine it, underscores the critical contribution of psychological, cognitive, social, and behavioral factors.

Assessment and Diagnosis Issues

Like all chronic medical disorders, it is virtually impossible to separate the physical manifestations from the psychosocial aspects of this problem. However, DM is obviously a diagnosis made by primary care physicians (PCPs), based on established and well-accepted reliable and valid biological markers. In integrating care with the PCP, the cognitive-behavioral therapy (CBT) clinician must be aware of each of the points of contact in the course of the disease when cognitive-behavioral factors are implicated. There are many factors to which the CBT clinician must attend, and requires a thorough understanding about diabetes, the adjustment to having been diagnosed with a chronic disorder, the factors influencing this disorder, and associated factors that may sustain or exacerbate the condition.

Assessment and diagnosis of diabetic patients is important in identifying factors that are most likely to impede patients from assuming the stringent regimen of requisite self-care to address the problem. A thorough consideration of important psychological, behavioral, and emotional factors is critical in understanding the challenges faced by the diabetic patient. Gonder-Frederick et al. (2002) have provided a comprehensive model delineating major target areas for consideration in assessment of the diabetic patient, including initial and on-going adjustment to the disease, adherence, knowledge, skills, empowerment issues, health beliefs, self-efficacy, distorted thinking, health locus of control, psychological disorders (depression, anxiety, phobia, and eating disorders), psychological distress, and social-environmental factors (family, social support).

At the most basic level, the clinician must be thoroughly familiar with an understanding of factors related to the self-care process. The clinician must be aware that although DM is equally prevalent in males and females, the risk of developing noninsulin-dependent diabetes is higher in minorities and in those with a family history of the problem (Gonder-Frederick et al., 2002). Beyond these demographic factors, clinicians must be aware of numerous areas in need of assessment, including knowledge about diabetes, understanding and ability to perform self-care behaviors, nonadherence problems, depression, anxiety, hypoglycemia phobia, eating disorders, smoking, drinking, diet, exercise, family stress, and social support.

Adjustment

The initial psychosocial factor affecting those newly diagnosed with type 2 diabetes is usually stress related to the onset and subsequent lifestyle changes associated with the disease (Hoff et al., 2003; Trozzolino, Thompson, Tansman, & Azen, 2003; Zazworsky et al., 2006). A diagnosis of any disease can force an individual into a crisis period, especially for a disease that demands such an extreme lifestyle change such as type 2 diabetes. When patients first learn that they are diabetic, many times they initially experience denial, which may delay the action needed to control lifestyle changes and ultimately, glucose control. For many people in the United States, sugary and fatty foods are frequently the most conveniently available foods that they enjoy. Altering ingrained eating habits is often a source of distress for many individuals with type 2 diabetes (Jenkins, 2004).

Nonadherence

The question of nonadherence is an extremely important consideration for the clinician. Diabetes is a disease in which successful management depends primarily on self-care. Diabetics are expected to perform a variety of behaviors that are critical to maintaining tight blood glucose control. This demanding behavioral regimen includes things such as daily self-monitoring of blood glucose levels with a glucometer, pricking fingers to obtain blood samples, avoidance and/or limited intake of certain types of foods, taking daily medication, increasing exercise, and the like. An assessment of adherence across a variety of specific behavioral indicators is, therefore, necessary. A cognitive social learning indicator of relevance includes the extent to which the patient believes he/she is capable of implementing the behavioral regimen in an effective manner to produce necessary changes. Likewise, assessing whether a patient believes that successful disease management is a function of self-determined, internal factors possessed within versus factors outside of the self, including powerful others or random factors of chance, are important as well (Gonder-Frederick et al., 2002). In effect, diabetic patients are expected to engage in and sustain a demanding regimen to achieve metabolic control. The patient with an internal locus of control who has a great deal of self-efficacy about his/her ability to achieve the desired outcome would be expected to fare well. In contrast, the patient with little belief in his/her ability to perform the requisite tasks and who sees good health as determined solely by luck is another matter.

Attachment Style

Ciechanowski and colleagues (2001) conducted a study examining how a patient's attachment style in relationships may affect their self-care and health outcomes among patients diagnosed with diabetes. They speculated that attachment styles affect a patient's every interaction, especially those with their physicians and important others who assist in managing of their diabetes. They gathered self-report data from 4,095 primary care patients diagnosed with diabetes, assessing the patients' attachment styles (secure, dismissing, preoccupied, or fearful), patient-physician relationship, diabetic self-care, and depression status. Ciechanowski and colleagues also had access to pharmacy and laboratory information, as well as glycosylated hemoglobin levels of the participants. They hypothesized that patients with less secure attachments to their physicians would adhere less to their treatment than patients with a reported secure relationship. Results showed that patients who had a dismissing attachment style, characterized by perceiving others as emotionally unresponsive and untrustworthy, practiced significantly lower exercise, foot care, diet management, adherence to oral medications and smoked more. These patients may mistrust their physicians and exhibit a self-reliance that could be deterring them from participating in treatment planning and adherence. Patients who reported a preoccupied attachment style, characterized by overdependence on others, had significantly lower rates of unhealthy glycosylated hemoglobin levels as compared with those with a secure attachment style. Ciechanowski and colleagues posit that these patients may report more symptoms, present to physicians for treatment more often, and may try to please their health care professionals more by complying with treatment, which could result in healthier glucose levels. The results support the hypothesis that attachment styles play a role in patients' diabetic self-care.

Positive Affect

Whereas the relationship between depression and diabetes has been well established by research, Moskowitz, Epel, and Acree (2008) studied the role of positive affect in health outcomes of people diagnosed with diabetes. They reported that people with diabetes are prone to stress and depression because of the chronic nature of their illness, but hypothesize that positive affect can lower or buffer stress, and can contribute to a lower mortality rate among diabetics. Using a longitudinal cohort study design, Moskowitz et al. reviewed data from the National Health and Nutrition Examination Study I and the Epidemiologic Follow-Up Study, a nationwide study that interviewed people between the ages of 25 and 75 on various health-related topics. The participants were interviewed in 1973, 1982, 1987, and 1992. Moskowitz et al. hypothesized that, among people diagnosed with diabetes, positive affect is predictive of mortality, and that the association between positive affect and mortality differs from the association among people not diagnosed with a serious medical condition. They found that positive affect, as measured by the Center for Epidemiologic Studies Depression Scale, was significantly associated with a lower risk of mortality from any cause among diabetic patients. Patients who endorsed that they enjoyed life had a lower mortality risk, despite their reporting concurrent negative affect and subjective stress. Positive affect was not significantly associated with risk of mortality in a sample of patients who were not diagnosed with chronic medical illnesses. This study provides support to the notion that positive affect is predictive of better health outcomes among diabetics (Moskowitz et al.).

Depression

Another psychosocial factor affecting those diagnosed with type 2 diabetes is depression. Therefore, the CBT clinician should be attuned to potential issues related to depression. Diabetics are twice as likely to suffer from depression than those without diabetes (Hoff et al., 2003; Williams & Pickup, 2004). Given the overlap between diabetic symptoms and vegetative signs of depression, such as loss of energy, fatigue, and loss of motivation, the risk is that diabetic patients may go undiagnosed (Lustman et al., 1997). Among those with type 2 diabetes, the highest rates of depression are observed in hospitalized patients and those suffering from macrovascular disease, chronic foot ulceration, retinopathy, and previous psychopathology. Women with type 2 diabetes are more likely to suffer from depression than men with the disease (Hoff et al., 2003; Williams & Pickup, 2004), necessitating the need to carefully screen female patients. Although the precipitants of depression frequently stem from the medical complications associated with type 2 diabetes, depression is a serious consideration in all patients with type 2 diabetes, as it occurs in about one in five patients. Depression, therefore, may not only be caused by type 2 diabetes and its complications, but may also exacerbate the complications of the disease. Type 2 diabetics suffering from depression are less likely to control their sugar intake and to adhere to a treatment regimen (Boyle, Allan, & Millar, 2004; Ciechanowski et al., 2001; Hoff et al., 2003; Ismail et al., 2004). In some patients, the constant threat of serious complications, including loss of sight or a limb, could easily create a cycle of disillusionment and depression.

According to a meta-analysis of literature on depression and glycemic control, Lustman et al. (2000) reported that more than 25% of patients with diabetes report experiencing some type of depression, which has a negative effect on quality of life and daily functioning. In reviewing almost 30 relevant studies, they found that depression is linked to poor glycemic control, especially with hyperglycemia. They estimated that the treatment of depressive symptoms could increase the percentage of diabetic patients with good glycemic control from 41 to 58%. They also found some support for the hypothesis that there is a reciprocal relationship between hyperglycemia and depression, as depression may cause hyperglycemia and hyperglycemia may exacerbate depressive symptoms (Lustman et al.).

Anxiety and Phobia

Anxiety level and phobic reactions are other areas that should be assessed. Some patients, especially those high in trait anxiety who may be stress sensitive, may experience elevated blood sugars during sympathetic activation. Screening patients for anxiety levels is, therefore, important. Clinicians should also focus on family functioning, as chronic family stress may contribute to the brittle diabetic. Likewise, level of social support may also be important for promoting family functioning, reducing family stressors, and increasing adherence.

Collins, Corcoran, and Perry (2009) conducted a cross-sectional study of 2049 patients diagnosed with diabetes types 1 and 2 in Ireland, in order to determine prevalence rates and risk factors of anxiety and depression symptoms in the diabetic population. Using the Hospital Anxiety and Depression Scale (HADS), they identified that 32% of patients who responded scored with "mild to severe" anxiety and 22.4% scored with "mild to severe" depression. Structured general practitioner care, private medical insurance, and the perception of "about right" glycemic control were identified as protective factors, and significantly associated with lower anxiety and depression scores on the HADS. Medical complications from diabetes, smoking, unemployment, poor perceived glycemic control, and heavy drinking (or a history of heavy drinking) were significant risk factors for higher anxiety and depression scores on the HADS (Collins et al.).

The CBT clinician should assess patients for past episodes of hypoglycemia and their impact, as well. Symptoms associated with these episodes are often quite aversive and frightening, and create a significant level of distress and avoidance. These patients may be fearful of low blood sugar and may choose to keep their levels at dangerously high levels. Likewise, they may be so focused upon scanning for early potential signs and symptoms of hypoglycemia that panic episodes may be triggered. Some patients may even have difficulty distinguishing anxiety symptoms from glucose-related symptoms.

Wild et al. (2007) studied the phenomenon of fear of hypoglycemia among patients with diabetes and its impact on treatment. Hypoglycemia is one of the most common negative outcomes of insulin treatment for type 1 and type 2 diabetics. Whereas insulin is used to lower blood glucose levels in order to maintain normal glycated hemoglobin values, sometimes the insulin itself can cause blood glucose levels to drop lower than is needed, causing hypoglycemia. Hypoglycemia can occur suddenly and cause the patient to suffer the often unpleasant symptoms of shaking, nausea, confusion, negative mood, and, sometimes, unconsciousness. Although these symptoms are similar to those of anxiety, sometimes causing difficulties in distinguishing hypoglycemia and anxiety, hypoglycemia does not cause diarrhea, muscle tension, or dry mouth. An acute episode of hypoglycemia can be traumatic for patients with diabetes and can cause a fear of hypoglycemia, which further complicates their diabetic treatment (Wild et al., 2007).

Wild et al. (2007) further noted that fear of hypoglycemia is common among diabetics, and that the greatest risk factor for hypoglycemia appears to be a history of hypoglycemia, with three factor being significantly and positively correlated with fear of hypoglycemia: number of hospitalizations due to hypoglycemia, time since initial insulin treatment, and frequency of hypoglycemia symptoms affecting work life. It is also noted that diabetic patients with lower blood glucose levels and a higher blood glucose level variability reported greater fear of hypoglycemia (Wild et al.). Irvine, Cox, and Gonder-Frederick (1992) and Berlin et al. (1997) identified that fear of hypoglycemia, combined with other phobic symptoms related to diabetes, such as fears of blood and injection, contribute to increased psychological distress and anxiety and decreased the number of daily blood glucose level checks.

Both state and trait anxiety are linked to fear of hypoglycemia (Wild et al., 2007). Anxiety and its related physical arousal are considered a symptom of hypoglycemia, and higher levels of anxiety can make actual hypoglycemia harder to detect, increasing the risk of patients suffering from severe hypoglycemia episodes. Diabetic patients can develop further disorders, such as agoraphobia and panic disorder, as a result of their fear of hypoglycemia. Patients may form unhealthy habits in order to prevent hypoglycemia, such as maintaining dangerously high blood glucose levels. Research supports the efficacy of CBT interventions and blood glucose awareness training (BGAT) in treating the fear of hypoglycemia, and subsequently preventing its complications and effects on diabetic treatment (Wild et al.).

Eating Disorders

Given the increased incidence of eating disorders in adolescent and young adult female diabetics (Jones, Lawson, Daneman, Olmsted, & Rodin, 2000), the clinician should be aware of this possibility especially in female diabetics. One of the authors has seen several female diabetic adults whose eating problems significantly impacted their condition. In one instance, a female patient limited her eating to such an extreme that her usual insulin regimen precipitated repeated episodes of severe hypoglycemia. In a second instance, a middle-aged diabetic with a previously undiagnosed eating disorder of anorexia, and who lived alone, was found unconscious by family members on several occasions from hypoglycemia stemming from refusal to eat, related to a fear of becoming fat.

Smoking

Nicotine intake, which impacts the vascular system, is another area of concern requiring assessment. Diabetics who smoke are at increased risk for microvascular and macrovascular problems (Gonder-Frederick et al., 2002). Therefore, all patients should be screened for smoking behavior.

Alcohol

Drinking alcohol is another high-risk behavior in diabetics, as excessive alcohol use may increase blood sugar levels. The use of screening measures to assess the presence of alcohol abuse and dependence should be considered.

Food Intake

Diet and weight control are important areas to assess, as well. Asking patients to self-monitor types, quantities, and frequency of food intake and a thorough analysis of such information are indicated. Diets high in carbohydrates, starches, fats, and sugars are problematic for obvious reasons.

Physical Activity

Level of physical activity is another important area to assess. A careful examination of amount and types of physical activity should be conducted. In patients who are engaging in exercise, a consideration of proper footwear should be addressed.

Sexual Functioning

Sexual dysfunction is another psychosocial factor associated with type 2 diabetes and, therefore, requires assessment. Male diabetes are two times as likely to experience erectile dysfunction, loss of libido, and ejaculatory failure as men without diabetes (Williams & Pickup, 2004; Zazworsky et al., 2006). Though sexual dysfunction is less common in women, type 2 diabetic females are at a higher risk of vaginal dryness and impaired sexual arousal. The effects of the sexual dysfunction on the diabetic individual, including decreased self-esteem and increased relationship problems, can be the same as in medically well individuals. Also, the dysfunction may not solely be a result of a medical complication of diabetes, but can also be caused by psychological factors associated with the disease, such as depression and anxiety (Williams & Pickup; Zazworsky et al.).

Incidence and Clinical Manifstations

An estimated 11 million people in the United States were diagnosed with diabetes in the year 2000, 90% of those having type 2 diabetes (Hoff et al., 2003). Currently, 20.8 million children and adults (7.0% of the population) have diabetes. About 10.9 million, or 10.5% of all men, and 9.7 million, or 8.8% of all women ages 20 years or older, have diabetes. Of great concern, however, is that nearly one-third of them do not know they have the disease.

About 13.1 million, or 8.7% of all non-Hispanic Whites aged 20 years or older have diabetes, whereas 3.2 million, or 13.3% of all non-Hispanic Blacks aged 20 years or older have diabetes. Mexican Americans, the largest Hispanic/Latino subgroup, are 1.7 times as likely to have diabetes as non-Hispanic Whites. If the prevalence of diabetes among Mexican Americans were applied to the total

Hispanic/Latino population, about 2.5 million (9.5%) Hispanic/Latino Americans aged 20 years or older would have diabetes (Williams & Pickup, 2004).

Two complications resulting from type 2 diabetes are worthy of note: hypoglycemia and hyperglycemia (Williams & Pickup, 2004). Hypoglycemia, dangerously low blood sugar level, as noted previously, may result in shakiness, headaches, hunger, mood changes, and/or attentional difficulties. Hyperglycemia, dangerously high blood sugar level, on the other hand, may result in increased thirst, increased urination, and glucose in the urine.

Most of the long-term complications associated with type 2 diabetes stem from recurrent hyperglycemia (Hoff et al., 2003; Williams & Pickup, 2004). DM types 1 and 2 are associated with an increased risk for heart attack, stroke, and complications related to poor circulation. Diabetes can also cause damage to the kidney, resulting in impaired ability to filter out waste products and, ultimately, kidney failure. DM can also cause eye problems, eventually leading to retinopathy or blindness. A common complication of diabetes is diabetic neuropathy (Williams & Pickup), damage to the nerves that run throughout the body, connecting the spinal cord to muscles, skin, blood vessels, and other organs. Diabetics can also develop many different and severe foot problems, resulting from nerve damage in the feet or when peripheral blood flow is compromised. As many as one third of people with diabetes will have a skin disorder that is caused or affected by diabetes at some time in their lives. In fact, such problems are sometimes the first indicator that a person has diabetes (Williams & Pickup).

There are many demographic and genetic risk factors associated with developing type 2 diabetes that have significant implications for assessment and treatment. The greatest risk factor for diabetes is obesity (Hoff et al., 2003; Williams & Pickup, 2004), which contributes to diabetes by causing insulin resistance. About 80% of type 2 diabetics are, in fact, obese. The risk of developing diabetes increases progressively as body mass index (BMI) increases.

Even in the absence of obesity, physical inactivity is another potential risk factor for developing type 2 diabetes. Those who exercise the most have a 25–60% lower risk of developing type 2 diabetes, regardless of other risk factors (Williams & Pickup, 2004).

Another potential risk factor is age. Those over the age of 45 are at a higher risk of developing type 2 diabetes, and approximately 20% of people over the age of 65 are diagnosed with diabetes. Individuals with a first-degree relative that has been diagnosed with early-onset type 2 diabetes are 40% more likely to be diagnosed with it than people with no family history (Hoff et al., 2003). Geographic setting may also be a risk factor. In many regions, diabetes is more common in urban areas than rural areas. Unemployment, social deprivation, and poverty in city dwellers may make them more susceptible to physical inactivity and unhealthy diets (Williams & Pickup, 2004).

To prevent complications from type 2 diabetes, the newly diagnosed person must follow a complicated treatment regimen daily, usually consisting of a restrictive nutritional regimen, an exercise program, oral medications, and, in more serious cases, insulin injections (Hoff et al., 2003; Searight, 1999; Zazworsky et al., 2006). The person must restrict sugar and fat intake, must decrease the amount of calories consumed per day, and be encouraged to begin aerobic and muscle-strengthening exercises regularly (Williams & Pickup, 2004). The responsibility of controlling the diabetes through this treatment regimen falls mostly on the individual. Searight (1999) reports that 80% of patients do not take their insulin in the appropriate manner, between 35% and 75% do not adhere to their diets, and 40% fail to test their blood sugar regularly. These are important manifestations to which the PCP must be alert.

Brief Case History

Two years ago Maria, a 34-year-old, second-generation Italian who works as an admissions director of a local university, presented to her PCP with symptoms of frequent urination, excessive thirst, and fatigue. Maria is a moderately obese woman with poor eating habits. She also complained of numbness in her toes on both feet for the past 4 years, which she attributed to her high-heeled shoes. Her PCP diagnosed her with type 2 diabetes and initially prescribed glucophage—500 mg twice daily. Difficulty with tolerating side effects of this medication resulted in a switch to 2.5 mg of glipezide daily and 30 mg of Pioglitazone daily. She was also asked to monitor her glucose level, begin an exercise program, and to lose weight. After several months of being unable to bring her blood sugars into tight control and her lack of success in changing her lifestyle habits, her physician switched her medical regimen to insulin. Being high in trait anxiety, Maria has been undergoing a significant level of state anxiety related to recently developing problems tied to a marked decrease in applications to her college, probably secondary to the financial crisis. She has been worrying about a number of problems in her life, including job stressors, relationship issues, and her medical problems. About a week ago, Maria experienced a hypoglycemic episode that was extremely aversive. During this time, she became very shaky, disoriented, and confused. Since that time, Maria has become quite fearful of hypoglycemia, and panicky whenever she injects herself with insulin. She has become so focused on herself that she is in a constant state of anxiety and has difficulty distinguishing her anxiety from symptoms of low blood sugar. As a result, she carries a quart of orange juice with her wherever she goes, and has become obsessed with her sugar levels to the point where she is checking her sugars, in some instances, several times an hour.

Cognitive-Behavioral Case Conceptualization

The following case conceptualization is based on the model presented by Nezu, Nezu, and Lombardo (2004), described in an earlier part of this volume. The goal of the case conceptualization is to identify the patient's presenting problem, identify related variables in the patient's life, and delineate treatment targets, goals, and objectives. Maria's presenting problems include her consistent anxiety regarding diabetic symptoms, poor glucose control, and obsessively checking her blood sugar. Ultimate outcome goals for Maria are to decrease her symptoms of anxiety and to effectively maintain control of her type 2 diabetes. Instrumental outcome goals for Maria are to distinguish between her anxiety symptoms and symptoms of hypoglycemia, to learn to control her anxiety symptoms, and to learn techniques to maintain healthy blood glucose levels.

Problem behaviors are multifaceted, and symptoms can emerge from multiple paths, including cognitive, affective, behavioral, environmental, and biological factors. Maria's problem behavior of experiencing anxiety symptoms related to her diabetes and obsessively checking her blood sugar stem from a constellation of factors. Cognitive factors include her thoughts related to misinterpretation of physical symptoms. Affective factors include her trait anxiety, which affects her in many areas of life. Behavioral factors include her being reinforced for checking her blood sugar and practicing safety behaviors. Environmental factors include Maria's work stressors, relationship issues, medical problems, and her family's continued poor eating habits. Biological factors include her diabetes and predisposition toward anxious reactions. The constellation of factors contributes to her problem behavior in several ways. Maria's biological predisposition toward anxiety leads her to experience excessive worry regarding her diabetic symptoms. She misinterprets physiological symptoms of anxiety as symptoms of hypoglycemia, which contributes to her feelings of excessive worry. She then exhibits safety behaviors, such as checking her blood sugars and carrying orange juice with her, rather than focusing on more long-term means to control her diabetes, such as weight loss and diet adherence. Her symptoms of anxiety and worry are constantly exacerbated by stressors regarding work and relationship issues and other factors, including her history of anxiety and her family's modeling of unhealthy eating habits.

According to the Nezu, Nezu, and Lombardo (2004) model of case conceptualization, the treatment plan for Maria would then include a review of her instrumental outcome goals and variables related to the problem behaviors, and the development of alternative behaviors. Maria's first instrumental outcome goal is to learn to distinguish between her anxiety symptoms and symptoms of hypoglycemia. Distal variables that contribute to the problem behavior are Maria's trait anxiety and her diabetes. Antecedent variables that contribute to the problem behavior are experiencing physiological symptoms of anxiety that overlap with the recently experienced and highly aversive symptoms of hypoglycemia. The consequences of Maria checking her blood sugar frequently and engaging in safety behaviors are that she feels an immediate relief from her symptoms of anxiety, but inconveniences herself by checking her blood levels too frequently and carrying orange juice with her. The treating therapist must assist Maria to identify her specific symptoms of anxiety in detail and her symptoms of hypoglycemia in detail. The therapist and Maria can then realistically evaluate Maria's anxiety by eliciting some of the symptoms of anxiety in session, and having Maria predict her blood sugar level based on the physiological symptoms. Maria can then check her blood sugar level in session to test out her predictions regarding low blood sugar. The discrepancy between Maria's predicted sugar level based on her anxiety symptoms and her actual sugar level will help her to distinguish between anxiety and hypoglycemic symptoms. The therapist and Maria must continue to focus on appropriate means to prevent hypoglycemia and actions to take if Maria experiences real hypoglycemia.

Maria's next instrumental treatment goal is to control her symptoms of anxiety. Maria experiences trait and state anxiety often, regarding many stressors. Distal variables contributing to Maria's anxiety include her biological predisposition for anxious reactions and ongoing stressors in her life. Antecedent variables include work stressors related to the financial crisis and worry regarding symptoms and complications from her diabetes. The consequences of Maria's anxiety are that she feels worried and on edge much of the time, leading to an unhealthy lifestyle. The therapist treating Maria will assist her to learn relaxation techniques, such as progressive muscle relaxation, in order to decrease her physiological reactions to stress and to focus her mind. The therapist and Maria will also work on cognitive restructuring to assess Maria's thoughts and feelings regarding the stressors in her life and that contribute to her anxiety. The therapist will assist Maria to test how adaptive, realistic, and useful her anxious thoughts are and to develop more realistic, appropriate, and less anxiety-provoking thoughts.

Maria's third and final instrumental outcome goal is to develop techniques that will help her to maintain a healthy blood glucose level and to control her diabetes. Distal variables that contribute to Maria's lack of success in controlling her blood glucose levels include the lifestyle that she has developed in her family, cultural, and socioeconomic environment. Antecedent variables include Maria's and her family's eating habits, and Maria's excessive focus on immediate symptoms of hypoglycemia and her insulin injections. The therapist will assist Maria's to practice behavioral strategies focusing on stimulus and environmental controls that will contribute to changing her eating habits. Maria can also develop a self-reinforcing token economy system to increase her participation in an exercise routine. The therapist can assist Maria to participate in individual or group sessions of BGAT to help her learn strategies to control her blood glucose level through increased awareness. It is essential that the therapist involve Maria's family in order to achieve the instrumental goal of controlling her blood glucose levels and diabetic symptoms. The therapist can invite the family into specific sessions in order to discuss the role that eating and food plays in their household. The therapist will educate the family on healthy lifestyles and will emphasize their role in assisting Maria to lose weight and maintain healthy blood glucose levels.

Reviewing and considering the reciprocal interactions between the many factors that contribute to the development of Maria's problem behaviors will assist Maria and the therapist to target the areas in Maria's life that are most maladaptive and in need of change. Keeping this constellation of variables in mind throughout the treatment will assist the therapist and Maria to achieve her instrumental goals, while working toward her ultimate goals of decreasing her symptoms of anxiety and effectively maintaining control of her type 2 diabetes.

Identifying and Addressing Obstacles to Treatment

There are a number of factors that may interfere with the treatment of diabetic patients. The CBT clinician should be on the lookout for any number of relevant factors that may present obstacles.

Depression

Depression in people with diabetes is highly correlated with poor physical health outcomes (Sacco & Yanover, 2006). The prevalence rate of depression among those with diabetes is twice as high as that among the nondiabetic population, and those suffering from depression have a higher rate of medical complications and nonadherence.

Swenson, Rose, Vittinghoff, Stewart, and Schillinger (2008) investigated the influence of depressive symptoms on diabetic patients' perceived communication with health care clinicians. Patients with depression report less satisfaction with their medical care and more unfulfilled needs than nondepressed patients. Effective medical communication should enhance the clinician-patient relationship, and allow the physician to gather and share information, obtain the patient's perspective on his/her illness, and collaboratively negotiate the appropriate treatment for the illness. Depressed patients who perceive that their doctors share more information with them and work collaboratively are more engaged in their diabetic self-management and more likely to adhere to their antidepressant treatment. Swenson et al. conducted a study comparing a group of nondepressed diabetic patients with diabetic patients who reported having depressive symptoms. They found that the depressed group reported more unsatisfactory patient–clinician communication across several communication domains, including empowerment, patient explanations of conditions, and elicitation of patient concerns.

Swenson et al. (2008) hypothesized several explanations why depressed diabetic patients perceive less effective communication with their primary care givers. During the visit to their physician, diabetic patients may exhibit impaired social skills and express hopelessness and negative affect. According to Swenson et al., this depressed style of communication may lead to the patient being less well liked by the physician, which decreases collaboration and elicits a more directive, authoritarian communication style from the physician. Another explanation for the perceived poor communication is that the doctor and patient have mismatched expectations of the treatment that are not thoroughly expressed; comorbid depressive and diabetic symptoms create competing demands of the treatment, resulting in the depression not being detected or being mistreated by the physician. Finally, the perceived poor communication may result from memory deficits related to depression, causing the patient to be unable to recall specific aspects of physician visits, and from the negative cognitive bias often exhibited by patients with depression (Swenson et al.).

In an earlier study, Sacco et al. (2005) identified other factors that may increase the likelihood of depression among those diagnosed with type 2 diabetes. They studied the role of diet and exercise adherence, BMI, and self-efficacy in exacerbating depression in diabetic patients. Exercise interventions have been shown to decrease depression, and physical inactivity, weight gain, and the failure to lose weight have been shown to result in greater depression. Sacco et al. suggest that the inability to maintain a healthy BMI or having a high BMI may also contribute to depression. They posit that the failure to adhere to diet and exercise plans, as well as failing to maintain a healthy BMI, will contribute to low self-efficacy among patients with diabetes, which will manifest as increased depression. Self-efficacy is a person's beliefs and perceptions about their own abilities to achieve tasks and perform skills adequately (Bandura, 1998, as cited in Sacco et al.). Sacco et al. studied the self-reports of 56 people diagnosed with type 2 diabetes regarding diet and exercise adherence, self-efficacy, and depression, and obtained BMI information from medical records. They found that the results supported the notion that adherence and BMI both contributed to the patients' self-efficacy, which also contributed to the patient's adherence behaviors and depressive symptoms. Patients with high BMIs and low adherence had lower self-efficacy and were, in turn, less adherent with their diabetic treatment and suffered more severe depression (Sacco et al.)

Misunderstanding and Lack of Education

Another barrier to treatment is misunderstanding and lack of education regarding diabetes and its treatment. In a qualitative study of diabetic patient-physician interactions conducted in Sweden, Holmstrom and Rosenqvist (2005) reported several themes regarding patients' misunderstandings about their diabetic treatment, and suggested methods to improve patient understanding. They observed that diabetic patients expressed that type 2 diabetes is not "real" diabetes, had "horror visions," or simply suppressed knowledge regarding complications from diabetes, saw self-monitoring of blood glucose as merely a routine rather than a means to learn, expressed that reducing fat is the most important aspect of controlling diet, and reported that they knew exercise is good for them, but were unclear on the specific benefits of exercise. Holmstrom and Rosenqvist (2005) suggest patient education be tailored to each individual patient and his/her understanding and expression of diabetes.

Nagelkerk, Rieck, and Meengs (2006) found that the most commonly identified barriers to diabetes control were lack of knowledge about specific diet plans, feelings of helplessness and frustration at continued progression of the illness despite adherence, and lack of understanding of their treatment plan. Effective strategies to treat diabetes, such as maintaining a collaborative relationship with physicians, developing and keeping a positive attitude that encourages learning about the illness, and identifying support people to provide encouragement and assistance with treatment adherence are indicated (Nagelkerk, Rieck, & Meengs).

In sum, the clinician must be assured that potential obstacles related to the patient, such as lack of knowledge about the disease, its consequences, and what can be done to alleviate and offset health risks, are addressed. Facilitating family and other available means of social support in the patient's environment and vigorous treatment of other lifestyle habits that may prevent tight control must be examined and targeted.

Points of Collaboration With Physicians and Family

In efforts to assist patients with diabetes, it is critical to work closely with the PCP and to capitalize on every available opportunity that exists. First and foremost, whereas diabetes is a disease that requires self-management, the pathway to achieving this ultimate goal of tight control requires that the therapist collaborate with the patient and physician. Because the physician-patient relationship is such a potent mechanism for fostering adherence, the clinician must be prepared to assist the physicians in strengthening and solidifying the relationship. Patients are more likely to be influenced by medical providers whom they view as warm, understanding, and empathic. Second, good care necessitates keeping the physician apprised of the patient's progress, significant barriers to progress, and strategies that have the greatest likelihood of working. The clinician must bear in mind that physicians may not be knowledgeable about the theory, rationale, and evidence for psychological interventions. Explaining these matters to the treating physician beforehand may help to engender support for components of the treatment protocol. One of the authors had a brittle diabetic patient undergoing a significant amount of distress in his relationship with his wife. There had been a major ongoing disagreement about the patient's failure to complete a variety of needed tasks around the house. The amount of tension this caused in his relationship was marked. His physician was concerned about the level of stress and how it was affecting the patient's medical condition. Despite a variety of cognitively based interventions (e.g., cost–benefit analysis), the patient was unable to bring himself to replace a broken lock on the back door to the house that had existed for years. He also refused to pay someone else to do it. His wife was understandably becoming angrier by the minute. When the therapist decided to employ a paradoxical strategy (i.e., agree to never repair the lock on the back door once and for all and to welcome the consequences of his inaction), his physician was understandably perplexed. However, once the physician understood the rationale of the strategy, he was able to reinforce it with the patient. The very next week the patient came in to report that he had simply decided to change the lock and did so, to the surprise of both his wife and physician.

As a team member, the behavioral health clinician must be committed to keeping the physician apprised of the patient's progress, accompanied by suggestions about how to help the patient. These strategies must follow from the case formulation. Understanding the patient's personality and coping style can be quite helpful in advising the physician about what strategies to use. For example, the nonadherent patient who becomes easily overwhelmed by anxiety is one with whom the frustrated physician must be careful to avoid repeatedly sensitizing with threatening information and requesting multiple and immediate changes in behavior. Rather, gradually providing information in a realistic manner and a measured plan to integrate and build behaviors into the patient's repertoire would be prudent.

Regarding points of collaboration, the clinician must work with the physician and patient to address the importance of adjusting and adapting diabetes control to a changing situation. For example, one of the authors has encountered patients who are frustrated, related to working at jobs requiring variable hours and shifts, which can complicate management. Difficulty coping and adjusting often leads to noncompliance, with patients giving up on diabetes management for long periods of time until they are forced to stop work, due to the complications of uncontrolled diabetes.

Collaboration with family members is also critical with diabetics. The realization that the patient probably spends the bulk of his waking hours with family members whose attitudes and patterns of behaviors are likely to be as deeply engrained as those of the patient is essential. For this reason, it is prudent to educate family members about diabetes and its treatment, and to emphasize the importance of social support and reinforcement of new habits. Also, creating an environmental context that removes, or at least minimizes, cues for triggering negative behaviors is important. For example, the spouse of a diabetic who does the weekly food shopping and daily cooking needs to be educated and motivated to provide safe food choices and limited portions. Family members may also be powerful reinforcers in shaping and maintaining healthy habits and making it easier for the patient to adhere.

Identifying ongoing sources of family stress and working with the patient and family to address and resolve these issues are important. Whenever possible, family sessions including the physician, although costly in terms of time, may yield worthwhile benefits.

Finally, the adjustment of family members to the patient's disease is another target area. Feifer and Tansman (1998) suggest working with family members experiencing problems with adjustment to the disease and medical regimen. In effect, the adjustment of the patient is, in many ways, a direct function of the adjustment of family members.

Development of an Empirically Based Treatment Plan

The development and implementation of an empirically based treatment plan for the diabetic patient hinges upon a number of factors. First, the treatment plan must be based on a comprehensive case conceptualization that fully explains the patient's problems and develops specific targets for intervention. Second, the treatment plan must be tailored to the specific needs of the patients. Third, the treatment plan must be based on the empirical literature that supports the targeted application of interventions shown to have a maximal likelihood of impacting the patient problems.

In their classic and exhaustive summary of the literature on interventions for diabetics, Gonder-Frederick et al. (2002) have drawn several important conclusions. First, coping-skills treatments reduce the stress associated with diabetes, improve quality of life, and enhance blood glucose control in adolescents. Similarly, in adults, coping-skills treatments have also yielded benefits in anxiety related to diabetes, improved coping ability, self-care behaviors, and control of blood glucose. Specific interventions designed at cultivating a sense of personal empowerment and skills in managing the condition (Anderson et al., 1995) have also resulted in gains in self-efficacy, self-care repertoires, and glucose control. Second, behaviorally based intervention strategies, such as setting specific goals, contracting, and reinforcement related to specific behaviors fostering diabetes management (including blood glucose self-testing and caring for the feet), have been shown to enhance the management of diabetes and control. Third, CBT appears to be a promising treatment for adult depressed diabetics. Fourth, a specific program called Blood Glucose Awareness Training, combining cognitive and behavioral strategies aimed at enhancing self-care and decision making in adult diabetics, has produced durable effects. Among the outcomes observed have been improved ability to identify symptoms and a decrease in both hyperglycemic and hypoglycemic episodes. Fifth, treatments aimed at improving lifestyle habits related to diet and exercise delivered in the early stages of the disease are also effective in helping type 2 diabetics to improve blood glucose tolerance and control and in decreasing incidence of the disease. Sixth, progressive muscle relaxation training may be helpful in reducing high blood sugars and improving control in high-trait anxious patients whose glucose levels are stress sensitive.

Feifer and Tansman (1998) have made a number of useful suggestions in caring for patients with diabetes with specific strategies at different stages of the disease; specifically, during the first year of diagnosis, when elevated HgbA1c levels persist, and when complications begin to emerge. For the newly diagnosed patients, they recommend referral to a competent mental health practitioner with a focus on assessment of level of acceptance of the disease, motivation to change lifestyle behaviors, and investigation of possible psychological comorbidity. Empirically based interventions aimed at relevant targets are necessary, when indicated. During the second phase, after appropriate medical intervention, when HgbA1c persists above 8%, they recommend further assessment related now to problems in coping with the treatment regimen, evidence of ongoing stressful life events, obstacles interfering with behavior change, and additional screening for psychological distress. In the subsequent paragraphs, we discuss some of the available treatments in more depth.

Blood Glucose Awareness Training

BGAT is a psychoeducational program designed to assist patients with type 1 diabetes to raise awareness of and better treat the symptoms of hyperglycemia and hypoglycemia (Cox et al., 2001; Schachinger et al., 2005). BGAT is usually conducted in a group format over an 8-week period. The training focuses on teaching patients to identify their personal symptoms and internal cues signifying they are experiencing extreme blood glucose levels, and to make decisions how to respond to and treat those symptoms. BGAT also focuses on teaching clients to anticipate extreme blood glucose levels based on external cues, such as foods, insulin treatments, and physical activity. The participants are expected to read chapters in the BGAT manual and to participate, and identify their symptoms and antecedents with the group. In a study of BGAT's efficacy, Cox et al. (2001) found that patients who completed the training demonstrated more accurate blood glucose estimates and better judgment as to when and how to treat extreme blood glucose levels. Patients also demonstrated better judgment as to when to drive a motor vehicle when experiencing hypoglycemia, as indicated by fewer motor vehicle accidents and legal violations. Patients also experienced fewer of the negative physical side effects from extreme blood glucose levels, as well as fewer psychological side effects. Patients report decreased stress related to diabetic symptoms and less fear of hypoglycemia, as well as an improved quality of life, after undergoing BGAT (Cox et al., 2001; Schachinger et al., 2005).

Patient Empowerment

Another treatment used to improve patient adherence to diabetic treatment is the patient empowerment approach, designed by Robert M. Anderson and colleagues (Funnell & Anderson, 2000, 2004; Funnell et al., 1991). Empowerment is a collaborative, patient-centered approach to diabetes treatment, where treatment providers assist patients to develop their capacity to be responsible for their own life and treatment. Treatment providers assist patients to express their feelings, report their problems, and to develop solutions to those problems. Treatment providers must also recognize individual factors of each patient's life, and that the patients are the primary decision-makers in their self-management of diabetes. In this approach, the role of the patient is to be well informed and active in their treatment, and the role of the treatment provider is to assist the patient to make informed decisions in their diabetes management. Patient education plays a large role in patient empowerment; treatment providers are expected to continuously educate patients regarding the illness, self-management strategies, and treatment option, all the time allowing the patient to make their own informed decisions. The treatment provider also assists the patient to learn from behavioral experiments and to continually develop treatment goals. According to the patient empowerment approach, each treatment and self-management strategy should be viewed as a learning experience, thus shifting the patient from a success-or-failure mindset, which can often discourage the patient from participating in treatment and adhering to healthy practices. According to Funnell and Anderson (2004), if the patient empowerment approach is used, treatment providers will no longer have to work to find external rewards for their patients' self-management. Rather, the patients will experience their own intrinsic rewards from their self-management, and will be more likely to successfully control their diabetes (Funnell & Anderson, 2000, 2004; Funnell et al., 1991).

Cognitive-Behavior Therapy

Snoek and Skinner (2002) conducted a review of the literature on psychological interventions for problematic diabetes, specifically the commonly identified problems of depression, anxiety, eating disorders, self-destructive health behaviors, and family conflict. Of the somewhat limited number of studies they reviewed, they found that CBT interventions were most effective for decreasing depressions, increasing self-care, and decreasing binge eating and self-destructive health behaviors, such as mismanagement of treatment and nonadherence with dieting. They suggest that physicians should avoid using psychological services as a last resort to assist their diabetic patients, but should rather refer them early for treatment if they show signs of these common comorbid psychological complications related to diabetes (Snoek & Skinner).

Studies on the impact of CBT on depression related to diabetes have also found that the interventions increase treatment compliance in diabetic patients (Gonder-Frederick et al., 2002; Hoff et al., 2003; Ismail et al., 2004). One study (Lustman, Griffith, Freeland, Kissel, & Clouse, 1998, cited in Hoff et al., 2003) compared two groups: one receiving CBT along with self-management training and one receiving only self-management training. The study found that 85% of those in the CBT group had experienced a remission in depression, compared with 25% in the self-management training-only group. Also, the CBT group showed greater improvements in controlling diet and blood sugar levels than the self-management training-only group. The CBT treatment of depression focuses on helping the patient identify and modify the dysfunctional thoughts and negative biases that maintain problematic behaviors and cause depression (Beck & Weishaar, 1989). The CBT treatment of depression with type 2 diabetes should focus specifically on thoughts, beliefs, and cognitive distortions related to type 2 diabetes and the effect the illness is having on the patient's life (Gonder-Frederick et al., 2002; Hoff et al., 2003).

Psychoeducation

Other CBT-based interventions are designed to prevent some of the psychological and medical complications that may develop from type 2 diabetes. Many of these interventions focus on preventing the psychological complications from even occurring, through properly controlling the diabetes by promoting and fostering appropriate treatment adherence. An initial intervention that is commonly used in CBT that can be most important to the overall health of a person with type 2 diabetes is psychoeducation (Hoff et al., 2003; Trozzolino et al., 2003). One form of psychoeducation for diabetics is called diabetes-specific coping skills training (DSCST). DSCST is a group intervention that focuses on increasing emotional functioning, self-management, and blood sugar level control. During the intervention, the group discusses the sources and complications of diabetes, patterns of and barriers to self-care, and methods to solve the problems they may encounter with self-care (Hoff et al., 2003).

Behavioral Rehearsal

Because so much of the treatment of diabetes relies on the patient's self-management and compliance with a new lifestyle, behavioral treatments that help the patient adhere to treatment are also used as an effective intervention (Gonder-Frederick et al., 2002; Leslie & Robbins, 1995). Behavioral rehearsals are often used initially to ensure that the patient knows how to enact the desired self-management behaviors. Continued rehearsals help to establish the behaviors as routine and familiar, and to make the patient more comfortable with performing them. After rehearsing and training the behaviors, another behavioral intervention that can be used is contingency contracting.

Contingency Contracting

In contingency contracting, the patient signs a contract stating that he/she will perform the behaviors when needed, often in return for a determined token or reward. When creating the contract, the person must determine what the rewards will be for performing the behavior and what the consequences will be for not performing the behavior. The therapist helping the patient create the contract must ensure that the rewards and consequences are healthy and coincide with his or her diabetes treatment. For example, a reward for exercising daily or for following a specific diet should not be eating junk food. These behavioral techniques have been shown to be effective in promoting healthy self-care and illness management for people with diabetes (Gonder-Frederick et al., 2002; Leslie & Robbins, 1995).

Motivational Interviewing

Because motivation to adhere to treatment is such an important factor in treating type 2 diabetes, the principles of motivational interviewing can also be used as an intervention to promote adherence (Ismail et al., 2004; Smith, Heckemeyer, Kratt, & Mason, 1997). Motivational interviewing was originally developed as a counseling style for people with unhealthy lifestyles, therefore, it is usually applied to those people who are not compliant with type 2 diabetes treatment. Motivational interviewing is not necessarily a set of techniques, but a style of counseling whose goals are to create motivational discrepancies, resolve ambivalence, and to get the patient to change problem behaviors (Miller & Rollnick, 2002, 2009). There are four fundamental principles that must be followed in motivational interviewing. The first is expressing empathy to the patient by communicating that he or she is accepted and safe to be open and honest. The second principle is developing discrepancies by pointing out the differences between how the patient is living and how the patient needs to be living. The third principle is responding to resistance through nonconfrontational communication and behaviors, and using different strategies when resistance arises to encourage the patient to change. The fourth principle is supporting self-efficacy and encouraging the patient that he or she is capable of changing. Motivational interviewing has been shown to be an effective technique in helping patients to become motivated to adhere to lifestyle changes needed for type 2 diabetes treatment (Ismail et al., 2004; Smith et al., 1997; Miller & Rollnick, 2002).

Relaxation Training

Researchers suggest that one major cause of noncompliance with diabetic patients is stress and anxiety (Boyle et al., 2004; Gonder-Frederick et al., 2002; Ismail et al., 2004). Relaxation training is often used as a CBT intervention for stress and anxiety related to type 2 diabetes (Gonder-Frederick et al., 2002; Hoff et al., 2003; Ismail et al., 2004; Jablon, Naliboff, Gilmore, & Rosenthal, 1997; Williams & Pickup, 2004; Zazworsky et al., 2006). Progressive relaxation therapy is a stress-reduction technique in which a patient is taught by an instructor to systematically tense and relax muscles in a predetermined order (DiTomasso, 2002). The technique is based on the empirically supported premise that tension and stress are relieved when the muscles are completely relaxed (Jablon et al., 1997). One study (Jablon et al., 1997) showed a significant decrease in stress and muscle tension in a group of patients with type 2 diabetes who were taught progressive relaxation techniques, when compared with a control group. Progressive relaxation training has also been found to improve glucose tolerance and reduce long-term hyperglycemia in people with type 2 diabetes (Gonder-Frederick et al., 2002; Hoff et al., 2003).

Training Professional Caregivers

One final area of focus that may promote adherence is training doctors, nurses, and health care professionals in behavioral methods to control diabetes, patient-centered approaches to treatment, and patient-empowerment techniques so as to foster a more appropriate patient–doctor relationship to increase the patient's treatment adherence (Gonder-Frederick et al., 2002).

Evaluation of Treatment Outcomes

In evaluating treatment outcomes for diabetics, the CBT clinician must select and tie valid and reliable measures to the targets of interest. Most certainly, self-monitoring blood glucose levels and periodic hemoglobin A1c levels may be particularly helpful in assessing the efficacy of a treatment plan. For depressed and anxious diabetics, standard CBT measures of depression and anxiety will suffice. Behavioral tests designed to assess the ability of diabetics to do what is needed to do to test and interpret blood glucose levels and to make appropriate food choices would also be useful. Much in line with what Nezu and colleagues (2004) have stated, the measurement of instrumental outcomes is critical in setting the stage for the achievement of ultimate outcomes. In this vein, if weight loss is considered an instrumental outcome to tight glucose control, the ultimate outcome, measuring weight over time can be an important indicator of the effectiveness or ineffectiveness of a treatment and signal the need for the use of some alternative strategy. These data may be useful in ensuring the probability of ultimate goal attainment.

Considerations With Special Populations/Diversity Issues

Treatment adherence and lifestyle changes necessary for healthy diabetic self-care often involve not just the patient, but the social network and cultural environment that they live in day to day. When treating those diagnosed with type 2 diabetes, clinicians must be sensitive to some of the socioeconomic and cultural issues that may arise for the patient living with the illness, including views of food and exercise, the doctor-patient relationship, the family's role in treatment, and lack of resources.

African Americans

Rajaram and Vinson (1998) report on some of the cultural aspects involved in treating people with diabetes, specifically among older, African American women. African American women are almost three times as likely to develop diabetes as Caucasian women, and are shown to have poorer glycemic control. Ranjaram and Vinson hypothesized that social and historic factors have forced many older African American women to live in poverty, thus having limited access to sufficient health care.

Gavin and Wright, Jr. (2007) report that lack of necessary medical insurance and the perception that diabetic treatment equipment, such as blood glucose monitors, are too expensive to afford keep many poor African Americans from seeking appropriate treatment. These economic factors, combined with transportation and wait time issues, contribute to failure to seek or receive appropriate health care for their diabetes. Lack of proper treatment along with the day-to-day stressors of living in poverty can lead to more adverse diabetic symptoms and side effects, including psychological issues related to diabetes (Gavin & Wright, Jr.,

2007; Ranjaram & Vinson, 1998). Clinicians treating minorities with diabetes should consider and educate themselves concerning the impact of social, behavioral, economic, and cultural factors on one's diabetic self-care.

The patient's cultural view of the doctor–patient relationship is another consideration. Studies of African Americans and diabetes (Gavin & Wright, Jr., 2007; Rajaram & Vinson, 1998) have shown that African Americans report communication barriers between themselves and physicians as an ultimate barrier to seeking and complying with treatment. African Americans can feel mistrustful of physicians and physicians, in turn, may not seek to develop a working relationship that fosters open communication and adherence. Gavin and Wright (2007) suggest that those treating African Americans with diabetes must work to build a trusting, honest relationship with their patients, one that respects and honors their cultural and religious beliefs and fosters necessary patient education in order to help to better treat the disease.

Chinese Americans

Chun and Chesla (2004) have highlighted some of the cultural issues in treating Chinese American patients with diabetes. They report that traditional Chinese culture views physical and mental health as a unified concept, and perceives illness as causing an imbalance in both the body and mind. Some Chinese Americans may perceive a strict behavioral interpretation of the disease and may experience guilt and shame in having been diagnosed with the disease and not having the "will power" to control it. They may also view food not just as sustenance, but as an important part of their quality of life, a tool to foster social relationships, and as something with healing qualities of its own. Chun and Chesla suggest that adhering to diets necessary for diabetic control may be especially challenging for Chinese Americans. They also report that Chinese Americans with diabetes may feel a sense of guilt in making their families provide accommodations to them because of their lifestyle changes, diet restrictions, and diabetic symptoms. They recommend that treatment providers consider these cultural factors when treating Chinese Americans with diabetes, and seek information from patients and their families regarding how their culture views diabetes and its treatment (Chun & Chesla).

Latino Americans

Caballero and Tenzer (2007) provide information on cultural issues relevant to the treatment of Latino Americans with diabetes. Because of the broad number of ethnicities included in the descriptor "Latino," such as Puerto Rican, Mexican, and people of Spanish decent, they suggest that clinicians treating Latinos with diabetes first seek information regarding the patient's unique cultural identity. The treatment provider should seek information from the patient regarding his/her level of acculturation to modern American culture and its medical practices. Caballero and Tenzer report that Latino American views of medicine differ throughout the culture, and range from trust of medical treatments and open relationships with physicians to mistrust and fear of physicians that encourages withholding information about symptoms for fear of being scolded. Like other cultures, Latino Americans view meals as a social gathering that brings people together, and see food as a connection to their culture, which may be a barrier to diet adherence. Latino Americans also experience the same barriers to health care as other cultures because of poverty and lack of resources (Caballero & Tenzer).

Clinical Pearls of Wisdom for Practitioners

1. Clinicians should recognize that diabetes self-care management is a challenging and complex process that is affected by a multitude of factors. Successful treatment necessitates a team-oriented approach that requires the collaboration of the patient, family, physician, and cognitive-behavioral therapist.
2. Clinicians should carefully assess the patient's adjustment to the diagnosis and carefully monitor adjustment over the course of the disease.
3. There are a multitude of factors that may impact diabetes and contribute to problems in management. Clinicians must take a comprehensive approach to assessing and pinpointing areas that need to be addressed in the individual patient, attending to psychological, social, biological, cognitive, emotional, cultural, and environmental factors.
4. Clinicians need to integrate the various facets of the comprehensive assessment into a case formulation and delineate key targets and goals that are specific to the patient.
5. Collaborating with and educating both the patient and the physician about how the cognitive-behavioral model can be applied in explaining, predicting, and ultimately altering the condition of the patient is critical.
6. Developing a multifaceted empirically driven treatment plan that is derived from the clinical research outcome literature and is tailored to the individual needs of the patient is necessary.
7. Developing a system for carefully monitoring the outcome of treatment is important in supporting the continuation of the treatment, or providing an early warning signal that adjustment to the treatment plan is required.

References

Anderson, R. M., Funnell, M. M., Butler, P. M., Arnold, M. S., Fitzgerald, J. T., & Feste, C. C. (1995). Patient empowerment: Results of a randomized controlled trial. *Diabetes Care, 18*(7), 943–949.

Beck, A. T., & Weishaar, M. E. (1989). Cognitive therapy. In R. J. Corsini & D. Wedding (Eds.), *Current psychotherapies* (7th ed., pp. 238–268). Belmont, CA: Brooks/Cole-Thomson Learning.

Berlin, I., Bisserbe, J. C., Eiber, R., Balssa, N., Sachon, C., Bosquet, F., et al. (1997). Phobic symptoms, particularly the fear of blood and injury, are associated with poor glycemic control in type I diabetic adults. *Diabetes Care, 20*, 176–178.

Boyle, S., Allan, C., & Millar, K. (2004). Cognitive-behavioural interventions in a patient with an anxiety disorder related to diabetes. *Behaviour Research and Therapy, 3*, 357–366. Retrieved October 3, 2007, from ProQuest database.

Caballero, A. E., & Tenzer, P. (2007). Building cultural competency for improved diabetes care: Latino Americans and diabetes. *Journal of Family Practice, Supplement*, 21–30.

Chun, K. M., & Chesla, C. A. (2004). Cultural issues for disease management for Chinese Americans with type 2 diabetes. *Psychology and Health, 19*, 767–785.

Ciechanowski, P. S., Katon, W. J., Russo, J. E., & Walker, E. A. (2001). The patient–provider relationship: Attachment theory and adherence to treatment in diabetes. *American Journal of Psychiatry, 158*, 29–35.

Collins, M. M., Corcoran, P., & Perry, I. J. (2009). Anxiety and depression symptoms in patients with diabetes. *Diabetic Medicine, 26,* 153–161.

Cox, D. J., Gonder-Frederick, L., Polonsky, W., Schundt, D., Kovatchev, B., & Clarke, W. (2001). Blood glucose awareness training (BGAT-2): Long-term benefits. *Diabetes Care, 24,* 637–642.

DCCT Research Group. (1993). The effects of intensive treatment of diabetes on the development and progression of long-term complications in insulin-dependent diabetes mellitus. *New England Journal of Meeicine, 329,* 977–986.

DiTomasso, R. A. (2002). Deep muscle relaxation: Update and future directions. In R. Rakel (Ed.), *Saunders' manual of medical practice.* Philadelphia: Saunders.

Feifer, C., & Tansman, M. (1998). Promoting psychology in diabetes primary care. *Professional Psychology: Research and Practice, 30*(1), 14–21.

Funnell, M. M., & Anderson, R. M. (2000). The problem with compliance in diabetes. *Journal of the American Medical Association, 284,* 1709.

Funnell, M. M., & Anderson, R. M. (2004). Empowerment and self-management of diabetes. *Clinical Diabetes, 22,* 123–127.

Funnell, M. M., Anderson, R. M., Arnold, M. S., Barr, P. A., Donnelly, M. B., Johnson, P. D., et al. (1991). Empowerment: An idea whose time has come in diabetes education. *Diabetes Education, 17,* 37–41.

Gavin, J. R., & Wright, E. E., Jr. (2007). Building cultural competency for improved diabetes care: African Americans and diabetes. *Journal of Family Practice, Supplement,* 14–20.

Gonder-Frederick, L. A., Cox, D. J., & Ritterband, L. M. (2002). Diabetes and behavioral medicine: The second decade. *Journal of Consulting & Clinical Psychology, 3,* 611–625.

Harris, M. I., Cowie, C. C., Reiber, G., Boyko, E., Stern, M., & Bennett, P. (Eds.). (1995). *Diabetes in America* (2nd ed.). Washington, DC: U.S. Government Printing Office.

Hoff, A. L., Wagner, J. L., Mullins, L. L., & Chaney, J. M. (2003). Behavioral management of type 2 diabetes. In L. M. Cohen, D. E. McChargue, & F. L. Collins, Jr. (Eds.), *The health psychology handbook* (pp. 303–324). Thousand Oaks, CA: Sage.

Holmstrom, I. M., & Rosenqvist, U. (2005). Misunderstandings about illness and treatment among patients with type 2 diabetes. *Journal of Advanced Nursing, 49,* 146–154.

Irvine, A. A., Cox, D. J., & Gonder-Frederick, L. (1992). Fear of hypoglycemia: Relationship to physical and psychological symptoms in patients with insulin-dependent diabetes mellitus. *Health Psychology, 11,* 135–138.

Ismail, K., Winkley, K., & Rabe-Hesketh, S. (2004). Systematic review and meta-analysis of randomised controlled trials of psychological interventions to improve glycaemic control in patients with type 2 diabetes. *Lancet, 363,* 1589–1597. Retrieved October 3, 2007, from http://www.thelancet.com/journals/lancet/article/PIIS0140-6736(04)16202-8/fulltext

Jablon, S. L., Naliboff, B. D., Gilmore, S. L., & Rosenthal, M. J. (1997). Effects of relaxation training on glucose tolerance and diabetic control in type II diabetes. *Applied Psychophysiology and Biofeedback, 22(3),* 155–166. Retrieved October 3, 2007, from http://proquest.umi.com/pqdweb?index=4&did=927134291&SrchMode=3&sid=3&Fmt=6&VInst=PROD&VType=PQD&RQT=309&VName=PQD&TS=1253222043&clientId=43854&aid=3

Jenkins, D. J. (2004). Psychological, physiological, and drug intervention for type 2 diabetes. *Lancet, 363*(9421), 1569-1570. Retrieved October 3, 2007, from http://proquest.umi.com/pqdweb?index=1&did=640512861&SrchMode=1&sid=4&Fmt=3&VInst=PROD&VType=PQD&RQT=309&VName=PQD&TS=1253222240&c lientId=43854

Jones, J. M., Lawson, M. L., Daneman, D., Olmsted, M. P., & Rodin, G. (2000). Easting disorders in adolescent females with and without type 1 diabetes: Cross sectional study. *British Medical Journal, 320* 1563–1566.

Leslie, R. D., & Robbins, D. C. (Eds.). (1995). *Diabetes: Clinical science in practice.* Cambridge, UK: Press Syndicate of the University of Cambria.

Lustman, P. J., Anderson, R. J., Freedland, K. E., DeGroot, M., Carney, R. B., & Clouse, R. E. (2000). Depression and poor glycemic control: A meta-analytic review of the literature. *Diabetes Care, 23,* 934–942.

Lustman, P. J., Griffith, L. S., Clouse, R. E., Freedland, K. E., Eisen, S. A., Rubin, E. H., et al. (1997). Effects of nortriptyline on depression and glycemic control in diabetes: Results of a double-blind, placebo-controlled trial. *Psychosomatic Medicine, 59*(3), 241–250.

Miller, W. R., & Rollnick, S. (2002). *Motivational interviewing: Preparing people for change* (2nd ed.). London: Guilford.

Miller, W. R., & Rose, G. S. (2009). Toward a theory of motivational interviewing. *American Psychologist, 64*(6), 527–537.

Moskowitz, J. T., Epel, E. S., & Acree, M. (2008). Positive affect uniquely predicts lower risk of mortality in people with diabetes. *Health Psychology, 27*, S73–S82.

Nagelkerk, J., Rieck, K., & Meengs, L. (2006). Perceived barriers and effective strategies to diabetes self-management. *Journal of Advanced Nursing, 54*, 151–158.

Nezu, A. M., Nezu, C. M., & Lombardo, E. (2004). *Cognitive-behavioral case formulation and treatment design*. New York: Springer Publishing Company.

Rajaram, S. S., & Vinson, V. (1998). African American women and diabetes: A sociocultural context. *Journal of Health Care for the Poor and Underserved, 9*, 236–247.

Sacco, W. P., Wells, K. J., Vaughan, C. A., Friedman, A., Perez, S., & Matthew, R. (2005). Depression in adults with type 2 diabetes: The role of adherence, body mass index, and self-efficacy. *Health Psychology, 24*, 630–634.

Sacco, W. P., & Yanover, T. (2006). Diabetes and depression: The role of social support and medical symptoms. *Journal of Behavioral Medicine, 29*, 523–531.

Schachinger, H., Hegar, K., Hermanns, N., Straumann, M., Keller, U., Fehm-Wolsdorf, G., et al. (2005). Randomized controlled clinical trial of blood glucose awareness training (BGAT III) in Switzerland and Germany. *Journal of Behavioral Medicine, 28*(6), 587–594.

Searight, H. R. (1999). *Behavioral medicine: A primary care approach*. Philadelphia: Brunner/Mazel.

Smith, D. E., Heckemayer, C. M., Kratt, P. P., & Mason, D. A. (1997). Motivational interviewing to improve adherence to a behavioral weight-control program for older obese women with NIDDM: A pilot project. *Diabetes Care, 1*, 52–54.

Smith, D. E., Heckemeyer, C. M., Kratt, P. P., & Mason, D. A. (1997). Motivational interviewing to improve adherence to a behavioral weight-control program for older obese women with NIDDM: A pilot study. *Diabetes Care, 20*(1), 52–54.

Snoek, F. J., & Skinner, T. C. (2002). Psychological counseling in problematic diabetes: Does it help? *Diabetic Medicine, 19*, 265–273.

Swenson, S. L., Rose, M., Vittinghoff, E., Stewart, A., & Schillinger, D. (2008). The influence of depressive symptoms on clinician-patient communication among patients with type 2 diabetes. *Medical Care, 46*, 257–265.

Trozzolino, L., Thompson, P. S., Tansman, M. S., & Azen, S. P. (2003) Effects of a psychoeducational group on mood and glycemic control in adults with diabetes and visual impairments. *Journal of Visual Impairment & Blindness, 97(4)*, 230–239. Retrieved October 3, 2007, from http://web.ebscohost.com/ehost/detail?vid=3&hid=5&sid=e78280b1-e71a-4d29-89b4-67b65c067da3%40sessionmgr14&bdata=JnNpdGU9ZWhvc3QtbGl2ZSZzY29wZT1 zaXRl#db=aph&AN=9541001

Wild, D., von Maltzahn, A., Brohan, E., Christensen, T., Clauson, P., & Gonder-Frederick, L. (2007). A critical review of the literature on fear of hypoglycemia in diabetes: Implications for diabetes management and patient education. *Patient Education and Counseling, 68*, 10–15.

Williams, G., & Pickup, J. C. (2004). *Handbook of diabetes* (3rd ed.) Malden, MA: Blackwell Publishing.

Zazworsky, D., Bolin, J. N., & Gaubeca, V. B. (Eds.). (2006). *Handbook of diabetes and diabetes management*. New York: Springer Publishing Company.

Obesity

27

Adam G. Tsai
Raymond Carvajal
Rebecca Egner
Thomas A. Wadden

Introduction

Obesity is a chronic disease that results from a genetic predisposition in combination with an environment that facilitates weight gain. The recent rise in the prevalence of obesity appears to be attributable mostly to environmental factors that lead to a final common pathway of increased caloric intake and decreased energy expenditure (Finkelstein, Ruhm, & Kosa, 2005). The prevalence of obesity has reached epidemic proportions in industrialized countries, as well as in many developing nations, with dramatic consequences for population health status and health care spending (Banks, Marmot, Oldfield, & Smith, 2006; Flegal, Graubard, Williamson, & Gail, 2005; Fontaine, Redden, Wang, Westfall, & Allison, 2003; Thorpe, Florence, Howard, & Joski, 2005).

Improvements in the clinical treatment of obesity have led to greater success in the induction and maintenance of weight loss (Buchwald et al., 2004; Li et al., 2005; Wadden, Butryn, & Wilson, 2007). Yet, the increased prevalence of obesity during this same time (Wang & Beydoun, 2007) underscores the importance of a multifaceted approach to the obesity epidemic, including primary prevention, as well as environmental and policy change (Hill, Wyatt, Reed, & Peters, 2003).

Efforts to promote increased physical activity and reduced consumption of high-calorie, high-fat foods remain a priority that must be addressed at both an individual and societal level.

This chapter provides an overview of obesity. The first section defines the condition and reviews its epidemiology and etiology. The latter part of the chapter addresses the treatment of obesity, including behavior modification, dietary interventions, medications, and weight loss surgery, as well as the management of obesity in primary care practice.

Definition

Obesity refers to an excess of adipose (i.e., fat) tissue that results from a consistently greater energy intake than expenditure. The body mass index (BMI) provides the easiest and most widely accepted method to measure obesity (National Institutes of Health [NIH], 1998). BMI is calculated by dividing weight in kilograms by height squared in meters. A BMI of 18.5–24.9 kg/m^2 represents "normal" weight, whereas a value of 25.0–29.9 is associated with increased risk of morbidity. Increased risk of mortality occurs with a BMI ≥ 30 kg/m^2 (NIH). We note, however, that these definitions were developed using data from non-Hispanic White populations (Adams et al., 2006); important differences in health risk based on BMI exist for persons from different ethnic groups (Cossrow & Falkner, 2004; Razak et al., 2007). Figure 27.1 presents a chart for determining BMI from height and weight.

Assessment and Diagnostic Issues

Clinicians and researchers use BMI to assess obesity because it generally correlates well with the amount of adipose tissue. However, because height affects the value of BMI nonlinearly, the BMI gives a distorted measure of body fat in very tall or short persons. An increase in body fat would increase the value of BMI more in a very short individual than in a very tall person. Furthermore, BMI depends on sex and age: in women and in older people, adipose tissue usually comprises a greater portion of total body mass. Thus, BMI may overestimate health risk in some muscular individuals (e.g., professional athletes), and underestimate risk in others (e.g., elderly individuals with little muscle mass, or so-called "sarcopenic obesity").

Incidence and Clinical Manifestations

Increasing rates of obesity represent an important public health problem for industrialized nations, as well as many developing countries. In the United States, 34% of the population is overweight, and an additional 32% is obese (Ogden et al., 2006). Obesity increased from 22.9 to 30.5% from 1988–1994 to 1999–2000, including an increase in extreme obesity (BMI > 40 kg/m^2) from 2.9 to 4.7% (Must et al., 1999; Ogden et al., 2006).

In the U.S. population, ethnic minority populations suffer from higher rates of obesity than non-Hispanic Whites. For example, in 2003–2004, 45% of non-Hispanic Blacks were obese, as compared with 30.6% of Whites (Ogden et al., 2006).

27.1

Body mass index chart.

	NORMAL						OVERWEIGHT					OBESE										EXTREME OBESITY		
BMI	19	20	21	22	23	24	25	26	27	28	29	30	31	32	33	34	35	36	37	38	39	40	41	42
Height (Feet-inches)	Weight (Pounds)																							
4'10"	91	96	100	105	110	115	119	124	129	134	138	143	148	153	158	162	167	172	177	181	186	191	196	201
4'11"	94	99	104	109	114	119	124	128	133	138	143	148	153	158	163	168	173	178	183	188	193	198	203	208
5'00"	97	102	107	112	118	123	128	133	138	143	148	153	158	163	168	174	179	184	189	194	199	204	209	215
5'01"	100	106	111	116	122	127	132	137	143	148	153	158	164	169	174	180	185	190	195	201	206	211	217	222
5'02"	104	109	115	120	126	131	136	142	147	153	158	164	169	174	180	186	191	196	202	207	213	218	224	229
5'03"	107	112	118	124	130	135	141	146	152	158	163	169	174	180	186	191	197	203	208	214	220	225	231	237
5'04"	110	116	122	128	134	140	145	151	157	163	169	175	180	186	191	197	204	209	215	221	227	232	238	244
5'05"	114	120	126	132	138	144	150	156	162	168	174	180	186	192	198	204	210	116	222	228	234	240	246	252
5'06"	118	124	130	136	142	143	155	161	167	173	179	186	192	198	204	210	216	223	229	235	241	247	253	260
5'07"	121	127	134	140	146	153	159	166	172	178	185	191	198	204	211	217	223	230	236	242	249	255	261	268
5'08"	125	131	138	144	151	158	164	171	177	184	190	197	204	210	216	223	230	236	243	249	256	262	269	276
5'09"	128	135	142	149	155	162	169	176	182	189	196	203	210	216	223	230	236	243	250	257	263	270	277	284
5'10"	132	139	146	153	160	167	174	181	188	195	202	209	216	222	229	236	243	250	257	264	221	278	285	292
5'11"	136	143	150	157	165	172	179	186	193	200	208	215	222	229	236	243	250	257	265	272	279	286	293	301
6'00"	140	147	154	162	169	177	184	191	199	206	213	221	228	235	242	250	258	265	272	279	287	294	302	309
6'01"	144	151	159	166	174	182	189	197	204	212	219	227	235	242	250	257	265	275	280	288	295	302	310	318
6'02"	148	155	163	171	179	186	194	202	210	218	225	233	241	249	256	264	272	280	287	295	303	311	319	326
6'03"	152	160	168	176	184	192	200	208	216	224	232	240	248	256	264	272	279	287	295	303	311	319	327	335
6'04"	156	164	172	180	189	197	205	213	221	230	238	246	254	263	271	279	287	295	304	312	320	328	336	344

Adapted from George Bray, Pennington Biomedical Research Center, *Clinical Guidelines on the Identification, Evaluation, and Treatment of Overweight and Obesity in Adults: The Evidence Report.* National Institutes of Health, National Heart, Lung, and Blood Institute.

The high prevalence of obesity among minorities appears attributable primarily to lower income and educational attainment rather than to race or ethnicity (Drewnowski & Specter, 2004). Obesity also is more prevalent among women of low socioeconomic status (SES), as compared with women of high SES, although recent changes in weight suggest that all SES groups are susceptible to weight gain (Chang & Lauderdale, 2005). Both genetic and cultural factors appear to play a role in the higher prevalence of obesity among African American women (Foster, Wadden, & Vogt, 1997; Kumanyika, 2005).

Unfortunately, overweight and obesity are also increasing in children and adolescents. In 2003–2004, an estimated 17.4% of 12- to 19-year-olds were overweight, as were 18.8% of 6- to 11-year-olds and 13.9% of 2- to 5-year-olds, compared with 10.5, 11.3, and 7.2%, respectively, in 1988–1994 (Ogden et al., 2006). The prevalence of overweight non-Hispanic Black and Mexican American adolescents increased more than 10 percentage points between 1988–1994 and 1999–2000, but increased only 3–4% in White adolescents (Ogden, Flegal, Carroll, & Johnson, 2002).

Etiology

Obesity is thought to result from an interaction of genetic and environmental factors, such that a genetically susceptible individual may gain weight in an environment that facilitates energy imbalance. The influence of heredity is strong, accounting for up to 40% of the variation in weight (Bouchard, 1997). However, the gene pool could not have changed enough since the 1960s to account for the marked rise in the prevalence of obesity in recent decades. Thus, the rise in obesity is best explained by behavioral and environmental changes. A smaller number of individuals also have psychiatric and/or medical causes of obesity, as will discussed in the text that follows.

Brief Case History

Mrs. G. is a 45-year-old, Caucasian female, who presented to her primary care physician for distress related to her obesity. She is 66 inches tall, with a weight of 212 lb., and BMI of 34 kg/m^2. Mrs. G. was diagnosed as overweight (BMI = sex-specific 95th percentile) at age 10 years. She continued to gain weight through adolescence and adulthood, which consequently impaired her physical health and quality of life. She was diagnosed with hypertension and type 2 diabetes in her early 30s, and she reports having experienced widespread prejudice and discrimination as a result of being obese. She has attempted to lose weight on several occasions through a variety of self-directed diets, commercial programs, and over-the-counter medications. Unfortunately, these approaches yielded minimal weight losses. Although she has experienced distress and embarrassment related to her obesity, Mrs. G. denied any significant history of psychiatric difficulties.

Assessment of Mrs. G.'s eating behaviors indicated that she eats two meals per day, snacks on high-sugar foods, and drinks large amounts of sweetened beverages (e.g., soda). She frequently consumes large portions of calorically dense foods. She tends to skip breakfast as a result of being in a rush to leave for work in the morning. As a result, she often is very hungry by the time she eats lunch, which results in her consuming more calories than she had planned. Because she does not regularly pack her lunches to bring to work, Mrs. G. often buys her lunches from outdoor food vendors, most of whom only serve high-fat foods (e.g., hot dogs). For dinner, Mrs. G. occasionally prepares meals at home, but more often stops and eats at her favorite fast-food restaurant that is located on her route home from her place of work. At home, she tends to snack while watching television, in different rooms of her house, and late at night. Mrs. G. is especially susceptible to overeating during periods of emotional distress. She consumes large amounts of food (particularly carbohydrates) when she is experiencing a high level of stress or anxiety, which consequently provides her a sense of relief from these adverse emotions. Despite recognizing the negative implications of her current eating behaviors on her ability to lose weight, Mrs. G. has been unsuccessful in modifying these behaviors in the long term.

Cognitive-Behavioral Case Conceptualization

Given the large body of evidence supporting the efficacy of behavior therapy (lifestyle modification) in the management of obesity (Foster, Makris, & Bailer, 2005; Wadden, Crerand, & Brock, 2005), Mrs. G.'s case is conceptualized from a behavioral perspective. Behavior therapy assumes that eating behaviors are conditioned phenomena that are amenable to modification through the application of behavioral principles and techniques. Accordingly, classical conditioning and operant conditioning serve important functions in treatment (Foster et al.; Wadden et al). In terms of classical conditioning, behaviors that are repeatedly paired with other activities are believed to gain associative strength, such that the presence of one event automatically triggers the onset of the other event (Pavlov, 1927). Repeatedly pairing the act of eating with different stimuli, therefore, compromises the ability to control weight as these latter stimuli become strongly linked with the consumption of food. Operant conditioning theory posits that the frequency at which a behavior occurs also is influenced by the consequences of the behavior (Skinner, 1953). Thus, if people experience a sense of pleasure after consuming food, then they may have difficulty modifying their eating habits as a consequence of the reinforcement that is gained from eating. Identifying discriminative stimuli and consequences that maintain maladaptive eating behaviors, and learning healthier responses to them, represent central goals in behavior therapy (Foster et al.; Wadden et al.).

Mrs. G.'s overeating and/or consumption of unhealthy foods is being triggered by a variety of events. For example, skipping breakfast in the morning increases her risk of overeating at lunch; failing to pack lunches increases her risk of consuming high-fat foods; and being exposed to her favorite fast-food restaurant increases her risk of eating at that restaurant. Mrs. G.'s eating has also become associated with certain activities (i.e., watching television), places (i.e., rooms in her house), times (i.e., late at night), and affective states (i.e., stress, anxiety). Because her eating repeatedly has been paired with these stimuli, Mrs. G. is prone to eat in the presence of these cues, regardless of her level of physiological hunger. In addition, Mrs. G. has been conditioned to overconsume carbohydrates when she is experiencing high levels of emotional distress. Furthermore, her carbohydrate intake is being negatively reinforced (strengthened) by providing her relief from such distress. The array of stimuli associated with her eating, along with the comfort that her eating provides, have impaired Mrs. G.'s ability to control her weight. Behavior therapy is designed to help her modify these conditions in order to achieve weight loss and improve her health.

Identifying and Addressing Obstacles to Treatment

Environmental Causes

The eating and physical activity environments of industrialized countries, especially the United States, are obesigenic. Some experts have labeled the current obesity epidemic, "a normal response to an abnormal environment" (Horgen & Brownell, 2002). The availability of highly palatable, energy-dense foods has never been greater, and less than 50% of Americans are regularly physically active (Centers for Disease Control and Prevention, 2006). Advances in technology facilitate sedentary behavior, and the wide-scale availability of energy-dense foods with large portion sizes have made it easy for individuals to overeat. The importance of environmental influences on eating and activity is evident in a study of the Pima Indians. Some of the highest rates of obesity occur in the Pima Indians in the Gila and Slat River areas of southern Arizona, where about two thirds of adults in this group also have diabetes. Increases in obesity in the Pima closely parallel trends in acculturation during the past 50 years. A Pima tribe that lives in Sonora, Mexico, and that is very closely genetically related to the Pima of Arizona maintains a traditional lifestyle and continues to have low rates of obesity and diabetes today (Ravussin, Valencia, Esparza, Bennett, & Schulz, 1994).

High-Fat, High-Calorie Palatable Diet

Changes in the food supply closely parallel increases in the prevalence of obesity in the U.S. According to the United States Department of Agriculture, the number of calories available for consumption has increased substantially over the past century, and most significantly over the past few decades. This has occurred through an increase in both the total amount of food available, as well as from an increase in dietary fat. Specifically, the number of calories available for consumption per capita per day increased from 3,200 calories in 1980 to 3,900 calories in 2004 (United States Department of Agriculture, 2009). Similarly, the number of calories consumed has increased by approximately 12% between 1971–1974 and 1999–2002 (Kant & Graubard, 2006). The percent of calories ingested from fat increased from 32 to 41% between 1910 and 2004, whereas the percentage obtained from carbohydrate decreased from 59 to 49%, and the percentage obtained from protein remained constant at approximately 11% (United States Department of Agriculture, 2009). An extensive body of literature shows that both animals and humans gain weight when fat in the diet is high, independent of the total weight or volume of food ingested (Bray & Popkin, 1998; Lissner & Heitmann, 1995). Weight gain occurs for several reasons. First, fat has a higher energy value per weight of food (9 kcal/gram) than does protein or carbohydrate (4 kcal/gram). Second, fat has a highly palatable flavor and texture. Third, dietary fat is converted to body fat with greater energy efficiency than is carbohydrate, leading to greater fat storage (i.e., weight gain) when consuming a hypercaloric diet with the same number of total calories but with a higher fat content (Golay & Bobbioni, 1997).

Although food has become higher in fat and more palatable, it has also become more available than ever. Fast food restaurants have exploded in number, offering package meals and massive serving sizes that easily allow the ingestion of an entire day's needed calorie intake in one meal. Most service stations have been remodeled to have convenience food markets, typically stocked with high-calorie snacks. Malls, airports, and train stations offer few healthy eating options, and many of the nation's large hospitals have fast food franchises in their lobbies (Cram, Nallamothu, Fendrick, & Saint, 2002; Lesser, 2006). Some public schools have soft drink vending machines, and even fast food outlets, as a result of contracts with the food industry. Fast food is the most obvious example of the obesigenic eating environment, but serving sizes of commonly consumed foods also have increased throughout the United States (Nielsen & Popkin, 2003).

Declining Physical Activity

A decrease in energy expenditure from physical activity has also contributed to weight gain in the U.S. population. Daily energy expenditure decreased substantially as our nation changed from an agricultural to an industrial economy and, more recently, from a service to information economy. For example, energy expenditure from low-level activities is thought to have decreased by 300–500 calories per day since the 1950s (Steffen et al., 2006). Modern society is highly reliant on technology, such that sedentary behavior is the norm and individuals must "swim upstream" in order to have regular physical activity. The trend toward sedentary behavior begins in childhood, with less than 10% of public schools providing physical activity classes daily (Centers for Disease Control and Prevention, 2006).

Public Policy

A number of policy decisions in the United States are thought to have contributed to the obesity epidemic. U.S. government subsidies for corn have lowered the market price for corn products, including high fructose corn syrup. Studies have shown that individuals who regularly consume high fructose corn syrup (e.g., soda) are more likely to gain weight over time (Malik, Schulze, & Hu, 2006). Corn subsidies also provide cheap feed for animals, lowering the price of meat and, via supply and demand, increasing meat consumption (Tillotson, 2004). Public policy also has reduced opportunities for transportation as physical activity, through zoning laws that have created neighborhoods where it is virtually impossible to leave one's house without driving (Sallis, Kraft, & Linton, 2002). The lack of a uniform system to educate the public about the nutritional value of foods (Katz, Njike, Zubaid, & Rhee-Baez, 2008) may have also contributed to weight gain. However, progress in this last area has been made, as with New York City's efforts to document the effect of required calorie labeling of foods (Bassett, Dumanovsky, & Huang, 2008) and the subsequent enactment of a law requiring labeling.

Genetic Causes

Genetic makeup plays a major role in the development of obesity. Genes can lead to a positive energy balance (i.e., weight gain) by predisposing an individual with normal energy requirements to overeat, or contributing to a lower energy requirement in individuals with a normal drive to eat. No single gene candidate has emerged as a cause for obesity in a large percentage of affected individuals. Rather, the heritable component of obesity is thought to result from the interaction of many genes.

Hormonal Regulation of Appetite and Body Weight

Recent studies have identified a variety of genetic products that appear to inhibit appetite and food intake in laboratory animals. The best known is leptin, a protein that is synthesized in adipose tissue, and acts on central neural networks that control ingestive behavior and energy expenditure. Under normal conditions, leptin inhibits food intake and increases energy expenditure. As an animal's adipose mass increases, leptin secretion increases proportionately, thus reducing food intake and eventually body fat. The ob/ob mouse, because of a mutation in the ob gene, produces no leptin. As a result, the animal is hyperphagic and extremely sedentary, producing its marked obesity. Peripheral or central administration of recombinant leptin in the ob/ob mouse results in rapid normalization of food intake, activity, and body weight.

In addition to leptin, numerous other peptides circulate in the bloodstream and interact in the brain to control food intake (Murphy & Bloom, 2006). Some of these, like leptin, inhibit appetite and decrease food intake, such as cholecystokinin (CCK), peptide YY ($PYY_{3\text{-}36}$), and glucagon-like peptide (GLP-1), and others increase hunger and food intake, such as ghrelin. CCK is produced in the stomach during gastric distension and acts via the vagus nerve to decrease meal size (Kraly, Cary, Resnick, & Smith, 1978; Liebling, 1975) and terminate eating. GLP-1 and $PYY_{3\text{-}36}$ are also satiety factors, but they are released further down in the gut, by cells in the ileum. GLP-1 stimulates the release of insulin, and GLP-1 mimetics are used as antidiabetic agents (Baggio, 2007). Ghrelin is a 28-amino acid peptide synthesized mainly in the stomach and small intestines (Tschoep, Smiley, & Heiman, 2000). Ghrelin levels increase during food deprivation and before meals in humans and decrease following food consumption. These peptides are but a handful of the large number of biological mediators that are involved in the regulation of body weight homeostasis.

Energy Expenditure

Genes can also cause obesity by lowering an individual's energy expenditure (i.e., their energy requirement). The three main factors that account for energy expenditure are: (a) resting metabolic rate (RMR), (b) spontaneous physical activity, and (c) the thermic effect of food (i.e., energy required to break down and absorb food). Of these, RMR is the largest component, accounting for 60–75% of total energy expenditure. Bouchard and colleagues have demonstrated genetic differences in RMR that could contribute to weight gain (Bouchard, 1997). Individuals with lower metabolic rates are more likely to become obese than are those with higher metabolic rates (Ravussin et al., 1988). For example, African American women were shown to have lower resting energy requirements than non-Hispanic White women (Foster et al., 1997). This genetic difference likely was an evolutionary adaptation that, through history, helped African women to survive during

times of food shortage, but that may contribute to weight gain in the current environment of food abundance.

Genes may also affect an individual's energy expenditure through spontaneous physical activity. For example, some data suggest that energy expenditure from physical activity is significantly correlated among sibling pairs, an effect that may have a genetic basis. Scientists have postulated that persons with a higher percentage of type II muscle fibers (i.e., "slow twitch" fibers, which use oxygen less efficiently) may be genetically predisposed to do less aerobic physical activity, and thus, to have a lower energy requirement. Similarly, preliminary evidence suggests that "nonexercise associated thermogenesis" (NEAT), the amount of energy expended during nonexercise activities throughout the day, may have a biologic basis (Levine et al., 2005).

Psychological Causes

Psychological status also may play a role in weight gain and the development of obesity (Stunkard, Faith, & Allison, 2003). Common psychological conditions in obese individuals include binge eating, night eating, and depression. The former two conditions both are associated with depression, although whether they represent atypical manifestations of depression is not clear.

Binge Eating

Among persons seeking professional assistance with weight loss, approximately 10–15% report binge eating, often in association with depressed mood. The prevalence of binge eating disorder in the general population is estimated to be 1.2% (Hudson, Hiripi, Pope, & Kessler, 2007). The diagnosis of binge eating disorder requires consumption of objectively large amounts of food in a discrete period of time, and the patient's subjective sense of loss of control over eating. Episodes of overeating cannot be followed by compensatory behavior, such as purging (e.g., vomiting, laxative or diuretic abuse), as is seen in bulimia nervosa. Persons with binge eating disorder also report eating very rapidly, eating alone, eating until uncomfortably full, and experiencing distress over bingeing episodes. The etiology of binge eating is not well understood, but has been hypothesized by some investigators to result from psychological distress that causes an individual to use food as an escape from unpleasant life circumstances. Anecdotes from individuals who suffer from binge eating include being "numb" during overeating episodes and using food to "block out the world."

Night Eating

Night eating syndrome, as defined by Stunkard and colleagues (Stunkard, Grace, & Wolff, 1955), is characterized by a lack of appetite for breakfast, intake of 25% or greater of total calories after the evening meal, and nocturnal awakening with food consumption several times per week. Thus, the normal circadian rhythm of food consumption is shifted toward later in the day in individuals with the condition. Night eating syndrome occurs in approximately 1.5% of the general population and in approximately 6 to 16% of obese individuals seeking weight loss treatment (Stunkard et al., 2009). The syndrome is not formally defined as an eating disorder in the *Diagnostic and Statistical Manual for Mental Disorders* (American Psychiatric Association, 2000). However, provisional criteria are being used to conduct studies that will improve understanding of the principal characteristics, prevalence, etiology, and treatment of night eating syndrome.

Depression

The relationship between mood and weight is a complex one. Obesity and depression appear to share a bidirectional relationship, such that weight gain can lead to depressed mood, and vice versa. This is contrary to older hypotheses that suggested that depression uniformly led to obesity. Individuals may either lose weight ("typical depression") or gain weight ("atypical depression") during an acute episode of depression, as noted by Stunkard and colleagues, who found that 38% of patients diagnosed with unipolar depression gained a significant amount of weight, as compared with 51% who lost weight (Stunkard, Fernstrom, Price, Frank, & Kupfer, 1990). Additionally, other forms of depression may be associated with weight gain, particularly seasonal affective disorder (SAD). Normal seasonal variation in appetite (greater appetite in winter, lesser appetite in summer) is more marked in persons with SAD (Rosenthal, Genhart, Jacobsen, Skwerer, & Wehr, 1987).

Medical Causes

The most common medical cause of weight gain is prescription medications. Agents that commonly cause large weight gains (5–10% of initial weight) include corticosteroids (e.g., prednisone), second-generation antipsychotics (e.g, olanzapine, quetiapine, risperidone), and certain mood stabilizing and/or antiepileptic drugs (lithium, valproic acid) (Aronne & Segal, 2003; Malone, Alger-Mayer, & Anderson, 2005). Among these, the centrally acting agents are thought to cause changes in neurotransmitters such as dopamine and serotonin. With steroids, the mechanism of weight gain is at least partially due to metabolic changes leading to increased central deposition of adipose tissue, with concomitant loss of lean body tissue. Among antidepressants, the most commonly used class of drugs, selective serotonin reuptake inhibitors (SSRIs), are associated with minimal weight gain, although some agents (e.g., paroxetine, citalopram) may cause large gains with chronic use (Malone et al.). Finally, a number of diabetes medications, including insulin, sulfonylureas (glyburide, glipizide), and thiazolidinediones (rosiglitazone, pioglitazone) cause weight gains of 3–5 kg. Although the weight gains from diabetes agents are smaller than those caused by steroids and antipsychotics, they are important from a population perspective, as most patients with type 2 diabetes are already overweight or obese.

Complications of Obesity

Obesity is associated with comorbid medical conditions that may be found in nearly every organ system of the body. Very clear epidemiological evidence indicates that obesity, particularly extreme obesity (BMI = 40 kg/m^2), both causes and

27.1 Health Consequences of Obesity

Cardiovascular disease	Sleep apnea
Type II diabetes	Osteoarthritis
Hypertension	Degenerative joint disease
Dislipidemia	Gout
Stroke	Infertility
Colon, endometrial, and postmenopausal breast cancer	Menstrual irregularities

Adapted from Pi-Sunyer, F. X. (1999). Comorbidities of overweight and obesity: Current evidence and research issues. *Medicine and Science in Sports and Exercise, 31*, S602.

exacerbates many illnesses. Table 27.1 lists the medical conditions most often associated with obesity. However, significant variability exists in the degree to which individuals are affected by their weight (Wildman et al., 2008). Some of the differences in individual susceptibility to obesity-related diseases can be predicted by observable factors, such as ethnicity (e.g., African Americans have lower rates of comorbidity compared with Whites at the same weight, whereas many Asian populations have higher rates of comorbid disease). The remaining component of disease susceptibility is likely due to nonobservable genetic differences. As described below, obesity also causes significant social, psychological, and economic problems, including overall decreases in quality of life.

Medical and Psychiatric Consequences

Medical Consequences

The most common medical diagnoses associated with obesity are coronary heart disease, diabetes, hypertension, dyslipidemia, osteoarthritis, gallbladder disease, sleep apnea, and cancers of the breast, colon, and uterus (Pi-Sunyer, 1993). Obese individuals may also have the metabolic syndrome, a constellation of abnormalities that represent precursors of cardiovascular disease (CVD) risk factors. Abnormalities that comprise the metabolic syndrome include: (a) high waist circumference (35 inches in women, 40 inches in men); (b) elevated blood pressure (130/85 mmHg); (c) elevated fasting blood glucose (100 mg/dl); (d) decreased high-density lipoprotein (i.e., "good cholesterol" < 40 mg/dl in men, < 50 mg/dl in women); or (e) high triglycerides (= 150 mg/dl) (Grundy, Hansen, Smith, Cleeman, & Kahn, 2004). Diagnosis of the metabolic syndrome offers an opportunity to motivate patients to lose weight, before they require pharmacotherapy to treat the condition.

The risk of medical comorbidity from obesity appears to be at least partially dependent on the regional distribution of body fat. Upper body fat distribution, particularly visceral adipose tissue (defined in clinical practice as an elevated waist circumference), is associated with an increased risk of coronary heart disease, insulin resistance, type 2 diabetes, and stroke, even after controlling for BMI (Zhu et al., 2002). In addition, visceral adiposity appears to lead to internal organ dysfunction, as with nonalcoholic fatty liver disease (NAFLD) and congestive heart failure. The mechanisms by which visceral fat leads to increased metabolic abnormalities are not well understood. They appear to be related to an increase in portal free fatty acid concentrations, which are associated with increases in hepatic gluconeogenesis and in very-low-density lipoprotein secretion, as well as decreased hepatic insulin clearance. The relationship of fat distribution to disease has important implications for the treatment of obesity. Specifically, individuals with greater upper body fat and, thus, a greater risk of comorbid disease should be targeted first for weight loss interventions. However, these higher risk individuals tend to be men ("apple shaped") who are less likely to enroll in weight loss programs. Conversely, women ("pear shaped") tend to have lower body fat distribution and are at less risk of obesity-related illness, yet they are more likely to enroll in weight loss programs.

Obesity and Mortality

The preponderance of research indicates a clear relationship between obesity and mortality. Several large cohort studies in different countries around the world have confirmed this association, with CVD being the principal cause of death among obese individuals (Whitlock, Lewington, Sherlicher, Peto, & The Prospective Studies Collaboration, 2009). Figure 27.2, from a large cohort study of over 1 million individuals in the United States (Adams et al., 2006), shows a strong relationship between increasing weight and the risk of premature death. This relationship was especially apparent after accounting for the effect of smoking and for medical conditions already present when individuals enrolled in the study.

Depression

As mentioned previously, depression is both a cause and a consequence of obesity (Stunkard et al., 2003). The relationship differs between the sexes, with a stronger relationship between obesity and depression among women than among men. The prevalence of mood disorders increases with increasing weight, such that depression is very common among severely obese individuals (e.g., those presenting for surgical treatment of weight loss) (Wadden et al., 2007). Persons presenting for weight loss treatment who have comorbid depression may need to have the two conditions treated together or to have their depression treated before they can lose weight. Alternatively, individuals whose depression is caused by weight gain may demonstrate improved mood after weight loss. Whether depression is the "chicken or the egg" requires individual clinical judgment.

Quality of Life

All of the previously mentioned consequences of obesity—medical, psychological, social, and economic—lead to a final common pathway of impaired quality of life in obese persons. Numerous surveys of obese individuals from population- and clinic-based samples have revealed complaints of reduced physical function,

27.2

Relationship between increasing weight and risk of premature death.

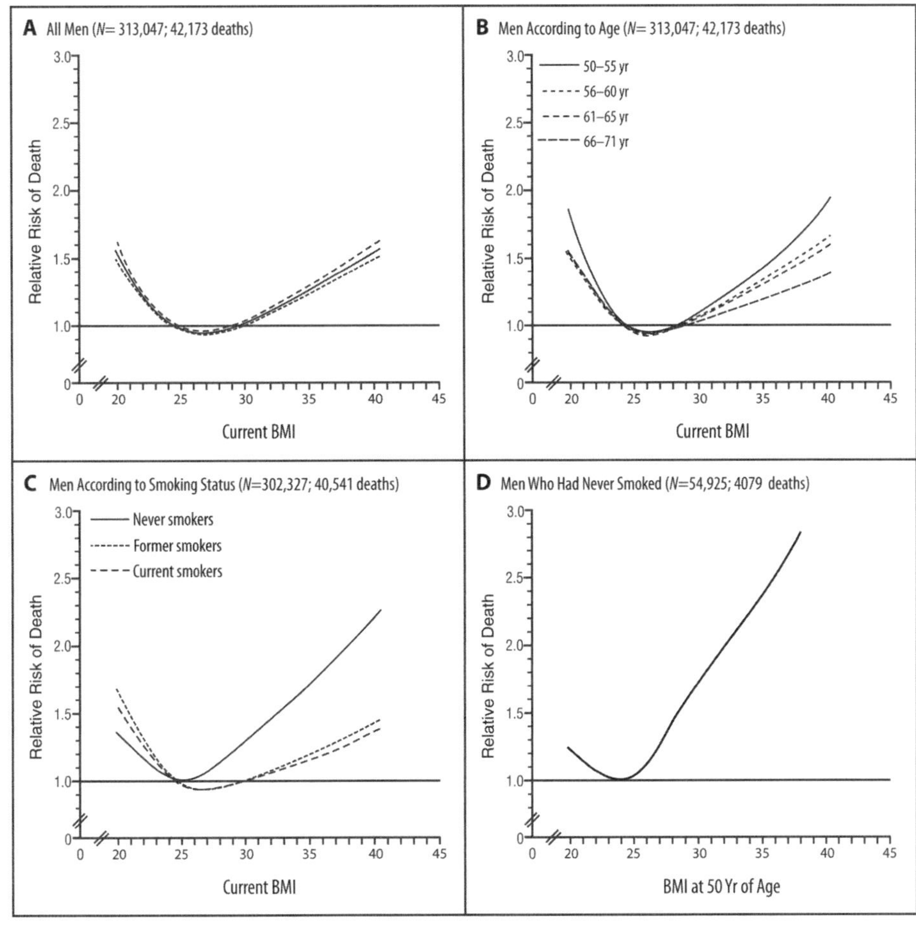

increased pain, reduced vitality, and impairment in social or occupational roles (Kolotkin, Meter, & Williams, 2001; Wadden & Phelan, 2002). Intentional weight loss in obese individuals leads to improvement in quality of life.

Development and Implementation of Empirically Based Treatment Plan

Selecting Weight Loss Interventions

A weight loss of 10% of initial weight is defined as therapeutic (i.e., clinically significant). Expert panels from the World Health Organization (WHO) and the

27.2 A Guide to Selecting Treatment [a]

Treatment	BMI Category (kg/m^2) 25–26.9	27–29.9	30–34.9	35–39.9	≥ 40
Diet, physical activity, and behavior therapy	With comorbidities	With comorbidities	+[b]	+	+
Pharmacotherapy		With comorbidities	+	+	+
Surgery			With comorbidities		

[a]Reprinted and adapted from National Heart, Blood and Lung Institute (2000).
[b]The "+" represents the use of indicated treatment regardless of comorbidities.

National Institutes of Health (NIH) have recommended that obese individuals seek to lose 10% of initial weight, no matter what their starting weight is (NIH, 1998).

Obese individuals are advised to lose weight through moderate caloric restriction (500–1000 kcal/day deficit) and increased physical activity (NIH, 1998). This lifestyle-modification approach is considered the cornerstone of treatment for all overweight and obese individuals (NHLBI/NAASO, 2000). The terms *behavioral treatment, lifestyle modification*, and *behavioral weight control* are often used interchangeably (Wadden, Butryn, & Byrne, 2004). They all encompass three principal components: (a) dietary change, (b) physical activity, and (c) behavior modification. This latter term, as applied to weight control, refers to a set of principles and techniques to help patients adopt new eating and activity habits (Wadden et al.).

Pharmacotherapy may be added to lifestyle modification for persons with a BMI = 30 kg/m^2 (or for those with a BMI = 27 kg/m^2 in the presence of comorbid conditions) who cannot reduce successfully with lifestyle modification (Table 27.2). Bariatric surgery is recommended for individuals with a BMI = 40 kg/m^2, or those with a BMI = 35 kg/m^2 with comorbidities. Even if pharmacotherapy or surgery is selected, patients must reduce their caloric intake and exercise regularly to maximize their health benefit (i.e., to lower CVD risk) (NHLBI/NAASO, 2000).

Lifestyle Modification for Obesity

The Diabetes Prevention Program (DPP) is a landmark study that demonstrated the benefits of lifestyle modification (Knowler et al., 2002). The trial recruited over 3,200 overweight and obese individuals with impaired glucose tolerance. Participants were randomized to one of three treatment conditions: (a) placebo, (b) metformin (850 mg twice daily), or (c) an intensive lifestyle intervention designed to induce a loss of 7% of initial weight and to increase physical activity.

27.3

Changes in body weight in participants in the Diabetes Prevention Program.

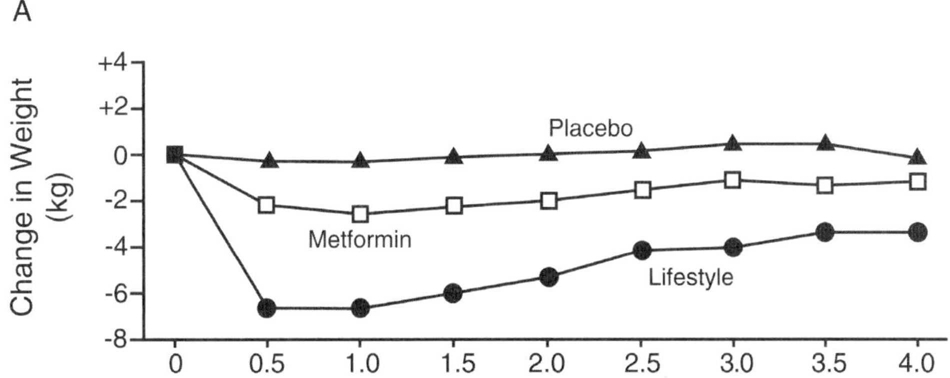

Participants randomized to the latter group received 16 individual weight loss sessions during the first 6 months, with counseling provided by registered dietitians (Diabetes Prevention Program Research Group, 2002; Knowler et al., 2002). Goals for dietary modification included reducing fat intake to less than 25% of total calories, as well as a total calorie limit of 1,200–2,000 kcal/day, based on the participant's initial weight. Recommendations for physical activity were to achieve at least 150 minutes per week of brisk walking or a comparable activity. Additionally, clinical sites offered supervised group exercise sessions twice per week. Behavior modification included self-monitoring of calorie intake, physical activity, and weight, as well as use of food scales and measuring utensils in order to accurately measure portion size (Wadden et al., 2004). Weight maintenance counseling sessions (group and individual) were provided for an average of 2.5 years after the initial 6-month intervention.

As shown in Figure 27.3, individuals assigned to the lifestyle intervention lost significantly more weight during initial treatment and kept off more weight at all follow-up points, as compared with persons in the metformin and placebo groups. The average duration of treatment was 2.8 years, at which time weight losses in the lifestyle, metformin, and placebo groups were 5.6 kg, 2.1 kg, and 0.1 kg, respectively. The primary endpoint of the study, the onset of type 2 diabetes, was lowered from 28.9% in the placebo group to 21.7% in the metformin group, and to 14.4% in the lifestyle group. Given the superiority of the lifestyle intervention, the intervention was stopped (one year earlier than originally planned) to allow participants in the placebo and metformin groups to receive lifestyle modification. Two similar studies (from Finland and China, respectively) of individuals at high risk for diabetes showed very similar results (Pan et al., 1997; Tuomilehto et al., 2001). Secondary analysis of the DPP indicated that the lifestyle intervention also significantly reduced the risk of developing metabolic syndrome, compared to metformin and placebo (Orchard et al., 2005).

Structure of Lifestyle Modification

The standard of care for lifestyle modification is similar to that provided in the DPP. Treatment is provided for an initial period of 16 to 26 weeks, often with every-other-week or monthly maintenance sessions afterwards (Wadden & Foster, 2000; Wing, 2002). Weight loss providers typically include registered dietitians, behavioral psychologists, exercise specialists, or related health professionals (Wadden & Foster; Wing). Treatment is usually provided in groups of 10 to 20 individuals. Group treatment may be more effective than individual counseling and is less expensive (Renjilian et al., 2001). Group sessions also provide empathy, social support, a healthy dose of competition among group members, and the opportunity for weekly weigh-ins (Wadden & Foster, 2000). Treatment of 16 to 26 weeks provides enough time for participants to achieve a 10% loss of initial weight, at which time weight loss reaches a plateau for the majority of individuals.

Lifestyle modification visits are best conducted with the help of a structured curriculum. Examples of such curricula include the Diabetes Prevention Program or the LEARN Program for Weight Control (Brownell, 2004; Diabetes Prevention Program Research Group, 2002). Group sessions typically last 60 to 90 minutes, begin with a weigh-in, and then proceed to a review of participants' food and activity records. Review of records creates an expectation among participants that they will be asked to share results of monitoring with the group. This record review also provides an opportunity for the group leader to help participants identify successes and challenges from the previous week, and to plan strategies that will increase adherence during the coming week. In the last part of the session, the group leader typically introduces a new topic area. This component of the visit also is meant to be interactive, as opposed to a lecture format (Wadden & Foster, 2000). The group session concludes with a review of "homework" assignments for the upcoming week. Participants' completion of food records and of other self-monitoring activities consistently predicts success in initial weight loss (Berkowitz, Wadden, Tershakovec, & Cronquist, 2003; Wadden et al., 2005).

Dietary Options for Weight Loss

Dietary interventions for weight loss historically have been consistent with those recommended by the U.S. Department of Agriculture (2005). This diet is based on the consumption of whole grains, vegetables, fruits, and low-fat dairy products, as well as restriction of fat to less than 30% of calories (including less than 10% of calories from saturated fat). However, several other dietary approaches can be incorporated in a behavioral intervention. This section briefly reviews alternative dietary approaches to weight loss.

Meal Replacements

Meal replacement products include liquid shakes and bars, as well as shelf-stable frozen food entrees. These products facilitate the consumption of a known number of calories, simplify food choices, and require little or no preparation (Gilden Tsai & Wadden, 2006). The set calorie value and smaller portion size of these foods are particularly helpful, given that obese individuals underestimate calorie intake by an average of 40–50% (Lichtman et al., 1992). Use of meal replacements also appears to provide good control of appetite, possibly because of sensory-specific satiety (Rolls & Bell, 2000). Taken together, these benefits improve adherence to a calorie goal (Gilden et al., 2006).

Several studies found that the use of meal replacements led to larger weight losses than an isocaloric diet comprised of conventional foods. In a study by Ditschuneit Flechtner-Mors, Johnson, and Adler (1999), patients were randomly assigned to meal replacements (Slim-Fast® liquid supplements used for two meals and two snacks per day) or to conventional foods. After 3 months, individuals who used meal replacements lost 8% of initial weight, compared with 1.5% for those who consumed a diet of conventional foods (Ditschuneit et al., 1999). Long-term follow up of participants in the meal replacement group revealed that individuals who continued to replace one meal and one snack a day with shakes after the first 3 months maintained a loss of 11% at 27 months and 8% at 51 months (Flechtner-Mors, Ditschuneit, Johnson, Suchard, & Adler, 2000). A meta-analysis by Heymsfield, van Mierlo, van der Knapp, Heo, & Frier (2003) of six trials that randomly assigned participants to isocaloric diets of conventional foods or to meal replacements concluded that use of meal replacements led to an additional weight loss of 2.4 kg in 3 months (Heymsfield et al.).

Low-Carbohydrate Diets

Low-carbohydrate diets, as championed by Atkins (1998), have been a popular alternative to a traditional low-fat diet. This diet nearly completely eliminates one of the three macronutrient groups (i.e., carbohydrate) while allowing unlimited consumption of the other two (i.e., protein and fat). Despite the unlimited amount of protein and fat intake allowed, dieters appear to reduce overall caloric intake, perhaps because of increased satiation (from high protein intake) and/or a relative decrease in dietary variability (Makris & Foster, 2005). The majority of studies, including a meta-analysis of four randomized trials comparing low-carbohydrate with standard low-fat diets, found that low-carbohydate regimens led to greater weight losses at 6 months, but similar losses at 1 year (Brehm, Seeley, Daniels, & D'Alessio, 2003; Foster et al., 2003; Nordmann et al., 2006; Samaha et al., 2003; L. Stern et al., 2004; Yancy, Olsen, Guyton, Bakst, & Westman, 2004). Two recent studies found greater losses with the low-carbohydrate regimen at 1 year (Gardner et al., 2007; Shai et al., 2008).

The most comprehensive study to date revealed that macronutrient composition, per se, has little impact on weight loss when calorie deficit is held constant. Sacks and colleagues (2009) had all study participants reduce their caloric intake by 750 kcal/d. Participants were randomly assigned to one of four diet groups in which the carbohydrate intake was as low as 35% of calories or as high as 65%. Fat in the diet was prescribed at either 20% of calories or 40% of calories, whereas protein constituted either 15 or 25% of calories. Weight losses among the four groups did not differ significantly from each other either at month 6 or month 24. The study provides the most definitive evidence to date that calorie restriction is the key to weight loss. Macronutrient composition does not appear to affect the amount of weight loss, as long as dieters meet their goals for caloric restriction.

No strong evidence to date suggests that low-carbohydrate diets are associated with adverse health consequences of the diets. The lack of documented long-term adverse effects may be due, in part, to the low likelihood of adhering to a low-carbohydrate eating plan for an extended period of time. Low-carbohydrate diets may be particularly useful, compared with low-fat diets, for improving glycemic control (reducing HbA_{1C}) in patients with type 2 diabetes. Long-term studies of this issue are needed.

Low-Glycemic-Index Diets

The glycemic index of a food is calculated by measuring the increase in blood glucose following consumption of 50 grams of a target food, compared with the increase after an equal amount of a standardized food (e.g., white bread, glucose) (Brand-Miller, Wolever, & Foster-Powell, 2000; Makris & Foster, 2005). A low-glycemic-index diet encourages consumption of whole grains, legumes, vegetables, and certain fruits. This may be associated with smaller postprandial excursions of glucose and insulin, which may facilitate greater satiation and not require marked restriction of the amount of food eaten (Brand-Miller et al., 2000). Short-term feeding studies have confirmed that consumption of low-glycemic-index foods may temporarily reduce energy intake (Dumesnil et al., 2001; Ludwig et al., 1999).

Despite the theoretical benefits of a low-glycemic-index eating plan, studies to date have not demonstrated greater weight losses in obese participants who followed this approach compared with standard low-fat diets (McMillan-Price et al., 2006; Raatz et al., 2005). Rather, the potential benefits of the glycemic index may be in reducing other CVD risk factors. Two studies demonstrated larger reductions in LDL cholesterol in persons on low glycemic index diets, compared with standard diets, despite equivalent weight losses (McMillan-Price et al.; Sloth et al., 2004). Similarly, a meta-analysis concluded that low glycemic index diets led to greater improvements in glycemic control (HbA1c), as compared with a higher glycemic index regimen (Knoops et al., 2004).

Mediterranean Diet

A Mediterranean diet is defined by a relatively balanced consumption of macronutrients, although allowing higher consumption of unsaturated fats, such as olive oil and fish. The diet is also characterized by moderate alcohol consumption, especially red wine. Although the foods that comprise a Mediterranean eating plan may be more difficult to find on a day-to-day basis in the United States, the diet is likely to be more palatable, as compared with the low-glycemic-index diet, and is perhaps healthier than a low-carbohydrate diet containing large amounts of saturated fat. Longitudinal cohort studies have confirmed that greater adherence to a Mediterranean diet is associated with lower mortality from CVD (Brand-Miller, Hayne, Petocz, & Colagiuri, 2003). A recent randomized trial (described previously) showed greater weight losses with Mediterranean or low-carbohydrate diets, as compared with a standard low-fat diet (Shai et al., 2008).

Physical Activity for Cardiovascular Health and Weight Management

Physical activity is crucial for improving and maintaining cardiovascular health, particularly in those who are at increased risk of complications (e.g., obese individuals; Blair & Leemakers, 2002; Foreyt & Poston, 1999). Longitudinal cohort studies suggest that regular physical activity reduces CVD mortality more in men than in women (Hu et al., 2004; Lee, Blair, & Jackson, 1999; Lee, Jackson, & Blair, 1998; Stevens, Cai, Evenson, & Thomas, 2002). However, there is a broad consensus that both fitness and fatness are independent risk factors for cardiovascular morbidity and mortality. Thus, both aspects of health should be targeted in comprehensive weight management programs (Blair & Leemakers, 2002).

Physical Activity, Weight Loss, and Weight Maintenance

Increased physical activity without accompanying caloric restriction is unlikely to produce significant weight loss (Wadden et al., 2004). This is because of the extensive amount of exercise (i.e., 35 miles of walking per week) needed to achieve even moderate weight loss (i.e., 0.5 kg per week). Rather, weight loss is more easily achieved by reducing food intake by 500 kcal/day (a change most individuals can achieve in the short term without undue burden). A study by Slentz et al. (2004) demonstrated the modest effect of exercise on weight loss. In this trial, persons who ran 20 miles per week (but were not instructed to restrict caloric intake) lost 3.5 kg after 8 months (Figure 27.4), whereas individuals who walked 12 miles a week at a moderate intensity (i.e., six half-hour bouts of walking a week) lost only 1.1 kg. The results of this study underscore advice to obese patients that exercise will improve overall health (including cardiovascular risk), but will not improve short-term weight loss (Wadden et al., 2004).

Regular exercise, however, is a crucial component of long-term weight management (Jakicic, Winters, Lang, & Wing, 1999; Jeffery, Wing, Sherwood, & Tate, 2003; Wing, 1999; Wing & Hill, 2001). A randomized trial by Jeffery et al., for example, showed that obese individuals who were instructed to engage in 2500 kcal/week of physical activity lost similar amounts of weight at 6 months, but maintained greater weight losses at 12 and 18 months than did persons instructed to expend 1000 kcal/week (Jeffery et al., 2003). Several other studies have demonstrated the long-term benefits of physical activity for weight management (Jakicic et al., 1999; Jeffery, Wing, Thorson, & Burton, 1998; Rippe & Hess, 1998; Wadden, Vogt, Foster, & Anderson, 1998; Wing, 1999; Wing & Hill, 2001). Research suggests that patients may achieve optimal long-term weight control by expending 2500–3000 kcal/week (e.g., walking 25–30 miles a week, or about 1 hour per day, 7 days per week) (Rippe & Hess, 1998).

Type of Physical Activity

The physical activity goal of 30 minutes per day can be achieved in two general ways—programmed or lifestyle activity (Andersen et al., 1999; Blair & Leemakers,

27.4

The relationship between weight change and amount of exercise. Error bars show standard error of the mean (SEM).

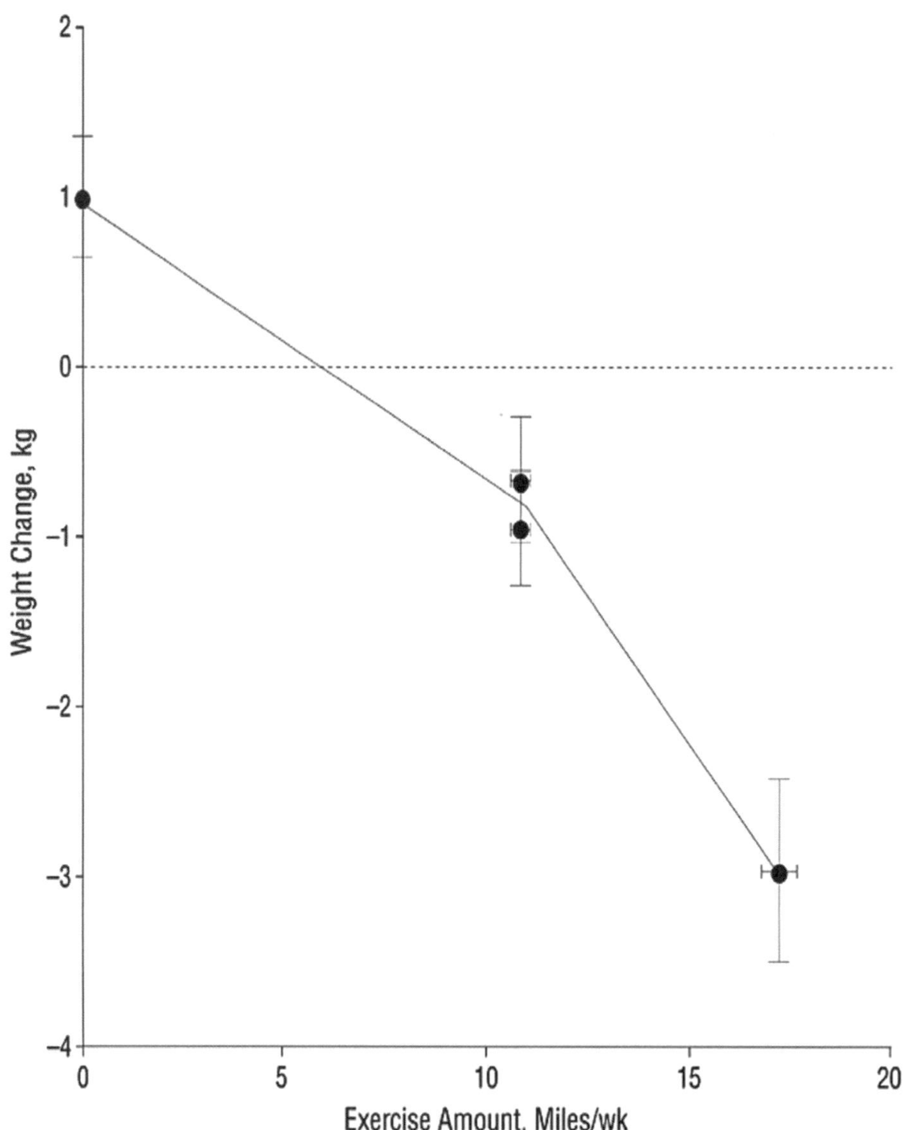

2002; Epstein, Wing, Koeske, & Valoski, 1985). Programmed activity (i.e., "exercise") typically requires more planning, is completed in a discrete period of time (i.e., 30–60 minutes), and is done at a relatively high level of intensity (i.e., 60–85% of maximum heart rate). Examples of programmed activity include jogging, biking, swimming, or exercising to a video. Lifestyle activity, by contrast, involves expending calories throughout the day, without concern for the intensity of the activity. Examples of lifestyle activity include walking rather than riding, using the stairs rather than the elevator, and walking down the hallway to talk to a colleague rather than e-mailing). The energy expenditure associated with such events may sum to 300 kcal/d, the equivalent of walking 3 miles (Blair & Leemakers, 2002). Two studies, one in children and one in adults, suggest that lifestyle activity is at least as effective as programmed activity for weight management (Andersen et al., 1999; Epstein et al., 1985). Thus, lifestyle activity may be ideal for patients who report that they do not enjoy exercising or do not have time for programmed activity.

Pharmacotherapy for Obesity

Two weight loss medications are approved for long-term use in the United States. They are orlistat (Xenical™) and sibutramine (Meridia™). Both orlistat and sibutramine have been used successfully for the induction and maintenance of weight loss.

Orlistat

Orlistat inhibits intestinal lipase, which, in turn, blocks the absorption of up to one third of the fat contained in food. (The blocked fat is excreted in stool.) Orlistat (sold over the counter as alli™) must be taken within 1 hour of eating, typically before each meal, for it to be effective. Numerous studies and several meta-analyses have demonstrated that orlistat, combined with lifestyle modification, produces weight losses of 8–10 kg in 12 months, which are 3–4 kg greater than those resulting from placebo combined with lifestyle changes (Hutton & Fergusson, 2004; O'Meara, Riemsma, Shirran, Mather, & ter Riet, 2004). The main side effects of the drug are related to steatorrhea (excretion of fat in the stool) and include gas, bloating, abdominal discomfort, loose and/or oily stools, and occasionally incontinence. Adherence to a low-fat diet (15 grams or less of fat per meal (e.g., a quarter-pound hamburger, without french fries or salad dressing) minimizes side effects of the drug. Use of orlistat can lead to deficiency of the fat-soluble vitamins A, D, E, or K. However, this risk is minimized by taking a daily multivitamin (at least 2 hours before or after taking orlistat).

Sibutramine

Sibutramine is a serotonin-norepinephrine reuptake inhibitor (SNRI). Thus, its mechanism of action is similar to that of several approved antidepressants, although the drug is not approved for use with depression (and SNRI antidepressants are not approved for weight loss). Numerous studies and two meta-analyses have shown that sibutramine induces placebo-subtracted weight losses of approximately 5 kg (that are slightly larger than those with orlistat) (Arterburn, Crane, & Veenstra, 2004; Li et al., 2005). Absolute losses of 10–12 kg have been observed in studies in which the drug was combined with intensive lifestyle modification (James et al., 2000; Wadden et al., 2005). Although sibutramine is slightly more effective than orlistat, it is contraindicated in patients with established CVD (i.e., coronary disease, cerebrovascular disease, congestive heart failure), in those with uncontrolled hypertension, and in individuals who take any medications with a serotonergic mechanism of action, including the commonly used SSRI antidepressants (Abbott Laboratories, 2008). Thus, sibutramine cannot be used by a significant percentage of individuals who could benefit from it.

We note that neither orlistat nor sibutramine is prescribed widely by primary care physicians (PCPs), for several reasons. First, PCPs may have general concerns about the safety of weight loss medications after the results of the "phen-fen" (phentermine + fenfluramine) experience in the 1990s. This very effective (and popular) pharmacologic approach was found to be associated with cardiac valvular disease and primary pulmonary hypertension. Second, some PCPs may be reluctant to prescribe a drug for what is perceived as a lifestyle problem (Foster et al., 2003). Third, even when prescribed, the drugs are not likely to be covered by insurance, and thus cost patients approximately $100 per month out of pocket. Fourth, the literature shows that the medications must be continued long-term to prevent weight regain (James et al., 2000; Sjostrom et al., 1998); some patients and PCPs may not be comfortable with the indefinite use of weight loss medications.

Investigational Agents for Weight Loss

No new weight loss medications have been approved in the United States since 1999. Recently, the cannabinoid receptor (CB-1) antagonist rimonabant (Despres, Golay, & Sjostrom, 2005) appeared to be poised for approval, after previously being approved by the European regulatory agencies. However, concerns about rimonabant's association with depression and suicidal ideation led the Food and Drug Administration not to approve the agent. Rimonabant's manufacturer subsequently suspended marketing the medication worldwide, when further reports of suicidal ideation and other psychiatric complications surfaced.

Several other weight loss agents are currently in development. The recognition that body weight is a highly defended and redundant pathway in the central nervous system has led to the strategy of combining medications that may have complementary mechanisms of action. Two such combination drugs currently in development include buproprion-naltrexone (Contrave™) (Greenway et al., 2009) and phentermine-topirimate (Qnexa™) (Cooke & Bloom, 2006). The former is a combination of an approved antidepressant (buproprion) and an approved agent for treatment of alcohol and narcotic addiction (naltrexone). The latter is the combination of a drug approved for short-term use in obesity (phentermine) and an antiepileptic medication, noted to have weight loss as a side effect (topirimate). Both medications have produced placebo-subtracted weight losses of approximately 4–5 kg. They are likely to be reviewed by the Food and Drug Administration as early as 2010.

Bariatric Surgery for Extreme Obesity

Several reviews have concluded that bariatric surgery is the most effective method to induce and maintain large weight loss of 15–25% of initial weight (Buchwald et al., 2004; Maggard et al., 2005). Surgery has been shown to dramatically improve several weight-related conditions, most notably type 2 diabetes. Generally, individuals with a BMI = 40 kg/m^2 are considered eligible for surgery, as are those with a BMI = 35 kg/m^2 who have weight-related comorbidity. The two most common surgical procedures in the United States are Roux-en-Y gastric bypass (RYGB) and laparoscopic adjustable gastric banding (LAGB). The latter procedure involves placing a horizontal band around the upper part of the stomach, such that a small stomach pouch (approximately 30 ml) remains, allowing the consumption of only a small amount of food. The band is adjustable and, if necessary, reversible. Conversely, RYGB involves creating a small pouch (i.e., 30 ml) at the upper part of the stomach, which is then anastamosed (i.e., connected) to the midpart of the small intestine, thus bypassing most of the stomach and the first part of the small intestine. RYGB induces weight loss by restricting food intake (with the small pouch) and potentially increasing the activity of satiety-related hormones such as GLP-1. Patients who undergo RYGB must be monitored for the development of micronutrient deficiencies (including iron, calcium, and vitamin B12).

RYGB induces significantly larger weight losses than LAGB, although banding is associated with lower complication rates. Weight loss surgery, in general, is associated with significant perioperative morbidity, including wound infection, blood clots, and other complications (e.g., breakdown of the intestinal anastomosis). The risk of perioperative (30-day) mortality with RYGB is approximately 0.5%, whereas the risk with banding is less than 0.1% (Flum et al., 2005). However, the Swedish Obese Subjects study found that extremely obese individuals who underwent surgery (RYGB or LAGB) had lower mortality after 10 years, compared with a matched control group that lost no weight (Sjostrom et al., 2007). Thus, despite the risk of perioperative mortality, bariatric surgery ultimately appears to extend life expectancy.

Evaluating Treatment Outcomes

Benefits of Weight Loss

Just as obesity is associated with decrements in physical and mental health, significant weight loss can ameliorate these complications. Improvements in health conditions can occur after a loss of as little as 5% of initial weight (World Health Organization, 1998). Numerous studies have demonstrated improvements in blood pressure, blood sugar, triglyceride levels, sleep apnea, and other health outcomes following modest weight loss (Knowler et al., 2002; NIH, 1998). Psychosocial benefits of weight loss may also be seen, although these are more commonly associated with large, rather than modest, weight losses (Fontaine & Barofsky, 2001).

Points of Collaboration With Physicians and Families

Primary care physicians play an important role in encouraging families to support patients' efforts to lose weight. The involvement of families of patients who are obese appears to improve patients' weight control and, thus, may enhance their weight loss outcomes (McLean, Griffin, Toney, & Hardeman, 2003). Families can support patients in many ways. First, they can provide patients with emotional support through displays of warmth, concern, and understanding. As noted previoously, obesity is a complex illness that is influenced by an interrelated set of physiological and environmental mechanisms. It is important that patients and families alike have a basic understanding of the various factors that serve to initiate, maintain, and exacerbate obesity so as to prevent "blaming the victim" for his/her weight problem, potentially leading to demoralization and impaired weight control. Displaying empathy, respect, and appreciation of patients' weight loss efforts, in lieu of insensitivity and criticism of their obesity, is an important step that families can take to support members who are obese. In addition, families can accompany patients to their medical appointments, which would help families become educated about obesity and ways in which they can help members lose weight.

Primary care physicians can also encourage families of obese patients to provide instrumental support, which refers to the provision of help with tangible needs (Ostberg & Lennartsson, 2007; Taylor, 2006). Examples of instrumental support include helping patients shop for healthy foods, assisting them with cooking, transporting them to their medical visits, and volunteering to complete household chores to allow them time to exercise. It is also important that families help patients control their household environments involving food (i.e., stimulus control). Strategies include storing high-fat, high-sugary foods out of sight, keeping serving dishes off the table, and serving modest portion sizes (Brownell, 2004; Wadden, Crerand, et al., 2005). In addition to eliminating triggers to overeating, families can be encouraged to add cues to their household environments that promote healthful behaviors. For example, placing a pair of sneakers at the front door may prompt members to exercise. Finally, from a broader perspective, primary care physicians should encourage all family members to engage in appropriate eating and physical activity behaviors to promote healthful changes on a systemic level.

Considerations With Special Populations/Diversity Issues

As noted earlier, African Americans and Latinos have higher rates of obesity in the United States. Many experts believe that a slightly different approach is useful in the treatment of obesity for ethnic minority populations, as compared to Whites. For example, the more social approach to health among African Americans suggests that weight loss could be increased by including friends and family in weight loss counseling sessions (Kumanyika, n.d.). Regardless of cultural differences in views of weight and weight loss, the higher rate of obesity among African Americans and Latinos has led to a much greater burden of diabetes, hypertension, and other weight-related conditions in these populations. Obese African American patients are open to counseling, provided that their physicians address the issue in a respectful and positive manner, and weight loss goals are individualized (Ward, Gray, & Paranjape, 2009).

Prevention of overweight and obesity in children has become a national priority in recent years, with the Robert Wood Johnson Foundation alone giving $500 million to study and mitigate the problem. Modification of the food and physical activity environment in schools is one of the most important ways to approach childhood obesity. Schools can require daily physical education classes, increase the quality of food served in their cafeterias and vending machines, limit the availability of high-fat, high-calorie food on its premises, and report children's BMI to parents. Clinical treatment of obesity for children, most often provided as group counseling, also may "bend the curve" of BMI in overweight and obese children. The labor intensity of group counseling limits the reach of this approach, but it may be appropriate for children who have failed other attempts and who are motivated to participate. Diet and behavior modification interventions for children and adolescents are likely to be more effective if parents are involved.

Clinical Pearls of Wisdom for Practitioners

Management of Obesity in Primary Care Practice

The U.S. Preventive Services Task Force (2003) has recommended that "clinicians screen all adult patients for obesity and offer *intensive counseling and behavioral interventions* to promote sustained weight loss for obese adults" (p. 930). However, most PCPs are neither trained nor reimbursed to treat obesity. Thus, clinicians are in the unfortunate position of treating comorbid conditions without the capacity to address the underlying cause.

Assessing and Discussing Weight

The PCPs' main responsibility, for which they are trained and reimbursed, is to assess and treat CVD risk factors. Tight control of these risk factors—all of which are common among overweight and obese individuals—is associated with reductions in morbidity and mortality (Ross et al., 1999; Thavendiranathan, Bagai, Brookhart, & Choudhry, 2006; U.K. Prospective Diabetes Study [UKPDS] Group, 1998).

After evaluating and treating CVD risk factors, PCPs who wish to initiate a discussion of weight must be prepared to take at least five minutes and to listen to patients' concerns (rather than lecturing). PCPs should use patient-friendly language to open a discussion about weight. For example, the term obesity, although clinically correct, tends to offend patients (Wadden & Didie, 2003). They are unable to disentangle the medical denotation of the term (excess body fat) from its pejorative social connotations (i.e., unattractive, lazy, weak-willed). Obese individuals find the terms *weight* or *BMI* most acceptable in discussing weight management, as shown in a pilot study (Wadden & Didie, 2003). PCPs should ask patients whether their weight affects their health or daily activities (and, if so, how). This relationship may be more readily apparent for some conditions (e.g., knee osteoarthritis) than for others (e.g., hypertension). If time allows, the patient's personal and family history of obesity can be reviewed, including previous weight loss attempts and periods of weight gain (Kushner, 2003). Finally, the PCP should determine what patients' current goals are for their weight. The Stages of Change Model can be used to help decide whether the patient is ready for weight loss (Hawkins, Hornsby, & Schorling, 2001). The brief "5A" intervention (*Assess* weight and BMI; *Ask* permission to discuss weight; *Advise* weight loss, using a personalized message; *Assist* in selecting an appropriate regimen; *Arrange* follow-up to discuss progress), as developed originally for smoking cessation, also has been used for weight management (Simkin-Silverman & Wing, 1997).

Weight Management Options for PCPs

The literature on the treatment of obesity in primary care reveals that PCPs have two primary weight management options they can use in their own practice, as well as two referral options. PCPs "in-practice" options are to: (a) manage obesity themselves using frequent counseling visits, with or without the addition of pharmacotherapy; or (b) treat patients collaboratively, working with other health professionals (e.g., dietitians, nurses) in their practice or health system. Their two principal referral options are to refer patients to community interventions for weight management, such as commercial or organized self-help programs, or enlist obesity treatment specialists, who offer medically supervised interventions or bariatric surgery.

PCP Counseling and/or Pharmacotherapy

Four randomized trials have assessed the effects of brief physician counseling on weight loss (Christian et al., 2008; Cohen, D'Amico, & Merenstein, 1991; Davis Martin et al., 2006; Ockene et al., 1999). Patients in these studies lost from 0.1 to 2.3 kg (with differences between treatment and control groups ranging from 0.7 to 2.3 kg). Three additional randomized trials combined brief PCP counseling with pharmacotherapy. Orlistat was used in two studies, and sibutramine in one. Absolute weight losses among active treatment groups in the two studies of orlistat were 1.7 kg (Poston et al., 2006) and 4.5 kg (60 mg tid) or 5.0 kg (120 mg tid) (Hauptman, Lucas, Boldrin, Collins, & Segal, 2000), with differences between treatment and control groups of 3–4 kg. In the study of sibutramine, medication alone induced a weight loss of 5.0 kg, whereas the combination of medication and brief PCP counseling produced a weight loss of 7.5 kg (Wadden et al., 2005). Collectively, these studies suggest that periodic, brief physician counseling is not sufficient to induce clinically significant weight loss, although the combination of brief counseling and pharmacotherapy may be more efficacious.

Collaborative Obesity Treatment

PCPs also can enlist other health professionals in their practice (e.g., registered dietitians, nurses) to provide weight loss counseling. The inclusion of other professionals as counselors could reduce the burden on PCPs to provide all acute, chronic, and preventive services for their patients (Frank, 1998; Yarnall, Pollak, Ostbye, Krause, & Michener, 2003). Two studies achieved clinically significant weight losses using a collaborative treatment model that included a combination of frequent dietitian counseling and meal replacements (Ashley et al., 2001; Bowerman et al., 2001). In one investigation, patients were randomly assigned to dietitian counseling, nurse/physician visits plus meal replacements, or dietitian counseling plus meal replacements. After 1 year, weight losses in the three groups were 3.4, 3.5, and 7.7 kg. Losses in the third group were significantly greater than those in the first two (Ashley et al., 2001). In a second study (a case series, with no control group), patients were provided five PCP visits, monthly telephone calls from dietitians, and meal replacements. Of the 48% of patients that remained in the study after 6 months, men lost 7.0 kg and women lost 8.6 kg.

Two other collaborative treatment studies that used frequent telephone support in the active treatment arm found smaller weight losses (Ely et al., 2008; Logue et al., 2005). One study used counselors trained in motivational interviewing, and achieved weight losses of 4.3 kg in the treated group and 1.0 kg in the control group at 6 months (Ely et al.). However, these results must be interpreted in light of a 49% attrition rate at 6 months. The second study used frequent phone support from dietitians and found small losses after 2 years of treatment (0.2 and 0.4 kg in the control and treated groups, respectively) (Logue et al., 2005). Collectively, these studies suggest that the largest weight losses may be achieved with the combination of dietitian counseling and meal replacements.

Referral to Community Program

PCPs who do not have the opportunity to treat obesity in their practice settings can refer patients to community-based programs. Popular interventions include commercial and organized self-help programs, such as Weight Watchers®, Jenny Craig, and Take Off Pounds Sensibly (TOPS) (J. S. Stern et al., 1995; Tsai & Wadden, 2005). A review of the literature found that individuals who completed commercial programs lost 4–7% of initial weight after 1 year (Tsai & Wadden). However, estimates of weight loss and of attrition from these studies may be optimistic. For example, a randomized trial of the Jenny Craig program reported weight losses of 6.5% of initial weight, with only 7% attrition at 1 year (Rock, Pakiz, Flatt, & Quintana, 2007). However, a naturalistic evaluation of the same program observed 50% attrition after 11 weeks of treatment. Patients who remained in the program at week 11 lost 5.5% of initial weight (Finley et al., 2007). Primary care patients, who represent a less selected population, are likely to achieve results closer to those reported in the latter study.

Many patients in primary care settings do not have access to intensive lifestyle modification for obesity, as is recommended by the U.S. Preventive Services Task Force. One way to offer such treatment would be to have behavioral psychologists working within medical practices alongside primary care physicians. So-called "co-location" of primary care and behavioral health could facilitate not only treatment of obesity, but also other health promotion counseling (e.g., smoking cessation, medication adherence). Co-location of primary care and mental health appears to improve patient care and provider satisfaction. However, mental health services provided in primary care settings are not adequately reimbursed. The unfortunate result of this is that primary care providers and mental health professionals usually do not work in the same office.

Referral to Obesity Specialists

Numerous studies have reported large weight losses (i.e., 15–25% of initial weight) with medically supervised low- or very-low-calorie diets (VLCD) (Anderson, Grant, Gotthelf, & Stifler, 2007; Anderson, Vichitbandra, Qian, & Kryscio, 1999; Donnelly et al., 2007; Wadden, Foster, & Letizia, 1994; Wadden, Foster, Letizia, & Stunkard, 1992). Because very-low-calorie diets (< 800 kcal/day) are costly and have equivalent long-term outcomes when compared with more moderate caloric restriction (total intake of 1000–1800 kcal/day) (Tsai & Wadden, 2005), they have been largely replaced by low-calorie diets (Anderson et al., 2007; Donnelly et al.; Wadden et al., 1997, 2004).

Weight regain is common after undergoing a medically supervised regimen. However, the provision of long-term weight-maintenance therapy may reduce the risk of regain (Anderson et al., 1994; Anderson et al., 1999). In addition, sibutramine was shown in one study to facilitate excellent maintenance of weight loss achieved with a VLCD (Apfelbaum et al., 1999).

Pharmacotherapy also is frequently used by obesity treatment specialists. Large weight losses (of 8–12% of initial weight) have been reported in several interventions in which pharmacotherapy was combined with an intensive lifestyle modification (Davidson et al., 1999; James et al., 2000; Wadden, Berkowitz, Sarwer, Prus-Wisniewski, & Steinberg, 2001; Wadden et al., 2005). We note, however, that modifications must be used long-term to facilitate the maintenance of weight loss. Weight is often regained rapidly following the termination of medication.

Summary

Obesity is a complex problem with causes and consequences that cut across many aspects of life—psychosocial, medical, and economic. There can be little doubt that obesity is a serious public health problem, amelioration of which will require widespread societal changes. These changes must include individual efforts to improve nutrition and increase physical activity, and equally important, economic incentives and policy changes that facilitate better choices. The concerted action needed among sectors of U.S. society—individuals, employers and schools, health care providers, the food industry, and government—may take a generation or more to achieve. Despite what may appear to be an uphill climb, advocates for obesity treatment should be heartened by other movements that successfully produced large-scale population improvements in health. Tobacco control is perhaps the best example, which offers many important lessons for the prevention and management of obesity.

Acknowledgments

This chapter was completed with the support of the Mid-Career Patient-Oriented Research Award from the National Institutes of Diabetes, Digestive, and Kidney Disease (K24-DK-065018) to Thomas Wadden.

References

Abbott Laboratories. (2008). *Meridia: Sibutramine hydrochloride monohydrate: Product monograph.* Retrieved May 25, 2008, from http://www.abbott.ca/static/content/document/meridia_2005 05-26_cxe.pdf

Adams, K. F., Schatzkin, A., Harris, T. B., Kipnis, V., Mouw, T., Ballard-Barbash, R., et al. (2006). Overweight, obesity, and mortality in a large prospective cohort of persons 50 to 71 years old. *New England Journal of Medicine, 355*(8), 763–778.

American Psychiatric Association. (2000). *Diagnostic and statistical manual of mental disorders* (4th ed., text rev.). Washington, DC: Author.

Andersen, R. E., Wadden, T. A., Bartlett, S. J., Zemel, B., Verde, T. J., & Franckowiak, S. C. (1999). Effects of lifestyle activity vs structured aerobic exercise in obese women: A randomized trial. *Journal of the American Medical Association, 281*(4), 335–340.

Anderson, J. W., Brinkman-Kaplan, V., Hamilton, C. C., Logan, J. E., Collins, R. W., & Gustafson, N. J. (1994). Food-containing hypocaloric diets are as effective as liquid-supplement diets for obese individuals with NIDDM. *Diabetes Care, 17*(6), 602–604.

Anderson, J. W., Grant, L., Gotthelf, L., & Stifler, L. T. (2007). Weight loss and long-term follow-up of severely obese individuals treated with an intense behavioral program. *International Journal of Obesity, 31*(3), 488–493.

Anderson, J. W., Vichitbandra, S., Qian, W., & Kryscio, R. J. (1999). Long-term weight maintenance after an intensive weight-loss program. *Journal of American College of Nutrition, 18*(6), 620–627.

Apfelbaum, M., Vague, P., Ziegler, O., Hanotin, C., Thomas, F., & Leutenegger, E. (1999). Long-term maintenance of weight loss after a very-low-calorie diet: A randomized blinded trial of the efficacy and tolerability of sibutramine. *American Journal of Medicine, 106*(2), 179–184.

Aronne, L. J., & Segal, K. R. (2003). Weight gain in the treatment of mood disorders. *Journal of Clinical Psychiatry, 64*(Suppl. 8), 22–29.

Arterburn, D. E., Crane, P. K., & Veenstra, D. L. (2004). The efficacy and safety of sibutramine for weight loss: A systematic review. *Archives of Internal Medicine, 164*(9), 994–1003.

Ashley, J. M., St. Jeor, S. T., Schrage, J. P., Perumean-Chaney, S. E., Gilbertson, M. C., McCall, N. L., et al. (2001). Weight control in the physician's office. *Archives of Internal Medicine, 161*(13), 1599–1604.

Atkins, R. C. (1998). *Dr. Atkins' new diet revolution*. New York: Avon Books.

Baggio, L. L., & Drucker, D. J. (2007). Biology of incretins: GLP-1 and GIP. *Gastroenterology, 132*(6), 2131–2157.

Banks, J., Marmot, M., Oldfield, Z., & Smith, J. P. (2006). Disease and disadvantage in the United States and in England. *Journal of the American Medical Association, 295*(17), 2037–2045.

Bassett, M. T., Dumanovsky, T., & Huang, C. (2008). Purchasing behavior and calorie information at fast-food chains in New York City. *American Journal of Public Health, 98*(8), 1457–1459.

Berkowitz, R. I., Wadden, T. A., Tershakovec, A. M., & Cronquist, J. L. (2003). Behavior therapy and sibutramine for the treatment of adolescent obesity: A randomized controlled trial. *Journal of the American Medical Association, 289*(14), 1805–1812.

Blair, S. N., & Leemakers, E. A. (2002). Exercise and weight management. In T. A. Wadden & A. J. Stunkard (Eds.), *Handbook of obesity treatment* (pp. 283–300). New York: Guilford.

Bouchard, C. (1997). Genetics of human obesity: Recent results from linkage studies. *Journal of Nutrition, 127*(9), 1887S–1890S.

Bowerman, S., Bellman, M., Saltsman, P., Garvey, D., Pimstone, K., Skootsky, S., et al. (2001). Implementation of a primary care physician network obesity management program. *Obesity Research, 9*(Suppl. 4), 321S–325S.

Brand-Miller, J., Hayne, S., Petocz, P., & Colagiuri, S. (2003). Low-glycemic index diets in the management of diabetes: A meta-analysis of randomized controlled trials. *Diabetes Care, 26*(8), 2261–2267.

Brand-Miller, J., Wolever, T. M. S., & Foster-Powell, K. (2000). *The glucose revolution pocket guide to sugar and energy.* New York: Marlowe and Company.

Bray, G. A., & Popkin, B. M. (1998). Dietary fat intake does affect obesity! *American Journal of Clinical Nutrition, 68*(6), 1157–1173.

Brehm, B. J., Seeley, R. J., Daniels, S. R., & D'Alessio, D. A. (2003). A randomized trial comparing a very low carbohydrate diet and a calorie-restricted low fat diet on body weight and cardiovascular risk factors in healthy women. *Journal of Clinical Endocrinology & Metabolism, 88*(4), 1617–1623.

Brownell, K. D. (2004). *The LEARN program for weight management* (10th ed.). Dallas, TX: American Health Publishing.

Buchwald, H., Avidor, Y., Braunwald, E., Jensen, M. D., Pories, W., Fahrbach, K., et al. (2004). Bariatric surgery: A systematic review and meta-analysis. *Journal of the American Medical Association, 292*(14), 1724–1737.

Centers for Disease Control and Prevention. (2006). *SHPPS: School health policies and programs study.* Retrieved December 7, 2008, from http://www.cdc.gov/HealthyYouth/shpps/

Chang, V. W., & Lauderdale, D. S. (2005). Income disparities in body mass index and obesity in the United States, 1971-2002. *Archives of Internal Medicine, 165*(18), 2122–2128.

Christian, J. G., Bessesen, D. H., Byers, T. E., Christian, K. K., Goldstein, M. G., & Bock, B. C. (2008). Clinic-based support to help overweight patients with type 2 diabetes increase physical activity and lose weight. *Archives of Internal Medicine, 168*(2), 141–146.

Cohen, M. D., D'Amico, F. J., & Merenstein, J. H. (1991). Weight reduction in obese hypertensive patients. *Family Medicine, 23*(1), 25–28.

Cooke, D., & Bloom, S. (2006). The obesity pipeline: Current strategies in the development of anti-obesity drugs. *Nature Reviews Drug Discovery, 5*(11), 919–931.

Cossrow, N., & Falkner, B. (2004). Race/ethnic issues in obesity and obesity-related comorbidities. *Journal of Clinical Endocrinology & Metabolism, 89*(6), 2590–2594.

Cram, P., Nallamothu, B. K., Fendrick, A. M., & Saint, S. (2002). Fast food franchises in hospitals. *Journal of the American Medical Association, 287*(22), 2945–2946.

Davidson, M. H., Hauptman, J., DiGirolamo, M., Foreyt, J. P., Halsted, C. H., Heber, D., et al. (1999). Weight control and risk factor reduction in obese subjects treated for 2 years with orlistat: A randomized controlled trial. *Journal of the American Medical Association, 281*(3), 235–242.

Davis Martin, P., Rhode, P. C., Dutton, G. R., Redmann, S. M., Ryan, D. H., & Brantley, P. J. (2006). A primary care weight management intervention for low-income African-American women. *Obesity (Silver Spring), 14*(8), 1412–1420.

Despres, J. P., Golay, A., & Sjostrom, L. (2005). Effects of rimonabant on metabolic risk factors in overweight patients with dyslipidemia. *New England Journal of Medicine, 353*(20), 2121–2134.

The Diabetes Prevention Program (DPP) Research Group. (2002). Description of lifestyle intervention. *Diabetes Care, 25*(12), 2165–2171.

Ditschuneit, H. H., Flechtner-Mors, M., Johnson, T. D., & Adler, G. (1999). Metabolic and weight-loss effects of a long-term dietary intervention in obese patients. *American Journal of Clinical Nutrition, 69*(2), 198–204.

Donnelly, J. E., Smith, B. K., Dunn, L., Mayo, M. M., Jacobsen, D. J., Stewart, E. E., et al. (2007). Comparison of a phone vs. clinic approach to achieve 10% weight loss. *International Journal of Obesity, 31*(8), 1270–1276.

Drewnowski, A., & Specter, S. E. (2004). Poverty and obesity: The role of energy density and energy costs. *American Journal of Clinical Nutrition, 79*(1), 6–16.

Dumesnil, J. G., Turgeon, J., Tremblay, A., Poirier, P., Gilbert, M., Gagnon, L., et al. (2001). Effect of a low-glycaemic index, low-fat high-protein diet on the atherogenic metabolic risk profile of abdominally obese men. *British Journal of Nutrition, 86*(5), 557–568.

Ely, A. C., Banitt, A., Befort, C., Hou, Q., Rhode, P. C., Grund, C., et al. (2008). Kansas primary care weighs in: A pilot randomized trial of a chronic care model program for obesity in 3 rural Kansas primary care practices. *Journal of Rural Health, 24*(2), 125–132.

Epstein, L. H., Wing, R. R., Koeske, R., & Valoski, A. (1985). A comparison of lifestyle exercise, aerobic exercise, and calisthenics on weight loss in obese children. *Behavior Therapy, 16*, 345–356.

Finkelstein, E. A., Ruhm, C. J., & Kosa, K. M. (2005). Economic causes and consequences of obesity. *Annual Review of Public Health, 26*, 239–257.

Finley, C. E., Barlow, C. E., Greenway, F. L., Rock, C. L., Rolls, B. J., & Blair, S. N. (2007). Retention rates and weight loss in a commercial weight loss program. *International Journal of Obesity, 31*(2), 292–298.

Flechtner-Mors, M., Ditschuneit, H. H., Johnson, T. D., Suchard, M. A., & Adler, G. (2000). Metabolic and weight loss effects of long-term dietary intervention in obese patients: Four-year results. *Obesity Research, 8*(5), 399–402.

Flegal, K. M., Graubard, B. I., Williamson, D. F., & Gail, M. H. (2005). Excess deaths associated with underweight, overweight, and obesity. *Journal of the American Medical Association, 293*(15), 1861–1867.

Flum, D. R., Salem, L., Elrod, J. A., Dellinger, E. P., Cheadle, A., & Chan, L. (2005). Early mortality among Medicare beneficiaries undergoing bariatric surgical procedures. *Journal of the American Medical Association, 294*(15), 1903–1908.

Fontaine, K. R., & Barofsky, I. (2001). Obesity and health-related quality of life. *Obesity Review, 2*(3), 173–182.

Fontaine, K. R., Redden, D. T., Wang, C., Westfall, A. O., & Allison, D. B. (2003). Years of life lost due to obesity. *Journal of the American Medical Association, 289*(2), 187–193.

Foreyt, J. P., & Poston, W. S., 2nd. (1999). The challenge of diet, exercise and lifestyle modification in the management of the obese diabetic patient. *International Journal of Obesity and Related Metabolic Disorders, 23*(Suppl. 7), S5–11.

Foster, G. D., Makris, A. P., & Bailer, B. A. (2005). Behavioral treatment of obesity. *The American Journal of Clinical Nutrition, 82*(1), 230S-235S.

Foster, G. D., Wadden, T. A., Makris, A. P., Davidson, D., Sanderson, R. S., Allison, D. B., et al. (2003). Primary care physicians' attitudes about obesity and its treatment. *Obesity Research, 11*(10), 1168–1177.

Foster, G. D., Wadden, T. A., & Vogt, R. A. (1997). Resting energy expenditure in obese African American and Caucasian women. *Obesity Research, 5*(1), 1–8.

Foster, G. D., Wyatt, H. R., Hill, J. O., McGuckin, B. G., Brill, C., Mohammed, B. S., et al. (2003). A randomized trial of a low-carbohydrate diet for obesity. *New England Journal of Medicine, 348*(21), 2082–2090.

Frank, A. (1998). A multidisciplinary approach to obesity management: The physician's role and team care alternatives. *Journal of the American Dietetic Association, 98*(10 Suppl. 2), S44–S48.

Gardner, C. D., Kiazand, A., Alhassan, S., Kim, S., Stafford, R. S., Balise, R. R., et al. (2007). Comparison of the Atkins, Zone, Ornish, and LEARN diets for change in weight and related risk factors among overweight premenopausal women: The A to Z weight loss study: A randomized trial. *Journal of the American Medical Association, 297*(9), 969–977.

Gilden Tsai, A., & Wadden, T. A. (2006). The evolution of very-low-calorie diets: An update and meta-analysis. *Obesity (Silver Spring), 14*(8), 1283–1293.

Golay, A., & Bobbioni, E. (1997). The role of dietary fat in obesity. *International Journal of Obesity and Related Metabolic Disorders, 21*(Suppl. 3), S2–11.

Greenway, F. L., Whitehouse, M. J., Guttadauria, M., Anderson, J. W., Atkinson, R. L., Fujioka, K., et al. (2009). Rational design of a combination medication for the treatment of obesity. *Obesity (Silver Spring), 17*(1), 30–39.

Grundy, S. M., Hansen, B., Smith, S. C., Jr., Cleeman, J. I., & Kahn, R. A. (2004). Clinical management of metabolic syndrome: Report of the American Heart Association/National Heart, Lung, and Blood Institute/American Diabetes Association conference on scientific issues related to management. *Circulation, 109*(4), 551–556.

Hauptman, J., Lucas, C., Boldrin, M. N., Collins, H., & Segal, K. R. (2000). Orlistat in the long-term treatment of obesity in primary care settings. *Archives of Family Medicine, 9*(2), 160–167.

Hawkins, D. S., Hornsby, P. P., & Schorling, J. B. (2001). Stages of change and weight loss among rural African American women. *Obesity Research, 9*(1), 59–67.

Heymsfield, S. B., van Mierlo, C. A., van der Knaap, H. C., Heo, M., & Frier, H. I. (2003). Weight management using a meal replacement strategy: Meta and pooling analysis from six studies. *International Journal of Obesity and Related Metabolic Disorders, 27*(5), 537–549.

Hill, J. O., Wyatt, H. R., Reed, G. W., & Peters, J. C. (2003). Obesity and the environment: Where do we go from here? *Science, 299*(5608), 853–855.

Horgen, K., & Brownell, K. D. (2002). Confronting the toxic environment: Environmental, public health actions in a world crisis. In T. A. Wadden & A. J. Stunkard (Eds.), *Handbook of obesity treatment* (pp. 95–106). New York: Guilford.

Hu, F. B., Willett, W. C., Li, T., Stampfer, M. J., Colditz, G. A., & Manson, J. E. (2004). Adiposity as compared with physical activity in predicting mortality among women. *New England Journal of Medicine, 351*(26), 2694–2703.

Hudson, J. I., Hiripi, E., Pope, H. G., Jr., & Kessler, R. C. (2007). The prevalence and correlates of eating disorders in the national comorbidity survey replication. *Biological Psychiatry, 61*(3), 348–358.

Hutton, B., & Fergusson, D. (2004). Changes in body weight and serum lipid profile in obese patients treated with orlistat in addition to a hypocaloric diet: A systematic review of randomized clinical trials. *American Journal of Clinical Nutrition, 80*(6), 1461–1468.

Jakicic, J. M., Winters, C., Lang, W., & Wing, R. R. (1999). Effects of intermittent exercise and use of home exercise equipment on adherence, weight loss, and fitness in overweight women: A randomized trial. *Journal of the American Medical Association, 282*(16), 1554–1560.

James, W. P., Astrup, A., Finer, N., Hilsted, J., Kopelman, P., Rossner, S., et al. (2000). Effect of sibutramine on weight maintenance after weight loss: A randomised trial. STORM study group. Sibutramine trial of obesity reduction and maintenance. *Lancet, 356*(9248), 2119–2125.

Jeffery, R. W., Wing, R. R., Sherwood, N. E., & Tate, D. F. (2003). Physical activity and weight loss: Does prescribing higher physical activity goals improve outcome? *American Journal of Clinical Nutrition, 78*(4), 684–689.

Jeffery, R. W., Wing, R. R., Thorson, C., & Burton, L. R. (1998). Use of personal trainers and financial incentives to increase exercise in a behavioral weight-loss program. *Journal of Consulting and Clinical Psychology, 66*(5), 777–783.

Kant, A. K., & Graubard, B. I. (2006). Secular trends in patterns of self-reported food consumption of adult Americans: NHANES 1971–1975 to NHANES 1999–2002. *American Journal of Clinical Nutrition, 84*(5), 1215–1223.

Katz, D. L., Njike, V., Zubaid, F., & Rhee-Baez, L. Q. (2008, October). *Overall nutritional quality index: A consumer empowerment tool*. Paper presented at the American Public Health Association 136th annual meeting and expo: Public health without borders, San Diego, CA.

Knoops, K. T., de Groot, L. C., Kromhout, D., Perrin, A. E., Moreiras-Varela, O., Menotti, A., et al. (2004). Mediterranean diet, lifestyle factors, and 10-year mortality in elderly European men and women: The HALE project. *Journal of the American Medical Association, 292*(12), 1433–1439.

Knowler, W. C., Barrett-Connor, E., Fowler, S. E., Hamman, R. F., Lachin, J. M., Walker, E. A., et al. (2002). Reduction in the incidence of type 2 diabetes with lifestyle intervention or metformin. *New England Journal of Medicine, 346*(6), 393–403.

Kolotkin, R. L., Meter, K., & Williams, G. R. (2001). Quality of life and obesity. *Obesity Review, 2*(4), 219–229.

Kraly, F. S., Carty, W. J., Resnick, S., & Smith, G. P. (1978). Effect of cholecystokinin on meal size and intermeal interval in the sham-feeding rat. *Journal of Comparative and Physiological Psychology, 92*(4) 697–707.

Kumanyika, S. (2005). Obesity, health disparities, and prevention paradigms: Hard questions and hard choices. *Preventing Chronic Disease, 2*(4), A02.

Kumanyika, S. (n.d.). *SHARE overview.* Retrieved September 21, 2009, from http://www.cceb.upenn.edu/pages/share/overview.html

Kushner, R. F. (2003). *Roadmaps for clinical practice: Case studies in disease prevention and health promotion-assessment and management of adult obesity: A primer for physicians*. Chicago: American Medical Association.

Lee, C. D., Blair, S. N., & Jackson, A. S. (1999). Cardiorespiratory fitness, body composition, and all-cause and cardiovascular disease mortality in men. *American Journal of Clinical Nutrition, 69*(3), 373–380.

Lee, C. D., Jackson, A. S., & Blair, S. N. (1998). US weight guidelines: Is it also important to consider cardiorespiratory fitness? *International Journal of Obesity and Related Metabolic Disorders, 22*(Suppl. 2), S2–S7.

Lesser, L. I. (2006). Prevalence and type of brand name fast food at academic-affiliated hospitals. *Journal of the American Board of Family Medicine, 19*, 526–527.

Levine, J. A., Lanningham-Foster, L. M., McCrady, S. K., Krizan, A. C., Olson, L. R., Kane, P. H., et al. (2005). Interindividual variation in posture allocation: Possible role in human obesity. *Science, 307*(5709), 584–586.

Li, Z., Maglione, M., Tu, W., Mojica, W., Arterburn, D., Shugarman, L. R., et al. (2005). Meta-analysis: Pharmacologic treatment of obesity. *Annals of Internal Medicine, 142*(7), 532–546.

Lichtman, S. W., Pisarska, K., Berman, E. R., Pestone, M., Dowling, H., Offenbacher, E., et al. (1992). Discrepancy between self-reported and actual caloric intake and exercise in obese subjects. *New England Journal of Medicine, 327*(27), 1893–1898.

Liebling, D. S., Eisner, J. D., Gibbs, J., & Smith, G. P. (1975). Intestinal satiety in rats. *Journal of Comparative and Physilogical Psychology, 89*(8), 955–965.

Lissner, L., & Heitmann, B. L. (1995). Dietary fat and obesity: Evidence from epidemiology. *European Journal of Clinical Nutrition, 49*(2), 79–90.

Logue, E., Sutton, K., Jarjoura, D., Smucker, W., Baughman, K., & Capers, C. (2005). Transtheoretical model-chronic disease care for obesity in primary care: A randomized trial. *Obesity Research, 13*(5), 917–927.

Ludwig, D. S., Majzoub, J. A., Al-Zahrani, A., Dallal, G. E., Blanco, I., & Roberts, S. B. (1999). High glycemic index foods, overeating, and obesity. *Pediatrics, 103*(3), E26.

Maggard, M. A., Shugarman, L. R., Suttorp, M., Maglione, M., Sugerman, H. J., Livingston, E. H., et al. (2005). Meta-analysis: Surgical treatment of obesity. *Annals of Internal Medicine, 142*(7), 547–559.

Makris, A. P., & Foster, G. D. (2005). Dietary approaches to the treatment of obesity. *Psychiatric Clinics of North America, 28*(1), 117–139, viii–ix.

Malik, V. S., Schulze, M. B., & Hu, F. B. (2006). Intake of sugar-sweetened beverages and weight gain: A systematic review. *American Journal of Clinical Nutrition, 84*(2), 274–288.

Malone, M., Alger-Mayer, S. A., & Anderson, D. A. (2005). Medication associated with weight gain may influence outcome in a weight management program. *Annals of Pharmacotherapy, 39*(7-8), 1204–1208.

McLean, N., Griffin, S., Toney, K., & Hardeman, W. (2003). Family involvement in weight control, weight maintenance and weight-loss interventions: A systematic review of randomised trials. *International Journal of Obesity, 27,* 987-1005.

McMillan-Price, J., Petocz, P., Atkinson, F., O'Neill, K., Samman, S., Steinbeck, K., et al. (2006). Comparison of 4 diets of varying glycemic load on weight loss and cardiovascular risk reduction in overweight and obese young adults: A randomized controlled trial. *Archives of Internal Medicine, 166*(14), 1466–1475.

Murphy, K. G., & Bloom, S. R. (2006). Gut hormones and the regulation of energy homeostasis. *Nature, 444*(14), 854–859.

Must, A., Spadano, J., Coakley, E. H., Field, A. E., Colditz, G., & Dietz, W. H. (1999). The disease burden associated with overweight and obesity. *Journal of the American Medical Association, 282*(16), 1523–1529.

National Heart Lung, and Blood Institute (NHLBI). (2000). *The practical guide: Identification, evaluation, and treatment of overweight and obesity in adults.* Bethesda, MD: National Institute of Health.

National Institutes of Health. (1998). Clinical guidelines on the identification, evaluation, and treatment of overweight and obesity in adults—The evidence report. *Obesity Research, 6*(Suppl. 2), 51S–209S.

Nielsen, S. J., & Popkin, B. M. (2003). Patterns and trends in food portion sizes, 1977–1998. *Journal of the American Medical Association, 289*(4), 450–453.

Nordmann, A. J., Nordmann, A., Briel, M., Keller, U., Yancy, W. S., Jr., Brehm, B. J., et al. (2006). Effects of low-carbohydrate vs. low-fat diets on weight loss and cardiovascular risk factors: A meta-analysis of randomized controlled trials. *Archives of Internal Medicine, 166*(3), 285–293.

O'Meara, S., Riemsma, R., Shirran, L., Mather, L., & ter Riet, G. (2004). A systematic review of the clinical effectiveness of orlistat used for the management of obesity. *Obesity Review, 5*(1), 51–68.

Ockene, I. S., Hebert, J. R., Ockene, J. K., Saperia, G. M., Stanek, E., Nicolosi, R., et al. (1999). Effect of physician-delivered nutrition counseling training and an office-support program on saturated fat intake, weight, and serum lipid measurements in a hyperlipidemic population: Worcester area trial for counseling in hyperlipidemia (WATCH). *Archives of Internal Medicine, 159*(7), 725–731.

Ogden, C. L., Carroll, M. D., Curtin, L. R., McDowell, M. A., Tabak, C. J., & Flegal, K. M. (2006). Prevalence of overweight and obesity in the United States, 1999–2004. *Journal of the American Medical Association, 295*(13), 1549–1555.

Ogden, C. L., Flegal, K. M., Carroll, M. D., & Johnson, C. L. (2002). Prevalence and trends in overweight among US children and adolescents, 1999–2000. *Journal of the American Medical Association, 288*(14), 1728–1732.

Orchard, T. J., Temprosa, M., Goldberg, R., Haffner, S., Ratner, R., Marcovina, S., et al. (2005). The effect of metformin and intensive lifestyle intervention on the metabolic syndrome: The diabetes prevention program randomized trial. *Annals of Internal Medicine, 142*(8), 611–619.

Ostberg, V., & Lennartsson, C. (2007). Getting by with a little help: The importance of various types of social support for health problems. *Scandinavian Journal of Public Health, 35,* 197–204.

Pan, X. R., Li, G. W., Hu, Y. H., Wang, J. X., Yang, W. Y., An, Z. X., et al. (1997). Effects of diet and exercise in preventing NIDDM in people with impaired glucose tolerance. The Da Qing IGT and Diabetes Study. *Diabetes Care, 20*(4), 537–544.

Pavlov, I. P. (1927). *Conditioned reflexes.* New York: Liveright.

Pi-Sunyer, F. X. (1993). Short-term medical benefits and adverse effects of weight loss. *Annals of Internal Medicine, 119*(7 Pt. 2), 722–726.

Pi-Sunyer, F. X. (1999). Comorbidities of overweight and obesity: Current evidence and research issues. *Medicine and Science in Sports and Exercise, 31,* S602.

Poston, W. S., Haddock, C. K., Pinkston, M. M., Pace, P., Reeves, R. S., Karakoc, N., et al. (2006). Evaluation of a primary care-oriented brief counseling intervention for obesity with and without orlistat. *Journal of Internal Medicine, 260*(4), 388–398.

Raatz, S. K., Torkelson, C. J., Redmon, J. B., Reck, K. P., Kwong, C. A., Swanson, J. E., et al. (2005). Reduced glycemic index and glycemic load diets do not increase the effects of energy restriction on weight loss and insulin sensitivity in obese men and women. *Journal of Nutrition, 135*(10), 2387–2391.

Ravussin, E., Lillioja, S., Knowler, W. C., Christin, L., Freymond, D., Abbott, W. G., et al. (1988). Reduced rate of energy expenditure as a risk factor for body-weight gain. *New England Journal of Medicine, 318*(8), 467–472.

Ravussin, E., Valencia, M. E., Esparza, J., Bennett, P. H., & Schulz, L. O. (1994). Effects of a traditional lifestyle on obesity in Pima indians. *Diabetes Care, 17*(9), 1067–1074.

Razak, F., Anand, S. S., Shannon, H., Vuksan, V., Davis, B., Jacobs, R., et al. (2007). Defining obesity cut points in a multiethnic population. *Circulation, 115*(16), 2111–2118.

Renjilian, D. A., Perri, M. G., Nezu, A. M., McKelvey, W. F., Shermer, R. L., & Anton, S. D. (2001). Individual versus group therapy for obesity: Effects of matching participants to their treatment preferences. *Journal of Consulting and Clinical Psychology, 69*(4), 717–721.

Rippe, J. M., & Hess, S. (1998). The role of physical activity in the prevention and management of obesity. *Journal of the American Dietetic Association, 98*(10 Suppl. 2), S31–S38.

Rock, C. L., Pakiz, B., Flatt, S. W., & Quintana, E. L. (2007). Randomized trial of a multifaceted commercial weight loss program. *Obesity (Silver Spring), 15*(4), 939–949.

Rolls, B. J., & Bell, E. A. (2000). Dietary approaches to the treatment of obesity. *Medical Clinics of North America, 84*(2), 401–418, vi.

Rosenthal, N. E., Genhart, M., Jacobsen, F. M., Skwerer, R. G., & Wehr, T. A. (1987). Disturbances of appetite and weight regulation in seasonal affective disorder. *Annals of the New York Academy of Science, 499*, 216–230.

Ross, S. D., Allen, I. E., Connelly, J. E., Korenblat, B. M., Smith, M. E., Bishop, D., et al. (1999). Clinical outcomes in statin treatment trials: A meta-analysis. *Archives of Internal Medicine, 159*(15), 1793–1802.

Sacks, F. M., Bray, G. A., Carey, V. J., Smith, S. R., Ryan, D. H., Anton, S. D., et al. (2009). Comparison of weight-loss diets with different compositions of fat, protein, and carbohydrates. *New England Journal of Medicine, 360*(9), 859–873.

Sallis, J. F., Kraft, K., & Linton, L. S. (2002). How the environment shapes physical activity: A transdisciplinary research agenda. *American Journal of Preventive Medicine, 22*(3), 208.

Samaha, F. F., Iqbal, N., Seshadri, P., Chicano, K. L., Daily, D. A., McGrory, J., et al. (2003). A low-carbohydrate as compared with a low-fat diet in severe obesity. *New England Journal of Medicine, 348*(21), 2074–2081.

Shai, I., Schwarzfuchs, D., Henkin, Y., Shahar, D. R., Witkow, S., Greenberg, I., et al. (2008). Weight loss with a low-carbohydrate, Mediterranean, or low-fat diet. *New England Journal of Medicine, 359*(3), 229–241.

Simkin-Silverman, L. R., & Wing, R. R. (1997). Management of obesity in primary care. *Obesity Research, 5*(6), 603–612.

Sjostrom, L., Narbro, K., Sjostrom, C. D., Karason, K., Larsson, B., Wedel, H., et al. (2007). Effects of bariatric surgery on mortality in Swedish obese subjects. *New England Journal of Medicine, 357*(8), 741–752.

Sjostrom, L., Rissanen, A., Andersen, T., Boldrin, M., Golay, A., Koppeschaar, H. P., et al. (1998). Randomised placebo-controlled trial of orlistat for weight loss and prevention of weight regain in obese patients. European Multicentre Orlistat Study Group. *Lancet, 352*(9123), 167–172.

Skinner, B. F. (1953). *Science and human behavior.* New York: Macmillan.

Slentz, C. A., Duscha, B. D., Johnson, J. L., Ketchum, K., Aiken, L. B., Samsa, G. P., et al. (2004). Effects of the amount of exercise on body weight, body composition, and measures of central obesity: STRRIDE—A randomized controlled study. *Archives of Internal Medicine, 164*(1), 31–39.

Sloth, B., Krog-Mikkelsen, I., Flint, A., Tetens, I., Bjorck, I., Vinoy, S., et al. (2004). No difference in body weight decrease between a low-glycemic-index and a high-glycemic-index diet, but reduced LDL cholesterol after 10-wk ad libitum intake of the low-glycemic-index diet. *American Journal of Clinical Nutrition, 80*(2), 337–347.

Steffen, L. M., Arnett, D. K., Blackburn, H., Shah, G., Armstrong, C., Luepker, R. V., et al. (2006). Population trends in leisure-time physical activity: Minnesota Heart Survey, 1980-2000. *Medicine & Science in Sports & Exercise, 38*(10), 1716–1723.

Stern, J. S., Hirsch, J., Blair, S. N., Foreyt, J. P., Frank, A., Kumanyika, S. K., et al. (1995). Weighing the options: Criteria for evaluating weight-management programs. The Committee to Develop

Criteria for Evaluating the Outcomes of Approaches to Prevent and Treat Obesity. *Obesity Research, 3*(6), 591–604.

Stern, L., Iqbal, N., Seshadri, P., Chicano, K. L., Daily, D. A., McGrory, J., et al. (2004). The effects of low-carbohydrate versus conventional weight loss diets in severely obese adults: One-year follow-up of a randomized trial. *Annals of Internal Medicine, 140*(10), 778–785.

Stevens, J., Cai, J., Evenson, K. R., & Thomas, R. (2002). Fitness and fatness as predictors of mortality from all causes and from cardiovascular disease in men and women in the lipid research clinics study. *American Journal of Epidemiology, 156*(9), 832–841.

Stunkard, A. J., Allison, K. C., Geliebter, A., Lundgren, J. D., Gluck, M. E., & O'Reardon, J. P. (2009). Development of criteria for a diagnosis: Lessons from the night eating syndrome. *Comprehensive Psychiatry.*

Stunkard, A. J., Faith, M. S., & Allison, K. C. (2003). Depression and obesity. *Biological Psychiatry, 54*(3), 330–337.

Stunkard, A. J., Fernstrom, M. H., Price, A., Frank, E., & Kupfer, D. J. (1990). Direction of weight change in recurrent depression. Consistency across episodes. *Archives of General Psychiatry, 47*(9), 857–860.

Stunkard, A. J., Grace, W. J., & Wolff, H. G. (1955). The night-eating syndrome; A pattern of food intake among certain obese patients. *American Journal of Medicine, 19*(1), 78–86.

Taylor, S. E. (2006). Social support. In H. S. Friedman & R. C. Silver (Eds.), *Foundations of health psychology* (pp. 145-171). New York: Oxford University Press.

Thavendiranathan, P., Bagai, A., Brookhart, M. A., & Choudhry, N. K. (2006). Primary prevention of cardiovascular diseases with statin therapy: A meta-analysis of randomized controlled trials. *Archives of Internal Medicine, 166*(21), 2307–2313.

Thorpe, K. E., Florence, C. S., Howard, D. H., & Joski, P. (2005). The rising prevalence of treated disease: Effects on private health insurance spending. *Health Affairs, 24*(1), (Suppl. Web Exclusives), 317–325. Retrieved November 15, 2008, from http://web.ebscohost.com/ehost/detail?vid=4&hid=3&sid=873d3e77-8ec3-4bd2-a203bc7c9a74db78%40sessionmgr4&bdata=JnNpdGU9ZWhvc3QtbGl2ZSZzY29wZT1zaXRl#db=aph&AN=18282085db=aph&AN=18282085

Tillotson, J. E. (2004). America's obesity: Conflicting public policies, industrial economic development, and unintended human consequences. *Annual Review of Nutrition, 24*, 617–643.

Tsai, A. G., & Wadden, T. A. (2005). Systematic review: An evaluation of major commercial weight loss programs in the United States. *Annals of Internal Medicine, 142*(1), 56–66.

Tschop, M., Smiley, D. L., & Heiman, M. L. (2000). Ghrelin induces adiposity in rodents. *Nature, 407*, 908–913.

Tuomilehto, J., Lindstrom, J., Eriksson, J. G., Valle, T. T., Hamalainen, H., Ilanne-Parikka, P., et al. (2001). Prevention of type 2 diabetes mellitus by changes in lifestyle among subjects with impaired glucose tolerance. *New England Journal of Medicine, 344*(18), 1343–1350.

U.K. Prospective Diabetes Study (UKPDS) Group. (1998). Intensive blood-glucose control with sulphonylureas or insulin compared with conventional treatment and risk of complications in patients with type 2 diabetes (UKPDS 33). *Lancet, 352*(9131), 837–853.

United States Department of Agriculture. (2005). *Dietary guidelines for Americans.* Retrieved October 1, 2005, from http://www.usda.gov

United States Department of Agriculture. (2009). *Nutrient availability data, 1909 to 2004.* Retrieved December 1, 2008, from http://www.usda.gov

U.S. Preventive Services Task Force. (2003). Screening for obesity in adults: Recommendations and rationale. *Annals of Internal Medicine, 139*(11), 930–932.

Wadden, T. A., Crerand, C. E., & Brock, J. (2005). Behavioral treatment of obesity. *Psychiatric Clinics of North America, 28*(1), 151–170.

Wadden, T. A., Berkowitz, R. I., Sarwer, D. B., Prus-Wisniewski, R., & Steinberg, C. (2001). Benefits of lifestyle modification in the pharmacologic treatment of obesity: A randomized trial. *Archives of Internal Medicine, 161*(2), 218–227.

Wadden, T. A., Berkowitz, R. I., Womble, L. G., Sarwer, D. B., Phelan, S., Cato, R. K., et al. (2005). Randomized trial of lifestyle modification and pharmacotherapy for obesity. *New England Journal of Medicine, 353*(20), 2111–2120.

Wadden, T. A., Butryn, M. L., & Byrne, K. J. (2004). Efficacy of lifestyle modification for long-term weight control. *Obesity Research, 12*(Suppl.), 151S–162S.

Wadden, T. A., Butryn, M. L., & Wilson, C. (2007). Lifestyle modification for the management of obesity. *Gastroenterology, 132*(6), 2226–2238.

Wadden, T. A., & Didie, E. (2003). What's in a name? Patients' preferred terms for describing obesity. *Obesity Research, 11*(9), 1140–1146.

Wadden, T. A., & Foster, G. D. (2000). Behavioral treatment of obesity. *Medical Clinics of North America, 84*(2), 441–461, vii.

Wadden, T. A., Foster, G. D., & Letizia, K. A. (1994). One-year behavioral treatment of obesity: Comparison of moderate and severe caloric restriction and the effects of weight maintenance therapy. *Journal of Consulting and Clinical Psychology, 62*(1), 165–171.

Wadden, T. A., Foster, G. D., Letizia, K. A., & Stunkard, A. J. (1992). A multicenter evaluation of a proprietary weight reduction program for the treatment of marked obesity. *Archives of Internal Medicine, 152*(5), 961–966.

Wadden, T. A., Foster, G. D., Sarwer, D. B., Anderson, D. A., Gladis, M., Sanderson, R. S., et al. (2004). Dieting and the development of eating disorders in obese women: Results of a randomized controlled trial. *American Journal of Clinical Nutrition, 80*(3), 560–568.

Wadden, T. A., Vogt, R. A., Andersen, R. E., Bartlett, S. J., Foster, G. D., Kuehnel, R. H., et al. (1997). Exercise in the treatment of obesity: Effects of four interventions on body composition, resting energy expenditure, appetite, and mood. *Journal of Consulting and Clinical Psychology, 65*(2), 269–277.

Wadden, T. A., Vogt, R. A., Foster, G. D., & Anderson, D. A. (1998). Exercise and the maintenance of weight loss: 1-year follow-up of a controlled clinical trial. *Journal of Consulting and Clinical Psychology, 66*(2), 429–433.

Wang, Y., & Beydoun, M. A. (2007). The obesity epidemic in the United States—gender, age, socioeconomic, racial/ethnic, and geographic characteristics: A systematic review and meta-regression analysis. *Epidemiology Review, 29*, 6–28.

Ward, S. H., Gray, A. M., & Paranjape, A. (2009). African Americans' perceptions of physician attempts to address obesity in the primary care setting. *Journal of General Internal Medicine, 24*, 579–584.

Whitlock, G., Lewington, S., Sherliker, P., Peto, R., & the Prospective Studies Collaboration. (2009). Body-mass index and mortality—Author's reply. *Lancet, 374*(9684), 114.

Wildman, R. P., Muntner, P., Reynolds, K., McGinn, A. P., Rajpathak, S., Wylie-Rosett, J., et al. (2008). The obese without cardiometabolic risk factor clustering and the normal weight with cardiometabolic risk factor clustering: Prevalence and correlates of 2 phenotypes among the US population (NHANES 1999–2004). *Archives of Internal Medicine, 168*(15), 1617–1624.

Wing, R. R. (1999). Physical activity in the treatment of the adulthood overweight and obesity: Current evidence and research issues. *Medicine & Science in Sports & Exercise, 31*(11 Suppl.), S547–552.

Wing, R. R. (2002). Behavioral weight control. In T. A. Wadden & A. J. Stunkard (Eds.), *Handbook of obesity treatment* (pp. 301–316). New York: Guilford.

Wing, R. R., & Hill, J. O. (2001). Successful weight loss maintenance. *Annual Review of Nutrition, 21*, 323–341.

World Health Organization. (1998). *Obesity: Preventing and managing the global epidemic*. Geneva, Switzerland: Author.

Yancy, W. S., Jr., Olsen, M. K., Guyton, J. R., Bakst, R. P., & Westman, E. C. (2004). A low-carbohydrate, ketogenic diet versus a low-fat diet to treat obesity and hyperlipidemia: A randomized, controlled trial. *Annals of Internal Medicine, 140*(10), 769–777.

Yarnall, K. S., Pollak, K. I., Ostbye, T., Krause, K. M., & Michener, J. L. (2003). Primary care: Is there enough time for prevention? *American Journal of Public Health, 93*(4), 635–641.

Zhu, S., Wang, Z., Heshka, S., Heo, M., Faith, M. S., & Heymsfield, S. B. (2002). Waist circumference and obesity-associated risk factors among whites in the third national health and nutrition examination survey: Clinical action thresholds. *American Journal of Clinical Nutrition, 76*(4), 743–749.

Acute and Chronic Pain in Primary Care Settings

28

Barbara A. Golden
Robert J. Gatchel
Scott Glassman

Introduction

Pain is a subjective experience that may often be inadequately treated. It is a universal stress response that has often been dismissed as "all in your head." Although medicine has advanced significantly since the 1950s, the study of the pain experience has lagged behind. However, in the last decade, dedicated researchers across many disciplines have shown that pain is not simply a physiological response, but rather a multidimensional response with far-reaching consequences.

Pain is a national epidemic that affects more than 25% of Americans, or an estimated 76.5 million individuals over the age of 20. The impact on productivity, lost wages, and health care expenses is enormous, exceeding $61 billion each year (National Center for Health Statistics, 2006; Stewart, Ricci, Chee, Morganstein, & Lipton, 2003). Pain complaints are one of the most common reasons for medical visits, and they occur at relatively high rates in all medical settings. It is estimated that up to 63% of patients have seen a primary care physician (PCP), 45% have consulted with an orthopedist, 25% have visited a chiropractor, and 38% of patients in pain have seen more than one practitioner in the medical community for treatment (American Pain Foundation, 2009). Accurate diagnosis and case formulation can prove challenging in fast-paced primary care clinics, where patient contact is often brief. In addition, lack of standardized pain assessment protocols, or limited access to an interdisciplinary team, may increase the difficulty of treatment planning. Therefore, a collaborative approach to the problem of pain is imperative for positive outcomes.

Assessment and Diagnostic Issues

There is evidence that complex pain presentations are increasing among U.S. adults, with a nearly 40% rise in chronic pain reported among the entire full-time workforce between 1996 and 2006 (National Center for Health Statistics, 2006). In these cases, treatment goals are more likely to extend beyond the acute phase of pain, which is defined as a period of symptoms lasting fewer than 6 months. Acute pain assessment has traditionally involved simple, reliable, and straightforward measures such as numerical ratings, visual analog scales, and the use of graphic "pain faces" with children (Breivik et al., 2008).

Chronic pain, on the other hand, requires a more complicated, multidimensional framework that addresses the interdependent biological, social, cognitive, and emotional factors that contribute to disability. Due in large part to advancements in the field of behavioral medicine, the biopsychosocial model for evaluating and treating chronic pain has gained widespread acceptance (Gatchel, Peng, Peters, Fuchs, & Turk, 2007; Hunter, Goodie, Oordt, & Dobmeyer, 2009; Nielson & Weir, 2001; Okifuji & Ackerlind, 2007; Scascighini, Toma, Dober-Spielmann, & Sprott, 2008). This perspective recognizes that pain is both a nociceptive, or sensory, experience, and a subjective one that can be influenced by psychological status, social functioning, and contextual factors. Specifically, the model describes a process whereby distorted cognitions and emotional responses to pain (e.g., catastrophizing thoughts, dysfunctional pain beliefs, and dysphoric mood) can interact with poor social support and environmental contingencies to negatively impact coping behavior. This, in turn, may exacerbate psychosocial distress, functional disability, biological processes, and pain severity in what can become a recalcitrant, self-sustaining feedback loop (Finestone, Alfeeli, & Fisher, 2008; Keefe et al., 2002).

Accordingly, national medical organizations have begun to incorporate this multidimensional view of pain into their practice guidelines. The American College of Physicians recommends that physicians routinely assess psychosocial factors when evaluating patients with low back pain (American College of Physicians, 2006). Similar guidelines have been issued for individuals diagnosed with chronic pain conditions, such as fibromyalgia, osteoarthritis, and rheumatoid arthritis (American Pain Society, 2002, 2005). Three main assessment methods can assist clinicians in formulating treatment plans that are sensitive to biopsychosocial concerns: the clinical interview, objective measures, and self-report questionnaires. Although the clinical interview is the primary method for gathering information in behavioral medicine and primary care settings, the health care team can supplement its findings with objective measures and standardized self-report inventories (Okifuji & Ackerlind, 2007). Case conceptualization can also benefit from assessing potential barriers to success and motivational variables such as treatment readiness. Belar and Deardorff (2009) provide a useful three-dimensional framework that can help physicians organize the data they gather during a clinical interview. Their model suggests breaking information down by history (past and present functioning), unit of assessment (individual, family, health care system, culture), and domains of functioning (biological, cognitive, affective, behavioral).

For instance, in the cognitive domain at the patient level, a physician might ask about the individual's pain beliefs, expectations for improvement, and self-efficacy perceptions. Focusing on behavioral targets at the family level could help determine whether caregivers are reinforcing pain behaviors. In the affective domain at the patient level, the interview might address the presence of pain-related anxiety, depression, fear of activity, or reduced enjoyment in recreational activities. Questions with a combined biological and behavioral focus could center on the location, duration, and severity of pain, along with possible functional impairment. One might ask about role limitations at home or work, or whether the patient avoids certain social or recreational activities. Exploring the patient's financial resources, occupational functioning, and social security status addresses key sociocultural targets. Belar and Deardorff (2009) stress the importance of gathering information about changes over time in any of these pertinent domains. Pain-specific application of their framework expands on the six core outcome domains recommended by the Initiative on Methods, Measurement, and Pain Assessment in Clinical Trials (IMMPACT; Dworkin et al., 2005). Four of these domains are specifically relevant to pretreatment evaluation: pain, physical functioning, emotional functioning, and patient disposition or characteristics. IMMPACT highlights the clinical importance of measuring quality of life indicators, such as depression and anxiety levels, the adaptivity of family and social relationships, and the individual's ability to engage in physical and social activities (Dworkin et al., 2008).

In step with IMMPACT's recommendations, Okifuji and Ackerlind (2007) propose a three-part interview protocol for pain patients that incorporates a domain-by-level approach. Not only does it seem feasible for busy primary care settings, but it moves progressively outward from the patient's perspective to include historical and systemic factors. It also pays particular attention to possible comorbid psychological disorders. Part 1 covers pain-related biological and cognitive targets at the individual level. The physician collects data about the patient's experience of pain as far as symptoms, aggravating or relieving factors, functional impairment, beliefs about pain, expectations about the future, and other relevant medical history. Part 2 concentrates on changes in psychosocial functioning over time. It evaluates the patient's use of coping resources, potential barriers to or facilitators of treatment success, and psychiatric history. It also covers any family and social factors that may affect the treatment course. Part 3 involves a thorough psychosocial examination, looking at the patient's current behavior, mood, and mental status.

This last step recognizes that mood disorders are two to seven times more common in populations of chronic pain sufferers, as reported in a recent comprehensive review of psychological comorbidity (Tunks, Crook, & Weir, 2008). This includes major depression, dysthymia, anxiety disorder, agoraphobia, social phobia, and posttraumatic stress disorder (PTSD). Depression shows an especially strong association with chronic pain, as prevalence rates ranged between 18–55.9% across the studied samples. Fibromyalgia, back pain, and rheumatoid arthritis have some of the highest incidences of accompanying depression (Dickens &

Creed, 2001; Patten et al., 2005). In their overview, Tunks et al. (2008) highlight studies showing that psychosocial distress predicts poorer pain prognosis and greater functional impairment. They also point out that pain increases the chance of developing psychological disorders if they are not already present. One large prospective study found that long-term pain problems at baseline approximately doubled the odds that individuals would suffer from major depression two years later (Patten, 2001). Thus, standard practice for conducting clinical interviews should include screening for comorbid psychosocial disorders, as well as evaluating the risk of developing these conditions in response to the pain course.

Given the time constraints in primary care settings, physicians would likely benefit from having a behavioral health consultant or multidisciplinary team that could separately administer structured clinical interviews for suspected psychological disorders. In addition, the *Diagnostic and Statistical Manual of Mental Disorders* (*DSM-IV-TR*; American Psychiatric Association [APA], 2000) and *International Statistical Classification of Diseases* (*ICD-10*; World Health Organization, 1993) can help distinguish between those pain presentations arising from general medical conditions, those that are intentionally caused (factitious disorders), and those whose onset, maintenance, and severity are closely associated with psychological factors (somatoform disorders). An important but difficult dimension to assess would be whether, in the absence of any physical evidence, the patient believes a pain condition exists. This profile may indicate a somatoform pain disorder, which the *ICD-10* defines as a persistent, severe distressing pain lasting at least six months, and which cannot be explained physiologically. The pain also dominates the patient's attention. It is important to note that some investigators question the validity and clinical utility of diagnosing "pure" pain or somatoform syndromes using these classification systems. They cite highly variable prevalence rates based on unclear diagnostic definitions. Moreover, most pain conditions have a mixed presentation of psychosocial and somatic factors (Nordin, Eisemann, & Richter, 2006; Sharpe & Williams, 2002). Although attention to different possible pain etiologies is necessary, strict adherence to diagnostic categories risks overemphasizing psychosocial or physical contributions to the patient's pain experience. Consequently, this may lead to less effective treatment planning.

Clinical Interview

An effective clinical interview will assess for possible psychosocial disorder comorbidity, evaluate multiple targets and levels of functioning, and involve other family members in data gathering. Providers in primary care settings will also want to administer confirmatory measures that can fill out the clinical picture of pain. Taking time constraints into consideration, a biopsychosocial interview protocol might also benefit from a heuristic-based "flagging" method. This involves identifying key psychosocial and behavioral symptoms that signal increased risk for developing long-term pain chronicity. Pertaining to musculoskeletal pain, these "yellow flags" have been described as having clinically significant prognostic value with the potential to guide early interventions (Finestone, Alfeeli, & Fisher, 2008; Kendall, Linton, & Main, 1997). Such markers may include beliefs that the pain is harmful or disabling, fear avoidance behavior, suppressed activity, depressed mood, social withdrawal, and social or financial problems (Samanta,

Kendall, & Samanta, 2003). They also can be validly and reliably assessed through brief screening instruments, building the case for their use in primary care settings (Grotle, Vollestad, & Brox, 2006). Supporting a heuristic-based approach, Hallner and Hasenbring (2004) demonstrated 83% accuracy in predicting long-term pain intensity in back and leg pain patients using an algorithm derived from three salient chronic pain characteristics: depression, behavior suppression, and thoughts about suppressing behavior. Although additional clinical research is necessary with varied populations and pain conditions, clinical heuristics show promise as an adjunct to a standardized assessment protocol.

Initially, a brief screening checklist, along with a Mini-Mental Status Examination (Folstein & Folstein, 2001), is quite useful for initially alerting the clinician to potentially major issues. Gatchel (2005) proposes several examples of brief forms for this purpose. The brief checklist will assess behavioral and psychosocial issues that may affect treatment, such as potential noncompliance issues, disincentives for improvement, medical problems, extremely negative affect, and so on. The Mini-Mental Status Examination will help to immediately determine patient disorientation and/or possible cognitive impairment. This, in turn, may signal the need for a referral for neuropsychological testing to determine the extent of such possible problems. Other issues that are important to cover in the interview include those that involve possible barriers to recovery that may negatively affect a positive response to treatment. Some of these include the following (Gatchel, 2005):

- There is a patient or family history of mental health disorders, such as anxiety, depression, or substance abuse
- A poor work history, such as job losses, job dissatisfaction, or frequent changing of jobs
- Any litigation or workers' compensation claim that is pending and related to the patient's current medical and pain problem
- A history of head injury, convulsions, or impairment of physical/cognitive functioning
- Any stressful changes in the patient's lifestyle or relationship/marital status before or after the injury/event initially causing the pain.

The above psychosocial interview information will provide the clinician with a starting point from which to decide the following: What more formal psychosocial testing (discussed below) will be needed, whether a referral is needed for medical or impairment issues, whether the patient will benefit from the pain management program available, and whether medication issues will be a problem that will require detoxification. Before any treatment planning can be formulated, all of this comprehensive evaluation information is needed to guarantee that a treatment program can be specifically tailored to the needs of the patient.

Measures

Along with the clinical interview, many self-report measures have been used in primary care settings to describe central features of the pain experience. In a sample of chronic pain patients, Davidson, Tripp, Fabrigar, and Davidson (2008) examined the relationship between nine commonly used instruments: the McGill

Pain Questionnaire-Short Form (MPQ-SF; Melzack, 1987); Pain Disability Index (PDI; Tait, Pollard, Margolis, Duckro, & Krause 1987); Tampa Scale of Kinesiophobia (TSK; Kori, Miller, & Todd, 1990), Pain Catastrophizing Scale (PCS; Sullivan, Bishop, & Pivick, 1995); Chronic Pain Coping Inventory (CPCI; Jensen, Turner, Romano, & Strom, 1995); Multidimensional Pain Inventory (MPI; Kerns, Turk, & Rudy, 1985); Beck Depression Inventory (BDI; Beck, Ward, Mendelson, Mock, & Erbaugh , 1961); Beck Hopelessness Scale (BHS; Beck, Weissman, Lestern, & Trexler, 1974); and Beck Anxiety Inventory (BAI; Beck, Epstein, Brown, & Steer, 1988). Across the 32 subscales of these measures, they identified 7 factors that captured important constructs of chronic pain: pain and disability, pain description, affective distress, positive coping, negative coping, support, and activity. Although the authors concluded that no single measure captures the entire clinical picture of chronic pain, the MPI subscales accounted for substantial variability in three of the seven factors, most notably activity performance (social activities, activities away from home, and household chores). The BHS and BAI are widely used instruments that primarily represent the affective domain. Items that contributed meaningful variance focused on expectations for failure or success, subjective anxiety, and somatic complaints. Three MPQ subscales uniquely measured sensory and affective dimensions of pain quality that constituted a separate, but related, factor of pain description. The CPCI identified crucial indices of positive coping that may anticipate more adaptive outcomes. These included coping self-statements, relaxation, and exercise or stretching. Davidson and colleagues (2008) recognize the separate, significant contributions made by these measures to understanding the central aspects of biopsychosocial functioning in pain patients. In a parsimonious method fitting for primary care settings, they recommend selecting one or two representative subscales across instruments for each of the seven factors. They argue that this would increase efficiency without sacrificing symptom sensitivity or specificity. It further promises to lighten the item-load on patients and ease the demand on health care workers.

Karoly, Ruehlman, Aiken, Todd, and Newton (2006) additionally emphasize the value of developing brief, reliable, and maximally informative multidimensional pain-screening instruments for use in medical settings. Appropriate measures include the Medical Outcomes Short Form-36 (SF-36; Ware & Sherbourne, 1992), Brief Pain Inventory (BPI; Daut, Cleeland, & Flanery, 1983) and Oswestry Disability Index (ODI; Fairbank, Couper, Davies, & O'Brien, 1980). All are self-administered and can be completed in less than 10 minutes. The SF-36 is a widely used, more general measure of health that assesses physical and social functioning, role limitations, emotional difficulties, vitality, bodily pain, general health perception, and mental health. It has the added benefit of normative data in the general population to guide interpretation (Hopman et al., 2006), along with empirically valid results for diverse conditions that include low back pain and arthritis (Bergman, Jacobson, Herrstrom, & Petersson, 2004; Veehof, ten Klooster, Taal, van Riel, & van de Laar, 2008). Similar to the SF-36, the BPI assesses interference and severity dimensions. It asks patients to rate how much pain affects their general activity, mobility, work, mood, sleep, and life enjoyment. It also captures variation in pain intensity over the last 24 hours. The BPI has shown strong psychometric properties with noncancer pain patients and responsiveness to disability change after primary care treatment (Keller et al., 2004). The ODI, a more disease-specific measure, consists of 10 questions examining patient disability related to personal care, daily physical activity, and social life. When compared with the SF-36 and MPI, this index demonstrated the lowest response burden and good reliability, validity, and sensitivity to change in patients undergoing multidisciplinary pain treatment (Wittink, Turk, Carr, Sukiennik, & Rogers, 2004). Although the SF-36, MPI, and ODI display substantial conceptual and empirical overlap, they also make specific contributions to describing pain impact. For instance, the SF-36 identified unique changes in general health and vitality, whereas the MPI was particularly attuned to significant-other support and activity changes. Questions remain as to whether the SF-36 and MPI's emotional domains are sufficiently sensitive to detect changes in affective distress. Nevertheless, the use of Beck Depression and Anxiety inventories could complement any potential weakness in this area.

The Profile of Chronic Pain: Screen (PCP:S; Ruehlman, Karoly, & Newton, 2005) is another easily administered instrument that has shown promise for use in primary care. It devotes more items to the affective dimension of pain than the SF-36 or BPI. This 15-item self-administered questionnaire takes 5–10 minutes to complete, and measures three integral domains previously discussed: pain severity, functional impairment, and emotional burden. Karoly, Ruehlman, Aiken, Todd, and Newton (2006) adapted its use from a telephone interview format to a paper-and-pencil version in a sample of 244 chronic pain patients, recruited from five different primary care locations. Questions include six items related to interference (e.g., "How often over the past 6 months have you had to give up enjoyable activities because of your pain?"), five emotional burden items (e.g., "How often has your pain caused you to feel sad or depressed?"), and four severity items (e.g., "How often during the past 6 months have you had physical pain or discomfort that has lasted for more than a few minutes?"). The PCP:S showed adequate reliability, internal consistency, and construct validity with regard to its three main factors. Suggesting its clinical utility, the PCP:S successfully differentiates patient treatment status, ability to work, and whether or not they were receiving compensation. When evaluating related measures, the time frame examined can be an important point of divergence. The authors compared the PCP:S with the MPI, and observed that the MPI is a broader, more general measure that uses different time frames for its severity and interference scales. All the PCP:S items, on the other hand, measure symptoms experienced in the six months prior to assessment. In selecting an ideal combination of instruments or subscales, clinicians may want to consider using items that examine both short-term and long-term symptom ranges.

When brief supplementary measures such as the BPI and SF-36 are used in primary care, they can strengthen the clinician's ability to direct treatment goals and successfully measure change in clinical outcomes. They also can help the treatment team more accurately identify acute pain conditions that could become chronic. Research has further underscored the importance of considering patients' readiness to change as a factor that can positively or negatively affect pain self-management (Burns, Glenn, Lofland, Bruehl, & Harden, 2005; Glenn & Burns, 2003). Specifically, increased commitment to pain self-management strategies learned in multidisciplinary programs can enhance treatment compliance. Burns and colleagues found that patients who became more ready to take responsibility for their outcomes, as evidenced by "forward stage movement," experienced less pain interference and severity later in treatment (Burns et al.). They also reported higher activity levels. This effect was observed independently of changes in mood following individual and group cognitive-behavioral therapy (CBT). Studying spinal cord injury and arthritis patients, Nielson, Jensen, Ehde, Kerns, and Moulton (2008) also describe encouraging preliminary findings for the use of the Multidimensional Pain Readiness to Change Questionnaire (MPRCQ2; Nielson, Jensen & Kerns, 2003). Patients' readiness to engage in exercise, activity pacing, relaxation, and cognitive techniques, but also to persist in these activities, represent two significant motivational constructs that clinicians ought to consider.

Although a consensus may not yet exist around what constitutes optimal behavioral medicine assessment for pain, there appears to be support for certain basic requirements. These include the following: knowledge about the biopsychosocial implications of pain, screening checklists and a protocol-guided clinical interview that pays attention to risk factors, brief self-assessment instruments that can bolster treatment planning, evaluation for possible comorbid psychological disorders, and a sensitivity to a wide range of treatment targets and potential barriers. Cognitive, behavioral, and affective dimensions deserve particular attention, as these domains contribute significantly to functional aspects of pain syndromes. Helplessness, hopelessness, depression, anxiety, and maladaptive pain beliefs can all act as sustaining mechanisms that contribute to poor prognosis. Ongoing empirically based clinical research on process, measures, and outcomes with diverse pain populations is necessary to sharpen the focus of multidisciplinary assessment. Growing commitment to the biopsychosocial approach continues to stimulate research into the efficiency and accuracy with which chronic pain treatment can be conducted in primary care environments. Finally, for a more comprehensive review of pain assessment instruments/approaches, the reader is referred to Gatchel (2005), Gatchel and Weisberg (2000), and Turk and Melzack (2001).

Incidence and Clinical Manifestations in Primary Care

The PCP is often the first contact for a person experiencing pain. The presentations may range from acute pain to chronic pain. Often, the primary care patient is familiar with his/her physician and feels comfortable with addressing these concerns. Von Korff et al. (2005) in a large-scale epidemiological study estimated 19% of the population suffers from chronic spine pain. The American Academy of Pain Management reports that up to 57% of American adults report experiencing chronic pain within the last year. Approximately 62% of the individuals report being in pain for more than one year, and 40% of these persons noted that they are in constant pain. Additional data suggests that the prevalence of chronic pain exceeds 35% of the general population, or approximately 105 million people (Harstall, 2003). Although the most common reports of pain in primary care practices are musculoskeletal, pain complaints also include headaches, gastrointestinal disturbances, and other general unspecified complaints (Gureje, Von Korff, Simon, & Gater, 1998; Reid et al., 2002). The PCP is limited in the amount of time available to thoroughly assess this pain complaint, and may often resort to medication to help with the symptoms. Unfortunately, this may only address the problem for the short term. Thus, the patient remains in distress, and is compromised in activities of daily living.

Brief Case History

A 52-year-old man, Mr. S., was referred by his PCP because he had persistent knee pain caused by a tear in the cartilage. He had the cartilage repaired in a laparoscopic surgery and had completed a 6-week course of physical therapy. He described the pain as "shooting and burning" every time he tried to exercise. He was a foreman in a factory, and the pain was present when he walked around the factory floor for any period of time. He was faced with the option of taking short-term disability from work in order to participate in additional physical therapy, with the goal to improve his functioning. This was extremely stressful for him, as he prided himself on his role as primary breadwinner for his family, his general physical appearance and athletic prowess, and his continued participation in coaching his son's track team. He had become more agitated at work and at home, and had started to drink more than he had ever done in the past.

A comprehensive medical evaluation revealed a resolution of the tear and no musculoskeletal or tissue damage associated with his pain. Initial psychological assessment with the Brief Symptom Inventory (Derogatis, 1994), the BDI-II, and the Short-Form SF-36 revealed that the man was suffering from a moderate level of depression and anxiety and emotional difficulty related to his limited ability to function in his general roles. In addition, during the clinical interview, a determination was made that the man was quite concerned that he appear in control of his pain with an ability to "fight through the pain" no matter what the cost. He did admit that he was concerned about taking short-term disability because of the present economy, and had also never been out of work since he started to work as a teenager. He had stopped taking any medication, and admitted that his use of alcohol was "to cope with the stress" of all that was going on in his life. This also included a certain amount of marital discord.

A comprehensive treatment plan included the following:

- A return to physical rehabilitation with the goal to increase his flexibility and tolerate more strenuous activity and weight-bearing exercise;
- The pursuit of short-term disability was abandoned at this time, and a change in his work requirements included more office work with a reduction in his need to walk the factory floor;
- Prescribed use of an antidepressant medication;
- CBT was initiated to address his feelings of depression, anger, and lack of control. In addition, the patient agreed to work to minimize his alcohol use and to spend more time engaged in pleasurable activities at home with his wife and family.

After 2 weeks, the patient was feeling less anger with greater control over his daily functioning. He had greatly reduced his alcohol consumption and, according to his self-report and confirmed by his wife, his overall mood had improved.

Cognitive-Behavioral Case Conceptualization

The cognitive model provides a framework for understanding a patient who is struggling with chronic pain. According to this model, beginning in early childhood, an individual develops certain beliefs about self, the world, and the future, *the cognitive triad* (Beck, Rush, Shaw, & Emery, 1979). These beliefs are central to the person's worldview, influencing thoughts, emotions, and behaviors. These core beliefs become guides to certain rules or assumptions that then produce automatic thoughts, thus, determining behaviors. Certain compensatory strategies are practiced in order to shield a person from experiencing distress. Thus, each situation produces an automatic thought that is connected to the core belief. This results in continued distress for the individual who is constantly attempting to reconcile this negative thinking with the world.

Mr. S. was the first-born of three children in a family that prided itself on hard work and education. His parents did not complete high school and they were determined that their three sons would finish high school and be steadily employed. Also, family values included a strong work ethic and a volunteer spirit, thus, Mr. S's pride in coaching his son's track team. His core belief, "if I am not productive, I am useless," after his injury caused significant depression. Mr. S. was unwilling to admit that perhaps he needed to take a break from work and physical exercise for his injury to heal. According to his beliefs, he should work so as to be admired by his family and others, and his future will only decline, to the point of divorce, if he is not in the most optimal physical condition. These assumptions began to pervade the thoughts of Mr. S. Consequently, he engaged in distorted thinking styles including "all-or-nothing," personalization, catastrophizing, and others. These added to his general feelings of distress. Thus, in CBT, steps to adopt new skills, pinpoint problems, and work to restructure distorted thinking and activate healthy behaviors became the targets of treatment.

Identifying and Addressing Obstacles to Treatment

It is critical to identify the progression from acute pain to chronic pain so as to identify potential obstacles to treatment. Gatchel (1991, 1996, 2005) has suggested a three-stage model. Stage 1, the acute phase, is a normal reaction to a patient's perception of pain (anxiety, worry, etc.). These reactions help to prompt the patient to intervene appropriately to address the pain and, if necessary, to seek medical attention. If the pain persists beyond a 2–4-month period, the time considered normal for healing, psychological and behavioral problems are usually present. In the case of Mr. S., he did seek medical attention shortly after he experienced pain in his knee. However, his expectation that the pain would be gone completely, and that he would be restored to 100% physical functioning, interfered with his ability to see progress with his treatment. The belief that physical functioning should improve completely, coupled with unrealistic estimates of the time needed for recovery, are often obstacles to treatment. These factors should be considered when evaluating the patient's beliefs about an injury. Stage 2 marks the development or exacerbation of problems such as learned helplessness, depression, anger, and/or substance abuse. These problems depend on the individual's level of premorbid functioning, personality functioning, socioeconomic, and environmental factors. Given that Mr. S. was generally in good health, exercised regularly, and was able to engage in physical activities such as coaching his son's track team while enduring this knee pain, it was notable that his depression increased, his anger and agitation were directed toward his wife, and his alcohol use increased. At Stage 2, the danger of secondary gain is present. Although Mr. S. did not consciously seek secondary gain, as a result of his change in behavior, his wife, children, friends, and work staff began to be more attentive to him and more solicitous of his needs. This resulted in further withdrawal and anger from Mr. S. The chronic phase of the three-stage model is marked by significant interactions among physical, psychological, and social processes. In Stage 3, the patient's life focuses on the pain itself and all the behaviors associated with it. This is the time when patients adopt the "sick role" and start to develop self-focus behaviors, avoid general responsibilities, and exhibit maladaptive behaviors (Gatchel, 2005). These three stages often are marked by physical deconditioning, where the individual engages in less physical activity, which results in more atrophy and discomfort in the injury (Gatchel; Mayer et al., 1988). For Mr. S., his total withdrawal from previous pleasurable activities and his inability to pace himself during his recovery resulted in some physical deconditioning, and he did become more self-focused.

Additional obstacles to treatment during the acute phase may include a patient's lack of appropriate initial care for the injury. For example, with a low back pain injury caused by a pulled muscle, a patient may ignore the injury and inadvertently exacerbate the injury by continuing to work through an exercise regimen that may be too strenuous. The patient may ignore the injury with the belief that "if I work through this pain, I will be stronger in the end." In contrast, the better course of action would be to attend to the injury and perhaps seek medical intervention. A basic relief of symptoms with the knowledge that the pain is temporary and will resolve is the best course of intervention in the Stage 1, acute phase. In addition, some education about the general pain course associated with the injury and the role of biological, affective, cognitive, and behavioral factors should be assessed and addressed early in the acute phase.

If the patient moves into Stage 2, the obstacles become more challenging. Treatment needs to address the psychosocial factors inhibiting the resolution of the pain. Patients who suffer from premorbid conditions of depression, anxiety, and/or the potential to abuse substances are vulnerable in this stage. Awareness is the first step toward resolution of the Stage 2 obstacles. Patients may focus more on the injury and deny the presence of psychosocial factors. The PCP is a key figure in identifying the presence of psychosocial factors for the patient. If the relationship between the PCP and the patient is one of trust, it is more likely that the patient will agree with the physician, as opposed to the judgment that the doctor "thinks this is all in my head." Also, often, it is helpful to not use the term *psychological/psychiatric problems* because of the social stigma associated with them; rather, it is recommended to use terms such as *stress* or *emotional distress*, because these are everyday words that do not have such a stigma associated with them. It is also helpful to have the presence of family members and other social supports to help the patient realize the presence or exacerbation of "stress-related" concerns. Interventions may include pharmacological treatment, cognitive-behavioral treatment, or increased activity scheduling to prevent physical deconditioning.

Stage 2 is also often accompanied by a sense of learned helplessness (Gatchel, 2005). Learned helplessness for a chronic pain patient is generally marked with feelings of being overwhelmed, hopeless, and depressed, and patients may perceive themselves as a burden on others. When this occurs, it is critical to assess for suicidal ideation. Because PCPs are often not adequately trained nor experienced in dealing with suicidal patients, a referral list of mental health specialists in suicide prevention should always be available.

Secondary gain issues can be a significant potential obstacle to the success of pain management treatment. Historically, secondary gain issues have been associated with those patients who have been injured as a result of a work-related injury, motor vehicle injury, or a related injury where the person has a potential for financial gain. However, secondary gain is not limited to this group of patients. Leeman, Polatin, Gatchel, and Kishino (2000) suggest that secondary gain may be viewed on a continuum; that is, secondary gain develops from primary gain mechanisms. When a patient attempts to alleviate guilt or conflict as present in physical symptoms (primary gain), the patient would then be able to avoid certain activities in order to receive support from the environment that may otherwise not be present (secondary gain). Although patients who have a potential for financial gain may or may not be engaging in secondary gain, this is a potential problem for all patients who have suffered from chronic pain over a period of time. A multidisciplinary team must be established to address the issues of secondary gain. This team should include medical providers, family members, attorneys, the patient, and any others who will help to ensure the successful resolution of this rehabilitation. In passing, it should also be noted that there is another phenomenon, coined "tertiary gain" (Dersh, Gatchel, & Kishino, 2005), which should be recognized. This refers to the gains sought or attained from a patient's pain/illness other than from the patient, who can significantly perpetuate it. For example, a spouse may become overly solicitous of the patient because it gives him/her a sense of power in the relationship. Likewise, health care providers may require multiple visits and complex treatments because of the financial gains to their practices.

Patients who reach Stage 3 of the progression into severe disability due to chronic pain are at risk for permanent disability. These patients need an intensive, interdisciplinary approach to treatment. The move toward functional restoration involves repeated measures to assess physical deficits to guide treatment, psychosocial and socioeconomic assessment to guide disability behavior interventions, the delivery of cognitive-behavioral approaches to provide multimodal disability management, and a medical treatment team working in a multidisciplinary fashion to direct intensive attention to restore functioning and ongoing assessment to review objective outcomes (Gatchel, 2005; Mayer et al., 1988). To avoid the progression from Stage 1 to Stage 3, physicians and family members must work collaboratively with the patient to realistically assess and appropriately treat all the biopsychosocial aspects of the pain problem.

Points of Collaboration With Physicians and Family

Working in a multidisciplinary model involves the patient's family and social support networks. The clinicians should include the family in all parts of the assessment and intervention process. It is more likely that a patient will respond more favorably when all members of the treatment team *believe and act* that the pain is real and not just "all in one's head." Education for patients and families is a key element for effective pain management. A treatment plan should take into account the patient's strengths, biases, and expectations, in addition to physical factors. Because family members provide a vast majority of care for the patient, it is helpful when their attitudes and behaviors target more realistic thinking patterns and behaviors. Solicitous behavior (anxious, concerned, hovering) may tend to decrease the patient's ability to engage in more functional behaviors. The nonverbal messages that may be communicated may elicit more pain behaviors. Supportive families are appropriate, and patients with support systems tend to report less pain intensity, less reliance on medications, and greater activity levels. The PCP is a key resource for families to obtain a realistic plan for patients' care.

Empirically Based Treatment Approaches

The current biopsychosocial model of pain is founded, in large part, on the "gate control" theory proposed by Melzack and Wall (1965). Their theory details the physiological pathway by which psychosocial factors are believed to affect pain perception. They propose the existence of a gating mechanism in the dorsal horn of the spinal cord that can either facilitate or inhibit the transmission of peripheral sensory signals. "Opening the gate" leads to increased pain, whereas "closing the gate" reduces pain by constricting the flow of signals to the point at which perception occurs. The pain experience thus depends on "bottom-up" sensory input, as well as "top-down" perceptual factors subject to individual control. These may include positive or negative expectancies, beliefs, and attributions about pain. Expanding on the biopsychosocial model, Maier (2003) hypothesizes a bidirectional stress-pain cycle, where maladaptive cognitive and affective processes interact with immune functioning and the release of proinflammatory chemicals to maintain acute and chronic pain.

CBT for pain management is based on the idea that changing pain-related schemas, or how an individual processes information about pain-associated events and sensations, can reduce pain severity and impairment. This "top-down" process is thought to operate via the gate control and stress-pain pathways. More specifically, it is thought that exaggerated emotional responses, distorted interpretations of painful events, and negative beliefs about pain can interfere with coping behavior and the physiological processes that increase pain perception (Molton, Graham, Stoelb, & Jensen, 2007). A self-sustaining feedback loop develops, where learned maladaptive behavioral patterns (e.g., avoidance, passive coping) reinforce the cognitive, affective, biological, and environmental reactions that contribute to increased disability (Okifuji & Ackerlind, 2007). For example, in a large prospective study of patients with low back pain, Swinkels-Meewisse et al. (2006) found that fear of movement/(re)injury was a more powerful predictor of reduced participation in activities and perceived disability than baseline pain intensity. Catastrophizing thoughts such as "it is terrible and I feel that it is never going to get any better" can also independently contribute to pain interference and poorer psychological functioning (Hanley, Raichle, Jensen, & Cardenas, 2008). In terms of a causal pathway, these types of cognitions may contribute to fear, supporting avoidant coping strategies, which subsequently result in reduced mobility and increased pain. Fear-based avoidance sustained by negative reinforcement and environmental contingencies may play a critical role in moving an individual from an acute to chronic stage of illness (Vlaeyen, Kole-Snijders, Rotteveel, & Ruesink, 1995).

Evidence-based pain management includes a combination of cognitive, behavioral, and psychoeducational approaches that intervene across multiple domains in order to interrupt this cycle. Scascighini, Toma, Dober-Spielmann, and Sprott (2008) reviewed 27 randomized controlled outcome studies of multidisciplinary treatments for pain, and found that all used CBT techniques. They most commonly included operant-behavioral methods, patient education, progressive muscle relaxation (PMR) or autogenic training, and exercise to improve activity tolerance. Fifteen of these studies demonstrated superior results when compared with treatment as usual or wait-list control conditions. Morley, Eccleston, and Willams (1999) similarly found that CBT interventions that used coping skills training, both with and without cognitive therapy, produced significantly greater changes in pain experience, cognitive coping, and pain behaviors than comparison treatments. Though research has not yet indicated an ideal combination of components, Nielson and Weir (2001) suggest that moderate treatment efficacy appears to depend on cumulative effects as individual components are brought together. Okifuji and Ackerlind (2007) identify three specific domains central to CBT: pain education, behavioral skill training, and cognitive restructuring. They are organized around the common goal of enhancing patient self-management, often situated within the broader context of pharmacological treatment, physiotherapy, and general medical care.

Educating patients and their families about pain is an important aspect of CBT, many times occurring early in treatment and prior to skill building. In this phase, clinicians teach patients about the interdependent relationship between pain, cognition, affect, and physiology. They may also engage the patient in collaborative goal-setting and treatment planning tailored to individual circumstances (Turk, Vierck, Scarbrough, Crofford, & Rudin, 2008). Another essential part of patient education involves correcting misinterpretations about pain and identifying environmental barriers or supportive resources (Lohnberg, 2007). Prior to treatment engagement, one study found that 39% of patients viewed pain as a sign of damage, and 60% reported strong avoidance of painful activities (Dobscha, Corson, Leibowitz, Sullivan, & Gerrity, 2008). Accordingly, education during initial sessions may address patients' fear-related beliefs and the connection between quality of life and resuming normal activities (Von Korff et al., 2005). To reduce the effects of secondary gain, patients' families or significant others may also receive instruction to ignore unhelpful pain behaviors (e.g., resting, passive coping) and reward alternative positive behaviors (e.g., exercise, activity engagement; Molton, Graham, Stoelb, & Jensen, 2007). More commonly, these educational components of CBT are integrated with exercise regimens or included as part of more comprehensive self-management programs, often delivered in group settings. Psychoeducation applied in this way has demonstrated positive effects on pain outcomes for patients experiencing cardiac pain, chronic headaches, and musculoskeletal pain (McGillion et al., 2008; Mongini et al., 2008).

The behavioral component of CBT encompasses a variety of interventions: activity pacing, graded activity as usual, PMR, autogenic training, breathing exercises, attentional control training (e.g., use of imagery or distraction), hypnosis, muscle strengthening, and biofeedback. Scascighini and colleagues (2008) have recommended that a minimum standard of behavioral treatment focus on relaxation, activity pacing, and exercise. Activity pacing is a widely taught technique that consists of breaking activities into more manageable parts, limiting activity duration, prioritizing activities, and increasing activity amounts gradually (Birkholtz, Aylwin, & Harman, 2004). This is thought to prevent underactivity that can lead to increased disability, or overactivity that can precipitate long periods of rest or guarding. Graded activity as usual is an operant-behavior approach aimed at increasing healthy behaviors through reinforcement. Patients are rewarded for meeting activity quotas within a given time frame and encouraged to engage in these activities until pain impedes their progress (Lohnberg, 2007). Recently, a variation of graded activity, or graded exposure in vivo, has been developed for patients particularly affected by pain-related fear. Patients undergo systematic desensitization to a feared movement hierarchy followed by clinician-guided practice of these movements. Early trials of exposure-based treatment have led to significant and lasting reductions in fear of movement/(re)injury and catastrophizing (Vlaeyen, de Jong, Geilen, Heuts, & van Breukelen, 2002).

Relaxation and attentional control techniques also occupy a prominent position in many CBT protocols for pain self-management. PMR is a systematic tension-release procedure designed to eliminate tension throughout various muscle groups in the body. It has received substantial empirical support in the literature, especially for arthritis pain (Kwekkeboom & Gretarsdottir, 2006). In comparison, autogenic training asks that patients focus on physically relaxing sensations in the body, such as heaviness in limbs, regular heart beat, and warmth in the abdomen. Although conclusions about its efficacy remain limited, autogenic training has shown positive effects when used with tension headache sufferers and patients with postoperative pain (Stetter & Kupper, 2002). Guided imagery is another method of redirecting attention as a means of inducing relaxed physiological responses. Clinicians use live or recorded verbal prompts to help patients focus on imagined visual, auditory, tactile, and olfactory sensations. When combined with PMR or other CBT components, guided imagery techniques have effectively decreased pain in patients with arthritis, chronic headaches, and fibromyalgia (Baird & Sands, 2004; Mannix, Chandurkar, Rybicki, Tusek, & Solomon, 1999; Menzies & Kim, 2008). Research has further suggested that different imagery content might have different effects on pain. One study of hypnosis found that focused analgesia suggestions (e.g., "imagine a blue analgesic stream reaching different parts of the body") led to greater reductions in pain intensity than relaxation suggestions or PMR with diaphragmatic breathing (Castel, Perez, Sala, Padrol, & Rull, 2007). Relaxation treatments can vary widely in frequency of application from a single session to several times a week. In reviewing 15 studies of stand-alone relaxation interventions for pain, Kwekkeboom and Gretarsdottir (2006) observed that more frequent use of relaxation produced more positive outcomes, suggesting a dose-response relationship. They also speculate that individual differences in cognitive and coping skills may moderate the effects of relaxation, which is particularly relevant when considering that relaxation is typically used in conjunction with behavioral and cognitive strategies. Highlighting this point, Wachholtz and Pargament (2005) found that incorporating spirituality into relaxation practices increased participants' pain tolerance, relative to meditation and relaxation without a spiritual element.

Cognitive-skills training in CBT for chronic pain directly targets individual beliefs, attributions, and expectations that can improve coping skills, social functioning, and psychological outcomes. Studying rheumatoid arthritis patients, Covic, Adamson, Howe, and Spencer (2002) reported that catastrophizing thoughts such as "I feel my life isn't worth living" and helplessness strongly predicted pain and disability. Catastrophizing is believed to increase the lack of control individuals experience over their pain, resulting in poorer coping and emotional adjustment. Catastrophizing beliefs, viewing pain as harmful or a sign of damage, and blaming others for one's pain can also contribute to reduced self-efficacy, or the expectation that one does not have the resources to cope effectively with pain. Low self-efficacy, in turn, can lead to greater pain and disability (Shelby et al., 2008). Additionally, self-appraisals regarding one's coping resources can be domain-specific, expressed at different levels related to pain control, managing emotional symptoms, and physical functioning.

Evaluation and Treatment Outcomes

Evidence from treatment outcome studies targeting the sources of chronic pain supports a multidimensional view of the biopsychosocial model. Studies have found that pain sufferers improve significantly on mood and coping measures after receiving cognitive-behavioral interventions, and also on various indices of pain (CBT; see Morley et al., 1999, for a detailed summary). One review examined 35 randomized, controlled studies of multidisciplinary treatments for pain that all included cognitive-behavioral components. The authors concluded that integrated regimens were more effective than standard medical treatment, wait list control conditions, or no treatment (Scascighini et al., 2008). As outcomes research continues to highlight the underlying cognitive, behavioral, and affective mechanisms of pain, it also can help focus assessment strategies as part of effective evidence-based practice.

CBT aims to enhance perceived control by helping individuals monitor situational or cognitive triggers, increase positive self-talk, and reduce global-stable attributions for pain (e.g., pain affects all areas of life; Okifuji & Ackerlind, 2007). At the same time, it seeks to increase internal attributions for success. Consistent with the biopsychosocial model, cognitive restructuring, when combined with small, gradual accomplishments (achieved through activity pacing or graded exposure), can reinforce self-efficacy and have a positive impact on psychological functioning. Empirical support is growing for this mechanism of action. One randomized controlled trial of CBT for chronic temporomandibular pain showed that increased perceived ability to control pain after treatment explained 81% of the total effect across outcomes of pain, activity interference, and disability (Turner, Holtzman, & Mancl, 2007). Decreased catastrophizing and harm beliefs were also substantial mediators of improvement. When patients view themselves as less disabled by pain and feel more in control over their symptoms after multidisciplinary treatment, they report lower pain intensity, fewer depressive symptoms, and less activity restriction (Jensen, Turner, & Romano, 2001). Early treatment reductions in helplessness are also associated with late-treatment decreases in pain severity and interference (Burns, Kubilus, Bruehl, Harden, & Lofland, 2003).

Using advanced statistical methods, Burns and colleagues describe a causal relationship between changes in appraisals and improvements in functioning. The effects of cognitive change extended beyond those attributable to mood changes. Heapy, Stroud, Higgins, and Sellinger (2006) suggest that individually tailoring CBT based on patient preferences should take into account self-efficacy beliefs related to various coping strategies. Before treatment, patients could rate their perceived effectiveness on a variety of skills and their confidence in their ability to learn them. This information could then be used to individualize treatment plans and appropriately match patients with intervention components. An individually tailored approach could also increase a patient's readiness to change, promoting greater adherence and treatment retention. A form of motivational enhancement sensitive to individual variations in maladaptive beliefs and behavioral propensities promises to maximize the effectiveness of CBT approaches. As CBT for pain is commonly administered in group settings, it could potentially help patients view the process as more personal or relevant to their specific concerns.

Considerations With Special Populations/Diversity Issues

Pain is a significant problem for many Americans; however, there are some populations who may be more vulnerable. These groups may include children, older adults, women, and persons of color. When these groups are identified, it is important that assessment and treatment follow certain considerations. Health care professionals should be aware of their own biases when treating people with chronic pain. Although this is not an exhaustive review of differences, a few populations will be discussed.

Children

All children will experience pain, whether it is from an acute injury or a more chronic condition. Research suggests that as many as 40% of children and adolescents complain of pain at least once a week, and chronic pain affects between 15 to 20% of children (Goodman & McGrath, 1991). Many children who are postsurgery receive inadequate pain management. Approximately 20% of children 5 to 17 years of age suffer headaches. Juvenile arthritis, causing joint inflammation and aches, affects approximately 250,000 people under the age of 16 years. By 2010, 1 in every 1,000 U.S. children will be survivors of childhood cancer, and may be dealing with late and long-term effects of treatment (American Pain Foundation, 2009).

Common causes of pain in children include scrapes and bruises, needlestick pain from immunizations, sports injuries, chronic illnesses, headaches, and abdominal pain. It is difficult to understand and treat these pain complaints in children because of physical and psychosocial changes that occur during child development. Some factors to consider in the pain experiences of children include age, beliefs about pain, coping ability, previous pain experiences and responses to these, and support from parents and other caregivers. Addressing these factors will have a great influence on a child's quality of life, and may interfere with mood, sleep, school attendance, academic performance, and participation in sport and social activities. It is important that pediatric providers approach the assessment and treatment of pain in a systematic and multidisciplinary manner in order to minimize children's distress and reduce pain-related disabilities.

Older Adults

Pain may be more prevalent in older adults, due to chronic and progressive age-related conditions. It is estimated that up to 50% of older adults living in the community have pain interfering with daily functioning, and between 60–80% of persons in nursing homes experience chronic pain. Diagnosing and treating chronic pain in older adults is challenging, as they often present with multiple medical problems, taking multiple medications, and may have poor nutritional habits. Additional factors may include inability to adequately communicate the presence of pain, possibly due to dementia or other communication limitations. Common pain conditions in older adults include: musculoskeletal pain concerns due to arthritis and other bone and joint problems; abdominal pain; neuropathic pain due to diabetes, herpes zoster, or other medical problems; muscle cramps; injury from falls; and cancer-related pain.

Assessment and appropriate treatment should include a thorough medical evaluation to appropriately diagnose and treat pain conditions. It should also address any mental health concerns that may be exacerbating the pain experience, including assessment of family and social support the older adult may need. It is not a consequence of the aging process to be in pain. Quality of life should not be compromised (American Pain Foundation, 2009).

Women

Although it has been thought that women and men have similar pain experiences, research has shown that there are differences in the way males and females process pain, and women's expression of pain and their response to analgesics and pain stimulation (Paulson, Minoshima, Morrow, & Casey, 1998). Women have been categorized as emotional and overly sensitive to pain, and this may influence the way physicians treat women in pain. However, now it is known that women suffer from higher incidences of chronic pain conditions than men. These include migraine headaches, irritable bowel syndrome, fibromyalgia, and osteoarthritis. Women also report pain more often than men, and this may be due to cultural conditioning, where as children, girls are permitted to express pain and show emotion more than boys. It is important for professionals dealing with women to recognize these gender differences, and to more effectively target and treat women suffering from chronic pain conditions.

Culturally Diverse Patients

Growing evidence suggests that there are significant disparities in the assessment and treatment of medical conditions in different ethnic groups. For patients in chronic pain, surveys suggest that racial and ethnic differences influence access to care. A cross-sectional telephone survey was performed in a national sample with patients who were in pain for longer than 3 months. Hispanics were less likely to have consulted a PCP for pain (70%) than Whites (84%) or African Americans (85%). Reduced likelihood for consultation was associated with speaking Spanish, being younger or male, having limited education and low income, and being unemployed (Nguyen, Ugarte, Fuller, Haas, & Portenoy, 2005). A national sample of U.S. English-speaking adults when questioned about pain experience and psychosocial outcomes did report some differences. African American and Caucasian adults did not differ significantly on pain severity, emotional burden, and current treatment status; however, multivariate analyses revealed differences in psychosocial functioning. African Americans reported greater interference with daily living, deficiencies in coping, and counterproductive attitudes and beliefs than the Caucasian sample. Greater impatience and insensitivity from the most important person in their lives was reported by the African American sample (Ruehlman, Karoly, & Newton, 2005). Practitioners sensitive to cultural differences including beliefs about pain, access to medical care, and psychosocial stressors relative to the population they are treating will fare much better for successful treatment outcomes.

Clinical Pearls of Wisdom for Practitioners

1. Educate patients to the biopsychosocial assessment and treatment of chronic pain. Often, patients and family members are not aware that appropriate pain management is a basic right of patient care. They are entitled to understand the scope of pain treatment and receive the resources needed for successful treatment planning.
2. Empower patients to be active in managing their pain. If patients view themselves as effective managers for their pain, they are more likely to engage in realistic thinking and healthy behaviors to maximize their quality of life.
3. Encourage communication with all members of the multidisciplinary treatment team, including the patient. Patients are more likely to express concerns, fears, and obstacles they encounter in treatment when they feel that the clinician is open to listening to them and not dismissive. This will lead to more active participation in treatment.
4. Address the physical and psychosocial needs of the patient. Patients are generally not aware of all the resources available to address chronic pain. Many self-help books, wellness programs, and support groups may be accessed within the community.
5. Help the patient improve daily functioning with the development of a realistic treatment plan. A *realistic* plan with small steps to pain management will maximize positive outcomes and overall improvement in patient and family quality of life.

References

American College of Physicians. (2006, June). Special focus: Low back pain. *Observer, 6*. Retrieved September 26, 2009, from http://www.acpinternist.org/archives/2006/06/special.htm

American Pain Foundation. (2009, May 12). *Special considerations: Pain specific populations*. Retrieved April 23, 2009, from http://www.painfoundation.org/

American Pain Society. (2002). Guideline for the management of pain in osteoarthritis rheumatoid arthritis and juvenile chronic arthritis. *Clinical practice guidelines series* (2nd ed.). Glenview, IL: Author.

American Pain Society. (2005). Guideline for the management of fibromyalgia syndrome pain in adults and children. *Clinical practice guidelines series* (4th ed.). Glenview, IL: Author.

American Psychiatric Association. (2000). *Diagnostic and statistical manual of mental disorders* (4th ed., text rev.). Washington, DC: Author.

Baird, C. L., & Sands, L. (2004). A pilot study of the effectiveness of guided imagery with progressive muscle relaxation to reduce chronic pain and mobility difficulties of osteoarthritis. *Pain Management Nursing, 5*(3), 97–104.

Beck, A. T., Epstein, N., Brown, G., & Steer, R. A. (1988). An inventory for measuring clinical anxiety: Psychometric properties. *Journal of Consulting & Clinical Psychology, 56*(6), 893–897.

Beck, A. T., Rush, A., Shaw, B., & Emery, G. (1979). *Cognitive therapy of depression*. New York: Guilford.

Beck, A. T., Ward, C. H., Mendelson, M., Mock, J., & Erbaugh, J. (1961). An inventory for measuring depression. *Archives of General Psychiatry, 4*, 561–571.

Beck, A. T., Weissman, A., Lester, D., & Trexler, L. (1974). The measurement of pessimism: The hopelessness scale. *Journal of Consulting & Clinical Psychology, 42*(6), 861–865.

Belar, C. D., & Deardorff, W. W. (2009). *Clinical health psychology in medical settings: A practitioner's guidebook* (rev. ed.). Washington, DC: American Psychological Association.

Bergman, S., Jacobson, L. T. H., Herrstrom, P., & Petersson, I. F. (2004). Health status as measured by SF-36 reflects changes and predicts outcome in chronic musculoskeletal pain: A 3-year follow up study in the general population. *Pain, 108*(1–2), 115–123.

Birkholtz, M., Aylwin, L., & Harman, R. M. (2004). Activity pacing in chronic pain management: One aim, but which method? Part two: National activity pacing survey. *British Journal of Occupational Therapy, 67*(11), 481–487.

Breivik, H., Borchgrevink, P. C., Allen, S. M., Rosseland, L. A., Romundstad, L., Hals, E. K., et al. (2008). Assessment of pain. *British Journal of Anaesthesia, 101*(1), 17–24.

Burns, J. W., Glenn, B., Lofland, K., Bruehl, S., & Harden, R. N. (2005). Stages of change in readiness to adopt a self-management approach to chronic pain: The moderating role of early-treatment stage progression in predicting outcome. *Pain, 115*(3), 322–331.

Burns, J. W., Kubilus, A., Bruehl, S., Harden, R. N., & Lofland, K. (2003). Do changes in cognitive factors influence outcome following multidisciplinary treatment for chronic pain? A cross-lagged panel analysis. *Journal of Consulting and Clinical Psychology, 71*(1), 81–91.

Castel, A., Perez, M., Sala, J., Padrol, A., & Rull, M. (2007). Effect of hypnotic suggestion on fibromyalgic pain: Comparison between hypnosis and relaxation. *European Journal of Pain, 11*(4), 463–468.

Covic, T., Adamson, B., Howe, G., & Spencer, D. (2002). The role of passive coping and helplessness in rheumatoid arthritis depression and pain. *Journal of Applied Health Behaviour, 4*(1–2), 31–35.

Daut, R. L., Cleeland, C. S., & Flanery, R. C. (1983). Development of the Wisconsin brief pain questionnaire to assess pain in cancer and other diseases. *Pain, 17*(2), 197–210.

Davidson, M. A., Tripp, D. A., Fabrigar, L. R., & Davidson, P. R. (2008). Chronic pain assessment: A seven-factor model. *Pain Research & Management, 13*(4), 299–308.

Derogatis, L. (1994). *Symptom checklist–90–R: Administration, scoring, and procedures manual*. Minneapolis, MN: National Computer Systems.

Dersh, J., Gatchel, R. J. & Kishino, N. (2005). The role of tertiary gain in pain disability. *Practical Pain Management, 5*, 13–28.

Dickens, C., & Creed, F. (2001). The burden of depression in patients with rheumatoid arthritis. *Rheumatology, 40*(12), 1327–1330.

Dobscha, S. K., Corson, K., Leibowitz, R. Q., Sullivan, M. D., & Gerrity, M. S. (2008). Rationale, design, and baseline findings from a randomized trial of collaborative care for chronic musculoskeletal pain in primary care. *Pain Medicine, 9*(8), 1050–1064.

Dworkin, R. H., Turk, D. C., Farrar, J. T., Haythornthwaite, J. A., Jensen, M. P., Katz, N. P., et al. (2005). Core outcome measures for chronic pain clinical trials: IMMPACT recommendations. *Pain, 113*(1–2), 9–19.

Dworkin, R. H., Turk, D. C., Wyrwich, K. W., Beaton, D., Cleeland, C. S., Farrar, J. T., et al. (2008). Interpreting the clinical importance of treatment outcomes in chronic pain clinical trials: IMMPACT recommendations. *Journal of Pain, 9*(2), 105–121.

Fairbank, J. C., Couper, J., Davies, J. B., & O'Brien, J. P. (1980). The Oswestry low back pain disability questionnaire. *Physiotherapy, 66*(8), 271–273.

Finestone, H. M., Alfeeli, A., & Fisher, W. A. (2008). Stress-induced physiologic changes as a basis for the biopsychosocial model of chronic musculoskeletal pain: A new theory? *Clinical Journal of Pain, 24*(9), 767–775.

Folstein, M., & Folstein, S. (2001). *The Mini-Mental State Examination.* Lutz, FL: Psychological Assessment Resources.

Gatchel, R. J. (1991). Early development of physical and mental deconditioning in painful spinal disorders. In T. G. Mayer, V. Mooney, & R. J. Gatchel (Eds.), *Contemporary conservative care for painful spinal disorders* (pp. 278–289). Philadelphia: Lea & Febiger.

Gatchel, R. J. (1996). Psychological disorders and chronic pain: Cause and effect relationships. In R. J. Gatchel & D. C. Turk (Eds.), *Psychological approaches to pain management: A practitioner's handbook* (pp. 33–52). New York: Guilford.

Gatchel, R. J. (2005). *Clinical essentials of pain management.* Washington, DC: American Psychological Association.

Gatchel, R. J., Peng, Y. B., Peters, M. L., Fuchs, P. N., & Turk, D. C. (2007). The biopsychosocial approach to chronic pain: Scientific advances and future directions. *Psychological Bulletin, 133*(4), 581–624.

Gatchel, R. J., & Weisberg, J. N. (Eds.). (2000). *Personality characteristics of patients with pain.* Washington, DC: American Psychological Press.

Glenn, B., & Burns, J. W. (2003). Pain self-management in the process and outcome of multidisciplinary treatment of chronic pain: Evaluation of a stage of change model. *Journal of Behavioral Medicine, 26*(5), 417–433.

Goodman, J. E., & McGrath, P. J. (1991). The epidemiology of pain in children and adolescents: A review. *Pain, 46*(3), 247–264.

Grotle, M., Vollestad, N. K., & Brox, J. I. (2006). Screening for yellow flags in first-time acute low back pain: Reliability and validity of a Norwegian version of the acute low back pain screening questionnaire. *Clinical Journal of Pain, 22*(5), 458–467.

Gureje, O., Von Korff, M., Simon, G. E., & Gater, R. (1998). Persistent pain and well-being: A World Health Organization study in primary care. *Journal of American Medicine, 280*(2), 147–151.

Hallner, D., & Hasenbring, M. (2004). Classification of psychosocial risk factors (yellow flags) for the development of chronic low back and leg pain using artificial neural network. *Neuroscience Letters, 361*(1–3), 151–154.

Hanley, M. A., Raichle, K., Jensen, M., & Cardenas, D. D. (2008). Pain catastrophizing and beliefs predict changes in pain interference and psychological functioning in persons with spinal cord injury. *Journal of Pain, 9*(9), 863–871.

Harstall, C. (2003). How prevalent is chronic pain? *Pain: Clinical Updates, 11*, 1–4.

Heapy, A. A., Stroud, M. W., Higgins, D. M., & Sellinger, J. J. (2006). Tailoring cognitive-behavioral therapy for chronic pain: A case example. *Journal of Clinical Psychology, 62*(11), 1345–1354.

Hopman, W. M., Berger, C., Joseph, L., Towheed, T., VandenKerkhof, E., Anastassiades, T., et al. (2006). The natural progression of health-related quality of life: Results of a five-year prospective study of SF-36 scores in a normative population. *Quality of Life Research: An International Journal of Quality of Life Aspects of Treatment, Care & Rehabilitation, 15*(3), 527–536.

Hunter, C. L., Goodie, J. L., Oordt, M. S., & Dobmeyer, A. C. (2009). *Integrated behavioral health in primary care.* Washington, DC: American Psychological Associataion.

Jensen, M. P., Turner, J. A., & Romano, J. M. (2001). Changes in beliefs, catastrophizing, and coping are associated with improvement in multidisciplinary pain treatment. *Journal of Consulting and Clinical Psychology, 69*(4), 655–662.

Jensen, M. P., Turner, J. A., Romano, J. M., & Strom, S. E. (1995). The chronic pain coping inventory: Development and preliminary validation. *Pain, 60*(2), 203–216.

Karoly, P., Ruehlman, L. S., Aiken, L. S., Todd, M., & Newton, C. (2006). Evaluating chronic pain impact among patients in primary care: Further validation of a brief assessment instrument. *Pain Medicine, 7*(4), 289–298.

Keefe, F. J., Smith, S. J., Buffington, A. L. H., Gibson, J., Studts, J. L., & Caldwell, D. S. (2002). Recent advances and future directions in the biopsychosocial assessment and treatment of arthritis. *Journal of Consulting and Clinical Psychology, 70*(3), 640–655.

Keller, S., Bann, C. M., Dodd, S. L., Schein, J., Mendoza, T. R., & Cleeland, C. S. (2004). Validity of the brief pain inventory for use in documenting the outcomes of patients with noncancer pain. *Clinical Journal of Pain, 20*(5), 309–318.

Kendall, N., Linton, S. J., & Main, C. J. (1997). *Guide to assessing psychosocial yellow flags in acute low back pain: Risk factors for long-term disability and work loss* (1st ed.). Wellington, New Zealand: Accident Rehabilitation and Compensation Insurance Corporation of NZ and the National Health Committee.

Kerns, R. D., Turk, D. C., & Rudy, T. E. (1985). The West Haven-Yale multidimensional pain inventory (WHYMPI). *Pain, 23*(4), 345–356.

Kori, S. H., Miller, R. P., & Todd, D. D. (1990). Kinesiophobia: A new view of chronic pain behavior. *Pain Management, 3*(1), 35–43.

Kwekkeboom, K. L., & Gretarsdottir, E. (2006). Systematic review of relaxation interventions for pain. *Journal of Nursing Scholarship, 38*(3), 269–277.

Leeman, G., Polatin, P., Gatchel, R., & Kishino, N. (2000). Managing secondary gain in patients with pain-associated disability: A clinical perspective. *Journal of Workers Compensation, 9*, 25–44.

Lohnberg, J. A. (2007). A review of outcome studies on cognitive-behavioral therapy for reducing fear-avoidance beliefs among individuals with chronic pain. *Journal of Clinical Psychology in Medical Settings, 14*(2), 113–122.

Maier, S. F. (2003). Bi-directional immune-brain communication: Implications for understanding stress, pain, and cognition. *Brain, Behavior, & Immunity, 17*(2), 69–85.

Mannix, L. K., Chandurkar, R. S., Rybicki, L. A., Tusek, D. L., & Solomon, G. D. (1999). Effect of guided imagery on quality of life for patients with chronic tension-type headache. *Headache, 39*(5), 326–334.

Mayer, T. G., Barnes, D., Kishino, N. D., Nichols, G., Gatchel, R. J., Mayer, H., & Mooney, V. (1988). Progressive isoinertial lifting evaluation: I. A standardized protocol and normative database. *Spine, 13*(9), 993–997.

McGillion, M. H., Watt-Watson, J., Stevens, B., Lefort, S. M., Coyte, P., & Graham, A. (2008). Randomized controlled trial of a psychoeducation program for the self-management of chronic cardiac pain. *Journal of Pain & Symptom Management, 36*(2), 126–140.

Melzack, R. (1987). The short-form McGill Pain Questionnaire. *Pain, 30*(2), 191–197.

Melzack, R., & Wall, P. D. (1965). Pain mechanisms: A new theory. *Science, 50*, 971–979.

Menzies, V., & Kim, S. (2008). Relaxation and guided imagery in Hispanic persons diagnosed with fibromyalgia: A pilot study. *Family & Community Health, 31*(3), 204–212.

Molton, I. R., Graham, C., Stoelb, B. L., & Jensen, M. P. (2007). Current psychological approaches to the management of chronic pain. *Current Opinion in Anaesthesiology, 20*(5), 485–489.

Mongini, F., Ciccone, G., Rota, E., Ferrero, L., Ugolini, A., Evangelista, A., et al. (2008). Effectiveness of an educational and physical programme in reducing headache, neck and shoulder pain: A workplace controlled trial. *Cephalalgia, 28*(5), 541–552.

Morley, S., Eccleston, C., & Williams, A. (1999). Systematic review and meta-analysis of randomized controlled trials of cognitive behaviour therapy and behaviour therapy for chronic pain in adults, excluding headache. *Pain, 80*(1–2), 1–13.

National Center for Health Statistics. (2006). *Chartbook on trends in the health of Americans* (pp. 68–71). Hyattsville, MD: U.S. Department of Health and Human Services.

Nguyen, M., Ugarte, C., Fuller, I., Haas, G., & Portenoy, R. (2005). Access to care for chronic pain: Racial and ethnic differences. *Journal of Pain, 6*(5), 301–314.

Nielson, W. R., Jensen, M. P., Ehde, D. M., Kerns, R. D., & Molton, I. R. (2008). Further development of the multidimensional pain readiness to change questionnaire: The MPRCQ2. *Journal of Pain, 9*(6), 552–565.

Nielson, W. R., Jensen, M. P., & Kerns, R. D. (2003). Initial development and validation of a multidimensional pain readiness to change questionnaire. *Journal of Pain, 4*(3), 148–158.

Nielson, W. R., & Weir, R. (2001). Biopsychosocial approaches to the treatment of chronic pain. *Clinical Journal of Pain, 17*(4 Suppl.), S114–S127.

Nordin, H., Eisemann, M., & Richter, J. (2006). The accuracy of the DSM-IV pain disorder and the ICD-10 persistent somatoform pain disorder in chronic pain patients. *Journal of Clinical Psychology in Medical Settings, 13*(3), 307–314.

Okifuji, A., & Ackerlind, S. (2007). Behavioral medicine approaches to pain. *Anesthesiology Clinics, 25*(4), 709–719.

Patten, S. B. (2001). Long-term medical conditions and major depression in a Canadian population study at waves 1 and 2. *Journal of Affective Disorders, 63*(1–3), 35–41.

Patten, S. B., Beck, C. A., Kassam, A., Williams, J. V. A., Barbui, C., & Metz, L. M. (2005). Long-term medical conditions and major depression: Strength of association for specific conditions in the general population. *Canadian Journal of Psychiatry/La Revue Canadienne De Psychiatrie, 50*(4), 195–202.

Paulson, P., Minoshima, S., Morrow, T., & Casey, K. (1998). Gender differences in pain perception and patterns of cerebral activation during noxious heat stimulation in humans. *Pain, 76*(1–2), 223–229.

Reid, M. C., Engles-Horton, L. L., Weber, M. B., Kerns, R. D., Rogers, E. L., & O'Connor, P. G. (2002). Use of opioid medications for chronic noncancer pain syndromes in primary care. *Journal of General Internal Medicine, 17*(3), 173–179.

Ruehlman, L. S., Karoly, P., & Newton, C. (2005). Comparing the experiential and psychosocial dimensions of chronic pain in African Americans and Caucasians: Findings from a national community sample. *Pain Medicine, 6*(1), 49–60.

Ruehlman, L. S., Karoly, P., Newton, C., & Aiken, L. S. (2005). The development and preliminary validation of the profile of chronic pain: Extended assessment battery. *Pain, 118*(3), 380–389.

Samanta, J., Kendall, J., & Samanta, A. (2003). 10-minute consultation: Chronic low back pain. *BMJ, 326*(7388), 535.

Scascighini, L., Toma, V., Dober-Spielmann, S., & Sprott, H. (2008). Multidisciplinary treatment for chronic pain: A systematic review of interventions and outcomes. *Rheumatology, 47*(5), 670–678.

Sharpe, M., & Williams, A. C. (2002). Treating patients with somatoform pain disorder and hypochondriasis. In D. C. Turk & R. J. Gatchel (Eds.), *Psychological approaches to pain management: A practitioner's handbook* (2nd ed., pp. 515–533). New York: Guilford.

Shelby, R. A., Somers, T. J., Keefe, F. J., Pells, J. J., Dixon, K. E., & Blumenthal, J. A. (2008). Domain specific self-efficacy mediates the impact of pain catastrophizing on pain and disability in overweight and obese osteoarthritis patients. *Journal of Pain, 9*(10), 912–919.

Stetter, F., & Kupper, S. (2002). Autogenic training: A meta-analysis of clinical outcome studies. *Applied Psychophysiology and Biofeedback, 27*(1), 45–98.

Stewart, W. F., Ricci, J. A., Chee, E., Morganstein, D., & Lipton, R. (2003). Lost productive time and cost due to common pain conditions in the US workforce. *Journal of the American Medical Association, 290*(18), 2443–2454.

Sullivan, M. J. L., Bishop, S. R., & Pivick, J. (1995). The pain catastrophizing scale: Development and validation. *Psychological Assessment, 7*(4), 524–532.

Swinkels-Meewisse, I. E., Roelofs, J., Schouten, E. G., Verbeek, A. L., Oostendorp, R. A., & Vlaeyen, J. W. (2006). Fear of movement/(re)injury predicting chronic disabling low back pain: A prospective inception cohort study. *Spine, 31*(6), 658–664.

Tait, R. C., Pollard, C. A., Margolis, R. B., Duckro, P. N., & Krause, S. J. (1987). The pain disability index: Psychometric and validity data. *Archives of Physical Medicine & Rehabilitation, 68*(7), 438–441.

Tunks, E. R., Crook, J., & Weir, R. (2008). Epidemiology of chronic pain with psychological comorbidity: Prevalence, risk, course, and prognosis. *Canadian Journal of Psychiatry/Revue Canadienne De Psychiatrie, 53*(4), 224–234.

Turk, D. C., & Melzack, R. (Eds.). (2001). *Handbook of pain assessment* (2nd ed.). New York: Guilford.

Turk, D. C., Vierck, C. J., Scarbrough, E., Crofford, L. J., & Rudin, N. J. (2008). Fibromyalgia: Combining pharmacological and nonpharmacological approaches to treating the person, not just the pain. *Journal of Pain, 9*(2), 99–104.

Turner, J. A., Holtzman, S., & Mancl, L. (2007). Mediators, moderators, and predictors of therapeutic change in cognitive-behavioral therapy for chronic pain. *Pain, 127*(3), 276–286.

Veehof, M. M., ten Klooster, P. M., Taal, E., van Riel, P. L., & van de Laar, M. A. (2008). Comparison of internal and external responsiveness of the generic medical outcome study short form-36 (SF-36) with disease-specific measures in rheumatoid arthritis. *Journal of Rheumatology, 35*(4), 610–617.

Vlaeyen, J. W., de Jong, J., Geilen, M., Heuts, P. H., & van Breukelen, G. (2002). The treatment of fear of movement/(re)injury in chronic low back pain: Further evidence on the effectiveness of exposure in vivo. *Clinical Journal of Pain, 18*(4), 251–261.

Vlaeyen, J. W. S., Kole-Snijders, A. M. J., Rotteveel, A. M., & Ruesink, R. (1995). The role of fear of movement/(re)injury in pain disability. *Journal of Occupational Rehabilitation, 5*(4), 235–252.

Von Korff, M., Balderson, B. H., Saunders, K., Miglioretti, D. L., Lin, E. H., Berry, S., et al. (2005). A trial of an activating intervention for chronic back pain in primary care and physical therapy settings. *Pain, 113*(3), 323–330.

Wachholtz, A. B., & Pargament, K. I. (2005). Is spirituality a critical ingredient of meditation? Comparing the effects of spiritual meditation, secular meditation, and relaxation on spiritual, psychological, cardiac, and pain outcomes. *Journal of Behavioral Medicine, 28*(4), 369–384.

Ware, J. E., Jr., & Sherbourne, C. D. (1992). The MOS 36-item short-form health survey (SF-36). I. Conceptual framework and item selection. *Medical Care, 30*(6), 473–483.

Wittink, H., Turk, D. C., Carr, D. B., Sukiennik, A., & Rogers, W. (2004). Comparison of the redundancy, reliability, and responsiveness to change among SF-36, Oswestry disability index, and multidimensional pain inventory. *Clinical Journal of Pain, 20*(3), 133–142.

World Health Organization. (1993). *The ICD-10 classification of mental and behavioural disorders. Diagnostic criteria for research.* Geneva, Switzerland: Author.

29 Headaches in Primary Care

Dawn C. Buse
Frank Andrasik

Introduction

Headaches are a common medical condition with a high prevalence in the general population, affecting 91% of males and 96% of females at some point during their lifetime (Rasmussen, 1995). Fortunately, the majority of headaches are benign, and less than 0.1% of the lifetime prevalence of headache is associated with life-threatening conditions (Silberstein & Lipton, 1993). At the same time, headaches can have a significant impact on daily life.

In this chapter we review background information on headache disorders and aspects pertinent to assessment, as well as treatment. Our chapter is guided by the biopsychosocial model, which posits that biological, psychological, and social or environmental factors all play significant roles in medical disorders. This model provides an ideal framework in which to conceptualize management of patients with primary headache disorders, where factors of biology, environment, behaviors, and beliefs are interwoven with the development, maintenance, progression, and remission of headache disorders (Andrasik, Flor, & Turk, 2005).

Assessment and Diagnostic Issues

The *International Classification of Headache Disorders* (*ICHD*), first introduced in 1988, was instrumental in standardizing headache diagnosis in clinical practice and research worldwide. In 2004, the classification system was updated and revised (*ICHD-II*) (Headache Classification of the International Headache Society, 2004). The *ICHD-II* is divided into three sections: (a) primary headache disorders (i.e., headaches not attributable to another medical condition), which has 4 major categories and 57 subtypes; (b) secondary headaches (i.e., headaches attributable to another medical condition), of which there are 8 major categories and 152 subtypes and subforms; and (c) cranial neuralgias, facial pain, and "other headaches yet to be defined." This chapter focuses on primary headache disorders or those that cannot be attributed to another medical condition.

Primary headaches can be subdivided into migraine, tension-type headache (TTH), cluster headache (CH) and other trigeminal autonomic cephalalgias, and other primary headaches. TTH is the most common type of primary headache. TTH is subdivided into infrequent episodic (headaches occurring less frequently than 1 day per month), frequent episodic (headaches on 1–14 days per month), and chronic daily headache (headaches on 15 or more days per month). The primary features of TTH are bilateral location (pain on both sides of the head), nonpulsating quality, and mild to moderate pain intensity, although features may vary by individual. Migraine, the next most common, but generally more disabling than TTH, has five major subtypes and may occur with (MA) or without aura (MO). It can also be subdivided by frequency into episodic migraine (EM) (with headache occurring on 14 or fewer days per month) and chronic migraine (CM) (headache occurring on 15 or more days per month). In general, migraine headaches tend to include moderate to severe pain that lasts at least four hours. The pain is often unilateral or one-sided, may have a pulsating quality, and may be aggravated by movement and activity. The migraine sufferer may experience nausea or vomiting, photophobia (sensitivity to light), and phonophobia (sensitivity to sound). Aura is characterized by focal neurologic features that usually occur in the hour preceding the headache. Aura symptoms may include seeing flickering lights, spots or lines, loss of vision, feelings of "pins and needles" or numbness, and other symptoms. CH is less common, but extremely debilitating. CH is a group of headache disorders characterized by trigeminal nerve and parasympathetic nervous system activation. CH is often described as an excruciating, sharp pain in or around the eye. CHs last approximately one hour and most often occur in clusters of multiple episodes over two weeks to three months; however, it is possible to experience more chronic forms of CH.

Incidence and Clinical Manifestations in Primary Care Settings

Headache is a common medical condition with a high prevalence in the general population, affecting 91% of males and 96% of females at some point during their lifetime (Rasmussen, 1995). The majority of headaches are benign, and less than 0.1% of the lifetime prevalence of headache is associated with life-threatening conditions (Silberstein & Lipton, 1993). TTH is the most common type in the general population, with a one-year-period prevalence ranging from 31 to 73%

(B. S. Schwartz, Stewart, Simon, & Lipton, 1998). Migraine is less common, but still takes a sizable toll with an annual prevalence of 12 to 13% (18.2% for women and 6.5% for men), with an estimated 31 million migraine sufferers in the United States (Lipton, Diamond, Diamond, & Reed, 2001). CH is rare, and is experienced by men four times more often than women (Finkel, 2003).

Headache can have a significant impact on daily life, and this impact increases as the frequency and severity of migraine or TTH increases (Holroyd et al., 2000). Primary headaches, such as migraine, can cause substantial functional impairment across all aspects of life and reduce health-related quality of life (HRQoL). The "Global Burden of Disease Study" by the World Health Organization ranked migraine in the most severe level of disability (along with dementia, psychosis, and depression) (Menken, Munsat, & Toole, 2000). The cost of migraine among the U.S. workforce has been estimated as approximately $13 billion per year, in terms of missed work days and lost productivity (Hu, Markson, Lipton, Stewart, & Berger, 1999). Approximately 31% of migraine sufferers miss work, and between 58 and 76% of migraine sufferers discontinue normal household activities or cancel family or social activities due to headache (Lipton, Stewart, Diamond, Diamond, & Reed, 2001).

Direct medical costs for migraine care in the U.S. have been estimated as $1 billion per year (Menken, Munsat, & Toole, 2000). Headache prompts several million outpatient medical visits annually, and results in over one million patient-days bedridden each month in the United States (Hu et al., 1999). The majority of people with headaches do not seek medical care, remaining without a diagnosis and without access to systematic treatment, despite the fact that they are likely to be experiencing considerable functional impairment and, consequently, personal distress (Lipton & Stewart, 1993; W. F. Stewart & Lipton, 1993). Of those who do seek care, 97% of this medical care occurs in the primary care setting (Latinovic, Gulliford, & Ridsdale, 2006).

Migraine is associated with increased rates of comorbidity for depression, anxiety, panic disorder, obsessive-compulsive disorder, and suicide attempts over controls (Breslau & Davis, 1993; Jette, Patten, William, Becker, & Wrebe, 2008). Gender-adjusted odds ratios for these disorders range from 2.6 for phobia to 6.6 for panic disorder. In a longitudinal, follow-up study, researchers found that migraineurs were more likely to experience future depressive and anxiety disorders. Migraine and depression have been shown to be bidirectional, so that no matter which occurs first, an individual who experiences one has a higher rate of risk for the other (Breslau & Davis). Anxiety and depression are correlated with greater impairment in functional ability and HRQoL in migraineurs, and lowered HRQoL is associated with increased migraine-related disability (Lanteri-Minet, Radat, Chautard, & Lucas, 2005). CM has been demonstrated to be associated with even greater levels of functional impairment, health service utilization, and psychiatric and medical comorbidities than EM (Bigal, Serrano, Reed, & Lipton, 2008; Buse et al. 2008; Lipton et al., 2008).

Migraine can place a significant burden on sufferers' lives, both during attacks (ictally) and also interictally (i.e., in between attacks). Interictal burden may include worry about the next attack and change or avoidance of commitments in the occupational, social, and personal arenas. For example, a patient may decide that she can not be a coach of her child's soccer team due to worry that she would have to miss too many practices and games due to headache. Patients with high levels of interictal headache-related burden have been demonstrated to experience higher rates of psychological disorders than those with lower levels of interictal burden (Buse et al., 2007). In a population-based study of interictal headache burden, of respondents with "severe" levels of interictal burden, 44% met criteria for an anxiety disorder, 47% for panic disorder, and 46% for a depressive disorder, compared with 20, 23, and 25%, respectively, of headache sufferers with low or no interictal burden (Buse et al., 2007). Results were controlled for frequency and severity of headache, demonstrating that interictal burden is not solely related to the severity of the disease, but rather a more complex interaction of disease severity with cognitions (e.g., expectations, anxiety) and behaviors.

Brief Case History

Donna is a 43-year-old, single, Afro-Caribbean woman who lives and works in a large U.S. city. Donna presented with a long history of episodic migraine, which had developed into chronic migraine, with headache occurring almost every day over the past 3 years. She described her headaches as bifrontal and temporal pain that radiated to the eyes and jaw, and lasted an average of 4 hours (maximum duration up to 8 hours). Exacerbating factors included stress, bright lights, heat, and noise, all of which were common aspects of her job. She had been taking over-the-counter nonsteroidal antiinflammatory medications (NSAIDs) daily for almost 2 years, but reported that they were no longer effective. The headaches interfered with work and caused emotional distress and impairment. In addition to headaches, Donna presented with high levels of depression, anxiety, and panic attacks, and reported feeling overwhelmed, helpless, and hopeless about her headaches and the future.

Donna, like most headache patients, was initially treated with acute and preventative migraine medications. Over the course of several months Donna's headaches did not improve; therefore, laboratory tests (including blood work, metabolic panel, liver enzyme panel, Lyme titer, thyroid function, and erythrocyte sedimentation rate) were ordered, and brain magnetic resonance imaging (MRI) and magnetic resonance venography scans were performed. All laboratory tests and imaging were normal. Over the next few months, Donna's headaches became more severe and debilitating, and she reported that she was missing a great deal of work and feeling very depressed. She subsequently was hospitalized so that intravenous therapies could be tried; however, after a week in the hospital and several courses of intravenous therapy options, she did not experience any relief from pain. She was discharged to home and her headaches continued to worsen in frequency and severity. She was considering taking a leave from work and applying for disability.

At this point, Donna was referred to a multidisciplinary headache center. She was seen by a neurologist, who took a comprehensive history and performed a physical examination. She was also evaluated by a psychologist who took a detailed history and administered several questionnaires, including the Patient Health Questionnaire (PHQ), a questionnaire that provides *Diagnostic and Statistical Manual of Mental Disorders* (*DSM-IV*; American Psychiatric Association, 2000) diagnoses for several Axis I disorders, to help guide treatment efforts (Spitzer, Kroenke, Williams, & The

Patient Health Questionnaire Primary Study Group, 1999). Donna, whose case we will return to at a later point in the chapter, represents one of the more extreme cases that is seen in primary care, but she was chosen to illustrate the complicated clinical picture that can arise and prompt interdisciplinary care.

Cognitive-Behavioral Case Conceptualization

Assessment, Diagnosis, and History

Treatment of headache should start with a complete medical evaluation by a neurologist or other qualified medical professional to rule out headache due to an acute medical condition, disease state, or structural abnormality. Once an acute problem is ruled out, a primary headache disorder can be diagnosed using *ICHD-II* criteria. In addition to a complete medical history, the initial evaluation should include assessment of comorbid psychiatric disorders (e.g., depression, anxiety), headache-related disability, including both ictal and interictal burden, impact of headache on occupational, academic, social, family, and personal functioning, and assessment of quality of life. Research has demonstrated that gathering information about headache-related disability leads to a more accurate recognition of the severity of the effect of migraine on the patient's life, and tends to result in more aggressive and comprehensive treatment plans (Holmes, MacGregor, Sawyer, & Lipton, 2001).

Headache diaries can be kept by patients for 1–2 months to gain a more complete and accurate picture of a patient's health, functioning, and quality of life (Andrasik, Lipchik, McCrory, & Wittrock, 2005). Data may include headache frequency, duration, and severity (rated on a scale of 0–10), presence of aura or focal neurological symptoms, associated features, medication use, female menstrual cycle, mood ratings, information about sleep, diet including meals, caffeine use, and alcohol, nicotine, weather (with a focus on barometric change), and life events. Maintaining this type of diary will provide a wealth of information to both the health care provider (HCP) and the patient, and help map out targets for behavioral intervention and help predict (and avoid) future attacks. During treatment, diaries may be used to record mood, relaxation practice, automatic thoughts, catastrophizing, and other relevant data.

Identifying and Addressing Obstacles to Treatment

There are several common obstacles to success in headache treatment and management, including problems with adherence, motivation, patient-provider communication, and access to care. Other patient characteristics that can create barriers to effective management include a lack of self-efficacy, an external locus of control, negative thinking styles such as "catastrophizing," an overfocus on medication, and unwillingness or inability to acknowledge and work on behavioral aspects or comorbid conditions, such as depression and anxiety, or to seek care when needed from a mental health provider.

Compliance refers to the degree to which patients follow medical recommendations of their HCPs (Rains, Lipchik, & Penzien, 2006). Adherence refers to an active and collaborative involvement by the patient in the implementation of a therapeutic regimen. These terms are often used interchangeably. We prefer the term adherence, in order to emphasize the importance of the patient's participation in effective treatment. Nonadherence can pose a significant barrier to effective headache management in many ways. Common problems areas in headache management include misuse of medication (including unfilled, overused, underused, incorrectly used, and nonadvised discontinuation of prescribed medications or treatments) (Gallagher & Kunkel, 2003), appointment keeping (Edmeads et al., 1993; Spierings & Miree, 1993), monitoring and diary keeping, and unwillingness or inability to follow clinical suggestions.

Improper medication use may not only limit relief, but may also aggravate the primary headache condition (and can lead to medication overuse headache or rebound headache) (Rains, Lipchik, et al., 2006). Adherence to pharmacological regimens declines when dosing regimens are more frequent and complex (Claxton, Cramer, & Pierce, 2001), side effects are increased (Dunbar-Jacob et al., 2000), and costs are greater (Motheral & Henderson, 1999), and is worse in chronic conditions, compared with acute conditions (Dunbar-Jacob & Mortimer-Stephens, 2001). The majority of these conditions apply to headache care. In addition, rates of adherence with behavioral recommendations, such as diary keeping, dietary modifications, weight loss, exercise, smoking cessation, proper sleep hygiene, and treatment for alcohol or substance use, are even lower than rates of compliance with prescribed medication regimens (Dunbar-Jacob et al.). These areas are an important target for behavioral interventions.

Social learning theory, the transtheoretical model, and motivational interviewing (MI) can be helpful in understanding barriers to behavior change and enhancing motivation for health-related behaviors (Bandura, 1986; Elder, Ayala, & Harris, 1999; Jensen, 2002). These theories are based on the hypothesis that health-related behavior change and motivation are based upon three basic components: (a) the patient's readiness for change, (b) self-efficacy (i.e., confidence in one's ability to perform an action), and (c) outcome efficacy (i.e., the belief that a behavior or set of behaviors will have a desirable result) (Bandura, 1977; Miller & Rollnick, 2002). Following this line of reasoning, skills or knowledge alone are not enough to ensure behavior change. Rather, the patient must want to change, believe that he or she can, and believe that the necessary actions will accomplish the desired goal(s).

The transtheoretical model proposes that patients' readiness and motivation for change can be categorized into one of five stages: (a) precontemplation (the patient is not thinking about changing behavior and does not recognize the need or a problem); (b) contemplation (the patient recognizes a need or problem and begins to think about changing behavior, and may be developing a plan, but has not taken any action); (c) preparation (the patient has done research, developed a plan, and may begin making minor changes or actions); (d) action (the patient is actively engaged in the behavior change or new actions); and (e) maintenance (the patient is continuing behaviors necessary to maintain changes) (Miller, 1996; Prochaska, Redding, & Evers, 1997). When the patient reaches the maintenance stage, behaviors and actions may be performed habitually and automatically.

Relapse may occur at any point in the process, and should be considered a challenge from which the patient needs to return to the steps of a previous stage and move through the course again. Relapse is not considered a failure or a permanent state, and it is understood that patients may move forward and backwards or even jump from one stage to another over time.

In providing headache treatment, providers should consider a patient's stage of readiness for change and tailor their interventions, clinical advice, and education accordingly. MI is a directive, patient-centered counseling style for eliciting behavior change by helping clients to explore and resolve ambivalence based on the transtheoretical model (Rollnick & Miller, 1995). MI focuses on the patient's stage of readiness, explores the patients' beliefs, concerns, perspective, and ambivalence about behavior change. The goal of the HCP is to help the patient realize the importance of change and maintain an empathic, supportive, and nonjudgmental atmosphere. Motivation for change is increased when patients examine the pros and cons of change and make decisions themselves, rather than receiving advice or instructions from a HCP or other person. HCPs can encourage patients to explore their ambivalence toward changing the identified behavior.

Effective patient-provider communication is essential for effective medical care. Communication between HCPs and patients is the basis of the therapeutic relationship, and is directly related to patient satisfaction (Frederikson, 1995; Hall, Irish, Roter, Ehrlich, & Miller, 1994; Hall, Roter, & Katz, 1988; Hulsman, Ros, Winnubst, & Bensing, 1999), medication adherence (Stevenson, Cox, Britten, & Dundar, 2004) and treatment compliance and medical outcomes (M. A. Stewart, 1995; M. Stewart, Meredith, Brown, & Galajda, 2000). Improved communication also decreases the risk of malpractice (Cole, 1997), HCP burnout, and HCP work-related stress (Graham, Potts, & Ramirez, 2002). Effective communication is even more important in the management of headache disorders, a condition where diagnosis is almost entirely based on patient-reported symptoms and resulting impairment, and where treatment success is largely dependent on a patient's level of treatment adherence with medication and behavioral recommendations (Buse & Lipton, 2008; Hahn, 2008).

Models of effective communication emphasize the importance of both the physical and psychological well-being of the patient, involve and empower the patient in decision making and responsibly for participation, and place attention and value on the relationship and interactions between the HCP and patient. These models incorporate the elements of effective communication to convey a sense of partnership and caring toward the patient. Strategies such as the use of open-ended questions (L. R. Martin, Jahng, Golin, & DiMatteo, 2003), the "Ask-Tell-Ask" technique (Back, Arnold, Baile, Tulsky, & Fryer-Edwards, 2005), active listening (Boyle & Dwinnell, 2005), and being fully present with the patient can significantly improve the quality of the relationship, with positive outcomes for both patient and HCP.

Points of Collaboration With Physicians and Family

As previously mentioned, responsible care by the nonmedical HCP begins by taking steps to ensure the headache patient has received a proper medical evaluation before initiating treatment. We recommend that HCPs maintain an ongoing relationship with a medical headache specialist, for several reasons. Even though medical factors have been ruled out prior to beginning treatment, they may surface as significant during the course of treatment. A list of "red flags" for the presence of serious underlying disorders as a cause of acute or subacute headache can be remembered by using the mnemonic SNOOP (Dodick, 2003): **S**ystemic symptoms or illness (including fever, persistent or progressive vomiting, stiff neck, pregnancy, cancer, immunocompromised state, anticoagulated); **N**eurologic signs or symptoms (including altered mental status, focal neurologic symptoms or signs, seizures, or papilledema); **O**nset is new (especially in those age 40 years or older) or sudden; **O**ther associated conditions (e.g., headache is subsequent to head trauma, awakens patient from sleep, or is worsened by Valsalva maneuvers); and **P**rior headache history that is different (e.g., headaches now are of a different pattern or are rapidly progressive in severity or frequency). When these red flags are present, neuroimaging such as computed tomography (CT) or MRI is indicated to investigate and make an appropriate diagnosis and treatment plan.

Patients whose headaches are exacerbated by medication overuse need to be withdrawn from the offending agents and to be placed on more appropriate medications. Physicians need to take the lead in these endeavors. When headaches are infrequent, less intense, and minimally disruptive, involvement by family members is rarely needed or encouraged. However, as headaches evolve to more chronic and debilitating forms, they often impact the family unit. Education can be helpful, as can instruction in ways to encourage and support the affected family member to cope and actively address the pain, and to minimize attention/reinforcement for pain complaints and absent coping skills.

Development and Implementation of Empirically Based Treatment Plan

Treatment of Headache

Both pharmacotherapy and nonpharmacological therapies play important roles in the management of migraine. Treatment should be individualized for each patient, taking into account such variables as frequency and severity of migraine episodes, identified triggers, comorbidities, the patient's lifestyle, and patient preferences (Dowson, Lipscombe, Sender, & Rees, 2002). The goals of pharmacological therapies are to avoid attacks when possible, treat attacks rapidly and consistently, avoid recurrence of pain, and restore the patient's ability to function and HRQoL (Silberstein, 2000). Pharmacological therapies can be divided into acute and preventive regimes. The majority of migraine sufferers use acute treatments (that include over-the-counter [OTC], prescription, or a combination of both). Acute therapies are taken at the onset of or during pain, and include certain nonspecific agents (e.g., aspirin, acetaminophen, NSAIDs) and migraine-specific agents (e.g., ergotamine, dihydroergotamine, and the triptans) (Bigal & Lipton, 2003). Triptans are a family of tryptamine-based medications. Their action is attributed to their binding to serotonin 5-HT1B and 5-HT1D receptors in cranial blood vessels (causing their constriction), and subsequent inhibition of pro-inflammatory neuropeptide release. Patients should be educated on the proper use of acute medications and that overuse can increase the frequency and severity of headaches (i.e., the patient can develop rebound headache or medication overuse headache) and reduce treatment efficacy (Andrasik, Buse, & Grazzi, 2009; Lake, 2006). Patients should also be educated that their acute medications should be taken at the first sign of pain for maximum effectiveness.

Preventative therapies are taken on a daily or other specified regimen. Approximately 40% of migraine sufferers meet criteria for preventive pharmacological treatment (Lipton et al., 2007). Preventive therapy is intended to reduce the frequency of attacks or eliminate them altogether, to reduce the cumulative impact of repeated attacks on the patient's HRQoL and level of disability, to improve the efficacy of acute therapy, and to prevent the transformation of EM to CM. FDA-approved preventive therapies for migraine in adults include the beta-blockers propranolol and timolol, and the neuromodulators divalproex sodium and topiramate (Ramadan, Silberstein, Freitag, Gilbert, & Frishberg, 2000). Other agents found to be useful in some patients as migraine preventives include antidepressants and calcium channel blockers, and natural products such as vitamin B2, botulinum toxin, petasites, and coenzyme Q-10 (Ramadan, 2006). More detailed information on pharmacotherapy for migraine has been extensively reviewed elsewhere (Bigal & Lipton, 2003; Bigal & Lipton, 2006b; Silberstein, 2000).

Although there are a range of relatively safe and effective pharmacological treatments for migraine, nonpharmacologic treatments also play a key role in comprehensive and effective headache management. Empirically validated nonpharmacological interventions have an important role in both the acute and preventive phases of the comprehensive headache management plan, and may be offered individually or in conjunction with pharmacotherapy (Goslin et al., 1999). A combination of pharmacological and nonpharmacological approaches has been demonstrated to be more effective than either approach on its own (Holroyd et al., 1995, 2001) to help maintain positive outcomes (Grazzi et al., 2002) and to improve treatment compliance (Andrasik, Blanchard, Neff, & Rodichok, 1984; Rains, Lipchik, et al., 2006; Rains, Penzien, et al., 2006). Behavioral interventions offer the benefit of being cost-effective without the potential for drug interactions or side effects. They are useful for patients who need or want to avoid medication use, such as women who are pregnant (Scharff, Marcus, & Turk, 1996) or trying to become pregnant, and they may augment the effectiveness of other treatments or minimize the need for their use (Penzien, Rains, & Andrasik, 2002). As a result, they have become standard components of specialty headache centers and multidisciplinary pain management programs, and are endorsed by the U.S. Headache Consortium, which is made up of several professional agencies, including the American Headache Society, the American Academy of Neurology, and the National Headache Foundation (Campbell, Penzien, & Wall, 2000). Nonpharmacological treatments for headache can be divided into the categories of behavioral treatments (cognitive-behavioral therapy [CBT] and biobehavioral training [i.e., biofeedback, relaxation training, and stress management]), physical therapies and education, and lifestyle modification. There is a large and constantly growing body of published evidence examining the use of behavioral therapies for headache and migraine, including meta-analytic studies and evidence-based reviews (Andrasik, 2007; Nestoriuc & Martin, 2007; Nestoriuc, Martin, Rief, & Andrasik, 2008). Meta-analyses comparing behavioral and pharmacological treatments have shown similar efficacy between the two approaches, and benefits from behavioral interventions are generally maintained over time (Holroyd et al., 1988; Mathew, 1981; Penzien, Johnson, Carpenter, & Holroyd, 1990).

The U.S. Headache Consortium recently published reliable, clinically pertinent and scientifically sound guidelines to inform the treatment of chronic headache in primary care settings (Campbell, Penzien, & Wall, 2000), and suggestions about how to improve diagnosis and treatment of migraine patients based on a review of the current literature (Goslin et al., 1999). Their guidelines divided treatments into those with Grade A or Grade B evidence. "Grade A" evidence includes treatments based on multiple soundly designed randomized clinical trials, considered of exact significance to the recommendation, which demonstrated a consistent pattern of results. Grade A treatments included relaxation training, thermal biofeedback combined with relaxation training, electromyographic biofeedback, and CBT (for prevention of migraine). "Grade B" refers to treatments for which there is some evidence from randomized clinical trials providing support, although not considered optimal, for the recommendation. These treatments included behavioral therapy combined with preventive drug therapy as a means to enhance clinical benefit for migraine.

Education

Headache is a unique medical condition in that the patient makes the majority of therapeutic decisions on his or her own. The patient decides which attacks to treat, when to treat them, with what to treat them, the desired level of compliance, whether to make healthy lifestyle changes, and many other decisions that are central to effective management. Therefore, patient education is essential to effective headache management. Patients must be taught the importance of their behaviors and lifestyle choices in their headache management, which helps to build self-efficacy, enhance an internal locus of control, and solidify the provider-patient collaborative relationship. Trials of educational interventions have demonstrated significant reductions in pain frequency, intensity, and duration, improvements in functional status and quality of life, reduced depression, and decreased service use (in terms of patient visits to both primary care providers [PCPs] and the emergency department) (Blumenfeld & Tischio, 2003; Harpole et al., 2003; Lemstra, Stewart, & Olszynski, 2002; Rothrock et al., 2006). One trial of a brief patient education intervention about abortive headache medication demonstrated improved adherence and efficacy (Holroyd et al., 1989).

Important components of education for headache management include the pathophysiology of migraine, the basic mechanism and purpose of medications, proper use of medication, potential drug interactions, the role of stress and sympathetic arousal in headache, common psychological comorbidities and consequences of headache, prodromal features, triggers, and the importance of maintaining a regular and healthy lifestyle. A patient should be informed of the expected course of a chronic disease with episodic manifestations, and also be reassured that the pain of primary headaches is relatively benign (once other causes of the pain have been ruled out). Patients should be taught the proper use of medications, including the importance of timing (e.g., take at the first onset of pain), potential for interactions, and danger of overuse of medication including both prescription and OTC. Studies with other medical disorders have shown that patients who understood the therapeutic mechanism of their prescription and its role in the treatment plan are twice as likely to fill the prescription (Cameron, 1996). Headache patients should be educated about the potential for medication overuse headache and the optimal timing and maximum use of abortive and analgesic medications. Patients should be warned of potential adverse effects of medications and informed in advance which symptoms typically resolve spontaneously. Because many patients also use OTC and herbal treatments, their potential effects and interactions should be discussed.

Some patients have the benefit of fairly predictable migraine attacks. For these patients, the prodrome provides a window of opportunity in which to use behavioral tools as a way to stop the process of migraine early, even before headache. Patients should be made aware of potential prodromal symptoms and triggers and asked to maintain a headache diary to identify their personal prodromal symptoms and triggers. Some triggers cannot be changed or avoided, such as the menstrual cycle, in which case patients should be aware of their vulnerability to headache during this time and protect themselves by taking extra care to maintain a healthy lifestyle. By doing so, they may reduce the number of headache attacks, although it is unlikely that the headaches will disappear altogether. Other triggers may be able to be eliminated or modified by patients. Common headache triggers and healthy lifestyle habits that patients should be educated about include diet and nutrition, sleep, exercise, stress management, and environmental factors.

Relaxation Training

Relaxation techniques help patients minimize physiological responses to stress and decrease sympathetic arousal. The U.S. Headache Consortium gave "Grade A" status to relaxation training for prevention of migraine (Campbell, Penzien, & Wall, 2000). Relaxation training may include a variety of techniques (Bernstein, Borkovec, & Hazlett-Stevens, 2000; Penzien & Holroyd, 1994). The classic procedure, progressive muscle relaxation training (PMRT), which was first reviewed in publication in 1938, involves tensing and relaxing various muscle groups while paying attention to the resulting contrasting sensations (Jacobson, 1938). Other relaxation techniques include visual or guided imagery, cue-controlled relaxation, diaphragmatic breathing, hypnosis, and self-hypnosis (Rime & Andrasik, 2007). However, patients may use any techniques or tools that quiet the mind and calm the body, including meditation, prayer, yoga, listening to pleasant music, listening to guided relaxation CDs or tapes, and any other method that a patient finds effective. Relaxation training is usually taught by clinical professionals, such as psychologists or other mental health professionals, but it can also be self-taught by patients with print or audio support materials. Although techniques can be learned during sessions in the office, they require regular practice in order to become effective, automatic responses, especially during stressful situations.

CBT for Headache

The U.S. Headache Consortium found "Grade A" evidence for CBT for preventive treatment of migraine (Campbell et al., 2000). CBT is an empirically validated, psychotherapeutic treatment comprised of cognitive and behavioral theories and strategies. Cognitive-behavioral interventions may be employed in headache management in several ways. With CBT, the patient may be able to directly manage and relieve symptoms, avoid headache-eliciting episodes or occurrences, and improve overall coping. CBT strategies may also help the headache sufferer manage comorbid symptoms, such as depression and anxiety, which have been demonstrated to increase the negative effects of migraine on a sufferer's life, including HRQoL and headache-related disability. Further, they may help target and eliminate potential risk factors for progression of the disease from EM to CM or daily headache (i.e., transformed migraine). Researchers have identified several risk factors for transformation that can be modified, including frequency of migraine attacks, obesity, acute medication overuse, caffeine overuse, stressful life events, depression, and sleep disorders (Bigal & Lipton, 2006a). These risk factors provide targets for CBT interventions. Several conditions, including obesity, depression, anxiety, and stressful life events have been established as common comorbidities of migraine with bidirectional influences (Bigal & Lipton, 2006a). Therefore, treating any of the conditions listed above may also have a benefit on migraine and vice-versa.

Cognitive strategies focus on identifying and challenging maladaptive or dysfunctional thoughts, beliefs, and responses to stress (Beck, Rush, Shaw, & Emery, 1979). Cognitive foci of CBT for headache management include enhancing self-efficacy (Bandura, 1977) (the patient's belief in his or her ability to succeed or accomplish a certain task), encouraging patients to adopt an internal locus of control (i.e., a belief that the mechanism for change lies within oneself, as opposed to an external locus of control or the belief that only the physician, medication, or medical procedures have the power for change) (Heath, Saliba, Mahmassani, Major, & Khoury, 2008), and eliminating catastrophizing (a hopeless and overwhelming way of thinking). Research has demonstrated that low self-efficacy, external locus of control, and catastrophizing predict poor outcomes to treatment and reduced quality of life in headache sufferers (Holroyd, Drew, Cottrell, Romanek, & Heh, 2007). Holroyd et al. (2007) examined catastrophizing, comorbid anxiety, depression, and headache characteristics among 232 migraine sufferers, and found that catastrophizing and severity of associated symptoms (photophobia, phonophobia, nausea) independently predicted quality of life, demonstrating that it is not just headache severity and frequency that predict quality of life, but that patient perception is directly related to quality of life. Other targets of cognitive interventions include assertiveness training, increasing coping skills, and cognitive reappraisal and restructuring (Holroyd & Andrasik, 1982; McCarran & Andrasik, 1987).

Behavioral strategies in headache management include helping patients identify behaviors that may increase or maintain headaches (including identification and avoidance of triggers, adoption of healthy lifestyle habits such as regular exercise, healthy eating habits, sleep hygiene, smoking cessation, and keeping headache diaries) (Nicholson, Nash, & Andrasik, 2005). Behavioral interventions for headache include education, the use of headache diaries, identification and avoidance of triggers, and lifestyle modification. To avoid and manage headache exacerbations, migraineurs should maintain a regular and healthy lifestyle, especially during times when they are most vulnerable to an attack (e.g., premenstrually for women with premenstrually related migraine or headache). This includes practicing proper sleep hygiene and maintaining a regular sleep-wake schedule, a regular and healthy diet, regular exercise, avoidance of excessive caffeine or alcohol consumption, smoking cessation, and regular practice of stress management, relaxation techniques, and self-care.

Biofeedback

Biofeedback involves monitoring physiological processes of which the patient may not be consciously aware and/or does not believe that he or she has voluntary control. Through various equipment and methods, biological or physiological information is converted into a signal that is then "fed back" to the patient. Through biofeedback training, the patient experiences increased awareness of physiological functions and learns to control his or her physiologic state (Penzien & Holroyd, 1994; M. S. Schwartz & Andrasik, 2005; Sovak, Kunzel, Sternbach, & Dalessio, 1981). While monitoring physiological responses, patients are taught relaxation skills, such as diagrammatic breathing or visualization, to induce the "relaxation response," which is comprised of calming of the sympathetic nervous system and activation of the parasympathetic nervous system (Andrasik & Flor, 2008; Benson, 1975).

Nestoriuc et al. recently conducted a comprehensive efficacy review of biofeedback for headache management in adults (Nestoriuc, Martin, Rief, & Andrasik, 2008). They examined data from 2 recently published meta-analyses, which included 150 outcome studies (Nestoriuc & Martin, 2007; Nestoriuc, Rief, & Martin, 2008). Ninety-four studies met inclusion criteria and were analyzed for effect sizes for the treatment of migraine and TTH. They reported medium to large mean effect sizes for biofeedback for the treatment of both types of headache, and found that treatment effects were maintained over an average follow-up period of 14 months, both in completer and intention-to-treat analyses. In addition to the reduction of frequency, significant effects were also found for perceived self-efficacy, symptoms of depression and anxiety, and medication use.

Many modalities may be monitored through biofeedback, including peripheral skin temperature (TEMP-FB) biofeedback, blood-volume-pulse (BVP-FB), electromyographic (EMG-FB), electroencephalographic (EEG-FB), and galvanic skin response (GSR-FB) feedback. The strongest evidence for migraine management is for thermal, EMG, and BVP biofeedback and relaxation training (Blanchard & Andrasik, 1987; Campbell et al. 2000). Thermal biofeedback, also known as "hand-warming biofeedback" or "autogenic feedback" (when combined with components of autogenic therapy), involves monitoring finger temperature (a measure of circulation) with a sensitive thermometer. Patients are taught that higher finger temperature corresponds to a more relaxed state, and their goal is to raise their finger temperature. During or preceding a headache, the body may enter the "fight or flight" state (activation of the sympathetic nervous system). As sympathetic activity increases, circulation to the extremities decreases and finger temperature decreases. Conversely, as parasympathetic activity increases and the relaxation response is activated, circulation and extremity temperature increases. The strongest evidence for biofeedback for TTH involves using EMG-FB with the goal of teaching patients to reduce pericranial muscle activity (Goslin et al., 1999; Holroyd & Penzien, 1990; McCrory, Penzien, Hasselblad, & Gray, 2001; Nestoriuc, Rief, & Martin, 2008). The Evidence-based Guidelines for Migraine

Headache: Behavioral and Physical Treatments (Campbell et al. 2000) reported that relaxation training and thermal biofeedback can produce significant improvements in headache activity (Blanchard, Andrasik, Ahles, Teders, & O'Keefe, 1980).

Biofeedback training generally requires several office visits, spaced one to several weeks apart. Providers are often psychologists who also incorporate CBT and relaxation training into sessions, but biofeedback may be successfully taught by a range of properly trained medical and mental health professionals. Patients are taught techniques in the office; however, home practice is also required between sessions. As the patient's ability to manipulate and control the targeted physiologic processes increases, the biofeedback device is gradually eliminated.

One of the biggest challenges for HCPs and patients can often be locating a biofeedback practitioner. The Association for Applied Psychophysiology and Biofeedback (AAPB) (www.aapb.org) and the Biofeedback Certification Institute of America (BCIA) list providers on their Web sites (www.bcia.org/directory/membership.cfm). Self-training and home-training biofeedback kits and manuals are also available, but many of these have not been subjected to rigorous analysis.

The Case of Donna, Revisited

Donna was experiencing CM with daily headache pain. She also had high levels of depression, anxiety, and panic attacks, and reported feeling overwhelmed, helpless, and hopeless about her headaches. She presented to a multidisciplinary headache center, where she underwent a comprehensive history and physical examination with a neurologist, and an evaluation with a psychologist. The general medical and neurologic exams were unremarkable. She completed several questionnaires. Results of the Patient Health Questionnaire (PHQ) (Spitzer et al., 1999) confirmed results of the clinical interview that the patient suffered from major depressive disorder (MDD), generalized anxiety disorder (GAD), and panic disorder. It was decided that Donna would be treated with a comprehensive pharmacological and nonpharmacological plan, which would be coordinated and managed by the neurologist and psychologist.

Donna's biobehavioral program included patient education, relaxation training, biofeedback, CBT, and stress management. Donna was taught to be aware of and avoid headache triggers, and how to apply effective stress management and assertion skills. She was also taught the importance of maintaining a healthy lifestyle (e.g., a regular sleep-wake cycle, proper diet and not skipping meals, regular exercise, pleasant activity planning, and use of her social support network). She was asked to maintain a headache, medication, activity, and mood diary to monitor progress. Biofeedback training and relaxation therapies, including diaphragmatic breathing training and exercises, progressive muscle relaxation, and guided imagery relaxation were initiated. She also signed up for a yoga class and began practicing yoga and meditation on a daily basis.

As the relationship grew with the psychologist, she revealed a number of personal factors having a bearing on her headaches. She revealed that she was from a Caribbean country where all of her family still resided. As a result, she often felt lonely and isolated in the large U.S. city where she lived. She also reported that her job working for the government was very stressful, and that customers often "yelled at" and complained to her. Her work space consisted of a small cubicle with a window for customers, one stool, and bright florescent lighting overhead. Although she was allowed breaks, she rarely took them, as she always felt that she had too much work to complete. In addition, she felt that there was no one at work with whom she would like to spend her break time. In fact, coworkers had asked her to join them before on breaks; however, she had declined in the past because she felt shy. Donna was given the homework assignment to build relationships with two coworkers with whom she was friendly, and to make any changes in her work environment that might lessen the likelihood of headache attacks. With the support of her supervisor and coworkers, she created a plan for work that included regular stretching and relaxation breaks, a change in the light source in her cubicle, and taking a walk with one of her coworkers during lunch.

Donna was motivated to learn and compliant with suggestions and homework practice. She practiced daily meditation and yoga and expanded her social support network by establishing relationships with colleagues at work and through her church. Over several months, a significant reduction in the severity of her headaches was observed. She reported substantial mood improvements, including a reduction in feelings of depression and anxiety and the elimination of panic attacks. She continued to have frequent headaches including migraine; however, they did not cause significant impairment at work, and she reported that she felt much more in control of her life and optimistic about the future. This raises an important point. Patients with long-standing headaches rarely become headache-free. Rather, a more realistic goal is to reduce headaches to the point where they are manageable and minimally disruptive.

Evaluation of Treatment Outcomes

One simple and very useful way to gather data and monitor treatment is to have patients keep a "headache diary." Diaries may include data such as headache frequency, severity, duration, medications taken, behavioral strategies practiced, diet, exercise, hormonal factors and menstrual cycle, and other potential triggers.

Several instruments are available for assessing and monitoring patients with headache. The Migraine Disability Assessment (MIDAS) questionnaire is a self-administered questionnaire consisting of five items that assess days of missed activity or substantially reduced activity due to headache in three domains: school work/paid employment, household work or chores, and nonwork (family, social, and leisure) activities. Two additional questions pertain to pain frequency and intensity (W. F. Stewart et al., 1999). The Headache Impact Test (HIT-6) is also a brief instrument that measures lost time in three domains and other areas of impact (e.g., pain severity, fatigue, and mood) (Pryse-Phillips, 2002). The Migraine Interictal Burden Scale (MIBS-4) is a self-administered questionnaire that measures migraine-related interictal burden (i.e., between headache attacks) in four domains: impairment in work or school, impairment in family and social life, difficulty making plans or commitments, and emotional/affective and cognitive distress (Buse et al., 2007).

The most widely used generic measures of HRQoL are the 36-and 12-item short-form health surveys (SF-36 and SF-12). The SF-36 assesses a range of symptoms associated with common diseases (Ware & Sherbourne, 1992). Migraineurs have significantly lower SF-36 scores than nonmigraineurs, and migraine adversely affects functioning at least as much as depression, diabetes, and recent myocardial infarction (Osterhaus, Townsend, Gandek, & Ware, 1994). Also, migraineurs have significantly lower HRQoL than those in the general population without any chronic condition (Bussone et al., 2004). One of the instruments specifically designed to assess the impact of migraine on HRQoL, the Migraine-Specific Quality of Life Questionnaire (MSQ) (version 2.1), consists of 14 items that measure the degree to which migraine affects the patient's daily activities (social life, work) and emotions over a 4-week period (B. C. Martin et al., 2000).

Brief screening instruments can be used to assess and monitor psychological functioning and comorbid conditions. The Patient Health Questionnaire is a brief, self-administered questionnaire that provides screening for several of the primary Axis I psychological disorders, based directly on *DSM-IV* criteria (Spitzer et al., 1999). The PHQ-2 is a two-item screening instrument that has been empirically shown to detect the presence of depression (Kroenke, Spitzer & Williams, 2003). The PHQ-9 can be used to conduct a more detailed, yet still time-efficient, evaluation for depression (Kroenke, Spitzer, & Williams, 2001). Clinically significant anxiety can be evaluated using the Generalized Anxiety Disorder-7 (GAD-7), a seven-item, self-administered questionnaire (Spitzer, Kroenke, Williams, & Lowe, 2006).

Considerations With Special Populations/Diversity Issues

Headache prevalence varies by race, gender, and socioeconomic status (SES), with individuals who are Caucasian, female, and of low SES sharing a greater proportion of the burden (Bigal & Lipton, 2009). Beyond this basic epidemiologic information, little is known about if and how these differences impact treatment. A recent comparison of Caucasians and African Americans found both groups to have similar responses to treatment that was provided at a headache specialty clinic, with results enduring through 6 months of follow-up (Heckman et al., 2009). These results held when SES and psychiatric comorbidity were controlled. One difference was notable, however, in that headache sufferers who were African American had headaches that were more frequent and disabling, and that led to lower quality of life after treatment was completed. What is needed to enhance overall outcomes for African American headache sufferers could not be determined from this investigation.

Headache occurs across the lifespan, but little attention has been directed to individuals at either end of the age spectrum. Some data suggest that older adults respond less favorably to biobehavioral treatments than their younger counterparts. However, when slight modifications were made to treatment procedures (taking greater care to ensure understanding, allowing geriatric patients to proceed at their own pace, repeating information as needed, compensating for decreased vision and hearing, etc.), outcomes rivaled those obtained with younger adults (Arena, Hannah, Bruno, & Meador, 1991; Kabela, Blanchard, Appelbaum, & Nicholson, 1989).

At the younger end of the age spectrum, children and adolescents tend to have more favorable outcomes from behavioral treatments. A meta-analytic comparison of pediatric and adult headache patients documented significantly better outcomes for children (Sarafino & Goehring, 2000). As was true for older adults, outcomes were enhanced when age adjustments were made (i.e., realizing that "child" headache sufferers are not merely "tiny adults" with headache and taking into account important developmental differences). Andrasik, Powers, and McGrath (2005), Andrasik and Schwartz (2006), and Powers, Gilman, and Hershey (2006) provide helpful suggestions for tailoring treatments for children and adolescents.

Clinical Pearls of Wisdom for Practitioners

1. Headache is a unique medical condition, in that the patient makes the majority of therapeutic decisions on his or her own. Patient education is essential to effective headache management. Rains, Penzien, et al. (2006) provide the following recommendations for effective education: (a) Limit instructions to three or four major points during each discussion; (b) use simple, common language and avoid complex medical terms, especially when explaining diagnoses and treatment instructions (model or demonstrate, when possible); (c) supplement oral instructions with written materials; (d) involve the patient's family members or significant others; (d) ask patients to restate recommendations; and (e) repeat and reinforce the concepts that were discussed.
2. Relaxation techniques should be practiced on a regular basis in order to maintain homeostasis and manage stress, so that the patient does not trigger a headache attack in the first place. Headache sufferers should be aware of times and states in which they may be most vulnerable to an attack (e.g., premenstrually, during final exams, etc.). During this time period, they need to be especially aware of potential triggers, avoid stress, engage in relaxing and nurturing activities, and maintain a very regular and healthy lifestyle. It is important for patients to use a diary to note such associations.
3. Depression, anxiety, and other psychological conditions have elevated rates of comorbidity with migraine. Patients should be routinely assessed and appropriately treated or referred for psychological comorbidities. Successful treatment of the headache disorder may improve the psychological condition and vice-versa.
4. Multidisciplinary treatment approaches are often the most effective for the management of headache, as the case of Donna illustrates (Harpole et al., 2003; Lemstra, Stewart, & Olszynski, 2002). Multidisciplinary headache and pain programs typically employ a range of pain specialists that may include physicians, nurses, psychiatrists, psychologists, physical therapists, occupational therapists, and social workers, among other providers. When a multidisciplinary program is not available, patients can be managed

through coordinated care between appropriate providers. For more information about finding specialists and making referrals, see Buse and Andrasik (2009).

Summary

Headache is a multifaceted disorder that can affect all aspect of sufferers' lives. Both pharmacotherapy and nonpharmacological therapies play key roles in the management of headache. Treatment plans must be individualized for each patient, taking into account such variables as frequency and severity of headache, comorbid conditions, family, social and occupational factors, and patient preferences.

Nonpharmacological treatments consist of a host of cognitive and behavioral approaches (CBT, biofeedback, relaxation training, and stress management), physical therapies, psychoeducation, and lifestyle modification. The cognitive-behavioral treatments have extensive support, derived from several evidence-based reviews (such as the U.S. Headache Consortium mentioned earlier and others) and meta-analyses. Further, the benefits from behavioral treatments have been shown to endure over extensive follow-up periods, with or without repeated contact. Finally, meta-analyses comparing behavioral and pharmacological treatments have shown similar efficacy between the two approaches.

Empirically validated nonpharmacological approaches to headache management include education, CBT, biofeedback, and relaxation training. Patients can be taught to modify thoughts, feelings, and behavior through cognitive-behavioral interventions. CBT interventions aid in headache management by making patients aware of triggers, including the relationship between stress and headache, and by identifying and challenging counterproductive or self-defeating beliefs and ideas. Patients should be encouraged to consider treatment a collaborative process. Patients can also learn to manage the physiological effects of stress with biofeedback and relaxation training. For the most effective outcomes, patients must consider their headache care a collaborative process. HCPs can facilitate this through education, enhancing a patient's self-efficacy, and encouraging a patient to adopt an internal locus of control.

Pharmacological therapies fall into two categories: acute, taken at the onset of or during an attack (e.g., aspirin, acetaminophen, NSAIDs); and migraine-specific agents, such as ergotamine, dihydroergotamine, and the triptans, and preventive regimes, taken on a regular basis. Nearly half of migraine sufferers meet criteria for preventive pharmacological treatment. The goals of preventive agents are to reduce or eliminate the frequency of attacks, reduce the cumulative impact of recurrent attacks, to enhance the efficacy of acute therapy, and to prevent the transformation of EM to CM. As mentioned earlier, preventive therapies approved by the FDA for migraine in adults include the beta-blockers propranolol and timolol, and the neuromodulators divalproex sodium and topiramate. Other agents found of value include antidepressants and calcium channel blockers, and natural products such as vitamin B2, botulinum toxin, petasites, and coenzyme Q-10.

References

American Psychiatric Association. (2000). *Diagnostic and statistical manual of mental disorders* (4th ed., text rev.). Washington, DC: American Psychiatric Press.

Andrasik, F. (2007). What does the evidence show? Efficacy of behavioural treatments for recurrent headaches in adults. *Neurological Sciences, 28*, S70–S77.

Andrasik, F., Blanchard, E. B., Neff, D. F., & Rodichok, L. D. (1984). Biofeedback and relation training for chronic headache: A controlled comparison of booster treatments and regular contacts for long-term maintenance. *Journal of Consulting and Clinical Psychology, 52*, 609–615.

Andrasik, F., Buse, D. C., & Grazzi, L. (2009). Behavioral medicine for migraine and medication overuse headache. *Current Pain and Headache Reports, 13*, 241–248.

Andrasik, F., & Flor, H. (2008). Biofeedback. In H. Breivik, W. I. Campbell, & M. K. Nicholas (Eds.), *Clinical pain management: Practice and procedures* (2nd ed., pp. 153–166). London: Hodder & Stoughton.

Andrasik, F., Flor, H., & Turk, D. C. (2005). An expanded view of psychological aspects in head pain: The biopsychosocial model. *Neurological Sciences, 26*, S87–S91.

Andrasik, F., Lipchik, G. L., McCrory, D. C., & Wittrock, D. A. (2005). Outcome measurement in behavioral headache research: Headache parameters and psychosocial outcomes. *Headache, 45*, 429–437.

Andrasik, F., Powers, S. W., & McGrath, P. J. (2005). Methodological considerations in research with special populations: Children and adolescents. *Headache, 45*, 520–525.

Andrasik, F., & Schwartz, M. S. (2006). Behavioral assessment and treatment of pediatric headache. *Behavior Modification, 30*, 93–113.

Arena, J. G., Hannah, S. L., Bruno, G. M., & Meador, K. J. (1991). Electromyographic biofeedback training for tension headache in the elderly: A prospective study. *Biofeedback and Self-Regulation, 16*, 379–390.

Back, A. L., Arnold, R. M., Baile, W. F., Tulsky, J. A., & Fryer-Edwards. K. (2005). Approaching difficult communication tasks in oncology. *CA: A Cancer Journal for Clinicians, 55*(3), 164–177.

Bandura, A. (1977). Self-efficacy: Toward a unifying theory of behavioral change. *Psychological Review, 84*, 191–215.

Bandura, A. (1986). *Social foundations of thought and action: A social cognitive theory*. Englewood Cliffs, NJ: Prentice Hall.

Beck, A. T., Rush, A. J., Shaw, B. F., & Emery, G. (1979). *Cognitive therapy of depression*. New York: Guilford.

Benson, H. (1975). *The relaxation response*. New York: William Morrow.

Bernstein, D. A., Borkovec, T. D., & Hazlett-Stevens, H. (2000). *New directions in progressive relaxation training: A guidebook for helping professions*. Westport, CT: Praeger.

Bigal, M. E., & Lipton, R. B. (2003). Acute treatment of migraine headache. *Current Treatment Options in Neurology, 5*, 423–430.

Bigal, M. E., & Lipton, R. B. (2006a). Modifiable risk factors for migraine progression. *Headache, 46*, 1334–1343.

Bigal, M. E., & Lipton, R. B. (2006b). The preventive treatment of migraine. *Neurologist, 12*, 204–213.

Bigal, M. E., & Lipton, R. B. (2009). The epidemiology, burden, and comorbidities of migraine. *Neurologic Clinics, 27*, 321–334.

Bigal, M. E., Serrano, D., Reed, M., & Lipton, R. B. (2008). Chronic migraine in the population: Burden, diagnosis, and satisfaction with treatment. *Neurology, 71*, 559–566.

Blanchard, E. B., & Andrasik, F. (1987). Biofeedback treatment of vascular headache. In J. P. Hatch, J. G. Fisher, & J. D. Rugh (Eds.), *Biofeedback: Studies in clinical efficacy* (pp. 1–79). New York: Plenum.

Blanchard, E. B., Andrasik, F., Ahles, T. A., Teders, S. J., & O'Keefe, D. (1980). Migraine and tension headache: A meta-analytic review. *Behavioral Therapy, 14*, 613–631.

Blumenfeld, A., & Tischio, M. (2003). Center of excellence for headache care: Group model at Kaiser Permanente. *Headache, 43*, 431–440.

Boyle, D., & Dwinnell, B. (2005). Invite, listen and summarize: A patient-centered communication technique. *Academic Medicine*, 80(1), 29–32.

Breslau, N., & Davis, G. C. (1993). Migraine, physical health and psychiatric disorder: A prospective epidemiologic study in young adults. *Journal of Psychiatric Research, 27*, 211–221.

Buse, D. C., & Andrasik, F. A. (2009). Behavioral medicine for migraine. *Clinical Neurology*, 27(2), 321–582.

Buse, D. C., Bigal, M. E., Rupnow, M. F. T., Reed, M., Serrano, D., Biondi, D., et al. (2007). The migraine interictal burden scale (MIBS): Results of a population-based validation study. *Headache, 47*, 778.

Buse, D. C., Bigal, M. B., Rupnow, M., Reed, M., Serrano, D., & Lipton, R. B. (2007). Development and validation of the migraine interictal burden scale (MIBS): A self-administered instrument for measuring the burden of migraine between attacks. *Neurology, 68*(Suppl. 1), A89.

Buse, D. C., & Lipton, R. B. (2008). Facilitating communication with patients for improved migraine outcomes. *Current Pain and Headache Reports, 12*, 230–236.

Buse, D. C, Manack, A., Serrano, D., Grosberg, B., Bigal, M. E, Biondi, D., et al., (2008, June). Summary of disability, treatment, and healthcare utilization differences between chronic migraine and episodic migraine populations. *Headache, 48*(Suppl. 1), S18. Presented at the 50th Annual Scientific Meeting of the American Headache Society.

Bussone, G., Usai, S., Grazzi, L., Rigamonti, A., Solari, A., & D'Amico, D. (2004). Disability and quality of life in different primary headaches: Results from Italian studies. *Neurology Science, 25*(Suppl. 3), S105–S107.

Cameron, C. (1996). Patient compliance: Recognition of factors involved and suggestions for promoting compliance with therapeutic regimens. *Journal of Advanced Nursing, 24*, 244–250.

Campbell, J. K., Penzien, D. B., & Wall, E. M. (2000). Evidence-based guidelines for migraine headaches: Behavioral and physical treatments. *Neurology, 54*, 1553.

Claxton, A. J., Cramer, J., & Pierce, C. (2001). A systematic review of the associations between dose regimens and medication compliance. *Clinical Therapy, 23*, 1296–1310.

Cole, S. A. (1997). Reducing malpractice risk through more effective communication. *American Journal of Managed Care, 3*, 649–653.

Dodick, D. W. (2003). Clinical clues and clinical rules: Primary versus secondary headache. *Advanced Studies in Medicine, 3*, S550–S555.

Dowson, A., Lipscombe, S., Sender, J., & Rees, T. (2002). New guidelines for the management of migraine in primary care. *Current Medical Research and Opinion, 18*, 414–439.

Dunbar-Jacob, J., Erlen, J. A., Schlenk, E. A., Ryan, C. M., Sereika, S. M., & Doswell, W. M. (2000). Adherence in chronic disease. *Annual Review of Nursing Research, 18*, 48–90.

Dunbar-Jacob, J., & Mortimer-Stephens, M. K. (2001). Treatment adherence in chronic disease. *Journal of Clinical Epidemiology, 54*(Suppl. 1), S57–S60.

Edmeads, J., Findlay, H., Tugwell, P., Pryse-Phillips, W., Nelson, R. F., & Murray, T. J. (1993). Impact of migraine and tension-type headache on life-style, consulting behaviour, and medication use: A Canadian population survey. *Canadian Journal of Neurological Sciences, 20*, 131–137.

Elder, J. P., Ayala, G. X., & Harris, S. (1999). Theories and intervention approaches to health-behavior change in primary care. *American Journal of Preventive Medicine*, 17, 275–284.

Finkel, A. G. (2003). Epidemiology of cluster headache. *Current Pain and Headache Reports, 7*, 144–149.

Frederikson, L. G. (1995). Exploring information-exchange in consultation: The patients' view of performance and outcomes. *Patient Education and Counseling, 25*, 237–246.

Gallagher, R. M., & Kunkel, R. (2003). Migraine medication attributes important for patient compliance: Concerns about side effects may delay treatment. *Headache, 43*, 36–43.

Goslin, R. E., Gray, R. N., McCrory, D. C., Penzien, D., Rains, J., & Hasselblad, V. (1999, February). *Behavioral and physical treatments for migraine headache. Technical review 2.2.* Available from the National Technical Information Service; NTIS Accession No. 127946. Retrieved May 25, 2008, from http://www.ntis.gov/search/product.aspx?ABBR=PB99127946

Graham, J., Potts, H. W., & Ramirez, A. J. (2002). Stress and burnout in doctors. *Lancet, 360*, 1975–1976.

Grazzi, L., Andrasik, F., D'Amico, D., Leone, M., Usai, S., Kass, S. J., et al. (2002). Behavioral and pharmacologic treatment of transformed migraine with analgesic overuse: Outcome at three years. *Headache, 42*, 483–490.

Hahn, S. R. (2008). Communication in the care of the headache patient. In S. D. Silberstein, R. B. Lipton, & D. W. Dodick (Eds.), *Wolff's headache and other head pain* (pp. 805–824). New York: Oxford University Press.

Hall, J. A., Irish, J. T., Roter, D. L., Ehrlich, C. M. & Miller, L. H.. (1994). Satisfaction, gender, and communication in medical visits. *Medical Care, 32*, 1216–1231.

Hall, J. A., Roter, D. L., & Katz, N. R. (1988). Meta-analysis of correlates of provider behavior in medical encounters. *Medical Care, 26*, 657–675.

Harpole, L., Samsa, G., Jurgelski, A., Shipley, J. C., Bernstein, A., & Matchar, D. B.. (2003). Headache management program improves outcome for chronic headache. *Headache, 43*, 715–724.

Headache Classification of the International Headache Society: The international classification of headache disorders, 2nd edition. (2004). *Cephalalgia, 24*(Suppl. 1), 1–160.

Heath, R. L., Saliba, M., Mahmassani, O., Major, S. C., & Khoury, B. A. (2008). Locus of control moderates the relationship between headache pain and depression. *Journal of Headache and Pain, 9*(5), 301–308.

Heckman, B. D., Holroyd, K. A., Tietjen, G., O'Donnell, F. J., Himawan, L., Utley, C., et al. (2009). Whites and African-Americans in headache specialty clinics respond equally well to treatment. *Cephalalgia, 29*, 650–661.

Holmes, W. F., MacGregor, E. A., Sawyer, J. P., & Lipton, R. B. (2001). Information about migraine disability influences physicians' perceptions of illness severity and treatment needs. *Headache, 41*, 343–350.

Holroyd, K. A., & Andrasik, F. (1982). A cognitive-behavioral approach to recurrent tension and migraine headache. In P.C. Kendall (Ed.), *Advances in cognitive-behavioral research and therapy* (vol. 1, pp. 275–320). New York: Academic.

Holroyd, K. A., Cordingley, G. E., Pingel, J. D., Jerome, A., Theofanous, A. G., Jackson, D. K., et al. (1989). Enhancing the effectiveness of abortive therapy: A controlled evaluation of self-management training. *Headache, 29*, 148–153.

Holroyd, K. A., Drew, J. B., Cottrell, C. K., Romanek, K. M., & Heh, V. (2007). Impaired functioning and quality of life in severe migraine: The role of catastrophizing and associated symptoms. *Cephalalgia, 27*, 1156–1165.

Holroyd, K. A., France, J. L., Cordingley, G. E., Rokicki, L. A., Kvaal, S. A., Lipchik, G. L., et al. (1995). Enhancing the effectiveness of relaxation-thermal biofeedback training with propranolol hydrochloride. *Journal of Consulting and Clinical Psychology, 63*, 327–330.

Holroyd, K. A., Holm, J. E., Hursey, K. G., Penzien, D. B., Cordingley, G. E., Theofanous, A. G., et al. (1988). Recurrent vascular headache: Home-based behavioral treatment vs. abortive pharmacological treatment. *Journal of Consulting and Clinical Psychology, 56*, 218–223.

Holroyd, K. A., O'Donnell, F. J., Stensland, M., Lipchik, G. L., Cordingley, G. E., & Carlson, B. W. (2001). Management of chronic tension-type headache with tricyclic antidepressant medication, stress management therapy, and their combination: A randomized controlled trial. *Journal of the American Medical Association, 285*, 2208–2215.

Holroyd, K. A., & Penzien, D. B. (1990). Pharmacological versus non-pharmacological prophylaxis of recurrent migraine headache: A meta-analytic review of clinical trials. *Pain, 42*, 1–13.

Holroyd, K. A., Stensland, M., Lipchik, G. L., Hill, K. R., O'Donnell, F. S., & Cordingley, G. (2000). Psychosocial correlates and impact of chronic tension-type headaches. *Headache, 40*, 3–16.

Hu, X. H., Markson, L. E., Lipton, R. B., Stewart, W. F., & Berger, M. L. (1999). Burden of migraine in the United States: Disability and economic costs. *Archives of Internal Medicine, 159*, 813–818.

Hulsman, R. L., Ros, W. J., Winnubst, J. A., & Bensing, J. M. (1999).Teaching clinically experienced physicians communication skills: A review of evaluation studies. *Medical Education, 33*, 655–668.

Jacobson, E. (1938). *Progressive relaxation*. Chicago: University of Chicago Press.

Jensen, M. P. (2002). Enhancing motivations to change in pain treatment. In D. C. Turk & R. J. Gatchel (Eds.), *Psychological approaches to pain management: A practitioner's handbook* (2nd ed., pp. 71–93). New York: Guilford.

Jette, N., Patten, S., Williams, J., Becker, W., & Wiebe, S. (2008). Comorbidity of migraine and psychiatric disorders: A national population-based study. *Headache, 48*, 501–516.

Kabela, E., Blanchard, E. B., Appelbaum, K. A., & Nicholson, N. (1989). Self-regulatory treatment of headache in the elderly. *Biofeedback and Self-Regulation, 14*, 219–228.

Kroenke, K., Spitzer, R. L., & Williams, J. B. (2001). The PHQ-9: Validity of a brief depression severity measure. *Journal of General Internal Medicine, 16*(9), 606–613.

Kroenke, K., Spitzer, R. L., & Williams, J. B. (2003). The patient health questionnaire-2: Validity of a two-item depression screener. *Medical Care, 41*(11), 1284–1292.

Lake, A. E. (2006). Medication overuse headache: Biobehavioral issues and solutions. *Headache, 46*(Suppl. 3), S88–S97.

Lanteri-Minet, M., Radat, F., Chautard, M. H., & Lucas, C. (2005). Anxiety and depression associated with migraine: Influence on migraine subjects' disability and quality of life, and acute migraine management. *Pain, 118*, 319–326.

Latinovic, R., Gulliford, M., & Ridsdale, L. (2006), Headache and migraine in primary care: Consultation, prescription and referral rates in a large population. *Journal of Neurology, Neurosurgery, & Psychiatry, 77*, 385–387.

Lemstra, M., Stewart, B., & Olszynski, W. (2002). Effectiveness of multidisciplinary intervention in the treatment of migraine: A randomized clinical trial. *Headache, 42*, 845–854.

Lipton, R., Buse, D., Serrano, D., Manack, A., Biondi, D., & Bigal, M. E. (2008). Differences in rates of common comorbid medical and psychiatric conditions in chronic and episodic migraine individuals. *Headache, 48*(Suppl. 1), S4.

Lipton, R. B., Bigal, M. E., Diamond, M., Freitag, F., Reed, M. L., & Stewart, W. F. (2007). American migraine prevalence and prevention (AMPP) advisory group. Migraine prevalence, disease burden, and the need for preventive therapy. *Neurology, 68*, 343–349.

Lipton, R. B., & Stewart, W. F. (1993). Migraine in the United States: A review of epidemiology and health care use. *Neurology, 43*(Suppl. 3), 6–10.

Lipton, R. B., Stewart, W. F., Diamond, S., Diamond, M. L., & Reed, M. (2001). Prevalence and burden of migraine in the United States: Data from the American migraine study II. *Headache, 41*, 646–657.

Martin, B. C., Pathak, D. S., Sharfman, M. I., Adelman, J. U., Taylor, F., Kwong, W. J., et al. (2000). Validity and reliability of the migraine-specific quality of life questionnaire (MSQ version 2.1). *Headache, 40*(3), 204–215.

Martin, L. R., Jahng, K. H., Golin, C. E., & DiMatteo, M. R. (2003). Physician facilitation of patient involvement in care: correspondence between patient and observer reports. *Behavioral Medicine, 28*(4), 159–64.

Mathew, N. T. (1981). Prophylaxis of migraine and mixed headache: A randomized controlled study. *Headache, 21*, 105–109.

McCarran, M. S., & Andrasik, F. (1987). Migraine and tension headaches. In L. Michelson & M. Ascher (Eds.), *Anxiety and stress disorders: Cognitive-behavioral assessment and treatment* (pp. 465–483). New York: Guilford.

McCrory, D., Penzien, D. B., Hasselblad, V., & Gray, R. (2001). *Behavioral and physical treatments for tension-type and cervicogenic headaches*. Des Moines, IA: Foundation for Chiropractic Education and Research.

Menken, M., Munsat, T. L., & Toole, J. F. (2000). The global burden of disease study: Implications for neurology. *Archives of Neurology, 57*, 418–420.

Miller, W. R. (1996). Motivational interviewing: Research, practice, and puzzles. *Addictive Behaviors, 21*, 835–842.

Miller, W. R., & Rollnick, S. (2002). *Motivational interviewing: Preparing people for change* (2nd ed.) New York: Guilford.

Motheral, B. R., & Henderson, R. (1999). The effect of copay increase on pharmaceutical utilization, expenditures, and treatment continuation. *American Journal of Managed Care, 5*, 1383–1394.

Nestoriuc, Y., & Martin, A. (2007). Efficacy of biofeedback for migraine: A meta-analysis. *Pain, 128*, 111–127.

Nestoriuc, Y., Martin, A., Rief, W., & Andrasik, F. (2008). Biofeedback treatment for headache disorders: A comprehensive efficacy review. *Applied Psychophysiology and Biofeedback, 33*, 125–140.

Nestoriuc, Y., Rief, W., & Martin, A. (2008). Meta-analysis of biofeedback for tension-type headache: Efficacy, specificity, and treatment moderators. *Journal of Consulting and Clinical Psychology, 76*, 379–396.

Nicholson, R. A., Nash, J. M., & Andrasik, F. (2005). A self-administered behavioral intervention using tailored messages for migraine. *Headache, 45*, 1124–1139.

Osterhaus, J. T., Townsend, R. J., Gandek, B., & Ware, J. E. (1994). Measuring the functional status and well-being of patients with migraine headache. *Headache, 34*(6), 337–343.

Penzien, D. B., & Holroyd, K. A. (1994). Psychosocial interventions in the management of recurrent headache disorders—II: Description of treatment techniques. *Behavioral Medicine, 20*, 64–73.

Penzien, D. B., Johnson, C. A., Carpenter, D. E., & Holroyd, K. A. (1990). Drug vs. behavioral treatment of migraine: Long-acting propranolol vs. home-based self-management training. *Headache, 30*, 300.

Penzien, D. B., Rains, J. C., & Andrasik, F. (2002). Behavioral management of recurrent headache: Three decades of experience and empiricism. *Applied Psychophysiology and Biofeedback, 27*, 163–181.

Powers, S. W., Gilman, D. K., & Hershey, A. D. (2006). Suggestions for a biopsychosocial approach to treating children and adolescents who present with headache. *Headache, 46*(Suppl. 3), S149–S150.

Prochaska, J. O., Redding, A., & Evers, K. E. (1997). The transtheoretical model and stages of change. In K. Glanz, F. M. Lewis, & B. K. Rimer (Eds.), *Health behavior and health education* (pp. 60–84). San Francisco: Jossey-Bass.

Pryse-Phillips, W. (2002). Evaluating migraine disability: The headache impact test instrument in context. *Canadian Journal of Neurological Sciences, 29*(Suppl. 2), S11–S15.

Rains, J. C., Lipchik, G. L., & Penzien, D. B. (2006). Behavioral facilitation of medical treatment for headache–Part I: Review of headache treatment compliance. *Headache, 46*, 1387–1394.

Rains, J. C., Penzien, D. B., & Lipchik, G. L. (2006). Behavioral facilitation of medical treatment for headache–Part II: Theoretical models and behavioral strategies for improving adherence. *Headache, 46,* 1395–1403.

Ramadan, N. M. (2006). Migraine headache prophylaxis: Current options and advances on the horizon. *Current Neurology and Neuroscience Reports, 6*(2), 95–99.

Ramadan, N. M., Silberstein, S. D., Freitag, F. G., Gilbert, T. T., & Frishberg, B. M. (2000). *The US Headache Consortium. Evidence-based guidelines for migraine headache in the primary care setting: Pharmacological management for prevention of migraine.* American Academy of Neurology, US Headache Consortium, 1–55. Retrieved December 2008 from www.aan.com/professionals/practice/pdfs/gl0090.pdf

Rasmussen, B. K. (1995). Epidemiology of headache. *Cephalalgia, 15,* 45–68.

Rime, C., & Andrasik, F. (2007). Relaxation techniques and guided imagery. In S. D. Waldman (Ed.), *Pain management* (Vol. 2, pp. 1025–1032). Philadelphia: Saunders/Elsevier.

Rollnick, S., & Miller, W. R. (1995). What is motivational interviewing? *Behavioural and Cognitive Psychotherapy, 23,* 325–334.

Rothrock, J. F., Parada, V. A., Sims, C., Key, K., Walters, N. S., & Zweifler, R. M. (2006). The impact of intensive patient education on clinical outcome in a clinic-based migraine population. *Headache, 46,* 726–731.

Sarafino, E. P., & Goehring, P. (2000). Age comparisons in acquiring biofeedback control and success in reducing headache pain. *Annals of Behavioral Medicine, 22,* 10–16.

Scharff, L., Marcus, D. A., & Turk, D. C. (1996). Maintenance of effects in the nonmedical treatment of headaches during pregnancy. *Headache, 36,* 285–290.

Schwartz, B. S., Stewart, W. F., Simon, D., & Lipton, R. B. (1998). Epidemiology of tension-type headache. *Journal of the American Medical Association, 279,* 381–383.

Schwartz, M. S., & Andrasik, F. (Eds.). (2005). *Biofeedback: A practitioner's guide* (3rd ed.). New York: Guilford.

Silberstein, S. D. for the U.S. Headache Consortium. (2000). *Practice parameter: Evidence based guidelines for migraine headache (an evidence based review).* American Academy of Neurology, U.S. Headache Consortium, 1–11. Retrieved Decemeber 2008 from www.neurology.org/cgi/reprint/55/6/754.pdf

Silberstein, S. D., & Lipton, R. B. (1993). Epidemiology of migraine. *Neuroepidemiology, 12,* 179–194.

Sovak, M., Kunzel, M., Sternbach, R. A., & Dalessio, D. J. (1981). Mechanism of the biofeedback therapy of migraine: Volitional manipulation of the psychophysiological background. *Headache, 21,* 89–92.

Spierings, E. L., & Miree, L. F. (1993). Non-compliance with follow-up and improvement after treatment at a headache center. *Headache, 3,* 205–209.

Spitzer, R. L., Kroenke, K., Williams, J. B., & Lowe, B. (2006). A brief measure for assessing generalized anxiety disorder: The GAD-7. *Archives of Internal Medicine, 166*(10), 1092–1097.

Spitzer, R. L., Kroenke, K., Williams, J. B. W., & the Patient Health Questionnaire Primary Care Study Group. (1999). Validation and utility of a self-report version of PRIME-MD: The PHQ primary care study. *Journal of the American Medical Association, 282*(18), 1737–1744.

Stevenson, F., Cox, K., Britten, N., & Dundar, Y. (2004). A systematic review of the research on communication between patients and health care professionals about medicines: The consequences for concordance. *Health Expectations, 7,* 235–245.

Stewart, M., Meredith, L., Brown, J. B., & Galajda, J. (2000). The influence of older patient–physician communication on health and health-related outcomes. *Clinics in Geriatric Medicine, 16,* 25–36.

Stewart, M. A. (1995). Effective physician-patient communication and health outcomes: A review. *Canadian Medical Association Journal, 152,* 1423–1433.

Stewart, W. F., & Lipton, R. B. (1993). Migraine headache: Epidemiology and health care utilization. *Cephalalgia, 13*(Suppl. 12), 41–46.

Stewart, W. F., Lipton, R. B., Kolodner, K., Liberman, J., & Sawyer, J. (1999). Reliability of the migraine disability assessment score in a population-based sample of headache sufferers. *Cephalalgia, 19*(2), 107–114.

Ware, J. E., & Sherbourne, C. D. (1992). The MOS 36-item short-form health survey (SF-36). I. Conceptual framework and item selection. *Medical Care, 30*(6), 473–483.

Irritable Bowel Syndrome in Primary Care

30

Brenda B. Toner
Immaculate A. Antony

Introduction

Functional bowel disorders are stress-related gastrointestinal (GI) disorders with symptoms attributable to the middle or lower GI tract (Drossman et al., 2006). These include irritable bowel syndrome (IBS), functional bloating, functional constipation, functional diarrhea, and unspecified functional bowel disorder. The most common of the functional bowel disorders is IBS, which is characterized by severe abdominal pain, bloating, and other bowel symptoms (Toner, Segal, Emmot, & Myran, 2000). IBS is a costly and a disabling GI disorder, for which there is no universally agreed upon medical treatment (Camilleri et al., 1999).

Assessment and Diagnostic Issues

The diagnosis of IBS is based on identifying positive symptoms consistent with the condition, and excluding other conditions with similar clinical presentation (Drossman et al., 2006; Russo, Gaynes, & Drossman, 1999). Medical conditions that should be ruled out through a medical workup include inflammatory bowel disease, intestinal parasites, lactose intolerance, or other GI diseases.

Criteria to diagnose IBS (i.e., the ROME III criteria) (Drossman et al., 2006) are characterized by the continuous or recurrent symptoms for at least 3 months of the following:

1. Abdominal pain or discomfort, relieved with defecation or associated with a change in frequency or consistency of stool;
2. Two or more of the following, with at least one occurring on one fourth of occasions or days:
3. Altered stool frequency;
4. Altered stool form (hard or loose/watery stool);
5. Altered stool passage (straining or urgency, feeling of incomplete evacuation);
6. Passage of mucus;
7. Bloating or feeling of abdominal distension.

The diagnosis of IBS is usually made by a primary care physician (PCP) or a gastroenterologist. Patients who have received a diagnosis of IBS are sometimes referred to a psychologist, psychiatrist, or other mental health care professional for cognitive-behavioral therapy (CBT) and other psychotherapeutic treatments (Drossman, 1995a). Before individuals with IBS begin treatment with a health psychologist or other mental health professional, they may have experienced frustration with the health care system searching for an explanation for their IBS. There are a few considerations that physicians should recognize throughout the diagnosis process. Patients seeking diagnosis and treatment often report an unsatisfactory experience. Patients also often report a lack of empathy, adequate treatment, and sufficient medical explanation (Betram, Kurland, Lydick, Locke, & Yawn, 2001). Patients often report that their experiences are not taken seriously, and that their conditions are not fully recognized or appreciated.

Although the opportunity to make a positive diagnosis is available through the Rome III diagnostic criteria, most PCPs and some gastroenterologists are unaware of the criteria, and only a portion of those even use them in clinical practice (Drossman et al., 2006; Toner, 2005). Patients seeking clear explanations may encounter uncertain or even conflicting views. Therefore, it is important at the time of diagnosis to ensure that the patient receives a clear explanation of his/her diagnosis, and also encourage the view of IBS as a legitimate diagnosis with treatment and management options (Toner, 2005).

Biopsychosocial Assessment

Following the completion of a medical evaluation, a thorough and detailed psychological assessment should be conducted. The formulation of a testable and understandable explanation of symptoms serves both to relieve the client's anxiety and concerns about being seen as having imaginary complaints, and to devise tests of working hypotheses based on the formulation, which can be modified in response to progress or lack of it. The medical history should be reviewed with the client. The patient can be asked for the history of the condition and to describe the relevant psychosocial events surrounding the symptoms. How chronic the condition is for the patient should be examined; chronic conditions often are associated with greater psychosocial concomitants, either contributing to or resulting from the medical condition. The patient's individual perceptions of the course of the illness and its impact on his or her quality of life, relationships, and abilities are central in the formulation of the meaning of the illness to the patient. During this assessment, it is important to discuss the potential stressors and triggers of symptoms, such as their diet, fatigue, work pressures, or other psychosocial stressors.

A recent large online survey based on 1,966 individuals with a diagnosis of IBS produced several key findings about the impact of IBS. Results of the study showed that 78% of those with IBS reported having continuous or frequently recurring abdominal pain in the prior 6 months, and of those who experience pain, one-fourth have described their pain as constant (Drossman et al., 2009). The study also suggested that IBS sufferers restricted their usual activities due to their health symptoms. Individuals reported an average of greater than 73 days where they restricted their daily activities (20% of the entire calendar year). The survey also suggested that more than 40% of respondents reported feeling a great loss of control over their lives because of their IBS diagnosis. The survey also examined the variety of medications that are taken for IBS, and the experience of multiple medication use among IBS sufferers. They found that only 8% are very or extremely satisfied with all types of IBS treatment. They also found that 37% of individuals with IBS have used complementary and alternative forms of medicine. Clearly, these results suggest the need to continue to develop and implement new treatments such as CBT for individuals with IBS.

Incidence and Clinical Manifestations in the Primary Care Setting

IBS is one of the most common syndromes seen by primary health care providers and gastroenterologists. It is the most common GI diagnosis seen in primary care (Thompson, Heaton, Smyth, & Smyth, 2000). Health-related quality of life is poorer than in healthy patients with diabetes, chronic renal disease, or functional dyspepsia (Gralnek, Hays, Kilbourne, Niliboff, & Maya, 2000). Persons afflicted with IBS have more hospitalizations, outpatient visits, and are given more total outpatient prescriptions than non-IBS patients (Longstreth et al., 2003); diagnosis is associated with unnecessary tests, procedures, and surgeries. Difficulties in diagnosis and treatment produce uncertainty, frustration, and dissatisfaction within the patient-physician relationship (Drossman, 1993, 1995b; Toner, 2005).

The experience of having IBS is one that impairs physiological, as well as sociological, functioning of the affected individual. In a quantitative survey of 277 women and 73 men who reported symptoms that occurred weekly or more frequently, the majority of respondents described major interferences (i.e., disturbances to work or social/leisure activities) with daily life due to symptoms (International Foundation for Functional Gastrointestinal Disorders [IFFGD], 2002). To address the significant impairments that exist in all aspects of the patient's life, clinicians and researchers are turning to a more integrated approach (i.e., a biopsychosocial perspective) for the treatment of IBS.

Biopsychosocial Perspective

Increasing evidence suggests that the impact of IBS is best understood within a biopsychosocial context that is more integrative than focusing on the IBS symptoms alone (Drossman, 1999; Toner, 2005). Within the past decade, an increasing body of evidence supports the concept that IBS is a multidetermined disorder of brain-gut function, in which emotional and cognitive areas of the brain modulate bowel motility, visceral hypersensitivity and inflammation, and that altered bowel function has psychosocial consequences (Drossman et al., 2003). The gut interacts directly with the brain, providing a bidirectional interaction along the brain-gut axis. There is reliable evidence that supports the view that social and psychological stressors and associated alterations in mood alter the function of the gut and IBS symptoms (Levy et al., 2006).

Many of the approaches used in the psychosocial assessment for IBS have been adapted from cognitive-behavioral models that were developed by investigators and clinicians working with individuals who presented to mental health professionals with depression and anxiety disorders (Toner, 2005). Although there is increasing evidence that there is an association between individuals with psychological distress (i.e., anxiety and depression) and IBS, the general consensus reveals that this is not specific to IBS, but this association occurs in a variety of illnesses. Individuals with IBS may also experience symptoms such as gynecological and urinary conditions, headaches, chronic fatigue syndrome, and fibromyalgia. It is helpful for the health care professional to work in collaboration with the client to identify which associations may be relevant to and interact with his or her IBS. Three pathways have been postulated as likely biopsychosocial mechanisms by which psychological factors influence the expression of IBS (Sperry, 2009). The first pathway is directly through the biological systems that mediate gut function and sensation. The second is through the adoption of illness behaviors that exacerbate IBS symptoms (i.e., anxiety of leaving home). The third pathway is through the social context mediating the risk of IBS onset (i.e., physicians telling patients that nothing is wrong with them) (Kirmayer & Robbins, 1991; Lackner, Quigley, & Blanchard, 2004).

As reviewed by Drossman (1999), the varied influence of environmental stress, thoughts, and emotions on gut function effected through neurotransmitter release or receptor activity may explain the extraordinary variation in symptoms of patients having these disorders. This suggests how psychosocial trauma (e.g., physical, emotional, or sexual abuse) or unhelpful coping style (e.g., catastrophizing) can profoundly affect symptom severity and health outcome. Psychosocial factors in general, and cognitive-behavioral perspectives in particular, can play a central role in both our understanding and treatment of IBS (Toner et al., 2000). Research has repeatedly demonstrated a significant psychological component in patients who seek specialized medical consultation for IBS. In particular, numerous studies have demonstrated various characteristics reported in patients, such as severe life stress that has been found immediately at onset of functional bowel disorder (Levy et al., 2006). For many patients, social stress has importance in the exacerbation of symptoms. Patients with IBS have higher psychosocial distress scores than a non-IBS population with similar GI complaints (Drossman et al.,

1988; Whitehead, Bosmajian, Zonderman, Costa, & Schuster, 1988). IBS patients have also been found to have more anxiety and depression than patients with other GI complaints (Talley, Boyce, & Jones, 1997). The implication of these findings is that patients with IBS may benefit from psychological interventions, which, in addition to reducing GI symptoms, may also reduce subjective distress and may enable them to cope with this chronic disorder (Toner et al., 2000).

Cognitive-Behavioral Model for IBS

According to a cognitive-behavioral model, IBS symptoms and distress are perpetuated by an interaction between psychological, social, and physiological factors. Certain cognitions can lead to certain behaviors that increase hypervigilance of bodily symptoms, increased anxiety and arousal that ultimately leads to hypersensitivity to pain. For example, someone with IBS who has the cognition "there must be a medical explanation for this pain" may experience repeated hospital visits, resulting in more attention to bodily sensations (Toner et al., 2000). During this process, the bodily sensations become even more heightened, and are experienced as more intense. These amplified sensations may then be taken as confirmatory evidence of a physical cause. Consistent with an information-processing model, people selectively attend to those cognitions and perceptions that confirm their explanatory hypotheses and selectively ignore evidence that is inconsistent with their beliefs (Toner et al.). Accordingly, other possible contributing factors such as life stressors, psychological distress, overwork, interpersonal conflict, or loss may be minimized by an individual's conceptualization of their IBS symptoms (Toner et al.). There is empirical support for this model in the work of Levy, Cain, Jarriett, and Heitkemper (1997), who found that patients with IBS were less likely to report an association between IBS symptoms and stressors, relative to IBS nonpatients (Toner, 2005). These results suggest that persons with IBS might benefit from a treatment program that assists individuals to cope with the stress that may be perpetuating their bowel symptoms.

The general goal of cognitive-behavioral treatment for IBS is to help the client develop a reconceptualization of their bowel symptoms. This reconceptualization should shift their view of their IBS being a medical problem to the belief that the IBS symptoms are subject to the patient's control. Thus, these reconceptualized beliefs may help to generate a more adaptive way of coping with IBS (Sperry, 2009). The treatment teaches the patient a range of coping skills to assist them in dealing with unhelpful thoughts and feelings that exacerbate their bowel symptoms.

For physicians and health care professionals, the cognitive-behavioral framework addresses the limitations of the disease-based model of GI disorders. The biopsychosocial model of IBS addresses the maladaptive thoughts and behaviors that emerge from and perpetuate symptoms of IBS. This treatment approach is highly focused toward helping patients achieve the means of managing their symptoms, and complements medical care by providing techniques for the patient's health care professional (Toner, 2005). This chapter will provide the biopsychosocial assessment and treatment approach to IBS, as well as the points of collaboration with PCPs and mental health care professionals.

Brief Case History

The following example highlights the ways that cognitive-behavioral principles can be incorporated within the larger social context, to understand the issues encountered when working with individuals with IBS.

Ms. L. R. is a single, 37-year-old accountant in a prominent accounting firm. She has experienced IBS for the past five years and has consulted several gastroenterologists to find out what is causing her unpredictable bouts of diarrhea and intense abdominal pain.

She describes herself as a confident person with great ambition, but has felt somewhat dissatisfied with her career because she has not been promoted in her firm. She has witnessed employees junior to her obtaining promotions, and she believes that she is doing something wrong. When she attempted to assertively state her needs and expectations to her supervisors, she was met with resistance. She explains that her contributions and ideas are not taken seriously, compared with her male colleagues, and she feels isolated at work as one of the few women employees, and the only female accountant in the firm. Aside from her professional relationships, her personal relationships are limited, and she explains that with her demanding career, she rarely has time for her personal life. She has been single for quite some time, and is worried that she will never find a satisfying relationship and will never be married. She also fears that she will be alone forever and that her biological clock is running out.

Regarding her medical symptoms, she is convinced that something has been missed, and that the doctors are not taking her seriously and are treating her like an "hysterical" woman. In spite of her symptoms, she has never taken a day off and is considered by her colleagues and friends as always being "in control" and "on top of things." She describes herself as a very considerate person who will always go out of her way to help colleagues or friends, but recently, she has been thinking that others are taking advantage of her. She finds it difficult to express any anger she feels about this situation. Also, she seldom has time for herself, and confesses that she has not taken a vacation in over 2 years.

Whenever L. R. is invited to attend dinners with her friends, she thinks of excuses to avoid the event. Subsequently, this has limited her social networks and her friends now rarely invite her out for dinner. On one occasion, in an attempt to go out one night for dinner, she limited her food intake for 2 days prior to the night of the event. She also arrived at the restaurant early to find out where the restrooms were so that she could select a table as close as possible in case she became symptomatic. In these types of situations, she would barely eat anything and would become incredibly embarrassed and anxious if her stomach rumbled, causing her to have mild diarrhea. She experiences intense shame and anxiety about her problem, and she has ultimately decided that going out with friends is simply not possible for her. To address questions from friends about her frequent washroom trips, she typically lied and said she had a kidney and bladder problem. She was convinced that if she told them that her doctors could not provide a treatment or cure they would think it was all in her head. Overall, in her professional and personal life experiences, L. R. has become increasingly depressed, tense, and exhausted.

The first step to understanding Ms. L. R.'s challenge is to examine her experiences and realities and the possible distortions in her thinking. It is important to check out whether Ms. L. R. is behaving, thinking, and feeling in agreement with her understanding of society's expectations for her (Worell & Remer, 1992). In addition to discussing possible errors in thinking (e.g., "I may never find a satisfying relationship," "I'm a failure at work because I have not been promoted," "If I have difficulty being assertive and expressing anger, there must be something wrong with me," "Something must be missed because I have so much abdominal pain"), the health care professional could increase the patient's awareness and understanding of the impact of gender role socialization, especially the societal messages about the "good woman" (i.e., a good woman marries and has children, never gets angry, puts other's needs before hers, never looks flustered or needy), stereotypes about single women (i.e., "old maid"), fears about living without a partner (i.e., women are helpless and need to be taken care of), and stereotypes about pain and organic cause (i.e., if it is "really" painful, there must be an organic etiology).

In discussions of general role issues with Ms. L.R., it is important to address whether she may have internalized society's expectations by thinking that she should prioritize professional productivity, even if that means sacrificing relationship goals. In addition to the more generic discussions about gender roles, cognitive restructuring techniques and behavioral experiments can be used to explore her specific thoughts and underlying assumptions about IBS. Through a careful exploration of the internalization effects of gender role expectations and power imbalance, one could assist Ms. L. R. to choose which of society's expectations that she wants to keep as her own.

Another area of examination could be the persistent apprehension around Ms. L. R.'s bowel symptoms, causing her to leave or avoid social contexts. This heightened anxiety is commonly associated with cognitions such as "if I have bowel symptoms, then I am a weak person," "I cannot go to any social activity unless I have total control over my bowel symptoms," "if I need to use the toilet several times in an evening, people are going to think that I am abnormal." A suggested area for a cognitive-behavioral intervention is to discuss the degree to which failure to meet their standards for acceptable GI behaviors warrants the sense of overwhelming shame. This exercise can help sensitize the patient to the overgeneralization of one behavior being representative of her whole character.

It is important to encourage individuals with IBS to monitor both their automatic thoughts and the influence of gender role and societal messages. In this process, we can aid clients in understanding that, regardless of external realities, some thoughts and behaviors are not helpful, and can contribute to dysphoric moods and somatic distress.

Accordingly, CBT techniques such as cognitive restructuring can be implemented without using pathologizing labels and client-blaming attributes (Worell & Remer, 1992). The integration of the social context into CBT shifts the focus to identifying and changing the unhealthy external situation, and to identifying and changing the internalized effects of the external social context.

Identifying and Addressing Obstacles to Treatment

There are many obstacles and challenges that PCPs may experience when working with patients with IBS. During the assessment and diagnosis phases, many physicians experience similar frustration that patients experience from a poorly understood condition and limited effective treatments (Dixon-Woods & Critchley, 2000). Following the completion of several tests to rule out organic or biochemical abnormalities and finding no conclusive answers, patients are often told that "there is nothing organically wrong" (Thompson, Heaton, Smyth, & Smyth, 2000). For the patient who is experiencing an intense, painful, and chronic condition, this message is difficult to hear, let alone accept.

A challenge with the assessment and treatment process for IBS patients involves the stigma associated with it. Within western society, illness is viewed as a biological affliction that befalls patients, whereas anything that is psychological in nature is self-controlled and caused by one's own volition (Kirmayer & Robbins, 1991). The western perspective of functional disorders is that anything psychological most likely has moral and depreciatory attributions to the self (Fabrege, 1991). The myths and stigmas associated with IBS demoralize the person seeking diagnosis, and often can become an obstacle to treatment. The patient may come into the physician's office with the belief, that like the rest of society, his or her physician will not see the IBS symptoms as "real" or serious (Toner et al., 2000). Therefore, it is important at the beginning of the diagnosis process to validate the patient's symptoms and challenge society's negative view of functional disorders.

Points of Collaboration With Physicians and Family

From the assessment stages and through the treatment process, it would be helpful for health care professionals to examine the contextual perspective of the patient (i.e., their social networks and family relations). In the initial phases, a physician may ask about a patient's relationships and examine the possible links between their relationship issues and their bowel disorder (Chang et al., 2006). Health care professionals should also convey to patients that information about their relationships and the larger context in which they live is important in the assessment and treatment process. It is important to help patients to begin to contextualize their issues, so that they can begin to think differently about their bowel disorder. The goal is to help the patient gain a new perspective on the link between his or her physical symptomology and the external environment. This approach to health care recognizes the role of the family in providing medical and supportive care, encourages collaboration among the patient, family, and health care professionals, and honors individual and family strengths and culture's traditions (Chang et al., 2006).

If the patient is involved in a relationship, it may be useful to explore how the bowel disorder fits within the relationship. Questions about the partner's knowledge of and reaction to the patient's symptoms can elicit important information about the degree to which they feel supported (Toner et al., 2000). It might also be helpful to explore the types of communication regarding the bowel symptoms, and can also prove to be useful in determining the impact the relationship may have on the bowel symptoms. When one partner has a medical disorder, it is not unusual for couples to experience some impact on various aspects of their relationships, including their sex life, the division of household labor, parenting responsibilities, and their social lives. Individuals with IBS also report that aspects of their relationships can have an effect on their symptoms, and for some people, can perpetuate them further. Patients may also have difficulties in explaining their illness to loved ones because it can further feelings of shame (Toner & Akman, 2000). Some individuals might hide the nature of their illness from family and friends, because they may find it difficult to explain their illness where there is no actual disease in their body. In such instances, health care professionals could provide the patient with a language for talking about functional somatic disorders and for illnesses without clearly elaborated physical causes. This will allow patients to share their experiences of IBS with family without evoking tremendous personal shame and guilt. The physician, with the patient, can evaluate the stressors and triggers that perpetuate their symptoms, and then evaluate the potential supports that exist, as well as exploring and maximizing the client's support system (Akman & Toner, 1999).

Many people who suffer from debilitating medical ailments, including bowel disorders, experience worry or guilt about being a burden to those around them. In addition, because having a bowel problem is such a shameful experience for many people, it is often kept hidden from the rest of the world, resulting in a vicious cycle of isolation. Oftentimes, the more the patient is isolated, the stronger the feelings of shame; strengthening their reluctance to ask for help and support from family and friends.

Some patients may be unable to identify a source of support. It is important to determine whether they are predicting that no one would be willing to support them or that they do not actually have a system of support in place. In the case of the patient predicting that no one would be willing to provide support, it would be important to examine beliefs about the significant people in his or her life. If the patient truly does not have a support system in place, it would be beneficial to work to broaden the support system. With patients who are unable to identify any sources of support, an important goal is to reduce the sense of isolation that is being experienced by helping them to reconsider their relationships and expand their social network (Toner et al., 2000).

The very nature of asking for and receiving support can be both foreign and threatening to many people for several reasons (Toner et al., 2000). People who have come to view themselves as caring for others, rather than caring for themselves, often have never entertained the idea that they are someone who legitimately needs and deserves support from others. They also have trouble conceiving of the notion that they can and should be supportive of themselves. To be truly self-supportive means to allow room for flexibility, for flaws, for nurturance, and for fun, and many people abandon these notions for fear of feeling like a failure, and for fear of public embarrassment. With people who seem to be lacking support from others and tolerance from themselves, it may be necessary to begin by addressing the contribution that self-understanding and self-care can make to their emotional and physical well-being.

The primary step to asking for support is to know when and in what way one needs support. For example, if a person is feeling fatigued, they would first need to recognize the fatigue, then they would need to determine what would alleviate their symptoms and know how to go about getting that relief. When a person is worried about their presentation in public and is preoccupied with caring about others, self-awareness is often sacrificed. For individuals with functional bowel disorders, it is quite common for them to explain that they do not know what they need most from others, because they are too busy focusing on keeping their world in order. A useful avenue to travel with these patients may be one that explores their understanding of themselves and the level to which they allow themselves to be fully functioning persons. The following questions are designed to introduce and validate these ideas to people who are reluctant to allow themselves to need, and then ask for, support.

When do you feel truly free from the responsibilities of your life?

What are you like when you are really being yourself?

When was the last time you were really yourself?

When was the last time you acted silly or playful? How did it feel? How do people around you respond when you act that way? How do you respond when you see others acting silly or playful?

Development and Implementation of Empirically Based Treatment Plan

Cognitive-behavioral treatment consists of a wide range of strategies and techniques designed to bring about changes in the clients' perceptions of their situation, and thus, their ability to control their condition. The rationale for cognitive-behavioral strategies assumes that individuals can learn new ways of thinking and behaving through personal experience and practice (Toner, 2005).

The general goal of cognitive-behavioral treatment for IBS is to help the patient develop a reconceptualization of his or her bowel symptoms. This reframing process should shift the view of IBS as a medical problem to the belief that IBS symptoms are subject to the patient's control. The treatment teaches the client a range of coping skills to assist them in dealing with unhelpful thoughts and feelings that exacerbate their bowel symptoms.

The cognitive-behavioral model presented for patients with IBS has been adapted from a model developed by Sharpe, Peveler, and Mayou (1992) for functional somatic syndromes. Central to the cognitive-behavioral model is the way the person thinks about his/her bowel symptoms. In a treatment study with patients with functional somatic syndromes, the tasks of therapy were divided into helping the patient change their cognitions and their methods of dealing with stressors. The treatment also encouraged behavioral change that would produce changes in cognitions. These researchers suggested a bidirectional view of treatment, working with cognitions that influence behavior and working with behavioral change to facilitate changes in cognitions that were contributing to their symptoms.

In recent clinical treatment studies, this cognitive-behavioral approach was adopted for the treatment of persons with IBS (Toner et al., 2000). The cognitive-behavioral treatment approach with clients with IBS has three major objectives: (a) to help the patient to reconceptualize her/his view of IBS from helplessness to hopefulness, (b) to help patients identify relationships among thoughts, feelings, behaviors, the environment, and IBS symptoms, and (c) to empower patients to develop and implement increasingly more effective ways of coping with IBS, and achieve an improved quality of life. Cognitive-behavioral treatment focuses on the cognitive variables as targets of therapeutic change. Cognitive change occurs in part through interventions that target the behavioral components of functioning. In cases where IBS is maintained by avoidant patterns (e.g., social withdrawal), behavioral tasks (e.g., exposure tasks) can be used so that patients are desensitized to catastrophic expectations when presented with evidence against their expectations (Toner et al.). Unlike a strictly behavioral approach, the cognitive-behavioral approach employs behavioral strategies with the ultimate goal of addressing IBS-related cognitions.

There have been numerous cognitive-behavioral strategies for addressing IBS-related thinking patterns. The focus of these strategies is on addressing automatic thoughts and common "distorted" thoughts (Toner et al., 2000). Some of these techniques include designing experiments and operationalizing negative constructs. The CBT therapist also considers strategies for dealing with core beliefs, attitudes, and assumptions that play a key role in the amplification of bowel symptoms, followed by a discussion of the different types of rule-breaking experiments, helpful responses, and hot thoughts (i.e., thoughts that are perpetuating their anxiety) that may be contributing to their ability to cope with their bowel symptoms.

With more women than men experiencing IBS, there are a number of reports that have suggested treating gender as an important variable in cognitive-behavioral therapies. Davis and Padesky (1989) have suggested that it is particularly crucial to incorporate issues of gender into CBT, because research has suggested that gender plays a role in influencing individuals' reactions to various situations, as well as their perception of themselves (Deaux, 1984). Cognitive-behavioral therapists would encourage patients with IBS to monitor their automatic thoughts and their gender role messages. The therapist would then use techniques such as cognitive restructuring, especially when discussing themes that are related to coping with IBS, including shame, anger, assertion, self-efficacy, social approval, perfectionism, and control (Toner et al., 2000).

Greenberger and Padesky (1995) discuss the concept of "hot" thoughts or automatic thoughts that are strongly associated with the emotions one experiences. Often, these automatic thoughts are connected to critical self-statements that may contribute to the exacerbation of the IBS symptoms. For example, if an individual felt the urgent need to pull off the highway to look for a bathroom while driving with a colleague, there are number of thoughts that she may have had: "this may make us late for the appointment" (anxious, 60%) and "my colleague will think that there is something wrong with me and that I'm weird" (anxious, 80%). In this example, the fear of being seen as weak or inadequate by her colleague increases her anxiety and exacerbates her symptoms. Greenberger and Padesky suggest that the individual select the automatic thought that causes the highest negative mood levels and evaluate the thought by searching for evidence that supports the hot thought, and evidence that does not support the hot thought. The evidence that does not support the hot thought does not have to be incredibly compelling, however, the existence of evidence is often persuasive enough to help the patient begin thinking about alternative interpretations of external events.

Toner and colleagues (2000) provide a detailed treatment program for different themes that are relevant for persons with IBS. For example, with a theme such as the association among thoughts, feelings, behaviors, and bowel symptoms, a CBT therapist would begin with identifying the specific patterns of thinking that are associated with IBS, associated with the behaviors, and associated with the client's mood. The therapist would then validate the reality of the physical and environmental stressors present in the IBS patient's life. The therapist and patient would then discuss the different parts of the stress reactions (i.e., the physical, the behavioral, and cognitive), and then go on to discuss how events and the patient's appraisal of these events lead to emotional reactions. The patient would then have to engage in an automatic thought exercise (i.e., identifying a thought that contributes to the most difficult emotional reaction experienced). The therapist would also encourage the patient to engage in a daily thought record, to assess the fluctuations of their emotions and cognitive activity.

Another common theme that is discussed in CBT therapy for IBS patients is pain management (Drossman, 1999). Because many people with IBS experience high levels of frequent abdominal pain, the therapist might introduce techniques to make it easier for the patient to cope with their discomfort and pain. CBT therapists use a variety of techniques, such as distraction methods for pain, relaxation for pain control, and guided imagery for pain control. For example, for guided imagery, the therapist would ask the patient to select a scene with personal meaning, that is, a situation in which the patient felt safe and peaceful. The therapist would ask the patient to think about the scene with all sensory modalities (i.e., visual, olfactory, auditory, and tactile). After practicing this guided-imagery technique in the sessions, the client would be asked to engage in this imagery exercise during experiences of pain. The rating of pain before and after would show the patient whether this was an effective technique, and if not, then the therapist would work with another therapeutic intervention (Toner et al., 2000).

Another theme that is frequently examined in CBT therapy is "shame" associated with having IBS, a common feeling associated with the condition. Shame has been defined as a humiliating sense of exposure of personal inadequacies (Toner, 2005). Toner and colleagues (2000) have suggested that shame is an important facet of suffering from IBS, and has been found to underlie other IBS-related symptoms of avoidance, depression, and anxiety. In this therapeutic setting, the therapist would help the clients identify social/cultural sources of shame reactions to the IBS symptoms. The therapist might also identify and question the following cognitive sources of shame reactions to IBS. The therapist would challenge any "distorted cognitions," such as the client overgeneralizing one problem he or she is experiencing as representative of the individual's whole character (Toner, Segel, Emmot, & Myran, 2000).

An important theme that is extremely common among persons with IBS is bowel performance anxiety (Toner, 2005). Individuals with IBS are often hypervigilant to the expectations of socially acceptable behaviors with regard to digestion. Bowel performance anxiety refers to the persistent, distressing apprehension of bowel symptoms in a public setting, which leads to future avoidance of such situations.

Evaluation of Treatment Outcomes

One of the preliminary studies to examine the treatment outcomes of CBT for patients with IBS was conducted by Neff and Blanchard (1987), within a multicomponent treatment program (educational information, progressive relaxation therapy, thermal biofeedback treatment, coping skills). Individuals who received the multicomponent treatment program experienced a reduction in GI symptoms, whereas individuals in the control self-monitoring group showed little change. The control group engaged in their own symptom monitoring and received no active treatment; however, they were later offered the multicomponent treatment, where more than half the group improved. Because this was a multicomponent treatment, it is not possible to identify which component of treatment contributed most to the improvement and whether it was the cognitive-behavioral components. In an effort to address this limitation, Shaw and colleagues (1991) combined CBT strategies, relaxation techniques, and educational components in their stress-management program for IBS. The results suggested that this program appeared to be more effective in reducing the frequency and intensity of symptoms, compared with "conventional" drug treatment. Rumsey (1991) also conducted a similar study that combined muscle relaxation training with education and CBT. At the end of treatment, those patients who received this multicomponent therapy showed a reduction in GI symptoms that had declined to a similar extent in the two groups, but the CBT group showed greater reduction in depression and anxiety, compared with the group that received psychotropic drugs. In an effort to address the methodological issues of the prior studies, Greene and Blanchard (1994) conducted a well-controlled cognitive-therapy intervention for clients with IBS. They found a greater reduction in GI symptoms for IBS patients in the cognitive-therapy group, compared with the self-monitoring controls.

Van Dulmen and colleagues (1996) found improvement in abdominal pain, coping strategies, and avoidance behavior in their CBT group relative to the wait-list control group. Toner and colleagues (1998) conducted a well-designed study that compared a sample of IBS patients who were randomly assigned to three groups: a cognitive-behavioral group treatment, a psychoeducational group treatment, and a conventional medical treatment. The results suggested that the cognitive-behavioral group treatment had a greater improvement in bowel symptoms in comparison with the other treatment groups. In a more recent study by Drossman and colleagues (2003), researchers found that those individuals who had moderate to severe symptoms had greater improvement of symptoms from the CBT treatment, compared with those individuals who experienced low to moderate symptoms.

Within the recent literature, there has been evidence emerging that the various combinations of cognitive and behavioral techniques lead to noticeable improvement in most individuals experiencing IBS (Lackner et al., 2008). Drossman and colleagues (2003) conducted a single blind trial of CBT for 12 weeks. The study demonstrated that CBT was significantly more effective than a weekly educational group control. Improvements were seen in global satisfaction and quality of life, but not in pain (Drossman et al., 2003). For detailed qualitative and quantitative reviews, refer to Scharff (2002) and Blanchard and Scharff (2005).

A recent development in IBS treatment is the second generation of CBT treatment as self-administrated or home-based treatments (Lackner et al., 2008). In its standard form, CBT has inherent limitations (i.e., cost, shortage of trained therapists, long waiting lists, time requirements) that can limit clinical utility. In an effort to economize therapist contact time in this study, self-management skills were introduced during the therapist sessions, but most of the learning of techniques occurred at home using self-study materials. This minimal contact CBT (MC-CBT) approach only required 4 clinic sessions, instead of the 10–20 weekly sessions that are most commonly found in other treatment studies. Lackner and colleagues (2008) conducted a pilot study where IBS patients were randomly assigned to the standard CBT therapy (i.e., 10 sessions), the patient-administered treatment (i.e., 4 sessions), or waiting list controls. The majority of the patients assigned to self-administered CBT described their IBS symptoms as improved and reported adequate relief. The proportion of IBS patient with self-administered CBT exceeded patients assigned to the waiting list control, and showed comparable improvements with patients who received standard therapist-administered treatment. The overall proportion of patients reporting adequate relief was 72% for self-administered CBT, 60.9% for standard CBT, and 7.4% for waiting list control. This pilot study provides the preliminary empirical support to support a more brief and patient-administered CBT treatment protocol.

Overall, a number of clinical trials have provided empirical support of the efficacy of CBT, and suggested significant treatment outcomes which include improvements in key GI symptoms (pain, bowel dysfunction), quality of life, and psychological distress.

Considerations With Special Populations: The Influence of Gender, Society, and Culture on IBS

Researchers and clinicians have now recognized that IBS exists within a larger socially constructed context, which is made up of factors such as gender, society, and culture that can influence the patient. In this section, we will examine how each of these factors is related and can perpetuate a patient's IBS symptoms. A health care provider can provide the patient with a framework to understand and legitimize their symptoms and identify factors that contribute to symptoms that the patient can control or influence.

Gender

The term *gender* is used to refer to the nonbiological aspects of being female or male (i.e., the social or cultural expectations associated with femininity and masculinity (Chang et al., 2006). From a psychological perspective of gender and IBS, there appear to be clear gender role differences to the experience of stress and the psychological manifestation and presentation in men and women. Women with IBS were more likely to report difficulties or problems with eating than normal control or patients with organic GI diseases. There is also an association that has been found between bowel symptom severity and subscales (i.e., perfectionism and ineffectiveness) for the Eating Disorder Inventory (Garner, Olmstead, & Polivy, 1983). There is a higher prevalence of anxiety and depression in female IBS patients, in comparison with men. A Swedish study by Simren and colleagues (2001) compared patients with IBS referred to a hospital center and those seen in primary care. The results suggest that IBS female patients seen in referral centers may be psychologically different from those who are seen in primary care, and this relationship does not appear evident in men.

Finally, the social determinants of health need to be incorporated into our understanding of IBS, including gender role socialization, early abuse, life stressors, and social support. The literature has suggested that many of the physical and mental health concerns experienced by women are influenced by the socialization of the female gender role (Worell & Remer, 1992). Toner and colleagues (2000) identified several themes that have been common to women with IBS; these include shame and bodily functions, bloating, physical appearance, pleasing others, assertion, and anger.

Society

There are pervasive societal myths and stigma associated with IBS in the health care system and society as a whole (Chang et al., (2006). The stigma of psychosomatic disorders is developed by the lack of medical explanation for symptoms and, as a result, society mistakenly views the IBS sufferers as malingerers seeking unnecessary medical attention. Also, the general social expectations of bowel habits magnify the shame and embarrassment experienced when IBS patients hide their condition and restrict their life experiences, including travel, diet, employment, social life, and sexual intimacy. The final example depicts the degree of stigma that society holds about bowel functions, which was reflected through a 1999 television media advertisement by the IFFGD. In 1999, the IFFGD produced an informational public service announcement about IBS. Prior to the distribution, 50% of the major media outlets surveyed stated that they could not air the ad if the word *bowel* was used. Therefore, it is no surprise that patients with IBS often find it embarrassing and difficult to discuss their debilitating condition.

Individuals who have received a diagnosis of IBS report feeling demoralized and believe that their illness is not taken seriously, even within the health care system. Letson and Dancey (1996) reported that overall, nurses held negative attitudes towards IBS patients, which was conveyed in a subtle manner through the communication between the nurse and patient.

In summary, it is important to recognize the multitude of social factors that influence and perpetuate IBS symptoms. By understanding the influence of the social context and IBS, physicians can provide clear information to patients about the possible contributing factors to their condition.

Culture

The prevalence of IBS appears to be lower in non-western countries, which may reflect the limited number of studies that have been conducted in these countries (Drossman et al., 2006). There is an interaction between culture and health that affects the interpretation of medical conditions and health outcomes. Culture refers to the values, beliefs, norms, and practices of a particular group that are learned and shared, and also guide thinking, decisions, and actions in a patterned way (Leninger, 1985). Cultural/ethnic factors may influence the patient-physician relationship, the diagnostic process, and health outcomes, thus, it is important to understand how certain cultural populations differ from others in terms of health care. If the significance of cultural differences goes unnoticed, then this may cause significantly poorer outcomes for these patients. In the clinical research context, cultural issues can cause methodological limitations that lead to results that are limited in applicability. In many clinical trial studies, participants have been predominantly Caucasian IBS patients. The limitation of this approach is clear to IBS patients from various ethnic and cultural backgrounds. Studies have demonstrated that the patient's ethnicity exerts an enormous influence on doctors' behaviors in ordering diagnostic studies, as well as the medications prescribed (Dimsdale, 2000). Also, some individuals in cultural groups do not have the skills required to function in the health care process; for example, they have limited literacy and language skills that can limit their understanding of the diagnosis. Therefore, cultural competence (i.e., the ability of the health care profession to recognize and perform under cross-cultural circumstances) is necessary to ensure the treatment compliance of the patient and positive treatment outcome.

Clinical Pearls of Wisdom for Practitioners

The Patient-Physician Encounter

The patient-physician encounter in IBS is challenging and often frustrating to both parties. Patients who seek diagnosis and treatment often report an unsatisfactory or unhelpful experience with health care professionals. Physicians share frustration with the patients over the poorly understood nature of IBS as a disease, as well as the lack of treatments. To the patient, unsatisfactory explanations may be experienced as a denial of the legitimacy of their reported symptoms, an implication that negative test results imply an absence of cause, and a lack of understanding or belief in their suffering.

Integrating the Patient's Perspective Into Assessment and Treatment

Although the experience of individuals living with IBS has not been formally integrated into assessment protocols, it is essential for health care professionals to elicit patients' concerns and experiences, and reaffirm them throughout the treatment and assessment process (Toner et al., 2006).

CBT distinguishes itself from other psychotherapeutic interventions by its focus on a collaborative empiricism (i.e., to work together in targeting problems and generating strategies). The model is based on a constructivist view that encourages the clinician to understand the patient's situation from the point of view of the patient. Health care professionals can work in partnership with individuals with IBS by eliciting their concerns and discussing them in ways that are individually relevant and affirming (Toner et al., 2006).

It is important to recognize that language and labels that are used in the health and mental health professions may serve to further invalidate the experience of patients with IBS. Certain cognitive concepts or labels, like cognitive distortions and irrationality, may facilitate the belief that patients' symptoms result from their own individual pathology and minimize the influence of social and biological determinants.

One concern commonly expressed by individuals with IBS has been the stigma of living with a chronic and debilitating condition that has been trivialized by society, and often misunderstood by health care professionals (Bertram et al., 2001; Toner et al., 2006). Often, individuals who have received a diagnosis of IBS come in to see health care or mental health care professionals feeling demoralized and thinking that their illness is not taken seriously. This may not be a cognitive distortion, but rather, an accurate reflection of the stigma associated with functional somatic disorders. Therefore, it important for health care professionals to incorporate the patient's perspective through the treatment process and encourage partnership and collaboration.

The Patient and Physician: The Collaborative Process

A collaborative patient–physician relationship is a fundamental component for the assessment and treatment of IBS. This process should begin at the time of diagnosis with a clear, understandable, and legitimizing explanation of the condition. Patients need clear explanations about the diagnosis and nature of their symptoms that encourages the view of IBS as a legitimate diagnosis with treatment and management options (Rumsey, 1991). Self-care is integral to coping with chronic IBS, and thus, patients should initiate a self-management process and feel some control over their symptoms (Toner, 2005).

A patient's understanding of his or her own health problems is influenced by everyday experiences, as well as cultural, social, and media interactions. The physician's recognition of these factors and of the patient's individual experience of IBS will facilitate a collaborative and strong therapeutic alliance. An empowering physician-patient relationship can be an affirming and validating process that provides the patient with a framework in which to understand and legitimize her/his symptoms, reduce self-doubt or blame, and identify the external or internal trigger factors for their symptoms (Toner et al., as cited in Drossman et al., 2006). Finally, the physician and patient should become partners, working together in the management of the condition. As Drossman et al. have noted, "self management support involves collaboratively helping patients and their families acquire the skills and confidence to manage their chronic illness, providing self-management tools and routinely assessing problems and accomplishments" (Drossman et al., 2006, p. 322).

Summary

IBS can be a challenging experience for both the physician and the patient. IBS patients place significant demands on health services, both in terms of numbers of consultations, and the challenges of diagnosis and treatment. Physicians can help their patients by eliciting and addressing patient concerns, by offering positive diagnosis, and clear, understandable, and legitimizing explanations of the disorder. Furthermore, physicians can provide patients with a language for discussing IBS in a non-self-effacing manner. Through a collaborative process, the patient and physician should work together by identifying factors that influence or perpetuate IBS symptoms. By supporting IBS patients and their families and providing them with the most effective way to manage the impact of IBS on their everyday lives, physicians may enter into a meaningful collaboration with their patients. This partnership and supportive health care can help individuals with IBS to replace feelings of helplessness with a sense of empowerment.

References

Akman, D., & Toner, B. B. (1999). *Including families in the treatment of irritable bowel syndrome.* Unpublished manuscript.

Bertram, S., Kurland, M., Lydick, E., Locke, G. R., III, Yawn, B. P. (2001). The patient's perspective of irritable bowel syndrome. *Journal of Family Practice, 50*, 521–525.

Blanchard, E. B. (2005). A critical review of cognitive, behavioral and cognitive-behavioral therapies for irritable bowel syndrome. *Journal of Cognitive Psychotherapy, 19*, 101–123

Blanchard, E. B., Scharff, L. (2002). Psychosocial aspects of assessment and treatment of irritable bowel syndrome in adults and recurrent abdominal pain in children. *Journal of Consulting and Clinical Psychology, 70*(3), 725–738.

Camilleri, M., Mayer, E. A., Drossman, D. A., Heath, A., Dukes, G. E., McSorley, D., et al. (1999). Improvement in pain and bowel function in female irritable bowel patients with alosetron, a 5-HT3 receptor antagonist. *Alimentary Pharmacology and Therapeutics, 13*(9), 1149–1159.

Chang, L., Toner, B. B., Fukudo, S., Guthrie, E., Locke, G. R., Norton, N. J., & Sperber, A. D. (2006). Gender, age, society, culture and the patient's perspective in the functional gastrointestinal disorders. *Gastroenterology, 130*, 1435–1446.

Davis, D., & Padesky, C. (1989). *Enhancing cognitive therapy with women. Comprehensive handbook of cognitive therapy* (pp. 535–557). New York: Plenum Press.

Deux, K. (1984). From individual differences to social categories: Analysis of a decade's research on gender. *American Psychologist, 39*(2), 105–116.

Dimsdale, J. E. (2000). Stalked by the past: The influence of ethnicity on health. *Psychosomatic Medicine, 62*, 161–170.

Dixon-Woods, M., & Critchley, S. (2000). Medical and lay views of irritable bowel syndrome. *Family Practice, 17*, 108–113.

Drossman, D. A. (1995a). Psychosocial factors in the care of patients with gastrointestinal disorders. In T. Yamada (Ed.), *Textbook of gastroenterology.* Philadelphia: J.B. Lippincott.

Drossman, D. A. (1995b). Diagnosing and treating patients with refractory functional gastrointestinal disorders. *Annals of Internal Medicine, 123*(9), 688–697.

Drossman, D. A. (1999). Review articles: An integrated approach to irritable bowel syndrome. *Alimentary Pharmacological Therapy, 13* (Suppl. 2), 3–14.

Drossman, D. A., Corazziari, E., Delvaux, M., Spiller, R. C., Talley, N. J., Thompson, W. G., et al. (2006). *Rome III: Functional gastrointestinal disorders* (4th ed.). Lawrence, KS: Allen Press.

Drossman, D. A., Li, Z., Andruzzi, E., Temple, R., Talley, N. J., & Thompson, W. G. (1993). U.S. Householder survey of functional gastrointestinal disorders: Prevalence, sociodemography and health impact. *Digestive Diseases Science, 38*, 1569–1580.

Drossman, D. A., McKee, D. C., Sandler, R. S., Mitchell, C. M., Cramer, E. M., Lowman, B. C., et al. (1988). Psychosocial factors in the irritable bowel syndrome: a multivariate study of patients and non-patients with irritable bowel syndrome. *Grastroenterology, 95*, 701–708.

Drossman, D. A., Morris, C. B., Schneck, S., Hu, Y. J., Norton, N. J., Norton, W. F., et al. (2009). International survey of patients with IBS: symptom features and their severity, health status, treatments and risk taking to achieve clinical benefit. *Journal of Clinical Gastgroenterology, 43*(6), 541–550.

Drossman, D. A., Toner, B. B., Whitehead, W. E., Diamant, N. E., Dalton, C. B., & Duncan, S. (2003). Cognitive-behavioral therapy versus education and desipramine versus placebo for moderate to severe functional bowel disorders. *Gastroenterology, 125*(1), 19–31.

Fabrege, H. (1991). Somatization in cultural-historical perspective. In L. J. Kirmayer & J. M. Robbins (Eds.), *Current concepts of somatization: Research and clinical perspectives*. Washington, DC: American Psychiatric Press.

Garner, D. M., Olmstead, M. P., & Polivy, J. (1983). The Eating Disorder Inventory: A measure of cognitive-behavioral dimensions of anorexia nervosa and bulimia. In D. Coscina & L. M. Dixon (Eds.), *Anorexia nervosa: Recent developments in research* (pp. 173–184). New York: Alan R. Liss.

Gralnek, I. M., Hays, R. D., Kilbourne, A., Naliboff, B., & Mayer, E. (2000). The impact of irritable bowel syndrome on health related quality of life. *Gastroenterology, 119*(3), 655–660.

Greenberger, D., & Padesky, C. (1995). *Mind over mood: Change how you feel by changing the way you think*. New York: Guilford.

Greene, B., & Blanchard, E. B. (1994). Cognitive therapy for irritable bowel syndrome. *Journal of Consulting and Clinical Psychology, 62*, 576–582.

International Foundation for Functional Gastrointestinal Disorders (IFFGD). (2002). *IBS in the real world survey [pamphlet]*. Milwaukee, WI: International Foundation for Functional Gastrointestinal Disorders.

Kirmayer, L. J., & Robbins, J. M. (1991). Functional somatic syndromes. In L. J. Kirmayer & J. M. Robbins (Eds.), *Current concepts of somatization* (pp. 79–105). Washington, DC: American Psychiatric Association.

Lackner, J. M., Jaccard, J., Krasner, S. S., Katz, L. A., Gudleski, G. D., & Holroyd, K. (2008). Self administered cognitive behavior therapy for moderate to severe irritable bowel syndrome: Clinical efficacy, tolerability, feasibility. *Clinical Gastroenterology and Hepatology, 6*(8), 899–906.

Lackner, J. M., Quigley, B. M., & Blanchard, E. B. (2004). Depression and abdominal pain in IBS patients: The mediating role of catastrophizing. *Psychosomatic Medicine, 66*, 435–441.

Leininger, M. (Ed.). (1985). *Qualitative research methods in nursing*. Orlando, FL: Grune & Stratton.

Letson, S., & Dancey, C. P. (1996). Nurses' perceptions of irritable bowel syndrome (IBS) and sufferers of IBS. *Journal of Advanced Nursing, 23*, 969–974.

Levy, R. L., Cain, K. C., Jarriett, M., & Heitkemper, M. M. (1997). The relationship between daily life stress and gastrointestinal symptoms of women with irritable bowel syndrome. *Journal of Behavioral Medicine, 20*, 177–193.

Levy, R. L., Olden, K. W., Naliboff, B. D., Bradley, L. A., Francisconi, C., Drossman, D. A., et al. (2006). Psychosocial aspects of the functional gastrointestinal disorders. *Gastgroenterology, 130*, 1447–1458.

Longstreth, G. F., Wilson, A., Knight, K., Wong, J., Chiou, C. F., Barghout, V., et al. (2003). Irritable bowel syndrome, health care use, and costs: A US managed care perspective. *American Journal of Gastroenterology, 98*, 600–607.

Neff, D. F., & Blanchard, E. B. (1987). A multi-component treatment for irritable bowel syndrome. *Behavior Therapy, 18*, 70–83.

Rumsey, N. (1991). Group stress management programmes vs. pharmacological treatment in the treatment of irritable bowel syndrome. In K. W. Keaton, F. Creed, & N. L. M. Goeting (Eds.), *Current approaches towards confident management of irritable bowel syndrome*. Lyme Regis, UK: Lyme Regis Printing.

Russo, M. W., Gaynes, B. N., & Drossman, D. A. (1999). A national survey of practice patterns of gastroenterologists with comparison to the past two decades. *Journal of Clinical Gastroenterology, 29*(4), 339–434.

Sharpe, M., Peveler, R., & Mayou, R. (1992). The psychological treatment of patients with functional somatic symptoms: A practical guide. *Journal of Psychosomatic Research, 36*, 515–529.

Shaw, G., Srivastaa, E. D., Sadlier, M., Swann, P., James, J. Y., & Rhodes, J. (1991). Stress management for irritable bowel syndrome: A controlled trial. *Digestion, 50*, 36–42.

Simren, M., Abrahamsson, H., Svedlund, J., & Bjornsson, E. S. (2001). Quality of life in patients with irritable bowel syndrome seen in referral centers versus primary care: The impact of gender and predominant bowel pattern. *Scandinavian Journal of Gastroenterology, 36*, 545–552.

Sperry, L. (2009). *Treatment of chronic medical conditions: Cognitive-behavioral therapy strategies and integrative treatment protocols*. Washington, DC: American Psychological Association.

Talley, N. J., Boyce, P. M., & Jones, M. (1997). Predictors of health care seeking for irritable bowel syndrome: a population based study. *Gut, 41*, 394–398.

Thompson, W. G., Heaton, K. W., Smyth, G. T., & Smyth, C. (2000). Irritable bowel syndrome in general practice: Prevalence, characteristics, and referral. *Gut, 46*, 78–82.

Toner, B. B. (2005). Cognitive-behavioral treatment of irritable bowel syndrome. *CNS Spectrums, 10*(11), 883–890.

Toner, B. B., & Akman, D. (2000). Gender role and irritable bowel syndrome: Literature review and hypothesis. *American Journal of Gastroenterology, 95*, 11–16.

Toner, B. B., Chang, L., Fukudo, S., Guthrie, E., Locke, R., Norton, N., et al. (2006). Gender, age, society, culture and the patient's perspective in the disorders of gastrointestinal function. In D. A. Drossman, E. Corazziari, N. J. Talley, W. G. Thompson, & W. E. Whitehead (Eds.), *The functional gastrointestinal disorders* (pp. 231–294). (Rome III). Mclean, VA: Degnon Associates.

Toner, B. B., Segal, Z. V., & Emmot, S. (1998). Cognitive-behavioral group therapy for patients with irritable bowel syndrome. *International Journal of Group Psychotherapy, 48*, 215–243.

Toner, B. B., Segal, Z. V., Emmot, S. D., & Myran, D. (2000). *Cognitive-behavioral treatment of irritable bowel syndrome: The brain-gut connection*. New York: Guilford.

Van Dulmen, A. M., Fennis, J. F., & Bleijenberg, G. (1996). Cognitive-behavioral group therapy for irritable bowel syndrome: Effects and long term follow up. *Psychosomatic Medicine, 58*, 508–514.

Worell, J., & Remer, P. (1992). *Feminist perspectives in therapy: An empowerment model for women*. Toronto, Ontario: Wiley.

Whitehead, W. E., Bosmajian, L., Zonderman, A. B., Costa, P. T., & Schuster, M. M. (1988). Symptoms of psychological distress asociated with irritable bowel syndrome. *Gastroenterology, 95*, 709–714.

10/22 Paper

31 Cognitive-Behavioral Therapy for Insomnia: Evidence-Based Treatments and Encouraging Innovations for Primary Care

Bradley Rosenfield
J. Russell Ramsay
Stacey C. Cahn
Philip J. Pellegrino

Introduction

One of the great ironies of life is that we spend one third of it asleep. Sleep is such an essential process that its disturbance is directly related to poor health, impaired functioning, economic burden, and shorter life expectancy (e.g., Kripke, Simons, Garfinkel, & Hammond, 1979). Although the literature reflects a plethora of definitions of insomnia, most descriptions encompass problems in initiating sleep, maintaining, or returning to sleep once one has awakened (American Psychiatric Association [APA], 2000). Insomnia is the most frequent sleep complaint in primary health care facilities (Patinen & Hublin, 2005), and the majority of primary care patients may report a history of insomnia (Schochat, Umphress, Israel, & Ancoli-Israel, 1999). Primary care clinicians will inevitably be confronted with patients who have insomnia. Moreover, because insomnia can be such a complicated and debilitating disorder, a thorough knowledge of assessment, diagnosis, empirically validated interventions, and strategies to overcome obstacles to effective treatment is essential to providing optimum treatment.

Assessment and Diagnostic Issues

According to the *Diagnostic and Statistical Manual of Mental Disorders* (*DSM-IV-TR*: APA, 2000), insomnia is a constellation of symptoms including the following criteria: difficulties initiating or maintaining sleep, or the absence of feeling rested upon waking (APA, 2000; Ohayon, 2002). The symptoms associated with insomnia often result in daytime fatigue and impairments in important areas of functioning. A diagnosis of insomnia requires at least one month in duration. Some researchers have categorized insomnia as either "primary" or "secondary." Primary insomnia occurs independently of any other relevant medical or psychiatric conditions, whereas secondary insomnia is conceptualized as developing from or being exacerbated by the influence of other mental disorders or medical conditions (e.g., APA; Ohayon). Other research has suggested that insomnia can be a precursor to psychological conditions, particularly mood disorders (Ford & Kamerow, 1989).

Buysse (2008) posits that the distinction between primary and secondary insomnia is of no clinical relevance. However, if one has the symptoms of insomnia, one needs to be treated for sleep difficulties in conjunction with any other presenting problems, because comorbid conditions can exacerbate insomnia symptoms and complicate treatment (Krystal, 2006).

Distinguishing between primary and secondary insomnia can be difficult, and requires clinicians to be aware of psychiatric and medical disorders that are associated with sleep disturbances. In considering when to refer patients with insomnia for a medical evaluation, one should consider the variety of Axis III (medical) disorders that can cause or exacerbate sleep disorders.

Sleep-disrupting medical disorders include, but are not limited to, the following: various cardiovascular and lung conditions, hyper- and hypothyroidism, adrenal disease, bladder and kidney ailments, a variety of arthritic conditions, chronic and idiopathic fatigue syndromes, conditions related to headaches, menopause, periodic limb movements (restless leg syndrome), sleep apnea conditions, peptic and duodenal ulcers, numerous neurological disorders, asthma, sinusitis, gastroesophageal reflux disorder, colitis and ileitis, and any other condition that causes pain or discomfort (see Kryger, Roth, & Dement, 2005; Plotkin, 2004).

The broad range of medications that can interfere with sleep may be surprising. According to Noble, Greene, and Levinson (2001), the following medications can cause insomnia: antihypertensives (clonidine, alpha methyldopa, reserpine); beta-blockers (propranolol, timolol, atenolol); bronchodilators (terbutaline, albuterol, salmeterol, metaproterenol, theophylline, and other methylxanthines); decongestants (phenylpropanolamine, pseudoephedrine); hormones (oral contraceptives, cortisone, progesterone, thyroid hormone); sympathomimetics (amphetamines, epinephrine, ephedrine, pseudoephedrine); and antineoplastics (alpha interferon, goserelin acetate, leuprolide acetate, medroxyprogesterone, pentostatin, daunorubicin). Potentially sleep-impairing psychiatric medications include levodopa, monoamine oxidase inhibitors, methylphenidate, manzidol, and selective serotonin reuptake inhibitors (SSRIs), among many others (see Kryger et al., 2005). Even some sedatives such as traditional benzodiazepines have been clearly shown to disrupt "sleep architecture" or the sequence and duration of sleep stages (Barbera & Shapiro, 2005).

Psychiatric disorders frequently associated with insomnia include the full gamut of anxiety and mood disorders. Additionally, insomnia is not uncommon among individuals with attention-deficit/hyperactivity disorder (ADHD), psychotic disorders, certain personality disorders, and substance abuse. Of course, various endocrine, neurological, and other medical conditions may also be associated with these psychiatric disorders (APA, 2000).

Mood and anxiety disorders have been found to be highly comorbid with insomnia (APA, 2000; Ohayon, 1997). Individuals diagnosed with insomnia are likely to be at risk for developing depression and alcoholism (Ford & Cooper-Patrick, 2001). Insomnia has also been found to be highly prevalent in individuals with alcohol use problems (Brower, Aldrich, Robinson, Zucker, & Greden, 2001). Conversely, individuals with alcohol and substance-use disorders and comorbid depression or anxiety often report sleep problems predating their psychiatric difficulties (Currie, Clark, Rimac, & Malhorta, 2003).

For example, Brower et al. (2001) found that 61% of individuals seeking treatment for alcohol dependence experience insomnia symptoms. In this same study, individuals with insomnia were more likely to report using alcohol as a sleep aid, albeit a maladaptive one. Those with insomnia symptoms at baseline were also more likely to use alcohol five months posttreatment. Thus, clinicians may want to screen for substance use when evaluating a patient with sleep complaints.

Interestingly, a significant number of individuals meeting criteria for ADHD are notoriously poor sleepers. The relationship between ADHD and insomnia warrants attention, as cognitive deficits secondary to insomnia, such as inattention, working memory impairment, distractibility, and disinhibition may mimic or exacerbate ADHD symptoms (Ramsay & Rostain, 2008; van der Heijden, Smits, & Gunning, 2005). Adults with ADHD report elevated rates of sleep and circadian problems related to delayed sleep onset, more interrupted sleep, and, in some cases, greater need for sleep than controls, as well as increased likelihood of having an evening orientation, that is, being a self-described "night person." In fact, there has been concern among some sleep researchers that many cases of childhood ADHD are actually misdiagnosed sleep disturbances (Boonstra et al., 2007; Gau et al., 2007; Rybak, McNeely, Mackenzie, Jain, & Levitan, 2006, 2007). Moreover, insomnia is a frequent negative side effect of stimulants, the medication of choice for ADHD (e.g., Ramsay & Rostain, 2008).

Assessment

Given the complicated nature of sleep problems, a comprehensive evaluation is essential to generate accurate diagnoses, case conceptualizations, and treatment plans. Multiple assessment methods are recommended for differential diagnosis and to rule out various comorbidities. Moreover, it is essential to identify specific sleep patterns and sleep-related behaviors.

Assessment Tools

A thorough insomnia assessment may include structured interviews, self-report questionnaires, psychological testing, sleep logs, polysomnography (PSG), and actigraphy. The American Sleep Association (ASA) provides clinicians with an excellent downloadable database of useful instruments for assessing insomnia and other sleep disorders (see www.sleepassociation.org), including the *New Patient Form, Sleep Disorder Screening Questionnaire, Sleep Diary*, and *Sleep Log*. In addition, Perlis, Jungquist, Smith, and Posner (2008) offer a number of elegant instruments for assessing sleep difficulties, such as a *Sleep Environment Checklist* and *Motivation for Change Index*, among others that are appropriate for primary care settings.

The ASA's *New Patient Form* is a self-report, detailed history and symptom questionnaire covering substance/alcohol and caffeine use, general medical history, medication use, and family history. The *Disorder Screening Questionnaire*, another self-report measure, used in conjunction with a thorough interview, allows the clinician to quickly rule out sleep disorders. The *Sleep Diary* and *Sleep Log*, also available from ASA, can be used to establish baseline sleep behaviors. A 1- or 2-week pretreatment baseline period is recommended (Sateia, Doghrami, Hauri, & Morin, 2000) to allow patient and clinician to establish pretreatment patterns. These same measures may be used throughout treatment to monitor progress on objective behaviors, such as patterns leading up to bedtime, time going to bed, sleep-onset time, middle and terminal awakenings, sleep quality, and other disturbed sleep patterns. Patients are also able to monitor wake and sleep patterns throughout the day.

Psychological testing is recommended to rule out the frequent clinical comorbidities. Frequently co-occurring Axis I clinical syndromes can be assessed via the Structured Clinical Interview for *DSM-IV* Axis I Disorders (SCID-I; First, Spitzer, Gibbon, & Williams, 1996), the Beck Depression Inventory II (BDI-II; A. T. Beck, Steer, & Brown, 1996), the Beck Anxiety Inventory (BAI; A. T. Beck & Steer, 1990), and the Beck Hopelessness Scale (BHS; A. T. Beck & Steer, 1988). The Structured Clinical Interview for DSM-IV Personality Disorders (*SCID-II*; First, Gibbon, Spitzer, Williams, & Smith, 1997) is useful for identifying Axis II disorders that can cause sleep-impairing anxiety and stress. It should be noted, however, that structured clinical interviews such as the SCID-I and SCID-II may be time- and cost-prohibitive in primary care settings, and are more appropriate for use when patients are referred for assessment and treatment in clinical settings.

When ADHD is suspected, a number of psychometrically sound instruments may be used to rule out this disorder, including ADHD symptom checklists for both childhood and adult symptoms, such as both self-report and observer report forms (Barkley & Murphy, 2006), the Brown Attention Deficit Disorder Scale for Adults (BADDS; Brown, 1996), and the Conners' Adult ADHD Rating Scales (CAARS; Conners, Erhardt, & Sparrow, 1999). Because adults with ADHD may have difficulties related to accurate self-monitoring, it may be useful to elicit feedback from significant others who may be able to comment on patients' sleep patterns.

The practice guidelines of the American Academy of Sleep Medicine (AASM; Standards of Practice Committee of the American Academy of Sleep Medicine, 2006) do *not* recommend routine PSG for transient insomnia, chronic insomnia, or insomnia associated with other psychiatric disorders. However, the AASM does prescribe referral for PSG when one suspects a sleep-related breathing disorder, periodic limb movement disorder, treatment for insomnia fails, the patient experiences precipitous arousals with violent or injurious behavior, or there is doubt about the provisional diagnosis. PSG can also provide invaluable data for other sleep conditions that frequently go undiagnosed, even by the best clinicians, such as breathing-related sleep disorders, sleepwalking disorder, circadian rhythm sleep disorders, narcolepsy, and sleep terror disorder (APA, 2000). These other sleep disorders may require additional treatment, and insomnia symptoms are likely to subside in the event that another primary sleep disorder is treated (Krystal, 2006).

Incidence and Clinical Manifestations in the Primary Care Setting

Insomnia is the most frequent sleep complaint in primary health care facilities (Patinen & Hublin, 2005). However, epidemiology findings regarding insomnia in the primary care setting are variable. One study determined that up to 69% of primary care patients report a history of insomnia, with 19% chronic and 50% experiencing occasional sleep difficulties (Schochat et al., 1999). If accurate, this means that the majority of primary care patients experience insomnia at some point. Kushida et al. (2000) found that approximately 32% of primary care patients experience chronic insomnia. Yet another study determined that approximately 10% of primary care patients aged 18 to 65 complain of significant insomnia symptoms, specifically, 6% with onset insomnia, 7% middle waking, and 5% awakening early and could not return to sleep, with overlap between varieties.

In the general population, it appears that 10–15% of adults experience insomnia persisting for one month or longer (Roth, 2001). However, 95% of randomly selected adults surveyed in a Gallup poll reported that they experienced insomnia at some point in their lives (Gallup Organization, 1979). In a survey of over 50 studies, Ohayon (2002) found that approximately one third of the adult population in the United States experienced symptoms of insomnia. Yet, there was great inconsistency in prevalence rates among these studies, which ranged from 4.4 to 48%. Much of the difference was accounted for by operational definitions of insomnia. Among these studies, inclusion criteria generally fell into the following four categories: (a) insomnia, (b) insomnia and dissatisfaction with sleep, (c) insomnia, with daytime sequelae, and (d) *DSM-IV* criteria for the diagnosis. Using the more stringent *DSM-IV* criteria reduced prevalence rates to only 6% of the population. However, a significant portion of those seeking treatment for insomnia, using sleep medication, or reporting sleep dissatisfaction fail to meet threshold for the *DSM-IV* criteria. Thus, strict adherence to *DSM-IV* criteria may drastically underestimate the scope of the problem (Edinger & Means, 2005).

It should be noted that the prevalence of primary insomnia is relatively rare, with only 4.9% of insomnia cases lacking at least one other comorbid disorder (Weissman, Greenwald, Nino-Murcia, & Dement, 1997). This means that one should expect that approximately 95% of insomnia cases will be complicated by an additional disorder. A number of variables increase the risk of insomnia, including advanced age, gender, psychiatric comorbidity, and occupation.

Notwithstanding these grim statistics, insomnia is rarely the chief complaint in primary care, leaving the disorder to be underdiagnosed and untreated in too many patients (National Heart, Lung, and Blood Institute Working Group on Insomnia, 1999). The resulting lack of appropriate treatment may account for the fact that primary care patients with insomnia experience significant functional impairment, use more medical services, and are disabled for more days due to poor health than patients with properly treated insomnia. Patients with insomnia are also more likely to use medication, with 28% taking psychotropic drugs, such as benzodiazepines and antidepressants (Simon & VonKorff, 1997). Such findings underscore the burden of insomnia to both the individual and society as a whole.

Brief Case History

To better illustrate the comorbidity and complicated clinical nature of patients presenting with complaints of insomnia in primary care, we present the case of Andre.

Andre, a married, Caucasian, 27-year-old computer programmer, active in an adult football league, initially presented for treatment with chronic insomnia, moderate depression, and attention-deficit disorder, predominantly inattentive type. Because of the combination of his superior intellect and psychiatric problems, he had a long history of academic and vocational success punctuated by painful setbacks. Andre and all who knew him agreed that he was not living up to his potential. Most distressing to Andre was the fact that he was now experiencing terrifying nightmares. Although Andre was recently married, he lamented that he and his wife were already experiencing a "stormy relationship" resulting from his wife's perceptions of his "childish irresponsibility, temper, and inability to communicate verbally." According to Andre, his sleep deficit was compounding his mood- and ADHD-related cognitive and behavioral difficulties, which have plagued him since childhood. He had reached a new nadir in concentration (e.g., failing to attend to conversations with his wife and employer).

Moreover, Andre's employer, a very tolerant uncle, was becoming increasingly annoyed with Andre's inability to finish tasks because of compulsive Internet surfing, missing important appointments, tardiness, impulsivity, and his obvious inability to focus his attention in important business meetings. The latter was manifested as blurting out disruptions when others were talking, missing major points, and repeating questions that others had already asked. To his dismay, Andre was also beginning to nod off during meetings. Thus, although his intentions were admirable, others perceived him to be rude, irresponsible, and uninterested.

As early as high school, Andre's primary care physician (PCP) had attempted to treat his ADHD symptoms with a variety of stimulant medications. Methylphenidate (Ritalin) provided Andre with the greatest relief, enabling him to surpass his family's expectations by graduating from both high school and college. However, all of the stimulants produced distressing insomnia, which was never properly treated. In fact, his sleep disturbance was so distressing that medication compliance had recently gone from spotty to nonexistent.

At age 27, his psychiatrist prescribed atomoxetine HCl (Strattera), a nonstimulant medication, which greatly ameliorated his ADHD symptoms and improved his performance at work. Andre acknowledged that the medication had been immensely helpful in increasing attention, impulse control, organization, follow through in important activities, and reducing forgetfulness and distractibility. Moreover, with his newfound success, his mood elevated greatly as his self-efficacy and self-image improved. Furthermore, he had learned that more adaptive behavior could bring social reinforcement in the form of compliments and affection, both at home and work. Another benefit was that the chronic insomnia secondary, in part, to the stimulant medication had vanished—at least for the first month of treatment—until the nightmares began.

Cognitive-Behavioral Case Conceptualization

Perlis, Jungquist, Smith, and Posner (2008) propose a cognitive-behavioral case conceptualization model that recognizes predisposing, precipitating, and perpetuating factors. Predisposing factors include inherited genetic and biological predispositions, such as hyperarousal (elevated metabolism and cortisol levels), hyperactivity (exaggerated startle response and subsequent sustained arousal; Perlis, Smith & Pigeon, 2005), and an "inherently weak sleep generating system" (Perlis et al., 2008, pp. 7–8). Other predisposing factors include a tendency to worry, family history of insomnia, depression, or anxiety.

According to the diathesis-stress model, *predisposing* factors make individuals vulnerable to *precipitating* events to varying degrees. Precipitants then interact with predispositions and trigger insomnia. Relevant precipitants may include current psychological problems (depression, anxiety, delusions, or obsessions); physiological issues (medical illness, pain, or discomfort); or social, financial, or family stressors that can increase cognitive and physiological arousal and impede sleep. These predisposing factors constitute the diathesis (a constitutional predisposition toward illness), whereas the precipitating stressors trigger insomnia (Perlis et al., 2005, 2008).

Although the majority of the population has experienced brief periods of insomnia, the presence of *perpetuating* factors differentiates the transient from the chronic varieties of insomnia. Individuals with insomnia may inadvertently perpetuate sleep disturbance by employing maladaptive compensatory strategies in an attempt to deal with sleep disturbance. Maladaptive coping behaviors may include excessive time in bed (TIB), non-sleep-related behaviors in bed, and resulting conditioned arousal. Moreover, poor diet and lack of exercise can perpetuate sleep disturbance (Bootzin & Nicassio, 1978; Perlis et al., 2008; Spielman, Saskin, & Thorpy, 1987; Spielman & Glovinksy, 2004). Compensatory behaviors stem from individuals' belief systems regarding themselves, others, their future, health, and sleep (see Figure 31.1, p. 712).

Individuals with insomnia also tend to underestimate their total sleep time. The resulting frustration, often stemming more from cognitive distortion than reality, can increase both day- and nighttime irritability (Bonnet, 1990). This phenomenon implicates sleep-related cognitions as a perpetuating factor in insomnia, as cognitive distortions related to the amount of sleep and actual sleep needed to function can lead to hypervigilance during presleep and sleep hours. An example is the individual who has the erroneous belief that he/she must go to bed earlier in order to get more sleep. This individual is likely to end up spending more TIB with less sleep, which conditions the association between the bed and arousal.

Physiological hyperarousal, both during daytime and nighttime hours, appears to be a major contributor to insomnia. Specifically, hyperarousal of the autonomic nervous system during sleep, manifested as increased heart rate, peripheral vasoconstriction, and elevated body temperature (Noble et al., 2001), and the stress response appear to be strongly related to insomnia symptoms (Noble et al.; Perlis, Merica, Smith, & Giles, 2001). To complicate matters, the relationship between insomnia and many of the aforementioned conditions may be multidirectional creating a vicious Axis I–Axis III circle. For example, headaches may interfere with sleep onset, and the resulting fatigue makes one more prone to headaches, which can then impede sleep.

To further complicate matters, individuals with personality disorders (Axis II) experience social and emotional conflict and impaired functioning, which can induce sleep-impairing stress and increase the vicissitudes of social and environmental stressors on Axis IV (A. T. Beck, Freeman, & Davis; 2004, Millon, 1996, 2000). For instance, the employer of an individual with a dependent personality disorder may label the employee as "high maintenance." In difficult economic times, such an employee may be more likely to be terminated, leading to the type of distress that can interfere with good sleep. Consequently, the combination of the Axis I, II, III, and IV factors understandably produces a vicious spiral that increases dysphoria, promotes dysfunction, impairs health-preserving behavior, and increases physiological arousal. On the other hand, a complete diagnostic picture facilitates proper case conceptualization and allows treatment planning for all of the relevant complications, which can ensure treatment of the other deleterious conditions, and thereby improve treatment outcome. Consequently, when treating insomnia, a thorough assessment is essential to identify previously undiagnosed relationships between disorders and obstacles to effective treatment.

Identifying and Addressing Obstacles to Treatment

Effective treatment requires an evolving case conceptualization that helps to explain the current predicament, identify obstacles to treatment adherence, and to maximize the effectiveness of chosen interventions. For instance, in primary care settings, approximately half of older patients with disturbed sleep attribute their sleep problems to the aging process or general medical conditions. As a consequence of these maladaptive beliefs, they show little interest in receiving behavioral treatment (Cahn et al., 2005), and up to 75% fail to adhere to treatment regimens (Salzman, 1995). Thus, for these patients, appropriate treatment may begin with increasing awareness of the deleterious effects of insomnia (to increase cognitive dissonance and motivation for change) and psychoeducation regarding effective treatment (to provide hope for better sleep and a healthier life).

Another potential obstacle to good sleep and treatment adherence occurs when individuals compulsively engage in stimulating activity prior to bedtime, such as television viewing, Internet surfing, excessive exercise, or ingesting stimulants. These behaviors are particularly common in individuals with ADHD, and are associated with hyperarousal (Ramsay & Rostain, 2008). On the other hand, theta waves are characteristic of daydreaming and the transition to stage 1 sleep (e.g., Klinkerfuss, Lange, Weinberg, & O'Leary, 1965). Interestingly, reading can induce theta waves in some people with ADHD (and those who find reading to be relaxing or "boring") (Monastra et al., 1999). Consequently, an innovative treatment for insomnia would be to prescribe light, dull, or even familiar reading for this population. Listening to books on tape, repetitive prayer, meditation mantras, or relaxing music may produce the same effects. The predictable structure of *familiar* material may be particularly soporific because it activates the same sleep mechanisms inherent to the children's proverbial bedtime story, which seem to increase in sleep-inducing effect with repetition.

Thus, replacing late-night television viewing with the incompatible response of reading, with specific instructions to relax, use diaphragmatic breathing, and *not actively attempt to remember anything* may help to reduce hyperarousal and, instead, produce sleep-inducing brain waves. In this way, a complete diagnosis and case conceptualization allows the clinician to *use the pathology in the service of the patient*, for example, with individuals with ADHD.

Cognitive-behavioral interventions for insomnia are clinically effective without the aforementioned risks attendant to pharmacotherapy. Nonetheless, specific risks associated with cognitive-behavioral therapy (CBT) do exist, including the fact that sleep restriction can trigger episodes in both bipolar and seizure disorder patients (Colombo, Benedetti, Barbini, Campori, & Smeraldi, 1999; Fountain, Kim, & Lee, 1998). Even relaxation-based interventions are not completely without minor risks, as the paradoxical phenomenon of relaxation-induced anxiety occurs in approximately 15% of individuals attempting relaxation methods (Heide & Borkovec, 1983, 1984).

For example, a surprising obstacle arose while treating Andre. Prior to the onset of insomnia, Andre's new psychiatrist prescribed Strattera to treat his ADHD. Andre was "amazed" by how effectively this drug directly ameliorated his ADHD symptoms, and consequently, improving his adaptive functioning and mood. However, there was a fly in the ointment. During the first month of pharmacotherapy, he began to experience terrifying nightmares, in which he dreamed that a monstrous assailant was choking him. During these episodes, he awoke breathlessly gagging for air, disoriented, and with the near-delusional idea that his wife was strangling him. He attributed the onset of these nightmares to the medication. As a result, he abruptly ceased taking his ADHD medication in the fourth week of pharmacotherapy, even though he found the prospect of abandoning the first truly effective treatment to be intensely distressing. Various sleep medications only increased the frequency of the nightmares.

Perpetuating insomnia were anxiogenic cognitions ("I'm going to die in my sleep" or "I'll be a zombie tomorrow!") and safety behaviors, such as avoiding sleep and engaging in arousing late-night activity in bed (reading, loud music, and TV viewing).

With such obstacles to effective pharmacological treatment, it was at this point that Andre's psychiatrist referred him to a psychologist for assessment and CBT treatment of the now untreated ADHD, insomnia, depression, and anxiety.

As Andre described awaking to the sensation of choking during his initial CBT session, one could not help but be struck by his rather large neck, with a circumference in excess of 19 inches, resulting from football exercises designed to prevent catastrophic spinal injuries and "just to look tough." Choking, large neck circumference, and nightmares are all common among individuals with obstructive sleep apnea hypopnea syndrome (OSAHS; Guilleminault & Bassiri, 2005).

On consultation, it appeared that previous clinicians had not suspected OSAHS because Andre appeared to be in such great physical shape, rather than the stereotypically obese OSAHS patient. However, knowing that neck circumference (>40 cm) correlates more strongly with the disorder than body mass (Guilleminault & Bassiri, 2005) prompted our referral for PSG, which confirmed a mild form of the disorder, and the end to the mystery of the nightmares was now in sight (see the Development and Implementation of an Empirically Based Treatment Plan section).

Points of Collaboration With Physician and Family

Because insomnia is a truly biopsychosocial phenomenon, proper treatment often requires a multidisciplinary approach. For example, because of the contemporary time constraints attendant to providing good medical care, busy physicians generally do not have the hours needed to conduct a detailed psychological interview and objective assessment necessary to make an accurate differential diagnosis on Axis I and II. For this reason, physicians often refer to a psychologist. Conversely, when psychologists diagnose insomnia, it is often prudent to refer to a physician to rule out a plethora of serious medical conditions that may interfere with healthy sleep, as illuminated previously. Moreover, when indicated, clinicians of all stripes can benefit from PSG to ferret out all of the possible sleep disturbances.

Physicians may also refer complicated cases or cases in which sleep medication has failed, such as Andre, for CBT. Ongoing collaboration between psychologists and physicians is often essential to ensure that patients receive the best possible care, whether or not sleep medications are indicated.

Development and Implementation of an Empirically Based Treatment Plan

Because every patient is a unique individual, an effective treatment plan stems directly from a thorough assessment and case conceptualization specific to that person. Treatment goals should be collaboratively generated with the patient to increase motivation and treatment adherence (Meichenbaum & Turk, 1987).

For example, Andre agreed to treatment goals, including a return to a normal sleep schedule of roughly 8 hours per night and resumption of ADHD medication. The first step was psychoeducation to help Andre understand that, rather than being "crazy," what he was experiencing was perfectly logical. His large neck and the laws of gravity made it more likely that his upper airways would collapse during sleep. When this happened, he was deprived of oxygen and suffered the dreaded choking sensation. As per the activation-synthesis theory of dreaming (Hobson & McCarley, 1977), his dream that someone was choking him likely resulted from his brain's attempt to explain his physical sensations and oxygen deprivation. This produced dream imagery consistent with choking. For instance, most individuals will readily remember having incorporated such environmental stimuli as the sound of a storm or the sensation of being touched into a dream. The sound of heavy rain may be transformed into a roller coaster or a light touch on the arm as a spider. Although Andre initially looked confused by this explanation, he could recall similar experiences. This cognitive reframe was transcribed onto a coping card, which Andre agreed to place on his nightstand so that he could refer to it immediately upon awakening.

At the beginning of the next session, Andre announced that he slept fine throughout the week, even though he had two similarly bad dreams. However, "this time, instead of panicking, I just said to myself, I got a big neck and I probably just stopped breathing temporarily." He was then encouraged to seek treatment for the OSAHS, for which he was prescribed a continuous airways pressure (CPAP) device. Additionally, stimulus control therapy (SCT), sleep restriction therapy (SRT), relaxation, and paradoxical intention were added to maintain positive treatment effects. Although the behavioral techniques, such as SRT and SCT, are first-line treatments for insomnia (Morgenthaler et al., 2006; Perlis et al., 2008), Andre's case clearly illustrates the importance of cognitive intervention in understanding and treating certain cases of insomnia.

Evaluation of Treatment Outcomes

Notwithstanding the potential adverse effects, pharmacotherapy is still the most frequently used treatment among PCPs (Chesson et al., 1999). Medication is most effective for acute insomnia (Smith et al., 2002), producing good results within one week, which is generally quicker than the effects of CBT. However, by 4–8 weeks and longer, both pharmacotherapy and CBT are essentially equally effective (Smith et al., 2002; Wu, Bao, Zhang, Deng, & Long, 2006). Limitations of medication are well known and include the risk of dependence, tolerance, withdrawal, and high and precipitous relapse rates once medication ceases. Additionally, because pharmacotherapy requires repeated visits to physicians for prescriptions, and the fact that the treatment may require chronic use, the long-term cost-effectiveness is questionable. In other words, pharmacotherapy reliably increases health care use and health risks.

Conversely, CBT reduces both risk and use (Morin, Bastein, & Savard, 2003) and provides even more enduring treatment effects than drug treatments (Hryshko-Mullen, Broeckl, Haddock, & Peterson, 2000; Morin, 2004; Morin, Stone, McDonald, & Jones, 1994). Moreover, evidence-based CBT has been found to be effective for all varieties of insomnia (Morin, Colecchi, Stone, Stood, & Brink, 1999; Smith et al., 2002), regardless of comorbidity or subtype (Goodie, Isler, Hunter, & Peterson, 2009). Recently, there have been a number of methodologically sound controlled clinical trials conducted specifically in primary care settings.

For example, Goodie et al. (2009) used CBT with adult insomnia patients in two primary care settings. The treatment protocol included psychoeducation and specific individualized behavioral recommendations to improve sleep, based on Morin (1993). Interventions were framed as experiments. Specific interventions included sleep hygiene education (Riedel, 2000), stimulus control (Bootzin & Epstein, 2000), sleep restriction (Spielman, Saskin, & Thorpy, 1987), relaxation

(Morin & Espie, 2003), and bibliotherapy (Jacobs, 1998). The results were impressive. After only three brief behavioral consultations, 83% were successful in reducing insomnia, defined as greater than 85% sleep efficiency or meeting their own sleep goals.

What is even more impressive about this study is that participants included complicated cases, such as those taking multiple medications, comorbid medical or psychiatric conditions, and history or current use of sleep medication. Limitations of this study included a relatively high dropout rate (18 dropouts versus 29 completers), with the only significant difference between groups being that those who completed had a "more diverse set of diagnoses compared to those who were non-completers, who generally presented with a sleep-related problem as their primary diagnosis" (Goodie et al., 2009, p. 299). The study also failed to use a no-treatment comparison group. However, the authors justify their design by citing the following research regarding the stability of insomnia symptoms (Edinger & Sampson, 2003; Morin et al., 1999) and the fact that they used a clinical series design. Despite its limitations, the importance of the study is that it demonstrated treatment effectiveness, in both cost and outcome, in real-world clinics with a diverse sample of primary care patients, many of whom had comorbid disorders.

In another study, 139 randomly assigned primary care patients compared CBT for insomnia with a self-monitoring control group (Espie, Inglis, & Harvey, 2001). Primary care nurses administered CBT in a small group format in only six sessions. Patients in the CBT groups improved on sleep latency, middle waking, and overall sleep time. These gains were maintained at a 1-year follow-up.

Additional randomized controlled trials have been conducted using various behavioral and CBT approaches. The salubrious and enduring effects of CBT have been replicated many times in other randomized controlled studies, for individuals (Wang, Wang, & Tsai, 2005), in group formats (Jansson & Linton, 2005), and for those with medical or psychiatric comorbidities (Rybarczyk, Lopez, Benson, Alsten, & Stepanski, 2002). In a review of CBT treatment for comorbid medical and psychiatric illnesses, Smith, Huang, and Manber (2005) determined that CBT improved sleep and comorbid psychiatric and medical conditions. Consequently, the evidence is that CBT has been empirically validated for the treatment of insomnia, in a wide variety of patient populations, treatment formats, and treatment settings, including primary care.

CBT has also proven to be quite efficient and cost-effective in ameliorating primary insomnia in primary care settings. Significant improvements can be achieved in as few as two sessions in the primary care setting (Edinger & Sampson, 2003). Furthermore, CBT can effectively reduce secondary insomnia, even when medical and psychiatric conditions are the primary source of sleep disturbance (Smith, Huang, & Manber, 2005).

Cognitive-Behavioral Interventions: How to Help Patients Sleep

Following is a synopsis of a number of behavioral and cognitive interventions and empirical evidence for their effectiveness in treating for insomnia.

Stimulus Control

Of all the behavioral interventions for insomnia, stimulus control therapy (SCT) (Bootzin & Epstein, 2000; Bootzin & Nicassio, 1978) has the greatest empirical support (Chesson et al., 1999). In SCT, individuals are instructed to use the bed only for sleep and sex. If the person does not fall asleep within 15 minutes, he or she is advised to leave the bedroom and engage in a calming activity until they are sleepy. Only then is the individual instructed to return to bed.

The rationale for SCT for insomnia is based on a classical conditioning paradigm. The theory posits that individuals with insomnia associate frustration and arousal with the bed (conditioned stimulus [CS]). Conditioning occurs over time, as the individual tosses and turns, worries in frustration, or watches TV during bouts of insomnia, so that the bed elicits arousal à la conditioned response (CR). In behavioral terms, the goal of treatment is counterconditioning, so that the CR is extinguished and the bed is conditioned to only elicit sleep. In operant terms, going to bed becomes a discriminative stimulus for sleep, which is positively reinforced by refreshing sleep.

Sleep Restriction

The goal of sleep restriction, sometimes referred to as sleep compression, is to increase sleep efficiency. Sleep efficiency is a percentage, which is computed by dividing the time spent physically lying in bed by the time that an individual is asleep, multiplied by 100 (Morin et al., 2006). A sleep efficiency of >85% (85% of the TIB is spent sleeping) is normally considered to be desirable. After establishing a baseline of total daily sleep time, including naps, via the sleep log, the patient is instructed to remain in bed for only the time *sleeping*. Napping is usually proscribed. By reducing the amount of TIB to only sleep time, patients are able to increase the percentage of sleep time while in bed. This accomplishes bed-sleep conditioning fundamental to SCT. Patients keep track of their sleep using a sleep diary.

Patients are taught to go to bed at the same time each night and to wake up on a regular schedule each morning. Most approaches recommend starting SRT with five hours or more in bed per night (Perlis et al., 2008). This mild sleep deprivation produces fatigue as an establishing operation that increases the likelihood of sleep. If patients sleep 90% of their TIB in a given week, then the TIB is increased by 15 minutes per night. If their sleep efficiency is below 85%, then they are to decrease their sleep time by 15 minutes. This approach reduces sleep onset latency, decreases middle waking after sleep onset, and improves sleep efficiency by inducing mild sleep deprivation and reducing anticipatory anxiety (Morin, 2005). Many controlled studies have evaluated the efficacy of sleep restriction for treating insomnia (Morin et al., 1999).

Sleep Hygiene Education

Psychoeducation regarding behaviors that can facilitate or prevent restorative sleep can be valuable. The following sleep hygiene instructions are based mainly on Morin (2005), Perlis et al. (2008), and Riedel (2000):

- Maintain a regular sleep schedule to "train" circadian rhythms to facilitate sleep compression.

- Abstain from caffeine (coffee, tea, caffeinated sodas, chocolate), nicotine, and alcohol, especially in the late afternoon, which can impede or fragment sleep.
- Engage in moderate, regular exercise, particularly late in the afternoon and early evening.
- Modify the bedroom to promote sleep: make it comfortable, quiet, dark, cool, and, if necessary, add a *white noise device* to mask extraneous noise;.
- Avoid bright lights when going to the bathroom at night, in favor of small night-lights, to avoid "resetting" circadian rhythms.
- Avoid excessive drinking after dinner to avoid waking as a result of the need to urinate.

Obstacles to implementing these recommendations are appropriate targets for cognitive interventions or a problem-solving approach, the latter to ameliorate practical issues, such as noisy roommates, shift work, overwork, or habitual television viewing or compulsive Internet-surfing activities.

- Eating a light snack or having a glass of milk (containing tryptophan) before bedtime can facilitate sleep.
- Turn the clock away from the bed, to avoid stimulating frustration and worry.

Interestingly, individuals who exercise regularly have been found to have improved sleep and moods (Blumenthal et al., 2007).

Relaxation and Breathing Retraining

Because a combination of cognitive arousal (racing thoughts, performance anxiety) and maladaptive physiological activation (sympathetic nervous system arousal, including elevated heart rate, rapid breathing, muscle tension, vasoconstriction) interfere with normal sleep and perpetuate insomnia, it is logical that treatment attempts to deescalate arousal to help the individual to relax facilitate sleep. Relaxation-based interventions accomplish this task by reducing sympathetic nervous system arousal and promoting calming parasympathetic nervous system activity, resulting in decreased heart and respiration rates, muscle relaxation, and even vasodilation. Various relaxation techniques have demonstrated effectiveness in this regard, including passive relaxation, progressive muscle relaxation (PMR), guided imagery, autogenic training, biofeedback, meditation, and hypnosis (Bernstein, Borkovec, & Hazlett-Stevens, 2000; Jacobson, 1964).

According to Morin (2005), "relaxation is the most common nondrug therapy for insomnia" (p. 728). Some of the more commonly used techniques include diaphragmatic breathing and PMR. Diaphragmatic breathing teaches patients to inhale slowly with their diaphragm (e.g., inhale to a count of four and exhale to a count of four). Decreasing respiration rate correlates with a reciprocal decrease in other sympathetic nervous system (SNS) activity, such as heart rate, brain waves, muscle tension, and so on (Craske & Barlow, 1993). PMR teaches patients to alternately tense their muscles and then release the muscle tension. During treatment sessions, teaching patients effective ways to quickly reduce physiological arousal inspires self-efficacy in patients and imputes credibility to the clinician (Bernstein, Borkovec, & Hazlett-Stevens, 2000; Jacobson, 1938).

Whereas PMR targets physiological arousal, imagery-based relaxation techniques focus on reducing worry, as well as racing and intrusive thoughts that comprise cognitive arousal (Morin, 2005). However, identification of appropriate imagery requires careful assessment, as triggers for relaxation are idiosyncratic. For example, although few would endorse the notion of boxing to be a relaxing activity, Joe, a former amateur boxer, found "imagining boxing with an opponent, totally relaxed and in slow motion" to be very helpful in inducing sleep. Another, more aesthetic insomnia patient, Rosalind, found imagining "walking through Monet's *Poppy Field near Giverny* painting" to be particularly soporific.

Cognitive Restructuring for Reducing Cognitive Arousal

Recent research has also illustrated the pivotal impact of cognitive arousal (unwanted intrusive and worrisome thoughts) and attention to insomnia symptoms (e.g., see Perlis et al., 2008) on insomnia. Anyone who has ever lain in bed unable to sleep will quickly recognize the relevance of these cognitive processes. According to the cognitive model (e.g., A. T. Beck, Rush, Shaw, & Emery, 1979; J. Beck, 1995), like the roots of a tree, schema and core beliefs underlie and powerfully influence the expression of the other cognitive processes, mood, and behavior. For instance, dysfunctional beliefs, such as "if I don't fall asleep immediately, I will be up all night, and tomorrow will be a disaster," may give rise to a confirmation bias, in which the individual becomes hypervigilant for evidence of obstacles to sleep (e.g., to internal symptoms of arousal or external noise) and a resultant cognitive overreaction (catastrophizing) to any stimuli that may be a potential threat, ambiguous, or even neutral (Harvey, Tang, & Browning, 2005). This confirmation bias is further confirmed as individuals with insomnia are more likely than good sleepers to insist they were awake at times, even when their own REM sleep patterns confirmed they were fast asleep (Mercer, Bootzin, & Lack, 2002). This indicates a tendency to misperceive and misinterpret sleep among individuals with insomnia.

Clinical research supports the propensity for insomnia patients to catastrophize, especially regarding the consequences of not sleeping (Harvey & Greennall, 2003; Perlis et al., 2000). Such an overreaction can then produce a physiological arousal, which is perceived as evidence for the dysfunctional belief. This produces a vicious circle and reinforces the individual's confirmation bias and interoceptive conditioning for arousal. Andre experienced such a vicious circle, as illustrated in Figure 31.1.

Consequently, cognitive interventions for insomnia directly target all of the cognitive processes, such as the dysfunctional beliefs that maintain cognitive distortions and intrusive thoughts, maladaptive beliefs regarding sleep, and cognitive arousal that perpetuates insomnia (see Harvey, Tang, & Browning, 2005, for a review of the cognitive research).

Despite evidence for these cognitive tendencies, debate still abounds in the sleep community regarding the necessity of adding cognitive techniques to behavioral interventions for the treatment of insomnia. Indeed, it is reasonable to ask, with the demonstrated effectiveness of behavioral treatments, what is the value of cognitive therapy for insomnia? One reason to use cognitive techniques is that

31.1

Insomnia's physiological arousal–dysfunctional belief cycle.

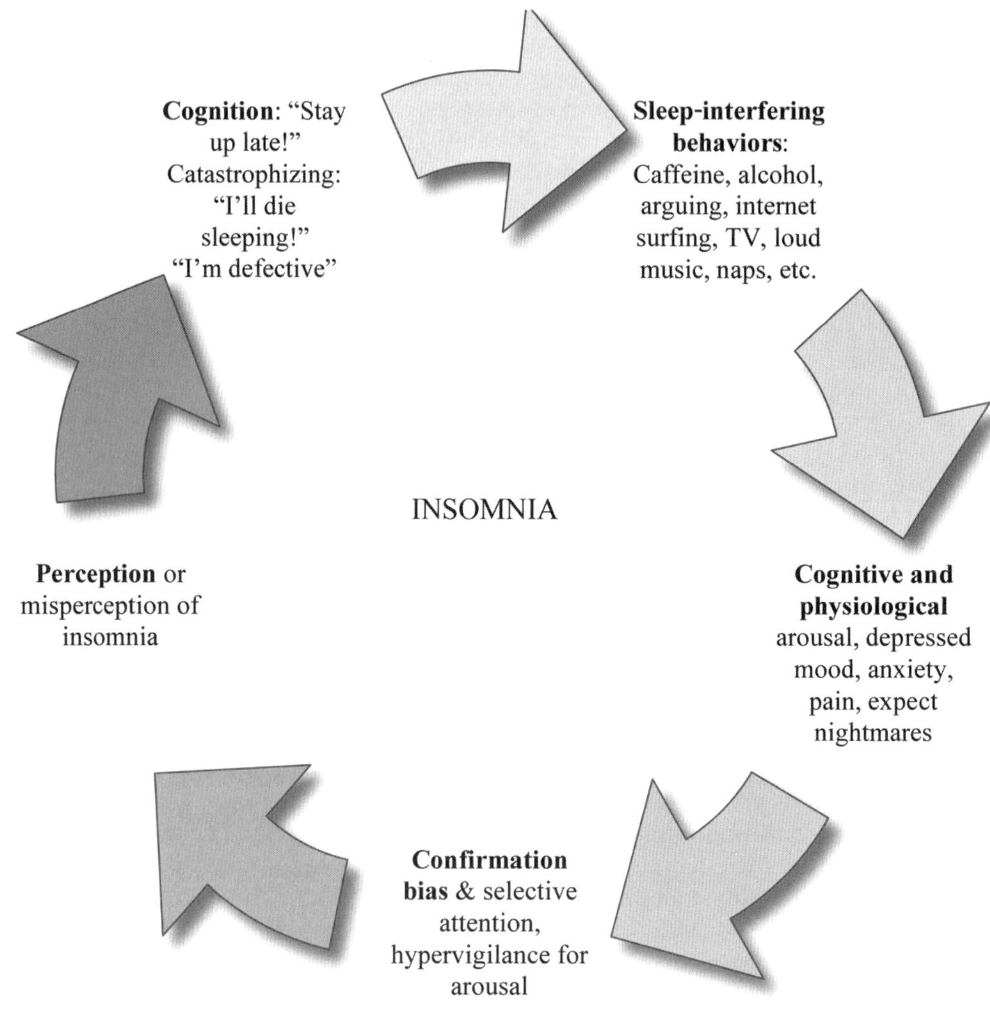

barriers sometimes prevent adherence to first-line behavioral techniques, such as SRT and SCT (Perlis et al., 2008). Treatment adherence to SRT and SCT has ranged from 55% to 89% (Bouchard, Bastien, & Morin, 2003; Perlis et al., 2004; Sexton-Radek & Overton, 1996). For example, patients who fail to adhere to behavioral recommendations, such as getting out of bed when one cannot sleep, claim that annoyance, discomfort, and boredom prevent treatment adherence. Vincent, Lewycky, and Finnegan (2008) significantly increased treatment adherence to SRT and SCT in adult insomnia patients by adding cognitive components in a 6-week group format. Importantly, increased adherence correlated with improvements on sleep measures, such as total sleep time (TST), reduced nocturnal awakenings and insomnia-related impairment. Treatment included psychoeducation to anticipate, problem solve, and cope with discomfort, annoyance, and boredom arising from behavior-therapy techniques. Additional CBT included anxiety reduction and positive self-talk, and encouragement to discontinue sleep medication (Vincent et al., 2008).

Edinger, Wohlgemuth, Radtke, Marsh, and Quillian (2001) demonstrated that CBT actually reduced dysfunctional sleep-related beliefs in patients diagnosed with primary insomnia, as compared with relaxation and placebo treatment groups. Significantly, improvements in cognition correlated with improvements in PSG measures and symptom reduction. At a 6-month follow-up, reductions in dysfunctional cognitions were also associated with subjective patient ratings of improved restfulness and sleep quality. These findings were replicated in a sample of older adults with insomnia (Morin et al., 1999). Other researchers determined that treatment failure was more common among individuals receiving behavioral therapy alone, *without a cognitive component*, versus those receiving CBT (Verbeek, Schreuder, & Declerck, 1999).

In summary, in the treatment of both chronic primary and secondary insomnia, CBT enjoys robust support, with moderate-to-large treatment effects (see Edinger & Means, 2005; Smith, Huang, & Manber, 2005, for reviews). In addition, the interested reader is referred to Smith, Huang, and Manber (2005) for recommendations for adapting CBT to specific comorbid conditions.

Additional Cognitive Interventions

Cognitive treatments involve strategies that are intended to alter the individual's thoughts and beliefs about sleep and sleep behaviors. The goal of these strategies is for the client to learn to identify and modify maladaptive thinking patterns that interfere with sleep. Once aware, individuals can then learn how to challenge dysfunctional thinking, allowing the individual to learn more adaptive beliefs and behaviors (Harvey, 2005; Perlis et al., 2005).

Perlis, Jungquist, Smith, and Posner (2008) assert that cognitive interventions are most useful for individuals presenting with intrusive ideation and worry, or who are preoccupied with their insomnia and its feared consequences. Such cognitions are problematic, as they are likely to correlate with both SNS and cognitive arousal. Cognitive restructuring can be accomplished by using a number of effective means. For instance, Harvey (2005) proposes using self-monitoring strategies to allow the client to identify specific negative automatic thoughts (AT–), either in vivo, while attempting to sleep, or through imagery during treatment sessions.

The Dysfunctional Thought Record (DTR; J. Beck, 1995) is very useful in helping patients to identify the relationship between insomnia, AT–, and the disturbing emotions and physiological correlates of these cognitions. Once the automatic thoughts are identified, the DTR provides Socratic questions to test their validity. Cognitions that are distorted can then be replaced by more accurate and adaptive cognitions. For example, the automatic thought "tomorrow will be a disaster if I don't sleep right now" can be replaced with the more rational "I've had sleepless nights in the past and survived, made it to work, and it is rare that

Exhibit 31.1

Socratic Vertical Arrow Questioning

I'll be awake all night! (AT-)
⇩
I'm frustrated, anxious, and angry (emotions)
⇩
I'll be a zombie tomorrow! (Expectation)
⇩
I must fall asleep quickly and sleep without interuption. (Expectation)
⇩
Watch TV in bed, worry, and ruminate, napping, irregular bed and wake times, alcohol, stimulant use (Compensatory strategies)
⇩
If I don't sleep now, tomorrow will be a disaster and I'll bomb the presentation! (Assumption)
⇩
I'm a loser and a total failure (Core belief)
⇩
Helplessness (Schema)
⇧
Hostile, perfectionistic, authoritarian parenting in childhood (Relevant childhood data)
⇧
Hyperactive, distractible, difficult (Temperament/Neurobiology)

anyone else ever even noticed any difference." On the other hand, rational negative thoughts, such as "My roommate's nocturnal partying is going to keep me awake all night," indicates a real-life problem and an opportunity to teach problem-solving skills, such as increasing assertiveness and communication skills to deal effectively with the roommate, moving, getting support from others, purchasing a white noise device, or getting a new roommate (Burns, 1999).

Once AT– are ameliorated, it is sometimes necessary to focus attention on underlying assumptions, expectations, beliefs, and schemas that maintain the automatic thoughts that perpetuate insomnia and influence mood. The vertical arrow technique allows one to identify these underlying cognitions (Burns, 1999) and can be used to flesh out a cognitive-behavioral case conceptualization. For example, with Andre, Socratic vertical arrow questioning in response to the AT– "I'll be awake all night!" involved asking him "What does that mean and why does it bother you?" and revealed the following (indicated in Exhibit 31.1) (each arrow represents a Socratic question).

The vertical arrow technique begins with AT– and then distills intermediate cognitions, compensatory strategies, and core beliefs from the original and more

31.2

Andre's case conceptualization.

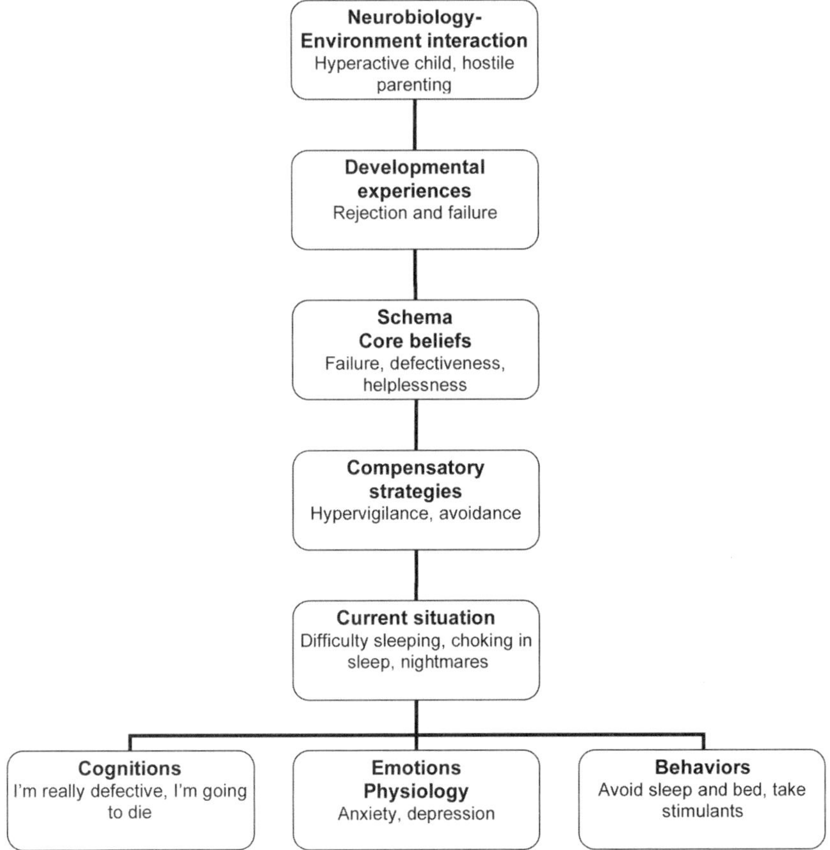

readily accessible AT−. This information, along with information gathered during assessment and treatment, is then used to flesh out a cognitive-behavioral case conceptualization illustrating the impact of the interaction among environment, biology, and early childhood experience on cognition and insomnia (adapted from A. T. Beck et al., 1979; J. S. Beck, 1995; Ramsay & Rostain, 2008). A case conceptualization diagram is also useful to draw connections between these cognitive structures and insomnia (Ramsay & Rostain, 2008). Figure 31.2 illustrates Andre's case conceptualization.

Behavioral Experiments

Another way to modify maladaptive cognitions is through behavioral experiments, which require patients to perform certain behaviors to test their thoughts and beliefs. For example, Andre held the negative belief, "this treatment will not work." The thought was framed as a hypothesis that could then be tested in the context of SCT. After a baseline of 4 hours sleeping per night was established in his sleep diary, Andre left the bedroom during periods of sleeplessness. The sleep diary for the following two weeks provided objective data to challenge the negative belief, as he added an average of 2.5 hours of sleep per night. Establishing the negative beliefs *prior* to the behavioral experiment allows the patient to actively challenge task-interfering beliefs in a way that augments effective cognitive and behavioral change. When performed correctly, behavioral experiments are some of the most effective cognitive interventions (A. T. Beck et al., 1979).

Paradoxical Intention

Dostoyevsky (1863/1997) originally observed, "After all, it is like trying not to think of a polar bear. Try to pose for yourself this task: not to think of a polar bear, and you will see that the cursed thing will come to mind every minute" (p. 49). In other words, attempting to suppress a thought only made it more salient. Harvey (2005) suggests that clinicians can demonstrate such paradoxical phenomena to patients by asking those who worry about falling asleep to imagine similarly notable animals or objects, such as a white bear. Then they are instructed to try *not* to think about the white bear. When questioned as to how well they are able to suppress thoughts or imagery about the bear, most quickly recognize the paradoxical effects of thought suppression. This allows a discussion with the client on how trying to stop worrying about sleeping can actually exacerbate it. This is also an example of a behavioral experiment in which a patient's belief that suppressing thoughts is an effective strategy to stop worrying.

Paradoxical intention is a cognitive intervention that counterintuitively involves passively attempting to stay awake although remaining in bed. Paradoxically, when the patient passively tries to stay awake, performance anxiety diminishes and sleep may occur more naturally (Ascher & Efrem, 1978; Broomfield & Espie, 2003; Morin et al., 2006). The goal of the intervention is extinguish performance anxiety that inhibits sleep onset.

The American Academy of Sleep Medicine (AASM; 2006) recommends paradoxical intention as an effective treatment for chronic onset insomnia. In practice, this technique is often administered after other approaches have failed. Clinical experience demonstrates that paradoxical intention works best along with SRT and SCT, and in combination with diaphragmatic breathing and other relaxation techniques.

Consideration With Special Populations and Diversity Issues

Older adults, adolescent females, and certain demographic groups are at elevated risk for insomnia. Older adults are notoriously poor sleepers. As we age, both deep sleep and total sleep time diminish (Ohayon, Carskadon, Guilleminault, & Vitiello, 2004). In a sample of adults in primary care, aged 65 and older, Morgan and Clarke (1997) determined that approximately one-third experienced chronic insomnia. But there was an interesting interaction between insomnia and age, with the highest rates (44%) among women, aged 70 to 74. The lowest rates (11%) were among men, aged 75 to 79. Notably, physical illness and unhealthy lifestyle posed the highest risk, and depression was most highly related to insomnia among older patients. These factors were more significant predictors of insomnia in older patients than age and sex. CBT has good empirical support for treating insomnia in this population (Espie, Inglis, & Harvey, 2001).

Curiously, 25% of older people nap (Beh, 1994), which is generally discouraged by SRT and sleep hygiene recommendations. Although these behavioral interventions and CBT have been shown to be effective treatments for insomnia in older populations, proscribing napping, typical of this age group, may not be empirically supported in all cases, and particularly for older adults. The research is inconsistent, with results ranging from no relationship between daytime napping and sleep disturbance to higher mortality, to, alternatively, positive effects of napping, including improved sleep quality, total sleep time, and improved cognitive and psychomotor performance (Ancoli-Israel & Martin, 2006; Campbell, Murphy, & Stauble, 2005; McCrae et al., 2006). Thus, additional research is needed to determine when sleep restriction and sleep hygiene treatments may be modified for treating older adults.

Forty percent of adolescents experience insomnia. Although prepubertal rates are similar for boys and girls, menarche was associated with a 27.5% increase in insomnia among girls (Johnson, Roth, Schultz, & Breslau, 2006). This gender difference has been attributed to hormonal changes, fatigue, sexual abuse, prevalence of psychiatric illness, sensitivity to familial disruption, and increased domestic and grooming expectations (Vallido, Jackson, & O'Brien, 2009). CBT and family therapy can both be useful in addressing issues of adolescence that impair sleep.

Finally, ethnicity and gender can be risk factors for sleep difficulties. In a recent study of 1,440 multiethnic women conducted in Brooklyn, females of Eastern European ancestry had the highest rate of insomnia symptoms (77%). These women were followed by Dominicans (73%), African Americans (71%), English-speaking Caribbeans (34%), and Haitians (33%). Socioeconomic status and physical health influenced rates of insomnia, with White women reporting more physical illness and being more likely to get medical treatment than the others. The author suggested that different coping mechanisms may explain the low rate of insomnia among English-speaking Caribbeans and Haitians (Jean-Luis, 2008).

However, a national study found contradictory results. Sleep time among Black women was more extreme, that is, either of unusually long or short duration as compared with their White counterparts, placing them at increased risk for the medical conditions associated with these sleep patterns (Nunes et al., 2008). All in all, the research on insomnia and the influence of ethnicity and culture is less developed than that of gender.

In conclusion, insomnia is a common problem in primary care facilities. Thankfully, there are numerous evidence-based resources available to aid multidisciplinary primary care teams treating this disorder. Overall, behavioral and cognitive interventions enjoy good empirical support for promoting healthy sleep, with or without medication. Proper treatment, enumerated above, can provide welcome relief for those suffering from the debilitating effects of insomnia. The influence of social cognition and cultural/ethnic factors on insomnia should be the subject of future research.

Clinical Pearls of Wisdom for Practitioners

- Medication has the greatest support for short-term treatment of transient insomnia, but is limited by potential negative side effects.

- Of all of the behavioral interventions, stimulus control and sleep restriction enjoy the greatest empirical support.
- Behavioral interventions can be augmented by behavioral experiments specifically designed to challenge maladaptive cognitions.
- Cognitive interventions are best for addressing cognitive arousal associated with insomnia.
- White noise devices can be invaluable for "light sleepers."

Acknowledgments

Thanks to Anthony L. Rostain and Lofton Harris of the University of Pennsylvania's Adult ADHD Treatment and Research Program for their valuable contributions to this work.

References

American Academy of Sleep Medicine. (2006). Practice parameters for the psychological and behavioral treatment of insomnia: An update. An American Academy of Sleep Medicine report, *Sleep, 29*(11). Retrieved March 3, 2009, from http://74.6.239.67/search/cache?ei=UTF-8&p=%22paradoxical+intention%22+insomnia&fr=slv8-frz6&u=www.aasmnet.org/Resources/PracticeParameters/PP_BTInsomnia_Update.pdf&w=%22paradoxical+intention%22+insomnia&d=Xn1oC52uSWIa&icp=1&.intl=us

American Psychiatric Association. (2000). *Diagnostic and statistical manual of mental disorders* (4th ed., text rev.). Washington, DC: Author.

Ancoli-Israel, S., & Martin, J. L. (2006). Insomnia and daytime napping in older adults. *Journal of Clinical Sleep Medicine, 2*, 333–342.

Ascher, L., & Efrem, J. (1978). Use of paradoxical intention in a behavioral program for sleep onset insomnia. *Journal of Consulting and Clinical Psychology, 46*, 547–550.

Barbera, J. & Shapiro, C. (2005). Benefit-risk assessment of zaleplon in the treatment of insomnia. *Drug Safety, 28*(4), 301–318.

Barkley, R. A., & Murphy, K. R. (2006). Identifying new symptoms for diagnosing ADHD in adulthood. *ADHD Report, 14*(4), 7–11.

Beck, A. T., Freeman, A., & Davis, D. D. (2004). *Cognitive therapy of personality disorders*. New York: Guilford.

Beck, A. T., Rush, A. J., Shaw, B. F., & Emery, G. (1979). *Cognitive therapy of depression*. New York: Guilford.

Beck, A. T., & Steer, R. A. (1988). *Manual for the Beck Hopelessness Scale*. San Antonio, TX: Psychological Corporation.

Beck, A. T., & Steer, R. A. (1990). *Manual for the Beck Anxiety Inventory*. San Antonio, TX: The Psychological Corporation.

Beck, A. T., Steer, R. A., & Brown, G. K. (1996). *Beck Depression Inventory: Manual (BDI-II)*. San Antonio, TX: The Psychological Corporation.

Beck, J. S. (1995). *Cognitive therapy: Basics and beyond*. New York: Guilford.

Beh, H. (1994). A survey of daytime napping in an elderly Australian population. *Australian Journal of Psychology, 46*, 100–106.

Bernstein, D. A., Borkovec, T. D., & Hazlett-Stevens, H. (2000). *New directions in progressive relaxation training*. Westport, CT: Praeger.

Blumenthal, J. A., Babyak, M. A., Doraiswamy, P. M., Watkins, L., Hoffman, B. M., Barbour, K. A., et al. (2007). Exercise and pharmacotherapy in the treatment of major depressive disorder. *Psychosomatic Medicine, 69*, 587–596.

Bonnet, M. H. (1990). The perception of sleep onset in insomniacs and normal sleepers. In R. R. Bootzin, J. F. Kihlstrom, & D. L. Schacter (Eds.), *Sleep and cognition* (pp. 148–158). Washington, DC: American Psychological Association.

Boonstra, A. M., Kooij, J. J. S., Oosterlaan, J., Sergeant, J. A., Buitelaar, J. K., & Van Someren, J. W. (2007). Hyperactive night and day? Actigraphy studies in adult ADHD: A baseline comparison and the effect of methylphenidate. *Sleep, 30*, 433–442.

Bootzin, R. R., & Epstein, D. R. (2000). Stimulus control. In K. L. Lichstein & C. M. Morin (Eds.), *Treatment of late-life insomnia* (pp. 167–184). Thousand Oaks, CA: Sage.

Bootzin, R. R., & Nicassio, P. M. (1978). Behavioral treatments for insomnia. In M. Hersen, R. Eissler, & P. Miller (Eds.), *Progress of behavior modification* (pp. 1–45). New York: Academic Press.

Bouchard, S., Bastien, C., & Morin, C. M. (2003). Self-efficacy and adherence to cognitive-behavioral treatment of insomnia. *Behavioral Sleep Medicine, 1*, 187–199.

Broomfield, N. M., & Espie, C. A. (2003). Initial insomnia and paradoxical intention: An experimental investigation of putative mechanisms using subjective and actigraphic measurement of sleep. *Behavioural and Cognitive Psychotherapy, 31*, 313–324.

Brower, K. J., Aldrich, M. S., Robinson, E. A. R., Zucker, R. A., & Greden, J. F. (2001). Insomnia, self-medication, and relapse to alcoholism. *American Journal of Psychiatry, 158*, 399–404.

Brown, T. E. (1996). *Brown attention deficit disorder scales*. San Antonio, TX: Psychological Corporation.

Burns, D. D. (1999). *The feeling good handbook*. New York: Penguin.

Buysse, D. J. (2008). Chronic insomnia. *American Journal of Psychiatry, 165*, 678–686.

Cahn, S. C., Langenbucher, J. W., Friedman, M. A., Reavey, P., Falco, T., & Pallay, R. M. (2005). Predictors of interest in psychological treatment for insomnia among older primary care patients with disturbed sleep. *Behavioral Sleep Medicine, 3*(2), 87–98.

Chesson, A. L., Anderson, W. M., Littner, M., Davila, D., Hartse, K., Johnson, S., et al. (1999). Practice parameters for the nonpharmacologic treatment of insomnia. *Sleep, 22*, 1128–1133.

Campbell, S. S., Murphy, P. J., & Stauble, T. N. (2005). Effects of a nap on nighttime sleep and waking function in older subjects. *Journal of the American Geriatrics Society, 53*, 48–53.

Chesson, A. L., Anderson, W. M., Littner, M., Davila, D., Hartse, K., Johnson, S., et al. (1999). Practice parameters for the nonpharmacologic treatment of insomnia. *Sleep, 22*, 1128–1133.

Colombo, C., Benedetti, F., Barbini, B., Campori, E., & Smeraldi, E. (1999). Rate of switch from depression into mania after therapeutic sleep deprivation in bipolar depression. *Psychiatry Research, 86*(3), 267–270.

Conners, C. K., Erhardt, D., & Sparrow, E. (1999). *Conners' adult ADHD rating scales*. North Tonawanda, NY: Multi-Health Systems.

Craske, M. G., & Barlow, D. H. (1993). Panic disorder and agoraphobia. In D. H. Barlow (Ed.), *Clinical handbook of psychological disorders* (pp. 1–47). New York: Guilford.

Currie, S. R., Clark, S., Rimac, S., & Malhorta, S. (2003). Comprehensive assessment of insomnia in recovering alcoholics using sleep diaries and ambulatory monitoring. *Alcoholism: Clinical and Experimental Research, 27*, 1262–1269.

Dostoyevsky, F. (1863/1997). *Winter notes on summer impressions*. Evanston, IL: Northwestern University Press.

Edinger, J. D., & Means, M. K. (2005). Cognitive-behavioral therapy for primary insomnia. *Clinical Psychology Review, 25*, 539–558.

Edinger, J. D., & Sampson, W. S. (2003). A primary care "friendly" cognitive behavioral insomnia therapy. *Sleep, 26*, 177–182.

Edinger, J. D., Wohlgemuth, W. K., Radtke, R. A., Marsh, G. R., & Quillian, R. E. (2001). Cognitive behavioral therapy for treatment of chronic primary insomnia: A randomized controlled trial. *Journal of the American Medical Association, 285*(14), 1856–1864.

Espie, C. A., Inglis, S. J., & Harvey, L. (2001). Predicting clinically significant response to cognitive behavior therapy for chronic insomnia in general medical practice: Analysis of outcome data at 12 months posttreatment. *Journal of Consulting and Clinical Psychology, 69*(1), 58–66.

Espie, C. A., Inglis, S. J., Tessier, S., & Harvery, L. (2001). The clinical effectiveness of cognitive behaviour therapy for chronic insomnia: Implementation and evaluation of a sleep clinic in general medical practice. *Behaviour Research and Therapy, 39*, 45–60.

First, M. B., Gibbon, M., Spitzer, R. L., Williams, J. B., & Smith, B. L. (1997). *Structured clinical interview for DSM-IV Axis II personality disorders (SCID-II)*. Washington, DC: American Psychiatric Press.

First, M. B., Spitzer, R. L., Gibbon, M., & Williams, J. B. (1996). *Structured clinical interview for the DSM-IV Axis I disorders*. Washington, DC: American Psychiatric Press.

Ford, D. E., & Cooper-Patrick, L. (2001). Sleep disturbances and mood disorders: An epidemiological perspective. *Depression and Anxiety, 14*, 3–6.

Ford, D. E., & Kamerow, D. B. (1989). Epidemiologic study of sleep disturbances and psychiatric disorders. *Journal of the American Medical* Association, 262, 1479–1484.

Fountain, N. B., Kim, J. S., & Lee, S. I. (1998). Sleep deprivation activates epileptiform discharges independent of the activating effects of sleep. *Journal of Clinical Neurophysiology, 15*, 69–75.

Gallup Organization. (1979). *The Gallup study of sleeping habits*. Princeton, NJ: Author.

Gau, S. S. F., Kessler, R. C., Tseng, W. L., Wu, Y. Y., Chiu, Y. N., Yeh, C. B., et al. (2007). Association between sleep problems and symptoms of attention-deficit/hyperactivity disorder in young adults. *Sleep, 30*, 195–201.

Goodie, J. L., Isler, W. C., Hunter, C., & Peterson, A. L. (2009). *Journal of Clinical Psychology: In Session, 65*, 1–11.

Guilleminault, C., & Bassiri, A. (2005). Clinical features and evaluation of obstructive sleep apnea-hypopnea syndrome and the upper airway resistance syndrome. In M. H. Kryger, T. Roth, & W. C. Dement (Eds.), *Principles and practice of sleep medicine* (4th ed., pp. 1043–1052). Philadelphia: Saunders/Elsevier.

Harvey, A. G. (2005). A cognitive theory and therapy for chronic insomnia. *Journal of Cognitive Psychotherapy: An International Quarterly, 19*, 41–59.

Harvey, A. G., Tang, N. K. Y., & Browning, L. (2005). Cognitive approaches to insomnia. *Clinical Psychology Review, 25*, 593–611.

Harvey, A. G., & Greennall, E. (2003). Catastrophic worry in insomnia. *Journal of Behavior Therapy and Experimental Psychiatry, 34*, 11–23.

Hryshko-Mullen, A. S., Broeckl, L. S., Haddock, C. K., &. Peterson, A. L. (2000). Behavioral treatment of insomnia: The Wilford Hall insomnia program. *Military Medicine, 165*, 200–207.

Heide, F. J., & Borkovec, T. D. (1983). Relaxation-induced anxiety: Paradoxical anxiety enhancement due to relaxation training. *Journal of Consulting and Clinical Psychology, 51*, 171–182.

Heide, F. J., & Borkovec, T. D. (1984). Relaxation-induced anxiety: Mechanisms and theoretical implications. *Behavior, Research and Therapy, 22*, 1–12.

Hobson, J. A., & McCarley, R. (1977). The brain as a dream state generator: An activation-synthesis hypothesis of the dream process. *American Journal of Psychiatry, 134*, 1335–1348.

Jacobs, G. D. (1998). *Say good night to insomnia: The 6-week solution*. New York: Henry Holt.

Jacobson, E. (1938). *Progressive relaxation*. Chicago: University of Chicago.

Jacobson, E. (1964). *Self-operations control*. Philadelphia: Lippincott.

Jansson, M., & Linton, S. J. (2005). Cognitive-behavioral group therapy as an early intervention for insomnia: A randomized controlled trial. *Journal of Occupational Rehabilitation, 15*, 177–190.

Jean-Luis, G. (2008). Study suggests ethnicity may affect sleep patterns in women. *Newswise*, Mon 31-Mar-2008. Retrieved March 7, 2009, from http://www.newswise.com/articles/view/539225/

Johnson, E. O., Roth, T., Schultz, L., & Breslau, N. (2006) Epidemiology of DSMIV insomnia in adolescence: Lifetime prevalence, chronicity, and an emergent gender difference. *Pediatrics, 117*(2), 247–256.

Klinkerfuss, G. H., Lange, P. H., Weinberg, W. A., & O'Leary, J. L. (1965). Electroencephalographic abnormalities of children with hyper-kinetic behavior. *Neurology, 15*, 883–891.

Kripke, D. F., Simons, R. N., Garfinkel, L., & Hammond, E. C. (1979). Short and long sleep and sleeping pills. Is increased mortality associated? *Archives of General Psychiatry, 36*, 103–116.

Kryger, M. H., Roth, T., & Dement, W. C. (2005). *Principles and practice of sleep medicine*. Philadelphia: Elsevier Saunders.

Krystal, A. D. (2006). Psychiatric comorbidity: The case for treatment insomnia. *Sleep Medicine Clinics, 1*, 359–365.

Kushida, C. A., Nichols, D. A., Simon, R. D., Young, T., Grauke, J. H., Britzmann, J. B., et al. (2000). Symptom-based prevalence of sleep disorders in an adult primary care population. *Sleep and Breathing, 4*, 9–14.

McCrae, C. S., Rowe, M. A., Dautovich, N. D., Lichstein, K. L., Durrence, H. H. Riedel, B. W., et al. (2006). Sleep hygiene practices in two community dwelling samples of older adults. *Sleep, 29*(12), 1551–1560.

Mercer, J. D., Bootzin, R. R., & Lack, L. C. (2002). Insomniacs' perception of wake instead of sleep. *Sleep, 25*, 559–566.

Meichenbaum, D. & Turk, D. C. (1987). Facilitating treatment adherence. In D. Meichenbaum & D. C. Turk (Eds.), *Treatment adherence: Terminology, incidence and conceptualization* (pp. 19–39). New York: Plenum.

Millon, T., & Davis, R. D. (1996). *Disorders of personality: DSM-IV and beyond* (2nd ed.). New York: Wiley.

Millon, T., & Davis, R. D. (2000). *Personality disorders in modern life*. New York: Wiley.

Monastra, V. J., Lubar, J. F., Linden, M., VanDeusen, P., Green, G., Wing, W., et al. (1999). Assessing attention deficit hyperactivity disorder via quantitative electroencephalography: An initial validation study. *Neuropsychology, 13*, 424–433.

Morgan, K., & Clarke, D. (1997). Longitudinal trends in late-life insomnia: Implications for prescribing. *Age and Ageing, 26*, 179–184.

Morgenthaler, T., Kramer, M., Alessi, C., Friedman, L., Boehlecke, B., Brown, T., et al. (2006). Practice parameters for the psychological and behavioral treatment of insomnia. An update. An American Academy of Sleep Medicine Report. *Sleep, 29*, 1415–1419.

Morin, C. M. (2004). Cognitive-behavioral approaches to the treatment of insomnia. *Journal of Clinical Psychiatry, 65*, 33–40.

Morin, C. M. (2005). Psychological and behavioral treatments for primary insomnia. In M. H. Kryger, T. Roth, & W. C. Dement (Eds.), *Principles and practice of sleep medicine* (pp. 726–737). Philadelphia: Elsevier Saunders.

Morin, C. M., Stone, J., Trinkle, D., Mercer, J., & Remsberg, S. (1993). Dysfunctional beliefs and attitudes about sleep among older adults with and without insomnia complaints. *Psychology and Aging, 8*(3), 463–467.

Morin, C. M., Bastien, C., & Savard, J. (2003). Current status of cognitive-behavior therapy for insomnia: Evidence for treatment effectiveness and feasibility. In M. L. Perlis & K. L. Lichstein (Eds.), *Treating sleep disorders: Principles and practice of behavioral sleep medicine* (pp. 262–285). New York: Wiley.

Morin, C., Bootzin, R. R., Buysse, D., Edinger, J., Espie, C., & Lichstein, K. (2006). Psychological and behavioral treatment of insomnia: Update of the recent evidence (1998–2004). *Sleep, 29*, 1398–1414.

Morin, C. M., Colecchi, C., Stone, J., Stood, R., & Brink, D. (1999). Behavioral and pharmacological therapies for late-life insomnia. *Journal of the American Medical Association, 281*, 991–999.

Morin, C. M., & Espie, C. A. (2003). *Insomnia: A clinical guide to assessment and treatment*. New York: Kluwer Academic/Plenum Publishers.

Morin, C. M., Hauri, P. J., Espie, C. A., Speilman, A. J., Buysse, D. J., & Bootzin, R. R. (1999). Nonpharmacological treatment of chronic insomnia. *Sleep, 22*, 1134–1156.

Morin, C. M., Stone, J., McDonald, K., & Jones, S. (1994). Psychological treatment of insomnia: A clinical replication series with 100 patients. *Behavior Therapy, 25*, 159–177.

National Heart, Lung, and Blood Institute Working Group on Insomnia. (1999). Insomnia: Assessment and management in primary care. *American Family Physician, 59*, 3029–3038.

Noble, J., Greene, H. L. II, & Levinson, W. (2001). *Textbook of primary care medicine* (3rd ed.). St. Louis, MO: Mosby.

Nunes, J., Jean-Louis, G., Zizi, F., Casimir, G. J., von Gizycki, H., Brown, C. D., et al. (2008). Sleep duration among black and white Americans: Results of the national health interview survey. *Journal of the National Medical Association, 100*(3), 317–322.

Ohayon, M. M. (1997). Prevalence of DSM-IV diagnostic criteria of insomnia: Distinguishing insomnia related to mental disorders from sleep disorders. *Journal of Psychiatric Research, 31*, 333–346.

Ohayon, M. M. (2002). Epidemiology of insomnia: What we know and what we still need to learn. *Sleep Medicine Reviews, 6*, 97–111.

Ohayon, M. M., Carskadon, M. A., Guilleminault, C., & Vitiello, M. V. (2004). Meta-analysis of quantitative sleep parameters from childhood to old age in healthy individuals: Developing normative sleep values across the human lifespan. *Sleep, 27*(7), 1255–1273.

Patinen, M., & Hublin, C. (2005). Epidemiology of sleep disorders. In M. H. Kryger, T. Roth, & W. C. Dement, *Principles and practice of sleep medicine* (pp. 626–647). Philadelphia: Elsevier Saunders.

Perlis, M., Aloia, M., Millikan, A., Boehmler, J., Smith, M., & Giles, D. (2000). Behavioral treatment of insomnia: A clinical case series study. *Journal of Behavioral Medicine, 23*, 149–161.

Perlis, M. L., Jungquist, C., Smith, M. T., & Posner, D. (2008). *Cognitive behavioral treatment of insomnia: A session-by-session guide*. New York: Springer.

Perlis, M. L., Merica, H., Smith, M. T., & Giles D. E. (2001). Beta EEG activity and insomnia. *Sleep Medicine Reviews, 5*, 365–376.

Perlis, M. L., Smith, M. T., Orff, H., Enright, T., Nowakowski, S., Jungquist, C., & Plotkin, K. (2004). The effects of modafinil and cognitive behavior therapy on sleep continuity in patients with primary insomnia. *Sleep, 27*, 15–25.

Perlis, M. L., Smith, M. T., & Pigeon, W. R. (2005). Etiology and pathophysiology of insomnia. In M. H. Kryger, T. Roth, & W. Dement (Eds.), *Principles and practice of sleep medicine* (4th ed., pp. 714–725). Philadelphia: Elsevier Science.

Plotkin, K. E. (2004). Insomnia caused by medical and neurological disorders. In H. P. Attarian (Ed.), *Clinical handbook of insomnia* (pp. 109–125). New York: Humana Press.

Ramsay, J. R., & Rostain, A. L. (2008). *Cognitive-behavioral therapy for adult ADHD: An integrative psychosocial and medical approach*. New York: Routledge.

Riedel, B. W. (2000). In K. Lichstein & C. Morin (Eds.), *Treatment of late-life insomnia* (pp. 125–146). Thousand Oaks, CA: Sage.

Roth, T. (2001). New developments for treating sleep disorders. *Journal of Clinical Psychiatry, 62*(10), 3–4.

Rybak, Y. E., McNeely, H. E., Mackenzie, B. E., Jain, U. R., & Levitan, R. D. (2006). An open trial of light therapy in adult attention-deficit/hyperactivity disorder. *Journal of Clinical Psychiatry, 67*, 1527–1535.

Rybak, Y. E., McNeely, H. E., Mackenzie, B. E., Jain, U. R., & Levitan, R. D. (2007). Seasonality and circadian preference in adult attention-deficit/hyperactivity disorder: Clinical and neuropsychological correlates. *Comprehensive Psychiatry, 48*, 562–571.

Rybarczyk, B., Lopez, M., Benson, R., Alsten, C., & Stepanski, E. (2002). Efficacy of two behavioral treatment programs for comorbid geriatric insomnia. *Psychology and Aging, 17*, 288–298.

Salzman, C. (1995). Medication compliance in the elderly. *Journal of Clinical Psychiatry, 56*(1), 18–22.

Sateia, M. J., Doghramji, K., Hauri, P. J., & Morin, C. M. (2000). Evaluation of chronic insomnia: An American Academy of Sleep Medicine review. *Sleep, 23*, 243–308.

Schochat, T., Umphress, J., Israel, A., & Ancoli-Israel, S. (1999). Insomnia in primary care patients. *Sleep, 22*, S359–S365.

Sexton-Radek, K., & Overton, S. (1996). Practical treatment considerations: Compliance with sleep restriction treatment in a non-disordered sample of sleepers. *Psychotherapy in Private Practice, 15*, 1–13.

Simon, G. E., & VonKorff, M. (1997). Prevalence, burden, and treatment of insomnia in primary care. *American Journal of Psychiatry, 154*(10), 1417–1423.

Smith, M. T., Huang, M. I., & Manber, R. (2005). Cognitive behavior therapy for chronic insomnia occurring within the context of medical and psychiatric disorders. *Clinical Psychology Review, 25*(5), 559–592.

Smith, M. T., & Perlis, M. L. (2006). Who is a candidate for cognitive-behavioral therapy for insomnia? *Health Psychology, 25*, 15–19.

Smith, M. T., Perlis, M. L., Park, A., Smith, M. S., Pennington, J., Giles, D. E., et al. (2002). Comparative meta-analysis of pharmacotherapy and behavior therapy for persistent insomnia. *American Journal of Psychiatry, 159*, 5–11.

Spielman, A. J., & Glovinksy, P. (2004). A conceptual framework of insomnia for primary care practitioners: Predisposing, precipitating and perpetuating factors. *Sleep Medicine Alerts, 9*, 1–6.

Spielman, J. A., Saskin, P., & Thorpy, M. J. (1987). Treatment of chronic insomnia by restriction of time in bed. *Sleep, 10*, 45–56.

Standards of Practice Committee of the American Academy of Sleep Medicine Practice. (2003). Parameters for using polysomnography to evaluate insomnia: An update for 2002. *Sleep, 26*(6), 754–760.

Vallido, T., Jackson, D., & O'Brien, L. (2009). Mad, sad and hormonal: The gendered nature of adolescent sleep disturbance. *Journal of Child Health Care, 13*(1), 7–18.

van der Heijden, K. B, Smits, M. G., & Gunning, W. B. (2005). Sleep-related disorders in ADHD: A review. *Clinical Pediatrics, 44*(3), 201–210.

Verbeek, I., Schreuder, K., & Declerck, G. (1999). Evaluation of short-term nonpharmacological treatment of insomnia in a clinical setting. *Journal of Psychosomatic Research, 47*, 369–383.

Vincent, N., Lewycky, S., & Finnegan, H. (2008). Barriers to engagement in sleep restriction and stimulus control in chronic insomnia. *Journal of Consulting & Clinical Psychology, 76*(5), 820–828.

Wang, M. Y., Wang, S. Y., & Tsai, P. S. (2005). Cognitive behavioural therapy for primary insomnia: A systematic review. *Journal of Advanced Nursing, 50*, 553–564.

Weissman, M. M., Greenwald, S., Nino-Murcia, G., & Dement, W. C. (1997). The morbidity of insomnia uncomplicated by psychiatric disorders. *General Hospital Psychiatry, 19*, 245–250.

Wu, R., Bao, J., Zhang, C., Deng, J., & Long, C. (2006). Comparison of sleep condition and sleep-related psychological activity after cognitive-behavior and pharmacological therapy for chronic insomnia. *Psychotherapy and Psychosomatics, 75*, 220–228.

Part V

Conclusions and Future Directions

Conclusions: The Future of Cognitive-Behavioral Approaches in Primary Care

32

Robert A. DiTomasso
Barbara A. Golden
Harry J. Morris

The purpose of this handbook was to provide a comprehensive and detailed overview of the applications of cognitive-behavioral approaches in primary care. Our intent was to provide practitioners with a resource for addressing the unique problems associated with practicing CBT in a primary care setting. Although much of what has been presented focused on the practitioner working side by side with the primary care physician (PCP), we believe that what is offered here is directly applicable to practitioners working with primary care patients in a separate location. The important point is for practitioners, wherever they may physically practice, to be aware of and sensitive to the unique and challenging aspects of working with primary care patients. Expanding models of practice and integrating services will likely yield the most benefit.

Based on the information provided in this book, we can draw a number of conclusions. *First*, there is clearly a place for cognitive-behavioral practitioners in the primary care setting. Scientist-practitioners from the cognitive-behavioral tradition have contributed much of the clinical research and applications in this area. These scientists and practitioners are providing cutting-edge applications designed to improve the health of patients. In so doing, they have expanded the scope of factors to consider for maximizing outcomes.

Second, cognitive-behavioral therapists must honor the empirical basis of their model, which guides their craft, and continue to work diligently to ensure that science affects practice and practice affects science. This goal requires a great deal of skill in customizing applications to fit within the context of primary care. We believe that this can be achieved only by thoroughly appreciating the role of the PCPs and understanding the clinical manifestations of common problems in primary care.

Third, there is little doubt that the integration of findings from three main influences, the biopsychosocial model, cognitive-behavioral theory, and behavioral medicine and health psychology, will continue to shape the future in identifying and offering unique and innovative assessments and treatments.

Fourth, the application of empirically supported approaches is absolutely critical in paving the way toward improving the health of our population. In the age of the empirical clinician, cognitive-behavioral therapists must continue to forge ahead. In the spirit of the well-known psychologist Neal Miller, in our efforts to help others, we must be daring in what we attempt, but careful about what we assert (Weiss, 1982).

Fifth, PCPs are a critical component of the health care service delivery system in this country, and serve on the front lines on a day-to-day basis waging war against disease. Their skillful efforts have a direct impact on the health of this country. As such, innovative cognitive-behavioral approaches that provide added value to what physicians offer are welcome. Cognitive-behavioral clinicians must partner with physicians, patients, families, other health care professionals, and communities to revolutionize the health care system. This effort requires the identification of problems in the primary care setting that undermine the work of the PCPs and the ability of patients to make the requisite changes to rehabilitate themselves, enhance their health, and ensure long-term maintenance of changes.

Sixth, through clinical practice, research, teaching, and consultation, cognitive-behavioral clinicians can have a significant impact in shaping the course of clinical care in communities at large. Concerted efforts to transport and test the effectives of approaches found to be efficacious will be necessary.

Seventh, the application of empirical findings rests upon accessing available information and developing case-conceptualization models that provide an adequate explanation of patient behaviors, reliably predict patient behaviors, and drive the development of effective treatment plans. Clinicians must not only be adept at recognizing patient problems, but must also be capable of building explanatory models of patient behavior, seeking input from a number of sources, including the patient.

Eighth, forging relationships with PCPs and working as an integral part of the medical team will likely provide comprehensive care. To achieve this end, therapists and physicians must find and fertilize the common ground, specifically, the health of the patient, in their combined efforts to treat the whole patient, as opposed to the patient's problem.

Ninth, therapists should focus on the critical tenets of primary care, especially continuity of care, comprehensiveness of care, patient education, and the biopsychosocial model, and seek opportunities to use these constructs in the service of the primary care patient.

Finally, there is clearly much more work to be accomplished in transporting, testing, refining, and evaluating assessment and treatment approaches in the primary care setting. Demonstrating the added value offered by cognitive-behavioral approaches over and above traditional, standard medical treatment is the task for today and the goal of the future. We believe that ongoing collaboration with PCPs and the integration of cognitive-behavioral approaches in the primary care setting will ensure our future success.

Reference

Weiss, S. M. (1992). Health psychology: The time is now. *Health Psychology, 1*(1), 81–91.

Index